PRAEGER ADVANCED GEOGRAPHIES

Edited by S. H. Beaver

THE WESTERN MEDITERRANEAN WORLD

PRAEGER ADVANCED GEOGRAPHIES
edited by S. H. Beaver

THE
WESTERN MEDITERRANEAN
WORLD

An introduction to its regional landscapes

J. M. HOUSTON

with contributions by
J. ROGLIĆ
and
J. I. CLARKE

FREDERICK A. PRAEGER, *Publishers*
New York · Washington

BOOKS THAT MATTER

Published in the United States of America in 1967
by Frederick A. Praeger, Inc., Publishers
111 Fourth Avenue, New York, N.Y. 10003

First published in England in 1964 by Longmans, Green & Co., Ltd.

The author has made corrections of the original text for this first
American edition.

© J. M. Houston, 1964, 1967

Library of Congress Catalog Card Number: 67-25037

Printed in Great Britain

To my Wife

PREFACE

This work makes no attempt to be encyclopaedic. If this besetting sin of the regional textbook has not been avoided entirely, at least I am conscious of its threat to serious geographic thought. Even narrowed to the theme of Mediterranean landscapes the facts are infinite and the scope of this book very limited. This therefore can only be an introductory text to a vast subject, and the reader is encouraged to use the selected bibliography for more detailed studies. Evidently, the Mediterranean sunshine is an attraction to many foreign scholars, just as the cool mountains of the Mediterranean lands tend to be popular *loci* for field studies in the summer vacation by its own scholars. To wade through the published material is itself a task of some magnitude and apart from my own field studies, this has been my pre-occupation for eighteen years, at times to the point of obsession.

My indebtedness to the French geographers, in particular, is immense. As early as 1913, M. Sorre emphasised: 'we wish to state freely that the whole content of geography lies in the analysis of the landscape' (*Les Pyrénées Orientales*, p. 10). He himself was inspired to think so by the writings of de Martonne and Flahault. This attitude to geography is now being revived by such Italian geographers as R. Biasutti and A. Sestini, and by some Iberian geographers trained in France. The fellowship of geographic scholarship is particularly a wide one, but I am most indebted to the important work by P. Birot and J. Dresch, *La Mediterranée Occidentale*.

It is only an arbitrary act that decides when a book is published, containing as it does material of such dynamic character. I am grateful to have had a patient publisher in delaying as long as I have. The encouragement of Mr E. W. Parker, of Longmans, Green, and of his successor Mr J. R. C. Yglesias, has been an inspiration. The skill and generous help given by the editor Professor S. Beaver is most appreciated also. Much emphasis has been laid on the maps, since the study of the landscape is essentially a sensual art. Although I have produced two basic series of maps dealing with the two most diverse elements of landscape, the types of landforms and the impact of man as measured by the population distribution, I am indebted directly or indirectly to the map-work of many people. Of particular value have been the maps of landform types in the Admiralty *Handbook of Italy*, Professor O.

Ribeiro's map of population distribution in Portugal, and a wide range of authors for individual maps.

In the preparation of this book, I am grateful to the companionship and guidance of numerous Mediterranean geographers on field trips, made annually since 1946. To the late Professor A. G. Ogilvie and to Professor E. W. Gilbert, who first set my course on Mediterranean studies, I have a special debt. To my friends Mr R. Aitken and Mr A. F. Martin who read several chapters, and gave much valued criticism I am most grateful. The chapter on climate was helped by notable suggestions from Professor K. Hare and from Dr D. Houghton of the Meteorological Office. Professor Gilbert F. White laboriously read most of the text and promoted some stimulating ideas. The two contributors, Professor J. Roglić and Dr J. I. Clarke were most obliging in their prompt response. To all these, and to some other of my colleagues, with whom this work has been often discussed, I am much indebted, although the mistakes and blemishes of this work are mine alone. Miss M. Potter undertook a heavy task with much care and cheerfulness in the preparation of so many of the maps and in the creation of the drawings. I am also grateful to Mr A. M. Carson Clark for the completion of a number of other maps. Mr E. J. S. Parsons, Superintendent of Maps in the Bodleian Library and his assistants obliged in the endless requests to consult topographic maps. I am indebted to several generations of students who helped with the preparation of the population maps, especially Messrs J. O. Arnold, J. H. Greenacombe, A. Gurtin, M. Mackenzie and A. A. H. Mayhew. To my wife, I am most in debt for her long-suffering and her scrutiny of the English in the text.

Oxford, July 1963.   J. M. H.

CONTENTS

10 Population and Settlement 223

11 The Regions of Spain: The Peripheral Provinces 251

12 The Regions of Spain: The Central and Southern Provinces 286

13 The Regions of Portugal 336

PART III: ITALY

14 Structures and Landforms 370

15 The Rural Landscapes   415

16 The Population and Settlements   444

17 The Regions of Northern Italy   469

18 The Regions of Peninsular Italy and Sicily   499

PART IV: PERIPHERAL LANDS OF THE NORTHERN MEDITERRANEAN AND THE MEDITERRANEAN ISLANDS

19 The Yugoslav Littoral: by Prof. J. Roglić   546

PLATES

MAPS AND DIAGRAMS

ACKNOWLEDGEMENTS

For permission to reproduce photographs we are indebted to the following: Aerofilms Ltd for Plates 1, 48, 49, 50, 60, 65, 67 and 89; Agencija Zm. Fotodokumentaciju Zagreb for Plates 69, 70, 71, 72, 73 and 74; Air France for Plate 46; M. W. Bruce Esq., for Plate 80; Crown Copyright, R.A.F., for Plates 9, 64, 66, and 78; Ente Nazionale per le industrie turistiche, Rome for Plates 2, 3, 8, 58, 59, 61 and 63; Ente per lo sviluppo dell' irrigazione e la transformazione fondiaria in Puglia e Lucania, Bari for Plate 31; Fotocielo, Rome for Plates 19, 20, 62 and 68; G. D. B. Jones, Esq., for Plates 22, 23, 24, 25 and 26; Prof. E. W. Gilbert for Plates 12, 79 and 82; Institut Géographique National, Paris for Plates 75, 76 and 77; Dr M. W. Mikesell for Plates 17 and 18; Ministère des Affaires Algériennes (through the kind services of Prof. J. Dresch) for Plate 86; Moroccan Tourist Office for Plates 5, 16, 31, 85, 87 and 88; Dr P. Niewolt for Plates 15, 80 and 83; Portuguese Tourist Office for Plates 13, 14, 42, 43 and 44; the Provincial Art Gallery of Valencia for permission to photograph oil painting, Plate 27; and the Spanish Tourist Office for Plates 4, 7, 10, 11, 21, 28, 32, 33, 34, 38, 40, 41, 45, 47 and 52. Photographs taken by the author are Plates 35, 36, 37, 39, 53, 54, 55, 56, 57 and 84.

For permission to reproduce maps and figures that are copyright we are indebted to the following: Fig. 57, 147, 160 and 193 from Almagià, *L'Italia* (Unione tipografico-editrice Torinese); Figs. 8, 19 from Birot and Dresch, *La Méditerranée Occidentale* (Presses Universitaires de France); Fig. 75 from Aranegui, *Geología y Geografía del Pais Vasco* (Museo nacional de Ciencias naturales); Fig. 111 from Boesch, *Helvetica* X, 1955, 136; Fig. 240 from Bowen-Jones, *Malta*, p. 35 (Department of Geography, Durham College); Fig. 37 from Bonatti, MS; Fig. 44 from Camps-Fabrer, F., *L'olivier et l'huile dans l'Afrique Romaine*, Service des Antiquities, Algiers, 1953, map II; Fig. 46 from Castagnoli, F., *Le richerche sui resti della centuriazone*, Rome, 1958, fig. 5, pp. 32–3; Fig. 177 from Desplanques, *Revista Geografica Italiana*, LXVI, 1959, p. 29; Fig. 255 from Despois, *Annales, Economies, Sociétés, Civilisations*, 1954; Fig. 50 from F.A.O. Report on the Mediterranean, Interim Report, M.S.; Fig. 146 from MS. map belonging to Dr M. Feio; Fig. 38 from Florchütz and Menéndez Amor, INQUA V Congrès International, *Livret-guide de l'excursion C3 et C4*, 1957, p. 34; Figs. 5 and 27 by permission of H. Gaussen; Fig. 180 from Guisti, *Caretteristiche ambientali, Italiane*, p. 256 (Fausto Failli, Rome); Fig. 139 by permission of Hayes, *Geographical Journal*, CXXII, 1956, p. 63; Fig. 47 from *Atlas des Centuriations Romaines* (Institut Géographique National); Fig. 200 from Judson and *Papers of the British School at Rome* 1963, pp. 76, 78; Fig. 254 simplified from Lalue and Marthelot, *Annales, Economies, Sociétés Civilisations*, 1962; Fig. 41 from Lombard, *Annales, Economies, Sociétés, Civilisations* XIV, 1959; Figs. 87, 88 and 98 from Lautensach, *Pet. Mitt.* 1951, *Estudios Geog.* 1956, and *Erdkunde* 1953; Fig. 36 from Marchesoni *N.G. Bot. Ital.* LXVI, 1959; Fig. 249 from Mikesell, *Northern Morocco* (University of California Publications in Geography, 1961; Figs. 63, 82 and 84 from Martin Echeverría, *España*, (Ed. Atlante), pp. 62, 73, 74; Figs. 208 and 235 from Milone, *Memoria illustrativa della carta della utilizazione del suolo della Calabria* (Consiglio nazionale delle ricerche), p. 26 and *L'Italia nell' economia delle sue regioni* (Edizioni Scient. Einaudi), p. 1054; Fig. 35 from Paganelli, *Studi Trentini di Sc. Nat.*, XXXVI, 1959; Fig. 28 from Pavari, *Monte e Boschi*, S(10), 1954; Figs. 181 and 236 from Pinna, *La Carta della densità della popolazione in Italia* (Com. Naz. Ricerche), Rome 1960, and *La Distribuzione della popolazione ... della Sardegna* (Publ. Ist. Georg. Univ. Pisa); Figs. 53 and 100 from Prof. O. Ribeiro, MS material; Figs. 13, 155 and 158 from *Revista Geográfica Italiana* 1958, p. 139 and *L'Italia Fisica* (Touring Club Italiano, 1957, pp. 77, 79); Figs. 161, 163 and 215 from Sestini, *Il Paessaggio* (Touring Club Italiano) 1963, pp. 165, 119 and 42); Figs. 15, 64, 66, 70, 79 and 80 from Solé Sabaris, *Geografía de España y Portugal* (ed. M.de Terán) vol. 1, pp. 99, 181, 212, 281, 340 and 367 (Montaner y Simon, S.A.); Figs. 86 and 245, permission to use material for maps, from Walter and Lieth, *Klimadiogramm Weltatlas* (Veb Gustav Fischer Verlag), Jena 1960, 1_2 and 3_3. All these maps and figures have been redrawn and modified.

GLOSSARY OF TERMS

A. = Arabic, B. = Berber, Ba = Basque,
Fr. = French or Provençal, It. = Italian,
M. = Maltese, P. = Portuguese, Sp. = Spanish

This glossary makes no pretence to be a linguistic study, nor is it comprehensive. Its purpose is to permit the reader to understand quickly terms in common usage in the Western Mediterranean, that are of geographical interest. The district where the term is most common is bracketed at end of definition.

Acequia (Sp.): an irrigation channel (see *sequia*).
Actus (Latin): a Roman land unit, of variable extent.
Adret (Fr.): sunny slope of valley as opposed to *ubac*.
Adritto (It.): see *adret*. Opposite is *opáco*.
Agouni (B.): valley, sheltered depression.
Aiguille (Fr.): slender, sharply-pointed peak (Alps).
Aïn, plural *aïouan* (A.): spring, well.
Aldea (Sp.): a hamlet.
Almendrella (Sp.): difficult clay soil, unsuited for cultivation of cereals.
Año y vez (Sp.): biennial system of cultivation followed by fallow.
Arrabal (Sp.): summer residence in suburbs of Arab town in Spain.
Barbecho (Sp.): practice of worked fallow, leaving soil uncultivated for a period of time. (In Fr. *jachète travaillé, intégrale*.)
Barraca (Sp.): peasant-dwelling (Valencia).
Barranco (Sp.): ravine, torrent bed.
Behetría (Sp.): a Military lordship (Santander).
Bejedal (Sp.): garrigue of box and associated plants.
Bocarribeira (Sp.): a scarped hill (Galicia).
Bonifica (It.): reclaimed land.
Bretema (Sp.): mist from the sea (Galicia).
Brughiera (It.): garrigue, heath, moorland.
Bruno (It.): heath of *calluna vulgaris* (Piedmont, Lombardy).
Burronamento (It.): gully erosion.
Calanque (Fr.), *Cales* (Catalan): a sea inlet on rugged coast.
Calar (Sp.): limestone relief (Baetic mountains).
Canuto (Sp.): deeply trenched interfluve.

Cascina, plural *cascine* (It.): farm building.

Caserío (Sp.): a group of houses, hamlet.

Castro (Sp. and P.): hill-top settlement of Celtic origin.

Ceduo (It.): undergrowth, brush wood, coppice.

Centuria (Latin): A Roman land unit of 200 *jugera quadrata* with a side of usually 20 *actus* (776 yards, 710 metres).

Châaba, plural *Châabi* (A.): a ravine.

Chano (Sp.): a gentle plateau (Galicia).

Chebka, plural *Chebket* (A.): a steep narrow ridge (W. Algerian Sahara).

Chirimire (Ba.): gentle, persistent rain (Basque provinces).

Coltura promiscua (It.): tree crops scattered in fields, in interculture with other crops.

Coltura specializzata (It.): compact groves of tree crops.

Comarca (Sp.): a country district, recognised as a historic unit by its inhabitants.

Concejo (Sp.), *Concelho* (P.): a small administrative district.

Coppa (It.): a height, hill (Gargano).

Corte (It.): farm yard, hamlet; in Sardinia, a feudal property.

Corte y dente (Sp.): upper zone of pastures (Asturias).

Cugno (It.): a summit (Sicily).

Daya, plural *dayet* (A.): enclosed natural basin where water may accumulate seasonally.

Derrumbe (Sp.): a landslide.

Dolina (It.), *doline* (Fr.): a basin or closed depression in limestone country. There are many other terms used locally, e.g. *bofies* (Catalonia), *carreggiate* (Istria), *hoyo* (Cantabrians), *nevazo* (Andalusia), *puli* (S. Italy) and *torca* (Cuenca).

Douar, singular *dour* (A.): a circle, group of tents or houses, a village.

Dugale (It.): artificial water-course (Lombardy).

Encinar (Sp.): holm oak woodland or scrub.

Erg (A.): a hill of sand dunes.

Erial (Sp.): uncultivated fallow.

Ericeto (It.): a scrub association of tree heath.

Esplegaras (Sp.): a scrub association of lavender.

Feligresia (Sp.): a rural parish (Galicia).

Fiumara or *Fiumare* (It.): torrent bed, flooded river (S. Italy).

Forteto (It.): secondary tree growth of holm oak woodland.

Frana, plural *frane* (It.): a landslide.

Frequesia (P.): small administrative unit or parish.

Furriadroxu (Sardinia): scattered houses on high ground.

Garrigue or *garigue* (Fr.), *gariga* (It.), *garriga* (Sp.): low, stunted, ever-green shrub vegetation.

Giave (It.): association of species of *genistus* and rosemary (N. Italy).

Gaada (A.): a flat plateau.

Guttaru (Sardinia): gully, water-course.

Hamada (A.): desert, plateau, bare and dissected.

Hamri (A.): red soil, lightly sandy.

Hórreo (Sp.): storehouse (N.W. Spain and N. Portugal).

Huerta (Sp.): irrigated garden, area under intense irrigation practice.

Jachère pâturée or *Jachère inculte* (Fr.): uncultivated fallow.

Jaral (Sp.): rock rose scrub (S.W. Spain).

Jaro (Sp.): tree heath scrub (Santander).

Jazzo (It.): sheep fold (Apulia).

Jebel, diminutive *Jebilet* (A.): mountain.

Kasbah (A.): native quarters of town.

Kem-Kem (B.): denuded, desert plateau, dissected by numerous, in-cised valleys.

Kreb (A.): characteristic edge of desert plateau, consisting of a cap of hard rock overlying a soft rock which has a gentler slope.

Lapiés (Fr.): bare limestone surface, etched, pitted, fluted and grooved. Similar terms are: *campos de lanar* (Sp.), *campi solcati* (It.).

Lastra (Sp.): metamorphic slate relief (Baetic mountains).

Launa (Sp.): Triassic sandstone relief (S. Spain).

Levante (Sp. and It.): easterly wind.

Lido (It.): low islands bordering lagoons (Veneto).

Macchia (It.): scrub, undergrowth. *Macchia alta*, maquis 4 – 5 m. high; *Macchia bassa*, lower scrub 1.5 – 2 m.

Maggese (It.): fallow land.

Magredi (It.): scrub association of *calluna vulgaris*.

Marcite (It.): irrigated meadows (Lombardy).

Merja (A.): lagoon, marsh, marshy tract (Rharb of Morocco).

Mezzadria (It.): a system of land tenure, common in Central Italy whereby the tenant farmer has fixity of tenure.

Misra (M.): a wide open space.

Mistral (Fr.): cold, northerly wind from the Alps that sweeps down on to the coast of S. France. Word is derived from the Latin *magister*, indicative of its masterful character.

Monte (P.): a large estate (Alentejo).

Monte alto (Sp.): Maquis vegetation woodland.

Monte bajo (Sp.): scrub, evergreen vegetation.

Nava (Sp.): enclosed basin in mountains (Central Cordillera).

nevertheless tend to obscure the regional diversity of climatic types, e.g. between the interior and north coast of Spain, or between the mountains and lowlands of Italy. The significance of climatic limits in the Mediterranean world is a second and intriguing feature of the climate, a theme which Professor Roglić has ably developed in Chapter 19, with regard to Dalmatia. For there is a varied choice in the meaningful criteria for such a limit. At the same time, the lively relevance of the jet stream in the troposphere to the climatic limit of the northern Mediterranean is a new and fundamental study.[6] Thus the Pyrenees with almost half the altitude of the Alps are a more significant climatic divide, precisely because they run parallel with the approximate boundary of the jet stream in summer, whereas the Alps lie to the north and therefore do not reinforce at ground level the meaningful tropospheric barrier. This in turn means that the climates of the Ebro basin and the North Italian Plain are very different, their landscapes are contrasted, their human significance markedly distinct.

The sea is the second major element in the Mediterranean. Shut off by the sill of Gibraltar from the colder deep waters of the Atlantic, its vast resources of warm water make it a sort of central heating system to the coasts of the Old World. The sea also attracts the passage of low-pressure systems, acting as a meteorological catalyst. That is to say it has a vital, though essentially passive role in the promotion of the weather changes. Its submarine relief and geology, if we could but discern them, hold the key to the understanding of the origin and pattern of its mountains, land masses and islands. The oscillations of its water level have determined the configuration of the surrounding coasts, particularly that of Italy which must have looked very different even only 50,000 years ago (Fig. 150). Finally, its surface has provided the most important passageway for human migration and trade ever since Neolithic times; the concentration of cities around its coasts reveals the intensity with which foreign cultures have been transported along sea routes (Fig. 39).

The third major element is the land, and in this we must recognise two important imposing forces which are everywhere at work in moulding the landscape, but nowhere more starkly or crudely than in the Western Mediterranean. These are on the one hand the tectonic forces and processes associated with the shapes, sizes and general elevations of the land masses and sea basins, and on the other the sculpture, and the wearing down of the land by the physico-climatic forces of denudation. The broad outline of Mediterranean tectonics given in Chapter 4 may seem difficult and even unnecessary in a book of this nature, but without

a broad grasp of them no general appraisal of the shape and arrangement of the sea basins, of the folded ranges or the Pliocene-Pleistocene
troughs can be made. Folded ranges undoubtedly and traditionally
constitute the most important tectonic elements in the Mediterranean,
but at least in the most recent geological period, vertical crustal movements have been fundamental in determining both major achievements
and present altitudes of the relief (Fig. 17).

The tectonic units thus disposed have been subject as soon as they
were exposed to the atmosphere to the violent attack of sub-aerial,
erosive forces. In the sub-arid conditions these forces have bared the
bones of many landforms, so that even the so-called human geographer
cannot help being challenged by them. Flats, valley floors and slopes are
sharply distinguished. Rugged limestone slopes rise steeply and abruptly
from flat coastal plain, or intermontane basin floor. The sharp relief
changes are often underscored by vegetation changes consequent upon
soil and subsurface water conditions. The coloured mosaics of soils
and palaeosols are the pages of a complicated history of erosion. Most
Mediterranean landforms are youthful, both tectonically and in denudation, and there is a varied and complex time-scale to their morpho-
genesis. So youthful are they that the time-scale is often largely in prehistoric and even historical time. Man has been a major agent in
initiating accelerated erosion, and probably half the land area has been
eroded in this way. There is a growing literature on this topic and one
day it may be possible to map the chronology of man-induced erosion,
as well as recognise its types. Thus in the western mountains of Majorca
the most formative phase of erosion appears to be about 100,000 years
old, that is prior to human interference.[7] Very different are the findings
at lake Monterosi north of Rome, where C^{14} dating, pollen analysis
(Fig. 37) and chemical analyses of the sediments suggest erosion
became very marked during the first few centuries B.C. and continued
until the fifth century A.D., that is to say with Roman deforestation and
settlement.[8] In the coastal ranges of Catalonia, erosion may be dated
from about A.D. 256 to 400.[9] In south-east Spain there is much erosion
that dates only from the late Middle Ages, when the Moorish redoubt
of the Baetic mountains became overcrowded. With erosion, deltas
began to form along the coast between Málaga and Almería during the
fifteenth and sixteenth centuries. This human-induced erosion of varying
age has left great scars on the Mediterranean landscapes, ruining at
least 40 per cent of Italy's mountain slopes, vast areas of North Africa,
and much of the Spanish mountains.

The fourth major theme is provided by the mantle of vegetation, in which the transitory character noted in the relief and soils, is even more pronounced. Its contribution to the landscape is highly distinctive and is once more intricately intertwined with man's pervasive impact on the land. Indeed it may be said that this impact is most closely to be deciphered in the pattern of vegetation. Decisive from this point of view and characteristic of the Mediterranean world is the conflict between agriculture and pastoralism. Not only does this contrast differentiate two societies with different outlooks and values, but it also often demarcates completely different ecological situations. Under agriculture, land that is abandoned especially in lowland areas of deep soil, is associated with progressive ecological processes, so that eventually forest cover will be restored naturally unless the severity of summer drought is unusually marked. Only in marginal areas for cultivation that have steep slopes, will the progressive tendency be hindered.[9] With pastoralism, however, the ecological model is always regressive because of its associated scourges of fire and selective, intensive grazing. After land clearance, a scrubby growth of kermes oak and shrubs such as heath, cistus or euphorbia is characteristic. Further use leads to the dominance of herbaceous plants such as *Brachypodium* and bulbs, notably asphodels. The range lands then take on irrevocably a ruined aspect. On the slopes and limestone plateaux this rocky *garrigue* becomes leached of all finer particles, eventually leaving a rocky desert. Herein then lies a key to the history of man's cumulative impact on the landscape, decipherable in the vegetation mosaics.

The fifth of the dominant themes is the long and continuous tradition of urban life. Here in the Western Mediterranean urban life is of unique interest for at least two reasons: the sharp contrast between the advanced civilisations of the cities and the backwardness of much of the countryside; and the varied character of the urban civilisations as revealed in the town plans. Compared with the desolate, backward and thinly populated areas of many landscapes, there is a progressive atmosphere in the cities, usually with a long illustrious history, commercial prosperity, and often with densely populated and intensively cultivated environs. This contrast is traceable to the beginnings of classical civilisation, although it was much exaggerated during the Renaissance when mercantilism was favoured by the growth of sea routes and civic enterprise.[10] It is characteristic of the Mediterranean that major ports have led in economic activity ever since, with a few exceptions.

The physical continuity of urban sites is an important trait of the Mediterranean, but although the sites have often been continuously occupied the town plan often shows the evidence of distinct evaluation of the economic problems of urban life made by each of the various civilisations.[11] Rome tended to eliminate indigenous modes of town life by its efficient networks of military roads and the rigid conformity of its town plans. It sought a strong central government so that each town was as it were a 'package' arrangement, containing those physical facilities required to Romanise the populace. Very different was the Muslim emphasis on local rule, its acceptance of a pluralistic society composed of Mohammedans, Jews and Christians, and its evaluation of privacy in the enclosure of the various elements of the urban pattern. Local autonomy is a marked character of all the Christian towns, still seen in the strength of municipal government displayed by the central location of the town hall, the importance of a central square, the prominence given to the churches, and the more regular and wider pattern of streets than that seen in Muslim plans. The much higher densities of population in central Italy than in the Spanish Meseta have brought about notable differences. Indeed, even when Rome took Hispania under its rule as an underdeveloped country, the sophisticated humanised countrysides of central Italy and the wild isolation of much of Spain must have been strongly contrasted.

Finally, it must be recognised that man has evaluated what is meaningful and significant in the landscape from the beginning of the human race. The sacred groves, the templed promontories, the sanctified territory of the town site, were such early evaluations of selected sites and situations.[12] But with more sophisticated societies, similar environments long occupied by man have been very differently transformed by their inhabitants. That a region is 'a medal struck in the effigy of its people' (Vidal de la Blache) is frequently illustrated in the Western Mediterranean. On a broader basis the same is true, aş for example when two contrasted civilisations clashed in the Iberian Peninsula, each leaving a distinct imprint of its own evaluation and utilisation of resources. No student of Iberian landscapes can afford to neglect the study of the Reconquest in this peninsula. Equally there are marked contrasts in the North, Centre and South of Italy, for the historic context of each has been very different until their eventual unification only a century ago.

Just as history plays a part in the understanding of relatively small regional variations, so in modern times the diverse utilisation of resources, which once distinguished region from region is now projected on a much larger scale through national (not regional) policies. The legislative frameworks of each country have directed, if not dictated, policies in certain directions, which succeeding governments have found either difficult to alter, or else have been unconscious of the need to look for alternative solutions. For over half a century, Spain has been mesmerised by the challenge to extend its irrigation systems, regardless of such an alternative as the improvement of its dry-farming agriculture. Portugal, on the other hand, with relatively greater opportunities to extend its irrigation has neglected this officially, and has been more concerned with such problems as the break-up of its common lands. After the Unification of Italy, Piedmontese legislation, long concerned with the physical challenge of the river Po for drainage and reclamation, was imposed on the nation as a whole, despite the fact that the South had more pressing problems in other directions. Since 1950, Italian land reform has shown how contrasted national governments can modify the landscape according to very different policies. Spain, which needs land reforms just as much as Italy ever did, has still no such intentions, despite other programmes. The three North African countries of the Maghreb have until now followed distinct policies of conservation and development. This was not so much because of varying legislative frameworks and political structures, for all were controlled by France, but with perhaps greater realism of the differing environments. Irrigation has been somewhat of a fiasco in Algeria, more impressive in Morocco, and of meagre status in Tunisia. This is because in each country the water resources are very different. It will be of interest now to see how these three independent units diverge in their resource policies, to exaggerate further the differences between them.

These six themes or major elements in the geographical complex of this Western Mediterranean world will be found to recur in the understanding of almost every one of the landscape types encountered. Widely ranging in thought they seem to be and, indeed, are, but the touchstone, the justifying and unifying factor among them all is the description and understanding of the present landscapes in all their splendour and variety.

The book divides itself naturally into a sequence of three parts. The first deals with these six themes in their general outline, viewed systematically. Then in the introduction to each major unit of the Western Mediterranean, the specific regional details of morphology, ecology and man's impact upon the land in terms of settlement are given. The regional landscapes are then finally described, with a bias to their subjective impressions in order to appreciate their atmosphere, composition and unique character. Thus the book may be read at two levels: the regional descriptions may be studied first by the sixth form and first year University student, while the advanced student—for whom the book is primarily intended—can study it systematically

PART I

LANDSCAPES OF THE WESTERN MEDITERRANEAN WORLD—GENERAL FEATURES

CHAPTER 2

THE CLIMATIC SCENE

Geography's 'chief subject matter is the control of climates by
landscapes, and of landscapes by climates, and the control by both
of the environments of living beings. This is pure geography.'
(H. J. Mackinder, *The Times*, 9 February 1905)

This statement of Sir Halford Mackinder aptly describes the geographical significance of climate in the Mediterranean world. Here as effectively as anywhere else is demonstrated the control of relief and its disposition upon climate. The distinctive traits of climate are in turn
effectively imprinted in its landscapes, so that the Mediterranean climate
is the most important element in this habitat. It is logical then to
commence with this feature. The term 'Mediterranean climate' is so well
recognised that the popular assumption is often made that it has uniform climatic conditions within its region. There is an element of truth
in this of course. As an 'Etesian climate' (Gr. *etesios* = annual), the
marked seasonal change between hot, rainless summers and warm,
humid winters is its major characteristic. But as a regional example of a
type, the abnormalities of the Mediterranean region are great, more
so than in any other of the regions of comparable climate. For around
the shores of the Mediterranean there are stations recording the highest
precipitation in Europe, as well as the minimal amounts. One Dalmatian station has over 180 inches mean annual rainfall, while the Sahara
is the greatest desert on earth. Rainfall probability for the year ranges
from less than two to over 50 per cent. The coasts of Sardinia, Sicily
and Morocco have some of the minimum frequencies of thunderstorms
to be found in the northern hemisphere, while some of the highest
records occur at the head of the Adriatic and on the mountains of
Dalmatia. Maritime influences dominate the coasts, continental conditions in the interior. Weather changes associated with shallow air-
masses are extreme, ranging from the scorching blast of diverse Saharan
winds which may raise the temperatures of the North African coast to
110° (43·3)* or more, to the icy, though more limited flow, of the Bora
which may bring temperatures down suddenly to 20° (−6·7) or less at
the head of the Adriatic.

* All temperature figures are quoted as follows: °F. (°C.).

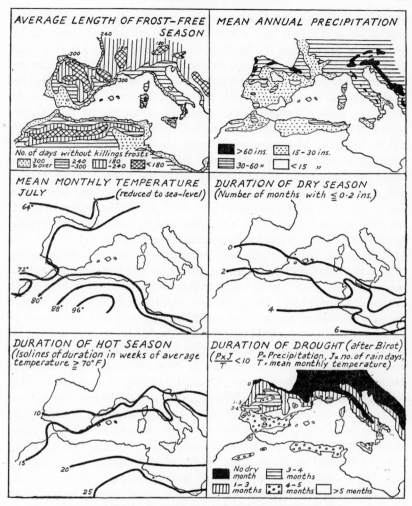

FIG. 1. Elements of climate in the Western Mediterranean

Another half-truth is that the Mediterranean is the controlling influence of its climate, a view that goes back to the ancients. Theophrastus, for example, observed what is still being repeated in textbooks today: 'In winter the sea is warmer than the land, so that if a cloud is formed over it, its formation is obviously due to a powerful active principle. For otherwise it would have been dissolved by the air by reason of its situation; while in summer, the sea is cold . . . and the land is warm.'[1] Certainly the extent of the Mediterranean sea has great significance. With a constant minimum temperature of 55° (12·8) at all depths below 1,000 ft and a low seasonal variation of some 17–20° (8·3–8·9) at the surface, the Mediterranean is 6 to 10° (3·3–5·5) warmer than the Atlantic at the same latitudes. In contrast to the marked seasonal changes of air temperature over its surrounding lands, the Mediterranean sea is responsible for vertical instability of air on an enormous scale. Cumulus skies, indicative of heating by the sea, are typical of the Mediterranean from early October until roughly mid-May. But to treat the Mediterranean climate as an isolated entity without reference to the general circulation is fallacious.[2] Thus in terms of the world conditions the Mediterranean plays the limited, more passive role of a catalyst in an area full of local heat sources and heat sinks. For despite their sub-tropical latitudes of 45–30 N., the climates of southern Europe and North Africa are dominated by polar and not tropical circulation.[3] The current and generally accepted model is that the Mediterranean lies in winter well north of the sub-tropical jet which crosses the north Sahara (at about 40,000 ft) and is detectable only in the winter half year. The tropical tropopause terminates not far north of the sub-tropical jet.[4] The Mediterranean typically lies in the weaker westerly circulation south of the polar front jet over and north-west of Europe. Thus in winter cold outbreaks in the Mediterranean are usually associated with a large amplitude oscillation in the atmospheric circulation wherein the polar jet stream is diverted southwards over the Mediterranean and into North Africa. Frequently a cold low persists over the Mediterranean in winter, moving a little to and fro but cut off from the main flow. In terms of local conditions, however, the controls of blocking anticyclones over Eurasia and of slit jets, make any detailed explanation extremely complicated.[5] Indeed it is questionable if a detailed synthesis of the Mediterranean climate is yet possible.

A third superficial generalisation usually made, is that with the seasonal swing of the equinoxes, the region lies within the westerly belt in winter and along the axis of the sub-tropical high-pressure belt in summer. Thus the drought of the Mediterranean summer is explained by the spread of the Azores anticyclone, extending with a feeble gradient over the Mediterranean. The immediate causes of drought are clear. There is the divergence of wind-flow at low levels on the poleward side of the trades. This causes a general subsidence of air throughout the lower troposphere and dynamical warming of the air inhibits convection currents. The ineffectiveness of disturbances to make rain in the troposphere, even when the air is humid, is a related factor. The anticyclonic regime of these latitudes in summer minimises the amplitude of wave-preturbations that account for a good part of the precipitation of the westerlies.[6]

Further explanation of the regional features is necessary. It appears that the roles of the Pyrenees and of the Alps are fundamentally different on the northern borders of the Mediterranean. In summer, except for occasional incursions of the polar front and its associated jet (then weak), the most significant factor is the position of the sub-tropical jet, moving slowly over North Africa as summer approaches. It reaches its most northerly position aligned approximately along the axis of the Pyrenees, though it may oscillate over the Mediterranean during the summer. In early summer it retreats southwards again. The relationship between the position of this jet and the surface synoptic features is not yet clearly understood, though the pronounced contrasts of the north and south flanks of the Pyrenees have been related to it by French writers.[7] The influence of the Alps is most important although in a completely different mechanism from that of the Pyrenees. During the winter the Alps seem to encourage a cut-off process whereby cold tropospheric pools get left in the central Mediterranean, especially near the Adriatic. These pools exist for some time and are only slowly warmed out. Thus frequently a mild south-westerly or westerly spell over France and Germany, following a north-westerly or northerly outbreak, is not felt over the Adriatic where the cold pool persists. This must be due, in part at least, to the Alps. The result is the small contrast in mean temperatures north and south of the Alps. Much of the thunderstorm activity over northern Italy and the Dalmatian coast occurs during the passage of such cold tropospheric troughs in the westerlies, over the moist surface air. To this extent there is a polar influence in the Mediterranean summer of the north central area.[8]

CLIMATIC FACTORS AND ELEMENTS

The Mediterranean regime is a transitional type of climate. It lies between the temperate climatic regime of western Europe, whose seasons are largely determined by thermal conditions affected considerably by outside controls, and the African tropics with their independent heat budget, with seasonal changes determined by precipitation. In the Mediterranean seasons both temperature and precipitation play an important role. The analysis of the Mediterranean climate is indeed as complex as any on earth, since its seasons are determined by both external and internal influences, and its detailed regional features are consequent on the interplay of sea, surface air and upper conditions.

1. *The Air Masses.* As the relations between the jet streams and synoptic conditions are not yet clear, what follows must be more descriptive than explanatory. In winter the Mediterranean lies between the cold Asian anticyclone and the Atlantic anticyclone of the Azores. It is a zone of relatively low pressure with minimal conditions over the sea basins of the Gulf of Lions, the Balearic, Tyrrhenian and Adriatic seas, making them centres of the greatest frequency of cyclogenesis in the whole of the northern hemisphere. In summer the anticyclonic cell of the Atlantic is developed but the continental cell disappears and the Mediterranean is under the former's control. Consequently, in winter the Mediterranean is dominated by the advection of air streams of markedly different characteristics and coming from distant sources, whereas in summer it has sluggish, much more uniform, conditions. The winter admixture of air streams is much more marked in the western than in the eastern Mediterranean because of its position.

Air Masses of the Western Mediterranean[9]

Air Mass	Source	Frequency
Arctic Maritime (mA)	Arctic ocean between Greenland and Scandinavia	Seldom more than 2–4 days; most likely at end of February
Arctic Continental (cA)	N. Russia, perhaps Siberia	Coldest air, occurring some 4 or 5 times annually
Polar Maritime (mP)	W. and S. of Iceland	Commonest type
Transitional (tmP)	Shifts from N.W. Atlantic to seas S. of lat. 44° N.	Frequent through Straits of Gibraltar
Polar Continental (cP)	Russia and Siberia via the Volga, Caspian and E. Europe	Not frequent
Tropical Maritime (mT)	Azores and ocean to the south	Not common and seldom penetrates to Cen. Medit. from Straits of Gibraltar
Tropical Continental (cT)	N. African deserts	Most frequent in late spring and autumn, but not very common
Mediterranean (M)	Stagnant air mainly of mP origin	Favoured by anticyclonic conditions over sea, especially in spring and autumn

Southerly airstreams are not important; mT air enters the Straits of Gibraltar only in the cool season when a deep depression is moving east across western Europe.[10] But as the cold front of the depression approaches the northern Mediterranean, the supply of mT air is cut off and replaced by cT air from North Africa. Nor is cT air relatively common because of the almost constant monsoonal inflow of air into Africa. Outbursts usually occur in spring and autumn when on-shore breezes are less marked than in summer, drawn into the Mediterranean by advancing depressions. Commonly called the *scirocco*, its structure over southern Italy is varied with usually cold air from eastern Europe in advance of the hot, dusty air from the desert.[11] The choking air with white or yellow haze and sometimes with rain falling as 'red rain' or 'yellow mud', carries great quantities of dust, the amount varying with the fetch across the deserts of Libya (Fig. 2).

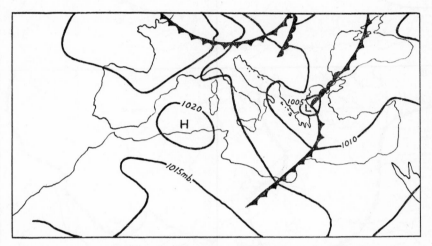

Fig. 2. Synoptic conditions showing the development of the scirocco over the Western Mediterranean, 13 September 1953

The cold northerly mA, mP, tmP air masses are of major importance to the Mediterranean in winter.[12] Warmed by 10–15° (5·5–8·3)—to about 500 millibars or 6,000 metres—they carry considerable quantities of moisture, recharged over the Mediterranean itself. This, and the warming of the surface layers, renews much instability causing rain and banks of cumulus cloud. They sweep the western basin five or six times monthly during the cool season (Fig. 3). Mediterranean air common in spring and autumn is mostly of polar origin.[13] At base it is therefore stable but convectionally unstable above. In areas of marked relief it is uplifted to give heavy orographic rainfall and thunderstorms.

It used to be fashionable to speak of Mediterranean storm tracks but their existence is not evidenced by daily analysis. There is a general tendency for cyclonic disturbances to move eastwards in the westerly

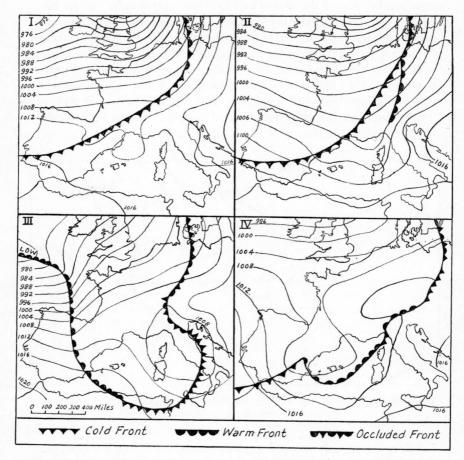

FIG. 3. Synoptic conditions, showing the advance of an Atlantic depression into the Mediterranean, 27–30 November 1954

belts. The position of the surface centre is often influenced in the Mediterranean by physiographic obstacles but the surface centre is not the important thing about an active disturbance. Mediterranean cyclones very rarely have clear-cut fronts. Most of them are moderately baroclinic. They hardly ever have warm fronts, however, and the cold fronts become distinct only after they move inland in Africa. Thus the classical frontal model does not satisfactorily fit the fronts which are found in Mediterranean depressions.[14] The greater part (more than nine-tenths) of Mediterranean depressions originate in the basin itself which is thus essentially a cyclonic source region. Of these, the great majority are generated within the northern sector as lee-depressions; about 69 per cent of all Mediterranean depressions originate in or near the Gulf of Genoa,[15] showing that unstable wave disturbances do not develop in a baroclinic field but as a result of a forced distortion, due to physiographic obstructions. In the south, although air masses are less impeded by relief, only deflected by the Saharan and Tell mountains and by the Libyan escarpments, the movements of air masses are much less significant.

2. *The Relief.* The relief of the northern rim of the Mediterranean has

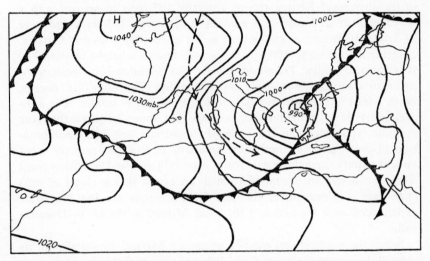

FIG. 4. Synoptic conditions, showing the invasion of the Mistral conditions into the Mediterranean, 3 March 1949. The broken line shows the previous trajectory of the maritime arctic air (mA)

at least three significant influences upon the air masses. It concentrates them to follow a few select routes, intensifying their effects. The trend of the mountain barriers, whether parallel or transverse, convex or concave to the air-stream, their mass, slope and their relative proximity to the sea are also important geographical factors in affecting air movements. Where the relief is high enough, that is 8,000–10,000 ft or more, lee-depressions are generated. The formation of a polar low over the Mediterranean, especially in the Gulf of Lions, appears to be critically dependent on the direction of the northerly or north-westerly flow which produces it. There must be some critical relationship between the wind direction at levels up to at least 500 mb, and the alignment of the mountain barriers. This accounts for the caprice of Mediterranean lows and their associated rainfall.

Fig. 4 indicates how a typical invasion of northerly air affects the western Mediterranean. Relatively cold air is advected with great force down the Rhône corridor and over the sill of Naurouze, to focus upon the Gulf of Lions. The force of its advent will depend upon the thermal nature of the air mass, whether mP, cP, mA or even cA, and also the degree to which it has been modified in its advance over Europe. The orographic 'funnels' generate masterful air jets; such is the name given to the *Mistral* (latin *magister*) in southern France.[16] Six stations in the Provençal Riviera record annually 105 days of *mistral* with a speed of over 27 knots, and another station with 103 days and over 21 knots. Its influence can extend as far as the Balearics and Corsica, covering a zone up to 100–200 miles wide and to a height of 10,000 ft. It is variously called *Tramontana* in eastern Spain and the western Po plain, or *Cirs*, *Cierze* in Aude and Roussillon. The *Bora* (Gr. *Boreas*, north wind) in the Adriatic and eastern Po valley is similar. The anticyclonic type is more limited in range but more frequent than the cyclonic type which can cover the whole Adriatic sea.[17] The combination of cold Arctic air and local katabatic effects, generate the most violent varieties, reaching gale force, especially on the Dalmatian coast when the waves are atomised to such an extent that a cloud of mist (*fumarea*) is formed over the sea. Similar winds are the *Maestrale* experienced near Genoa, and the local *Mistral* in the lower Durance valley.

When the northerly air meets a mountain barrier, the stability of its air will determine the proportion deflected; in unstable air much more is lifted over the obstacle. And as relief can influence the air to heights four or five times its own elevation, the relations between surface and upper air streams can become very involved.[18] It is thus one of the meteorological problems of the Alps, not yet fully understood, why in some cases the main polar front is delayed by the mountains, advancing only on narrow sectors and fanning out through the gaps, while at other times fronts of deep cold air pass quickly over the mountains without much obvious hindrance. In most cases, the immediate lees of the mountains are sheltered from frontal clouds by strong currents of air. Moreover, air lifted over mountains is subjected to intense convection and perhaps to heavy precipitation, so that the airstream loses much of its moisture on the leeward side, combined with a katabatic motion. These orographic controls explain the famous blue skies which are popularly associated with the Mediterranean winters.[19] In reality, they predominate only along limited sections of the coast, especially in the lee of the Alps (the Riviera) and of the Meseta (south-eastern Spain).

The most significant regional influence of mountains is, however, in the formation of lee-depressions. These occur sometimes in association with the so-called 'trade-wind fronts' in the lee of the Atlas.[20] But their great importance in the northern Mediterranean is consequent on particular geographical circumstances. The combination of favourable frontogenesis and cyclogenesis is induced by the advance across the Alps of a cold front or cold occlusion, the warm air from the Mediterranean sea and the orographic features. The convexity of the western Alps, reaching here their maximum elevation, with no important transverse defiles to the north-western airstreams, are all important factors.[21] If the advancing cold air is shallow, an incipient low depression will form either in the Gulf of Genoa, or in the western Po valley, or sometimes in both areas, later joining to move eastwards into Eastern Europe. Intense cold air over the Plain can discourage its local development but this may be offset to some extent by the warmer air above the Pre-Alpine lakes area. If the cold air is very deep, the cold front may flow directly over the Alps, creating much greater instability and then the lee-depression becomes a well established system, affecting perhaps the whole of the western Mediterranean. The airstream drawn down the Rhône valley may continue as a cold jet right across the sea to northern Africa, giving its coasts the cold, wet, stormy weather sometimes experienced. The trajectory of the lee-depressions commonly runs south-east along the Tyrrhenian coast in winter and spring, or across the Po valley in autumn and summer encouraged by the heating of the plain with its thundery instability.

The Mediterranean relief is also influential in determining the amount of precipitation, especially along its coastal ranges. Steep gradients of rainfall occur on the north and north-west coasts of the Iberian Peninsula, south-west Sierra Nevada, Rif, Moroccan and Tell Atlas, northern Sicily, Calabria, western Apennines, Riviera Levante and Dalmatian mountains

3. *Temperature*. Three factors affect to varying degrees the Mediterranean climate: latitude, continentality and altitude. Of these, latitude has least significance. Between Tortosa at the Ebro delta and Oran there is a latitudinal difference of 5° (2·7) but there is only a mean annual temperature difference of 7° (3·8). This is influenced by the western Mediterranean sea, whose water temperature varies little more than 59–68° (15–20)[22]. Between November and March the sea is warmer than the land areas, cooler from June to August and

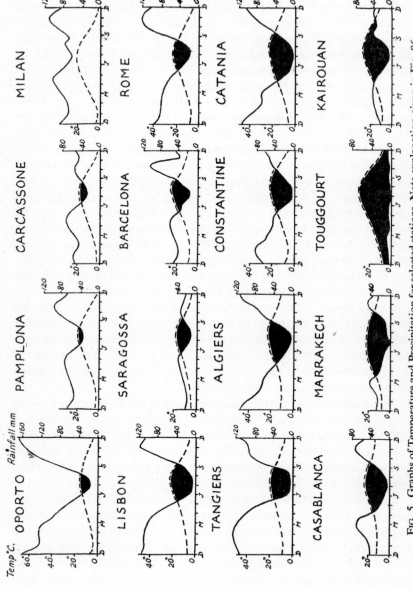

Fig. 5. Graphs of Temperature and Precipitation for selected stations. Note explanation given in Fig. 86

normally about the same temperature between April and May and again between September and October.[23] There is thus a marked contrast between maritime areas which have a total annual range of daily measured temperatures of only 50–59° (27–33) and the continental climates of the Spanish Meseta, the North Italian Plain and North Africa which have ranges of 66–75° (36–41) or even more. The lowest annual range occurs on the Atlantic coast, at Corunna, 47° (25), with its fresh maritime climate, and at Mogador, 43° (23), washed by the cold Canaries current offshore. In contrast, the shallow waters of the Syrte sea, readily heated in summer, explain Gabès' annual range of 61° (33).

The Italian Peninsula is little affected by continentality because of its narrow configuration between the two seas. It is only marked in the Po basin, enclosed by the Alps and Apennines, and having marked temperature inversion in winter, excessive heating in summer. The annual extreme range reaches over 75° (41) in the western plain between Vercelli, Asti and Saluzzo. There is therefore a marked contrast with the Ligurian coast, a difference of 16° (9) mean annual temperature in the distance of only 37 miles between Genoa and Alessandria. Influenced by the coasts of the Peninsula, the January isotherms run from north to south, and more clearly so in July from south to north[24] (Fig. 1). Apart from the Po valley, the highest temperatures in summer are recorded in the Tavoliere and Lucania, also in Catania and Campidano, all areas subject to rapid heating with scirocco and foehn influences.

The much greater dimensions of the Iberian Peninsula produce marked continentality, especially in the trough of the river Ebro and in New Castile, but it occurs to some extent everywhere that is within 50–100 miles from the coast.[25] Mean annual maximum temperatures reach 111° (43·9) at Saragossa and Murcia, and even 115° (46·1) at Seville, while mean annual minimum temperatures of 10·4° (−12) at Leon and 14° (−10) along the foothills of the Pyrenees, are recorded.[26] The seasonal range may indicate how varied are stations with the same mean annual temperatures. Corunna and Albacete have the same average annual mean of 56° (13·3) but the January figures are 48° (8·9) and 40° (4·4) respectively, the July figures 64° (17·8) and 75° (23·9). Continentality is even more marked in the interior of northern Africa. Diminution of winter temperatures are irregular there, compensated by relief and other local factors, but in summer the contrasts between the coasts and the interior are brutal, rising from a mean monthly daily maximum in July of about 81° (27·2) on the Algerian coast to 93° (33·9) on the high plains of Oran and Constantine, to 100° (37·8) in the Chéliff depression and to 108° (42·2) in the Tadla plains. But their absolute maximum may exceed 118° (47·8) or even 122° (50·0).

The distribution of the mean annual temperature reflects very closely the relief conditions, with temperature decrease of 0·46 to 0·64°C for every 100 m. But mountain basins tend to exaggerate markedly the features of continentality. For example, in the basin of Vich between the eastern Pyrenees and Montseny, a thermal inversion of over 36° (20) has been recorded. Similar phenomena occur in some of the Apennine basins such as Fucino and Aquila. In North Africa excessive day heating in summer with marked diurnal changes exaggerate the continentality in a distinct manner.

4. *Precipitation*.[27] The Italian peninsula also shows a rough approximation between the distribution of annual rainfall and the relief features[28] (Fig. 169). For their altitude two districts have markedly high precipitation, the Carnic and Julian Pre-Alps (Musi has the Italian record of 152 in) and the Apuan Alps, influenced by the orographic and cyclonic rainfall of lee-depressions, over the Gulf of Genoa and the head of the Adriatic. The Po plain has a relatively uniform distribution with more on the northern side (about 35 in) than on the south side (Bologna, 22 in). The Peninsula has a relatively uniform distribution, ranging from about 24 in along the coastal plains to over 40 in on the mountains, especially on the Abruzzi, Salentino and Calabrian mountains. Minimal amounts fall between the Tavoliere and the Gulf of Tarranto, S. Pancrazio Salentino near Lecce having only 7 in.[29]

In the Iberian peninsula there is a marked decline from north to south on both coasts (Oporto 48, Lisbon 22, and Sagres 14 in; Barcelona 24, Valencia 14·5, and Alicante 11·4 in). The contrast between the north-west (Pontevadra 61 in) and the south-east (Almeria 7 in) is most marked[30] (Fig. 87). This contrast from north to south, east to west is also seen in North Africa. The high relief of the Great Atlas, facing the Atlantic, receives the maximum rainfall at an altitude of 6,000–10,000 ft. But all areas with high relief and affected by frequent cyclonic conditions in winter notably the Rif, and Tell Atlas, receive over 24 in annually. The basins of the Tensift, Tadla, Moulouya and Chéliff reflect their rain-shadow position (Fig. 245).

The causes of rainfall seasonal distribution are very complex as it is now realised that their traditional interpretation by airmasses is not valid. Most precipitation comes from the middle and upper troposphere where the distinctions of airmasses are largely meaningless. Even in ideal situations it has proved impossible to establish any relationship

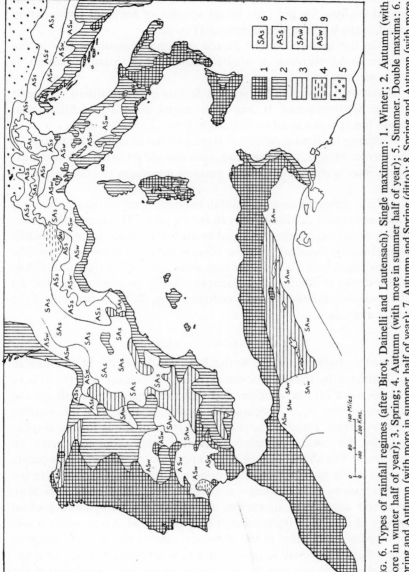

FIG. 6. Types of rainfall regimes (after Birot, Dainelli and Lautensach). Single maximum: 1. Winter; 2. Autumn (with more in winter half of year); 3. Spring; 4. Autumn (with more in summer half of year); 5. Summer. Double maxima: 6. Spring and Autumn (with more in summer half of year); 7. Autumn and Spring (ditto); 8. Spring and Autumn (with more in winter half of year); 9. Autumn and Spring (ditto)

between rainfall and upper air parameters, even such obvious ones as mean water vapour content. Thus we cannot yet be sure of the fundamental reasons for the four broad systems of seasonal precipitation found in the western Mediterranean (Fig. 6).

1. On the western oceanic facade and on the southern half of the western Mediterranean a single mid-winter maximum rainfall is characteristic.

2. Autumn maximum rainfall is a feature of the northern coastland of the Mediterranean. It has been associated with Mediterranean fronts but it is doubtful if they really exist.

3. Spring maximum rainfall is typical of the mountainous masses of the Iberian Meseta, the Moroccan Atlas and the Algerian high plateaux. These show a transition towards autumn maximum rainfall nearer the coast.

4. Late spring to summer rainfall maxima, grading into the Central European regime are found only in the Po plain. This is largely convectional, occasioned during the rapid heating of the plain when the middle troposphere is unusually cold for reasons already alluded to (see p. 13). Thus whereas only 10 to 15 per cent of the annual rainfall occurs elsewhere in the northern Mediterranean during the summer, in the Po plain summer thunderstorms contribute some 20 to 25 per cent of the yearly amount.

THE SEASONAL CHANGES

Unlike the conditions of the British Isles, weather in the Mediterranean is dominated by the climatic seasons. It is significant that the Greeks had no word for the weather, and that the latin peoples still use the same word for both a measurable period of time and the weather (*tiempo, tempo, temps*). The seasonal rhythm of life is further emphasised by the distinct calendars of annual grain crops and perennial tree-crops. The abrupt change of the upper-air circulation which occurs widespread in the Northern Hemisphere in June and October, is in the Mediterranean area markedly important for ground conditions also. It is still conjectural to explain its mechanism though the gradual change of insolation from summer to winter appears to produce a certain type of 'instability' in the upper air, causing the sudden change to take place. The result is rapid northward displacement of the intertropical convergence zone in June and an abrupt southward shift of the westerlies in October.[31]

1. *The Wet Season.* The most striking change in the Mediterranean year is the autumn break which brings the dry season to an end. On the

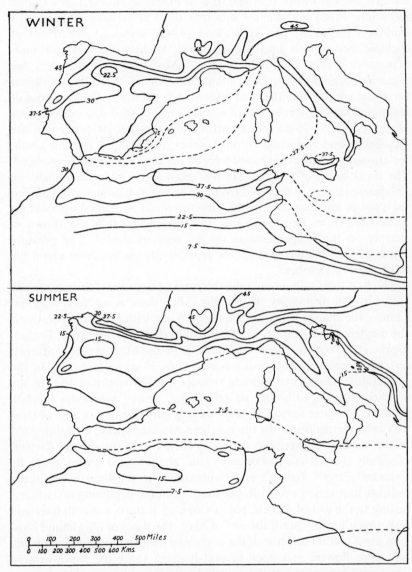

FIG. 7. Average number of days with rainfall in the summer and winter half-years
(after Reichel)

western seaboard as in Portugal, it is as dramatic almost as the Indian monsoon. From mid-August onwards there is a rising frequency of rain-days (10 to 50 per cent) along coastal stations, with traces of cyclonic penetration into the northern Mediterranean about mid-September.[32] (Fig. 7). In the southern Mediterranean, however, the regime of sluggish atmospheric circulation remains generally established for about another month. Thus beginning in the north, the assurance of getting at least one rain-day in a given pentad (five-day period) rises abruptly from 50–70 per cent in early October to about 90 per cent in late October to mid-November in most places, although the extreme south, for example Gibraltar, does not have 80 per cent until mid-November.[33] The break-down of the dry season is often spectacular, accompanying characteristically the first cold front. Ahead of it shallow warm scirocco air is swept northwards over the Mediterranean, to meet deep, cold air behind the front. Because of this, the seasonal break is not shown as sharply on the temperature as on the pressure curves. The pressure charts of the Mediterranean show prominently the break-up about the third week of October.

The first rains commonly take the form of occasional thunderstorms with air-mass instability. In the Po valley there is no such seasonal change, the change being more a thermal one with lower temperatures, the incidence of 50–60 days of frost and 8–10 days of snowfall. Excluding then the Po plain, there is on the Atlantic and Mediterranean littorals an almost continuous growing season with 50 or more weeks. In the mountains the effect of altitude reduces it to 30 weeks or less. In the southern littoral, although we talk of its 'winter' maximum rainfall, there is no winter season as such, having only one day or less of frost and mild temperatures. In the northern Mediterranean, a slightly cold winter is more appreciable, except in sheltered sectors of the Riviera, especially the Riviera di Ponente. Thus phenological studies made by Ottmar,[34] Peter[35], Barata[36] and Lautensach[37] in the Iberian peninsula, indicate that spring occurs in the south from the beginning of January, lasting to the end of March, but at Coimbra it starts a month later and lasts much longer—until the end of May. The dates of the almond blossom are a useful indicator of the beginning of spring (Fig. 88). Its white and pink flowers first open in mid-January along the south-western coast, and by the end of the month it is common along all the eastern littoral to Ampurdan. Majorca and most of the southern half of the Meseta do not, however, see it in flower, until the middle of February, while in the north the blossom does not appear until March. The contrast between the duration of spring in the northern and southern

Mediterranean, occurring in the former from February to May, in the latter only from January to March, is heightened by a marked difference in flora. The glories of the opening green foliage of the deciduous oaks, beeches and chestnuts during the month of April is reserved only for the better watered regions of the north, where the spring is longer and the dry summer is not so unkind (Fig. 88). But in the south there is 'none of the sudden green of thrusting buds which makes deciduous trees the very emblem of a northern spring; the change is one of light and shade rather than of colour and line; cypresses put on more uncompromising mourning and alchemist olives add silver to that mixing bowl in which every shade of green has a place; while the change of season in sea and sky is less marked even than in the landscape; their blues become perhaps more than ever interchangeable' (quoted from *The Golden Honeycomb* by V. Cronin). The crucial sign of a southern spring is invisible alike to ear and eye, for it is rather a sudden and steadily increasing surge of heat.

2. *The Dry Season*. Thus the transition to the dry summers is everywhere more gradual than the autumn break. Rain and its liability continue close to their winter maximum until about March on the littoral with an alternation of cyclonic activity and some quieter spells occurring especially from April onwards. In the southern Mediterranean this is related to the increasing stability of the air masses over the sea, rather than to any pronounced diminution of cyclonic activity.[38] Winds may continue to be quite violent despite increasingly sunny weather. Over the continental interiors, however, convectional activity and rain may continue to a marked extent until May or even June. With the anticyclonic subsidence of the Azores high pressure system, spreading east and northeast, the summer regime is established. It lasts from two to three months in the north with about two dry months, to six months or even more in the extreme south. Fig. 8 illustrates its progressive advance and duration towards the south.

This seasonal aridity constitutes probably the major factor of Mediterranean landscapes, contributing in large measure to their climatic, hydrographic, phytogeographic and even their morphological features. Summer drought is less severe in the north than in the south, in the west than in the east.[39] But its duration is not necessarily very much influenced by the total precipitation. This is especially so in North Africa, where for example it is as long at Tangier (35 in) as at Oudja (13 in), at El Milia (43 in) as at Batna (13 in). Neither is it always influenced by latitude, Matmata having a shorter season than Gabès, Barcelona less than Perpignan. Altitude, however, makes a marked

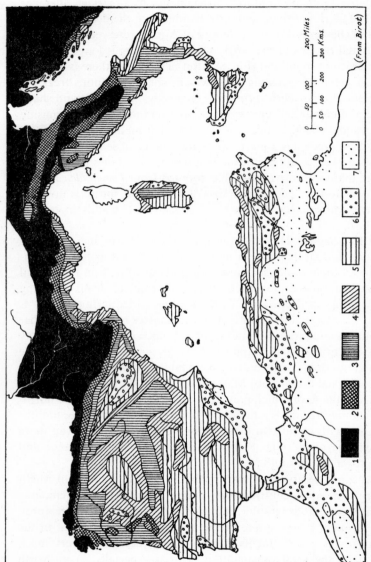

Fig. 8. Duration of the dry season. 1. No dry month. 2. From one to two dry months. 3. From three to four. 4. From two to three. 5. From four to five. 6. From five to seven. 7. More than seven months. A dry month is defined by the following formula:

$$\frac{PJ}{T} < 10$$

with P the monthly precipitation in mm.; J, the number of rain-days, and T, the mean monthly temperatures

(From Birot)

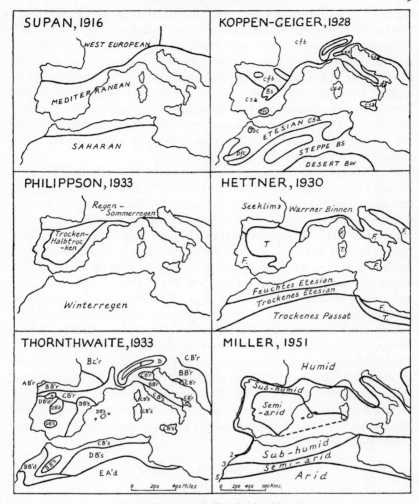

FIG. 9. Systems of climatic classification

difference, bringing a better distributed rainfall for example, to the Apennines. This is strikingly seen in the high mountains of North Africa, Djelfa in the Saharan Atlas (4,429 ft) having a shorter dry season than Maillot in the Tell Atlas (1,525 ft).

Aridity formulae can only approximate crassly to actual conditions, and are unrepresentative of actual conditions because they rely on mean values (Fig. 9). Nuances of geographic circumstance are too variable to be systematised, the length and distribution of the dry season fluctuating more or less markedly each year. Statistical difficulties are obvious. Meteorological observations have not been standardised; for example in Portugal they were taken until recently at 9, 15, 21 hours, while in Algeria they were at 7, 13, 18 hours. Rain-days are not always clearly defined and in the northern Mediterranean the use of June figures is critical, since the dry season usually comes after the middle of the month; thus the humid first half of the month can appreciably alter the statistical values. Paucity of stations, especially in North Africa, where the nearest Saharan stations are over 500 miles apart, should warn against any reliance on lines drawn on a map.[40]

De Martonne's formula ignores the intensity of precipitation and it can also be criticised for its inclusion of the Po plain in a similar context as central Portugal or even the north African littoral.[41] Birot's definition of the duration of the dry season does relate the number of rain-days to the precipitation,[42] but it fails to distinguish the type of rain, or to take account of the atmospheric humidity and its by-product dew (Fig. 8). Neither can it express the degree to which reserves of moisture carried by the soil from winter rains delay the influence of summer aridity to the plants. Gaussen's xerothermal index is a biological definition of the dry season and more satisfactorily defines the transition from the Mediterranean climates (subdivided as Meso-, Thermo- and Xerothermo-) to the subdesert and desert.[43] Thornthwaite's classification is particularly unsatisfactory in Spain with an unrealistic complexity. Miller's scheme, because of its simplicity, is much more practical (Fig. 9). The degree of coincidence of these various formulae is more marked in the definition of the arid and desert climates than in the subdivisions of the Mediterranean humid and sub-humid types.[44]

REGIONAL CLIMATES

The seas, mountains, and to the south the desert, all influence the marked diversity of regional types. But the climatic regions can be grouped simply under the three broad headings of littoral, continental and mountain climates.

1. *Littoral Climates.* The regional contrasts between the Atlantic and Mediterranean littorals in the Iberian peninsula are distinguishable primarily by the annual range of temperature, those on the Atlantic having much lower ranges. Also whereas the Mediterranean littorals are merely ameliorated by the sea, the western coasts are dominated by the more extensive pressure systems of the Atlantic. The most striking feature is the contrast in precipitation and the number of rain-days on

the two facades, reaching a minimum in the south-east, where steppe occurs along its coast. There can be few greater contrasts than that of the gentle, persistent rain of the north and north-west, and the few but violent downpours of the south-east (see Appendix I, table I).

In Southern France and Italy, the littoral climates are much more uniform. The main differences in the Tyrrhenian sea and the Gulfs of Genoa and Lions are thermal, especially winter temperatures. The mild Riviera di Ponente is in a similar position to the Provençal Riviera, both sheltered from the *mistral* winds. The Riviera di Levante and even more so Languedoc are exposed and have greater ranges in temperatures. The east coast of Italy, orographically more uniform than the west, has also less variable climate. But a gradual transition occurs near Ancona and again in the Gargano peninsula. The Adriatic itself, warmer south of the Gargano-Lagesta sill, gives milder winters to the south-east coast. But rainfall also decreases markedly in Apulia, while the Tavoliere has a high range of temperatures. The islands have strangely maritime temperatures but accompanied with a remarkably low rainfall.

In Morocco the Atlantic facade gives a climate unique in North Africa. Although the rainfall is steadily less southwards (Larache 28 inches, Casablanca 16, Agadir 8) and the rain-days diminish from 80 to 27, the coastal zone benefits from heavy summer dews. Along the Rif coast, towards the rain-shadow area of Oran, the rainfall again diminishes so that Melilla has only 16 inches in 66 rain-days. Eastwards again, these figures are doubled as far as the Tunisian Tell. Everywhere the cool sea breezes temper the summer heat and so the annual range is moderate. Eastern Tunisia, however, is plagued with the hot *scirocco*, and the limited effect of the sea-breezes only contributes a minor amount of the annual six to ten inches mean annual rainfall in the Sfax district.

2. *Continental Climates.* Position and the features of relief make these types more variable in their characteristics. The climate of the Po plain is, of course, quite distinct because of its pluviose and markedly summer rainfall regime, transitional to that of Central Europe. In the Iberian Peninsula, the interior relief influences markedly the character of its four climatic regions. The higher and more enclosed relief of Old Castile gives it colder winters than New Castile experiences, so that the southern flanks of the Central Cordillera are a significant limit for a number of plants, notably the olive, and the mean minimum temperature falls to 12° (−11·1) compared with 46° (7·8) in the southern plateaux (see Appendix I, table 2). The two depressions of the Ebro and

the Guadalquivir have hotter climates but the former is contrasted by its lower mean annual temperature, its great range between minimum and maximum values, its lower rainfall more of it in summer and by more days with snow.

The continental climates of North Africa have been described as 'cold climates where the sun is hot.' In Morocco there are two variants, the plateaux and high plains of the east which have very marked contrasts between summer and winter, with marked drought, and the more attenuated continental type characteristic of the Haouz and Tadla plains and the submediterranean eastern plains (Angad and Tafrata). In the inner Algerian Tell distinction is made between the high interior plains, with considerable continental conditions, and the lower plains such as the Chéliff and middle Medjerda, which are drier and hotter. The steppes to the south are secluded from Mediterranean influences and therefore even more continental. Extreme ranges of temperature increase from west to east, less because of the winter conditions than the very high summer temperatures.

3. *Mountain Climates*. Excluding the Alps, the Mediterranean mountains may be divided into two climatic types, the high summits above 6,500 ft and the lower ranges. In the Apennines, more important than merely altitude is also accessibility to maritime influences. Thus in the north, the Arno basin admits marine influences right into the centre of the peninsula, whereas further south a mountain climate is more recognisable in the massive Abruzzi ranges, in Sila and Etna (see Appendix I, table 3).

Areas above 3,000 ft cover about one-seventh of the Iberian Peninsula (34,750 sq. miles) so there mountain climates are significant. Apart from the high ranges of the central Pyrenees, the Sierra Nevada and isolated summits in the Cantabrians and Central Cordillera, that rise above 6,500 ft and have prolonged snow cover, the majority of the mountains lie between 3,000 and 6,500 ft. These have 15 to 60 days of snow, with moderate to heavy rainfall depending upon their orientation, local winds and angle of slopes. Two types are recognisable: the peripheral mountains, which have annual ranges of temperature less than 60° (33) with an average of 42–55 in precipitation; and the interior mountains which have 63–65° (35–36) range and only 25–40 in annually.

In North Africa, the Moroccan mountains are more distinctive than those to the east, because of their greater rainfall. Snow lies above 6,500 ft in the Rif for two to three months, three to four months in the northern Middle Atlas and even longer in the Great Atlas in wet years. Above 10,000 ft precipitation decreases once more. There are, however,

1 View of Vesuvius, looking south-east, with ancient crater of Mount Somma on the left. Note dark streaks of 1944 lava flows in centre of photograph

2 Summit of Etna, in winter   PRIMEVAL LANDSCAPES

3 The Aosta Valley, Ayas basin, Italian Alps

4 Viella, Val d'Aran, with lower slopes of Maladeta on right, Central Pyrenees

5 Toubkal, highest range of W. High Atlas (13,650 ft.) with village of Asni in the Rheraia valley

very few meteorological stations above 6,500 ft in all these Mediterranean mountains (three only in Spain) and so it is impossible yet to make many generalisations.

WATER RESOURCES

The western Mediterranean lands have widely differing hydrological conditions that reflect the contrasts of climate. In the Italian peninsula it is estimated that run-off represents 43 per cent of the total precipitation. In the Iberian peninsula it is about 35 per cent. Run-off is much less in North Africa and diminishes markedly to the east. Tunisia, for example, loses 91 per cent of its precipitation by evapotranspiration and a further 2·4 by percolation, leaving only 6·6 as run-off. The volume of run-off is also sharply contrasted. The river Po, fed by the great water resources of the Alps, drains about 34,000 million m³ annually, whereas all the rivers of North Africa draining into the Mediterranean scarcely contribute a total of 15,000 million m³. Between these two extremes, the Iberian peninsula shares out its outflow more evenly among its major rivers.

Of the factors affecting the volume and seasonal flow of the rivers, the rainfall regime in the catchment is, of course, most important. The melting of snow has little significance except in the Alps and the Pyrenees. Some regimes are influenced by the presence of karst relief, though it is not clear how much;[45] and the lakes have some effect, notably those of northern Italy. No attempt has yet been made to correlate on a broad scale the seasonal flow of these Mediterranean rivers with the seasonal and annual fluctuations of precipitation, but local studies indicate clear correlations. For example, annual precipitation and the surface flow have been correlated in Morocco.[46]

Broadly, there are three major types of river regime. The typical regime of the southern Mediterranean has a marked maximum flow in winter and a very poor summer coefficient of rainfall of only 0·00 to 0·15 (that is the division of the mean monthly precipitation in the catchment area by 12). The northern Mediterranean regime has a marked autumn maximum with summer co-efficients of 0·20 to 0·35. A third regime which is associated with the most abundant precipitation occurs where spring and autumn have dual maxima, and with summer values of 0·30 to 1·00.[47]

In Italy the striking feature is the dominance of the Po whose flow represents 38 per cent of the total annual run-off in Italy. The other Italian rivers flowing into the Adriatic contribute a further 31 per cent. The Tyrrhenian and the Ligurian seas receive only 21 from the peninsula and the islands contribute six per cent.[48] This leaves only a discharge of four per cent into the Ionian sea. There is thus much more discharge into the north than in the south and into the Adriatic than elsewhere. The Po has a complicated regime with flood periods in May and in November, low water in February and August. These reflect: an alpine regime in its headstreams with a nivo-pluvial peak in the spring that coincides with the maximum rainfall; subalpine regime with a slightly later pluvio-nival season; and on the southern tributaries, an Emilian regime, with floods in November and March. The lakes, which have a large volume compared with their catchment areas, especially Garda, retard the maximum flow by about a month and help to regulate the rivers Ticino, Adda, Oglio and Mincio. All these influences account for the relatively even flow of the lower Po, which is itself largely a man-directed channel between some 1,240 miles of protective dykes.[49] But, floods such as those of 1951, which inundated about 400 sq. miles, demonstrate that the Po is not yet tamed. In central Italy, with an annual precipitation of 24–28 in, there is only a moderate volume of flow in rivers such as the Reno, Arno, Ombrone, Tiber, Volturno and Pescara. Their regimes reflect closely the rainfall incidence, with floods in February and March and a secondary rise in November, with low water in the summer.[50] In limestone areas, such as the lower Tiber, Volturno and Pescara, there is a lag and the rainfall fluctuations are more evened out. In the south there is no secondary maximum in autumn, a single flood season occurring in late winter with a long, dry season in summer when many of the smaller streams dry out. The Tirso even, in Sardinia, has been known to remain dry for eight months. Modern hydraulic works, however, are modifying some of these larger rivers.

The majority of Iberian rivers have a modest flow of less than 700 $m^3/$sec, since one-third of the peninsula has less than 20 in of rainfall annually.[51] Much of the peninsula has 20 per cent or less as surface run-off. In the south, especially in La Mancha and in the Sa Morena, even large catchment areas dry out in summer (for example the Jabalon with 3,000 sq. miles). These areas of only seasonal flow would be much greater were it not for the mountainous watersheds that feed the main rivers. Apart from the pluvio-nival and the nivo-pluvial regimes above about 3,000 and 6,500 ft respectively, three broad distinctions are clear. First, there are in the north and the north-west rich resources that give its rivers the greatest run-off: the Minho at Orense has 19·4 litres/km², the Mondego at Coimbra 10·0, the Zezere at Castelo do Bode 27·7. There is a single maximum in February and a minimum in August.

Secondly, there are the Mediterranean rivers (including those of the Cévennes) which have autumn and spring maxima of rainfall, but their flow is complicated by karstic phenomena, notably on the rivers Mijares, Turia and Júcar. Flow is meagre (0·5 to 41 litres/km²) with late spring maximum and a secondary maximum in autumn. But as the floods of September 1962 in Catalonia have shown, these Levant rivers are all notorious for their inundations, especially the Llobregat, Turia, Júcar and Segura. Thirdly, in the south and south-east, where flow is meagre, the regimes are very irregular. Floods tend to occur in February, with minor ones in December. Small basins have only intermittent flow and even the upper Guadiana struggles to maintain its summer flow with an average of 1 litre/km² within the 1,200 sq. miles of its upper basin.

In north-west Africa, rough appraisals of its water resources suggest Morocco has half of the total, Algeria and Tunisia about one-quarter each.[52] Morocco is favoured because of its Atlantic position and the configuration of its mountains. About 21–22 per cent of its area receives over 24 in of rain annually, another 26 per cent has 12–24 in and the rest is steppe or desert. The chief rivers of Algeria and Tunisia, the Chéliff and Medjerda, have an even lower volume than some of the Moroccan tributaries, such as the Ouerrha and el Abid. Morocco's great river, the Oum-er-Rbia, is fed by springs and a pluvio-nival regime at its source in the Middle Atlas, so that it maintains a steadier flow of c. 35 m³/sec during the summer than the Sebou (12 m³/sec) which has greater floods. Compared with the flow of these rivers, the Tensift and Sous have meagre supplies, the former only blessed by the sub-surface supplies of the Haouz of Marrakech. The lengths of the Moulouya (280 miles) and especially the Dades-Dra (750 miles) are illusionary of the real importance, having only low or seasonal flow across steppe and desert. Thus the regime of the North African rivers is essentially pluvial, having a late winter or spring maximum, and most of the rivers dry out in summer.

The water resources of the western Mediterranean are meagre compared with those of western Europe. Even on the north coast of Spain and on the south flank of the Po valley there are average annual deficits of precipitation for maximum crop production of some 8–12 in (200–300 mm), while much of Spain and the south-east of Italy have deficits of over 24 in (600 mm). In the south-east of Spain and over much of North Africa deficits exceed 31 in (800 mm).[53] Supplemental irrigation which is desirable for high productivity in the north, and very important in the central Mediterranean lands, is essential in the south.

Great efforts have been made in Italy, Spain and in Morocco in recent decades to expand the irrigated areas. But in Algeria and Tunisia, where the water resources are more limited, small scale works will inevitably remain of primary concern.[54] With the sudden change of seasonal conditions from summer drought to winter rains, the climatic challenge is how to protect riverine communities from disastrous floods, and how to conserve the overall meagre water supplies for agriculture and other growing needs. This is probably nature's greatest challenge to man in the Mediterranean world.

SUMMARY

The Mediterranean region has a wide variety of climatic types, greater perhaps than any other comparable area of Europe. Its marked feature is the widespread summer drought, associated with the sub-tropical high pressure system. The sea has an ameliorating influence in winter but the nature of its cyclogenesis is distinct from the classical model of north-western Europe; its structure is closely related to the configuration of the relief, making weather forecasting more difficult. Local winds play a significant role in local climates. The climatic influence of the Pyrenees and the Alps are markedly contrasted creating fundamental differences in the human geography of the North Italian Plain and in the Ebro basin. Seasonal, rather than weather, changes rule in the Mediterranean climate with a dramatic break between the summer drought and the onset of the autumn rains. Flood control, difficult because of the high variability from year to year in any river flow is an exaggerated problem in the Mediterranean. There are three major types of river flow reflecting the contrasts between the northern, southern and most pluviose areas of the region. Italy has the most generous water resources, mainly because of the run-off from the Alps. But in varying degree all parts show some water deficiency for maximum crop production and so irrigation is important.

CHAPTER 3

THE MEDITERRANEAN SEA:
THE INVISIBLE LANDSCAPE

'In spite of the fact that the Mediterranean zone is remarkably uniform otherwise, there is no unity under the sea, and this emphasises the importance of the submarine highlands.'

(A. Siegfried, *The Mediterranean*)

The Mediterranean, which initiated Western civilisation, has more claim than any other region of the world to be the birthplace of the earth sciences. Herodotus the father of geography refers to a copper engraving that depicted the outline of the Mediterranean, dating from at least 500 B.C. The map made by Ptolemy in the second century A.D. was for long the most detailed, if not the most accurate, outline of its shores. The famous Portolan charts of the Middle Ages originated in the Western Mediterranean. The first special study of the sea was Bartholomew Crescention's *Della Nautica Mediterranea*, published in Rome, in 1602. Atlases and numerous maps followed rapidly, made especially by French and Italian cartographers. Count Marsilli carried out the first systematic investigations of salinity in the Mediterranean (in 1706–7) while Georges Aimé made a significant contribution to hydrography in his *Recherches physiques sur la Méditerranée* (1845). There followed an era of much oceanographical research, such as the contributions made by Smyth (1854), Carpenter (1870), Magnaghi (1881), Prince Albert of Monaco (after 1885) and Schmidt (1908–10). Since 1910 an international commission has been established by the Prince of Monaco to study the scientific problems of the Mediterranean Sea. Numerous expeditions continue and, within recent years, French and Italian surveys have been mapping the sea-floor in detail. Despite all these efforts this invisible landscape of the Mediterranean is still largely unknown.

The Mediterranean Sea is about 2,320 miles from Gibraltar to the Syrian coast. Its maximum width, between Genoa and Tunis, is about 500 miles. The western Mediterranean together with the Adriatic Sea are neatly divided from the eastern Mediterranean by the Silician-Ionian basin, and comprise about 38 per cent of the total area.[1] The

Mediterranean is a deep sea with a mean depth of about 4,500 ft and about 56 per cent of its area having depths of over 3,000 ft.

WATER CIRCULATION

Three characteristics of the Mediterranean Sea make it one of the most distinctive of the inland seas. Because of the lack of much tidal action, sea movements are dictated very largely by temperature and salinity differences. The physiographical features of the basins, the sills and the channels all influence greatly the water circulation, especially the sill of Gibraltar which virtually shuts out the Atlantic influences and creates a gigantic aquarium of warm water. The climate with its intense evaporation and the low annual increment of fresh river water flowing into the Mediterranean cause it to be markedly saline.

It is erroneous to imagine that the Mediterranean is tideless. The semi-diurnal tidal ranges are however, only of the order of 7–12 in. Maximum tidal ranges are 19–23 in and on the North African coast, but reaching 35–39 in along the coast of Provence. In the narrow channels, such as the Straits of Messina, the tidal velocity can be five knots or more, even though its tidal range is only about ten inches.[2]

The sill of Gibraltar plays a fundamental rôle in the Mediterranean circulation. It keeps out effectively the much colder currents that occur in the Atlantic at depths below 1,050 ft (that is below the sill). Homothermal temperatures at the bottom of the Mediterranean basins vary only slightly, from 12·8° (−10·7) in the Balearic sea to 13·7° (−10·2) in the eastern basin. But the sill does not prevent denser saline water from flowing out into the Atlantic, in currents which are traceable as far as the latitude of southern Africa. This deeper saline water, which escapes from the Mediterranean or sinks into the deeps in each basin, is replaced by the inflow of surface water from the Atlantic.[3] As the Mediterranean surface lies at 4–12 in below the ocean outside, water is driven in as a powerful surface current at four knots, aided also by wind and barometric gradients, to provide an easterly drift[4] (Fig. 11). The peninsulas of the Mediterranean deflect the easterly drift to form an anticlockwise movement of surface currents round their shores.

As the sea is surrounded by warm, dry lands with cloudless summers and few important rivers flowing into it, evaporation predominates over precipitation and run-off. It is estimated by Schott that there is an annual loss of nearly 3,400 km³/per annum. But the transport of fresh water from the Atlantic is calculated to be sufficient to ventilate the entire sea of the Mediterranean within seventy-five years (Fig. 10).

According to the estimates of Schott and Sverdrup, it is possible to illustrate the water budget in the following table:

Water Budget of the Mediterranean Sea[4]

Gains in m³/sec		Losses in m³/sec	
Inflow from the Atlantic Ocean	1,750,000	Outflow to the Atlantic Ocean	1,680,000
Inflow from the Black Sea	12,600	Outflow to the Black Sea	6,100
Precipitation	31,600	Evaporation	115,400
Run-off	7,300		
Total	1,801,500		1,801,500

Salinity is more excessive in the eastern Mediterranean because of the higher losses by evaporation. There is, therefore, a similar inflow of surface water over the Sicilian and Tunisian sill to compensate for this loss, estimated by Nielsen to be about four per cent of that passing through the Straits of Gibraltar.[5]

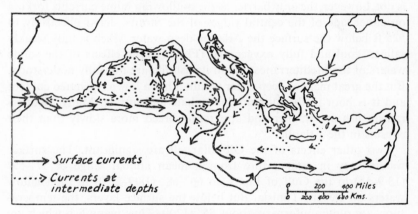

FIG. 10. The circulation of currents in the Mediterranean Sea

Within each Mediterranean basin there are three or four levels distinguishing different water bodies. The surface layer varies seasonally in depth from 350 to 700 ft, that is the depth to which convection currents ordinarily reach in winter, reflecting seasonal changes of temperature, and having a relatively low salinity. Below this is intermediate water with a salinity maximum at 1,000–1,300 ft. At depths of 5,000 to 6,500 ft minimum temperatures are reached and below this the temperature increases adiabatically to the sea-bottom.[7] The ultimate source of the bottom water of the western basins comes chiefly from the northern part of the Balearic and Ligurian seas, which contribute the main river flow into the sea, and eventually sinking into the deeps.

THE FISH HABITATS

About three-quarters of the fish tonnage landed in the countries that border the western Mediterranean come from the Atlantic. Yet it is wrong to exaggerate the poverty of the Mediterranean Sea. In the first place, statistics for the numerous rural ports of the Mediterranean often grossly underestimate the landings to avoid fiscal duties, whereas the more commercialised fishing of the Atlantic ports have probably more accurate returns. Secondly, the Mediterranean fishermen have been slow to develop techniques and the trawling grounds of the Mediterranean have not been fully explored. Thirdly, environmental conditions are so different that the contrast is rather one of relative difficulty of fishing than one of relative scarcity of fish.[8]

The sill of Gibraltar plays a fundamental role in creating the vast Mediterranean aquarium. The sill, rising to 1,051 ft below the surface is not, however, the only barrier as the outflowing saline currents forking on either side of the central ridges of the Straits, debar effectively to 525 ft below the surface the Atlantic deep water which is only weakly saline,[9] cool and fully oxygenated (Fig. 11). The effects of the saline waters of the Mediterranean upon its fish-life are not fully understood. But the great mass of deep water within it has a low oxygenated content and it is poor in the nutrients phosphate and nitrate. Many Mediterranean fish are smaller and apparently breed more slowly than their cousins in the Atlantic.

Two other effects of the Gibraltar sill are significant. The surface waters vary in temperature from a mean annual range of 57°–59° (13·9–15) in the Gulf of Lions, to 66°–68° (18·9–20·0) in the shallow waters off eastern Tunisia. But below the surface layers, the temperatures are quite uniform at about 55° (12·8). Thus many fish which are pelagic in the Atlantic can live several hundreds or even thousands of feet deeper in the Mediterranean. Vertical migrations of fish therefore tend to become exaggerated and the fish are more difficult to catch. Relative uniformity of water conditions makes some species more susceptible to temperature and salinity changes within narrow limits, that is they are stenothermic and stenohaline.

It is important to remember, however, that this Mediterranean 'aquarium' has been affected by climatic changes since late Tertiary times, with relict fauna ranging from Tertiary tropical to Quaternary glacial and temperate conditions.[10]

Does the south-eastern Mediterranean belong to a relic of the Tethys fauna of subtropical character? Is the western Mediterranean related more definitely to Atlantic fauna? What influence have the Quaternary land bridges had on the present fauna of the basins?[11] These biological problems remain still unsolved. Together with the highly variable bathymetrical and orographical conditions, there is therefore a great diversity of fish species. These create a market problem in each trawler's haul and the miscellany of teleostians comprises the major catch.

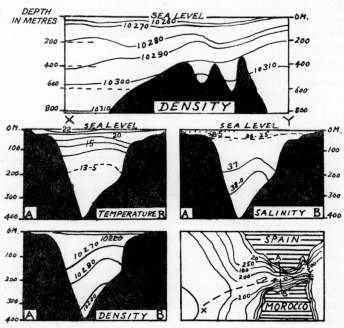

Fig. 11. Profiles of salinity and temperature in the Straits of Gibraltar

There are four major types of habitat for the Mediterranean fish. Of lesser importance, but providing winter employment for the fishermen when they cannot go to sea because of storms, are the lagoons and inland waterways.[12] The lagoons of the Languedoc coast (68,000 acres) the Ebro delta, the Valencian Albufera, the Mar Menor and the Po delta (Commachio), are still fished by traditional methods of traps, nets etc. for migrants such as the eel, shad, golden perch, mullet and bass.

The continental shelf is the most important zone of fish. But this is confined to narrow belts on most of the Italian and North African coasts, rarely more than 10–15 miles wide. The shallow waters of the

Adriatic are exceptional, and are the most intensively fished Italian waters, with large ports such as Chioggia. La Planasse, in the Gulf of Lions, is another broad sandy area, some 25–30 miles wide, but it is under-exploited[13] (Fig. 12). The Gulf of Valencia and especially the shallow waters of the Sicilian-Tunisian sill are important. During the spring and summer these shallow waters heat quickly and the cloudless skies intensify the photosynthesis that aids the rapid, rich growth of plankton and plants. The continental shelves are thus characterised by the intense seasonal migrations of blue fish, represented notably by the Cleipeides (sardine or young pilchard, sprat, tunny, bonito, alache), the Scombrides (mackerel, horse and cobs mackerel, melva, crab and spring lobster). Some fish, such as the tunny, fatten in these waters, obtaining their oil from the plant *Posidones*, before migrating south to the breeding grounds of the warm waters between Sicily and Tunisia.[14]

The third habitat occurs on the edges of the continental shelf and slope (at 900–3,000 ft), at present beyond the reach of most Mediterranean fishermen, where the continental slope plunges into the abyss beyond. Here an intense breeding life proceeds, of which little is yet known. Modern trawling techniques will eventually open up possibilities of rich returns on the unexploited coasts. In the deeps, pelagic fish such as the flatfish and crustacea, together with bathypelagic fauna share an unknown world, impossible to assess as yet.

The key to Mediterranean fishing is the recognition of the seasonal migrations of fish, on both horizontal and vertical scales. The gentle thermal gradient between the northern waters of the Planasse and the southern waters off Tunisia influences the breeding habits of the tunny in summer. The saline currents which sweep through the western Mediterranean from the Levant at shallower or deeper layers according to the seasonal conditions of the surface waters, act like some magic carpet, conveying the shoals of sardine, anchovy, mackerel, bonito and tunny. The thrust of the current and the state of the season determine the fill of the net and the welfare of the fisherman, no two seasons being exactly alike. Fishing communities like Ste Marie, on the Rhône delta, with its shallow waters, are more dependent on these seasonal vagaries than the deep rocky coasts which plunge steeply off the shelf. Liguria, Roussillon, Costa Brava, Alicante, eastern Andalusia, Algeria, have always enjoyed more fishing throughout the year because the sardines, anchovies and other vertical migrants are found in deeper water in winter, near the surface in summer. Methods have to be varied accordingly, using *lámpara*, seine, drift and drag nets in summer, deep trawling and net fishing in winter to catch the sardines and anchovy. Nets are used to catch the tunny in late spring (*courantelle* and *seche*), elaborate traps in the breeding season (*tonnara* in Italy, *almadraba* in Spain, *armacoe* in Portugal), and line fishing from pinnaces and fast cutters throughout the year.[14] Thus the skill, the variety of methods, the seasonal character of the work, all engender separate ways of life between the fishing societies and the agricultural peasants. Some societies such as those of El Palmar, in the Valencian Albufera, San Pedro in the Ebro delta, Commacchio in the Po delta, still have ways of life regulated by customs traceable from the Middle Ages.

The Atlantic fishing grounds are much more important than those of their Mediterranean counterpart. Morocco, for example, has five times more catch of fish than Algeria, and the Atlantic ports of Spain represent 74 per cent of the total Spanish tonnage. There are obvious reasons for this supremacy of the Atlantic coasts. The continental shelf, although only 18–25 miles wide off the Portuguese coast, broadens into the wide area of the Bay of Biscay and again south of the Straits of Gibraltar as far as Cap Cantin. In the whole of this zone, the habitat is remarkably uniform, since the warm Gulf stream gives positive anomalous temperatures to the northern sector, while the cold Canaries current off the North African coasts reduces the influence of sub-tropical latitudes. The seasonal migration of fish is on a vaster and more horizontal scale than in the Mediterranean, and so the trawlers of these Atlantic countries penetrate further south into Mauretanian waters and westwards to the Newfoundland banks. The pelagic fish, sardine (pilchard), hake and mackerel, together with others more usually associated with northern latitudes, mingle in these coastal waters.

The geographical position of the three Atlantic countries provides a number of contrasts. The ample shelf area of northern Spain means that long-distance fisheries do not need yet to be much developed and some 90 per cent of the fish caught in Spanish ports normally come from coastal waters. Portuguese fishermen on the other hand have had long-distance fisheries for over eight hundred years, fishing in British waters at least from the twelfth century, and on the Newfoundland banks from the sixteenth century. The disinterest of the Arabs in a fish diet perhaps explains the very recent development of Morocco's fisheries since the First World War.

THE SUBMARINE RELIEF

The western Mediterranean consists of several deep basins, separated by shallow sills and narrow straits. It is effectively limited to the west by the sill of Gibraltar and to the east by the Sicilian-Tunisian platform.

Bordering the Atlantic, the Gibraltar sill is a complex barrier with at least three summits rising to within 1,050 ft of the surface, plunging, however, to depths of over 4,500 ft in the western approaches (Fig. 11). On the sill is the volcanic islet of Alboran. The Straits of Gibraltar are presumed to have been formed during the Upper Pliocene (?Piacenza stage).[15] East of the sill, the sea-floor sinks rapidly to the Balearic basin, forming a plain some seventy miles wide at depths of 9,000–10,000 ft. Whereas a wide continental shelf extends from Spain to link it with the Balearic islands, the coastal margins of Corsica, Sardinia and North Africa are very narrow and plunge rapidly. Off Bonifacio for example a depth of 11,220 ft is found. Platforms exist between Sardinia and Algeria (4,200 ft) the Balearics and Sardinia (7,875–8,200 ft) and between Corsica and the Balearics (5,900–8,500 ft). A shallow sill seems to link Formentera with the Spanish mainland in northern Alicante,[16] reaching a maximum depth of 2,322 ft. But a ditch separates the other islands from it at a depth of 2,706 ft. Apart from these broad features little is yet known about this western or Balearic basin.

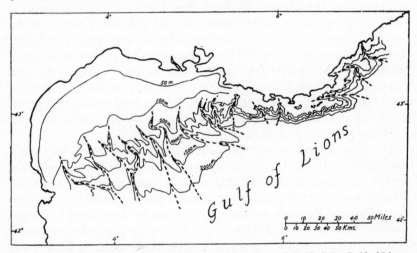

FIG. 12. Submarine canyons in the Planasse or continental shelf of the Gulf of Lions. Note the occurrence of these canyons showed by pecked lines between – 100–500 to over 2,000 m.

More is known about the Planasse, the shallow continental shelf of the Gulf of Lions, covering 2,800 sq. miles between the drowned ends of the eastern Pyrenees and the Maures-Esterel.[17] It forms a gently undulating plain dipping seawards to depths of 390–500 ft. On its lower slopes a network of some twenty submarine canyons appear and plunge down the continental slope to depths of 6,500–8,800 ft.[18] Some of these off the Riviera coast seem clearly to be seaward continuations of river valleys (Fig. 12). According to Bourcart, they are dated variously from the late Miocene to the Quaternary and related to movements of continental flexure, the Planasse and Riviera coast acting as a hinged structure.[19] Another series of submarine canyons off the west coast of Corsica are even more clearly continuations of river valleys.[20]

The Ligurian sea is bordered on the west by a submarine platform extending north from Cap Corse. This indicates linkage with the Riviera mainland rather than with the suggestion of a Corsican link with Elba and Tuscany.[21] The south-eastern flank of the Gulf of Genoa is a glacis which continues southwards as the mid-Tyrrhenian rise, supporting the islands of Gorgona, Capraia, Elba, Pianosa and Monte Cristo. Like the Maures system submerged in Miocene (Tortonian) times, the Gulf of Genoa also seems to represent a fractured and submerged mountain system, with faults running north-east to south-west and which influence two major canyons, the Bisagno and Policovera.

Between Corsica and the northern Tyrrhenian sea is a deep trench, the Corsican Canal (1,600–2,000 ft) running southwards for some 200 miles.[22] Bourcart has dated it as Pliocene. Within the northern Tyrrhenian, all the submarine features of relief appear related to the Tuscan structures and apart from the Corsican Canal, there are few depths below 2,000 ft. In contrast, the central and southern Tyrrhenian sea is very deep, reaching maximum depths of over 10,000 ft in the western Mediterranean, only exceeded by the Mediterranean record of 15,200 ft in the narrow Matapan trench. But much of the southern Tyrrhenian is a vast, almost level plain; north of the islet of Alicudi it has a constant depth of 11,650 ft for a distance of fifteen miles. Six large graben and several smaller ones have been identified, one of which plunges to a depth of 12,598 ft near the Ponza islands. The Lipari islands represent only a few of the submerged volcanoes which form a continuation of the Calabrian arc (Fig. 151). One major volcano situated about half-way between Naples and Palermo rises 10,170 ft to within 1,500 ft of the sea surface, having a height three times and a perimeter twice that of Vesuvius. According to Segre, lava dredged from the Tyrrhenian seafloor indicates a subaerial origin for at least some of the volcanoes, but this is dubious.[23] Evidence of volcanics dredged up from depths of 7,000–8,500 ft in Algerian waters perhaps indicates subsidence on a major scale within late Tertiary times. Some 137 submarine canyons border the continental shelf of the Tyrrhenian basin, and here evidence of subsidence is clearer (Fig. 13).

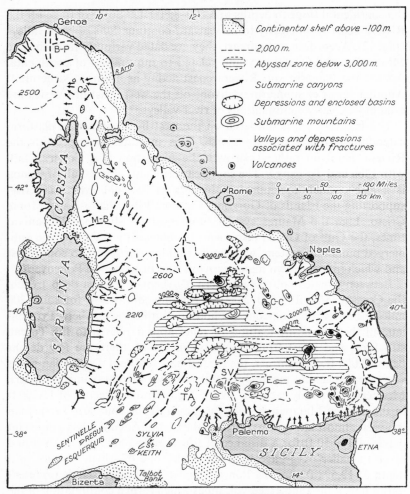

FIG. 13. Submarine relief of the Tyrrhenian Sea.
Letters C-T, TA, etc., refer to depressions and deep valleys

The Tyrrhenian basin is limited to the south by a platform 3,000 ft below the surface and extending from east to west between Sicily and Galita. Beyond it stretches a shallow sill between Sicily and Tunisia, most of it less than 2,000 ft below sea-level. This sill appears to be of continental origin, shattered by distension movements in the Pleistocene.[24] The submarine features of the sill appear to connect the folded structures of Tunisia with those of Sicily, in a series of submarine mountains, troughs and plateaux.[25] East of these the shelf rises again to form a shallow plain mostly less than 600 ft deep, linking east central Tunisia with the similar hills and plains of south and central Sicily. Malta, Lampedusa, Lampiane and the Graham Bank on which the volcano of Julia arose above the sea (in 1831 and 1863) are all situated on this sill. The sill is dominated by north-north-west to south-south-east fractures which have given the outline to some of the islands for example Malta.[26] Similar fractures opened up the Straits of Messina and Otranto in late Pliocene times. East of the sill which separates the western from the eastern Mediterranean, there is one of the steepest gradients anywhere in the Mediterranean, with slopes of 45° or more, plunging to depths of over 12,000 ft in the Ionian sea (Fig. 14).

CLASSIFICATION OF COASTS

The present outline of the Mediterranean sea has been finally determined by the Flandrian transgression, associated with the last postglacial phase. The same transgression that established the English Channel and drowned the rias of north-west Spain, fashioned the straits of Bonifacio[27] and overlapped the low-lying coasts of the mainland. Its chronology has been well studied by A. C. Blanc (1936) at Versilia, south of Spezia.[28] Recent deposition has affected the latest changes. The Tunisian Medjerda, for example, carries annually 17 million tons of alluvium into its delta, causing subsidence by such rapid accumulation. The Po valley with its 6,500 ft of Quaternary deposits has certainly experienced this in the northern Adriatic, and it is probable that it has occurred on a smaller scale at the mouth of the Rhône (the Fos gulf) and in the Pontine marshes.

A broad two-fold division of Mediterranean coasts can be recognised.[29] There are the primary or youthful coasts where structure is important, and there are the secondary or mature coasts where marine agencies have been significant. In view of the importance of recent tectonics in shaping the Mediterranean, the majority of its coasts belong to the first category (Fig. 14).

Rias flooded in the Flandrian transgression are a distinct type. Notable examples occur in Galicia and also in western Corsica.

The traditional distinction between transverse and longitudinal coasts is not very satisfactory as in a sense all coasts attain eventually a longitudinal form. Various degrees of straight and indented coasts may be a preferable distinction. A classic type is the coast of Dalmatia, resulting from the parallel alignment of anticlines which form the cliffs and 'peanut islands', and of synclines lying submerged in the intervening narrow straits and bays. This scheme applies only in the general form

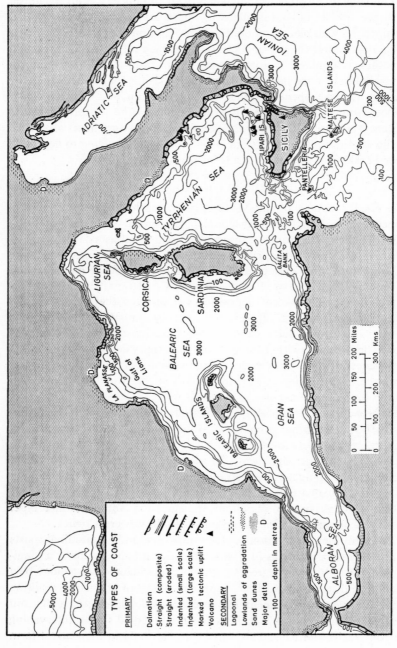

Fig. 14. The Western Mediterranean: classification of coasts and bathymetric features

however, as some of the islands offshore may have more complicated structures. Western Majorca has a comparable coast. Relatively straight coasts are composite. Faulted coasts give some good examples of straight coasts such as the Apulian plateau, some of the North African coasts, and the Provençal coast between Cap Sicie and Cavalaire. Mountain chains parallel to the coasts produce other types, as along the Málaga shore.

Indented coasts are also composite in character. In south-west Morocco the Great Atlas meets the coast transversely with a series of faults near Mazagan. In Algeria oblique structures result from the intersection of the east-north-east to west-south-west trends of the coasts and the north-east to south-west mountain folds. Thus a series of oblique headlands, corresponding to the anticlinal structures, shut off the intervening synclinal bays of Oran, Arzew and Algiers. Along the coasts of northern Tunisia and Sicily, and especially on the south-west coast of Calabria, the most significant feature is the rapid uplift since the Pleistocene with marine terraces rising to 2,000–2,700 ft (Fig. 14).

Coasts shaped by volcanic activity complete the list of primary coasts. Some result from lava flows and ash beds as occur in Campania and the Lipari Islands. A few examples of caldera subsidence are also found as in the famous example of Santorin in the Aegean.

Secondary or mature coasts shaped by marine action are associated particularly with lowland areas. Continuous coastal plains in areas of crustal stability are more typical of the southern and eastern Mediterranean. They are characteristic, for example, of the coastline between southern Tunisia and Egypt. In areas of late Tertiary fractures as along the Murcian and Valencian coasts, the plain of Languedoc and parts of western Italy, lowlands of aggradation have been built up. Deep troughs such as those of Roussillon, Ampurdán, Andalusia and the Gharb are more complex infills of glacis material and sedimentation.

Deltaic coasts are a special variant, subdivided according to their shape. Where alluviation is growing fast deltas are lobate, for example, the Ebro, Rhône and Po. Where marine erosion is more important concave crescents facing the sea are formed, as at the mouth of the Tiber. With active coastal currents rounded deltas are formed, for example, the Llobregat, Arno, Rion and Crati. At the Tet, Guadalaviar and Garigliano stunted deltas are caused by the dominance of marine action.

SUMMARY

Three main characteristics of the Mediterranean Sea are its relative absence of tidal action, the natural division of its series of deep basins by submarine sills at shallow depths, and the marked salinity of its waters. The effect of the Gibraltar sill is to make the Mediterranean into virtually an aquarium with distinct differences of temperature and of fish habitats from those of the Atlantic. The poverty of fishing in the Mediterranean has been exaggerated and more reference should be given to the difficulties of fishing and to the archaic practices still in use. The submarine features are now being explored in some detail, the knowledge of which is an essential key to the surer understanding of the patterns of Mediterranean tectonics. The present outline of the Mediterranean coasts was determined after the effects of the Flandrian transgression. The coasts may be broadly divided into two categories: the primary coasts, whose configuration depends on structural features, and the secondary coasts that were fashioned more directly by marine agencies.

CHAPTER 4

THE ANATOMY OF THE LANDSCAPES:
STRUCTURES, LANDFORMS AND SOILS

'Natura non facit saltus'

The mountains and the basins of the Mediterranean have been called the Enigma Variations of tectonic geology. Certainly it is a symphony of the earth that is not easy to understand. Consequently the geographer may best thread his way in observing certain principles. First, it is necessary to distinguish the broad contrasts of structures, even though a causal explanation of their origins is not always clear. Thus the rigid blocks of the Mediterranean region are contrasted with the mobile belts of plastic rocks. Secondly, it is probable that numerous geophysical processes have occurred depending both on the types of rocks, and on the scale involved. Undue attention to these processes readily results, however, in a confusion between the speculative and the known. Thirdly, it is important to emphasise that the mountain chains of the Mediterranean have been folded not once but many times, their orogenic processes being perhaps quite localised at a specific period. Some of the earlier geologists, notably Staub, tended to see everywhere evidence of alpine orogeny. Now it is recognised that while two general phases of alpine folding may be broadly distinguished, the Oligocene-Miocene and the Pontian-Pliocene, each may also be subdivided into phases and episodes. Moreover, mosaics of structures that were created prior to each orogeny reacted perhaps quite differently from each other during these principal epochs of mountain building. Finally, it must be admitted that a hiatus still exists between the broad, somewhat speculative synthesis of the tectonic geologist, and the narrower outlook of the geomorphologist, who is only concerned with those geological structures that explain relevantly the surface features of the landforms.

EVOLUTION OF MEDITERRANEAN STRUCTURES

Any structural explanation of the Mediterranean—considering its great dimensions—must recognise a hierarchy of geophysical causes[1] in relation to scale[2] both spatial and temporal. Four structural orders are recognised in this summary. The first order sees the Mediterranean as a seaway of Eurasia that has planetary scale and is traceable to the early history of the earth as a whole. Certainly, the precursor of the Mediterranean, the Tethys Sea, goes back to late Palaeozoic times, although it is uncertain what areas of the present sea—if any—have a direct ancestry. Some geologists imply the Mediterranean is the remnant of Tethys,[3] while others are sceptical.

Thermo-dynamic theories that postulate adjustment between the deep crustal contrasts of continental (sial) and oceanic (sima) structures belong to the second order of geotectonics. Broadly, geologists agree that the deep crustal movements of the European and African shields, separated by the sial of Tethys, have framed the general architecture of the Mediterranean lands and basins. There are, however, three different schools of interpretation. The first and most vocal postulate the advance of the African Shield northwards, compressing the sediments of the geosyncline between the two shields. This is the view of geologists such as Termier,[4] Argand,[5] Staub,[6] von Seidlitz,[7] Russo[8] and Fallot.[9] A second interpretation suggests an autonomous evolution of the orogenic zone between the two shields, associated with a magmatic genesis.[10] This is the least probable theory. A third group of geologists such as Holmes, Vening-Meinesz[11] and Umbrove use the concept of convection currents below the earth's crust, metamorphism of basic rocks (e.g. eclogite, which has a 10 per cent decrease in volume), and buckling. It is more reasonable to see at differing scales all three hypotheses, giving full recognition to the effects of the northwards push of Africa. In broad outline it seems clear that the mountains of the western Mediterranean have arisen along the major and bordering geosynclines during the struggle for space, resultant on the relative approach of Africa and Europe. Median areas in some cases have been squeezed up but in others, more numerous, they have been broken up and subsided wholly or in part.

Figure 15 summarises some of the attempts made to demonstrate a causal linkage in the evolution of the Alpine chains. Suess first assumed (in 1860) a unity of structure and relief in these chains.[12] Later (in 1909) he recognised distinct structures (Alpides and Dinarides) which he related to European and Asiatic movements respectively. In a modified way this distinction is still upheld, the Alpine structures being older and more complicated than the Dinarides. Suess envisaged a great alpine arc extending from the Cantabrians, via the Pyrenees, Alps, Apennines, Tell Atlas and the Rif, linking up with the Baetic Cordillera. Stille[13] and Cueto[14] have supported similar schemes. Argand rejected the dual distinction made of the Alpides and Dinarides but he was the first to show that the folds of the Rif and the Baetic are separate. He elaborated on a twofold system of Alpine-Pyrenean ranges in the north and an African-Apennine system in the south. Stille, von Seidlitz and

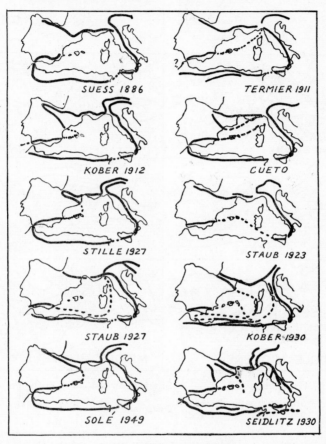

FIG. 15. Tectonic schemes of Alpine folded mountains, according to various geologists (after Solé Sabarís)

others have followed Kober's main thesis[15] though modifying it in detail. Now, due to the researches of Marín and Fallot,[16] it is recognised that there is no Gibraltar arc but a stratigraphical, tectonic and physiographical divide between them, the Palaeozoic rocks of the Rif and Malaga acting as one system (Fig. 15).

To summarise the features of the second order of tectonics two broad types of structures may be distinguished. First, there are the External

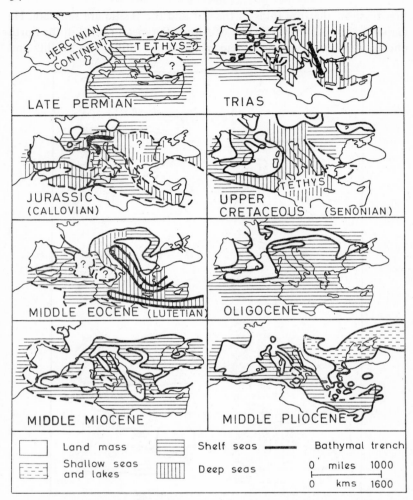

FIG. 16. The palaeogeographical evolution of the Western Mediterranean area since
late Permian times

structures, associated with the Shields and their outlying blocks, whose
borders were covered by the Secondary and the Tertiary epicontinental
seas. Fracture and folding of the superficial cover are typical features.
Secondly, there are the Internal structures, moulded from the abyssal
and the bathymal deposits of Tethys into young, folded mountains.
They are influenced in part, however, by the occurrence of ancient rocks,
promoting overthrust and nappes.

The Primary Mediterranean or Paleotethys has been commonly conceived as a trough of sima lying between the two sialic Shields of Europe and Africa. As the folded mountains developed on their peripheries, the two continents expanded until by Carboniferous times the Hercynian ranges completely filled in the hiatus between the two Shields.[17] Thus during the Upper Permian and Lower Trias, a continental land mass extended from the Sahara to the Ardennes and to Britain. After the Middle Trias, the land mass was disrupted, leaving only fragments of the ancient continent within the modern Mediterranean area.[18] A constricted sea in Mesozoic times, called 'Mesotethys', was deepest in the eastern Mediterranean. Along a geanticline following near the modern coast of North Africa semi-deltaic sediments were laid down (Fig. 16). The palaeogeography of Mesotethys suggests a variable nature and thickness of sediments around its shores and islands, so that the subsequent alpine folding of the geosynclines was probably very varied and even discontinuous.[19] Consequently, it is fallacious to assume a homogeneous and continuous orogeny in the Tertiary period. Moreover, as the African Shield lies some 1,200 miles from the Russian platform and only 300 miles from the Iberian Massif, it is to be expected that the trough tectonics of the Western Mediterranean are contrasted with the block tectonics commoner in the Eastern basin.

It is now necessary to introduce the third order of tectonics, that is of cratons (or regional blocks), individual ranges and basins, associated with isostatic movements of sub-crustal origin. From mid-Eocene to late Oligocene times, marked compression created a massive land surface sometimes called 'Tyrrhenides', which stretched from the Straits of Gibraltar to southern Italy. In the course of the orogenic folding of this period, the blocks of the Bohemian, Rhenish, French and Iberian Massifs to the north and west and the blocks of the Moroccan and Oran Mesetas to the south, had a profound influence on the folded zones., For in front of each there is a series of troughs, namely the Rhône-Saone, the Garonne-Ebro, and the Guadalquivir-Sebou basins, formed in early Tertiary times. The basins of Old and New Castile were also affected by distension movements. Two other groups of basins have significant relations. One is the oval basin on an East-West axis of the present Alboran-Algerian Sea, encircled by remnants of the Hercynian continent still visible in the blocks of Málaga-Rif, Oran-Kabylia, northern Sicily, Calabria and south western Sardinia (Fig. 17). The other is along the north-west/south-east axis of the Tyrrhenian and Ligurian Seas. There seems no other explanation to account for the thick accumulation of Oligocene flysch (maximum of 6,000 ft)

that occurs on both flanks of the Straits of Gibraltar, in western Catalonia, and in the Maritime Alps and the Northern Apennines,[20] than
the subsidence of great land masses from which the eroded materials
were derived. Compensating for the collapse of these ovals, was the
resurrection of the mountain borders by epeirogenic movements in the
Alps, Corso-Sardinia, southern Italy, North Africa, and the Baetic
and Pyrenean ranges. The role played by two of these blocks is still
obscure. Was the Corso-Sardinian craton associated with the African
Shield or not? The identity of the Adriatic block is even more uncertain. Von Seidlitz, Russo and others have argued that the spiral-like
arrangement of the structural lines, swinging out from the Provence-
Adriatic areas, can only be the result of the Adriatic block acting as the
appendage of the African Shield. That is to say, it has pushed from the
south-east and underpinned the Alpine folds, in what is now the North
Italian Plain.[21] But there is no definite evidence of this.

Deep-seated fractures are also associated with this third order of
tectonics. Some of these follow Hercynian folds across the western
Mediterranean. One important fracture runs north-south, separating
the blocks of Calabria-Messina from Sicily. Along this line of fracture
are situated the volcanics of the Lipari islands and Etna. Another
fracture, later rejuvenated, has provoked the subsidence of the Sicilian-
Tunisian Sill at the end of the Tertiary. Between Zaghouan and Kairouan another fracture neatly divides the coastal basins of eastern
Tunisian from the Tell. At least seven other fractures have fragmented
North Africa[22] (Fig. 17). The most western fracture follows off the
coast of Alicante to form the western border of the mountains of Oran.

Tectonics of a fourth order may be associated with those elements of
Plio-Pleistocene uplift which have an important influence on the configuration and on the divisions of the contemporary relief (Fig. 18).
Block movements at the end of the Pliocene (usually post-Astian)
created clusters of fractures, which van Cloos has called 'geosutures'.
One group occurs along the Cantabrian coast, explaining much of its
configuration. Another series of four or five fractures has divided the
major morphological units of Galicia. A master fault, running from the
Minho to south of the Mondego, abruptly terminates the Portuguese
mountains from the coastal lowlands. Other minor faults run along the
southern Algarve, and along the coasts of Malaga and Catalonia.
Master faults shape the edge of the Sierra Morena, the Tagus trough,
and the block mountains of the Central Cordillera.[23] Clusters of faults
explain the volcanics of Calatrava and Olot. The west coast of Majorca
and the coasts of Elba are neatly defined by faults, while the Straits of

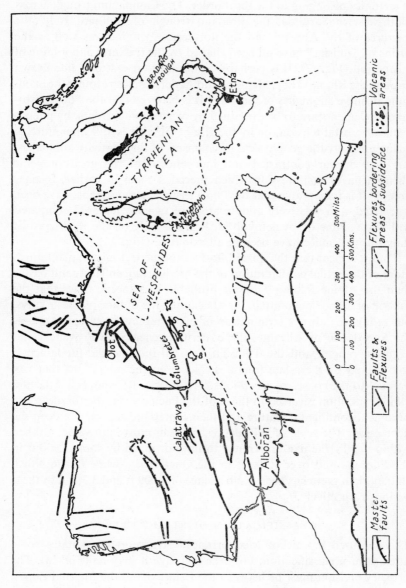

FIG. 17. Major fractures and faults of the W. Mediterranean

Messina show in detail fractures which have also elaborated aligments of tectonics belonging to the third order. The Campidano trough across south-western Sardinia, the Bradano trough of southern Italy, the fractures of the Abruzzi and the northern Apennines, as well as the basins of Tunisia,[24] have all been shaped by the fractures and folding of this period (Fig. 17). It is perhaps significant that east of a line drawn through the Rhône valley, Menorca and Algiers, there are found the maximum positive anomalies of gravity.[25] It is believed that the Plio-Pleistocene movements are to be explained by convection currents, by phenomena of crustal tension, or by the rise of sima. It is still premature to define precisely the geophysical mechanisms of these gravity anomalies, but they appear contrasted and independent of the great orogenic phenomena of compression which preceded them in earlier Tertiary times.[26] It is remarkable that the Plio-Pleistocene movements have been associated with relatively minute areas of igneous material compared with the volume of areas involved. For it is only on the west coast of Italy that volcanics have been at all extensive (Fig. 17).

Thus it is clear that these late Plio-Pleistocene tectonics explain much more of the actual configuration of the Mediterranean lands and basins than the Alpine folding.[27] It was probable in Miocene times that the folding of a Pacific mountain type fashioned the outline of Mesotythys, but today, the abrupt termination of many mountain systems such as the Sub-Baetic of Alicante, the eastern Pyrenees, the Provençal and Ligurian ranges, and the Tunisian Tell, all indicate the fundamental role played by these late fractures. Not even the mountains that run parallel to the coast are exceptions. The Baetic, Rif and Tell Atlas are all in a situation reversed to those of the Pacific style: the foredeep has become a continental feature and their hinterlands are now a deep sea depression. The scale of subsidence has been most impressive. Graben within the Tyrrhenian are known to have dropped by some 1,600 ft in the Pliocene and over 1,300 ft in the Quaternary, while in the North Italian Plain there has been a subsidence of 5,000 ft and 3,300 ft in these periods respectively.[28]

CLASSIFICATION OF STRUCTURES

The confused mosaic of Mediterranean structures necessitates some attempt at a classification, however tentative it may be (Fig. 18). The primary division must be between the External and the Internal Zones. The former is more characteristic of the Western Mediterranean, whereas the latter is commoner in the Eastern basin.

In the External Zone are found the ancient massifs that are the

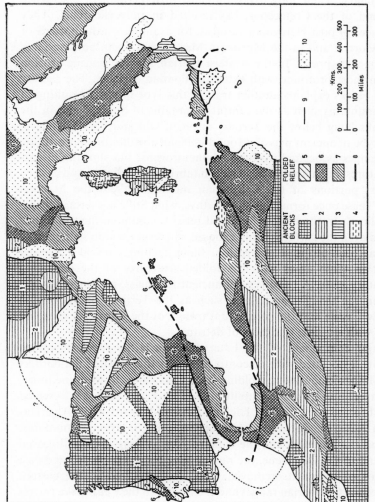

FIG. 18. Structural styles of relief in the W. Mediterranean. 1. Ancient blocks influencing actual relief. 2. Ancient blocks with discordant surface cover. 3. Ancient blocks affecting trend lines but not the surface features. 4. Ancient blocks, closely associated with Eogene folds. 5. Areas of Eogene folding. 6. areas of Neogene folding. 7. Areas of Eogene and Neogene folding intricately mixed. 8. limit between internal and external structures. 9. Limits of Hercynian blocks. 10. Tertiary sediments (unfolded)

appendages of the African and the Eurasian Shields. These are of three broad types. First, there are the Hercynian blocks of the Iberian, Moroccan and Oran massifs, whose Triassic outcrops provide a guiding boundary. Their long exposure since their permanent emergence at the end of the Cretaceous, has resulted in polycylic relief. They show traces of post-Hercynian surfaces, for example, on the borders of the Sa Morena and in the Moroccan Meseta, but Cretaceous surfaces are more widespread. In the western Iberian Meseta Eogene erosion has been most profound with extensive Pontian surfaces. The rigidity of these blocks explains another trait of this type of relief resulting in block mountains such as the central mountains of Spain,[29] and in the deep sinks lying below the Tertiary cover of Old and New Castile. A second type of ancient massif is found imbedded within the more plastic folded ranges associated with the Alpine orogeny, but showing discordant features. Such are the western Cantabrians, the central and eastern Pyrenees, portions of the Celtiberian mountains, and the Maures-Esterel. These once formed gulfs of Tethys, what Stille has termed 'parageosynclines'. In these areas fossilised relief is common, the old trends lines and even the surfaces being exposed wherever the thin sedimentary cover has been stripped by erosion. Block tectonics reveal a marked contrast in these areas with the folded structures of the encircling sedimentary stata. A third type of ancient landmass, no longer visible, occurs in the troughs and sinks, such as the Tertiary basins of Old and New Castile and the continental trough of the Ebro. These are all marked with a visible thickness of detritus.

A major component of the External Zone is the regularly folded sediments, associated with epicontinental seas that washed the borders of the Mesozoic continent. Folding from Cretaceous to Miocene times, and rejuvenation by vertical uplift in the Plio-Pleistocene, have created the great folded ranges of the High and the Middle Atlas, the Algerian-Saharan Atlas, the Sub-Baetic, Celtiberian, and Cantabrian mountains, as well as the Pyrenees and the western Alps. Where the uplift ceased by the end of the Oligocene, the ranges have been peneplaned and vast quantities of sediments removed. Such has occurred in the eastern Pyrenees, the Celtiberian ranges and the Aurès. In the Celtiberian ranges the late Tertiary surfaces even bevel their summits. In the east side of the High Atlas each stage of uplift has been related to a sequence of erosion surfaces. On the contrary, where tectonic movements have been gradual and prolonged, erosion has not had sufficient time to develop peneplains. This has occurred in the Tunisian Atlas and the Sub-Baetic. Where the surfaces have been carved out of limestones, they have been best preserved, as in Provence, in the Middle Atlas, and in the eastern High Atlas.

The very thick limestones of the Cevennes, Valencia, the central Apennines and the Middle Atlas have a distinct style of folding. Broad folds and heavy faulting characterise these mountains. Their instability has complicated and narrowed the effects of peneplanation.

Overthrusts, creating nappes and other complicated structures, characterise some of the borders of the External Zone. In the western Baetic and the southern Rif these nappes are associated with Triassic marls and gypsum, acting as a lubricant to foster diaperic mobility. In the Northern Apennines gravity flow of the plastic sediments, known as *Argille scagliose*, has caused extensive and chaotic transference of these structures. Links between the nappes of north-eastern Corsica are also postulated. It is now fashionable to reduce the distances, once exaggerated, to explain these complicated structures. Generally, these nappes were formed in the early Alpine orogeny, that is before the Oligocene.

In the Internal Zone of the Mediterranean area, the relations between the structure and relief become increasingly confused. The Mesozoic geanticline of the southern Mediterranean separated the epicontinental seas from the abyssal depths of the Mesotethys, like some mid-Atlantic rise. This was fractured by the Plio-Pleistocene tectonics and plastered partially by folded sediments. This confusion of compact, folded and rigid blocks, now seen in the Baetic, northern Rif, Algerian Tell, northern Sicily and Calabria, has disfavoured differential erosion. This is in marked contrast to the External Zone, whose landforms show sharply the effects of differential erosion. The Sicilian-Calabrian arc, reacting to the pressure of mid-Tertiary movements of the African Shield, has shown very marked instability in the Plio-Pleistocene; these oscillations have minimised the effects of erosion because of an insufficient time-scale.

The Tertiary Period with its remarkably warm climates and its great earth movements ends with the Villafranchian, when continental conditions and intense erosion prevailed. It has been suggested that the rise of the Thomson Ridge within the Atlantic cut off the Gulf Stream from the Arctic basin at the end of the Tertiary. If this did happen, it would have caused changes in the flow of the warm waters coming from the Caribbean.[30] Periodic opening and closing of the barrier to the Gulf Stream would then help to explain the interglacial and glacial climatic fluctuations which characterised the Quaternary. During the Tertiary, the north pole was centred over the Pacific where the water was too deep to freeze over. The displacement of the poles with the upheavals of the earth's crust are thus other primary causes of the climatic changes of the Quaternary. Within the Mediterranean the resultant features have been the succession of marine and riverine terraces, the traces of glacial action in the high mountains and of the more widespread 'periglacial' processes, and on the other hand of chemical weathering attributable to warm interludes. Finally, there are many soils and subsoils, which are still extant though formed under climatic and vegetational conditions no longer existing.

MARINE AND RIVERINE TERRACES

Attempts have been made to correlate the climatic fluctuations of the Quaternary with those of sea-level and thus to establish a chronology. At the beginning of this century, Dépéret[31] and Lamothe[32] distinguished four sea-levels in the Quaternary Mediterranean, which they associated with the following coastal terraces: Sicilian (Doderlein, 1872) at 100 m (280–320 ft); Milazzian (Dépéret) at 60 m (165–185 ft); Tyrrhenian (Issel, 1914) at 30 m (100 ft); and Monastirian (Dépéret) at 15 m (45–55 ft). Vertical differences between the four alpine glaciations (Günz, Mindel, Riss and Würm) were noted to be about the same as marine terraces and so they were related in the chronology. Marine terraces are certainly a striking feature of many Mediterranean coastlands, and are an important element in the geography of agriculture and settlement. They are prominent in many parts of Italy, particularly the Ionian coast, in Corsica, Tunisia, and parts of southern France and Spain. But continued investigation, especially in the last decade, has failed to confirm the formerly accepted scheme and Quaternary terminology has become almost anarchical. First, regression of sea-level was noted to be more relevant to glacial advances, and the direct effects of glaciation in the Mediterranean have been recognised to be very limited. Next, it was argued that glacio-eustatism implied that the Straits of Gibraltar were open to the Atlantic throughout the Quaternary which is unproven. Indeed, Blanc has suggested the Straits were dry land in the Mindel (Romanian) regression.[33] More seriously, the whole scheme of marine chronology based on altitude and even on fauna has been questioned.[34] It is still impossible to distinguish in the western Mediterranean between local epeirogenic movements and glacial eustatism as the causes of the earliest terraces.[35] The terms Milazzian[36] (since 1931–35) and Monastirian[37] (1953) have been discredited because the sites of their original identification lie in the areas of marked tectonic instability. Distinctions of terrace fossils made

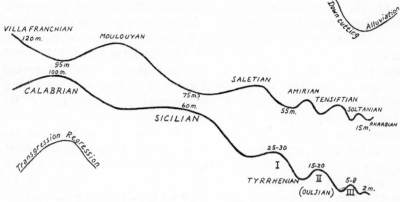

FIG. 19. Pleistocene and Quaternary chronology in Morocco (after Gignoux)

between cold and warm fauna suggesting temperature variations are now also questioned, since salinity changes and bathymetric oscillations may also explain the change in fossils.[38]

To sum up the present knowledge of the Mediterranean sea-levels, the older terraces are left in doubt and only Tyrrhenian levels are well established. The Calabrian, equated with the continental Villafranchian, followed by the Sicilian, are dubious, for they only occur in areas of marked instability. The 'Calabrian' terrace has been identified at 550 ft as well as at over 3,500 ft in southern Italy. In Sicily, the 'Sicilian' occurs at 2,500 ft. In fact, while there may be grounds for the existence of the Calabrian sea-level, the Sicilian transgression has still to be proved. There is surer evidence for perhaps three Tyrrhenian terraces in the Western Mediterranean. The Paleotyrrhenian may be the equivalent of the Mindel-Riss inter-glacial, the Eutyrrhenian with the Riss-Würm interglacial, and the Neotyrrhenian with the first Würm interstadial.[39] It is probable that the lowering of the sea during the Riss glaciation was not uniform. Of fundamental significance for the continental shelf areas of the actual Mediterranean was the great pre-Flandrian regression, associated with the Würm glaciation. At that stage the shoreline was about 100 m (328 ft) below present sea-level and all the northern half of the Adriatic sea was above sea-level[40] (Fig. 213). Submarine valleys that now terminate at about −75 or 80 m (−246 or 262 ft) were cut during this phase. Then followed the post-Würmian deglaciation when the Flandrian (generalised by Dubois, 1924) transgression drowned the rias of Galicia, the coastal plains of the Mediterranean and the Adriatic. Since then the deltas and beach terraces have been built up.

On the lower courses of the main rivers, the terraces are eustatic, corresponding to the transgressions. Some, however, as in Corsica have been affected by flexures. On the middle and upper sectors of the largest rivers the terraces are climatic, related to pluvial phases.[41] This is well seen in the five main rivers of the Iberian Peninsula, with four marked terraces at 300, 180, 90 and 30 ft above the rivers, with occasional benches between these levels.[42] On the right bank tributaries of the Tagus, coming off the Central Cordillera, only three terraces are seen however (at 150–160, 50–80 and 10–25 ft). Similarly in Morocco, the lower Moulouya and the coastal plain between Tetuan and the Gharb show a comparable sequence of eustatic levels.[43] But on the much larger course of the Oum-er-Rbia, five climatic terraces are distinguishable at 450, 300, 130, 50–65 and 15–25 ft above the river and its tributaries. In peninsular Italy the recent evolution of most rivers makes them less significant. Instead, the effects of deforestation upon their courses has shown startling results in the few cases studied, for example the lower Tiber.

PROCESSES OF EROSION

As a climatic borderland the Mediterranean region has been susceptible to distinct processes of erosion, ranging from humid climates in which linear erosion, sub-tropical chemical weathering and karst solution have been active, to arid climates with their distinct landforms. Reference must therefore be made first to the legacies of glacial, periglacial and other erosion during the Quaternary. Then it is necessary to summarise the present systems of Mediterranean processes.

Of the different glaciations only the Riss and the Würm are clearly evidenced in the landforms. Perhaps the Mindel moraines have been removed by the later Riss, particularly where the mid-Pleistocene earth movements raised the mountains higher than they had been during the Mindel, as for example in the Pyrenees. The Riss seems everywhere in the Mediterranean mountains to have been the maximum glaciation. It is therefore only in the lowlands that periglacial features suggest evidence of earlier glaciations. Blanc has described five, although only the last glaciation has morphological relevance in the Roman Campagna, where he studied the deposits.[44] Indeed, only in the northern Mediterranean has intense glaciation occurred wherever there was heavy precipitation (Fig. 150). Thus in the Ligurian Apennines the Würmian snowline lay as low as 4,000 ft and in the Apuan Alps its glaciers descended in some places to even 2,000 ft. In the Pyrenees, which was the most intensely glaciated apart from the Alps, a front of 186 miles

MEDITERRANEAN
COASTS

6 The Rock of Gibraltar
and the Straits

7 Peñon Ifach, N. Alicante, where the sub-Baetic ranges plunge
seaward towards the Balearic Islands

8 The Sorrento Peninsula

9 Arsa Channel, Istria. Note contrast between limestone plateau pock-marked with dolines and the cultivated coastal strip south of channel

10 La Herradura, Costa del Sol, with Baetic ranges running *en eschelon* to the sea

11 Coastal Plain of Benicarlo, Castellón, at mouth of R. Seco

was covered by glaciers (Fig. 78). The Würmian moraines descend to 1,300 ft on the French slopes but on the south-facing Spanish slopes only to 2,600–3,200 ft. Further south the limit of glaciation rises progressively: Central Cordillera 6,300 ft; Sa Nevada 8,200 ft; and Middle Atlas 9,500–9,800 ft. The narrow peninsula of Italy was unfavourable and so the Apennines generally show little glaciation (Fig. 157). It is absent in the Sila and restricted on Etna to the slopes near the summit.[45]

Much more widespread have been the effects of periglacial action. In the Roman Campagna frost action is strongly evidenced in the early Pleistocene rocks, but weak in the later periods.[46] In contrast, the more continental features of the Iberian Peninsula indicate much more vigorous frost action in the Riss and Würm. Severe cryoturbation of the Ebro terraces suggest a dry tundra climate there in the Würm.[47] Periglacial valleys have been identified in northern Portugal. In Morocco vast beds of periglacial solifluxion up to 3,000 ft thick have been recognised,[48] and in Algeria similar effects have been traced in deposits 2,500 ft thick. According to Büdel, a periglacial tundra climate characterised the high mountains of the Mediterranean in Würmian times, with cold temperate conditions and severe frost on the high plateaux, even in North Africa, to about 2,600 ft (Fig. 24).[49] In contrast to the intense solifluxion which seems to have affected so much of the North African plains, most of the Iberian plateaux were probably above its limits.[50]

The summer drought of the present climate does not favour chemical action. So the evidence of marked corrosion on some Mediterranean landforms can only be attributable to the warmer and more humid interglacial climates and even perhaps to late Tertiary times.[51] The granitic inselbergs of central Portugal may go back to the late Pliocene. Cavernous weathering of granites into curious forms is quite widespread (Fig. 21). It is found in northern Portugal, Corsica, Sardinia, Elba and even in the Sahara (Hoggar). It forms particularly grotesque landscapes in the Agriates of north-west Corsica (Fig. 21) and in the 'tufoni garden' of Marciana Marina in Elba. These forms decrease with altitude (limits of 1,600–2,600 ft in Elba, 5,000 ft in Corsica). Their chemical processes are not fully understood; they are probably the result of water, subject to recurrent evaporation, so that the salts increase and dissolve all but the resistant felspars. Other forms of chemical weathering have rotted the granitic outcrops in Portugal and Corso-Sardinia to depths of 50–65 ft.[52] Probably during the Riss/Würm interglacial water, enriched by humus and carbonic acid, penetrated deeply

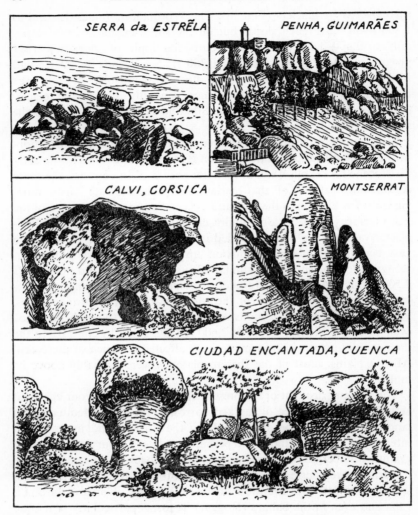

FIG. 20. Types of erosional forms. Serra da Estrēla—granitic tors; Penha, Guimarães —granitic cliffs; Calvi, Corsica—tuffoni; Monserrat—'monserratinos' carved out of Oligocene conglomerates; Ciudad Encantada, Cuenca—karst features in Cretaceous limestones

and stained the rock waste with iron oxide, features not found in the Würm and subsequent deposits.

Because of the widespread occurrence of limestones karstic relief and its associated development of *terra rossa* is typical of many areas of the Mediterranean (Fig. 21). These range widely in character according to the purity of the limestone, its solubility and corrosion, the nature of folding and fissures, the presence and quantities of calcium carbonate, and the climate. The landforms range widely therefore from limestone pavements of lapies to dolines, with various local names (see Glossary). Grottoes and caverns are particularly common in folded limestones where the strata are pitched at angles of 30° to 70°.[53] In many parts of the Western Mediterranean there is evidence of at least two cycles of karst, one more or less fossilised and the other still active. These cycles

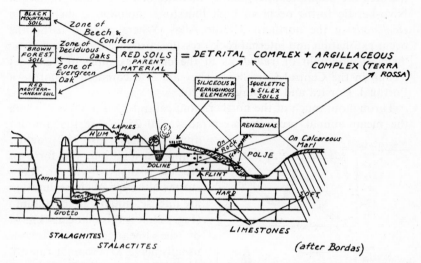

FIG. 21. Deposition of 'terra rossa' and its associated soils in the Mediterranean environment

frequently reflect the climatic changes of the Quaternary. Further, according to the climatic or altitudinal zones, some four climatic types of karst at least occur in the Mediterranean, ranging from the high areas of perennial frost, through the areas of low temperatures but spring melt, to the mild oceanic climate of the Atlantic coasts and the arid realm with its lack of water. The chief areas of karst in Italy occur in the Alps (which have over 5,000 of the 8,379 grottoes listed by Anelli, 1941).[54] In the Apennines there are a further 2,000 grottoes, notably in Umbria where an important series of polja follow the river systems and the monoclinal folds.[55] Where the sub-surface hydrology is deeply developed in relation to sea-level, the karst is most marked, as in Istria, Dalmatia and Apulia. In the Iberian Peninsula, the chief areas of karst are in the Pyrenees, the Picos de Europa and the Cantabrian

coast, the Cuenca-Valencian ranges (Fig. 21) and in the Baetic mountains.[56] In North Africa karst relief is best developed in the Middle
Atlas and in the Tell.

Apart from the processes enumerated above, many of them now
fossilised, there are four systems operative today. In the mountains
mechanical disintegration is marked, with river flow as the chief agent
of transport. Although there is little frost action below 3,000–5,000 ft
depending on latitude and the degree of continentality, periglacial
features are widespread, especially in limestone and marly outcrops.
Nivo-karstic forms occur in high limestone mountains, such as the
clochetons of the northern Middle Atlas. Where granitic batholiths
occur exfoliation and internal rock pressures produce the characteristic
'helmet' mountain or *yelmo*, as in the classic example of Peña del
Yelmo in the Central Cordillera. They are also common in northern
Portugal, Corsica and Sardinia (Fig. 20).

Throughout much of the northern and central Mediterranean where
the mean annual precipitation is above 20–25 in, or the amount
approximately lost by actual
evapo-transpiration, the form of
erosion is markedly linear. Rainstorms although of short duration
are intense, notably in the autumn
(Fig. 22). It is this that causes most
of the linear erosion. Streams
usually have a perennial run-off,
except for those that have small
catchment areas of less than 400–
500 sq. miles. Regional differences
naturally occur according to fluvial
conditions, gradients, rock types,
etc. For example the Po at Casal-
maggiore has a degradation of 300
tons per km² annually while the
Tiber at Rome has 473 and the
Adige at Trento only 160.[57] Rock

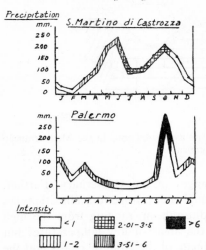

FIG. 22. Intensity of Rainfall for rain-day
(from Mennelli)

types show detailed differences. Generally, the schists have a marked
linear and rugged relief because of their impermeability. The granites,
especially those that are coarse-grained, preserve their erosion surfaces
more clearly because of the more effective absorption of surface water by
the sands and screes overlying much of the rock outcrops.[58] When the
vegetable cover is removed, however, linear erosion can be induced in

the rotten mantle of rock, producing deep valleys. In the softer outcrops such as the tuffs in central Italy, gulleys readily develop after deforestation.

There are three distinctive types of linear erosion related to geological conditions; badlands, the effects of landslides and *fiumare*. In Italy, badlands (or *calanchi*) occupy over 900 sq. miles in the peninsula in association with clayey deposits, especially the laminated clays called *argille scagliose* (see pp. 372, 391) and on the edges of the Pliocene shoreline in Basilicata. Badlands are also common in south-east Spain and on the borders of the Ebro basin. Landslips are most severe in Italy, especially on the central and southern flanks of the eastern Apennines and in Sicily (Fig. 160). Five main types have been distinguished: soil creep (*lame*) occurring especially during the rainy season; a more catastrophic and periodic form of soil creep (Plate 55); landslips along an underlying impervious bed that dips in the same direction; loosening by frost action; and undermining as a result of running water, producing often a scarp (*balza*) in the harder outcrop above.[59] Earthquakes can also exaggerate the extent of these landslides, especially in southern Italy. Characteristic of Calabria and north-east Sicily are the *fiumare*, short parallel streams that debouch steeply on to the coast every few miles (Fig. 168). They form deep gorges in their upper and middle courses but they widen in their lower courses with vast spreads of gravel often over half a mile wide. The severely seasonal rainfall, the impermeability of the crystalline massifs, the steep gradients and the marked instability of this area throughout the Pleistocene are all factors to explain their distinct features.

What may be called a semi-arid system of erosion occurs in North Africa and to a limited extent in south-east Spain. But as it is transitional climatically and temporally it may be described more as a tendency rather than as a well established system.[60] Lateral more than linear erosion by seasonal streams is the chief process, usually associated with pediments. Some of these slopes are bare, stony surfaces, others are covered with alluvium, indicative of one or more pluvial phases prior to subsequent desiccation. In eastern Morocco Raynal has recognised four glacis levels that might be correlated with four such pluvials.[61] But pediments are not directly the product of semi-arid climates for they occur in the well-watered Rif and northern Tunisia as well. Rather they are the combined product of slopes dependent on rock types, structures and drainage. Dresch has distinguished three types: those in synclinal, anticlinal and monoclinal depressions.[62] Thus two series of factors are responsible: the climatic alternation of a dry season with intense evaporation and a season of violent rains; and the marked structural contrast between the relief of hard rocks and the depressions carved out of softer rocks.

The arid system lies on the southern borders of the Mediterranean and is scarcely relevant to this outline. Dominated by wind action it is most marked where the material available consists of friable sandstones and fine-grained sediments. This explains the distribution of the Saharan ergs which cease wherever hard volcanic or crystalline rocks outcrop. On the borders of the Sahara the formation of the inland basins of the chotts has been developed partially by aeolian processes, for, after the dissolution of the Plio-Pleistocene limestones, there has been the deflation of their underlying Tertiary sands. The widespread distribution of light-coloured limon beds on river and marine terraces, indicates that aeolian action has been much more extensive in previous Quaternary periods. Probably the emergence of the continental shelf with the regressions of the Quaternary (notably in the Würm) with the exposure of sandy shorelines were important sources of limon around the Mediterranean.

It is impossible of course to delimit zonally these systems of erosion.[60] Not only have they fluctuated throughout the Quaternary, but they are unstable now. Even the approximate limit of 20–25 inches mean annual rainfall between the humid and semi-arid systems fluctuates from year to year. One system also interpenetrates into the realm of the other, wherever there are differences of altitude. Thus in Morocco the arid system invades the western Meseta via the great plains, while the mountain system penetrates into the desert lands to the south.[62] [63] The compression of climatic zones in North Africa and their changes in the Quaternary, complicates the whole question of erosion systems.

THE SOILS

In an environment where pedogenic processes are slow and where nature has donated few gifts, the Mediterranean peasant is utilising or exploiting the legacy of Quaternary climates and vegetation in the vital top few feet of the land surface. When the river Adonis is said to run red like blood to the sea after the heavy rains, the legend of a god wounded to death by the wild boar of Mount Lebanon has some substance. Its modern interpretation is that it demonstrates the ease with which the contemporary brown earths of the Mediterranean developed under evergreen forest cover, lose their decalcified, granular, A I horizon, once the plants are moved. Then follows the truncation of the Quaternary soils, exposing the red stains of the palaeo-sols that belong to the Pleistocene. It is no coincidence that on many a Mediterranean interfluve, such as the Pontian surfaces of the upper Tagus basin, the dull grey, ash or brown soils of the plateaux suddenly change to a colourful mosaic, red splashes on the steeper slopes of the valleys, with light-coloured outcrops of shallow rendzinas and xero-rendzinas on the calcareous banks, and with darker, brown-coloured soils on the flats. A traverse of western Morocco reveals even more strikingly a Quaternary sequence of landscape, from the black *tirs* of the Gharb plain, to the bright red soils of the *hamri* on the bordering sandy plateaux, and to the grey or ashen coloured soils beyond.[64] Soils may thus be considered in the Mediterranean as the pages of the history book of its landscapes. They cannot yet be all read or understood because of the limitations of soil chemistry and of the areal understanding of such concepts as soil catenas but their study attracts exciting prospects of a more detailed knowledge of the evolution of Mediterranean landscapes.

Colour is, however, an inadequate guide to distinguish the soils of the Mediterranean especially red soils which are so widespread, since they have many shades and diverse origins. Red Triassic clays and sandstones, continental Miocene sandstones, red earths of volcanic origin and the fine red dust brought by the hot winds of North Africa to the shores of Italy and Spain, all provide variants of red soils. Distinct from these soils of geological origin are those which reflect the physico-chemical processes of Quaternary climates.[65] Such is the true *terra rossa* of the Apulian peasants, a residue mantling the dolines and other karstic depressions (Fig. 22). Some pedologists have stressed the long process of decalcification required to bring about this residue, calculated at approximately one metre of terra rossa for every 400 metres of limestone. Presumably the presence of residual accumulations from erosion surfaces on the limestones or aeolian deposition can affect the accumulation of terra rossa.

As the process of rubification or red colouring affects other rocks beside limestones under certain climatic conditions, the term 'red earth' (Italian *ferretto*) is best used in this other context.[66] Such soils occur in rocks where alumino-silicates are always present, and the red colour is related not to the amount of iron contained but to the state in which it occurs. The profound alteration of the parent material under hot, humid conditions liberates important quantities of iron oxides and aluminium compounds, which form the silica complex and the iron oxides are acted upon by colloidal silicic acid.[67] Such hydro-morphic processes have occurred in several pluvial periods of the Villafranchian and the Quaternary. In North Africa there is an absence of recently-formed red earths where the annual rainfall is below 25 in, suggesting the critical importance of slight increase in precipitation during the pluvial phases on the plains of Morocco and Algeria, which today have only 15–20 in.[68] Red earths tend to be limited to areas below 5,000 ft in the Algerian Tell and in the Atlas mountains, suggesting also a thermal control.

There is still inadequate knowledge of the distinction between fossil red earths and recent ones. Most of the Moroccan red earths are clearly fossilised, occurring on the western Meseta and northwards in a belt from Rabat to Fes and Taza, often over three feet thick. Some are developed *in situ* and others have been transported by the rivers. Pujol believes that generally the Moroccan soils are going through modifications under the present climate, where erosion predominates over pedogenesis.[64] In the Rif, Algerian and Tunisian Tell, red earths may be more recent as the discoloration of Roman monuments,[69] recent rock breaks, etc. seem to suggest.[70] Some pedologists, notably Reifenberg[71] and Bordas, believe that the formation of red earths is still in process in some of the more humid habitats of the Mediterranean. At the beginning of the dry season, the ferro-silica complexes are dispersed in the profile towards the upper horizons by evaporation and capillarity. As the drought continues these complexes are destroyed and the increase in saline solution causes the precipitation and the crystallization of iron oxides. It is also possible that red palaeo-sols can be evolved towards a brown soil by the partial rehydration of iron oxides, a feature that has occurred in Istrian soils.[72]

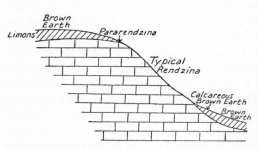

FIG. 23. Soil sequence on a calcareous slope (from Dauchaufour)

Although brown soils are of widely differing character, three types are characteristic of much of the northern and central Mediterranean lands. In the humid zones of northern Portugal, the Asturias[73] and much of peninsular Italy,[74] especially on the Adriatic slopes, brown forest soils are widely developed. There the mild winters and the lack of severe drought result in rapid, chemical decomposition of the abundant humus cover, hence their name of 'mull' soils.[75] They have a good soil structure and a neutral value of 7 pH. The profile is uniform —particularly over schistose rocks, and it is relatively stable on acid, crystalline rocks.[76] The vegetation cover associated with these soils is generally deciduous and mixed pine forests.

Compared with these dark coloured humus soils, the typical Mediterranean brown earths, termed 'siallitic' by del Vilar,[77] is much paler and less stable. It is the climax soil of the original evergreen oak forest (*Quercetum ilicis*) once prevalent in the Eu-Mediterranean zone (Fig. 27). Now that this forest has been largely destroyed, their soils are widely degraded or destroyed.

In the mountains where the rainfall is relatively high, podsolised soils result. Thus today in the Tell, especially Kabylia, the Rif, Atlas and on the south-western slopes of the Sierra Nevada, degraded podsolised soils have resulted from the leached, originally brown forest soils. Other forms are found in the Asturias and in northern Portugal. The parent rock has some influence on the changes with the predominance of chemical action on calcareous soils, and of mechanical action on siliceous soils.[76]

There are in addition to these main soil-forming processes, more localised physico-chemical processes, such as tirsification, crust formation and the modification of aeolian soils. Black soils called *tirs* occur under the most humid conditions. They are found in the lower plain of Andalusia between Cordoba and the coast, in the Moroccan Rharb between the Tensift and the Bu-Regreg near Rabat, and in the Mitidja plain of Algeria. Waterlogged during the Flandrian transgression, their black colour is related to the intensity of these conditions, reaching a climatic pluvial optimum that merges with the Neolithic.[78] Soil crusts of subaqueous origin are common in North Africa, some reflecting conditions of the Villafranchian and others of Quaternary pluvials. There are crusts however that betray evidence of deforestation in the semi-arid realm of North Africa.[79] Crusts have actually formed in abandoned Roman olive groves in central Tunisia, sealing the roots and trunks left in the subsoil.[80] Following the Arab destruction of the forests around Meknes the same process has occurred there.[81] Because of the friability of many Mediterranean soils skeletal soils are very common. In the Central Cordillera of Spain it is thought the soil profiles have nearly all been truncated. In Tunisia erosion was at a minimum in Roman times when terraces and centuriation protected the land so effectively; today the ravines of the Wadi-Kebir have a removal rate of about ten inches annually (25 cm).[82] In Algeria it is estimated there is an annual loss of about 100,000 acres to a depth of ten inches.[83] The mosaics of truncated soils in the lands around the Mediterranean are thus one of the greatest challenges both to the decipherment of their history and to the conservation of what is left of this precious heritage to the Mediterranean peasant.

QUATERNARY CLIMATES

The study of climatic changes in the Quaternary is very relevant to the geomorphology and pedology of the Mediterranean. Indeed, much of the evidence of climatic change is morphological. The pedogenetic power of the existing climate in the semi-arid lands of North Africa and south-east Spain is on the wane. Thus the Quaternary climates have left a distinctive mark on the soils of these regions that the present climate cannot obliterate. In vast areas of the Sahara a few inches below the reg, there are deep palaeosols that date from the last glacial period. These only need water and 'reseeding' with soil microbes to come to life again.[84] Palynological studies show them to have had a Mediterranean climate.

We have already seen that the traditional assumption of the four alpine glaciations (Günz, Mindel, Riss and Würm) forming the framework of Pleistocene chronology in the Mediterranean area is suspect. In the first place the glacial periods, although spectacular, occupied a very small part of the total time-scale. There is, moreover, doubt concerning the glaciations before those of the Riss and Würm in the Mediterranean area. Blanc's cold phases in the Campagna are not easy to equate with the alpine sequence.[85] All that can be asserted with some confidence is that of the climatic fluctuations that have occurred since the beginning of the Würm, some 25,000 or 30,000 years ago. Morphological evidence in the northern Mediterranean suggests the Würm began with a cold moist climate, followed by a colder, dry climate. Possibly, the maximum glaciation lagged behind the period of minimum temperatures. Then followed a rather warm climate that outlasted deglaciation.[86]

By a comparison of the present and Würmian snow lines Büdel has located the tree-line (that is to say the 42° F. July isotherm reduced to sea-level).[87] His reconstruction shows that the climatic zones of the Würm were not centred around the ice masses which were of very limited extent in the Mediterranean lands (Fig. 24) but displaced equatorwards in belts generally parallel with conditions today. Thus the Mediterranean lands had a wide cover of mixed deciduous forests, with forest tundra on the lower mountain ranges. The Mediterranean evergreen forests were displaced southwards into the Sahara (Fig. 24).

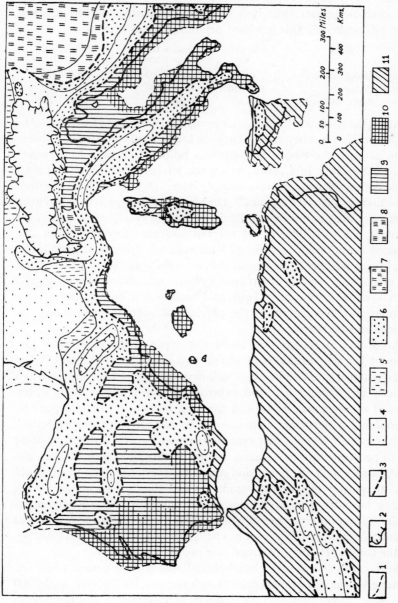

FIG. 24. Shorelines and vegetation cover in late Quaternary times (after Büdel and Troll). 1. Shoreline. 2. Ice sheet. 3. Limits of Taiga forests. 4. Tundra. 5. Loess tundra. 6. Shrub and woodland tundra. 7. Loess steppe. 8. Loess, woodland steppe. 9. Subpolar forests (of Scots pine, birch and meadows). 10. Mixed deciduous forests. 11. Mediterranean evergreen forests

Then as now, climatic differences within the Mediterranean were dominated by height above sea-level. The warming influence of the sea was perhaps greater than it is now. Consequently, marked regional contrasts occurred. This has been demonstrated in Provence.

Würm	Lower Rhône = feet	Middle Durance = feet	Maritime Alps = feet
Intense frost action	0–300	below 1300–1500	2000–2600
Stone alignment	300–650	1300	2200–3200
Amorphous solifluction	0–160	below 1300	1300–1600

Along the Riviera littoral, similar periglacial features to those found in the lower Rhône valley at 300 ft are not found until 1,000 ft above Nice. Then as now, the Rhône corridor was probably exposed to a violent mistral. Similarly in Corsica, as on the Riviera, it appears that cold phases of the Pleistocene have scarcely interrupted the typical torrential conditions of the river regimes.[86] The glacial periods such as the Würm, were associated in the Iberian Peninsula and in North Africa with cold climates but with little or no marked increase of precipitation. But reduced evaporation, associated with reduced summer temperatures, would give positive hydrological budgets, raising the levels of lakes and the inland seas. To this extent such a pluvial was more a morphological than a climatic pluvial.[88] Thus as Charlesworth has cautioned, the number and 'the picture of the pluvial belts can at present only be painted in light strokes'.[89]

According to Willett, two circulation types of the atmosphere can account for the variations of glacial and inter-glacial climates.[90] The zonal pattern, characterised by a well-developed jet stream and a marked pattern of subpolar low and subtropical high-pressure belts, is the normal of what may be termed the long periods of the interglacials. Meridional patterns are characterised by weaker planetary westerlies, with upper air troughs that extend far equatorwards and permit polar air to penetrate into the tropics. These are associated with ice-ages and cold, historic periods. Expansion equatorwards of the polar front would lead to greater temperature gradients and thus to storminess in the middle latitudes. This would increase the efficiency of the condensation cycle.[91] The primary cause of change from the zonal to the meridional circulation pattern might well be changes in solar radiation in addition to the causes already mentioned (see pp. 61–62).[92]

Succeeding the Würm glacial-pluvial was a long period when the climate was as dry or even drier than it is now. Then about 5000–2300 B.C. was a minor pluvial in the southern Mediterranean and the Sahara attested by the Neolithic cave-drawings of fauna and by the evidence of

Savanna-like vegetation. Since the close of the third millenium the climate has fluctuated slightly around a mean very little different from that of the present day. From studies in the Middle East, Butzer has postulated marked desiccation between 2350–500 B.C.[93] But archaeologists such as Adams[94] and Braidwood[95] are very sceptical of these lines of evidence. In Tunisia, Tixeront has studied the archaeological evidence carefully and come to the opposite conclusion that there has been a marked stability of the climate since the Atlantic sub-pluvial.[96] This is more in line with the views of other workers in Palestine and Iran. Another and more unlikely hypothesis is that put forward by Balout.[97] He suggests that the Atlantic subpluvial was associated with a northwards advance of Sudanese monsoonal winds into the Sahara. This theory fits nicely into the archaeological evidence of a northwards advance of Sudanese culture (Saharan Neolithic) but it is unrealistic with regard to the atmospheric circulation.

During the historic period there is every evidence of climatic stability, any changes being induced by man through deforestation and cultivation.[98] In Algeria for example, Budel has recognised crusts which suggest the influence of plough cultures, probably traceable for some three millenia, and destroying the older soil cover.[99]

SUMMARY

Any explanation of the Mediterranean structures must recognise a hierarchy of geophysical causes and their associated scales of both space and time. These are as follows: the existence of the Eurasian Seaway as a primary order of global significance; the juxtaposition of sial and sima as components of the second order; the regional blocks or cratons that are appendages of the two shields of Europe and Africa that have influenced structural features of the third order; and the more detailed configuration of relief associated with structures of the fourth order, mostly major fractures. In the 'alpine movements' it is fundamental to distinguish between the earlier Oligocene-Miocene orogeny marked by compression and Pacific-style mountains, from the Plio-Pleistocene vertical movements most characterised by fracturing. The latter has therefore most relevance in explaining the present configuration of the Mediterranean lands. It is necessary, however, to distinguish clearly between the External and the Internal Zones operative from much earlier periods and belonging to the second order of tectonics.

Together with the Villafranchian, the Quaternary processes have largely fashioned the details of the existing relief. But the chronology of the Quaternary is at present in confusion, particularly in reference to the marine terraces. Although these terraces are of minor significance as a feature of the landscape compared to their Atlantic counterpart, they play a key role in the chronology of the last one million years. Terraces on the major rivers indicate evidence of both climatic and marine oscillations. As a climatic borderland the Mediterranean lands reveal evidence of distinct geomorphic processes. During the glacial periods of northern Europe, much of the Mediterranean land area experienced periglacial conditions. During warmer and humid periods there is evidence of active chemical processes. Today, four systems of erosion may be broadly distinguished: marked mechanical action in high mountains; linear erosion by rivers in the humid areas; lateral erosion in semi-arid lands; and the marked effects of aeolian erosion in the arid realm.

The truncation of soil profiles formed during the Quaternary or earlier, reveal patterns of distinctively coloured soils. Colour, however, is not a sure guide, especially to the genesis of the red earths, which may be of several origins since the Tertiary. They are not to be confused with *terra rossa*, a residue of limestone areas, of varying ages since the Tertiary. Similarly the brown soils of the Mediterranean are at least of three types: the 'mull' soils of the more humid areas; the bleached and often radically altered profiles of soils which formed a climax under evergreen oak forest; and the soils which have been podsolised by the invasion of pine woods. Skeletal soils are very widespread because of the intensive effects of erosion, much accelerated since the Middle Ages by deforestation.

CHAPTER 5

THE VEGETATION COVER

'The trees once went forth to anoint a king over them; and they
said to the olive tree, "Reign over us".'　　　　(Judges IX, 8)

Trees give distinctive styles of Mediterranean landscape.[1] Without
reference to the stone pines of the Roman Campagna, the cork oaks of
Alentejo and Mamora, the evergreen oaks of Extremadura and the
cedars of the Atlas, their respective landscapes could not be adequately
described. Some trees symbolise the cultural characteristics of a landscape—singly, as in the vertical silhouette of the cypress alongside the
Provençal *mas* or Tuscan villa; in horizontal clusters of pines as around
the farms of northern Portugal; or in the shelter belts of Lombardy
poplar and Vauclusian cypress. But these are only vignettes of some
Mediterranean plants. In reality, vast stretches, especially in the Iberian
Peninsula and in North Africa, constitute degraded forms of thin
woodland, maquis, scrub or even bare rock. For despite the widespread
woodland associations that reach their climax in the Mediterranean,
man and his animals have caused much destruction.

CHARACTERISTICS OF MEDITERRANEAN PLANTS

The vegetation cover is the expression of complex interactions of
climatic, edaphic, palaeontological and biotic controls. It can unfold
the nuances of local and regional climates much more eloquently than
any statistics. For instead of isolating the climatic elements, the vegetation reflects the interrelationships of air and soil humidity, insolation,
radiation and air temperature. Unfortunately the writing of this ecological text is not yet fully decipherable. Its pages, however, may be
recognised as *plant associations*. In the Mediterranean climatic realm
proper the characteristic one is that of the evergreen or holm oak,
Quercetum ilicis.[2] Not all associations have the same significance, but
those that have a durable equilibrium between the climate and the soils
of an area form a *climax*, notably *Quercion ilicis*. Thus the soil too has
its climax, a profile that can readily be identified with a plant association,
producing a symbiosis which is mutually a *regressive* or *progressive*
evolution. In the precarious conditions of the Mediterranean environ-

ment, the mutual interdependence of soil and vegetation cover is seen clearly.[3]

1. *Plant Adaptations to Climate.* The Mediterranean climate is essentially hostile to many plants since the hydrotherm shows no parallelism between the curves of precipitation and temperature (Fig. 5). The perennial trees and the shrubs experience both the physiological drought of winter when low temperatures cause a decline in plant activity, and the physical drought of summer, when lack of rainfall is an even more effective check on plant growth. It is only when the two curves intersect during the autumn, and more especially in spring, that there is a favourable relationship and, in consequence, intensive plant growth can take place. The plant condition of physiological drought in winter is a characteristic of the northern Mediterranean, and of the continental interiors of the Iberian Peninsula and North Africa. The latter environments are particularly inimical to many plants, only compensated by marked diurnal changes of temperature which enable chlorophyllic processes to remain active, even in winter. The mountain frame of the Mediterranean lands, with its general increase of precipitation, changes the character of the hydrotherm to depict conditions approaching temperate Europe with its mesophytic flora. The prevalence of high relief or continental conditions explains the relatively few numbers of heat-loving plants or thermophytes which represent 25 per cent of the 4,963 species in Italy, and 27 per cent of the 5,589 species in the Iberian Peninsula.[4]

The evergreen plants constitute the characteristic plants of the Mediterranean because of the dominance of summer drought over all other climatic features. Broadly there are four ways in which plants deal with the problem of physical drought: by escaping, evading, enduring and being resistant to drought.

In the southern Mediterranean, the grasses such as false esparto (*Lygeum spartum*) and alfa (*Stipa tenacissima*) are well adapted to conditions where there are less than 12 inches of precipitation annually, growing rapidly in the season of autumn rains and then losing their external organs with the approach to summer. The bulbous plants, such as the narcissus and especially the asphodel, common in areas of thin, degraded soils, escape drought in this way.

The majority of Mediterranean plants evade drought by a wide range of xeromorphic adaptations.[5] Three principal means are by reduction of transpiration, by increase in osmotic pressure (that is the ability to draw moisture by suction) and by the growth of deeply penetrating roots. Some plants are seasonally wasteful of their water budget but they can reduce their transpiration rate to a minimum when a serious deficiency arises; the mastic tree (*Pistacia lentiscus*) does this in summer by closing its stomata.[6] Others have marked diurnal rates of transpiration, high in the early morning, very low in the early afternoon. Reduction of the transpiring surface is very common, sometimes by a seasonal change in leaf size, but more usually having a permanently small leaf (Fig. 31). The latter is characteristic of many of the *labiatae*, such as the garrigue plants, lavender (*Lavandula spp*), thyme (*Thymus spp*) and rosemary (*Rosmarinus oficialis*), etc. Some have reduced their leaf surface to mere thorns, such as the cistus species, or to needles as in the pines. The aromatic shrubs of the Mediterranean such as the fragrant myrtle and the *labiatae* already mentioned, are further aided by their oil content to reduce transpiration in the sap and this also seems to lower the external rates of evapo-transpiration. The glossy surface of some evergreens seems to reflect the sun's rays and prevents excessive heating of the leaves. Thick bark such as that grown by the cork oak (*Quercus suber*) and hair structures which protect the stomata of plants such as the *Ericae* species, are also typical forms of protection. With all these variable adaptations sclerophyllous evergreens have a wide range of transpiration rates. Plants like the laurel (*Laurus nobilis*), the strawberry tree (*Arbutus unedo*), aleppo pine (*Pinus halepensis*) (Fig. 26), the olive (*Oliva europaea*) and the carob (*Ceratonia siliqua*) save water carefully. Garrigue plants, such as rosemary and thyme, survive with still higher water deficits (Fig. 31).

Another xerophytic adaptation is the ability to increase osmotic pressure during drought. This can be extremely low in some plants during spring and autumn, from five to 20 atmospheres, whereas sclerophyllous plants have usually between 15 and 22 atmospheres. The holm oak (*Quercus ilex*) which has 20 to 22 atmospheres, is so well adapted in its climax, that the variation is less than 25 per cent throughout the year (Plate 41). Halophytes have 30 to 65 atmospheres reaching even 100 or more in the sebkhas of North Africa.[7] Many of the Mediterranean plants have the ability to change their osmotic pressure seasonally or according to soil differences, greater in limestone, less in sandy soils, or according to whether they are irrigated or not.

Long root systems are another adaptation, particularly with the holm oak, which anchors itself into fissures in the rock, less so for example with the cork oak, which possesses a dense root network in deep soils. The minority of plants, represented by the third category of drought endurance[8] also have long tap roots reaching down to the water-table

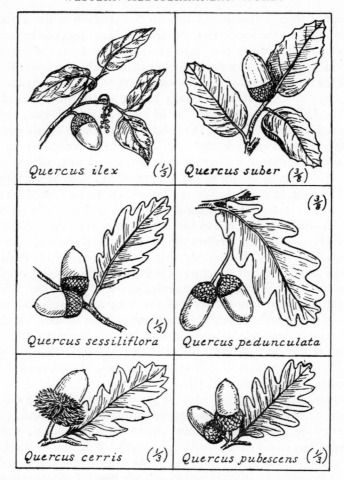

FIG. 25. Types of oaks found in the W. Mediterranean (fractions refer to approximate reduction shown from actual size)

such as the vine and the oleander (*Nerium oleander*) which also follows the water courses.

The final category, the drought resistant plants, are more typical of the arid realm than the Mediterranean proper. Such are the euphorbiae, the cacti and similar succulents that store their own independent supplies of water during prolonged periods. The prickly pear has, however, been widely introduced by man in the drier parts of the Mediterranean.

2. *The Climax Vegetation and its Degradation.* Within the characteristic or Eu-Mediterranean zone (Fig. 27), the evergreen associations

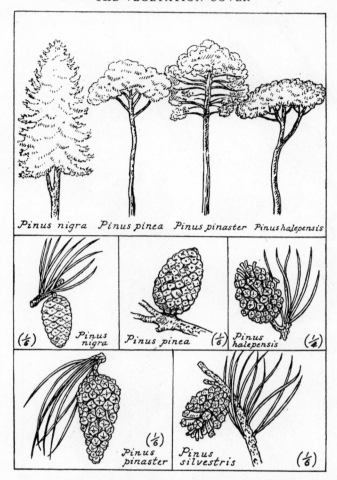

FIG. 26. Types of pines and their cones (fractions refer to approximate reduction shown from actual size)

of *Quercetum ilicis* with their climax of *Quercion ilicis* dominate. The latter is a veritable sub-tropical selva with four or five levels of vegetation.[9] First there are the mature trees composed almost entirely of evergreen oak with their magnificent crowns of foliage, rising 50–60 feet on good lands but more usually 25–40 feet. Then there are the lower tree shrubs, especially buckthorn (*Phillyria media*), 40–50 feet high, the strawberry tree (*Arbutus unedo*), sometimes over 40 feet, but more usually 10–15 feet, and frequently junipers (*Juniperus oxycedrus* and *Juniperus phoenicea*). They are bound by a dense canopy of creepers

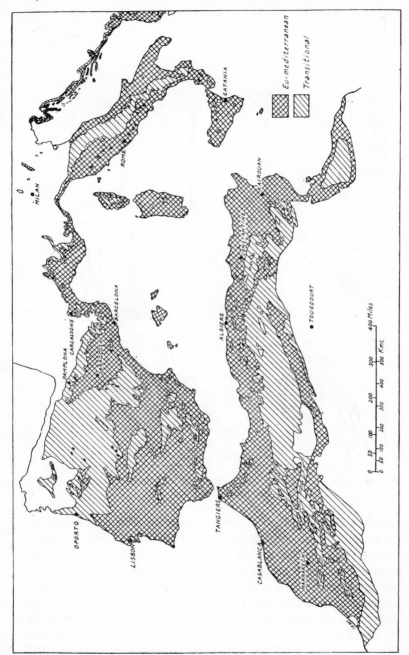

FIG. 27. The Eu-Mediterranean zone as defined by H. Gaussen

such as several species of clematis, smilax (*S. aspra*) and ivy. This zone grades into a lower one of evergreen shrubs, the mastic tree (*Pistacia lentiscus*), laurustinus (*Viburnum tinus*) and thick masses of privet (*Rhamnus alaternus*). A lower layer at 2·5 to 4 feet has a dense growth of butcher's broom (*Ruscus aculeatus*). Finally, the ground layer suffering from lack of light (only one-seventh or less of possible light), covers only about a third of the soil with lower herbaceous plants. The effect of this sequence of massive layers and canopies is to create several micro-climates, with various rates of evapo-transpiration, sunlight, heat amount and irregularity of moisture etc.[10]

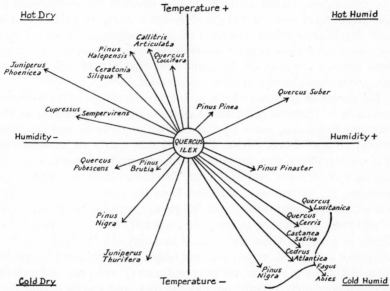

FIG. 28. Climatic conditions of the holm oak in its relations to possible rivals (after Pavari)

No tree is more widely represented in the landscape than the holm oak (*Quercus ilex*). With a xerothermal index from 0 to 130 it is so well adapted to widely varying conditions that it is probable there are several subspecies of palaeogenic origin.[11] From its climax, however, other flora show distinct ecological tendencies which may be summarised diagrammatically (Fig. 28). The transition from the meso-Mediterranean zone to a warm humid climate is seen in the appearance of the stone pine (*Pinus pinea*) (Fig. 26) and on siliceous soils, the cork oak (*Quercus suber*).[12] This explains the maritime location of the cork woodlands of Alentejo and the Moroccan forest of Mamora. The transition to colder, more humid conditions usually consequent upon increased altitude or position, is reflected in the appearance of deciduous oaks and the black pines. Common in sea-board areas is the occurrence, with its distinctive 'umbrella' canopy, of the maritime pine (*P. pinaster*), then on the mountain slopes the chestnut (*Castanea sativa*), the black pine (*Pinus nigra*), the cedar (*Cedrus atlantica*) chiefly located in the Atlas mountains, and the fir (*Abies alba*) form a sequence. On these regional and altitudinal climatic transitions there are also imposed micro-climatic changes affected by the destruction of the *Quercion ilicis*. The latter are associated usually with higher ground temperatures and desiccation.[13] Thus in the transition between the associations of *Quercetum ilicis* and the warmer *Oleo-lentiscatum*, as well as by the local degradation of the *Quercion ilicis*, the sequence of kermes oak (*Q. coccifera*), Aleppo pine (*P. halepensis*) and the juniper (*J. oxycedrus*) form distinct elements of the plant landscape. There are, however, many more mosaics of regressive associations.

The climax of *Quercion ilicis* is no longer widespread in the Mediterranean in its primeval splendour. Good examples are preserved in the Gargano Peninsula, some of the Catalan mountains and in some coastal areas of North Africa. Elsewhere it is nearly all secondary or in more degraded forms, for once destroyed, regressive species, such as kermes oak, intrude readily. When the lower levels of shrubs are removed, the kermes oak, excluded from the climax because of the lack of sunlight, begins to appear. Its greater regenerative powers with its rhizomes, enables the kermes oak eventually to triumph in a para-climax of garrigue. Once the original undergrowth of viburnum, box and privet is removed, greatly resistant to fire, it is supplanted by species much less resistant, such as rosemary and erica (*E. arborea*), and then by species immediately volatile, notably the rock rose species (*Cistus spp*) and greenwood (*Genista scorpius*). The cistus regenerates quickly and so eventually becomes a dominant association with the continuous results of burning.

The main types of regression and their associations are summarised in Fig. 30. From the gradual thinning of the cover of evergreen oaks and their associated species of woodland, there results a degenerate cover of tall sclerophyllous shrubs variously called *maquis* (Fr.), *matorral* (Sp.) and *macchia* (It.).[14] Tall maquis can reach 13–16 feet, often with a predominance of the strawberry tree, while the low maquis at 5–6 feet consists mostly of shrubs such as the cistus. Although botanists make a distinction between primary maquis resulting from climatic changes and the secondary forms consequent on human interference,

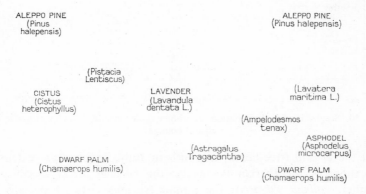

ALEPPO PINE
(Pinus
halepensis)

ALEPPO PINE
(Pinus halepensis)

(Pistacia
Lentiscus)

CISTUS
(Cistus
heterophyllus)

LAVENDER
(Lavandula
dentata L.)

(Lavatera
maritima L.)

(Ampelodesmos
tenax)

ASPHODEL
(Asphodelus
microcarpus)

(Astragalus
Tragacantha)

DWARF PALM
(Chamaerops humilis)

DWARF PALM
(Chamaerops humilis)

FIG. 29. Typical garrigue plants in the eastern coastal plain of Oran

in practice it is not easy to differentiate them. Eight or nine chief types of maquis association occur in the Mediterranean identified by their chief plant.[15] These are: cistus, red juniper (*Juniperus oxycedrus*), Spanish broom (*Spartium junceum*), the wild olive (*Oleaster*), laurel (*Laurus nobilis*), oleander (*Nerium oleander*), euphorbia (*Euphorbia dendroides*) and dwarf palm (*Chamaerops humilis*). In mixed, transitional types of maquis, the mastic tree, tree-heath (*Erica arborea*) and box (*Buxus sempervirens*) are very common. While some degenerate into a fire climax of mastic, strawberry tree and cistus, because of their resistance to fire or active regeneration, others degenerate into the humbler forms of plant life associated with the *garrigue*. This occurs particularly where drier and warmer conditions occur, either zonally in the southern Mediterranean or edaphically on the limestone. Its plant associations usually less than 4–5 feet high, consist predominantly of the kermes oak, the labiatae such as rosemary and lavender and the geophytes, notably asphodel (*Asphodelus*).[16] The constant use of fire by the pastoralists has created the dominance of some associations, covering a wide area. Such are the *giare* (rosemary and *genista* species)

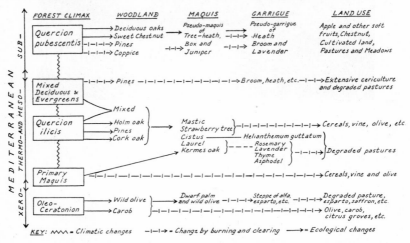

FIG. 30. Stages in the degradation of plants under Mediterranean climatic and cultural changes

and the *ericeto* (tree-heath) in southern Italy. Much more extensive are those of the Iberian Peninsula: the *brezales* (erica species and heather, *calluna vulgaris*); the *jarales* (various cistus, especially *C. landaniferus*); *bujedales* (box) and *goscojales* (Kermes oak). There are also numerous labiatae. The most degraded types of garrigue are associated with the erosion of limestone pavements and their geophyte plants, notably asphodels (an edaphic form), or with the steppes of esparto and alfa (a climatic form). In all the confusion of types of degraded vegetation, the definition of *maquis* and *garrigue* is somewhat arbitrary. The distinction reflects physiognomic, edaphic and biotic processes, the height of the plants and their struggle for space, the depth of the soil, and the frequency or lapse of time since man and his animals intervened in affecting the plant cover.

3. *The Plant Cover and Related Soils.* The distinction between organic and mineral soils is fundamental in the Mediterranean, since the

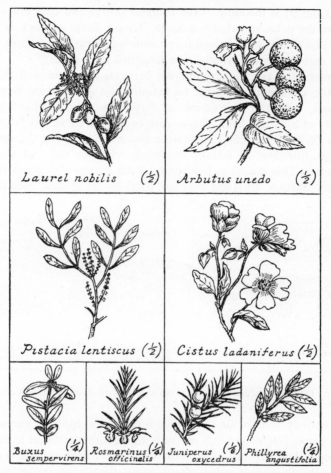

FIG. 31. Typical plants of the garrigue and of the maquis (fraction indicates approximate scale of reduction)

quality and the quantity of the humus determine the type of soil. The nutritive and progressive cycle between plant and soil (organic litter) and of soil and plant, is active and short in the *Quercion ilicis*. It is represented by brown, 'mull' soils that have little raw humus. Dense shade in the lower layers of the *Quercetum ilicis* favour mycological flora and the concentration there of carbonic gas is of major importance for the formation of the soil.[17] Each layer of plant cover has its corresponding influence in the soil profile: the A0 horizon is rich in fungi; the A1 is well aerated by the herbaceous plants in the wet season; the B1 is the zone of the roots of shrubs and creepers; the B2 is where the oaks, strawberry trees etc. have a dense network of roots. Under this climax light brown forest soils will form, irrespective of the parent material, transforming even fossilised *terra rossa*.[18]

Regression is equally a symbiosis between the plant and the soil. With the change from forest to maquis, the A0 horizon begins to disappear, with the destruction of shrubs and the resultant greater intensity of light and heat. This in turn causes the humus to deteriorate rapidly. With a garrigue cover, more and more exposing the soil as it regresses, the loss of humus eventually changes the soil structure completely. This occurs as the humus is the cement that binds the soil particles together. First the finer soil particles are eroded, then the soil

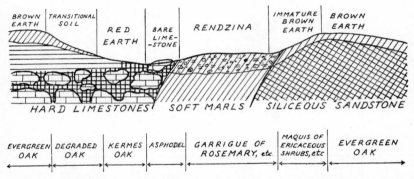

FIG. 32. Typical associations of soil types and of plant cover (from Dauchaufour)

itself, until eventually the soil profile is destroyed and thin gravels with scattered pockets of soil that can only support the asphodel are all that remains.[19] The pH values are also increased in the middle stages of regression, favouring some plants more than others, for example, rosemary. Fig. 32 shows how some of these stages can occur in the same area, accelerated by the angle of slope and by the nature of the parent material.[20] Active pedogenesis of eroded slopes, under soft parent rocks, such as limestone, can rejuvenate a soil. This will develop first some form of rendzina under a garrigue cover, while friable, schistose rocks can even create a canopy of maquis shrubs to form youthful brown soils (Fig. 32).[21] But hard, karstic limestones, once they have lost their evergreen cover, their brown forest soils and their underlying C cover of perhaps fossilised *terra rossa*, can at best only maintain a low coverage of kermes oak and dwarf palm, growing in red-stained gravels.[22] It is thus a general pedological principle in the

Mediterranean, that the more degraded the soil becomes with its commensurate plant cover, the more important becomes the character of its mineral content, and the clearer reflection it is of its parent material.

In the mixed deciduous forests of the mountains and the northern Mediterranean, the stages of regression are distinct. The soils are darker brown, richer in raw humus, with a slower nutritive cycle and therefore with a more acidic reaction. Pseudo-maquis and pseudo-garrigue associations show stages of plant regression (Fig. 30). Removal of the tree cover leads to active soil leaching, exaggerated with the high, more continuous rainfall. The deep, mull soils are thus destroyed, breaking down eventually into sandy, acidic soils. They are suited to pine woods, but unlike the natural Boreal climax, these induced podsols are regressive. In the northern half of Portugal where pines are the dominant vegetation cover, the forest soils, like their vegetation, are remote in character from their original climax.[23]

REGIONAL CLASSIFICATIONS OF PLANT COVER

1. *Limits of Mediterranean Vegetation.* At first sight, the relief barriers of the northern Mediterranean might suggest decisive phyto-climatic boundaries. More significant than altitude is, however, exposure to the cold mountain winds. It is for this reason that Mediterranean flora cannot ascend the upper valleys of Roussillon and Aude, the Ardeche or the upper tributaries of the Rhône. In Dalmatia, the effects of the bora restrict evergreen woody communities to the islands offshore; only from Sibenik southwards do they encroach on to the coastal ranges. Much, therefore, depends on the shelter from these cold winds and on the occurrence of dry soils. Even more elusive is the use of plants as limits of the Mediterranean. For example, the stone pine and the cork oak are both typical of its landscapes, but both are narrowly defined by edaphic conditions, preferring siliceous soils. The kermes oak, although such an important invading species in regressive stages of an association, lives well below the upper limit of Mediterranean flora, because of its marked sensitivity to low temperatures. Others like the dwarf palm and, in North Africa especially, the jujube (*Zizyphus lotus*) are very widespread in their areas of occurrence, but they are concentrated in the xero-Mediterranean and semi-arid regions. The list is inevitably reduced to the holm oak and the olive (*Olea europaea*), both indifferent to soil types and scaling to considerable altitudes. The adaptable evergreen oak is, however, too widespread, occurring as a relic flora of the warm interglacial periods, as far as Aquitaine and even to Limousin.

It is not known for certain if these species have evolved independently of their Mediterranean relatives to support greater cold and more humidity. Thus although the evergreen oak forms the Mediterranean climax, it is the olive plant which more faithfully reflects significant climatic limits of the Eu-Mediterranean zone (Fig. 27).[24]

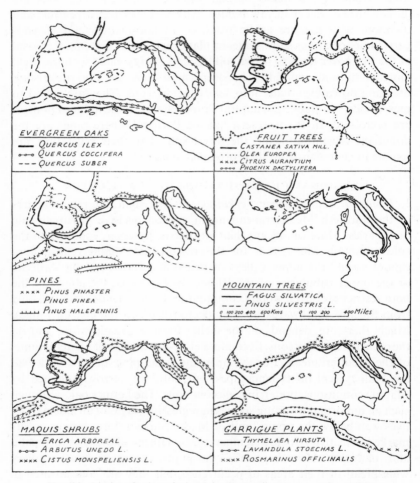

FIG. 33. Limits of selected plants in the Mediterranean (after Rikli)

Although pushed to its maximum limits in the eighteenth and early nineteenth centuries, the olive has since retreated to occupy more realistic, ecological limits today. These have been mapped carefully by Gaussen and Philippis.[25] There is no fixed lower temperature limit to the olive, though damp cold is more readily a cause of plasmolysis of the tissues and so the death of the plant. In broad terms, with humid cold the limit is set at a mean minimum of 30·2 to 28·4° (−1 to −2), and in dry cold at 26·6 to 14·0° (−3 to −10). A dry season is essential to enable the plant to develop its oil content, which Gaussen has estimated at 40 to 180 or 200 'dry' days. This is more precise than de Martonne's minimum of 240 days annually, with over 50° (10).

The actual limits of the olive vary with the climatic situation and the extent of its cultivation (Fig. 33). Summer humidity limits it in northern Portugal so that the olive lies south of the Mondego valley and the Sierra da Estrêla, except for an important outlier in the middle Douro valley, and other smaller stations on sheltered, limestone areas of northern Spain (Fig. 27). Winter cold limits the olive to south of the Central Cordillera, except in the Ebro valley. The high relief of the Guadalupe-Toledo mountains, the borders of La Mancha and the Sierra Nevada are also excluded. In the Ebro basin, the Pyrenean limit is a combination of summer humidity and winter cold, low in the west, but rising to 3,940 feet in the valleys of western Catalonia.[26] It is similarly complicated in southern France,[27] reaching to Belvianez in the valley of the Aude, the Lauraguais trough, the southern flanks of the Montagne Noire and the valleys of the Cevennes. Across the Rhône in the Robinet de Donzère, the olive rises to Remuzat in the Mont Ventoux, and up the Durance valley to Volonne. Similarly along the Provençal littoral, it follows up the valleys, reaching inland to Moustiers on the Verdon and Annot on the Var. Excessive humidity limits it on the Ligurian coast. In the Italian Peninsula it has a thermal limit, reached according to altitude: 1,300–1,600 feet in the north and west, 2,000–2,800 feet in the south. Similarly in the islands, the olive is limited by altitude: 2,900–3,200 feet in Corsica, 2,300–2,600 feet in Sardinia, and 2,600–3,300 feet in Sicily. The olive is generally absent from the North Italian Plain, but it recommences at Rimini, though limited by winter cold to below 1,000–1,300 feet in the Marches. Thus in Italy, the olive coincides roughly with Pavari's Lauretum zone and the isotherm of 37°F. mean monthly minimum. The olive occurs in sheltered pockets of the Veneto, but it is restricted to the Istrian coast.[28] In Dalmatia and Montenegro it rises to 650–1,150 feet, that is above even the *Quercetum ilicis*.

In North Africa the olive climbs the slopes of the western Atlas where it is limited by cold, but eastwards and southwards aridity checks its possible spread. The Moroccan coast, with its distinctive climate, has also little oleiculture. The limit follows the southern flanks of the

Algerian Tell, excluded by the winter cold of the High Plains, but growing to the south on the lower slopes of the Aurès and Batna massifs.
Tunisia, with its extensive groves, grows it widely, as far even as the
Monts des Sours. Scattered patches follow along the coast into Tripo-
litania.

Bordering the Eu-Mediterranean zone thus defined by the olive, there
are the contrasted humid and arid zones to the north and south respectively. More accurately, however, six phyto-climatic types may be
recognised in the western Mediterranean: the humid or sub-humid, the
meso-, thermo- and xero-Mediterranean subdivisions of Gaussen's Eu-
Mediterranean, the semi-arid or arid, and the high mountains.[29]

2. *The Transition to the Humid or Sub-Humid Vegetation.* Where the
maritime climates permit mild winters and the summer drought is
minimal a deciduous flora results, partially resistant to both conditions.
A number of oaks are characteristic therefore of the Northwestern and
Northern Iberian Peninsula and much of the Apennines. Where moisture is at a maximum on lowland sites, the common oak (*Quercus robur*)
occurs. In the Iberian Peninsula, the pubescent oak (*Q. pubescens*), the
sessile oak (*Q. sessiliflora*) and especially the Pyrenean (*Q. Pyrenaica*)
and the Portuguese (*Q. Lusitanica*) oaks are characteristic. The renewal
of the leaves each spring is the main adaptation, together with smaller
leaves and acorns in the species more resistant to summer drought. Thus
in the Iberian Peninsula, two northern zones may be distinguished: a
maritime, humid zone where the common oak is important, mingling on
the higher slopes with the sweet chestnut (*Castanea sativa*), and a transitional interior zone where the Pyrenean and Portuguese oaks mingle
with the evergreen oak. In Peninsular Italy the chief deciduous oak is
the Turkey oak (*Quercus cerris*). As in the Pyrenees, the low passes of
the Apennines have permitted many central European species to migrate
southwards. Relief features in the northern Mediterranean provide a
wide variety of local ecological conditions in this region of transition.
Q. robur may be found in cool, lower valleys where siliceous or alluvial
soils have a high water-table in summer, whereas *Q. pyrenaica* or *Q.
cerris* occurs perhaps on drier and steeper slopes. The holm oak will
predominate on limestone soils on the drier, lee-side of mountain slopes.
In this medley of deciduous types the surprising feature is the marked
absence of natural coniferous associations. Man has introduced, however, a great number of species, notably the maritime pine (*Pinus
pinaster*). The beech too has been extended by man's intervention in
cutting the fir for his needs. The beech, having more regenerative
powers, has competed successfully and especially in the Apennines it

has replaced the fir.[30] The sweet chestnut as a valued food in the past, has also been greatly spread by man.

Thus the contrast with the Eu-Mediterranean zone is clear. There, the ecological difficulties of tree-growth, once the *Quercion ilicis* is destroyed, tend to induce rapid regression. In the more favoured sylvatic northern zone, the variety of tree associations is such that it is impossible to conceive of the original climax. The distinction between primary and secondary forms remains obscure. The transition between the sub-humid and Eu-Mediterranean types is gradual if the distinction is a question of varying rainfall. A sharper break occurs when there is a marked thermal difference, such as occurs in the Rhône corridor and on the Dinaric Alps, where consequently mixed species are much less developed. It is the thermal factor too which accounts for regional transitions in the essentially central European flora of the North Italian Plain, with outlines of Mediterranean species, e.g. around Lake Garda and the south-east slope of the Euganean hills.

3. *The Transition to the Arid Vegetation.* Like the Mediterranean vegetation cover, the plants of the semi-arid realm have a tree climax. But in contrast to the northern borders, the number of species is much reduced and the dominance of a few species has been the consequence, not only of a more difficult environment, but of the struggle to survive against man's depredations. Broadly, three types of vegetation can be recognised in North Africa, south of the humid Mediterranean zone, and below an annual rainfall of 24 inches. These are: the degraded Mediterranean forests, the climax of jujube brushwood and the steppe climax of alfa.

In the degradation of *Quercion ilicis*, first the cork oak forests disappear (below 24 in), then the evergreen oak (below 12 in and a xero-thermal index of up to 250). In degraded forms, the woodlands of the Aleppo pine are very important, on all the drier slopes of the Tell, from Tunisia to the eastern Rif. Degraded forms of *Oleo-lenticion* are common, chiefly the dwarf palm, or *dourm* and the rock-rose. Transitional to these two forms are the woodlands of the Barbary thuya or *araar* (*Callitris articulata*), rising to 30–40 ft and often with a dense brushwood layer. Associated with them are the ubiquitous red juniper (*J. phoenicia*) and the prevalent juniper (*J. thuriferus*). All these trees are long-lived, with small, persistent scale-like leaves. The juniper, able to withstand the winter cold of the dry interior is typical also of the Ebro steppes and Teruel mountains, where it forms an association called by the Spaniards *sabinar*. The thuya is exceptional among conifers in being able to regenerate readily from the base of the cut-down trunk and the junipers, indifferent to poor soils, are able to throw up new stems from the lower branches. Thus on the High Plains of North Africa, precisely suited to extensive cereals and grazing, these trees can survive in their struggle against much human exploitation.

The camel thorn or jujube (*Zizyphus lotus*) may be considered as much the climax of the semi-arid realm as the evergreen oak is of the Mediterranean.[31] It has a wide ecological range, from Saharan to Mediterranean conditions, but as a plant of tropical origins it is largely confined to North Africa. Where the rainfall is 12–16 in it can form a dense, grey-coloured brushwood, 15–20 feet high. Adapted to shed its small leaves in winter, this deciduous tree replaces the Mediterranean hard-leaved communities where drought and cold are unfavourable to the latter. The jujube is often associated with the Atlantic turpentine or betoum tree (*Pistaccia atlantica*). In Morocco,[32] in the upper Moulouya basin and from the Sous valley southwards the argan or Barbary almond (*Argania spinosa*) covers vast areas which would otherwise be desert. This evergreen forms an open woodland or brushwood, rising to 18–25 feet. It is commonly associated with a spurge (*Euphorbia beaumierana*) and sometimes with the Atlantic turpentine tree. Northwards, the argan merges into open bush of gum acacia (*Acacia gummifera*), the camel thorn and a spurge (*E. resinifera*).

The steppe grasses may be considered transitional between the degraded Mediterranean forests and the jujube association, since some alfa steppe especially in North Africa is truly climatic, and others are degraded forms of woodland, for example in south-east Spain. Very few plants accompany the alfa (*Stipa tenacissima*), so it gives a characteristic landscape of grassy tufts that rise two to three feet, between eroded soils, called in Spain *calvero*. Coarse esparto (*Lygeum spartum*) grows in saline soils, often mixed with wormwoods. Both merge towards the desert into a lower, sparser cover of drinn (*Aristida pungens*). With increased aridity, these steppe plants reflect more sensitively the edaphic differences, some able to withstand salinity (the *halophytes*) in varying degrees.

4. *Mountain Vegetation Zones.** This zonal arrangement of vegetation from humid sub-mediterranean in the north, and Eu-Mediterranean to semi-arid in the south, is upset to some extent by the mountain chains, with their supra-mediterranean cover. To the geographer the mountain flora have a threefold significance: as indicators of climatic differences; as evidence of previous climatic changes; and as a measure of man's

---

* See, however, recent discussion raised by R. Corte, 'Esiste una vegetazione mediterranea montana?' *Ann. Accad. Ital. Sci.*, for. 7, 1958, pp. 61–86.

12 Maquis and garrigue with asphodel stalks in foreground, Col de Sevi (3,612 ft.), W. Corsica

13 Olive picking

14 Cork oak forest, Alentejo, with young shoots mingling with mature trees

15 Cactus hedge

16 Goats browsing on an argan tree, S. Morocco

17 Saint's tomb in relict woodland, Ghmaran hills, near Taza, Morocco

18 Saint's tomb, with its cover of original woodland, near Tetuan, N. Morocco

influence in changing the face of the landscape. These features are particularly interesting in mountains, because of the variety of climatic factors, the relic character of plants taking refuge there with climatic changes, and the preservation of natural vegetation less touched by man.

Broadly, the thermal differences affected by altitude are more important in the northern Mediterranean, where the latitudinal zones of vegetation are reflected on the mountain slopes. In the southern Mediterranean, however, summer drought is more general and determines more markedly the altitudinal succession of the tree cover. The climatic factor is, of course, much more complicated in any detailed analysis

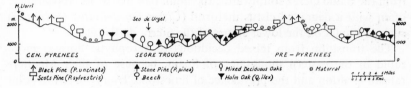

FIG. 34. Vegetation profile in the eastern Pyrenees

than this generalized principle. Aspect on the northern and southern flanks of major mountain ranges, sunny or shady valley slopes, protection from wind, the calcareous or non-calcareous soils, are all of major significance in determining the local zonation. It is characteristic of the northern Mediterranean mountains, that despite sharp contrasts of flora on the northern and southern flanks of the ranges, valleys that run north to south from one flank have markedly a mixed vegetation, alternating with the condition of sun and shade on either side of the valley (Fig. 34).[33] This feature is much less pronounced in valleys running east to west, where more normal altitudinal zones are characteristic. In the southern Mediterranean, as there are much fewer species, the mountain zonation is much clearer. That is to say, there are fewer plant-ecological options.

In the transition between the northern and southern mountains, there are distinct differences from one peninsula to another. Within the western Mediterranean, the Atlantic mountains of the Iberian Peninsula, the eastern mountains of the Meseta, the Sa Nevada, and the Italian peninsula are all different.

In the north and north-west of the Iberian Peninsula, the mild oceanic climate favours a deciduous flora. The common oak (*Quercus robur*) provides the basal climax though often replaced by chestnut or cultivated land. Mixed with it are associations of *Quercetum pubescentis* and *Quercetum pyrenaicae*, the latter also forming the lower mountain

W.M.W.—5

stage. Above it the beech is dominant in the western Pyrenees and the Cantabrians, descending even to sea-level along the humid Basque coast. The summits of the Cantabrian mountains consist of heaths of erica, heather, gorse and pasture, the latter important especially on the limestones. In Galicia and northern Portugal, the horizons are simplified by the absence of beech. The basal stage of common oak, often replaced by a paraclimax of cluster pine (*Pinus pinaster*) is succeeded by the submontane or montane zone of black oak (*Quercus pyrenaica*) and crowned by matorral or heath of juniper (*Juniperus communis*), gorse (*Genista lusitancia*) and ferns. On southern slopes from the Sa de Gerez southwards, the holm oak makes its appearance, often with a degraded cistus matorral (*Cistus landaniferus, C. crispus*) such as occurs on the lower slopes of the Sierra de Estrêla.

The transition from mixed deciduous to xerophytic flora is more rapid in the eastern mountains of Spain, because of their Mediterranean location and the prevalence of limestone. Everywhere the holm oak forms the basal stage, except in the Pre-Pyrenees and parts of western Catalonia, where the mixed pubescent and sessile oaks are the lowest stage, associated with box brushwood (Fig. 34). But even as far north as the Catalan limestones, the holm oak climbs to 5,500 ft though absent on the northern Pyrenees. On the higher slopes it is frequently mixed with the Aleppo pine. The beech is unimportant in the Catalan mountains, except in damper areas such as Olot where it descends even to the plain. But in the montane zone the beech is frequently replaced by the mountain pine (*Pinus mugo*) mingling with the Scots pine (*Pinus sylvestris*). The high summits have a sub-arctic flora of common juniper, bilberry, rhododendrons and pastures. South of the Catalan mountains, the increased summer drought eliminates the mixed deciduous oaks and the beech, so that the basal stage of the *Quercetum ilicis* is succeeded by the montane black pine (*Pinus clusiana*). The Scots fir pine suited to more continental conditions crowns the summits of the Celtiberian and central Cordilleras. To the south of these mountains the general impoverishment of species becomes more marked with the elimination of the Scots pine (except in the Sa Nevada) and the upward rise of the evergreen oak climax. Often it forms in the southern mountains a sub-montane stage, with mixed deciduous oaks on the lower summits.

The Italian peninsula illustrates some striking differences. There are no sharply marked changes between central European and Mediterranean flora in the Apennine ranges and in the north there is no comparable floristic barrier to the Pyrenees.[24] Everywhere in the Peninsula the basal stages have Mediterranean plants, the *Laurentum* zone[35] (according to Pavari) which roughly coincides with Gaussen's Eu-Mediterranean (Figs. 171 and 27). The basal zone terminates with the *Castanetum* with its sweet chestnut woods and mixed deciduous associations. Much of it consists of degraded brushwood of hairy oaks (*Quercus lanuginosa*) and Turkey oaks (*Quercus cerris*) or woodlands of pedunculate and sessile oaks. In the montane zone of the *fagetum* the beech is the chief constituent, aggressive in its encroachments on the white fir (*Abies alba*). It also occurs widely in a dense brushwood with alder (*Alnus cordata*) and sometimes with hazel undergrowth. This *folteto* is a typical degraded form of many mountain slopes. Scots pines and black pines form the culminating cover of the higher mountains. In the islands the basal evergreen climax, and especially its degraded macchia, form a wide expanse, notably in Sardinia. The lower montane stage in Corsica is well developed in the chestnut forests, the upper stages simplified by the dominance of the mountain pine (*Pinus laricio*). The montane stages are markedly unimportant in Sardinia because of its relief (Fig. 234), but in Sicily, especially Etna, the beech, climbing to over 6,000 ft, occupies a significant montane zone.

In North Africa, the great majority of the mountain forests are resinous (92 per cent in Morocco). Another distinctive feature is that the sub-alpine stage is replaced by steppe plants. In the central mountains of Morocco (the High and Anti-Atlas) these latter plants also comprise the basal stage, in which gum acacia and other parkland cover, succeeded by montane stages of thuya, red juniper, a narrow zone of holm oak, and thurifer, the latter displacing the cedar near the drier summits.[36] In the Middle Atlas the basal zone of *Oleo-lenticetum* is succeeded by the montane stage of evergreen and the cedar, the latter to the tree limit. The summits are covered with stunted brushwood of red juniper and dwarf palm. The Rif and the Tell have generally a richer sequence with the holm oak and aleppo pine in the basal stage, then some Afarès and Portugese oaks, and montane cedar forests. Southwards in the Aurès and Saharan Atlas, the holm oaks, aleppo pines and red juniper intermingle and scale the summits.

PALAEONTOLOGICAL CHANGES OF VEGETATION

To complete this brief outline of the climatic interpretation of the vegetation cover in the Western Mediterranean, it is necessary to consider the evidence of plant origins. These help to explain the discrepancies that exist between the actual distribution and the ideal climax. Many plants have an ancestry in the Tertiary flora[37], some like the cedar are even traceable to the Cretaceous. During the Tertiary there is evidence of two sources of relict flora. One is associated with the Macronesian plants found in Portugal, Morocco and the Canary Islands, a damp tropical flora, descendants of which may be the fig, magnolia, laurel, cluster pine, (*Pinus pinaster, P. canariensis and P. mesogenesis*) and possibly the cork oak. The argan in Morocco has a similar ancestry. More obscure is the origin of plants coming from Asia and the eastern Mediterranean, such as probably the aleppo pine, which may have been forced to migrate westwards with increased Pontian desiccation, although its occurrence in the Western Mediter-

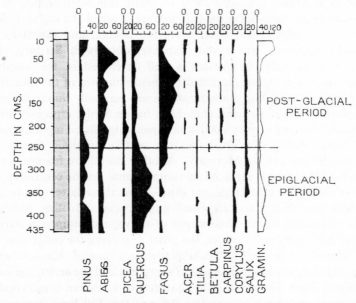

FIG. 35. Pollen diagram at Prato delle Nasse,1,475 m., near S. Martino di Castrozza, Trentino

ranean has itself a long Tertiary evolution[38]. The plant changes of the Tertiary are, however, less climatic—since the long epoch was marked by relatively uniform tropical conditions—as the consequence of land and sea changes. The palaeogeographic units of the Rif-Baetic massif, the Tyrrhenian continental connections of the Balearics[39] and Corso-Sardinia with Catalonia and Maures, and the Sicilian-Tell bridge, have influenced restricted and endemic distributions[40]. Such is the possible explanation of the distribution of *Callistris articulate* and *Abies pinsapo* on either side of the Alboran sea. A souvenir of the Tyrrhenian continent is *Pinus laricio*.

The distribution of plants in the Pliocene, such as the olive in the Po valley, the sequoia in the Rhône valley and the cedar in the Auvergne, are some indication of the marked climatic changes during the Quaternary. At the same time it is remarkable that of the species found in the Rhône valley in the Pliocene, most are still there. It appears that the *Quercus ilex* became a dominant species during the colder conditions of the Vallafranchian, adapting itself successfully to the subsequent changes, during which many of its earlier associates were eliminated. This would explain its present virility and its relict distribution outside the Mediterranean domain.

During the early Pleistocene the deterioration of climate from the warm conditions of the Tertiary resulted in a gradual elimination of species such as *Tsuga, Carya, Zelkova* and *Pinus haploxylon*. Pollen studies in Italy widely scattered from the Po delta[41] to the lakes of central Italy[42] and even in to Calabria[43] confirm this change (Figs. 35–37). Pollen samples are scarce in most Mediterranean areas as the pollen is only well preserved in acid or neutral soils, so the Italian studies which have grown rapidly in the last decade are of great importance. During the Quaternary glaciations southern Europe had dense coniferous forests, covering most of the Italian peninsula south of the Po valley[44] and on the borders of the Iberian Meseta[45], with taiga in the North Italian Plain and the Spanish interior (Fig. 38). White and red fir, and especially Scots pine were well represented. During the Würmian glaciation the Scots pine reached Leiria in Portugal and possibly even to the coast[46]; it was also in the Campagna. In the post-Würmian oscillations, first conifers, and then during the two Atlantic or 'ipsothermal' phases, mixed deciduous woods spread over the northern Mediterranean (6500–2500 B.C.). These comprised first a hotter, drier climate (*c.* 5000 B.C.) which permitted the Mediterranean xerothermal vegetation to extend north of the Pyrenees over low cols, and then a late Atlantic, cooler, wetter phase which encouraged a marked spread southwards of the beech and the fir[47]. The climatic optimum for much mixed deciduous flora was probably reached about 2500 B.C. in the Mediterranean[48], at a period when the chestnut was widely spread (though in retreat in the Po Plain). Since then the climate appears in terms of vegetation to have been slightly drier and hotter in the sub Atlantic II or catathermal phase, precisely at a critical stage when man has been active in destroying effectively so much of the Mediterranean forest[49]. This climax, built up in the post-Würmian oscillations with generally more humid conditions, has been unable to maintain its primeval splendour, once its micro-climatic conditions have been

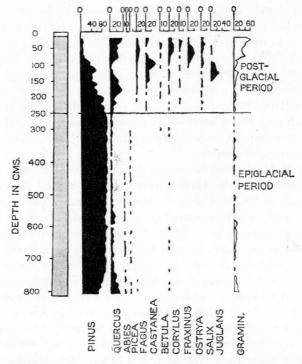

FIG. 36. Pollen diagram at Piano di Colfiorito, 750 m. upper Valle del Chianti

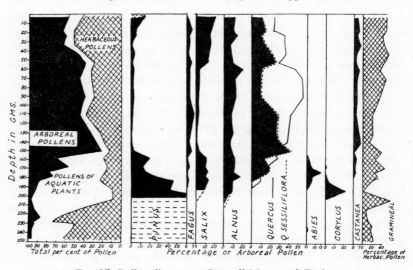

FIG. 37. Pollen diagram at Lago di Monterosi, Latium

irrevocably changed by deforestation. Since then, the forest has been in retreat. In this process, some species have been eliminated, such as the cedar in southern Europe, while others have spread, notably the mixed deciduous flora, the cypress and trees of food value (the stone pine, the olive, carob, etc.).

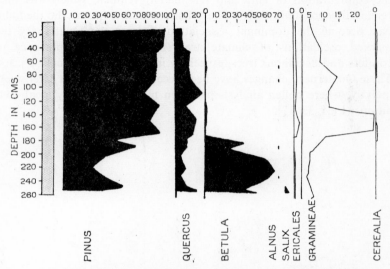

FIG. 38. Pollen diagram at Hoyos de Peñalara, Central Cordillera

SUMMARY

The characteristic plant association of the Mediterranean is the holm oak (*Quercetum ilicis*). The most marked feature of its plant cover is in the various adaptations to drought. Few areas however have the relics of the original cover of sub-tropical forests, in which the holm oak was supported by three or four other levels of vegetation. Much more common are the degraded stages of *maquis* and *garrigue*, distinguished by the height of the plants, the depth of the soil, and the dominance of biotic controls. The symbiosis of vegetation and soils is clearly reflected in the stages of plant regression.

Although the northern relief barriers might suggest decisive phytoclimatic boundaries, the limits of Mediterranean plants are varied and indecisive, although the olive is still the most satisfactory. North of this limit, is a transitional zone of humid or sub-humid conditions, where mixed deciduous flora predominate. To the south is another transition towards more xerophytic associations, where the camel thorn is a common climax. Mountain zones however complicate this simple threefold arrangement.

The present flora despite their dramatic modifications induced by man, reveal evidence of a long heritage. Many plants are traceable to Tertiary times, their distribution more affected perhaps by changes in the configuration of land and sea than by climate which was then remarkably constant. Only in the Villafranchian, however, did the holm oak become the dominant association. During the Quaternary the marked oscillations of climate are reflected in the importance of conifers and deciduous trees, especially in the cold or 'glacial' phases. These Quaternary changes have been recently studied most extensively in Italy, where pollen analysis has been most favoured by local conditions (Figs. 35–37).

CHAPTER 6

THE WESTERN MEDITERRANEAN
AS A MAN-MADE WORLD

'Natural resources are in fact cultural appraisals.' (Carl O. Sauer)

The vegetation cover that thickly mantled the Western Mediterranean during the pluvial regime of the Atlantic phase has been radically altered by man. At least half of the soil erosion that is prevalent in the region has been human induced, and the ecological balance has been severely impaired. On the positive side, however, the introduction of many plants, the domestication of animals, the spread of irrigation and drainage, the rise of cities and the close occupance of the land by peasants, have all helped to create new landscapes. Psychology, as well as physiology and technology, have contributed in these achievements, for varied societies have selected and emphasised differing values. The study of the evaluation and choice made by the settlers of the Mediterranean world is a historic and contemporary study of vast proportions that is still to be undertaken seriously. The cumulative effects of diverse cultures in a given area have contributed to the personality of historico-cultural regions, itself also a neglected study.

CULTURAL BACKGROUNDS

Of all the cultural regions in this study that of the Atlantic zone of Iberia perhaps stands out most clearly. Apart from its distinct climate and vegetation it has had a strong 'Celtic' culture. This was first fostered by an active bronze trade (based on Cantabrian copper and Galician tin) with Brittany and Britain commencing in the seventh century B.C.[1] Another distinct region is the North Italian Plain whose inhabitants have looked naturally towards the Adriatic Sea. The first trade over the Brenner Pass was associated with the amber route that linked the Baltic with Greece via the Adriatic. Ever since, notably during the Byzantine empire and later in the days of the Venetian republic, the shores of the Adriatic have had common links of trade. The Iberian shores of the Algarve and southern Spain turn towards Africa; they were most effectively united during the Arab domination and reinforced by the invasion of the Almoravides. More recently, the expulsion of the Moriscos (Fig. 40) in the seventeenth century[2] and the Spanish emigration since the nineteenth century have forged strong links. The islands of the western Mediterranean have had some of the oldest contacts with each other, ever since Neolithic and later Megalithic peoples used the islands as stepping stones from the Eastern Mediterranean during the second and first millennia B.C.[3]. The strategic position of southern Italy and Sicily, at the cross-roads of the Mediterranean Sea explains the numerous legacies of Greek towns, Norman castles and Spanish feudalism that have left their several imprints. In the northern Mediterranean, perhaps more significant than the sea has been the great Roman highway that united Etruria with the east coast of Spain. Subsequently, the influence of the Franks was to spread along this littoral. Later still mercantile rivalries were to divide this important coastline into numerous political units. The interpenetration of land and sea, the flow of the current, the location of islands and straits, all played a positive rôle in fashioning regional entities in this Mediterranean world. Only in the centre of Iberia was its territorial extent so extensive that semi-indigenous cultures emerged there.[4]

Archaeologists have been too ready to think of our predecessors in terms simply of technology and *en masse*. Yet factors of diverse social taste and individual decision have also helped to modify the landscape. Living in a lush forested world of mixed deciduous trees, the Etruscans showed such strong preferences for useful and non-productive trees, that they conceived the *arboles felices*, such as vine and the ivy, regulated in their own rhythm of growth and the full development of human beings.[5] Hemmed in by forest, the Etruscans were organised into self-governing towns, a system favourable to high levels of culture, but unable to withstand the pressures of larger and more coherent units (Fig. 39). The Etruscans were overrun by Celtic people from the Po valley (450 B.C.) and by the Romans from the south (*c.* 400–295 B.C.). By instinct the Phoenicians, though successful agriculturists, were traders and fisherman. They planted fruits widely throughout the Mediterranean—notably the pomegranate (*malum punicum*)—but their great achievement was the widespread creation of ports (Fig. 39). Pliny describes how lagoon fishing with nets and traps in shallow waters was a particular practice of the Phoenicians, [6] and doubtless they introduced the present-day methods of lagoon fishing into the western Mediterranean. It is thus not by chance that numerous Phoenician sites, such as Cádiz, Alcudia de Elche, Ibiza and Cagliari are near, or on the site of, natural salt pans, still being exploited. Tunny fishing too, figures on the earliest Phoenician coinage.[7] However, the widespread scatter of Punic and Carthaginian settlements suffered defeat for the same reason as the Etruscan towns; the countryside was not consolidated by rural settlement. Little is known of the topography of Etruscan and Phoenician towns, so effectively did the Romans destroy them. The Etruscans made full use of the edges of lava plateaux in Etruria for commanding sites. The Phoenicians showed a preference for limestone promontories, where cisterned water was available, or else for lagoonal sites, defensible and well-stocked with fish, salt and murex.

Very different was the agricultural colonisation of the Greeks in Sicily and southern Italy (Fig. 39). Population pressure in Greece prompted systematic colonisation of this classical land of promise. Many colonies were the result of private enterprise. First consideration was given to sites on or near alluvial plains which could be cultivated, such as those abounding on the south and east coasts of Sicily and the more isolated plains of Calabria and Campania. Sites with good harbours but without attractive lowlands, such as at Brindisi, were deliberately ignored. Ideal agricultural sites were chosen irrespective of distances involved for trade with the home country.[7] Such serious agricultural colonisation is also attested by the cults of fertility goddesses. It is to the Greeks that we may attribute the first scientific principles of land use, prompted by soil erosion in Attica and by population pressure. Thus Theophrastus in 313 B.C. formulated the following principle: 'Use your rich soils for grains and thin soils for trees. Grains and all other annuals take the nutriment from the surface soil which, therefore, ought not to be thin or of a quality to be quickly exhausted, as happens in a shallow layer of earth. But trees, equipped with long and strong roots, draw their nourishment from the depths. In rich soils, trees run to wood and foliage but yield little or no fruit. Hence a thin soil is superior from both standpoints; it produces a balanced foliage and fruitage.'[8] Views such as that of Agrigento in Sicily (Plate 20) illustrate how this established a triad of land use; at the foot of the mountains were located the olive groves with their thin soils, with vineyards either below them on stony pediments, rich in sub-surface water, or above them because of hardier crop resistance to winter cold; and the cereal lands (chiefly barley) on the plains, where winter rains made possible a seasonal use of otherwise parched land. The morphological sequence of calcareous or crystalline outcrops, flanked by Quaternary pediments and terraces, and a lowland plaster of clays, or alluvial sediments was thus admirably utilised. Moreover, the growth

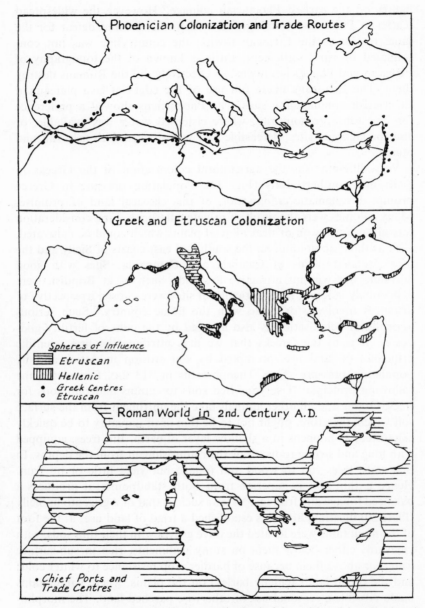

FIG. 39. Colonization of the Mediterranean in classical times: Phoenician, Greek and Etruscan, Roman in the 2nd century A.D.

and ripening of the annuals in the humid season and the harvest of the perennials at the close of the hot season integrated the seasonal rhythm of life as βιος. That is to say it was a diet whose 'life according to reason' engendered classical civilization.

The Greek view of the landscape was not merely utilitarian. Above all it was psychic, so that the study of their temple sites reveals the basic meaning of the environs to the Greeks.[9] Hera, the goddess who holds colonial lands for the settler, Demeter, the goddess of fruitfulness, and Athena, the giver of the olive, all have their dwelling in the plains and gently rolling hills. The Greek sense of pattern in the landscape shapes the void of earth and sky with sculptured clarity (Plate 20). Very different is Artemis, guardian of the untamed lands who must be propitiated even with human blood. Apollo, dweller of wooded groves and towering peaks, Zeus, god of things as nature decrees, dwell in the lofty mountains, where man has only a precarious footing in nature. Compromised by the needs of man to dwell in cities, templed promontories and mountain shrines shared with the city altars, a unity of man and nature.

Compared with the city states of the Greeks, Roman colonization is a more prosaic story of a pragmatic people who had shrewd rather than bright ideas, clothed in the homespun of peasant interests. Rome's territory was to begin with *ager Romanus*, conquered by the sword but subjected to the plough. Despite its huge overseas empire, Rome looked to the land and remained rooted in the soil. It was the massive consolidation of land ownership, the spread of colonization by the soldiery, and not by the tenuous, scattered creation of towns isolated from each other, that Rome's legacy has remained the most enduring and even the most beneficent of all the ancient peoples (Fig. 39). Varro gives us a fascinating picture of the Roman interest in agriculture. Looking at the map of Italy, he asks his readers, 'You men who have travelled over many lands, have you ever seen any which was better cultivated than Italy? My opinion is, said Agrius, that there is none that has so little of its land uncultivated'. Later he adds, 'What spelt is comparable with that of Campania, what wheat with the Apulian, what wine with the Falerian, what oil with the Venafrian? Is not Italy so stocked with fruit-trees as to seem one great orchard?'.[10] This is not just patriotism, for today Italy is still the most humanised of all Mediterranean landscapes. Certainly its climates are kinder than elsewhere but much of the credit must also go back to the Roman farmer. Centuriated field patterns, areas of specialised viticulture and of interculture, varied breeds of stock, are all traceable to the Roman heritage.

Above all the Roman empire was a vast city-building enterprise, leaving its imprint on hundreds of 'colonial' towns, as well as altering the features of many old established ones. It consisted of some 5,627 separate civic bodies at its apogee[11] (Fig. 39). At the time of the Roman conquest, for example, the Iberian Peninsula had an estimated population of some two million; by the fourth century A.D., after six centuries

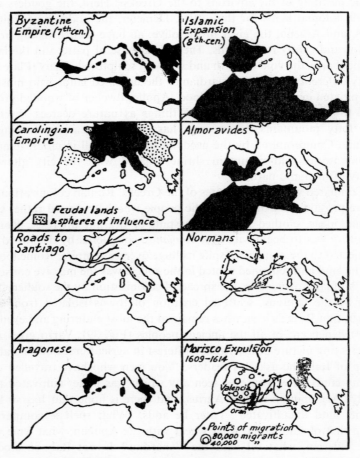

FIG. 40. W. Mediterranean cultures in the Middle Ages and later

of sustained peace and city life, it had nine million. To support this increase of population, the ordered planning of the landscape by new roads, grid-iron towns that commonly housed 50,000 inhabitants, and the careful survey of the land, all helped to integrate the needs of town and country, and to ensure an economic balance between supply and demand. Lip-service was still paid to the gods of the earth, but the peasant's dictum 'a man reapeth as he soweth' was of first concern.

The breakdown of Roman rule led to a fervent emphasis of local authority. In Italy this was exaggerated by the church dignitaries and later in the north by trade rivalries. In the Iberian Peninsula, the agriculturally-minded Visigoths and Muslims fostered regional discriminations that have never since been effaced. Unlike the Romans, the Muslims built few new cities but they radically transformed the layout of existing cities to meet their own needs. The Muslim lived in two realms; one was the Mesquita where he worshipped and the zoco where he traded, but the other was his walled home where seclusion was emphasised. Thus the foci of mosques, small squares and radiating streets, blend with the maze of cul-de-sacs and walled dwellings where tribal groups and individual families could keep to themselves. Another important element of Moorish life was the garden, retreats in a setting of nature, where the splash of water, the fragrance of myrtle and orange, and the seclusion for sensual delights gave men their paradise.[12] No wonder the Persian word for 'paradise' means a walled garden. The Crusaders learnt to appreciate the peculiar value set on gardens, and Provence especially became the setting for garden landscapes such as described by Albertus Magnus in his *de Vegetabilibus*. From the Muslims also came many vegetables, fruits and the arts of irrigation that have transformed so many of the lowlands of the Spanish Levante.

HUMAN MODIFICATIONS OF THE VEGETATION COVER

The role of man in changing the face of the landscape is still only inadequately understood. To assess the changes it would be necessary to know precisely what the original landscapes looked like, but this is a controversial topic among ecologists. The assumption that the evergreen oak and its associations were dominant everywhere in the lands of the western Mediterranean appears unlikely. Rupérez Cuellar,[13] for example, thinks the widespread ilex woodlands postulated by Font Quer in the Iberian Peninsula is exaggerated. The assumption that all maquis and garrigue are secondary in origin is also disputed.[14] On the limestone pavements of Bas-Languedoc, [15] Provence, and in other parts of the Karst, there appears rather the reverse evidence, that these are indigenous plant cover. If this is so, then the effects of the biotic factor in the spread of the degraded shrub associations may be sometimes exaggerated.

1. *Deforestation.* With this cautionary attitude, it is certain, however, that man and his animals have caused very great changes in the original

woodland cover[16]. The evidence of forest clearance has not yet been treated systematically in the Western Mediterranean but there are numerous clues.[17] The use of fire since upper Palaeolithic times has continued to the present day. One authority has stated that 'around the Mediterranean and in the present state of pastoralism the use of fire is as necessary as transhumance'.[18] The goat, sheep and pig from the seventh to the fifth millennium B.C., and since the fourth century A.D. the widespread introduction into North Africa of the camel,[19] have been important direct causes of deforestation. The ubiquitous use of charcoal in a world that lacks fuel resources, has been very important. Positive evidence is seen in the remnants of ancient woodlands today, isolated conspicuously in clumps.[20] Such are the beech woods and mixed oak woodlands of Tuscany and the pinewoods of the Calabrian Sila. In North Africa the remnants of natural plant cover preserved in cemeteries and around the shrines of holy men constitute important evidence, [21] kept sacred like the ancient groves of Palestine, alluded to in the Old Testament (see Plate 17). Indirectly, there is the evidence of floods and soil erosion. For example the floods on the Tiber became more significant after the second century B.C.,[22] and the study of the *cuniculi* or underground aqueducts of Etruria indicated clearly the rate of downcutting since they were made about the fifth century B.C., much accelerated subsequently by deforestation[23] (see Fig. 200).

The nature of the plants and their relative importance is other evidence, for their regenerative capacity varies widely. The Aleppo pine, for example, bears much more seed than the cluster pine and is therefore more regenerative. The cedar does not bear abundant seed until it is forty to fifty years old, a critical weakness in areas of sustained exploitation such as in North Africa. Pyrophytes, or rather plants that survive despite fire, form a number of associations, indicative of pastoral incendiarism. Some are of passive resistance because their materials do not readily burn, notably the black pines of Corsica and the cork oaks of southern Spain, Portugal and North Africa. Pyrophytes with biological reactions are of four main groups:[24] those able to survive despite the loss of surface organs and with powers of recuperation (e.g. the thuya and strawberry tree); those with deep root systems such as the kermes oak and bracken; pyrophytes only indirectly resistant (for example open ilex woods with little undergrowth to catch fire); and social pyrophytes that grow rapidly after repeated burning and form a dense flora, such as the cistus of Extremadura and Sardinia. Thus it is possible with ecological spectacles to map and study the effects of fire on the vegetation.

Deforestation, however, has been markedly accelerated by the series of processes set off by the Mediterranean civilizations. First, there have been the economic needs, resultant on the enormous growth of demands, provoked especially by the development of the Roman and Muslim worlds, requiring new fleets, new towns, many new cultural buildings, new irrigation zones needing wooden water-wheels and new mines whose minerals required fuel treatment. Secondly, there have been the technical needs of timber. Shipbuilding has been of paramount importance in a sea which has seen the rise and fall of Carthaginian, Roman, Byzantine, Muslim, Italian, Spanish and French sea-power, and from which vast trading empires were opened up to Portuguese and Spanish shipping.[25] Then too, the Roman civilisation with its industries of brick and tile making, oil refining, the arts such as ceramics and lesiure such as the heated baths, created unprecedented demands for timber as a source of fuel. To this demand the Moors added sugar-refining and their overall needs were exaggerated. Military strategy became dictated by the sources of ship timbers. Thus the Romans were better placed than the Carthaginians, since the mixed oaks, pines and firs of the Tiber and Arno basins could be conveniently floated down to the arsenals. The intensive trade in lumber with the eastern Mediterranean in classical times indicates the marked poverty of the Levantine forests compared with the richer western resources. The Muslims would have been unmatched against the Byzantine naval resources of the Balkans but for their North African, Iberian and North Sicilian forests. The naval struggle of Pisa and Genoa for the timber resources of Corsica was also significant. The rich Ligurian and Istrian forests gave Genoa and Venice a more equal rivalry.[26]

As each civilization made its inroads on the Mediterranean forests, so the processes of deforestation have varied regionally and temporally. First there was the Greek colonization of Magna Graeca on the coasts of Lucania, Calabria and Sicily. Then the Romans cleared the forested borders of the Etruscan city states, colonized Campania and later the Po valley. Apulia was already largely cleared for sheep walks, dating probably from its dense Neolithic settlement. But the highlands of Calabria, the Apennines and Corsica were virtually untouched in classical times. Tunisia, more easily cleared was intensely colonised in its eastern lowlands. But the Roman province of Mauretania was still heavily mantled in forest, transport costs limiting exploitation to select woods such as the thuya and the cedar.[27]

In the Middle Ages, the Muslims made great inroads into the forests of the North African littoral, also the valleys of the Sebou, Guadal-

FIG. 41. W. Mediterranean forests in the 7th–11th centuries

quivir, Ebro and the eastern coasts of Spain[28] (see Fig. 41). It is not
without significance that the great Arab cities were situated near a wide
radius of forests, for instance, Tunis, Fès, Seville, Córdoba and Granada.
The Moorish arsenals of Tunis, Almería and Tortosa completed the
clearance of forests in the hinterlands, and the tile industry of Quesada
helped to denude the Sub-Baetic mountains, especially in the Sierra
Cazorla. Where the low rainfall made reforestation impossible, the
Romans and Moors together stripped bare the mountains of the
Segura, to feed the mineral furnaces around Cartagena. In Spain,
after the Reconquest, deforestation became the accepted policy of the
pastoralists, especially after 1273 when the Mesta of Castile was established, first along the drove roads and then in the pastures.[29] Deforestation began in the plains of the Douro, and its limestone plateaux,
then along the Alberche and Tagus valleys, until within four centuries
much of the northern Meseta and Extremadura had been cleared.[30]
With their Spanish experience, the Aragonese did the same thing in
southern Italy after 1300. In Galicia, the Pyrenees, Catalonia and
southern France, the monasteries were the active colonizers of the
forested valleys, and in the notable example of the Cistercian granges

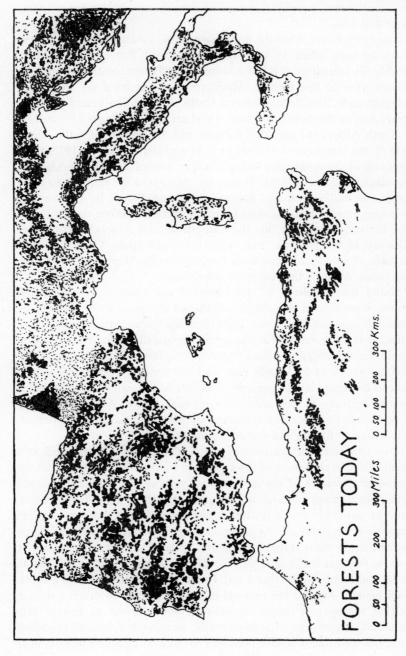

FIG. 42. W. Mediterranean forests today (from World Forest Atlas)

they contributed a unique system of equilibrium in the use of *ager*, *saltus* and *silva*.[31]

During the seventeenth and eighteenth centuries active forest clearance took place in the alpine valleys of Provence and Italy, notably for viticulture.[32] But it is since the early nineteenth century that deforestation in the western Mediterranean has been on an unprecedented scale. The Peninsular and Carlist wars in Spain, and the later Corn Laws of Alentejo have cleared vast areas of the Iberian Peninsula. In North Africa, the revolt of Kabylia and the Tell in 1871, the Aurès in 1879, the conquest of Tunisia in 1881 and the Rif war in 1923, took great toll of the remaining forests, further accelerated by the Algerian war since 1952. In Algeria, Boudy has estimated the deforestation at about one million hectares between 1870 and 1940.[33] In Tunisia and Morocco, much destruction had already occurred before the arrival of the French, especially in the Medjerda and Ouergha (principal tributary of the Sebou), fires being the chief agent. Over a million hectares of woodland have been removed on the slopes of the Middle and Great Atlas by the sedentary inhabitants.

Today the problems of deforestation are most severe in North Africa, especially in Algeria, in south-east Spain, and on the clay or shale hill lands of Peninsular Italy, causing intense erosion. In North Africa it is estimated that in the areas climatically suited the following species have receded as follows: cedar 76·6, thuya 75·7, evergreen oak 67·7, cork oak 61·5, Aleppo pine 53·5 per cent of their former areas. Instead of occupying 27 per cent of North Africa, which is suitable for forests, scarcely 11 per cent is so covered today. A comparison of Figs. 42 and 50 indicates the marked differences between lands potentially suited to forests and the actual distribution.

Two characteristic features of the landscape may be noticed as a result of the exploitation of the evergreen forest cover. There is first the oasis-like character of the *agri cultura*, with small, irregularly shaped fields, often surrounded by an enormous stretch of range-lands (*saltus*) and the generally more restricted woodland (*silva*), both in varying degrees of degradation. At different stages of culture, man has used discriminately these three fundamental units of land use. In a primitive system, the *ager* is cleared from the *silva* in order to exploit the benefit of natural humus in the forest soil. In the Mediterranean this is a short-lived benefit, without the renewal of animal humus or green fertiliser, so that the *ager* is readily abandoned and allowed to relapse into *saltus*. Such a system of semi-nomadic farming is *écobuage* (so-called from the instrument *écobue* used in Provence to clear the woodland.)[34]

It has been practised right to the present day in isolated districts of the French Midi and in the islands of Corsica and Sardinia. Equally the long rotations of *al tercio con encinar* in the ilex woods of the western Iberian Meseta and the gorse-heather rotations of the Atlantic lands of the same peninsula, are examples of such ancient practice. In some edaphic conditions, the *saltus* may never revert to secondary *silva*, and with the general anarchism of much Mediterranean pastoralism, the regressive tendency has been for the *saltus* to become of paramount importance in its extent, at the expense of the *silva*.

It is also a characteristic of these degraded woodlands that the distinction between forest and pasture is never clearly demarcated.[35] These two uses of land tend to be administered today by the same authority. Thus in Spain and in North Africa the forestry officials, theoretically at least, manage the grazing lands. But the problem of a human and ecological usage of range lands and forests, existing harmoniously, is probably the greatest challenge today in the Western Mediterranean landscapes. As Kuhnholtz-Lordat has aptly said 'Le désert a ses excuses . . . Mais la garrigue, en plein coeur des plus hautes civilisations qui se superposent depuis des millénaires autour de la Méditerranée, est un luxe qui fait figure de scandale'.[36] Pastoralism has always tended to be divorced from agriculture in this environment. The prestige of numbers in the flock or herd (*pecunia*) having the same root meaning for stock and wealth has not fostered good husbandry and the deterioration of the *saltus* has been the consequence of over-grazing. It is important also to remember that stock-raising is probably the oldest economy in the Mediterranean world. The *drailles* of Langue-doc and the *carraires* of Provence, sheep walks into the mountains date perhaps from the Bronze age.[37] Even earlier, the dolmens of the Cevennes, Pyrenees and Cantabrians may have been the summer residences of nomadic shepherds. The very name *Itali* (cattlemen) indicates the pastoral pursuits of the forebears of the Etruscans and Romans, while the Sabine and Alban wars reflect the need of the Romans for summer pastures in the Apennines. Zeuner[38] has reviewed the sequence of the domestication of animals as follows: first the dog (a scavenger) *c.* 8000 B.C.; then nomadic animals such as the pig, sheep and goat about 7000 B.C.; followed by cattle associated with a settled agricultural life during the Neolithic; and finally, transport animals such as the ass and horse in Crete, *c.* 1900 B.C. and in N. Italy, *c.* 1100 B.C.

2. *The Introduction of Food Plants.* Barley is probably the oldest grain crop to be extensively cultivated, useful for both bread and

drink.[39] According to Helbaek[40] the wild domesticable barley (*Hordeum spontaneum*) is distributed from Morocco to Turkestan, whereas wild emmer (*Triticum dicoccoides*) grows exclusively only in a small area of the Near East. The cultivation of emmer (*T. dicoccum*) is attested in the Kurdish Highlands during the sixth millenium B.C. Figs, flax, chick peas and some vegetables have also a long ancestry but for millennia barley[41] and emmer resisted any competition from other crops. But while barley remained the main crop of Greece, Italy forged ahead with bare wheats, which were developed for bread-making about the fifth century B.C. It is thought the Carthaginians in North Africa may have taught the Romans the art of dry-farming. Millet could not stand the low winter temperatures and as a summer crop was never profitable to irrigate, except in the Nile valley, having a low yield. Rye, a hardy winter crop, prefers markedly acid soils which only occur in the northern Mediterranean. Oats, a weed in the wheat fields in Pliny's time, was only developed as a fodder crop at the end of the classical period. Quick growing and adapted to being sown in spring, it suited the mountain areas of the northern Mediterranean.[42] Barley was the chief cereal in the drier areas until after the middle Ages. Because it has a shorter growing season than wheat, it is not susceptible to alkalinity or salinity. It also starts to grow early with autumn rains and needs less moisture in the ripening stage.[43] The food of the peasants, it was associated with a self-sufficient economy, whereas it was wheat that occupied the grain trade sponsored by the sophisticated tastes of the Roman citizens. Thus, until modern times barley was the chief crop of the Iberian Peninsula and North Africa, followed by the *durum* wheat, which was confined to the southern Mediterranean because of its sensitivity to cold winters. This hard-grained wheat was introduced into North Africa by the Arabs.[44] Sorghum introduced from India about A.D. 70 was not diffused in the Mediterranean realm until Arab times. Indeed in classical times the Nile Delta functioned as a conservatory for numerous exotics brought from the Far East, including sugar cane and rice (Fig. 43). These were only diffused much later, when the Arabs had perfected techniques of irrigation.

Two cereals have become significant in more recent times. Rice known to the Greeks as a medicine was also spread by the Arabs and introduced to the Spanish *huertas*. It remained long associated, however, with malaria so that legal prohibition was encouraged after epidemics. It is only in the last century that its cultivation has been more widely developed.[45] Maize was first brought to Seville from America in 1493, growing first on the Andalusian coast, then intro-

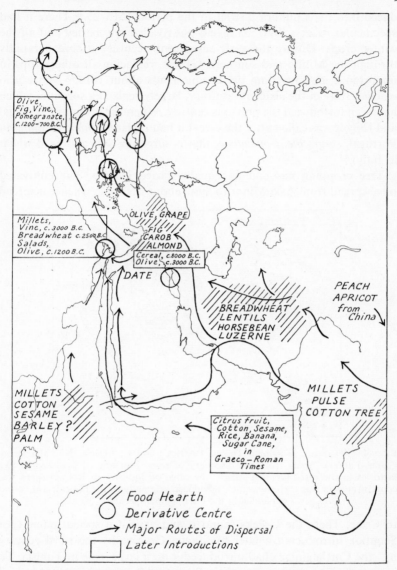

Olive,
Fig, Vine,
Pomegranate,
c. 1200-700 B.C.

OLIVE, GRAPE
FIG
CAROB
ALMOND

Millets,
Vine, c. 3000 B.C.
Breadwheat c. 2500 B.C.
Salads,
Olive, c. 1200 B.C.

Cereal, c. 8000 B.C.
Olive, c. 3000 B.C.

DATE

PEACH
APRICOT
from
China

BREADWHEAT
LENTILS
HORSEBEAN
LUZERNE

MILLETS
COTTON
SESAME
BARLEY?
PALM

MILLETS
PULSE
COTTON TREE

Citrus fruit,
Cotton, Sesame,
Rice, Banana,
Sugar Cane,
in
Graeco – Roman
Times

///// Food Hearth
◯ Derivative Centre
→ Major Routes of Dispersal
▭ Later Introductions

FIG. 43. Introduction and dispersal of cultivated plants within the Mediterranean area. Note the significance of the sea-route across the Indian ocean for perishable, tropical plants, while the hardier plants could be brought overland through western Asia. Syria, the Nile delta, the Rome district and the irrigated gardens of eastern Spain, have been of particular importance in the re-distribution of exotics within the Mediterranean area

duced into the Coimbra district in the period 1515–25.[46] There it had
spectacular success, by 1533 it had out-rivalled rye, barley and all the
winter crops. During the early seventeenth century it spread rapidly
through the Minho and southern Galicia, replacing all other crops in
importance, and reaching the Basque lands about 1615.[47] Maize also
reached Italy in the sixteenth century, largely replacing sorghum which
had been introduced the previous century. Wherever it went in Portugal
and Italy it was called after the cereal it had replaced (*milho* or millet in
Portugal, *sorgo, ble, fromentone,* that is sorghum, soft and hard wheat
in Italy).[48]

Tree cropping has had an equally varied history. The cultivated
olive spread from Asia Minor to Syria about 1,500 B.C. whence it spread

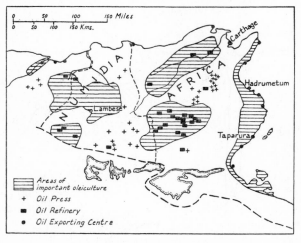

FIG. 44. Oleiculture in Roman Tunisia ('Africa') and E. Algeria 'Numidia' (from
Camps-Fabrer). Apart from the discovery of some fourteen oil presses and two
factories in the rest of North Africa, the olive oil industry in Roman times was
concentrated in this eastern sector. Introduced originally by the Phoenicians, it was
expanded in the Carthaginian period

to Crete. There the Greeks found it and gave it a special name (not
Semitic), introducing it later to Magna Graeca. By the third century
B.C. the Carthaginians had introduced it on a large scale in Tunisia. To
protect their trading monopoly in Sicily and Tunisia they cut down all
the trees in Sardinia. Meanwhile the Tartessians spread olive groves in
Andalusia. Preceding this culture of the grafted olive was the use of the
wild olive (*Oleaster sativa*) whose fruit may have been used from Upper
Palaeolithic times.[49] Rome profited from the Punic experiment in
North Africa, to establish there vast areas under olives (see Fig. 44) as

the instrument of Roman imperialism.[50] As the olive does not bear fruit until some ten years old, it could never be developed widely by the peasantry; it needed Pax Romana and all its administrative resources. On the semi-arid frontiers with the nomad, the Roman *limes* and the limit of the olive coincided. Planted on the hill terraces to counter soil erosion it was an elaborate process of sedentary cultivation, as the air photographs of Roman Africa still reveal.[51] Bearing its fruit in winter, when the nomads (*Getuli*) were safely away in their southern pastures, the calendar was admirable. The olive, the symbol of peace, was also the necessity for peace. Roman oleiculture reached its climax in the second century B.C. and the great domains of *saltus*, formerly wooded pasturage, [52] were converted into olive groves and vineyards. Tunisia, Andalusia, Tarragona and Lucca have maintained a reputation for their olive oil ever since, though it is ironical that the Berber fastnesses of Aurès, Kabylia and the Atlas, little reached by the Romans, have preserved most faithfully the traditions of Roman oleiculture.

It is probable the vine was spread from the coasts of Asia Minor much earlier than the cultivated olive, reaching Egypt perhaps in the third millenium B.C. Its name has a Semitic origin and its philology indicates that it came to Italy via Greece. The vine spread markedly in the consulate of Optimius *c*. 121 B.C., when vintages and vines became differentiated and were spreading in the south with the political overtones of *latifundia*.[53] Rome was thus the first civilisation to mass-produce vineyards and it is significant that the specialities today in Italy are not essentially different from those of the classical locations (Plates 25, 26). Around Etna the vineyards of Mamertine, Syracuse, Catania and Taormina are still there. In the time of Pliny, Campania was the richest province with specialized viticulture at Sorrento, on the slopes of Vesuvius, and at Faustino. In Latium and especially Tuscany, the vine was equally the basis for a prosperous peasantry of smallholders (*familia rustica*).[54] Then as now, viticulture was of less importance in northern Italy, with only small districts such as Ravenna, Istria, Asti and parts of Emilia and Liguria. The limited spread of the vine from Marsala along the via Augusta—via Domitia in southern France, gave no hint of the vast monoculture that was to develop in Bas-Languedoc during the nineteenth century.[55] In Spain, Cicero eulogised the wines of Tarragona but vineyards were not generally important in the provinces, except in the immediate hinterlands of home-sick colonials. The Moors spread the vine in the Iberian Peninsula ostensibly for their fruit, though Muslim theologians knew how to get over more difficult passages of the Koran when it concerned delectables such as Malagan wines! The monastic houses in the Iberian Peninsula, as in France, devoted great skill to viticulture, notably the Cistercians of Alcobaça in Estremadura. With the expulsion of the Moriscos in 1609–10, vineyards were planted by them in North Africa. But it was only during the latter part of the nineteenth century that the great vineyards of the Cheliff and other areas of French colonization took form.[56]

If Peninsular Italy was the classical and the Christian home of viticulture, it was also the centre for a wide variety of other tree fruits, some earlier ones being introduced via Greece, later ones direct from the Near East. Pliny says the cherry was introduced from Pontus about 74 B.C.*[57] Varro mentions new species of figs, vines and olives coming from Asia.[58] Martius, a friend of Octavian, brought apple trees.[59] Indeed by the middle of the first century B.C., horticultural science became highly developed in central Italy and Syrian gardeners were imported to foster this art. At that time the citron and the lemon were introduced into Italy. Tolkowsky and Andrews have used the evidence of Roman frescos to demonstrate that the sweet orange was also known in Italy in the first century A.D., in contradiction to the traditional view that citrus fruits were introduced into the Mediterranean by the Arabs.[60] The citron (*citrus medica*), spread by the Jews for religious purposes is more likely to have been the subject of these frescoes. There is also the argument that, as the Sanskrit word *naranga* is the root of the current Italian, Spanish and Portuguese words for orange, not the Latin *citrium*, it suggests the long period of Mediterranean acclimatisation before the orange, originally from S.E. Asia, was spread widely by the Arabs. But this is not proved. Plants which appear to have been introduced more definitely by the Arabs are the mulberry (in *c.* A.D. 553), sugar cane (grown in Palestine in the seventh century), black cherry, apricot, banana, carob, cotton, alfalfa, henna, saffron and some garden crops. During the fifteenth century, sugar cane became an important crop of the Spanish *huertas*, but it could not compete against American imports from the Caribbean which arose in the following century.[61] Mulberries, still an important tree in the North Italian Plain, were also developed intensely in the plains of Valencia and Bas-Languedoc for sericulture in the eighteenth century. But the silkworm epidemics of the 1850s and 1860s, the rising importance of the cotton industry and the intensive Italian competition, markedly reduced the areas of mulberries. Meanwhile after 1825, great increases in orange groves commenced in Valencia and Castellón, and more recently in Sicily and Calabria.

* Both Pliny and Varro have to be treated with reserve as they are much indebted to Greek writers, particularly to Theophrastus.

3. *Terraces and Land Reclamation.* In some areas of the Mediterranean, such as the valleys of Beira and Minho in Portugal, Liguria, Provence, and islands notably Malta, terracing is widespread in the landscape (Fig. 45).[62] Curiously in North Africa, terracing is relatively unimportant and where it does occur in the pre-Saharan mountains it is of recent origin. The use of a swing plough with a wide yoke for two oxen is unsuited to terraces in North Africa.[63] This Berber plough is remarkably like that shown on Phoenician pottery. Also the Arab abstinence from wine did not foster terraced vineyards, so common in the regions mentioned above. Terracing presupposes a certain density of population to carry out the laborious task of carving out mountain slopes and to make it worth while to maintain the system. Rural depopulation in southern France and in mountains such as the Pyrenees has caused abandonment of terraces, whereas in areas of strong population pressure such as Italy and northern Portugal they have been preserved. As measures of soil and moisture conservation they also meet an ancient necessity experienced since the dawn of agriculture in the Mediterranean lands. The lack of vegetation in summer, followed by autumn downpours on the baked earth creates the constant threat of erosion, while the thin calcareous or skeletal mountain soils can accumulate in terraces. It is impossible, therefore, to equate terraces with any one civilisation or to trace their ultimate origin. Yet it is obvious that terrace cultivation has a certain social and economic uniformity. It depends largely on the hoe not the plough, usually with an egalitarian social and political life. But the land use varies considerably from the garden terraces for vegetables, cereals and tree crops where irrigation is available, to the dry culture terraces usually under vines, olives, figs and other tree crops. Floodwater terraces in the steppes are even more distinct, with their seasonal cereal production. Certainly, it is the Muslim peoples that have introduced terrace cultivation into the Algarve, the Alpujarras, northern Alicante and Majorca. But elsewhere demographic necessity has produced the same effects as in north-central Portugal and Italy. In Malta, soil conservation has gone even further in the 'Red Earth Law' which decrees that all the precious *terra rossa* must be removed prior to new building, to save it for the terraced slopes.

Counter-measures to soil erosion arose very early in Latium, where the deforestation of the Sabine mountains quickly caused rapid downcutting in the soft tufa of the Campagna. Tunnels or *cuniculi* were cut by the Etruscans from the sixth century B.C. in southern Etruria and in the Alban Hills, to draw off surface run-off, serving the dual purpose of soil conservation on the slopes and irrigation on the plains (Fig. 200).

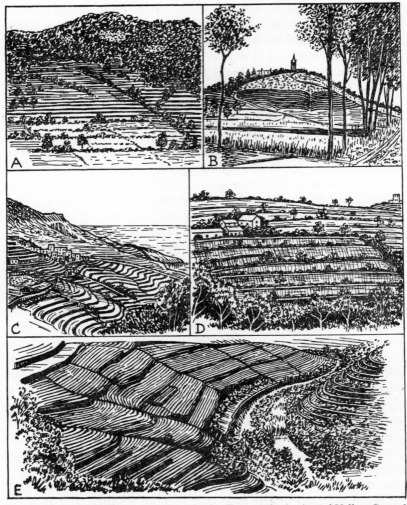

FIG. 45. Types of Mediterranean terraces. A—Terraces in the Arenal Valley, Central Cordillera. B—Piedmontese terraces in the Langhe. C—Terraces at Bañalbufar, western Majorca. D—Terraces near La Spezia. E—Vine terraces in Cioia, Port Wine district, Douro valley

Diverting the water also saved the valley floor for cultivation, and population pressure on the land can alone explain the prodigious efforts made in this way to save very limited areas.[64] Many of the crater lakes were tapped by long underground tunnels to maintain the lake-level, notably the emissarium of the Alban lake cut 1,300 yards to conserve a few hundred acres of arable land within the crater. A longer emissarium drained lake Nemi, and the basin of Fucino was partially drained by a double tunnel cut four miles through the mountains. In 1875 the same alignment, for a more successful Fucino scheme, was followed. The Romans also built a great drainage canal across the Pontine marshes to the coast of Terracina. Despite these efforts to reclaim both the Pontine and the Maremma marshes, continued geological subsidence made their task impossible to accomplish on a permanent basis.

In the hard school of Latium public works, the Romans learnt to accomplish feats of engineering. From the Etruscan *cuniculi* developed the Roman aqueducts, some of them on an impressive scale. Such were those of the Old Aniene (39 miles long, 27 underground), Aqua Marcia (56 miles), and the greatest of Rome's fourteen aqueducts which was fed by the Cerulea and Curzia springs in the upper Aniene, 83 miles away.[65] In the plain of Tunis, the aqueduct from the springs of Zaghouan to Carthage is still an impressive colonial monument. It may be that the *rhetaras* and *foggeras* of Marrakech and other plains of North Africa go back in origin to the ideas of the Etruscans, translated to Africa by the Carthaginians or the Romans.

Canalisation of the lower Po was begun by the Etruscans, though the Romans drained much more land, notably south of the Po between Placentia and Parma, especially when the Emilian Way was built in 109 B.C.[66] Evidence of Roman reclamation in the Iberian Peninsula appears limited to small irrigation schemes, not on the Italian scale. After the decline of Rome, reclamation lapsed until the sixteenth century in Italy, though the Moors had fostered irrigation and the cities of the North Italian Plain followed suit in the twelfth and thirteenth centuries. The creative planning of *bonifica*, as land reclamation is expressively termed in Italy, commenced afresh with the projects of Ferrara (1566–1580), Porto Viro in Venezia (1606), Bentivoglio (1576) between the Po, Crostolo and Enza and the Parmigiana-Moglia.[67] Others were more difficult to reclaim, such as that of Ravenna, begun in 1531. Ever since the sixteenth century, schemes of *bonifica* have figured prominently in the governments of the Italian states, especially in the Po plain (see pp. 438–9). Thus the Italian rural landscapes are largely heir to either the classical or post-medieval processes of reclamation and colonisation.

AGRARIAN SYSTEMS[68]

Related to the environment and the success of man's utilisation, have evolved a variety of agrarian systems, whose origins go back several millennia.[69] In the hilly country of Peninsular Italy, well exemplified by

Tuscany, is the classical type with its ancient triad of wheat, oil and wine, often in the interculture of trees and grain crops termed today *coltura promiscua*. A system of peasantry, it is frequently related to careful measurement of holdings and elaborate systems of land surveys, called centuriation. In less favoured or less settled lands, archaic and extensive systems of land use have produced a variety of types in the landscapes of Corsica, Sardinia, and much of North Africa, and in the poorer parts of the Iberian Peninsula. Evolving from them have developed since the Middle Ages, the great open field system of Castile and also systems of latifundia in the southern Mediterranean. Irrigation with its codification of water rights has created other distinct agrarian societies. What is important to stress is that each of these systems can be traced back over long periods of history, often maintaining an independent evolution from adjoining systems.

1. *Classical Landscapes*. From the writings of latins such as Cato, Varro, Columella, Strabo and Pliny, we have a clear picture of Roman cultivation in Italy, many of whose features are still recognisable.[70] Columella, biased towards viticulture, makes it clear that interculture, the *coltura promiscua* so characteristic of modern Italy, was well developed in his day. The land was planted with vine-laden trees, usually elms, poplars and ash (*arbusta*), and olive groves. Cereals were subordinated to the tree crops in central Italy, a reflection of the Sicilian, then Egyptian and African grain tribute which ousted the importance of cereals at home. Some of the *arbusta* were pollarded and their leaves were pruned for animal fodder. On the richest lands, vines could be grown at a density of 3,200 plants to the *jugerum*. A peasant family theoretically could be supported on an *heredium*, equal to two *jugera*; the *jugerum* was supposedly the area that a man and two oxen could plough in one day, equal to about five-eighths of an acre or a quarter of a hectare.[71] The work of Colonel Baradez in North Africa has indicated that many evolved systems of land-holding existed there in Roman times.[72] Blocks of small fields clustered around organised water-points or were dictated by the terrain; corn and olives were the staple crops. To this day, the family unit of cultivation ploughed by two animals is maintained, the *attelée*: in Morocco the *zoudja* averages ten ha, the *sekka* of Oran is the same and in Tunisia the *machia* is eight to fifteen ha. In the Iberian Peninsula the Romans left little imprint on the land, since the Tartessian society of Andalusia was already well established and elsewhere settlement tended to be peripheral to the Peninsula. However, modern dictatorships do not encourage free use of aerial photographs, and so new discoveries may yet be made.

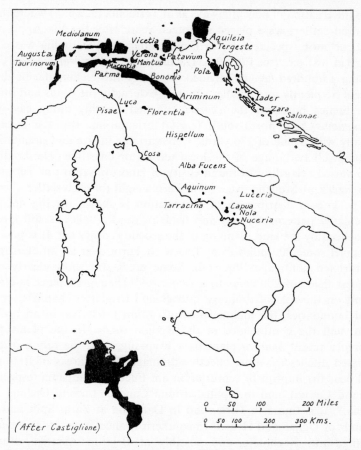

FIG. 46. Distribution of Roman centuriation in Italy and Tunisia (from Castagnoli).
During the last century of the Republic and the first century of the Empire, few things
better demonstrate the arbitrary and methodical qualities of Roman administration
than the system of *centuratio*. Note the contrasted environments in which this was
developed, from the well-watered, even marshy lowlands of the Po valley to the semi-
arid and sub-desert lands of Tunisia. Although of small extent, there is evidence of
much scattered centuriation around the towns of central Italy.

Centuriation was a special case of Roman state planning that has
stamped its abiding imprint on the landscape[73] (see Fig. 46). Carved
usually out of conquered territories, it served crucial periods of social
change, such as during peasant land hunger, the Gracchan reforms, the
settlement of veterans after the Civil Wars, and periods of town-
building. Centuriation was used as a convenient fiscal system in Africa,
or as the instrument of land reclamation. The latter was associated

with the creation of new highways as at Terracina (329 B.C.) where three hundred settlers were placed seventeen years after the Via Appia was built, or more spectacularly in Emilia, after the Via Emilia was completed in 187 B.C. (see Fig. 194). The unit was the *centuria quadrata* containing a hundred *heredia*, divided internally into rectangular holdings or less frequently into smaller squares. Externally the roads and drainage ditches bordered the *centurii*, aligned roughly along east-west (*decumanus*) and north-south (*cardo*) orientation. But the squares, usually with a side of 776 yards, were variable in size and orientation, to take full advantage of the local terrain or coastline. The holdings also varied according to the intensity of land utilisation: at Terracina two *jugera*, at Modena five, and at Parma eight for each settler.

The known distribution of centuriation is shown on Fig. 46. The reticulated pattern of roads and fields in the Po valley is still greatly influenced by the land planning of the second century B.C. It is possible to travel some 300 miles from Trieste to Turin over an uninterrupted centuriated landscape (Plate 66). Some areas still show clearly rectangular fields of 200 acres to a *centuria*.[75] Their persistence is consequent on the rôle of drainage ditches and irrigation channels on the field boundaries, the maintenance of *coltura promiscua* in an orderly plan, and the continuance of the Roman roads. In the plains near Florence recent *bonifica* plans have even suggested the re-use of centuriated ditches for more effective drainage. Other areas of Italy that still bear the imprint of centuriation are Fucino, Campania (especially around Capua), and in Apulia around Canosa, Lucera, Ordona and Troia.[76] It is found in Istria, and in Dalmatia at Zara, Split and the islands of Ugljan and Hvar.[77] In southern France, it occurs at Valence, Orange and Narbonne, and possibly at Beja in Alentejo. But in Tunisia, the centuriated landscape is vast[78] (see Fig. 47). There are two systems: the older one created about 122 B.C. for a Gracchan colony, and to the south and west an Augustan one probably from after 46 B.C.[79] The system doubtless aided dry-farming, the field boundaries helping to preserve the top soil from being removed by erosion. A comparison of Figs. 44 and 47 indicates how much of it was under olive groves.

The study of field sizes in areas still cultivated has not yet been systematically made, though doubtless it is related to the continuity of ploughing techniques. When the centuriation was over hilly country, later roads tended to follow the lie of the land and the old system was modified. Equally where large tracts were abandoned, as in Tunisia, the air-photograph is the only guide to the former layout (see Fig. 47). Also of geographical interest is the indirect evidence of interrupted

19 Etruscan tombs near Cerveteri

CLASSICAL
LANDSCAPES

20 Greek temple of Agrigento, S. Sicily

21 Roman town of Ampurias, near Ampurdán, N.E. Spain, founded in 45 B.C. It is built near earlier Greek and Iberian settlements

22 A 'cuniculated' valley, near Veii, N. Latium. The shaft heads of the *cuniculus* are covered by clumps of bushes in middle distance

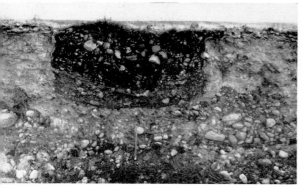

24 Cross-section of Roman olive trench, Apulia

23 Interior of a *cuniculus*. By error of judgment the passage has to bend to join up the excavations between two shafts

25 Ground view of Roman vine trenches, Apulia

26 Rectangular Roman farm enclosures, with vineyard trenches, connected to centuriated roads, north-east of Lucera, Apulia. They are superimposed on Neolithic circular enclosure

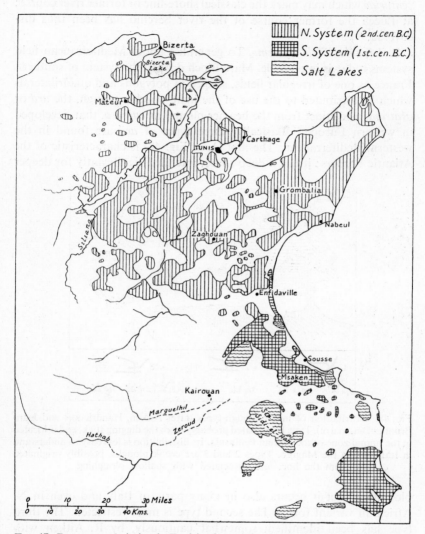

Fig. 47. Roman centuriation in Tunisia (from Atlas des Centuriations Romaines de Tunisie). The northern system of centuriation between Bizerta and Enfidaville was created during the first phase in the opening up of the country to Roman administration, *c.* 122 B.C. It covered about 5,800 sq. miles, much of it over hilly and wooded country. The southern system shows a different orientation, and spread over a long period from the reigns of Augustus and Tiberius. Easier to survey, it is impressive testimony of a well-developed policy for water conservation

centuriae which may mark the classical shore-line or former river course; at Lucca the former course of the river Serchio has been thus discovered.[80]

2. *Irregular Field Systems*. To generalise about Mediterranean field systems today is impossible. Marc Bloch defined the system of southern France as one of irregular fields, shaped in polygons and quadrilaterals which he attributed to the use of the light wooden plough, the *ard* or *aratrum*, as distinct from the heavier plough or *carruca*, that developed in western Europe.[81] Basically, three types of *ard* are found in the western Mediterranean. The first (1, in Fig. 48) is characteristic of the Atlantic borders; it has a deep share, intended significantly for deeper

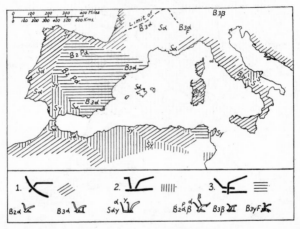

Fig. 48. Distribution of major plough-types (after Aitken, Haudricourt and Jean-Brunhes Delamarre). Type 1 originated probably from the digging stick, and is located in the humid zone of the Iberian Peninsula. Its distribution is less easy to understand in Italy and in the Magreb. Types 2 and 3 are crook ploughs, possibly originated from the hoe, and associated with shallow ploughing

ploughing. But it occurs also in many parts of Italy and even in N. Africa, in variant forms. The second type is more restricted. The third type has been identified, somewhat cautiously, by R. Aitken with Virgil's plough.[82] The types (2) and (3) specially are intended to pulverise the soil and not to turn the sod so that ploughing is done in both directions, criss-cross over the fields. When the field is small, the tendency towards a square shape is understandable.[83]

Sion has also pointed out that the accidented relief of Mediterranean lands is frequently reflected in irregular parcellation of land,[84] although irregular open fields occurred in the Apulian Tavoliere where it is flat.

Faucher too has emphasised that the variety of crops grown wherever possible, in order to mitigate seasonal risks of uncertain rainfall, would also create this tendency.[85] The irregular relations of *ager* and *saltus* are also fundamental. Cadastral maps of Corsica, dating from the late eighteenth century, indicate the co-existence of small individual properties of cultivated land, mountain pastures communally controlled and allocated, and a vast stretch of range-grazing, leased to individuals. Thus at Cargèse, a village created for Greek refugees in 1775, irregular fields lie next to the planned settlement.[86] In North Africa, the transitions from nomadic to sedentary settlement have also evolved numerous irregular systems. Thus irregular fields are not necessarily a generic system of Mediterranean society, but a reflection of many tendencies which in the past had their diverse origins in forms of shifting cultivation.

3. *Open Field System.* A major problem of agrarian history is the gap of knowledge between the Classical and later Middle Ages.[87] Thus it is not only difficult to know what happened to the classical landscapes during this period, but the origin of open fields is still in debate. Open fields occur notably in areas of little accidented relief, where a grain economy is markedly developed, that is in western Morocco, the Spanish Meseta, Trás-os-Montes, the Campidano of Sardinia and, possibly, in the Po valley and the Rhône terraces. In western Croatia Blanc has studied the similar organisation, called *bratstvo*.[88] In Old Castile, the cultivation of open fields is possibly traceable to the Pre-Roman *Vacci*, though the differences between Old Castile and New Castile are mostly post-Reconquest. In the latter area there was not a strict biennial system and the lands were not periodically re-allocated—they were only open fields in the sense that stock grazed on the stubble. In Old Castile and Trás-os-Montes both features were strictly observed.

In southern Sardinia, where Le Lannou has studied the open field system termed *vidazzone*, there is documentary evidence that it was already of ancient origin by the eleventh century A.D.[89] Rather fancifully he has suggested that lands peripheral to *Orbis Romanus*, such as Sardinia, felt more strongly the need of protection after the decline of the Roman Empire. As a measure of security the nucleated Sardinian village and a rigid communal organisation of open fields were created by its inhabitants, especially against the periodic incursion of the shepherds of central Sardinia, driven south when adverse climatic conditions forced them to look for food.[90] But there is no concrete evidence for this in the gap between the sixth and the eleventh centuries, when Le Lannou suggested the open field system began.

Whatever the origin of the open fields in the Mediterranean, the laws of succession and the enclosures of the nineteenth century have produced a tattered mosaic of small, rectangular strip-holdings (called *mthira* in North Africa). In Spain, where the concentration of properties has been going on since 1952, recent surveys have revealed some astonishing examples[91] (see Fig. 56). The hill villages of southern Italy have similar problems of scattered ownership, with small properties often several miles apart. Diversity of soils, inheritance laws and pressure of population on the land have thus created intense fragmentation of holdings in many parts of the Mediterranean.

4. *Irrigated Field Patterns.* Water rights explain why in irrigated communities, land holdings are generally consolidated. But in North Africa, water rights are often given with priority to certain families or clans, so that patches of land on alternate banks of channels are often characteristic, resulting in great wastage in the use of water for irrigation. Rectangular holdings parallel with the canals are common, and where seasonal irrigation is practised in piedmonts, the fields follow the gradients of the fans. The oases have markedly irregular plots while in mountain terraces the irrigated holdings are widely dispersed. Despois has studied a wide variety of all such field patterns especially in the Hodna,[92] and the Tunisian Sahel.[93] The *huertas* of Spain are often a composite pattern of small, irregularly shaped holdings in the old centres, neatly rectangular in areas more recently reclaimed.[94]

SUMMARY

The Mediterranean environment has been always a tantalising paradox of fruitfulness and of frugality, providing both suggestions and obstacles. The clearance of the Mediterranean woodland first begun effectively after the seventh millennium B.C. with the domestication of the sheep and the goat, was accelerated markedly with the rise of urban civilisations, notably the Roman, Muslim, and now in the modern, eras.

The Mediterranean World has been the experimental greenhouse, in which plants from the Near East were improved. More distant plants were introduced by two main routes: overland from Central Asia via the Fertile Crescent, and by sea from south-east Asia. Etruscans, Phoenicians, Greeks, Romans and Muslims have all contributed in this task of diffusion. But the Roman imprint upon the landscape has been the most extensive and durable, witnessed by the landmarks of centuriation. The model of Mediterranean land use has been of tree crops on the hills and of cereals on the plains. This has created a whole series of dual features: tree crops have tended towards polyculture,

FIG. 49. Types of field pattern in irrigated lands in E. Spain

cereals to monocultures; small-scale irrigation from springs and wells
has evolved on terraced hills, while dry farming techniques are characteristic of the plains; and hoe cultivation in small enclosed plots has
differed in social organisation from the communal ploughing of large
open fields. In the mountains the mode of life has been more conservative as in Corsica, Sardinia, and Kabylia, engendering a sturdy peasantry,
scornful of the fruitful animality of the richer lowlands. A striking

feature of Mediterranean society has been the marked absence of a middle class, between the serfdom of the large estates, typical of the southern plains, and the independent small cultivators of the hills.

The existing gap of knowledge in the evolution of field systems between the classical and the later Middle Ages makes it debateable how the open field systems have evolved. The regular open fields are commonest in the extensive cereal lands of the Spanish Meseta, Trás-os-Montes, the Campidano of Sardinia and central Sicily. Inheritance laws help to explain the minutely fragmented pattern of small fields (or minifundia). This presents today, perhaps, a severer problem than latifundia, though the latter is more of a political anathema.

CHAPTER 7

MODERN DEVELOPMENTS IN THE LANDSCAPES

'When a new idea about the environment was adapted, it was as if
the environment itself had been changed.'   (Isaiah Bowman)

Mediterranean landscapes have the enduring qualities of an eternal
present, like beaches on which the tides of successive civilisations have
heaped their ill assorted legacies. But they have frequently become
desolate, mournfully haunted by the memories of vanished glory.
Economic stalemate, especially since the late sixteenth century has been
a major factor. Everywhere, except in the North Italian Plain, there is
still a great gulf between the progressive atmosphere of the large cities
and the backwardness of the countrysides. This is partly a consequence
of the dominance of city mercantilism during the Renaissance, with its
great concentration of wealth and trade in the major ports of the Mediterranean and in some other favoured cities. The absence of coal fuel
has not made up for the deficiency in modern times. The great boot of
southern Italy, inadequately laced by modern lines of communication,
has hindered its progress. In North Africa, even two countrysides have
evolved, one Europeanised, the other still primitive and native. Thus
exaggerated contrasts between rich and poor regions of the western
Mediterranean are common. In some cases, these result from the undue
dependence of the national economy upon a few agricultural resources,
so that the geographic differences of each environment still dictate
imperiously. It is also important to realise that poor areas demand
development in many directions at once, tending to dissipate the
limited energies of a nation. Often it has therefore been more immediately advantageous to encourage the richer areas with a few, effective
contributions to their rapid progress. It is only recently that the 'southern problem' shared by Portugal, Spain and Italy, and the ethnic gulf
between European and native farming in North Africa have been
challenges to national progress, which can only be faced realistically
with international aid. How these major developments are changing the
face of the Mediterranean landscapes is clearly relevant to this study.
Before doing so, however, it is essential to describe broadly the salient
features of land utilisation today.

LAND UTILISATION

Land use in these Mediterranean countries is not easy to generalise about accurately. This is partly because of the paucity of reliable statistics and the lack of standard data for all its territories. Then there is the ecological problem of distinguishing forests, grazing lands and farmland. Multiple use of land also complicates matters. The irregularity of crop harvests reflecting uncertain rainfall, and the biological cycles of the tree crops, also make it difficult to describe 'normal' harvests. The tables shown in Appendix III are therefore only a broad summary of the salient features of land utilisation.

On an agro-climatic basis, the western Mediterranean may be divided into five broad zones: arid (under 12 in annual rainfall), semi-arid (12–20 in), sub-humid (20–30 in), humid (over 30 in) and mountain. Nomadic grazing is the only possibility of the arid zone, in transitions verging upon the Sahara desert. The average rainfall is under 4 in. Crop production in areas having between four and twelve inches is extremely hazardous without irrigation. Extensive grazing and shifting cereal cultivation are the chief forms of land use. In the semi-arid zone, characterised by an unreliable annual rainfall, cereal farming is prevalent. It is without other crops where the winters are cold, for example the northern Meseta of Spain, but with tree crops, notably the olive and almond, where winters are mild. In the sub-humid climate, dry farming is enriched by the growth of forage crops and the integration of crop cultivation and animal husbandry is possible. It is represented by such areas as south-west Italy, northern Sicily, the coastal belt of Algeria and northern Morocco and lower Andalusia. The humid Mediterranean zone is much more favourable to settled agriculture and permanent pastures. Restricted to small areas of North Africa, it is widespread in northern Portugal, northern Spain and western Italy north of Naples. In the Mediterranean mountains, the agricultural possibilities vary considerably but forests and pastures are the major features.

Mediterranean land use is also controlled by the soil conditions. Fig. 50 indicates the various potentials of land use on this basis.[3] Irrigable soils are chiefly alluvial in origin, mostly in areas of level relief. Dry farming is best suited to neutral or slightly alkaline soils. Grazing is often related to thin soils with insufficient moisture for crop production, while forestry is related to skeletal soils, steep slopes and high altitudes.

1. *Pastoralism.* In the Mediterranean lands, the wide diversity of

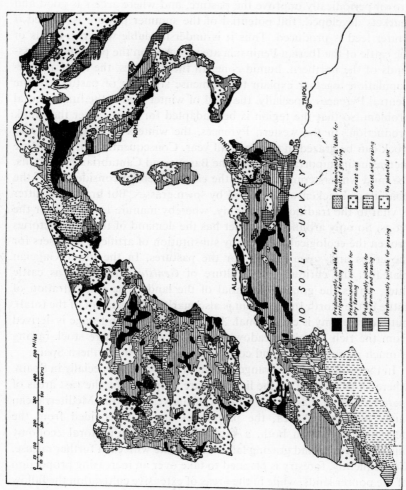

FIG. 50. Land utilisation potential of soils in the W. Mediterranean

relief, climate and human controls, explain the diverse types of stock-raising.[4] In the humid zone, cattle-grazing is ideal, especially when the relief is high and the population diversity is considerable. Potatoes grown periodically improve the pasture, and where access is good and markets developed, full potential of the summer pasture is utilised if winter feed is produced. Thus it is understandable why two-thirds of the cattle of the Iberian Peninsula are pastured on the permanent grass-lands of the northern, humid zone. In the Pyrenees, the relief and de-population together explain the immense stretches of pasture. In the Central Pyrenees especially, the need of winter feed is the fundamental problem, so that the region is best adapted for meat rather than milk production. In the western Pyrenees, the winters are less severe and stock can be grazed in the open all year. Consequently dairy cattle are increasing in importance. Along the Basque and Cantabrian mountains, the mild winters could increase the cattle potential considerably if the ubiquitous bracken was replaced by sown grasses. But bracken as litter is vital to the traditional economy, whereby manure is assured for the crops. So only around Santander has the demand of the milk factories broken the ecological balance, by substitution of artificial fertilisers for the crops and sown grasses for the pastures. In the lower Galician plateaux, the curious gorse culture of *Genista Welwitschii* as cattle litter, limits the grazing potential of the land.[5] The concentration of cattle in the North Italian Plain is also marked (70 per cent of the total), but the economy is exceptional. A third of the Italian forage is derived from the rich *marcite* meadows of the Po valley, where stock-raising is much more intensive and commercialised than in northern Spain.

In the semi-arid lands, range grazing is important, especially in Spain, where 68 per cent of all the livestock are supported by the vast areas of *matorral*, for at least seven months of the year.[6] In the Mediterranean lands of North Africa, the pasturages are also provided from the degraded forests. In both, a successful agro-sylvo-pastoral economy has been broken and grazing lands degenerate with each further misuse. Consequently, forestry is planned to take over an increasing proportion of the poorer lands, while in the areas of extensive cultivation the fallow land is likely to be reduced to forage crop.[7] Thus free range grazing will be rapidly reduced in the near future. Towards the North African steppe the ecological problems are different. Here the natural vegetation is not forest, and the removal of the plant cover by over-grazing soon diminishes the area of pasturage.

On the Mediterranean islands, pastoral land use is essentially a human problem. In Sicily, where the economy is orientated to cereals and now also to cellulose for the new factories, there is a diminishing interest in stock. Eventually the economy may become dictated by an agro-forestal policy, towards grain and eucalyptus production, with no place for pastoralism.[5] Population pressure leaves no significant place for stock in Malta and Majorca. In Corsica, the sylvo-pastoral economy has had a disastrous history. Excessive depopulation and the presence of a retired population with no interests in the soil, have exaggerated the importance of *maquis*, while the high prices paid by the Roquefort cheese producers for ewe milk in Corsica has increased the role of pastoralism.

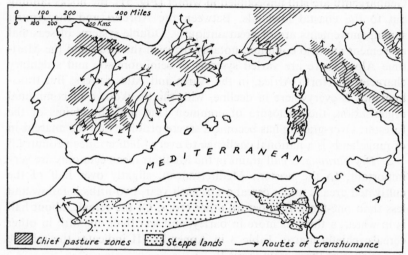

FIG. 51. Major routes of transhumance in the W. Mediterranean

The systems of transhumance, consequent on the climatic differences between the mountains and the semi-arid zones, have attracted much attention from geographers.[8] Many of them date from the Bronze Age[9] (e.g. in the S. of France). The distances involved in these seasonal movements may be as much as 300–400 miles, especially in Spain and North Africa (Fig. 51). The ancient network of the *tratturi* between Apulia and the Apennines, once covered 20,000 ha, and measured some 1,860 miles; elongated pastures, along which ebbed and flowed the pastoral resources of a nation. Similarly, the Mesta in Spain once controlled seasonal movements on the scale of four to five million sheep in the hey-day of the early sixteenth century. Normal transhumance, that is in search of summer pastures, is much less practised than formerly. In the northern Mediterranean, intensive cropping on the lower mountain slopes has tended to check it, while in the southern Mediterranean the intensity of summer drought increases the altitude necessary for profitable grass grazing, that is 10,000 to 12,000 ft.

Inverse transhumance is therefore more widespread for a variety of reasons. The inadequacy of many mountains to offset summer drought means that their cold winter temperatures became the more critical control. Thus in Castile, the flocks of Old Castile used to move south to the winter grazing lands of the upper and middle basin of the Guadiana. In the Pyrenees, inverse transhumance is still relatively important to the Aragonese steppes. In Sardinia, the *saltus* of Barbagia and Gennargentu are still unoccupied in winter (Fig. 51), the flocks fanning out to the coastal lowlands. Between the Abruzzi and the Apulia similar movements are of great antiquity. Double systems of seasonal movement are also common, notably between the Crau and the Maritime Alps. There are varied systems of semi-nomadic and sedentary character in North Africa, in the Aurès and Atlas ranges. But transhumance is everywhere in decline, with the breakdown of communal organisation, the enclosure of common land and the claims of the forester. Over-grazing has become a severe problem and the anarchism of rangelands is a national challenge to every Mediterranean country.[10]

2. *Dry Farming.* Small grains in the Mediterranean economy are very important. In the western Mediterranean, slightly over half of the cultivated area is under cereal crops each year, two-fifths is fallow and less than one-tenth is under all other crops. Of the cereals, about half is in wheat, a third or more in barley, and less than one-fifth in other cereals, chiefly maize. Table 3 in Appendix III indicates the relative importance of these grain crops.[11]

The variability of yield and of output tend to fluctuate in opposite directions, minimising to some extent the total effects. This results from the quite different levels of yield in peasant and mechanised farming, notably in North Africa. The climatic limits in North Africa are between the isohyets of 14 and 16 inches under European cultivation, and 9–12 inches for native barley cultivation. In general, however, the seasonal incidence of rainfall is more critical than its annual amount, especially that which falls during seed-time and harvest. In southern Italy, the following rainfall estimates have been found necessary for the maximum yields of durum wheat:

Rainfall Requirements of Durum Wheat, S. Italy

	Autumn Sowing	Winter Tilling	Spring Sowing	Summer Ripening
Maximum rainfall	8 inches	3·2	—	2·4
Minimum rainfall	2 inches	1·2	1·6	—

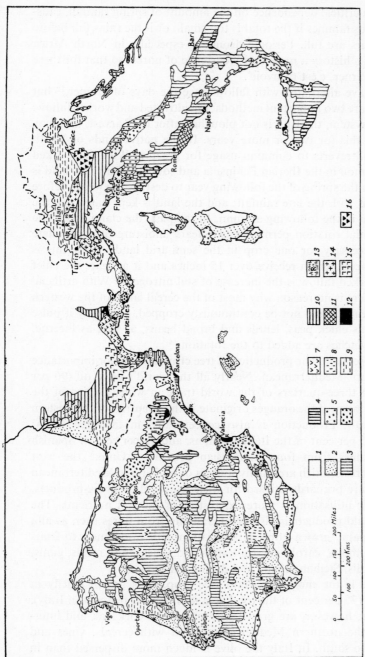

FIG. 52. Land utilisation in the W. Mediterranean, showing predominant economies. Explanatory notes: 1. mountains and waste; 2. scrub lands with some extensive cultivation; 3. extensive grain cropping; 4. rotation of cereals, with some root crops, etc.; 5. arboriculture (dry-farming); 6. arboriculture (irrigated—chiefly citrus crops); 7. vineyards; 8. olive groves; 9. polyculture (based on maize); 10. polyculture (based on grain and forage crops); 11. commercialised mixed farming (especially in Campania); 12. intensive irrigation (*huertas*); 13. rice cultivation; 14. hay and dairying (irrigated meadows or *marcite*); 15. East Aquitaine type (cereals and stock–transitional to Mediterranean cropping); 16. industrial cropping (especially in Po delta)

There is a critical dependence on the amount of spring rainfall, causing disastrous famines if the total is too small, or if the rains fall before
the grain ears are full. Periodic droughts, especially in North Africa
have given its history a measured recurrence of unrest so that for these
lands, 'gouverner, c'est pleuvoir'.

Cereals have alternated with fallow since the days of Homer,[12] but
today there are two important methods: uncultivated and worked fallow.
In the first system, the land is not ploughed after the harvest, and may
remain like this for two or more years. In the native lands of North
Africa it still reverts to common usage for grazing. With the worked
fallow, common in the Iberian Peninsula and southern Italy, the land is
cultivated in the spring of the following year to destroy the weeds before
they set seed with the late rainfall; and the land is kept bare until the
crop is sown in the following autumn. In the past, the claim was made
that a biennial rotation permitted two years' moisture to accumulate
and was necessary for one crop in the semi-arid lands. Now this is
denied for areas which receive over 15 inches and it appears the chief
merit of worked fallow is the increase of soil nitrogen.[13] With artificial
fertilisers there is no reason why most of the cereal lands of the western
Mediterranean should not be continuously cropped, especially if pulse
crops such as chick peas, lentils and broad beans, as well as lucerne,
lupins and vetches are added to the rotation.[14]

3. *Tree Cropping*. The production of tree crops is of major importance
in the western Mediterranean. Nearly all the world's olive oil (96 per
cent), about three-quarters of the world trade in wine, a third of the
lemons and many of the oranges originate in the countries of the western
Mediterranean. Production is also concentrated in favoured areas:
Sicily has 95 per cent of the Italian lemons, and 45 per cent of Spanish
olive oil comes from four Andalusian provinces. Unlike the west
European forests which are chiefly sources of timber, the Mediterranean
woodlands are primarily utilised for their fruit and other by-products,
so that their utilisation is more exhaustive of the soil nutrients. The
variety of wild products is also great, ranging from fibres such as alfa
and dwarf palm, grown often in association with woodlands, to fruits
such as the thuya, carob, chestnut, nuts and acorns, and resins, gums,
perfumery oils, Sicilian manna and dyeing materials.[15]

The olive is the most important tree crop. It is grown chiefly in
plantations (75 per cent of the total area in Spain, 62 per cent in Italy).
Some olives, however, are grown with chestnuts, cork oak and interculture in the northern Mediterranean, and with cereals, vines and
carobs in the south. In Italy the olive is much more dispersed than in

Spain, where it is a virtual monoculture in large areas of Andalusia, and in the Tunisian Sahel. Viticulture is also of major importance. Italy has the most extensive area of vineyards in the world, covering large areas both in monoculture and specially in interculture in Emilia and Tuscany. The vine has made the economy of Algeria since the third quarter of the nineteenth century. It is the chief export of Portugal. And with 44 per cent of the French area under vines, Bas Languedoc and Roussillon are the premier producers of France. Citrus fruits, though much more restricted in area, are a third important source of revenue, especially in eastern Spain, Sicily and Calabria.[16] Table 4 in Appendix III summarises the relative importance of these tree crops.

The indirect importance of woodlands is seen also in the forage value of trees, such as the argan (*Argania sideroxylon*) of south Morocco, where it covers some 700,000 hectares in open parklands.[18] The pine-woods of Portugal, Spain and southern France are also important sources of resin, edible nuts, as well as timber.

4. *Irrigation*.[19] The widespread practice and the antiquity of irrigation in the Mediterranean is proof of its necessity. It came as a revolution in organisation with city life, rather than as a technological achievement.[20] Three main systems have been developed in the western Mediterranean. In areas where water storage is essential to guarantee perennial canal irrigation because of the severe summer drought, the Moors especially pioneered with irrigated systems. Notable are the *huertas* of south-east Spain and similar gardens in Morocco and Sicily. A second type of irrigation is the seasonal use of flood water in winter and spring, such as the wadis of North Africa, notably in the plain of Kairouan. Whereas tree crops can be cultivated in the first type, only cereals are possible in the second system. From the twelfth century, a third system of irrigation was developed in the North Italian Plain, utilising the rivers and the springs (*fontanili*) for more intensive land use (see pp. 151–3). In the lower Durance, some canals date from the same period (see pp. 593–4). In these areas irrigation is not essential but it is desirable for more intensive production of crops.

Irrigation in modern times has produced some of the most significant changes of land use. The most spectacular recent increases have occurred in Spain, Italy and Morocco, harnessing the rich water resources of the Ebro, Douro, Tagus, Po, Sebou and Oum er Rbia. The World Food and Agricultural Organisation plan to see the irrigated area doubled by 1975, when production from irrigated land will account for at least 40 per cent of the total value of agricultural products in the Mediterranean.[21] This should double the existing population that is now dependent on irrigation. But much of the material progress in agricultural production in the last few years has been made at the expense of balanced land use. The truth is that though governments are rapidly changing the face of many landscapes, there is yet no comprehensive national policy to tackle all aspects of their agrarian and forestal problems.

NATIONAL DEVELOPMENTS SINCE THE NINETEENTH CENTURY

In the last few decades especially, the traditional apathy to change has been broken down and progress is now being accelerated fast. Land reclamation and irrigation, soil conservation and afforestation, concentration of land holdings and the construction of new rural settlements are all changing the face of the land. But these planned developments have not been pushed in a vacuum. They are usually compromises with the past, with the promises and slogans of previous governments, now expressed more realistically by the pressures of modern contingency. It is proper therefore to view these in the perspective of the last century. Each state has a distinctive policy, whose contrasts are creating new differences in these Mediterranean landscapes. Portugal, long concerned with the utilisation of its common lands, has been much less energetic in the utilisation of its rich water resources for irrigation. On the other hand, water control has been the panacea offered to the Spanish people for at least the last half century. Since the unification of Italy in 1861, legislation of Piedmontese origin has emphasised the importance of marsh reclamation to increase agricultural productivity in that over-populated land. In North Africa, European colonisation has produced a profound disparity between the landscapes of immigrant creation and native traditions. Thus each need to be discussed separately.

1. *Portugal.* The first legislation in Portugal to develop its natural resources was introduced in 1804, though the monarchy had shown personal interest in the conservation of its forests at least since the fifteenth century. In 1824, administration to define and protect the forests was set up, and ever since forestry has been a noble art, evidenced in the fine stands of woodland in central and north-west Portugal. But in the south, pastoralism in the hands of military lordship had created a vast terrain of over-grazed and continuously burnt scrublands since the time of the Reconquest. In 1885, Alentejo still had 1,647,000 ha uncultivated, a desolate waste of common lands (*charneca*), the extent of which is shown on Fig. 53.[23] The introduction of chemical fertilisers between 1884 and 1894, and the development of communications helped

to reclaim and colonise these poor, mostly schistose lands. Private migration of northern Portuguese into the newly opened farmlands started a process of colonisation south of the Tagus, that has continued to the present. Modernisation of large estates commenced in Alentejo in the early 1930s with the introduction of farm machinery and more recently small irrigation schemes have been developed, both privately and by the state.[25] Within the last decade, new forage crops have been introduced, notably *serradilla*, to intensify cattle production. There is, however, no market for more milk, and meat competes with the vital fishing industry, so agricultural progress in this direction is bound to be slowed to await a rising standard of living.

Second in importance to the revolutionary changes that private colonisation has made

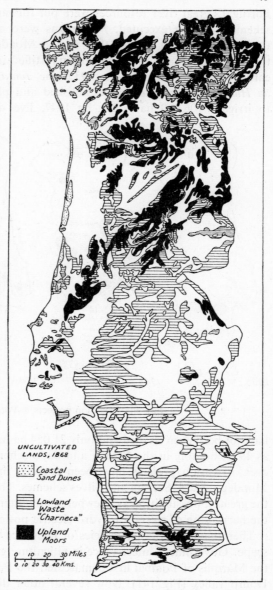

FIG. 53. Common and other waste lands of Portugal in 1868

in Alentejo, are the government-sponsored schemes of irrigation and re-settlement. Between 1877 and 1910 many projects to utilise

Portugal's great river resources were put forward, but only one small scheme was ever executed. New plans were suggested in 1927 and the first catchment board, that of the Mondego, was created. But the economic anarchy of the country stifled initiative until after the early reforms of Salazar. In 1935, the *Junta Autónoma das Obras de Hidraúlica Agrícola* was established and plans were put forward to irrigate 106,000 ha.[26] But by 1947, five of the twenty schemes

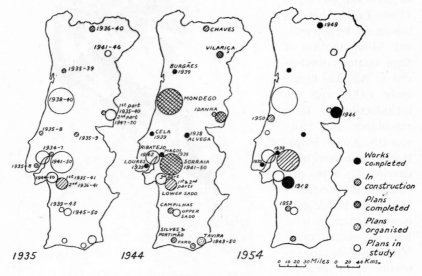

FIG. 54. Irrigation projects in Portugal

had not been even studied and only 21,054 ha had been irrigated as late as 1953, notably in the Idanha and Sado schemes.[27] Since then, however, irrigation projects have been speeded up, notably the Chaves, Mondego, Sado, Sorraia and Silves schemes. The Mondego scheme has the greatest possibilities, as elsewhere more interest has been focused on the harnessing of rivers for hydro-electric power.

There have been other policies of relevance to changes in the landscape. Government interference in viticulture goes back to 1756, when the Marquis of Pombal first demarcated the Port Wine district of the Douro valley (Fig. 141). Now several other districts of vintage wine have been created; and since 1926 it has been prohibited to grow vines freely. Another government interest has been the enclosure of common lands (*baldíos*), long a source of contention in Portugal. After unsuccessful attempts to deal with the problem, especially in 1925 and

1933, the *Junta de Colonizion Interna* was formed in 1936.[28] The remaining *baldíos* only occupy now less than 4 per cent of the total area, found chiefly in small scattered areas in the mountains. A serious problem is the fragmentation of holdings[29], and since 1881 the average size of holding has been halved in size.[30] In this matter little or no progress has been made to consolidate holdings. In the current five-year plan (1959–64) Portugal is making the first serious effort to modernise its agriculture.[31] But partly because of its colonial distractions and because of its cautious, independent financial policy, the changes in the landscape are slow and not readily perceptible. Apart from the new ricefields in the lower Sado and Tagus valleys, and afforestation in the northern mountains, modern changes are not marked.

2. *Spain.* Landscape changes are much more spectacular in Spain. As an agricultural country, nine-tenths of whose cultivated lands have been subjected to the vagaries of a low and uncertain rainfall, it is natural that Spain should have turned its attention to irrigation schemes. The first national plan of 1902 aimed to add 1·4 million hectares to the existing irrigated land, which then comprised 6 per cent of the cultivated land and yielded 15 per cent of the total value of crops grown. The Aragonese economist Joaquin Costa had already drawn attention to the need to develop the drainage basins of the country. Under Gasset in 1914, these catchment areas were designated and the following year a more realistic plan was put forward to irrigate one-quarter of the original area suggested in 1902. But little was done until 1925 when independent river board authorities were set up.[32] At the beginning of the present century there were only thirteen reservoirs with a capacity of 98 million cubic metres, but by 1936 there were seventy-four reservoirs retaining 4,000 million cubic metres. Since 1939, the economic *élan* of Spain has been striking: in 1951, one hundred and one major reservoirs could store 8,274 million cubic metres; in 1956 one hundred and thirty-eight reservoirs had a capacity of 13,664 million cubic metres and another thirty dams were in course of construction.[33] Today, some 13 per cent of the average precipitation over Spain or about 30 per cent of the river flow is controlled by these major schemes.[34] Some 217 miles of modern trunk canals irrigate 500,000 ha in addition to 300,000 ha under older systems of canals (Fig. 55). Even so, these systems represent only half of the total of 1,174,000 ha that are watered permanently, in addition to another 500,000 ha irrigated seasonally. Table 5, Appendix III, indicates the relative importance of these systems of canal irrigation. Since 1953, these ambitious projects have been substantially aided by American funds, some of them specifically earmarked for dam construc-

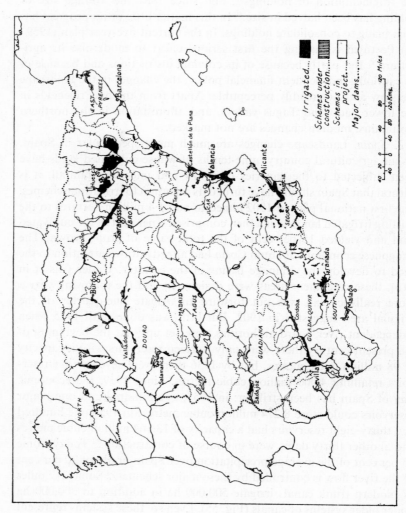

FIG. 55. Irrigation schemes of Spain, developed and in project

tion. Even so, these canal systems, old (300,000 ha) and new (500,000 ha), represent only about half of the total irrigated area for well irrigation is also important.[34]

A related feature has been the attempts to colonise the improved lands. The most ambitious was the ill-fated legislation of the Socialist government in 1933 to break up the latifundia estates of the south, but this foundered in the Civil War. In 1939, there was created the *Instituto Nacional de Colonisación* which seeks by technical, economic and social aids to improve the lot of the peasants in a series of large schemes. After 1948 some seventeen areas were declared of national interest (375,199 ha), increased to twenty-two in 1956.[35] The most ambitious of these has been the scheme to drain some 136,240 ha of salt marsh at the mouth of the Guadalquivir and to improve 73,000 ha in the Guadiana valley. A second approach was made in 1949, when legislation was passed to expropriate lands if the lack of initiative or capital on the part of the owners held up government schemes. This still makes little effort to tackle the problem of latifundia; in 1956 only 81,013 ha had been expropriated. A third function of the Institute is its assistance to landowners and tenants to improve their lands and at the same time make more use of the unemployed labour. Some 250,000 ha have improved (168,000 ha of them irrigated) by this assistance. The Institute has also created 112 new villages, and its policy of building nucleated settlements has been maintained since early experiments to build isolated farmsteads failed. This is in marked contrast to the Italian policy which has created groups of scattered dwellings.

Other energetic efforts to change the face of the landscape have been started since 1952 when a special office was created to consolidate scattered holdings. In 1954, minimum sizes of holdings were established, an important event in a country where 70 per cent of the holdings are under one hectare in size. But the consolidation of holdings is bound to be a slow and costly programme, involving no less than fifteen stages of technical and administrative organisation.[35] This is being energetically pursued, especially in Old Castile and the northern provinces of New Castile, a veritable enclosure movement which will gain momentum as the peasants realise the benefits it brings. However, at a cost of 5,000–10,000 pesetas for each hectare reformed, it will be many years before the tattered patchwork of open fields—where primogeniture has been little practised—will be renovated. By mid-1961, only 278,000 ha had been consolidated.[36]

More impressive still are the current regional plans, directed by a series of autonomous authorities which were first announced in 1951.

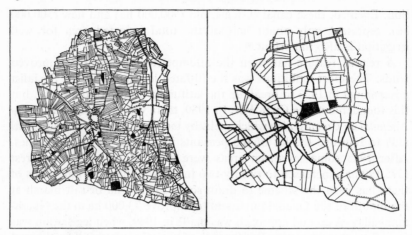

FIG. 56. A Castilian commune, before and after consolidation (La Minosa, Soria). Before consolidation in 1955, there were 1,056 holdings and subsequently 178

The Badajoz Plan, put into operation in 1953–4, aims to revolutionise the economy and the landscape of the largest province of Spain. It is based on the construction of the giant Cijara dam (and five ancillary ones) on the middle course of the Guadiana. Now completed, this dam will supply power for newly established industries and water for irrigation between Mérida and Badajoz. The completion of the plan is scheduled for 1965 when it is expected 60,000 families will cultivate some 300,000 ha of newly irrigated lands along this plain, in the midst of forty new villages and towns.[37] In the catchment area, a further 123,500 ha are being planted with trees. A similar but more modest scheme in Jáen has commenced with new dams on the Upper Guadalquivir and its tributary the Guadiana Menor, to water 98,800 ha. Twelve new villages to house 4,328 families are also being built.[38] In 1954, a more ambitious fourteen-year plan was started on the left bank of the Ebro. Encouraged by the successful scheme of the Violada on the lower Gállego, this new project is designed to benefit the steppes of Cinca, Bardenas and Los Monegros, among the most desolate landscapes of Aragon. Other regional plans are now being announced in rapid succession for the provinces of Cáceres, Salamanca, Seville and Granada. No other Mediterranean country has made such vigorous progress in afforestation, with plans to plant a further two million hectares in the decade 1956–66.[39] Even cactus is being grown in the salt-encrusted lands of the south-east to provide additional fodder. Rural roads have been improved and transport on them has doubled in a decade. All these developments demonstrate the revolutionary changes that are taking place in the Spanish countryside. Modernisation of Spanish agriculture is taking place also in other directions, such as the new fertiliser industry in Saragossa, the rapid production of agricultural machinery in centres such as Vitoria, even a national network of large freezing plants.

There is, however, a number of criticisms that can be made about Spanish regional planning. Large amounts of capital tend to get tied up in long-term, grandiose schemes, well suited to the national temperament of *mañana* and big dreams. Instead, more limited or make-shift plans more immediately realisable, would perhaps suit Spanish budgets much better. Meagre agricultural statistics, and few soil surveys, only show how much agrarian ignorance there is still. Too much trial-and-error planning is still being executed. Irrigation is perhaps being over-emphasised in the regional plans, consequent on past legislation. Land settlement schemes have been tied up almost exclusively with impressive irrigation projects. As they are costly, they can only serve the interests of a very limited number of the rural population. Yet at present there is no other solution to the improvement of rural welfare being so vigorously pursued, apart from the limited success in land consolidation. As the report of the International bank for Reconstruction and Development recently recommended, 'irrigation should be included (in colonisation schemes) only if economically justified in itself.'[40]

3. *Italy*. In Italy, especially in the south, herds of water buffalo have provided an oddly oriental touch in the otherwise Mediterranean landscapes. For centuries past, the melancholy coastal plains have been deserted at sunset by shepherds and labourers for their hill-top villages, leaving the marshy flats to the mosquito. Now all this is rapidly changing, though it has not all taken place suddenly. Since the Unification of Italy, this country of young, unstable mountains, juxtaposed with marshy plains and afflicted by rapid erosion, floods and malaria, has had nevertheless a proud record in its struggle against nature: 1,500,000 hectares have been irrigated, 23,000 km of irrigation canals built and 2,800,000 ha of marshes reclaimed.[41] The 500 pumping stations, constructed to maintain lowland drainage, have a capacity greater than the normal flow of the Po. No Mediterranean country has done more to change the face of its landscapes within the last century. And perhaps no other country in the world has published more detailed statistics on its rural life. Irrigated land is still more extensive in Italy than in Spain, despite the latter's greater climatic needs and its own recent progress with dam construction (see Appendix III, table 6). More

important than areal extent (9 per cent of the utilised land of Italy) is
the value of crops produced by Italian irrigation (25 per cent of agricultural output). Irrigation is, of course, not new in Italy. Ever since the
thirteenth century the river Po has been gradually harnessed. But it was
in the hands of the communes and therefore localised. Only the unification of Italy in 1861 made possible the utilisation of water in major
regional plans. Thus the Cavour Canal was built in 1866 to irrigate a
vast area of 150,000 ha, and also initiated a new policy of direct state

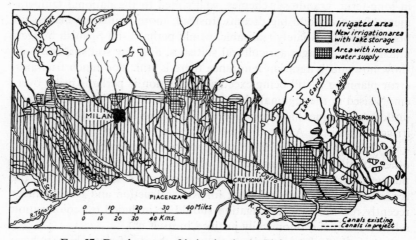

FIG. 57. Development of irrigation in the Plain of Lombardy

control. Since then rapid progress has taken place so that the million
hectares of irrigated land which had taken almost a millennium to
create, were more than doubled in the following century. Notable
among the schemes of the late nineteenth century were the Alto
Veronese and Agro-Veronese canals, deriving their water from the
Adige to water 366,000 ha. Since the beginning of this century most
spectacular progress has been made in the Po delta and eastern plains.
After 1948, new plans to add eventually 500,000 ha in the Po plain and
360,000 ha in the south and islands have been started. The Flumenosa-
Campidano scheme in Sardinia is the largest of the southern plans
(70,000 ha). Despite more widely distributed areas, irrigation is still
concentrated in the Po valley, whose great river supplies 70 per cent of
all the water used for irrigation in Italy.

In addition to irrigation, land reclamation of marsh (*bonifica*) has
played a very significant rôle in the cultural landscapes. In the period
1861–1915, attention was almost entirely confined to the Po Plain,

where 330,000 ha were drained, compared with only two thousand ha for the whole of the south.[42] Indeed, the first drainage law after Unification was a Piedmontese measure, and even the first national law of 1882 was focussed on the Po delta. This and other ninteenth-century legislation suffered from three major defects: the excessive specialisation of acts which dealt with isolated technical problems, rather than the integrated needs of drainage basins, mountains and plains; the neglect of socio-economic needs of the rural economy; and, above all, the ineffective checks to the growing disparity between economic progress in the north and retardation in the south. Soil erosion, agrarian problems and the toll of malaria—over two million suffered from malaria in the period between 1887 and 1920—were most aggravated in the south[43] (Fig. 179). Fascist legislation tried to remedy some of these problems. The act of 1923 widened the notion of *bonifica* to cover control of mountain streams, irrigation and malaria. Regional planning was formulated by the acts of 1928 and 1933.[44] Progress in reclamation schemes was rapid in the thirties, prompted by unemployment and political motives. Ambitious schemes were started, many not for the first time but more successfully than before, notably the Pontine Marshes (75,000 ha),[45] the Maccarese and other lowlands of the Roman Campagna (200,000 ha), the Sele Plain (41,200 ha)[46] and the Tirso in Sardinia (126,500 ha).[47] The control of the lower Piave in Venetia and soil conservation on the clay hill slopes of the Apennines between Florence and Ravenna (82,250 ha), were also attempted. Few were completed by 1939, but their initiation made the post-war achievements more rapidly possible. Indeed, 80 per cent of the lands now planned for re-development are located in the same areas that were selected in the fascist period. But further tasks remain on an immense scale. It is estimated that because of geological, hydrological and other physical considerations, 40 per cent of the whole agro-forestal area of Italy (13 million ha) still needs some measure of reclamation or conservation.[48] By 1950, land reclamation had been applied in some form or other to seven million hectares, but there were still 2·9 million hectares for which there was no active policy. Moreover, the achilles heel of Italian reclamation has always been the mistaken policy of first attempting the more spectacular schemes on the lowlands before commencing with land conservation in the remoter mountain areas, a slow and unspectacular programme in the eyes of the public. Specific Calabrian legislation in 1954 took a step in the right direction, involving a detailed soil and slope mapping programme in its mountainous terrain.

Many of the lands reclaimed since the nineteenth century have been

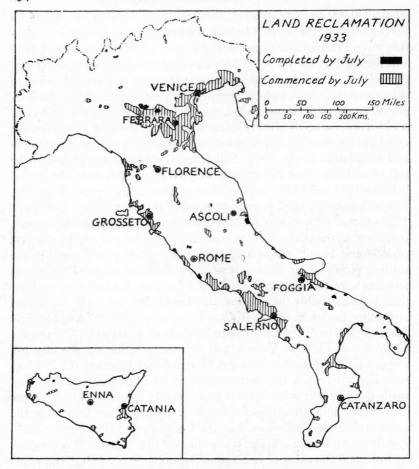

FIG. 58. Land reclamation and land improvement in Italy in 1933

developed by large commercial companies. *Latifundi* and their attendent
evils were not therefore faced by the earlier *bonificati*. However, a new
era began in 1950, when the Italian government, hard-pressed by the
threat of domestic communism, began to tackle land reforms so
vigorously that within a decade it has affected 29 per cent of the national
territory and settled over 100,000 families on the land.[49] In each region
affected, a land reform agency (*Ente*) with certain autonomous powers
has been set up (Fig. 60). The chief ones in the peninsula are: Ente
Maremma, comprising the coastal plains between Leghorn and Rome,
and some districts outside the geographical region, notably the volcanic

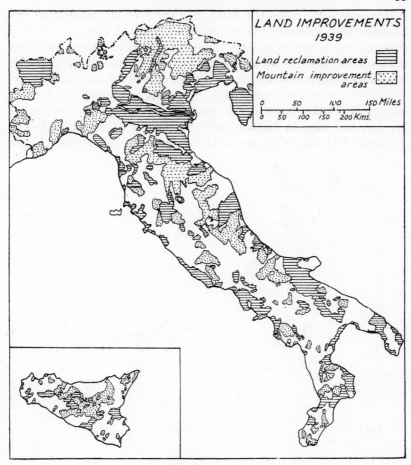

FIG. 59. Land reclamation schemes in Italy, 1939

lands of Tuscany and Latium;[50] Ente Puglia-Lucania-Molise, which
embraces the Murge, Tavoliere and the coastal plan around the Gulf of
Taranto;[51] and Ente Calabria, centred on the Sila but stretching to the
Ionian coast.[52] The two islands of Sicily and Sardinia are entirely
covered by reform legislation: ERAS (*Ente Riforma Agraria Siciliana*)[53]
and ETFAS (*Ente per la Trasformazione Fondiaria ed Agraria della
Sardegna*), which works in conjunction with the hydro-electric power
and irrigation project for southern Campidano, entitled *Ente Flumendosa*. There are also smaller district units such as those of the Po delta,
the Fucino basin and two in Campania (Volturno and Sele).

It is impossible to outline more than the general principles of this energetic land reform.[54] Expropriation of land has been on a sliding scale, to ensure the break-up of undeveloped, large estates, especially those on the plains. Other aims are to give some protection to energetic landowners and to discriminate in the use of land for cattle raising and woodlands in the catchment areas. According to the regional circumstances, legislation has varied in each *ente*. Although these measures are only one stage in tackling problems such as latifundia, table 7 in Appendix III indicates the spectacular progress made in the first decade

Fig. 60. Areas affected by land reform, 1949–60 (Note that within Sardinia there is the independent development area of the Flumendosa hydraulic scheme for irrigation and power)

of the *Cassa per il Mezzogiorno*, the state co-ordinating body which was established in 1950.[55]

Although the size of holdings will vary with the demographic pressure in each region, the aim of doubling productivity is the same. The reduction of the area under permanent pasture, the improvement of stock-raising, the expansion of tree crops and where possible of irrigated crops, are the common policy, guided by co-operative societies. Marked changes of the settlement pattern are being created. In place of the traditional villages perched remotely on hill-tops, the new settlers are being housed in gaily coloured houses that dot the new lands in the plains, usually aligned loosely along the roads.[56] Complete dispersion is not always possible as in Calabria and Sicily, where hamlets of ten to twenty farms are more practicable over the hilly terrain. Even on the plains, the social and economic needs of each community have favoured a loose grouping of dwellings, often on the isolated borders between communes.

These rapid and impressive changes in these poor regions of Italy naturally raise other problems.[57] It is now realised that land reform, which had such political urgency in 1950, is not the real solution of the south; indeed in central Sicily it has been a disastrous fiasco. The dissemination of settlement in the land reform areas was modelled on the assumption that the pattern of dispersed farms in central Italy was the ideal norm. But the social revolution today has made it unpopular for young people, who desire looser family ties and more social life. It has also created problems for education and cooperative marketing. Only in the newly irrigated areas is it likely to be sustained, for technical reasons. As only one out of twenty agricultural workers have benefited from land reform, it has done nothing to stem migration from the south. Indeed, in the decade 1950–60, almost two million migrated from the South to the North, thereby threatening the social disintegration of the South. Meanwhile in the South there has been slow economic development through its basic programme of public works. Now in the 1960s there is a race between the incipient industrialisation and the continued depopulation of the rural areas. But only in the three industrial pivots of the South, Naples-Salerno, Bari-Brindisi-Taranto and Messina-Augusta, with smaller outposts at Cagliari, Potenza, Foggia and Crotone, is industry likely to modify the countryside. Increasingly, vast areas of southern Italy will be left in the position of being unsuited either to industrial or to modern agricultural development. In these vast areas of Pliocene clays and rugged limestone terrain, forestry has no great future. A new agricultural policy will have to be devised for regions such as central Sicily, Calabria and much of Basilicata with a return to the integration of larger holdings and with new concepts of land use for pastoralism. Other Mediterranean peoples will watch these developments with much interest, for Italy has already executed Europe's greatest democratic regional plan since the war, and is now in the vanguard of Mediterranean advance.

4. *North-west Africa.*[58] The most striking feature of the countrysides in North Africa is the brutal contrast between the neat, gridiron pattern

of fields, roads and settlements built by European colonists, and the jig-
saw mosaic of native lands with their huddled mud villages and farms
that blend with the soil. Even so, the impact of European settlement
varies considerably in each territory and even in the types of colonisation (see Appendix III, table 7).

European colonisation began much earlier in Algeria than in the two
former protectorates, favoured also by legislation that made land expropriation much easier.[59] In 1830, French troops landed in Algeria, but
colonisation on a significant scale did not commence for another fourteen years. At first, small military holdings were set up, but malaria
caused a rapid decimation of the settlers and some villages were
colonised several times over in the Mitidja.[60] During the governorship
of Bugeaud (1840–47), sixty-one villages and hamlets were built, and
again in the mass exodus of exiled Parisians in 1848–9, forty-two new
centres were established. The first settlers of the Mitidja, scattered in
isolated farms, had to be evacuated, and the logical consequence of
defence was the creation of villages, further encouraged by the Kabylia
rebellion of 1871. In those early decades of Algerian colonisation
numerous experiments were tried: free military settlements, large-scale
commercial enterprises (after the sale of land became the policy in 1864,)
and a more energetic state-sponsored colonisation after 1871. The result
was the wide distribution of several dozens of villages scattered over the
plains of Oran,[61] Algiers, Philippeville, Bône, the Cheliff valley and
around Sétif. Then it spread to the eastern Mitidja and to the north of
Sétif and Constantine. The Phylloxera crisis in France gave Algeria its
greatest opportunity, vineyards there increasing from 23 ha in 1880 to
154,000 ha in 1900. Isnard has noted, however, that the distribution of
these lowland colonial lands determined the location of the vineyards,
whereas the zone of optimum climatic conditions at c. 2,500 ft on the
Tell slopes was overlooked, a fact which has determined the inferior
qualities of the Algerian wine trade.[62] Viticulture encouraged farm lots
to be erected near the villages after 1880, but the French village has given
the strongest imprint to these Tell plains. There are today over three
hundred villages and six hundred hamlets, all with the same regular
gridiron plan, tree-lined streets, houses of the same style and age, and
centred on the square and public buildings. After dry farming was first
developed in 1876 in the Cheliff plain,[63] colonisation pushed south of the
Tell mountains into the interior steppes in large farms, but 90 per cent
of the European population is still concentrated in the coastal plains.
It is more accurate, however, to speak of this colonisation as Mediterranean, since the immigrants that came in the nineteenth century were

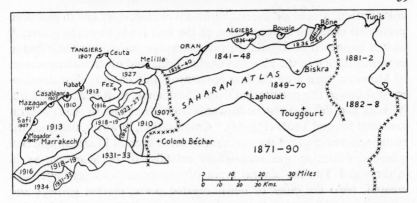

FIG. 61. The European pacification and conquest of the Maghreb (after Despois and Mensching)

primarily from the poorer lands of Languedoc and Corsica. After 1873, an influx of Spaniards from the eastern provinces and Andalusia settled around Sidi-Bel-Abbès, Oran and Tlemcen, while immigrants also came from the overpopulated lands of Campania, Calabria, Tuscany, Sardinia, Sicily and Malta into western Algeria.[64]

Towards the end of the nineteenth century, large capitalised estates were established in Tunisia, notably around Enfida and Sidi Tabet. This prompted the French to establish the country as a protectorate in 1881, and in 1885 legal status for the settlers further encouraged the creation of large olive groves in the hinterland of Sfax.[65] Numerous small-holders established vineyards in the north, around Tunis and the plain of the Cape Bon Peninsula. Many of these were Italian peasants. The Tunisian vineyards doubled in area between 1918 and 1933, and the influx of Italians so alarmed the French that further efforts to settle colonists from Constantine were made, chiefly in the wheatlands of north-west Tunisia and in the olive groves of Sfax. But territorial expansion of French colonisation had practically ceased by 1932 (Fig. 61). Unlike the Algerian villages, the red roofs of the French farms, isolated in their clumps of eucalyptus, are the familiar sight of Tunisia, stretching from Mateur to Zaghouan and from the Medjerda plain to Maktor, with scattered areas further south especially around Sfax and Kasserine.

In Morocco, colonisation had already commenced before the establishment of the protectorate in 1912; there were then 100,000 ha in European ownership. Most of the colonists came from other parts of North Africa, already experienced in the problems of environment and well versed with the trial-and-error lessons of Algerian colonisation. Moreover, the establishment of customary law in Morocco prevented excessive expropriation of the best lands from the natives,[66] as had happened in Algeria. Private enterprise started the colonisation movements, first in the plains of Oudja, Triffa and other eastern sectors of Morocco, then after the first movements in Chaouia, their development followed the pacification from Casablanca, to Rabat, the Gharb, Meknes and Fez and also southwards from Doukkala to Abda Marrakech and beyond Tadla (Fig. 61).[67] Colonisation, however, occupied the better watered lands of the north, or in areas such as Mazagan and Safi where dry-farming was successfully established. In Morocco, as in Algeria and Tunisia, several types of European holdings have been created. Near the cities or newly created ports, market gardens and orchards predominate. Vineyards are of variable size, with other specialised holdings occupied with olive or citrus groves. Grain farms, characteristic in the drier interiors, are commonly 150 to 500 ha but in Morocco there are also larger units of 500 to 3000 ha. As in Tunisia, the farm is the common unit of European settlement.

Another important change in the North African countryside has been the development of drainage schemes on some coastal plains. Despite a century of effort, few are yet completed because of geological and hydrological difficulties. The Mitidja plain in the hinterland of Algiers, whose malarial reputation gave it the title 'the graveyard of colonisation', has only been finally drained since the second world war. Other Algerian plains, notably the lowland behind Bône (now called Annaba) and the Macta plain, are still in process of reclamation. In northern Tunisia, a private company, the Mabtouha, initiated a drainage sector on the Medjerda. Now the state is completing a series of dams, an ambitious overflow canal and other works to control this river, and permit full-scale cultivation of this magnificent plain. In Morocco, the first drainage scheme on the right bank of the Sebou was also begun by a private company (in 1919) and subsequently the state has completed other sectors.[68] But the left bank of the Sebou is still a marshy waste.

Extensive technical progress has been made with irrigation projects (see Appendix III, table 9). In Algeria, the story is very largely an unhappy one of failure.[69] The first dam, Hamiz (1883), built near Algiers, and others in the period before the first world war, were rapidly silted. After 1924, another generation of dams focused attention on the drier, western section of the Tell, despite the fact that their rivers only account for about one-fifth of the total surface flow into the Mediterranean. In this inter-war period, some of the earlier dams were raised higher (eg. Perregaux and Hamiz) to make them more effective, and

27 The Tribunal of Waters (reproduction of oil painting by Ferrandis, 1865). The tribune of peasants outside the door of Valencia Cathedral giving judgment on the litigation of water-rights between two contestants

28 A *noria* driven by mules, raising water in the Huerta of Orihuela

29 View of the Alhambra and its watered gardens from the Generalife, Granada

WATER CONTROL, A MEDITERRANEAN NECESSITY

30 Dam of Im Fout on the Oum er Rbia, Central Morocco. The dam is 120 m. high capable eventually of irrigating 150,000 has. in the coastal plains of Doukkala. Its generating station can produce 130 million kWh.

MODERN DEVELOPMENT

31 Dispersed settlements at Melfi, in the northern part of the Ofanto valley, S. Italy

numerous works were completed for the control of the Cheliff. Since
1944, further dams have been built in Oran, on the Cheliff and in the
south. Nevertheless, less than half of the potential area irrigable has
been so far utilised, in some areas one-third of the irrigated perimeters
lie fallow for dry-farming. Perhaps more promising will be the exploitation of underground water resources at Biskra and notably in the
Chott ech Chergui (begun in 1944).

In Tunisia, the terrain is unsuited to large dams, and sub-surface
water resources are more important than surface discharge. Consequently, apart from the El Kebir (1928) and Ben Metir (1953) dams, the
only major irrigation scheme has been on the lower Medjerda, now
nearing completion. Apart from this, priority is given to flood control
in the Tunisian Tell, and to tapping underground supplies, notably
in the Kairouan plain, on the coast near Gabès, at Gafsa, and at
Kasserine.[70]

The Atlantic facade of Morocco provides it with the greatest water
resources of the Maghreb. It is estimated that one million hectares could
eventually be irrigated and the present programme aims to irrigate
500,000 hectares within twenty years.[71] This is favoured by the possession
of large rivers, notably the Sebou and Oum er Rbia. Before 1939, major
dams had been built on the O. Beth, a tributary of the Sebou in the
district of Sidi Slimane, on the O. Mellah near Casablanca, and on the
N'Fis, west of Marrakech. Since the war, major schemes have been
developed on the Oum er Rbia, notably in the Tadla plain, and at
Imfout to irrigate the Doukkala (Plate 30). The Triffa project on the
lower Moulouya is also partially completed. Other schemes are more
diversified, to improve indigenous systems with smaller works, such as
those of the Dra basin, the Sous plain, the Tafilalet and Fes, using both
surface and underground water.[72]

The criticism of many irrigation projects in the Maghreb is that they
have been too much orientated to meet European interests and have
often been technical schemes of engineering, inadequately related to
rural resettlement. However, since the war a third series of changes,
apart from reclamation and irrigation, the modernisation of native
agriculture is now changing the face of some countrysides. This is
challenged by the indigence of two-thirds of the fellahs. Each country
has put forward its own original scheme. In Algeria, about 2,000
families had been settled by 1958, but there were still about 600,000
landless peasants. Based on the earlier established insurance institutes
(*Societies Algériennes de Prévoyance*) modernisation was slowly being
introduced by the S.A.R. (*Secteurs d'Amélioration Rurale.*) Over two

hundred sectors were created to affect eventually 17·5 million hectares and 305,000 families. Since independence in 1962, radical changes are likely to develop. In Tunisia, a series of regional plans was conceived to deal with the particular problems of each climatic zone of the country: the north, the high steppes, the low steppes and the pre-Saharan zone. Since 1955, efforts have also been made to settle the southern nomads. But in general, Tunisian schemes of peasant reform have not so far been conspicuously successful. In Morocco, progress has been much more ambitious. In 1945, the *Conseil Supérieur du Paysannat* was formed to create S.M.P. (*Secteurs de Modernisation du Paysannat*). As the fellahs are more primitive and tribalised than in Algeria, these districts have been framed to suit the collective, patri-monial life of the countryside, to deal with such problems as micro-fundia, parcellation of holdings, etc. and to transform the tribal way of life into modern collective systems of farming. The most successful results have commenced in the Tadla plains where two nomadic tribes have been settled, and are being educated to irrigation farming. Major changes are also taking place in the Doukkala and Triffa plains.

In all these national schemes the Western Mediterranean generally is contrasted with the countries of the Eastern Mediterranean. In the latter, there have been spectacular increases in the cultivable area since the war, especially in Turkey. But the rapid changes of the western countries have been more qualitative, with little or no increase in the cultivable area. As such, these countries are now coming to grips more realistically with the social, as distinct from the technical problems, involved in changing the character of their landscapes. Moreover, the challenge of the European Common Market will mean that their re-form programmes will be guided less in future by the distinct moulds of national legislation and customs, and much more by international conditions.

PART II

THE IBERIAN PENINSULA

CHAPTER 8

STRUCTURES AND LANDFORMS
OF THE IBERIAN PENINSULA

'A glance at a map shows that one of the most distinctive features
of our Peninsula is diversity. Indeed, if a common attribute can be
found in the Hispanic landscape it is diversity, to an extent that no
other country in Europe can express.'   (L. Solé Sabarís)

The Iberian Peninsula is a continent in miniature and the most varied
of the three Mediterranean Peninsulas. Its massive form of 223,000 sq.
miles is dominated by the geological block of the Meseta which stands
at an average elevation of 2,000 to 2,300 ft above sea-level. Seven-
eighths of the Peninsula's borders are washed by the seas, and it is
further isolated by mountain walls. The monotony of its wide central
plateaux and the diversity of its peripheral structures emphasise its
continental character. The Peninsula shares with central Europe the
areal extent and the influence of Hercynian structures, while it also has
Alpine forms of relief that characterise southern Europe. Its rock types
reveal other features of diversity. Crystalline rocks dominate in the
west, clays and other sediments in the central and peripheral basins,
and limestones in the east and north. They reveal a long geological
evolution focused upon Hercynian block tectonics, Alpine folding and
prolonged erosion and sedimentation during Tertiary times (Fig. 18).

At least since the Mesozoic epoch three zones have been recognisable
in the palaeogeography of the Peninsula: the Meseta block, the epicontinental margins, and the geosynclinal depressions. The Meseta block—
not to be confused with the physiographic term used for the Castilian
tablelands—is the geological core of the Peninsula, occupying about
four-sevenths of its total area.[1] It is a remnant of the great Hercynian
continent that once extended from North Africa across Europe, and
was peneplaned at the close of the Carboniferous.[2] Evidence of a pre-
Palaeozoic or Huronian mountain system in Galicia is uncertain.[3]
Great thicknesses of Cambrian slates in the north and south-west
indicate relatively uniform marine conditions at the time of their
deposition, but the thick Silurian conglomerates and sands over the
south-west and the 'island block' over the Ebro basin[4] reflect the folded
relief already associated with the Caledonian orogenesis. In Galicia and

especially in the folds of the Sierra Morena the Caledonian trend lines are still clear. In the north of the Peninsula deep geosynclinal conditions prevailed until towards the end of the Carboniferous when the Culm series bear witness to the first Hercynian folds. Apart from this sequence of Palaeozoic strata on the borders of the Meseta block, there was also the widespread intrusion in the west and north-west of granitic batholiths. According to Cotelo Neiva there are five important magmatic phases in the Palaeozoic rocks of Portugal, ranging from basic to acid types.[5] Where the Palaeozoic geosynclines were deepest, especially in the Pyrenees and the interior of the north-west, the Armorican trend lines, from north-west to south-east, are still significant features.

The epi-continental margins of the Meseta block comprise the second palaeogeographic unit of the Peninsula. They reflect the prolonged period of orogenic tranquillity that existed throughout the Mesozoic and the early Tertiary, when marine transgressions laid down thick fine sediments, chiefly limestones. Three subdivisions were recognisable: a wide but shallow platform bordering the Meseta Block from near Oviedo to Albacete; a shallow sedimentary basin in the north-east; and a very deep geosyncline that stretched from Gibraltar to the Balearic Islands.[6] Some gentle folding in the Jurassic and Cretaceous produced oscillations of sea-level and varied facies but more marked continental conditions only commenced with the beginning of the Tertiary and the first phase of the Alpine movements. At the end of the Eocene, Alpine orogenesis began in the Pyrenees and the Penibaetic, moving outwards from the ranges in several phases. According to Stille these were: upper Eocene-Oligocene: Oligocene-Miocene; intra Miocene (Helvetian-Tortonian); and Pliocene (See table, Appendix II, for geological equivalents).[7] During the earlier Tertiary movements flysch and littoral deposits were laid down thickly in the geosynclines of the Pyrenees and the Sub-Baetic Straits between lower Andalusia and Majorca. But during the Miocene all the Peninsula was subjected to continental conditions except the Sub-Baetic Straits then wider than before.[8] This was only gradually narrowed and then closed by the end of the Pliocene (Fig. 81).

The third palaeogeographic unit of the Peninsula has been the sedimentary basins infilled with Tertiary deposits. Over the eastern Meseta block shallow lakes laid down unconformable deposits in Old and New Castile. The Ebro basin, an arm of the Eocene sea, became a trough of inland drainage in which thick deposits of continental origin were laid down.[9] Since the Pliocene, the basins of the Meseta block have initiated

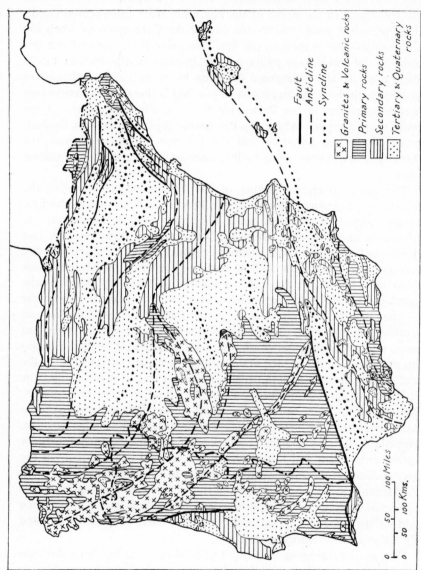

Fig. 62. The structure of the Iberian Peninsula (after Staub and others)

the proto-courses of the main lines of drainage, aided over the Meseta by a pronounced tilt towards the west and south-west.[10]

THE MESETA BLOCK AND ITS BORDERS

This core of the Peninsula may be divided broadly into the two zones of the Palaeozoic west, mostly a complex of Cambrian-Silurian crystalline rocks, and the east-central basins of Old and New Castile with their Tertiary cover. In the western zone Hercynian features are clear, both in granitic batholiths and in the trends, though subsequent erosion has so modified the relief that the north-west to south-east trend lines are commonly better seen on the geological rather than on the topographical maps. In the zone, variously termed *Hispanides* (Staub)[11] or *Hesperides* (E. Hernandez Pacheco)[12] four distinct types of landscape may be distinguished by the outcrop of slates, granites, quartzites and limestones respectively. The thick deposits of Ordovician and Silurian slates are generally softly contoured to form rolling plateaux with impressive peneplains, such as those of Alentejo, Extremadura, Beira and the Campo de Calatrava. The acid granites and the basic gneisses, more indifferent to change of relief, appear sometimes as plateaux such as Guarda and western Salamanca, sometimes as block mountains as in the Gredos and Guadarrama. Hard quartzites aligned along Hercynian synclines rise abruptly in inverted relief as ranges such as some of the Montes de Toledo, Castelo Branco and mountains bordering León and Galicia. Carboniferous limestones, folded and elevated to produce scenery that is alpine in scale in the eastern Cantabrians and in the Pyrenees, scarcely appear part of the Hercynian complex (Fig. 62).

Prolonged subaerial denudation has peneplaned the Meseta, probably many times. The oldest surface appears to be pre-Triassic but Fischer's assumption that it was widespread is not proven.[13] A pre-Cretaceous (Upper) surface has been identified to the west of Salamanca (Sa Bussaco).[14] A pre-Miocene cycle has been suggested in Alentejo.[15] But the fundamental surface of the Iberian Meseta is dated to between mid-Miocene and Pontian times, a pale flat skyline that dominates the scenery of so much of its rolling tablelands.[16] The varying altitude of this peneplain, ranging from 5,500 to 7,300 ft in the Central Cordillera to only 2,300–3,300 ft in the Douro valley implies that the original surface has been warped and flexured on an impressive scale.[17] Bores in the Henares valley indicate that it has been affected on a scale of some 10,000 ft by late Tertiary movements within the Meseta block.[18] On the mountain borders, a further sequence of pediments eroded by a Pliocene cycle, two detrital spreads of Villafranchian *rañas*[19] and a sequence of Quaternary river terraces complete the polcyclic chronology (See plates 33, 35, 36, 37, 41.)

In the eastern zone of the Meseta Block differential erosion is stripping the Tertiary cover. The dominant form is the tableland (*mesa*), consisting of unconformable Miocene strata, laid down by rivers (Tortonian), in brackish ponds (Sarmatian) and swamps (Pontian).[20] The flat, upper surface of hard limestone forms an eroded capping (*páramo*), protecting the softer, underlying marls that outcrop abruptly on the slopes (*cuestas*). The sands and clays of the lower slopes form plains (*campos, campiñas, llanuras*) (Fig. 63). There is, however, a

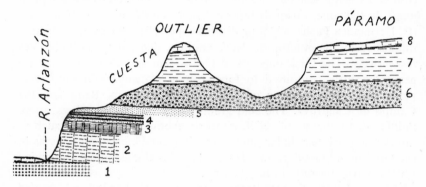

FIG. 63. Cross-section of a Castilian *páramo*, showing the Mircene strata: 1. clays and red sands; 2, marly clays; 3. fetid marls; 4. concretions in marls; 5. red sandstones; 5. fossiliferous marls; 7. other marls; 8. limestones

marked contrast between the basins of Old and New Castile. The former is an almost enclosed basin at an average elevation of 2,300 ft, in which the Douro is only slowly eroding its Miocene cover. The Douro plunges over the edge of the basin in a series of gorges at the Portuguese frontier. New Castile more open and more varied in relief, is drained by the Tagus and the Guadiana; its average elevation is some 650 ft lower. The marked dissection of the Alcarria indicates the relative ease with which the Tagus is cutting in its headwaters, because of the facility of the tectonic trough in its middle course (Fig. 64).[21] In contrast the river Guadiana, even more than the Douro, finds it difficult to cut through the south-western Meseta, so that the region of La Mancha is least affected by headward erosion.[22]

1. *Old Castile and the Leonese Borderlands.* Clearly defined by the mountainous rim to the north, east and south, this basin extends 140 miles from north to south and for about 110 miles from east to west.

The faulted, southern borders of the Cantabrians rise sharply above the Pontian *páramos* of Palencia and León, but to the east and south ramps of erosional debris mask the foot of the Iberian mountains and the Central Cordillera respectively. These pediments rise gradually towards the mountains, their preservation depending partly upon the nature of the parent rocks. Thus the granites of the Gredos and Guadarrama mountains, readily reduced to sands, are rapidly dissected, whereas the thick spreads of quartzitic pebbles and schistose gravels in the pediments fronting the Somosierra and Ayllon ranges are better preserved. These pediments rise from 2,500 to 3,000 ft and in the east from 2,500 to 3,500 ft in the north and south (Fig. 66).

Fronting the pediments, the tablelands (*páramos*) have been eroded

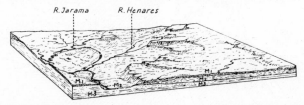

FIG. 64. Block-diagram of the upper Járama and the Henares tablelands. Note the Miocene clays and marls overlain by the hard capping of limestones that comprise the structural tablelands

into a series of interfluvial plateaux by the consequent streams. This is markedly so in the north, as the Cantabrian streams are supplied by more generous water resources.

The Castilian basin is not a continuous plain, but a complex fusion of troughs whose structures are obscured by the Tertiary deposits[23] and only partially revealed by the behaviour of the drainage systems. The Bureba-Burgos depression, the upper Douro valley, the Palencian and the Leonese basins, and the central Douro valley are distinct troughs. They are flanked to the north-west by the graben of the Bierzo, and to the south-west by the tectonic depression between Salamanca and Ciudad Rodrigo. The Esla and the Pisuerga control most of the northern drainage but in the south the drainage flows in a series of independent courses. Only the Tormes appears to have been deflected to enter the Salamanca basin. Differential erosion has created the landscape of buttes and cuestas, especially in the district between Valladolid and Tordesillas. Westwards beyond Zamora the plateau rises gradually over the Palaeozoic rocks, a vast peneplain of thin, poor soils that are covered extensively with scrub. To the north-west relief is Appalachian, with quartzitic ranges such as the Sa Cabrera.[24] The

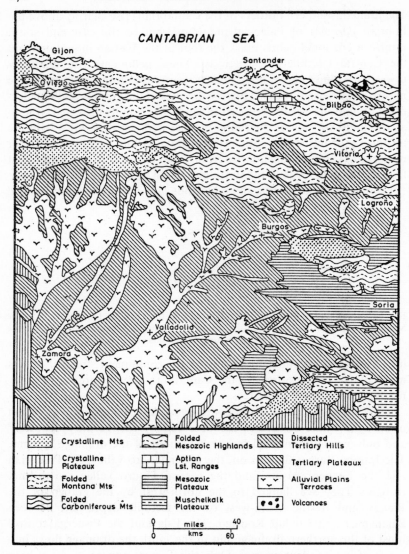

FIG. 65. Landscape types of Old Castile

granitic country of Sanabria with its glacial lake and moraines borders Galicia.[25]

2. *The Central Cordillera*.[26] These block mountains act as the backbone of the Meseta. Granites predominate in the Sa de Gredos and the western Sa de Guadarrama, and weather uniformly into great bosses,

rounded slopes and numerous tors. Metamorphic rocks are typical of the eastern Guadarrama and the Somosierra mountains, etched out by differential erosion so that the ancient Hercynian features are again recognisable. Early Tertiary movements shattered the Cordillera into a series of vertebrae but erosion has since then peneplaned the blocks and much debris has been deposited in the graben and on their flanks (Fig. 66). Glaciation has left its imprint, especially in the Gredos mountains, and moraines descend to 4,900 ft (Fig. 65).[27]

Five types of relief may be distinguished in the Cordillera. The high mountains, usually above 4,250 ft, run *en echelon* and culminate in

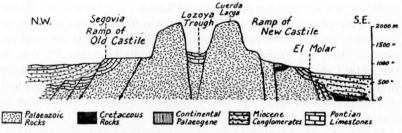

FIG. 66. Cross-section of the Central Cordillera. Note the block structures, bounded by faults and erased by erosion surfaces. A central graben in the Guadarrama has preserved the Cretaceous cover. The Pliocene erosion surface on the bordering ramps between 2,950 and 3,600 ft has reduced considerably the width of the elevated horsts. Abbreviations: P., Palaeozoic; Cr., Cretaceous; Pa., Palaeogene continental; M., Miocene; Mi., detrital course Miocene deposits on the borders of the cordillera; M_2, Pontian limestones

Peñalara (7,972 ft) in the Guadarrama, and Almanzor (8,727 ft) in the Gredos. In the Somosierra there is one main mountain block, but in the Guadarrama two parallel horsts are separated by a graben that is followed by the upper Lozoya valley. In the Gredos the sequence of horsts and graben is more complicated and impressive. The second type of relief consist of the interior basins. The higher ones are called *navas*, while longitudinal depressions have been excavated by subsequent streams along lines of fracture or softer rocks, such as the Lozoya, Tormes and Alberche. The mountain ramps are a third type of relief. These lie at about 3,300 ft on the northern flank, descending gradually into Old Castile. But on the south side they fall abruptly to the Tagus trough, lying at 2,600–2,300 ft. The last two types of relief are scarps and transverse fractures. Fault-line scarps are common as a consequence of late Tertiary erosion which has moved the scarps yards or even miles from the original faults. Often the main fault now runs along the pediment zone, with a secondary fault now separating the ramp from the mountain front. Transverse fractures run north-east to south-west in a Tertiary system to separate the Gredos and Béjar mountains from those further west. But other fractures follow probably Hercynian trends.[28] These permit the low cols, notably the Somosierra (4,650 ft) the easiest pass between the two Castiles, as well as the Navacerrada and the Guadarrama.

3. *The Southern Meseta.* The southern Meseta block is much larger than the northern area, extending 150 miles from north to south, and about 300 miles from east to west, occupying an area about the size of England. It consists of four major units: The Tagus trough; the table-lands of New Castile; the mountains of Toledo; and their continuation in the plateaux of Extremadura (Fig. 67). Faulted between the Central Cordillera and the Montes de Toledo, the Tagus trough is not a simple graben. There are several distinct basins, notably La Sagra, La Vera in the Tiétar valley, and the lower course of the Alagón.[29] The Tagus flows to the south of the trough, and in the Toledo area is actually antecedent in a deeply incised valley that cuts through an outlier of the Montes de Toledo.[30]

East of the clay lands of La Sagra, the trough merges with the table-lands of New Castile. In the north these are overlapped by a Plio-Pleistocene pediment to about the site of Madrid.[31] But south and east of the capital, the typical features of eroded Tertiary limestones and marls are apparent in the buttes and mesas occupying the interfluves between the broad ribbons of the riverine *vegas.*[32] The headstreams of the Tagus have trenched their courses some 300 to 500 ft below the *páramos* of western Alcarria and the Serranía de Guadalajara, and scarped relief is pronounced (Fig. 64). Beyond the Pontian surface of the tableland merges northwards and eastwards with the high plateaux of the Iberian mountains at 3,000–3,500 ft.

South of the Guadiela valley and the Mesa of Ocaña unfolds the flat, undissected relief of La Mancha; in the area of San Juan there is the flattest and most extensive interior plain in the Peninsula, scarcely affected by stream erosion.[33] Yet this monotony of relief in La Mancha rising very gradually between 2,200 and 2,600 ft towards the east, obscures a complex evolution. A mantle of Sarmatian clays and Pontian limestones covers the schistose and quartzite surfaces on the western borders, and lies over the Mesozoic limestones to the east and south of Albacete. Islands of quartz and Silurian slates stand out of the plain (Sierracilla de Alhambra, Herencia, Lillo), while cuestas of Triassic sandstone rise above the Campos of Criptana and Alhambra.[34]

In the north-west, the Montes de Toledo lack the continuity, the high altitude and the scale of fracture seen in the Central Cordillera. The highest range, the Sa de Guadalupe, rises only to 5,250 ft and so lacks the glacial features of mountains such as the Gredos. Eastwards

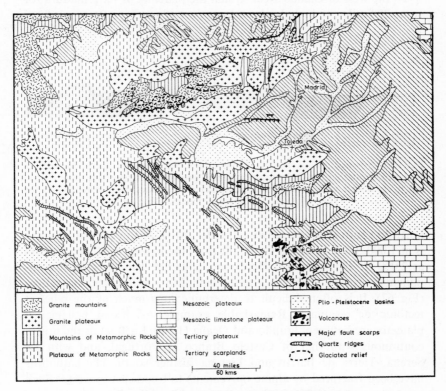

FIG. 67. Landscape types of New Castile and Extremadura

the Montes de Toledo disappear under the Miocene cover of the Campo de Criptana, and westwards they break up into detached hills. The most prominent relief is associated with the quartzitic ridges that once occupied the Hercynian synclines (Fig. 67). Denudation of the softer slates has thus inverted the relief.[35]

South of La Mancha is the Campo de Calatrava, pivoted between the Hercynian block of Extremadura and the Alpine or Baetic folds. In the west there is the subdued Appalachian relief so typical of Extremadura: a broad swelling relief of slates interrupted by quartzitic ranges, notably the Sa de Mestanza (6,430 ft). Further east, the north-west to south-east grain of the country is modified by the west to east alpine trends. Where they intersect is the volcanic district of Calatrava (some seventy Quaternary cones).[36] The recent uplift of this block has nearly severed the course of the upper Guadiana, here deeply incised.

To the west of Ciudad Real stretch the plateaux of Extremadura for some 200 miles, to include also a large part of southern Portugal; from

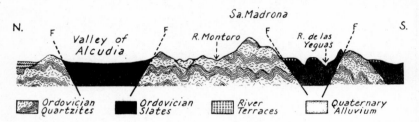

FIG. 68. Cross-section of the Sa Morena and Sa Madrona (after Hernández Pacheco). Note that the Ordovician quartzites provide the higher and more rugged relief, compared with softer and lower relief of the slates, most extensive in the Valley of Alcudia, a noted summer grazing ground

north to south they extend 90–120 miles. Most of this plateau country is at 1,000–1,500 ft with a gentle tilt from the higher, northern borders at 2,000 ft. This exhumed Hercynian landscape had three basic components: erosion surfaces, granite batholiths, and quartzitic ranges (Fig. 67). It is often difficult to determine how much of the relief is tectonic or residual.[37] Remarkable examples of broad peneplaned plateaux are between Trujillo and Ocaña (1,500–1,650 ft) in the north, continuous with that of Castelo Branco in Portugal, and with La Serena, Tierra de Barros and Llerena further south. The batholiths have been fractured by alpine movements to trend east to west.[38] Such are Montanchez (3,261 ft) Santa Cruz and Trujillo. Rugged ranges of quartz and hard palaeozoic limestones follow the Hercynian grain, especially in the mountains of Villuercas (4,330 ft), Altamira and San Pedro. Hernández Pacheco has recognised several erosion surfaces in Extremadura: an early Tertiary surface on the summits, the main Pontian surface on the plateaux, and two Plio-Villafranchian cycles associated with the *rañas*.[39] However, there has not yet been much morphological mapping. The drainage has been influenced by the Tertiary basins of La Serena and Tierra de Barros. But the antecedent course of the Tagus plunges through gorges 300–500 ft deep, and curiously avoids the early Tertiary basins of the Campo de Aranuela and Monforte.

The Sa de Aracena marks the southern borders of Extremadura where the Sa Morena begins. The latter, however, is only a continuation of the same structures and relief of Extremadura. It is not a mountain range but the dissected edge of the Meseta block which has been affected by flexures and down-warping and broken up by transverse fractures. Birot has aptly described it as a piano keyboard.[40] The proximity of the Baetic trough 300–750 ft below the Sa Morena has encouraged river capture on the plateau and intense erosion of the Morena front.[41]

4. *The Portuguese Borderlands.* The landforms of Portugal are essentially a western extension of the Meseta block. Protected from the more energetic orogenic movements that developed on the other borders of the Peninsula, block structures are the rule in Portugal with only limited folded relief of a relatively thin Mesozoic cover in Estremadura and the Algarve. Cretaceous movements upraised the batholiths of Monchique,[42] Sines and Sintra but prolonged denudation in early Tertiary times has smoothed out the general profile of much of highland Portugal. Another surface was carved between the Oligocene and the Miocene, probably the fundamental peneplain in the present relief, subsequently retouched by late Miocene cycles.[43] The extensive surfaces of Portugal although polycyclic, indicate the marked stability of this borderland. Mid-Tertiary movements, however, are evidenced by the lower Tagus-Sado troughs, and smaller grabens such as Chaves in the north.[44] More recent shattering of the blocks is demonstrated by the concurrence of drainage lines with fractures, mostly tranverse to the Hercynian trend, that is north-east to south-west. There is also the evidence of freshly formed fault scarps especially in the north, where blocks descend in steps from the Meseta block to the coast. During the Quaternary however the stability of the Atlantic coast is demonstrated by well developed eustatic terraces. These are clearly marked along the coast except north of the R. Cavado, where recent sinking has eliminated two of the lower terraces.[45]

Southern Portugal is a Palaeozoic block, mainly of Carboniferous schists, granites and other crystalline rocks, tilted and planed in a series of plateaux that descend south-westwards. A widespread surface occurs at about 650 ft clearly seen in the plains of Beja and Évora.[46] North-eastwards it rises in the plateaux of Upper Alentejo (1,000–1,500 ft) in the watershed area between the Guadiana and the Tagus; they are dominated by the Sa de S. Mamede (3,350 ft) an outlier of the central ranges of Extremadura. To the south east, the same surface locally termed 'flat mountain' (*Serra cha*) rises gradually to the Sa

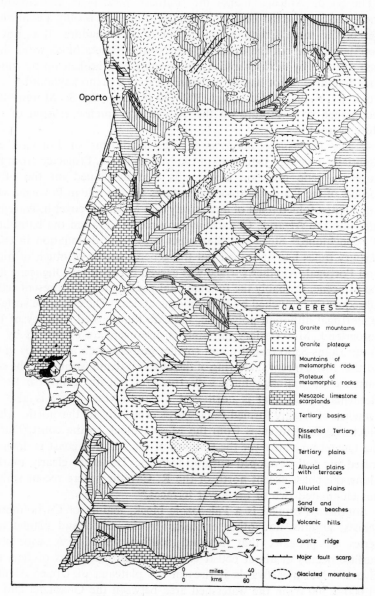

FIG. 69. Landscape types of Portugal

Caldeirao (1,885 ft) in northern Algarve.[47] To the east, the Guadiana has entrenched 350 ft below the plateau and partially destroyed this surface.[48] Rising about the plateaux of Alentejo are undulating ridges of schists (*cumeadas*) that are more dissected than the granites. There is also the residual relief of the quartzites with their Hercynian trend (Alcaria Ruiva, Fitalho hills); horsts such as Serra de Portel; and fault scarps (Grandola and Aljustrel hills).[49] In the Algarve, the relief is more varied, ranging from the dissected syenite massif of Monchique (2,734 ft) and the high, rolling plateaux of Caldeirao (1,000–1,800 ft) in the north to the Jurassic scarps, vales and faulted plateaux of the Barrocal and the coastal plain. Erosion surfaces occur discontinuously at 650–750 ft and 360–400 ft with a pronounced abrasion platform in the most westerly peninsula of Cape St Vincent.[50]

Across the plains of the Tagus that are mostly below 300 ft there is a marked change of landforms. These are: the Mesozoic hills and basins of Estremadura; the plateaux of Beira; and the central mountains of Estrêla and Lousa.[51] The Tagus or Ribatejo trough has a simple form, a Tertiary estuary infilled by marine and later detrital sediments which have been affected by eustatic changes of sea-level. There is also a sequence of Plio-Pleistocene terraces on the south side of the Tagus and in the Sado plain, but the northern side of the Tagus trough is a complex of faulted Meso-Tertiary rocks, dissected into hills that form the southern border of central Portugal.[52] The Mesozoic hills of Estremadura extend north-westwards along the coast for some 150 miles and 30 miles wide. Carved out of Jurassic and Cretaceous limestones, marls and clays, they have karstic features, hogsbacks, scarps and horsts, that are aligned from north-west to south-east. Relief rises to the maximum elevation in the Candeiros (2,011 ft) and Aire (2,221 ft). Differential erosion has been active in carving out a pattern of subsequent valleys and depressions in the lower relief.[53] It also explains the resistant massif of Sintra and the volcanic islets of Berlenga off the coast. Eastwards a major tectonic line of fracture divides this relief from the plateaux of Beira, framed by the lower course of the Zezere, the horst of Carmullo (3,509 ft) and other blocks further north that overlook the plains of the lower Mondego and Aveiro. Other faults let down the Beira surface (only 650 ft along the R. Ponsul) on the border with Alentejo. This plateau rises gradually to 2,000 ft in Beira Baixa, and to 2,500–3,000 ft in Beira Alta.[54] The latter is trenched by fractures traced by the northern flanks of the Estrêla mountains (6,530 ft) and Lousa (3,940 ft) and along the upper valley of the Zezere.[55] The Mondego valley is also guided by a system of north-east to south-west faults. The prevalence of granitic and schistose landforms and erosion surfaces gives unity to both the eastern plateaux and the western mountains of Beira (Fig. 69).

North of the Douro, block movements have destroyed much evidence of altitudinal homologues and the distinction lies between the coastal relief of Minho and the interior plateaux of Trás-os-Montes. Minho has a more broken relief, deeply dissected by rivers that are guided by north-east to south-west structural elements.[56] The mountain blocks that rise above the narrow coastal plain carry summit levels that evidence late-Tertiary uplift. Chief of these massifs are Gerez (4,600 ft), Alturas, Marao and Montemuro. To the east the mountains of Nogueira and Bornes merge into the high plateau that extends eastwards into Castile. This surface of 2,500–3,000 ft is broken by a series of faulted basins such as Regoa-Varim, Mirandela and Vilarica, and is also deeply trenched by the epigenetic course of the Douro and its tributaries.

5. *Galicia.* North of the Minho valley, the Galician landscape has many affinities with northern Portugal but perhaps with a greater series of contrasts between its youthful coasts and the senility of its interior plateaux. Galicia is bounded on the north-east by the tectonic alignments of the Navia basin, the Cua valley and the graben of the Bierzo, while to the south-east the mountainous watershed runs along the Culebra (3,440 ft) Segundera (6,700 ft) and Aquilinos range (7,180 ft). West of these limits, the Galician tableland averages 1,500 ft, stretching some 100 miles from east to west and 120 miles from north to south. Only in the south do the mountains bordering Orense rise to over 3,500 ft, notably San Mamede. The morphological zones of Galicia are threefold: the coasts and their rias; the central tablelands and depressions; and the interior mountain rim (Fig. 70).

The crenulate coasts have been drowned by the recent Flandrian transgression.[57] Narrow plains less than three miles wide, except in Betanzos, but with rias that penetrate deeply for twenty miles or more, have poorly developed marine terraces that suggest the importance of this submergence. It may be that continental flexuring of the interior has been commensurate with this, to explain the rejuvenated valleys such as the Jallas, that plunge over the edge of the plateau to reach the sea.[58] The major line of fracture that is traceable in the rectilinear coast of Portugal as far south as Espinho and then inland towards Tomar, is followed in western Galicia in the granitic headlands of the Rias Bajas and on the islands between them.[59] In the north-west the Rias Altas are structurally distinct, a radial pattern of drowned valleys between the promontories of Bergantinos and Ortigueira, that centre on a depression excavated in Cambrian slates. The interior of Galicia is a vast batholith, mostly of granites, that has been fractured by north to south step faults into the following units: the west coast block; the central mountains, for example the Lugo Meseta and the Sa del Suido in Pontevedra; the central depression occupied by the upper Minho and the Lugo basins; and the high mountains of the eastern

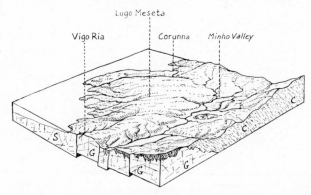

FIG. 70. Block-diagram of Galicia (after Llopis). Note the distinct morphological divisions: A. the coast with its rias; B. the central plateaux and mountains: 1—the Santiago plateau, 2—the Minho trough, 3—the Lugo tableland, and 4—the eastern border of the Minho; C. the High Mountains to the east, comprising: 1—the Sil valley, and 2—the Eastern Mountains. Abbreviations: S, Silurian, G, granites; C, crystalline rocks

interior[60] (Fig. 70). There is a pronounced tilt from north to south, which explains the flow of the Minho, rising only twelve miles from the north coast and then flowing one hundred and fifty five miles south-westwards. Significant erosion surfaces occur at 2,300–2,800 ft, 2,000–2,300 ft and at 1,400–1,600 ft.[61] The Sil basin comprises most of eastern Galicia, with impressive transverse gorges that link the Bierzo basin with the Orense trough lower down. Rugged slate and quartzitic mountains, with fault scarps, rise steeply on the east to over 6,000–7,000 ft. South of the Sil, a high tableland with relics of inland drainage has now been captured by the Limia which plunges steeply down to the Portuguese coast[62] (Fig. 71).

6. *The Cantabrians.* Compared with the other borders of the Meseta block, the Cantabrians are a more formidable mountain range that extends over 150 miles from east to west and from 30 to 60 miles in depth (Fig. 65). Fractures have sharply demarcated it from the Castilian tableland and from the Cantabrian Sea, but the eastern and western

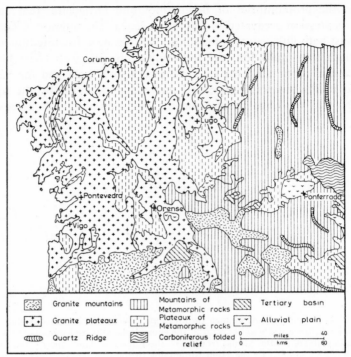

	Granite mountains		Mountains of Metamorphic rocks		Tertiary basin
	Granite plateaux		Plateaux of Metamorphic rocks		Alluvial plain
	Quartz Ridge		Carboniferous folded relief		

FIG. 71. Landscape types of Galicia

borders are less distinct. Short rivers plunge some 8,000 ft within distances of 10–20 miles to the sea. Consequently, erosion is very marked, effacing evidence of peneplantation although post-Miocene surfaces (*brañas*) are still preserved on the borders of the southern ranges. River piracy by Cantabrian streams has captured headstreams of the Douro, carving out defiles utilised by transverse lines of communication. Isostatic block movements have produced new cycles of erosion, whose evidence is better seen in the Palaeozoic rocks of Asturias than on the softer rocks to the east.[63] In the Cantabrians, there are three major and contrasted units: the Asturias in the west, the eastern Cantabrians, and the Montaña of Santander.

The Asturias is demarcated approximately by the valleys of the Navia and the Lesaya on the west and east. It has a complicated structure of thick Palaeozoic sediments, folded in late Carboniferous times, emergent since the Mesozoic, and fractured into blocks by early and mid-Tertiary movements. On its western coast, quartzites form pronounced headlands (Busto, Vidrio, and Peñas) but to the east, a submerged karstic relief explains some of the bays in what are drowned dolines.[64] As elsewhere along the north coast, coastal terraces are pronounced, probably of both marine and subaerial origin, and variously deformed (Fig. 72). Behind them the coastal ranges rise generally to 1,000–1,600 ft although in the anticlines of the Sa de Cuera and in Peña Turbina (4,300 ft) they are more steeply pitched and elevated. Behind the coastal ranges is a longitudinal depression, narrow in the east, but widening into the faulted trough of Oviedo; this merges southwards into the valley coalfields (*c.* 480 sq. miles) and the southern

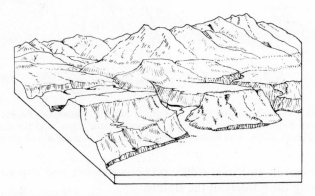

FIG. 72. Block-diagram of the Cantabrian coast (after Scheu). Looking south from the coast near Unquera, with the *rasas* in the foreground and the Picos de Europa in the distance

mountains. Beyond the coastal ranges in the eastern Cantabrians rise the massive limestone pile of the Picos de Europa (Fig. 73). It is a horst, divided by the deep canyons of the Sella, Duje and the Deva into three massifs: Covadonga in the west, Bulnes in the centre and Andara in the east. Apart from the scale of relief, glacial sculpture and the karstic forms (notably dolines) are the impressive features.[65] To the south-east these mountains overlook the graben of Liebana, while to the south-west are the most extensive interior ranges with a fault scarp running between Cervera and La Robla that bounds them from Castile. Eastwards into the Montaña of Santander, east to west folds and transverse fractures produce a more open relief in the Mesozoic rocks, such as in the longitudinal corridor of Las Caldas and in the Marina of Santander (Fig. 65). Anticlinal hills rise to only about 1,500 ft compared to the mountains further west.[66] In the south and south-east, other folds of Cretaceous and lower Tertiary rocks run north-west

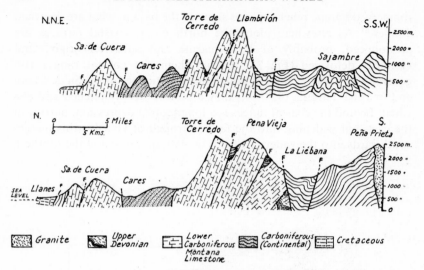

FIG. 73. Cross-sections of the Picos de Europa (after F. Hernández Pacheco). Note the imbricated structures formed by the 'Mountain limestones' and the continental Carboniferous slates. The faults (F) and the tectonic troughs are of alpine age

to south-east in anticlinal ridges between Reinosa and Espiñosa, and again along the borders of the Bureba.

7. *The Iberian Mountains.* The Iberian ranges are less like a mountain barrier than either the Cantabrians or the Central Cordillera, despite their distance of nearly 300 miles and general width of about 60 miles. Indeed, only the geological map indicates clearly their tectonic unity of Palaeozoic rocks flanks by Mesozoic rocks. Apart from a series of central depressions which have been exploited by the rivers Jalón, Jiloca and Turia, and the Pontian surface which has planed the Iberian mountains to its Castilian borders, there is no obvious morphological unity.[67] Folded ranges, horsts, graben and ancient tablelands provide a wide range of landscapes (Figs. 74 and 78). Two Mesozoic geosynclines situated over the north-west and south-east portions were separated by a central zone of shallow deposition. Tectonic movements, beginning in the late Cretaceous, folded these troughs into mountains and broke up the central sector into blocks. After the Miocene, intense erosion and the consequent infill of the fractured basins to depths of 3,000 to 4,500 ft have masked the earlier relief while subsequent faulting on a local scale has fragmented the erosion surfaces and modified the drainage of rivers such as the Jiloca. Despite their complicated evolution and confused relief, five major units may be distinguished: the north-western

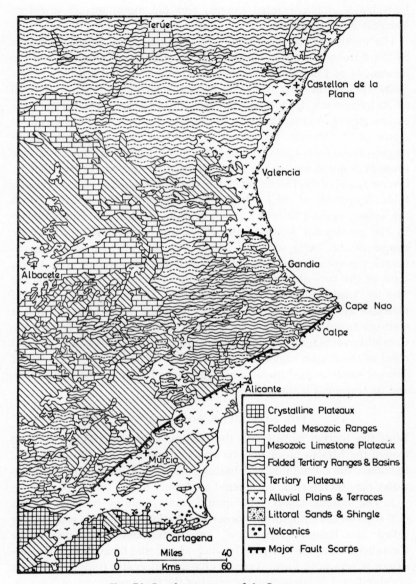

Fig. 74. Landscape types of the Levante

mountains; the Soria Plateau; the central depressions; the Montes Universales and associated ranges; and the mountains of northern Valencia and Castellón.

The north-western mountains are separated from the Cantabrians by the Bureba depression. In the slate mountains of Demanda and the limestones of Cebollera the relief is equally high and rugged (7,000–7,600 ft).[68] To the west and south lies the Soria plateau, some 60 by 10 to 20 miles wide. Its tabular and partially preserved erosion surfaces emphasise the residual character of much of this plateau.[69] In the central sector of the Iberian Mountains, a series of depressions varying in origin, extend from Calatayud to Daroca and Teruel, and then bifurcate towards Segorbe and to the south of Ademuz. Some are bounded by inverse faults in the Cambrian slates, while others are carved in Triassic folds. Amplitude of relief is from 2,300 to over 6,000 ft. Further south the Teruel corridor follows a syncline, linked with the Calatayud basin by the subsequent valley of the Jiloca and connected by the upper course of the Turia with the Mediterranean.[70] In the south-eastern ranges vigorous erosion has exaggerated the diversity of rock types, such as the two quartzitic ranges of the Albarracín, the karst of the Montes Universales and the Serranía of Cuenca and the faulted plateaux along the edge of the Meseta block which descend like a staircase towards the Valencian plain. The Júcar and its tributary the Cabriel have incised deep gorges on these eastern flanks. Similar wild relief in the Gudar and Javalambra (6,600 ft) has been carved out of Triassic sandstones, Jurassic and Cretaceous limestones by the Mijares and its torrential tributaries.

THE NORTHERN BORDERLANDS

With the Iberian ranges and the tectonic unit underlying the Ebro trough the Meseta block may be said to terminate. The Basque lands, Pyrenees, the mountains and basins of East Catalonia, and the Ebro valley may therefore be considered as distinct units.

1. *The Basque Lands*. The mountainous country between Valera (5,600 ft) on the Cantabrian border and Aralar (3,682 ft) is geologically called 'the Basque Depression', an independent unit between the Cantabrians and the Pyrenees.[71] Thick and plastic limestones and sandstones (Cretaceous-lower Tertiary) have been gently folded, but there are significant differences in the relief of the three provinces of Viscaya, Guipúzcoa and Alava. In Viscaya, the relief is predominantly structural, controlled by gentle folds west-north-west to east-south-east with denuded anticlinal ranges such as the Encartaciones, Salvada, and San

Adrian. There is a vast denuded anticline on the southern border, in which the rivers deeply dissect a series of Urgonian limestones (Gorbea, 5,043 ft; Aitzgorri, 5,082 ft). The coastal ranges are lower (c. 2,000 ft) and the majority of the rivers follow synclines, notably the basin of the Cadagua and the Ibaizába at the head of the Bilbao ria. East of the Deva valley, this corrugated relief of Viscaya is superseded by the gridiron frame of Guipúzcoa. The folds are still running west-north-west to east-south-east, but the superimposition of the drainage—probably from the mid-Tertiary surface—has resulted in the apparent indifference of the master streams to the structural grain.[72] However, two subsequent depressions carved out along bands of weaker rock and the asymmetrical flanks of denuded anticlines run transverse to the main lines of drainage. The proximity of the Pyrenees explains the closer folding, the uplift and the more intensive erosion of the superimposed drainage give character to the relief. Whereas the coast of Viscaya is more apparently drowned, that of Guipúzcoa is rectilinear, parallel to the monoclinal sierras of Eocene flysch. Only where these coastal ranges are breached, notably at San Sebastian, is submergence pronounced (Fig. 76).[73]

To the south of the Atlantic watershed, Alava is more a continuation of the Pre-Pyrenees than an independent unit. Its high cuesta of Urgonian limestone overlooks a depression at about 2,000 ft which connects the basins of Vitoria and Pamplona, via the valleys of the Alegría and the Araquil. Further south, two east–west folds mark the alignment of the Andia and Badayas ranges at about 3,400 ft.

2. *The Pyrenees.* From Cape Creus to Cape Higuet the Pyrenees stretch eastwards for 260 miles and cover an area of 15,000 sq. miles within Spain. The Pyrenees may be viewed

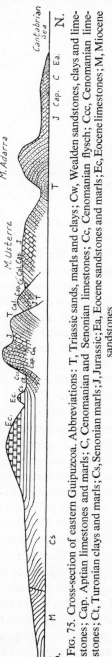

Fig. 75. Cross-section of eastern Guipuzcoa. Abbreviations: T, Triassic sands, marls and clays; Cap. Aptian limestones and marls; C, Cenomanian and Senonian limestones; Cc, Cenomanian flysch; Ccc, Cenomanian limestones; Ct, Turonian clays and marls; Cs, Senonian marls; J, Jurassic; Ea, Eocene sandstones and marls; Ec, Eocene limestones; M, Miocene sandstones; Cw, Wealden sandstones, clays and limestones

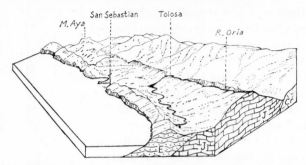

FIG. 76. Block-diagram of the coast of Guipuzcoa, east and west of San Sebastian (after Scheu). Note the gridiron relief with the trellis drainage, exposing the interior to coastal influences. Cr—Cretaceous; J—Jurassic; E—Eocene

zonally and regionally. The zonal division consists of the Central Axis, the series of discontinuous Central Depressions, and the Pre-Pyrenees (Fig. 77). Marked regional divisions are those of the western, central and eastern Pyrenees, distinguished by tectonic and morpho-climatic contrasts.

The Pyrenees show a marked zonal arrangement. First, there is the Central Axis of Palaeozoic metamorphic and granitic rocks, whose Hercynian structures have been exhumed below the Triassic cover to produce relief styles more Carpathian than Alpine.[74] These consist of mountains that rise in a continuous belt above 8,000 ft from the Pic d'Anie (8,215 ft) in the west to the Maladeta massif, which boasts of the highest summit at the Pic d'Aneto (11,168 ft). East of Montcalm (10,105 ft) the Central Axis broadens to include ranges that ring the Cerdaña basin (Carlitte, Puigmal, Canigou). High plateaux in mica granites preserve erosion surfaces, used by the shepherds as their summer pastures (*plas*).[75] More rugged relief is carved out of gneiss, granulite and porphyries. Immediately south of this zone run the Interior Sierras, an anticlinorium of Mesozoic limestones carved into magnificent mountains at about 6,500 ft. There is also a zone called 'Nogueras', a complex of small nappes, fractures and volcanics, but this is more localised.[76] Next in sequence is the discontinuous Central Depression, which has been opened by differential erosion at the point of contact between Eocene marls and Oligocene conglomerates. It is best developed in the upper Aragon (Canal de Berdún)[77] and in the upper Segre valley. But it is also traceable in the basins of Conflent, Capcir, Vall d'Ager and Vall d'Hospoles. To the south there rise the Exterior Sierras of the Pre-Pyrenees to about 4,000 ft, carved out chiefly in Eocene and Oligocene conglomerates. It is on these flysch deposits, formerly more extensive over the flanks of the Pyrenees, that the transverse rivers were superimposed.[78] They have had a pronounced influence in isolating the valley communities from each other (Fig. 108).

Imposed on these structural and zonal differences are the regional distinctions of the western, central and eastern Pyrenees. It is in the central Pyrenees that the zonal arrangement is broadest and most clearly developed. The relief is highest and the transverse rivers of the Gállego, Cinca and Segre provide the major water resources for the Ebro. Glaciation is at a maximum in the central ranges.[79] To the west, the folding of the deep Mesozoic sediments and the intense river erosion in the Atlantic zone, generously supplied by rain, have developed a complex tangle of mountainous relief, thickly covered in forest. Very different is the eastern or Mediterranean sector, to the east of the Col de la Perche, at the head of the Segre valley. Compared with the central sector's girth of nearly 80 miles, the eastern Pyrenees narrow to an average of 15 to 18 miles. The juxtaposition of the ancient Catalan 'continent' explains the thin Mesozoic cover, the prominence of the Central Axis, and the dominance of tectonic relief with graben such as Cerdãna and horsts.[80]

3. *The Ebro Depression.* Bounded by the Pyrenees, Iberian and Catalan mountains, the Ebro trough forms a triangle 220 miles from west-north-west to east-south-east and 100 miles wide between the valleys of the Segre and the Guadalope. It lies mostly between 600 and 1,000 ft but it is overlooked by residual hills such as the Sa de Alcubierre rising to over 2,000 ft. Upstream from Calahorra, the upper Ebro valley is enclosed by fold mountains, forming a threshold that leads into the Bureba basin of Castile. In the north-east, the plains of western Catalonia pass discontinuously over scarps and plateaux to the faulted basins of Olot and Ampurdán following the Tertiary axis of the depression, where sediments are thickest.[81] The south east exit now cut by the Ebro through the Catalan moun-

Fig. 77. Cross-section of the east-central Pyrenees (after Misch). Abbreviations: P, Palaeozoic; Tr., Triassic; J, Jurassic; Cr, Cretaceous limestones; Cr_2, upper Cretaceous marls; E, Eocene; O, Oligocene conglomerates.

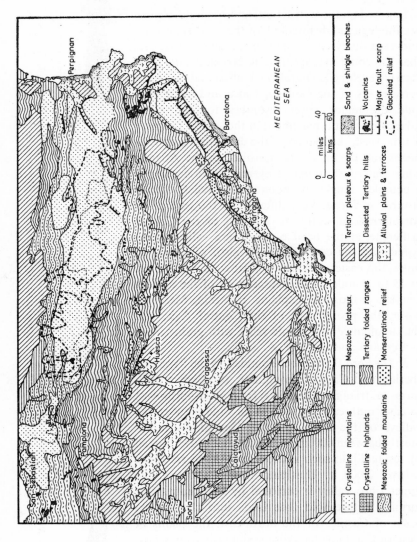

FIG. 78. Landscape types of the Ebro basin and eastern Catalonia

tains below Mequinenza is a late Tertiary episode in the history of the basin. A comparison of the relief and geological maps clearly shows that the morphological depression of the Ebro valley is much less extensive than the structural basin. Post-palaeogenic movements which folded the Pre-Pyrenees also produced gentle folded anticlines in the trough especially at the extremities of southern Navarre and western Catalonia, with diapetic structures over salt beds.[82] These folds, together with the dominance of the Pyrenean rivers over the meagre flow from the drier Iberian Mountains, also explain the asymmetrical position of the Ebro valley towards the south and south-west.

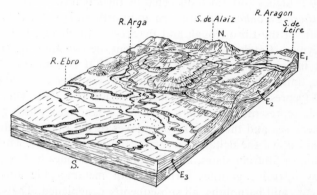

FIG. 79. Block-diagram of the upper Ebro trough in the Ribera of Navarre (after Llopis). Abbreviations: E_1, Lutetian limestones; E_2, Barthonian marls; E_3, Landenian-conglomerates, sandstones, marls and saline deposits

Associated with inland drainage for most of the Tertiary, there is a predominance of conglomerate beds and gravels around the borders of the trough, with sandstones then marls and clays towards the centre. The relief is largely the result of differential erosion, so that the same features are repeated throughout in a sequence of river valleys, terraces, mesas, cuestas and monadnocks. These features have progressed more vigorously than in either La Mancha or Old Castile because of the steeper gradients in the basin. The main rivers are transverse, super-imposed on the conglomerate cover, but some longitudinal tributaries have excavated a series of depressions at the foot of the Pre-Pyrenees, notably the Vega of Ayorbe, the Hoya of Huesca, and the Somontano (Fig. 119). Bordering the eastern trough are the *monserratinos*, residual bold relief carved out of thick conglomerates on the sites of Tertiary deltas, now separated from each other by basins excavated in marls, by the rivers Francoli, Anaia and Llobregat, viz. Barbera, Odena and

Bages (Plate 32). Below the mountains, on either side of the trough, extends a piedmont from the Lerín valley to the plains of Urgell and Caspe at 1,000 to 1,500 ft. The more extensive northern piedmont is divided by the main rivers into a series of tablelands: the Ribera, Bardeñas, Violada, Hoya de Huesca and Los Monegros (Fig. 108). On the right bank they form narrower platforms, less marked as natural regions. Climatic terraces border the main rivers, varying from 280–295, 160–200, 65, and 25–33 ft above the present flood plains.[83] East of the lower Cinca valley commence the plains of Lérida and western Catalonia that rise from a structural tableland at 1,300 ft to a piedmont border 650–850 ft higher and much dissected by the streams.

4. *Eastern Catalonia.* The western and northern borders of Catalonia form part of the Ebro trough and Pyrenees respectively. Remnants of a Hercynian Catalan—Balearic continent demonstrate however the distinct individuality of eastern Catalonia.[84] It is composed of four tectonic units: the Interior Serralada, the Transverse Serralada, the Central Depression, and the Coastal Serralada (Fig. 78). The Interior Serralada represents the western border of a landmass which bordered the Eocene sea and the later Tertiary lakes of the Ebro trough, whose rivers laid down the deltaic deposits of the *monserratinos.* This block, consisting of Silurian slates, and Devonian limestones had been indurated by intrusive granites forming both metamorphic aureoles of gneiss, etc., and batholiths, all subsequently peneplaned. The southern half had also been covered by the Mesozoic seas leaving a thick cover of Triassic rocks, Jurassic and Cretaceous limestones. Upraised and fractured by the Tertiary movements, the four units became distinct. The Transverse Serralada, infilled with Eocene sediments, was uplifted to separate the tectonic troughs of Ampurdán and the eastern continuation of the Ebro depression. The Central Depression was fractured and infilled with Miocene and later sediments, and the Campo de Tarragona also subsided as a basin of Tertiary deposition. Pyrenean compression folded the Mesozoic cover of southern Catalonia into roughly parallel ranges, north-east to south-west, with Miocene distension movements creating the subsidence of most of the Catalan continent below the Mediterranean. Since late Tertiary times, intense erosion has stripped the Tertiary cover of northern Catalonia, exposing the ancient Hercynian massifs. Differential erosion has exhumed the Central Depression, and reversal of drainage since Tertiary times explains the present courses of the Francolí, Llobregat and Ter.[85] Active erosion has infilled the coastal depression of Ampurdán, and has created deltas since the Flandrian transgression; the Ebro delta is

being built at the rate of thirty feet annually and the Llobregat at three feet.[86] But coastal plains only represent five per cent of Catalonia; three-quarters of the total area are high plateaux or mountains.

The interior Serraladas represent all the folded Mesozoic ranges of southern Catalonia, rising to 4,740 ft in the Ports de Tortosa. Northwards they continue in the Oligocene conglomerates of Montserrat (4,072 ft) and Montsant to the granites and gneisses of the Montseny (5,620 ft)[87] and Guillérias. Chemical and mechanical weathering have strongly eroded the conglomerates into great, chaotic masses of pinnacles and buttresses, while the thick mantles of rotten granite and

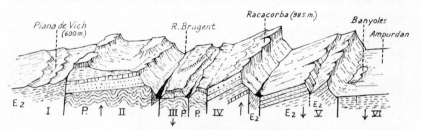

FIG. 80. Block-diagram of the Catalan Transverse Serralada between the Plana de Vich and the Ampurdán trough. The Roman numerals indicate the diverse blocks limited by faults, the direction of thrust indicated by the arrows. Abbreviations: E_2, Middle Eocene marine limestones and marls overlain by upper Eocene, marine deposits, and underlain by lower Eocene continental deposits. P. Palaeozoic; black areas indicate basalt cover

sands (to depth of 60 ft) preserve the surfaces of the northern mountains.[88]

The transverse Serralada blocks the northern outlet of the Eocene trough, a narrow zone only 13 miles wide between the Pyrenees and Guillérias. It consists of closely folded Eocene sediments, fractured by systems of north to south and east to west faults. A good example is the impressive fault scarp between the mountains of the Garrotxa and the Ampurdán basin. The Garrotxa is a complex horst and, to the west, the fractures of the Olot graben are pierced by some forty Plio-Pleistocene volcanoes and their basaltic lava flows.[89]

The Central Depression unites a number of basins, from Ampurdán and the Selva in the north, through the depression of Vallés with its dry lands, and the sandstone hills of Panadés to the undulating ridges of the Campo de Tarragona (Fig. 78). It averages from 300 to 800 ft. Superimposed drainage has maintained transverse courses across the Depression dividing it into a series of three hilly basins.

The Coastal Serraladas are shorter than those of the interior, turn-cated by the coast. With an altitude ranging from 900 to 1,600 ft, their scenery is diversified by the rock types. The Garraf has karstic relief, pitted with dolines and bare limestone pavements. The valleys of the Llobregat and Besos separate the Palaeozoic massifs of Tibidabo (1,680 ft) and the Sa de Levante, which continues to the transverse coast of the Costa Brava.

THE BAETIC SYSTEM

The mountain system of south-east Spain is in several respects a con-trast with the Pyrenees. The Baetic is more extensive, stretching for some 500 miles from north-east to south-west and in parts 150 miles wide. The system boasts of the highest summit of the Peninsula, the

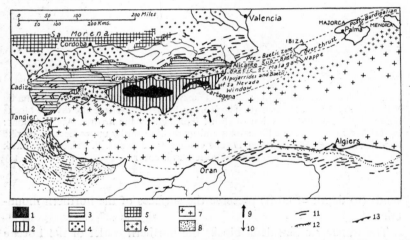

FIG. 81. Tectonic and structural units of the Baetic-Rif mountain system (after Fallot). 1. Baetic 'deep'; 2. nappes; 3. Sub-Baetic folds; 4. chief Neogene basins; 5. Meseta; 6. Malaga nappe; 7. sunken block—Rif-Baetic-Kabylia; 8. Tell folds and nappes. 9. direction of folding (Alpine); 10. ditto (post-Oligocene, pre-Burdigalian); 11. folds of Tell and Rif (pre-Burdigalian) and of Pre-Baetic and W. Sub-Baetic (post-Burdigalian); 12. nappes; 13. Sub-Baetic overthrust

Sa Nevada (11,420 ft). Despite these features, the Baetic cordillera is more broken and much less formidable as a mountain barrier. The Guadalquivir basin is also contrasted with its counterpart, the Ebro Depression, for it lies open to the sea, in a continuous plain.

Of all the geosynclines of the Western Mediterranean, the Baetic has been most persistently a segment of the 'Tethys sea'. Several thousands of feet of deep-sea deposits were laid upon Triassic clays and Marls which have acted as a plastic and slippery base, especially in the western

32 Oligocene conglomerates weathered into *monser-ratinos*, El Bruch, Catalonia

33 Gredos Mountains with interior basin (*nava*)

34 Badlands at Tabernes, Almería, during esparto harvest

35 Würm moraine in upper Gállego Valley, Aragón with Pyrenees in background

36 View looking north from La Muela over Ebro Plain. New afforestation terraces in foreground

37 Soria Plateau near Medinaceli. Note Pontian surface on skyline

or Sub-Baetic ranges. Tectonically, the Baetic and the Rif ranges are presumed by modern geologists to have been one unit.[90] Straits between this block and the Meseta block gradually narrowed during the Tertiary, to form a predecessor of the Straits of Gibraltar in what is termed the Sub-Baetic. Orogenic movements initiated in the late Cretaceous, compressed the Sub-Baetic geosyncline with a maximum intensity during the Oligocene-Miocene. Later epeirogenic movements broke up the Baetic ranges, induced vulcanicity, and at the end of the Pliocene opened up the present Straits of Gibraltar.[91] But tectonic geologists are divided on a number of problems posed by the Baetic structures, such as the roots and the mechanisms of the nappes,[92] the absence of littoral deposits around the Baetic-Rif block,[93] and lithological anomalies. There is a profuse literature on these problems and the reader is referred to these studies.[94] The Baetic province is usually divided into three units: the Baetic or Peni-Baetic Cordillera; the Sub-Baetic ranges; and the Guadalquivir basin (Fig. 82).

1. *The Baetic or Peni-Baetic Cordillera*. Compared with so much of the structural relief of the Pyrenees, created by Tertiary folding, the Baetic ranges show close relations between the tectonic units and differential erosion. Another contrast is in the much steeper descent to sea-level—11,000 ft in twenty miles in the Nevada mountains. This together with an absence of prolonged tranquillity have disfavoured the development of erosion surfaces. This morphological system may be conveniently divided into three units: the coastal Cordillera, the interior ranges and the interior depression (Fig. 81). The coastal mountains consist mostly of metamorphic rocks which have been shattered by a series of transverse fractures and rise steeply above the coast. Such are from west to east: Tejeda (6,700 ft), Almijara, Contraviesa, Gador (7,620 ft), and Alhamilla.

The interior Peni-Baetic Cordillera includes some of the highest ranges: Nevada (11,420 ft); Baza and Filabres. Each is an oval-shaped dome, orientated east-north-east to west-south-west and separated by synclinal depressions that are deeply dissected in Triassic rocks by two subsequents, the rivers Guadalfeo and Andarax (Fig. 83). In each mountain dome, there is a similar style of relief as that seen most spectacularly in the Sa Nevada. This consists of a central dome, fifty miles in length, with rounded, relatively smooth relief in metamorphosed slates. On the denuded and faulted anticlinal crest are the summits of the Valeta and Mulhacén. The mountain flanks are deeply dissected in Triassic sandstones and limestones with spectacular gorges.[95] Westwards however, around the basin of Malaga, relief is confused

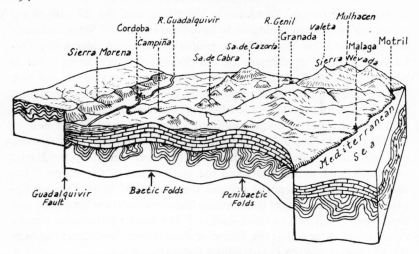

FIG. 82. Block-diagram of Andalusia (after Echeverría)

with coastal ranges carved out of Cambrian slates and interior limestone mountains such as the Cabras and the Torcal. Karstic relief is
best developed in the Liassic limestones of the Torcal de Antequera.
The western outpost of the cordillera is the Serranía de Ronda (2,064
ft) a crystalline tableland dominated in the west by the wild, limestone
country of the Sa de Grazalema (5,425 ft).[96]

The Peni-Baetic Depression is traceable for some 180 miles through
valleys and basins between Antequera and Baza, and again further
north-east from Lorca, down the Guadalentín valley to Murcia and
beyond (Fig. 83). It has no simple explanation, sometimes forming a
fractured basin as in the Miocene Vega of Granada, aided by synclinal
features, or a flexured trough floored by Tertiary detritus, or simply
the alignment of softer rocks removed by differential erosion. In the
valleys of the Guadiana Menor, Almanzora and Guadalentín, it comprises an extensive series of badlands. Elsewhere, the Tertiary plains
appear more docile and cultivated.

2. *The Sub-Baetic Ranges.* Much more extensive than the Peni-
Baetic are the Sub-Baetic ranges, running from the Campo de Gibraltar
to northern Alicante, and indeed to the islands of Ibiza and Majorca,
a distance of 500 miles (Fig. 81). Their style of relief is apparently
simple, gently folded and Jura-like, although their tectonics are complex.[97] Comprising Mesozoic and Tertiary folded rocks, they may be
divided into five sectors. In the first, between Algeciras and the Barbate,
mountains mostly of dissected sandstones (flysch) trend confusedly,

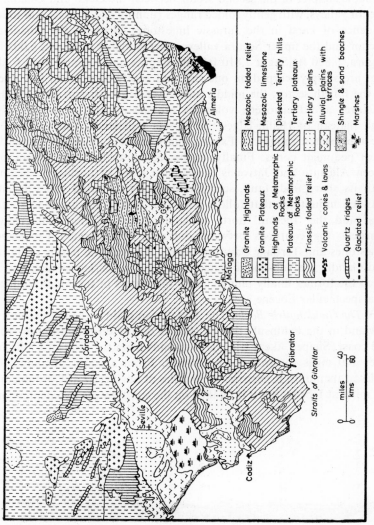

FIG. 83. Landscape types of Andalusia

first north-west to south-east in the Sa Cabras (3,580 ft) and then north-east to south-west in the mountains overlooking the Guadalete valley. Relief is simpler in the second sector between the Genil and Guadiana Menor valleys, with gently folded ranges running east to west and much evidence of karst in the Jurassic limestones. Between the Guadiana Menor and the upper Segura valleys relief is higher (Cazorla, 6,005 ft; Segura, 6,860 ft; Sagra 7,810 ft) with nappes and asymmetrical folds, that are steeply scarped on one side and gently dipping on the other. In the fourth sector, the middle and lower Segura basin, late Tertiary fractures and Pleistocene volcanics provide distinctive scenery. The high plateau of Hellín edges the Meseta tablelands, and south of it are the faulted ranges of Espuña and Carrascoy, partially buried by great pediment cones. Finally, in the sector north of the Segura, between Alicante and Játiva is the tangled relief of northern Alicante, with its sharp folds fault, scarps and deeply dissected valley basins, between mountains that follow both the 'Baetic' north-east to south-west and the 'Iberian' north to south trends. Differential erosion sharpens the contrasts between outcrops of indurated Cretaceous limestones and Tertiary clays and marls. Between the basins of Játiva and Gandía the Sub-Baetic ranges abut on the Iberian system, and at Ifach the former finally plunge below the waters of the Mediterranean in a spectacular Eocene arch.

3. *The Guadalquivir Basin.* The Andalusian plain is the only extensive lowland in the Peninsula that penetrates deeply into the interior from the coast. Shaped like a triangle it extends from the Gulf of Cádiz for over 200 miles towards the north-east. From a width of about 100 miles at its mouth it narrows to 50 miles at Seville, 37 at Córdoba and six miles at Úbeda, but it is flanked on the south by the two depressions

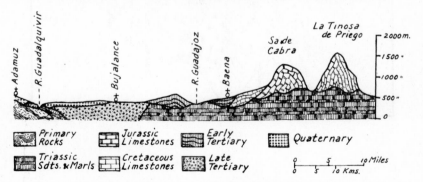

FIG. 84. Cross-section of the Andalusian Campiña (no attempt is made to show Triassic folds)

followed by the tributaries Genil and Guadiana Menor (Fig. 82). Reference has already been made to the contrast between this plain and the Ebro valley (p. 192). Unlike the continental features of the Ebro with its thick deposits of conglomerates, and tabular relief, the Guadalquivir valley was an arm of the sea throughout the Tertiary period. Its fine sediments have now been carved into undulating smooth relief. The physiographical distinction between the upper valley above Seville with its higher lands and more swelling relief, the lower plain, flatter, below 300 ft and with an absence of river terraces, is the consequence of the evolution of this marine trough and its retreating shorelines.[98]

With the Baetic folding in early Tertiary times, the axis of the geosyncline moved north-westwards, becoming the alignment of the Guadalquivir trough in mid-Tertiary times (with the Burdigalian folding of the Sub-Baetic ranges). A second series of post-Pliocene uplifts caused the evacuation of the Guadalquivir 'straits', probably in a series of stages. Four terraces can be recognised in the upper trough at 325, 200, 100 and 40 ft above the present course of the river, cut into wide platforms by the tributaries. Above these is an undulating plain rising from 300 ft above sea-level at Córdoba to an average of 600 ft.[99] On the borders with the southern Meseta, the Guadalquivir trough merges with pediments that slope up to 1,600 ft. The Despeñaperros gap is the main outlet through the eastern Sa Morena into Castile. The low basin opening out from Seville towards the coast, probably developed in later Quatenary times, since the river loops through it in wide meanders and is tidal for some 60 miles upstream. The marshes of the Marismas were in Roman times the extensive *Lacus Ligustinus*, ponded in by the old line of sand dunes, Arenas Gordas (Fig. 83).[100]

CHAPTER 9

THE RURAL LANDSCAPES

'All ideas of a biogeography are derived from the contemplation of the landscape.' (M. Sorre, *Les Pyrénées Orientales*)

Compared with the diversity of landforms, the ecological features of the Iberian Peninsula appear at first sight to have a disarming simplicity, Cultivated land occupies less than half the total area (Spain 43 per cent. Portugal 37 per cent). Range lands and pastoralism have long dominated in the Meseta. Uniformity of economy is emphasised by the climate, so that some 90 per cent of the cultivated area practises dry-farming techniques (*secano*), while monocultures are a characteristic; over 60 per cent of the cultivated land of Spain is devoted to wheat, vines and olives. There is also the simple contrast between the open field landscapes of the Meseta, and the various forms of enclosed cultivation that are typical of the peripheral regions. However, when the landscapes are viewed in detail, and in more than one dimension, their ecological and agrarian features are seen to have great complexity. Climatically, the usual distinction made between the Pluviose and Arid zones in the Peninsula is inadequate. Edaphically, the soil classification still leaves many problems unanswered. Botanically, the four influences of central European, Mediterranean, Atlantic and African flora are complex. Early cultures and their influence in changing the landscapes are only slowly being understood.

ECOLOGICAL CHARACTERISTICS

1. *Climatic Zones.* The primary division of the Peninsula into humid and arid zones was first recognised by Brunhes (1902).[1] He selected the mean annual isohyets of 600 mm (23·6 in) and 400 mm (15·7 in) to define them (Fig. 85). Although revised by Dantín (1912) this division makes no allowance for the seasonal incidence of rainfall, so that to include all Portugal in Dantín's humid zone is palpably false.[2] Exaggerated on the other side is the application of Thornthwaite's formula by Tames[3] and Llorente to the Peninsula. The extent of steppe shown has also no basis in reality. Other attempts have been made to define the climatic divisions notably by Sorre,[4] Dantín and Ravenga,[5] Lauten-

sach,[6] Birot[7] and Lopez Gomez[8] (Fig. 85). These all suggest that
there are several distinctions within the threefold division of maritime,
continental and mountain climate briefly summarised in chapter 2
(see pp. 30–33). Overlapping them are the zonal divisions of humid,
semi-arid and arid or sub-desert.

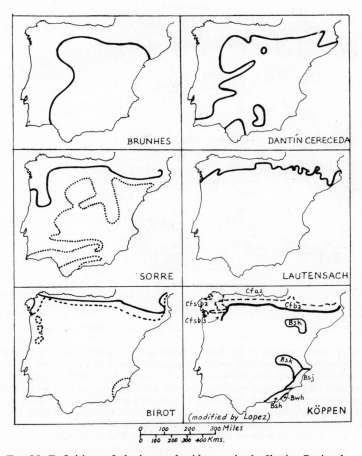

FIG. 85. Definitions of pluviose and arid zones in the Iberian Peninsula

The humid zone is usually demarcated from the lower Mondego or
even the Tagus along the northern coastal lands to the Basque provinces
(Fig. 85). Nevertheless, this may be subdivided on the basis of seasonal
rainfall into humid and sub-humid zones (Lopez Fig. 85). From eastern
Galicia to Gerona there is a similar humid climate, with distinctions

however between the milder coastal areas and the interior mountains that suffer from colder winters. This is the realm of the mixed deciduous forests. But in western Galicia and northern Portugal the absence of the beech reveals a significantly marked dry season in summer. The intensity

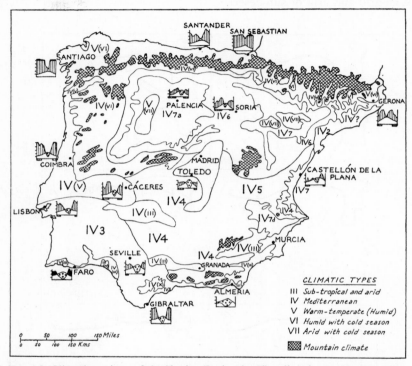

Fig. 86. Climatic regions of the Iberian Peninsula. The climatic graphs show mean monthly temperature and mean monthly precipitation drawn as curves. Using the fixed proportion (suggested by Gaussen) of a scale of ten degrees centigrade of temperature for twenty mm. precipitation, drought is shown by dotted area whenever the precipitation falls below this ratio. The hatched area indicates a humid climate above this ratio. At base of graph the black symbol indicates extent of frost when the mean minimum of a month falls below zero centigrade and stippled when the absolute minimum lies below zero (after Walter and Lieth)

of summer drought increases southwards towards the Tagus. Thus although the north-west of the Peninsula has some of the highest annual figures of precipitation, it receives less in summer than either the Basque lands or the eastern Pyrenees. The lower courses of the Minho and the Douro for example, have over 50 in. annually, but only one-tenth of this falls in summer, compared to one-fifth in the Basque mountains and one-third in the eastern Pyrenees.

Within the semi-arid realm that covers so much of the Peninsula, distinction is clear between the seasonal dry climates of the northern Meseta, with its marked seasonal amplitudes of temperature, and the southern Meseta with lower amplitudes of temperature and more

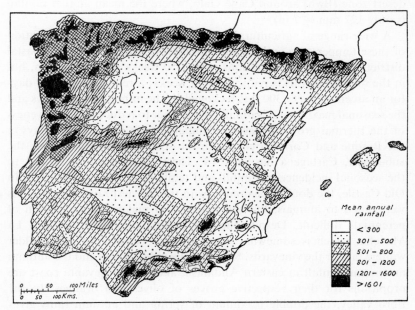

Mean annual rainfall

	< 300
	301 – 500
	501 – 800
	801 – 1200
	1201 – 1600
	>1601

FIG. 87. Mean annual precipitation in the Iberian Peninsula (1942–1952)

direct influence from the Atlantic (Fig. 86). The mountain climates are also clearly distinct, although lack of data makes them as yet unclassified. Orographic rainfall may produce impressive annual figures, but the disparity between the winter and summer totals is intensified. Thus the Serra da Estrêla, bordering the humid and semi-arid zones has stations registering 95–100 in but one-fifteenth only falls in the three summer months. As the growing season of these mountains is concentrated in the summer half year, the limited fall of precipitation at that season has much more significance than total figures might suggest.

Where the yearly rainfall is less than approximately 15 in. steppe climates are found. Several types may be distinguished. The cold winter steppe (BSk according to Köppen's system) is found in eastern La Mancha, an extensive district around Saragossa, and in a small area east of Zamora. Distinct from this are the mild winter steppes

(BShs and BSjs) on the south-east littoral, between Alicante and Almería, and again south of Granada.[9] In these dry zones the summer drought is crippling because the soil has little opportunity to store moisture during the rest of the year (Fig. 85). Worst of all is the sub-desert zone (Bwh) around Cape Gata, where the mean annual rainfall is only 122 mm (4·7 in).[11]

A wide range of agricultural conditions results from the combination of these temperature and rainfall variables (Fig. 88). In all the coastal districts, temperature conditions permit 50 weeks growing season, but in the mountains this is reduced to 30 weeks; a reduction of four days for an ascent of every 300 ft is reckoned.[11] The number of rain days and the seasonal maximum of rainfall tend further to reduce the effectiveness of the thermal growing season. Compared with over 175 rain days in the Basque and Corunna coasts, in the semi-arid zone bordering the sub-desert, Cartagena has only 14. These totals must be related to the seasonal incidence of rainfall and temperature (Figs. 6 and 86). In Old Castile, the double maximum, with the heaviest rainfall in May, is well suited to annuals, but the winter cold makes the cultivation of perennials difficult. Despite the low annual rainfall of western La Mancha, which is somewhat precarious for cereal crops, the milder winters favour the vineyards. Similarly the mild winters and the autumn maximum rainfall in eastern Andalusia and on the Levante coast are propitious for their respective groves of olives and oranges. In the Ebro valley, the double maximum of spring and autumn rains gives more rain in the summer half of the year, so that cereal cultivation is precarious wherever the annual total is low, as in Los Monegros. Moreover the winter cold, though generally less intense than on the higher plateaux of Old Castile and León, makes it essential to concentrate vineyards on southward facing slopes and to avoid lowlands subject to temperature inversions. Thus within the semi-arid zone of the Peninsula, there are numerous nuances ranging from the Eu-Mediterranean features of winter maximum rainfall, as in the cork forests and cornfields of the south-west, to the more intense drought and higher losses of moisture by evaporation on the east coast, characterised by the dwarf palm and near the coast by the carob and olive. It is thus in the reality of vegetation differences that our conception of climatic zones is modified or corrected.

2. *The Soils.* Edaphic differences are critical in lands which are mostly marginal to cultivation. In the semi-arid areas of the Peninsula, from 40 to 60 per cent of the rainfall may not be utilised by plants, according to the soil texture. Porous soils which give good harvests in rainy years,

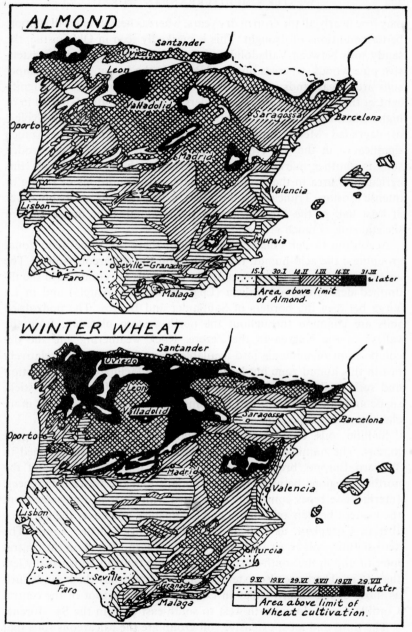

FIG. 88. Average dates for the flowering of the almond and for the harvest of winter wheat (1946–1952). The almond dates refer to the period 15 January to 31 March, and the wheat dates to 9 May to 29 June and later

may lose nearly all the crop in dry years, whereas heavy soils will support
better conditions of drought. This is markedly seen in Old Castile, the
sandy soils between Valladolid and Segovia being given over to extensive pine woods, whereas north of Palencia the heavy, yellow 'campo'
soils are wheat lands *par excellence*. Slope conditions are also significant in the semi-arid zone, the borders of the fields often lying 20 in or
higher than the centres to facilitate the absorption of rainfall. Typical
of degraded Mediterranean soils, the parent material has much
significance in the soil types, and the ruinous state of many eroded
soils is another marked feature. Approximately 40 per cent of this
agricultural area in the Peninsula is subject to conditions of strong or
intense erosion. Truncated soil profiles, called *calveros*, probably cover
at least half of the Meseta, and in the mountains the importance of
skeletal soils is much greater.

According to del Villar's classification, there are three main zonal
groupings: the acid-humid, the siallitic and the calcareous soils.[12] The
acid-humid soils are of two types. The peat soils are common in the ill-
drained depressions of Galicia (Lugo basin, lake Antela) and in La
Virga between the borders of Santander and Burgos. The podzolised
soils are common throughout the north-western plateaux, from the
valleys of the Narvea to the Zezere. Rock weathering and the decomposition of minerals into available plant foods proceed relatively
fast in this humid zone but leaching has been facilitated by cultivation
and soils easily deteriorate without due attention. The digging stick,
spade and hoe are traditional instruments, whereas the plough is more
characteristic of the semi-arid realm.

Siallitic soils, comprising the second broad group have only mild
humus. The humid type is the equivalent of those loosely termed in
Western Europe 'brown forest soils'. They are characteristic of the
northern regions between the Cantabrians and the western Pyrenees.
Intermediate types commonly associated with *Quercus Pyrenaica* flank
the western borders of Zamora and Salamanca, and cover the northern
Iberian Cordillera, as well as other high ranges further south. The
xero-siallitic soils cover vast areas of the western Meseta, in the central
interior and in the south-west, in areas where the rainfall is usually less
than 15 in. There are also extensive areas of uniformly thick sands such
as those of the Douro valley in Old Castile, at the foot of the central
Cordillera and along north-west to south-east belts in the Sa Morena.

The third and most extensive soil group are the calcareous soils that
cover most of eastern and southern Spain and Portuguese Estremadura.
They range widely in colour and texture from humid types in the eastern

Cantabrians to xerophytic types in the east. Widespread along the eastern littoral, in the Montes Universales and the Sub-Baetic hill lands are the red earths. Intrazonal varieties of the calcareous soils are the black earths of the Andalusian *campiñas* (see p. 74). Quaternary deposits of travertine and other calcareous matrix in association with siallitic types provide soils of high fertility and complex texture in the Campo de Tarragona, the southern Tagus trough near Toledo, in the Tierra de Barros (Badajoz), Alentejo, Huelva and the littoral between Málaga and Murcia.

The salt bush tracts of the Peninsula have particular edaphic conditions. Willkomm (1852) recognised the existence of 'climatic steppes' in La Mancha, the Levante and Aragon (*c.* 27,000 sq. miles)[13] but his views were castigated by Reyes (1915) who related them to the geological occurrence of salts.[14] In support of this del Villar has cited the saline lakes of western La Mancha, Zamora, S. Valladolid, the saline Triassic marls in Andalusia, and the extensive outcrops of Tertiary salts in the Ebro basin.[15] It is reasonable to explain the extensive salinity of southeast Spain in terms of both climate and rocks.[16] However, between the misconceptions of 'steppes' in the cultivated lands of the Meseta, and the 'deserts' of the eroded mountain borders, much exaggeration of Spain's sterility is still being made in textbooks. The distinction between human induced sterility and the original ecological conditions must always be made.

3. *The Vegetation cover.* About half of the Peninsula (Spain 49·6 per cent, Portugal 45·6 per cent) has a spontaneous cover of vegetation, 2 per cent is cultivated with periodic reversal to natural growth, and approximately one-tenth is unproductive waste (Spain 9·7 per cent, Portugal 4·3 per cent). Of the vegetation cover, one-tenth is dense woodland (mostly conifers), another tenth is light woodland, 7·5 per cent is coppice and deciduous undergrowth, and one-fifth of the total area is scrub and pasture (of which natural meadows represent only 2·5 per cent of the total).[17] Such have been the depredations of the Meseta woodland (see pp. 113-16) that the Iberian forests are to-day largely concentrated in the mountains. Their composition is summarised in Appendix III, table 10.[18] The dominance of the evergreen oak is clear; indeed the Peninsula has over half of the total Mediterranean area of its species (Fig. 89). Requiring less than 20 days of frost, over 1,000 hours of sunshine in winter and spring, and at least 150 mm (6 in) of rain in summer,[19] it is excluded from the humid zone, the central Ebro valley, eastern and south-eastern La Mancha, and much of the Andalusian trough. Elsewhere it is the dominant association. Its preserve is most

intact in the south-west of the Meseta where its acorn pastures feed over a million pigs, and lands are periodically cultivated, chiefly for barley. This is also the domain of the cork oak, especially in poor, siallitic soils. The Alentejo cork estates (*montados*) give Portugal a world lead in cork products (Fig. 145). In Spain, the cork industry centred on the small forested areas of northern Catalonia, is divorced from the much more extensive, although poorly developed woodlands of Cadiz.

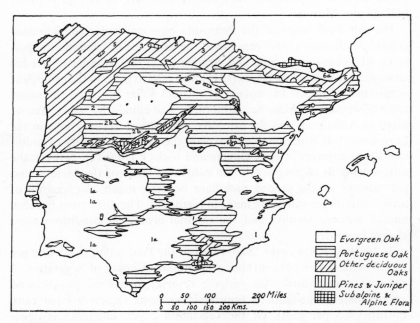

Fig. 89. Distribution of natural vegetation in the Iberian Peninsula (after Rivas Goday). Figures refer to plant stations, viz. 1. Evergreen oak; 1a *Pistacia lentiscus*; 2. *Q. lusitanica-Acer*; 2a. *Q. suber*; 2b. Q. ilex; 3. *Q. pubescens*; 4. *Q. tobut*; 5. *Fagus silvatica*; 6a. *P. uncinata-Juniperus nana*; 6b. *P. silvestris*; 7. Subalpine; 8. Alpine

Pines, such as *Pinus sylvestris*, have been a relic flora in the mountains of the Peninsula since the cold, continental climates of the Quaternary. But the maritime pine has replaced many of the deciduous forests of the humid zone, especially in northern Portugal, since prehistoric times. From the sixteenth century, when the first systematic efforts were made in the Peninsula to plant pines, their species have spread very rapidly and now dominate in the forests of the central Pyrenees, the Iberian ranges, in the central Sierras and throughout northern Portugal. On the lower lands, especially in Portugal and Old Castile the species *Pinus pinaster* dominates, and it is probable that the stone pine (*P. pinea*) is a late arrival. These pines are well adapted to the psammosiallitic soils, such as the 100,000 ha of southern Old Castile.[20] In Portugal, pine woods natural and planted now cover five times the area they had a century ago.

Since the end of the nineteenth century, two other trees have become significant in some landscapes. The poplar has been introduced in great numbers, some 21 million lining the banks of the Ebro and its tributaries, as well as many others in the Douro basin.[21] Nowhere has the eucalyptus spread more rapidly than in the province of Huelva, which has now more than all the rest of Spain. The necessity for wind-breaks to check the force of the desiccating winds of summer across the open landscapes, the drainage of marshy lands in the estuaries of the south-west, and the rapid cash returns of the eucalyptus (for cellulose), are some of the main reasons for the spread of these species. The Portuguese foresters have also found it successful to mix the *P. pinaster* with the *Eucalyptus globulus*, in new forests.[22]

As one-fifth of the total area of Spain consists of Mediterranean scrub (*monte bajo* or *matorral*), the vast expanse of bushes and ever-green shrubs is one of the chief characteristics. A wide range of species is grouped chiefly in the plant families of the *Cistaceae, Labiatae, Ericaceae* and *Leguminosae*. Constant burning by the pastoralists has induced certain fire-resistant species to form dominant associations over vast areas. This is particularly characteristic of the Cistus species, whose associations cover much of the southern Meseta between the Montes de Toledo, the Sa Morena and the northern Algarve; one of the commonest species is the gum cistus (*Cistus landiferus*). On the plains of La Mancha and in the Iberian ranges, aromatic labiatae form considerable covers, such as thyme, lavender, and rosemary. Box and kermes oak are also common in the southern and eastern mountains. Broom and gorse species are also very extensive, with great golden spreads of broom-heaths in northern Ciudad Real. Under the colder continental conditions of the central Ebro and Aragonese hills, juniper (*Juniperus thurifera*) is the chief constituent of the dull grey-green wastes. A species of esparto grass (*Lygeum Spartum*) frequently covers the 'steppes' of the south-east and in La Mancha, but the real source of the esparto products of Spain is the associated alfa (*Stipa tenacissima*), covering some 500,000 ha (see plate 34). In the coastal ranges of the north and north-west, heather and heath moors are characteristic with the plants *Calluna vulgaris, Erica cinerea, E. australis* and *E. arborea*. Thus the natural vegetation of the Peninsula, although floristically complex, has physiographically a relatively reduced number of formations. These emphasise the desolate monotony of the Peninsula's vast, empty spaces.[23]

THE RURAL ECONOMY

The marginal nature of so much of the land utilisation, and the extent of open woodland and scrub, has stressed the importance of pastoralism. Its influence has been fundamental in the history of the Peninsula, probably ever since the Bronze Age. From the Pyrenees to the Levante ranges, the plains of Old and New Castile, and along the Cantabrian mountains to the north-west, different cultures such as the Basque, Celtic, Celtiberian and Vetonic, have all been based on stock-raising (Fig. 93).[24] In favoured regions there is early evidence of agriculture. Lusitania, in central Portugal, was early in contact with the Greeks; oil and wine were produced and the goat domesticated. The Tartessian civilisation of Andalusia had rich agriculture, and mineral trade with Phoenicians and later merchants. There, and in the irrigated enclaves of the east coast, the plough was probably first introduced in the Bronze age. The Greeks, Romans, and Arabs all intensified and specialized production in these lands which had been enriched since the dawn of sedentary cultivation. Exceptional were the rich yellow soils of the central Douro which had become very early the focus of a collective form of agriculture, organised by the Vaccei, that is described by Diodorus (Fig. 93). The broad lineaments however of an agricultural South and East, intensified by the Moors, and a pastoral North and West, spreading out with the Christian Reconquest, remained until the introduction of maize and potatoes transformed the rural economy of the humid zone between the fifteenth and nineteenth centuries. Meanwhile, on the Meseta, the pastoralist has lost his former importance and cultivation has continued to expand over vast areas. Today, the economy may be summarised under the five broad headings of pastoralism, dry farming, tree and bush crops, maize meadow lands, and irrigation.

1. *Pastoralism and Stock-Raising*. Broadly, cattle tend to predominate in the humid zone, sheep over vast areas of the arid zone and goats in the dry zone. The importance of the evergreen oak woodlands of the south-west explains the significant concentration of pigs there. Pastures consist largely of edible shrubs within the scrub and woodland such as *Genista cinerea, G. scorpius, Ulex europeus, Atriplex halimus*, etc. as well as seasonal grasses. The latter are fugitive pastures, occurring in summer on the mountains, in spring and autumn on the lower lands, and in winter especially in the south-west. Like the rest of the Mediter-

ranean world, pastoralism has been divorced from agriculture and this together with the abrupt physical contrasts of relief and climate has encouraged transhumance.[25] Although cattle and pig transhumance are not unknown in the Peninsula, the sheep is the animal best suited to travel long distances (Fig. 51).

Local movements from pasture to pasture are traceable to remote antiquity. Notable are the inverse and normal forms still practised between the Pyrenees and the Ebro basin, notably in Andorra. In contrast the Basque lands have remained aloof from the semi-arid realm, because their humid, mild climate has made them more independent. In the south-east of Spain summer pastures are most readily burnt out, and in the east the cultivators have always fought to reduce transhumance to a minimum. Only the Meseta has been the realm of major movements of pastoralism, especially after 1273 when the Mesta was organised by the Crown.[26] Then a maze of pastoral routes of ancient origin were legalised (*cañadas*), rivers of pasture along which flowed the medieval wealth of Spain. Three routes were of particular importance: the royal highways of León, Segovia, and Cuenca, which led to the southern pastures of La Serena, La Alcudia and the Sa de Córdoba (Fig. 51). There were of course many other routes, such as that which followed the Portuguese coast from Galicia to the Sa Estrêla, but today transhumance is greatly in decline, and only 100,000 sheep from the mountains of León and another 80,000 from the east move each summer to the pastures of Extremadura, mostly by rail.

Over half of the cattle of the Peninsula are concentrated in the humid zone, because of its superior grazings. Most are all-purpose breeds, and the economy is commercialised. Another significant economy is that of pig-rearing in Extremadura and Alentejo where the mast of the extensive holm and cork oaks feeds about one-third of the Peninsula's pigs, a utility praised as far back as Greek and Roman times.[27] It is in these semi-arid zones of the Meseta and the south-west that the stock-keeper has an uncertain future. Squeezed as he is between the proprietary claims of the agriculturist and the ecological claims of the forester, over-stocking and archaic traditions do not favour the historic claims of the pastoralist to the Mediterranean ranges. Distinction however should be made between the shepherd and the destruction he has made of the woodland cover, and the pig-herder whose economy has favoured the perpetuation and improvement of the evergreen tree cover.

2. *Dry farming of Cereals.* Cereals are the backbone of the Iberian economy, and of these wheat is the most important, covering 26 per

cent of the cultivated land. Altogether, herbaceous plants are cultivated over 32 per cent of the total area of Spain (29·8 per cent of Portugal), but about one-third of this lies fallow every year. The cultivation of wheat is the basis of the open field landscapes of Old Castile, Aragón, La Mancha and Alentejo (Fig. 90). The 'bread-baskets' of the Peninsula are more narrowly contained by the regions of the Tierra de Campo, Tierra del Pan, the plains of Coca, Cuellar, Medina del Campo, Saragossa, La Sagra and La Mancha.[28] (Fig. 90). Other wheat districts extend from La Serena and Tierra de Barros into Alentejo (Fig. 90). In the South and East the hard wheats are locally important although their yields are poorer than the varieties grown in the more favoured Andalusian districts of La Campiña, El Alcor and El Condado. Barley, formerly more widespread is still the chief cereal of the south-east because of the drier climate. As the Murcian proverb says, 'If you wish to eat bread, grow barley'. The chief barley provinces however are Badajoz and Ciudad Real, cattle country that grows much barley as forage for the work animals. Rye is chiefly cultivated in the lean soils of the north-western Meseta (Beira, Zamora and Salamanca), and is next in importance to barley as a forage crop. Oats are concentrated on the calcareous, hilly lands to the north and east of La Mancha (Cuenca, Albacete), in Almería and on the thin soils of Extremadura.

Three factors have favoured the great increase in the cereal lands in the last century. The disamortisation laws (1836–68) in Spain enabled peasants and a new middle class of property owners to cultivate lands formerly held in church estates or grazed extensively by the communes.[29] Secondly, the wheat tariffs and the introduction of chemical fertilisers fostered especially in Alentejo important movements of land colonisation.[30] Thirdly, the boom in prices during the First World War expanded acreages in Castile and Aragón.[31]

The norm of cereal cultivation is still the biennial system of *año y vez*. The entire village lands are divided into large fields, or multiples of two, in which the cultivator has small parcels of land in each field. This practice is still typical of Trás-os-Montes,[32] León, the Castiles and Aragón.[33] The traditional rotations are still fallow-wheat or barley on the better lands, fallow-rye or oats on the poorer soils. An advance on this is the cultivation of legumes such as vetches instead of a rough fallow. In the system of *al tercio* used on the richest lands of Old Castile, Aragon and especially La Campiña, the rotation is fallow-wheat-wheat-forage crops or cash crops, such as sugar beet. Less intensive than the norm is *al tercio con encinar*, consisting of cereal-stubble-bare fallow in patches of land surrounded by scrub or woodland.

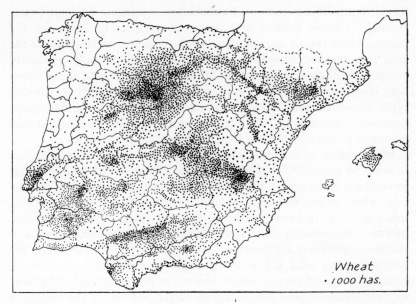

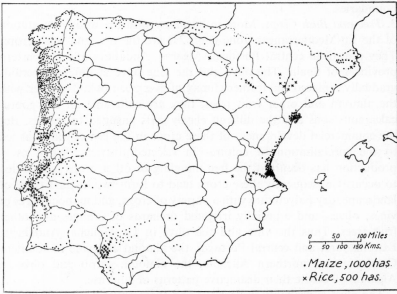

FIG. 90. Distribution of wheat, rice and maize in the Iberian Peninsula. Note the concentrated production of rice in the Ribera of Valencia and Ebro delta, and of maize in the pluviose north-western zone

This is common especially in Extremadura, stretching through Upper Alentejo, Castelo Branco, and western Salamanca to León. On the poorest lands cereals are cultivated until the soil is exhausted and the land may then be allowed to revert to scrub for as much as twenty years. Thus as the duration of the fallow period lengthens, so the open-field landscapes of *año y vez* or *al tercio* gradually merge into wooded types where the holm oaks prevail under the systems of large estates (*montados, montaderas*).[34] The tree products then become an essential source of livelihood with the long periods of fallow.

In the richer, cereal producing provinces, as in the Tierra del Pan it must be realised that while the broad plateaux and rolling plains provide the bread grains, the river valleys form ribbons of *vega* cultivation, where irrigation intensifies cultivation and changes the prevailing dusty ochreous or brown earths of the dreary landscape, to the varied greens of horticulture. The river terraces are usually under vines, and the bare limestone or quartzite crests under scrub. These are the features which bind whole districts into a community of interests, uniting a series of villages for the control of more distant hill pastures or river meadows, and influencing the shape and size of the commune boundaries.

3. *Tree and Bush Crops*. More in harmony with the woody vegetation of the Eu-Mediterranean zone (Fig. 27) are the tree and bush crops. They prevail in central Portugal, Algarve, Andalusia and the eastern provinces of Spain. The olive and the vine have at different periods gradually replaced the former climax of evergreen oak. Together with the almond and other fruit trees, they are cultivable on the poorer calcareous soils and the difficult clayey soils unsuited to cereals. But the commercial development of these crops in the last century has led to the specialisation of cultures in selected districts. When over-production has occurred the free mingling of other crops has tended to occur. Consequently these crops tend to form two distinct types of landscape, dry polyculture with a variety of crops, and monocultures of vines, olives, and especially irrigated orchards of oranges and other fruit trees. Thus the vine and the olive in La Mancha, Andalusia, Extremadura, and central Portugal, the almond and vine in southern Catalonia and northern Alicante, the almond, carob and olive in Algarve, all create their distinctive patterns of land use.

The olive is probably indigenous and there are still some 22,000 ha of wild olive (*acebuche*) in southern Spain, climbing the Baetic mountain slopes to heights of over 5,000 ft.[35] Spain leads the world in olive oil production, its groves comprising 10 per cent of the cultivated land. The

Andalusian provinces of Jaén, Córdoba and Seville have 40 per cent of the total area, and some communes (especially in Jaén) are like a sea of

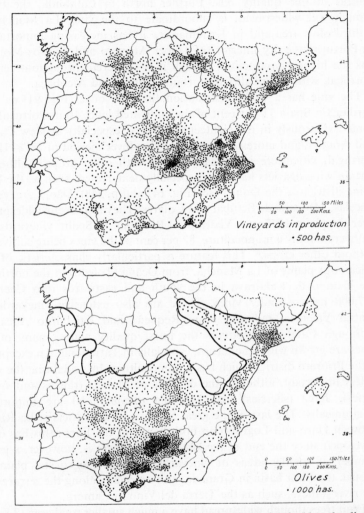

FIG. 91. Distribution of olives and vines in the Iberian Peninsula. Note the climatic limit of the olive in north central Spain, and the more widespread distribution of vines

olives, the trees covering 80–90 per cent of the surface (Fig. 91). Some specialisation occurs, the deeper soils of the plain around Seville being noted for their table olives, whereas the marly, hilly soils are generally utilised for oil-producing groves. A second concentration is in the basin of the lower Ebro between Alcaniz and Tortosa, centres of fine quality oils. Further north in Catalonia, the olive, though till widespread, is subordinate to the vine. La Mancha is a third olive area and in Extremadura it has increasing importance. In Portugal, the dry interior (of Upper Alentejo and Trás-os-Montes) has the highest production, though it is scattered throughout central Portugal, with fine quality oils around Tomar and Alcobaça.

The vine has a wider distribution than the olive (Fig. 91) as it is hardier (in Spain 11 per cent of the cultivated land, 10 in Portugal). It spread vigorously in the eighteenth century, especially in New Castile and Aragón, and more so during the 'vine-fever' period of 1878–91. In Portugal, viticulture is typically mixed with other crops,[36] although certain wine districts have been specially demarcated, such as the Port Wine district of the Douro (see Fig. 141 and p. 348), Dão, Carcavelos, Bucelas, Moscatel de Setúbal and Colares. They also occur widespread over the plains of Torres Vedras and Ribatejo. In Spain, vineyards are more commonly a monoculture, 82 per cent of the vines being cultivated without other crops.[37] This feature is particularly characteristic of the calcareous plains of La Mancha, from Ocāna (Toledo) in the north, to the Campo de Calatrava in the south and eastwards into Cuenca; 257,000 ha are under vines. There are also extensive vineyards in central Valencia, radiating from Requeña and Utiel into Alicante. Although Catalonia produces the finest quality wines, many of its vines are grown with other crops, especially in Tarragona. An exception is the Priorato district which has a monoculture. In Andalusia, the vine is less important, although the districts of Malaga (raisins and sweet wines), Jérez (sherries) and Montilla (amontillado) are important economically. The last of the great Spanish wine districts is La Rioja, between Haro and Logroño on both banks of the Ebro; this has only developed since the end of the last century. There is, however, a great number of smaller areas of vineyards, such as the coastal plain of Motril, the Baza basin in Granada, and especially along the terraces of the river valleys, such as the Tierra del Vino in Zamora.

Fruit trees though widespread have a much smaller total area (2·8 per cent of the cultivated land in Spain, 2·4 in Portugal). They form only significant elements of the landscape in certain areas: the apple and pear in the north and north-west; the fig in the Algarve; the peach and apricot in Murcia; and the pomegranate in Granada. Others are more strictly limited by climatic controls, such as the carob—a valued fodder crop (which never grows more than 1,000 ft above sea-level nor more than twenty miles inland from the east and south coasts)—or the prickly pear in the south-east, and the date palms grown commercially only at Elche. But the chief tree crops are the orange and the almond. Although found widely, even in sheltered coastal districts of the north

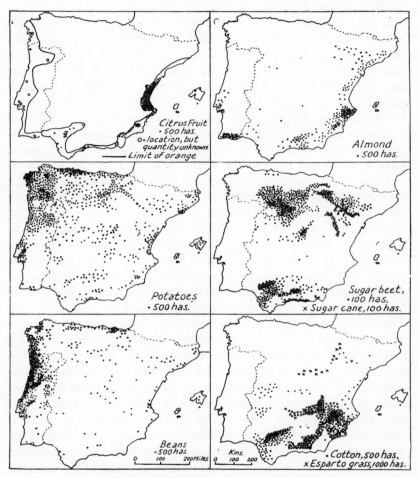

FIG. 92. Distribution of selected crops in the Iberian Peninsula

coast, oranges are now concentrated in the Levante (Fig. 92). The production of citrus fruits has halved in Portugal since the last century, whereas it has rapidly expanded in Valencia and Castellón where there is a belt of orange groves from Gandía, Alcira and Carcagente to Castellón de la Plana. The Spanish economy gambles as much as 20 per cent of its export trade on this one crop. The orange groves on the sandy hill slopes of the former Pleistocene shoreline reflect the farmers' knowledge of local climate, with shelter from cold winter air-streams and inversions of temperature. The almond is chiefly grown in the Algarve and Alicante.

4. *Irrigation and Huerta Cultivation*.[38] The widespread use of the water level and the water wheel reflect the age-long art of controlling water for agriculture in the Peninsula. In Portugal these primitive methods still water a larger surface than dams and canals. Three decades ago, before the modern developments of Spain, one-fifth of all its irri-gated surface was supplied similarly by wells, springs and storage tanks. Irrigation is an ancient practice in the Peninsula, dating back to the Tartessian and Iberian gardens, and to the Roman reservoirs of Cor-nalvo and Proserpina. But the cumulative effect, greatest in the Levante, must be attributed most to the Arabs, with their famous *huertas* of Valencia, Murcia and Granada; many others are scattered from the Llobregat delta along the east coast, south to Malaga (Fig. 55). Along these coasts the system is adapted to the climate and rivers. In the Levante, the simple division of water rights among the cultivators as practised in Valencia, becomes more complicated towards the south where drought is more severe.[39] From Murcia into Andalusia, private enterprise in storing water has superimposed a more realistic policy of selling water to the highest bidder. There is almost anarchy in the water laws of Murcia, in trying to distinguish between the 'old water' still distributed communally, and the 'new water' sold commercially.

Irrigated lands represent a wide range of agricultural practices, which may be grouped under six main categories. The first comprises the *huertas* such as those of the lower Llobregat, Valencia, Gandía, Murcia, Granada and Aranjuez in Spain, and the Loures basin north of Lisbon. These practise intensive horticulture, with short-term rotations, and have a wide variety of crops. Many of these districts have medieval institutions such as the 'Water Tribune' in Valencia[42] (Plate 27) and the 'Council of Good Men' in Murcia. The second type is the monoculture of rice, a crop used as an instrument of land reclamation[43] in the Ebro delta, Albufera of Valencia, the Marismas, Sado and Tagus estuaries, and Aveiro (Fig. 90). Rice cultivation, often banned in the past because of its association with malarial epidemics, has been rapidly expanded within the last few decades. The third type consist of the citrus groves of the Levante, also a specialised commercial system, developed with the use of the steam and electric pumps since the mid-nineteenth century. A fourth type is associated with the new irrigation zones, with extensive systems of irrigation on a large scale such as those of Lérida and Urgel, and more recently in the other major valleys. In the past these have not always been successfully developed, because they involve more than feats of engineering in building dams and canals. But as rural factories and new markets are opened, they develop the possibilities of mixed farming as well as of cash crops such as sugar beet and cotton. Contrasted with the modern systems, is the seasonal irrigation still poorly practised in the south-east, especially at Lorca, for the assurance of the cereal harvest. Finally in the north-west, where the short period of summer drought does not dry out the shallow sources of seepage water, well and spring irrigation is skilfully and extensively pursued.

5. *Maize-Meadow Cultivation.* This intensive form of polyculture coincides with the humid zone of the north and north-west. Thus Galicia has 42 per cent of the total area of maize grown in Spain, and the three north-western provinces of Portugal have 53 per cent of the Portuguese total (Fig. 90). The potato, though important, is more diffused, Galicia ranking only third in production after the Levante and Catalan provinces (Fig. 92). French beans are another important crop. Rotations are commonly four course, maize taking a place according to its relative importance with potatoes, vegetables such as beans and cabbages, forage crops and meadows. In the coastal districts of Oporto, Minho and Pontevedra the most intensive forms of polyculture prevail, maize being sown in May on the stubble of the winter-sown rye or other forage crop, and grown in the same field with beans, cabbage and even pumpkins. These crops are harvested in September or October, when another series of forage crops or potatoes are then sown. The small, fragmented fields, and the hedgerows of fruit trees, hazel and vines, present a mosaic of light and dark greens throughout the year. Where stock-raising is more important, as in the Asturias, lush fields of meadows and permanent grass cover the hill slopes, though in the populated districts green manuring by turning in clover, lupine or meadow grass is commonly the more intensive practice.

AGRARIAN STRUCTURES

1. *Land Holdings.* Historic factors have been more important in determining the character of land tenure than climatic. There is one exception however in the share-cropping of the south-east or arid zone, where the risk of crop failures has always been greatest.[44] In view of the prevalence of extensive cropping, the size of holdings is surprisingly small. Forty per cent of Spanish land-owners have less than one hectare of land, and three-quarters of them have less than five hectares (re-

presenting 36 per cent of the total land area).[45] Fragmentation of holdings (*minifundia*) is characteristic of the humid zone, while large estates (*latifundia*) are typical of the south and south-west. This contrast is most strikingly revealed in Portugal. In the north holdings average densities of over 600 per sq. mile, while the southern third has less than 60 per sq. mile.[46] In Spain twelve hundred families own over 40 per cent of all the agricultural land, their great estates requiring few permanent workers.[47] Thus almost half of the total agricultural labour force in Spain (46·7 per cent)—less in Portugal—is classified as casual labour that migrates seasonally to some mythical Eldorado in search of work. In Andalusia, the seasonal economic despair of the villagers is further deepened by the fluctuations of olive oil yields from year to year. Latifundia, however, is not the only problem of the south, for around the large agricultural villages there is excessive fragmentation of holdings. In some areas the capital resources of the large landowners have been used to good advantage, notably in parts of Alentejo where rural modernisation has proceeded fast in recent decades[48] (Fig. 146).

The humid zone is the classic region of minifundia. There is the Galician anecdote that 'one man's tethered cow will fertilise another man's crops'. Even single furrows are bought and sold, and one may own a plot on which another has a tree. A cadastral survey of such lands is a Herculean task and remains uncompleted. In the provinces of Corunna, Pontevedra and Minho, three-quarters of the proprietors own less than one hectare each. Small-holdings are only one aspect of the land problem. In Minho, over half of them are consolidated into one unit but in Beira alta and Beira littoral, 86 and 91 per cent respectively are scattered in the commune.[49] In a broad belt of country from central Portugal to Segovia, Soria and León, there is an average of at least 20 plots of land per owner. In many Castilian properties which have ten to fifteen hectares each, there may be 200 or more separate plots, notably in Soria and Guadalajara[50] (Fig. 56). The waste of manpower and of land is enormous and since 1952 a vigorous policy of land consolidation has been pursued, affecting 278,000 hectares (1960). But at a cost of 5–10,000 pesetas per hectare, it will be many years before this tattered patchwork of open field ownership will be reshaped (see also pp. 149–50). No attempt has yet been made in Portugal to tackle the problem.

2. *Regional Systems.* On the basis of the physical and cultural features of the Peninsula, it is clear that certain broad types of agrarian structure may be recognised. These are: the polyculture of the humid zone, mountain pastoralism, the Castilian open-field system, transitional open-field systems and the irrigation communities.

Along the densely peopled coasts of the humid zone between Beira littoral and the Basque lands, there are common features of landscape and culture.[51] This area forms part of that larger Atlantic community of western Europe, which since the Bronze Age quest for the tin islands, has been linked together. In this Iberian zone, intensive polyculture and strongly developed family life have been its main characteristics. Except in the Basque lands (which are ethnically distinct and have preserved the family property in primogeniture), the excessive minifundia of this zone has been aggravated by the practice of gavelkind,[52] that is to say, division of property among all the heirs. The heterogeneous features of relief and soil, promoted by active erosion and rapid decomposition of the rocks have produced a mosaic of slopes and flats, best utilised by individual rather than by collective farming (Fig. 45). The latter has been further discouraged by the careful and intensive utilisation of land in a rapid sequence of crops, with maize fields interlaced with fruit trees, some vines, orchards, meadows and chestnut groves (Fig. 139). It is perhaps an exaggeration to call it a matriarchal society, but the women often cultivate the land while the men act as pastoralists or fishers. All features of its rural life emphasise the familial unit, such as the house-types (see pp. 245–50), the stores, and the simple digging tools (such as the Asturian *cuchillo* or the Basque *laya*).

In the mountains, stretching from the Serra da Estrêla to the central Cordillera, Iberian and Cantabrian ranges, and to the Pyrenees, pastoralism is the traditional economy. These elaborate systems of collective organisation have sometimes evolved with the seasonal movement of stock. The fifteen communes of La Ceana in the Asturias used to distinguish three mountain zones: an upper zone of summer pastures, a middle zone of *brañas* where the herdsmen lived in temporary summer dwellings, and a lower zone of pastures which fed the work animals near the cultivated valleys.[53] More complex organisations in the Pyrenees have kept their cattle on the lower pastures and sheep on the higher *plas*. In the Sa de Gredos, the 'Universidad y Tierra de Avila' still controls 25,000 hectares of pasture for its 134 communes. The Sierra de Albarracin comprises the so-called 'Montes Universales' as common pasture and forest for its 23 communes, forming a unit since early times, even an independent kingdom for a short time in the eleventh century, and a Mesta after 1415.[54] A collective pastoral economy is still practised in some of the mountains of Burgos[55] and of León.

Usually side by side with the communal organisation of the pastures which may comprise nine-tenths of these large communes having 1,000 to 10,000 hectares or more, there are small individual holdings for cereals near the village. These fields are fragmented, especially in areas of marked relief or where irrigated; large and square-shaped in the broad intermontane depressions, narrow and following the contours on steep slopes. Since the eighteenth century, population pressure in the mountain valleys has encouraged sporadic enclosure of small clearings in the common pastures. The disamortisation law of 1836 also fostered private estates carved out of the common lands, which may have thousands of hectares.[56]

A third and the most characteristic system of the Meseta is the collective, biennial rotation of the open fields. This champagne landscape stretches from Trás-os-Montes (which still cultivates over half of Portugal's common lands) and Beira, throughout Old Castile, and into Aragón and New Castile. Numerous survivals of this agro-pastoral economy have been described.[57] This obligatory biennial rotation grouped the individual holdings into large fields and sometimes the

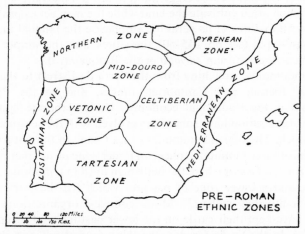

Fig. 93. Pre-Roman ethnic zones in the Iberian Peninsula (from Caro Baroja). Clearly, the environmental distinctions and locations of Andalusia, the Levante, the Lusitanian core area of central Portugal, the north-west and the north make these sharply different. The central area of the Meseta has been more remote, and semi-indigenous, less developed except for the advanced culture of the Vaccei in the Douro valley. (Unnamed zone in north refers to Basque area)

whole area of the commune might be divided into large blocks. A tattered patchwork of strip fields has been the result, which will take many years to consolidate under current land reform (Fig. 56). The origin of the system is obscure. Some authors suggest that it is traceable to proto-

historic times, and cite the evidence of the Vaccei who ploughed communal lands in the Douro valley.[58] It is more likely that the rigid system
was elaborated and spread during the Middle Ages, when municipal
authority was established at the Reconquest and colonisation was
effected by *presuria* (see p. 244).[59] Its rigid conservatism until modern
times may be explained primarily by the need to feed the flocks on the
stubble and to conserve nitrogen in the soil for the subsequent crop.
As population increased and agriculture was intensified, a more selective
use of the land was made, the best lands being reserved for grain and
the poorer soils used for vines. Grouping the vineyards into blocks had
the great advantage of more effective protection against animals, and
often municipal guards were employed in this task. After the vintage,
the sheep were permitted to feed on the leaves. Everywhere in this type
of landscape there is thus the stamp of a strong municipal authority.
Other elements are the groups of dove-cotes on the richer lands such as
the Tierras de Campo, which indicate the importance attached to these
birds to provide manure for the fields; and also the clusters of ventilation shafts of the wine cellars that form suburbs in all vine-growing
villages.

Towards the east and south of Old Castile, evidence of collective
organisation is more obscure, although today the landscape maintains
vast open-fields. The reasons are probably numerous and not all yet
recognised. In much of Aragón, a two-field system was only practised
along the valleys of the Ebro and its major tributaries, not on the interfluvial tracts. This was probably because much of the latter formerly
lay waste and flocks of sheep were permitted a right of way over
them. Subsequently when such lands were cleared for cultivation
a rigid open-field system could not be enforced.[60] In New Castile and
Extremadura, it is apparent that despite intensive cultivation in private
properties around the large villages, much of the communes lay waste
until the eighteenth and even nineteenth centuries. In some areas, such
as Ocaña in northern La Mancha, tree crops were more important than
cereals; in this commune olives and vines occupied almost half of the
total area, compared with 85 per cent under cereals today.[61] Irrigation
of small garden plots in some communes, and everywhere the pre-
occupation with the colonisation of waste, could not engender a rigid,
communal system. The radial plan of roads and fields in each commune,
centred on the large village, is a characteristic feature of such lands.

In Andalusia, the Moorish practice of garden cultivation and the later
imposition of an alien feudal system at the Reconquest have never
favoured collective systems. Historians have speculated whether the

latifundia, evolved from Castilian military overlords with their traditions of agropastoralism, would have been so marked if lower Andalusia
had been conquered instead by the Aragonese. Certainly, the Aragonese
conquerors of Valencia and later of Granada were sympathetic to maintain the *status quo* of the small cultivators on their *huertas*, familiar with
similar irrigation techniques in Aragón.

In the Levante, collective cultivation is generally unknown, with
some minor exceptions. In Tarragona, there is evidence of a communal
use of pasturage in the orchards. More significantly in Murcia, which
was conquered by Castile, there was a system of communal pasturage at
Mula, Priego, Cieza, Jurmilla, Ojos and Villanueva. The basis of
society in the Levante however has been irrigation, practised around all
the important settlements since Moorish and even Iberian times.
Although water rights have been communal, the strong individualism
has been fostered by the endless rotation of crops, as well as the commercial opportunism that has traded overseas and reclaimed the waste
for more cash cropping. The face of the *huertas* has thus constantly
changed, from the sugar cane plantations of the Middle Ages to the
wooded aspect of the mulberry trees and hemp during the next three
centuries, then to the more modern appearance of horticulture and
orange groves.

CHAPTER 10

POPULATION AND SETTLEMENT

'The Iberian Peninsula is either exposed to the influences that pour
in from the two continents which she links together, or else she
retires into the desolation that is due to her remote geographical
position.'   (Ramón Menéndez Pidal, *Spaniards in their History*)

To the climatic divisions of humid, semi-arid and arid zones discussed
in the previous chapter, there may be added two further series of regional
contrasts. The distribution of population clearly illustrates the physical
contrasts between the peripheral and central areas of the Peninsula
(Fig. 96). Differences also between the north and the south, partially
climatic, have been much accentuated by the historic evolution of land
holdings and settlements, especially as the result of the Reconquest
during the Middle Ages. Of course, the position and the size of the
Peninsula, as Menéndez Pidal has noted, have never favoured a cultural
unity so that the terms 'Iberia' (from its Greek settlers) and 'Hispania'
(from its Roman rulers) are perhaps misleading.[1] Rarely has the Peninsula been controlled in its entirety by one group of peoples. More
frequently its culture has been imposed by migrants settling in a limited
portion of this continent in miniature, coming either from Africa and
the Mediterranean, or from Europe. The Mediterranean Sea, the Straits
of Gibraltar, and the passes of the Pyrenees have formed the links for
these migrations. Naturally, it is the periphery of the Peninsula that has
been the most hybridised by the colonial development of alien city
life. Within the Peninsula itself, the dualism of mountain peoples and
plain dwellers, pastoralists and settled cultivators, rural and urban
civilisations, have complicated its personality, although it has always
tended towards conservatism. The historical geography of much of the
Peninsula may thus be viewed as the fundamental conflict of the age-
long interests, between the cultivators utilising the watered valleys and
the pastoralists ranging widely over the *páramos* and the sierras.

POPULATION: ITS CHANGES AND DISTRIBUTION

1. *Population Trends.* First, let us consider how the population trends
reflect these regional elements.[2] It is only from the sixteenth century
that it is possible to trace the trends of population with relative accuracy.

The Portuguese census of 1527 and the detailed survey of Philip II made for Spain in 1575–8, incorporated in the census estimates of 1594 for the whole Peninsula, provide useful bases.[3] Between 1594 and 1950, Portugal increased its population from 1·5 to 8 million (428 per cent) compared with Spain's increase from 9·5 to 27·2 million (294 per cent). The history of the Spanish people certainly appears to have been more chequered. First, there was the forcible expulsion of the Jews in the sixteenth century, followed by the disastrous expulsion of the Moriscos in 1610.[4] Then the collapse of the Spanish economy in the seventeenth century led to an overall decline of its population by some 25 per cent between 1600 and 1680, compared with the 15 per cent increase of the previous century. It was only during the eighteenth century that the more enlightened policy of the Bourbon rulers stimulated an increase of 75 per cent (10·5 million in 1797).[5] The increase has been accelerated since, rising by 77 per cent in the nineteenth century to 18·6 million in 1900, and a further 49 per cent increase since then, despite the grievous Civil War. The population of Portugal remained relatively stagnant until the nineteenth century (in 1732, 2·14 and in 1841, 3·39 million). But from 1845 to 1950 it increased by 131 per cent, and has now one of the highest rates in Europe.[6]

Population changes and distribution are, as we have noted, a demonstration of the physical contrasts between the periphery and centre of the Peninsula. The distribution of population (Fig. 96) clearly illustrated this dualism, although the map of population changes (Fig. 94) shows this less sharply. In fact the centre of the Peninsula may be divided into two demographic zones: the north centre of León, Old Castile and Aragón; and the south central provinces of Extremadura and New Castile. For long the north central area has been the demographic heart of Spain, having 56 per cent of the Spanish population at the end of the sixteenth century; now it represents less than one quarter. The reason is that despite high birth rates, this area has been for centuries the main migratory force within Spain, and in modern times especially to the industrialised areas of the north coast and eastern Catalonia. Thus Old Castile which had 2,247,882 in 1791, has now only 1,038,366. The average density is only 67 per sq. mile, whereas Andalusia with similar birth rates but little migration until recent years has a density of 168. Much of New Castile and Extremadura have always had low densities and migration has been insignificant, being more remote from the main centres apart from Madrid.

Very different has been the growth of population in the borders of the Peninsula. Catalonia, for example has multiplied its population over

38 Olive groves, Baños de la Encina, Jaen

39 Huerta crops, Valencia

40 Castilian wheatlands, Guadalajara

41 Cattle country, Estremadura, with holm oak woodlands

42 Peñafiel Plateau, with vineyards and woods

43 Terraces in the Douro Valley,
Port Wine district

44 Manteigas district, Serra de Estrêla

seven times[7] and Portugal four times since the sixteenth century. Here too are concentrated thirty-five Spanish cities (with over 50,000 inhabi-

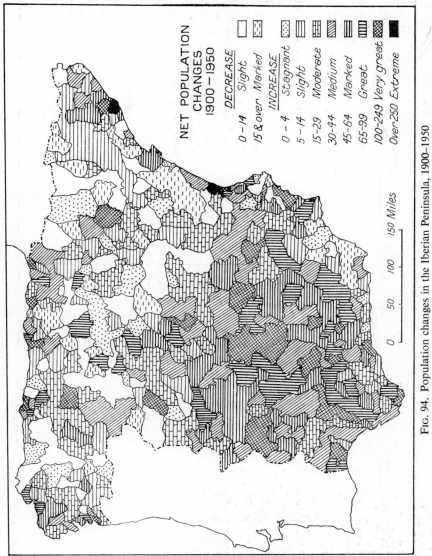

Fig. 94. Population changes in the Iberian Peninsula, 1900–1950

NET POPULATION CHANGES 1900–1950

DECREASE
0 – 14 Slight
15 & over Marked

INCREASE
0 – 4 Stagnant
5 – 14 Slight
15–29 Moderate
30–44 Medium
45–64 Marked
65–99 Great
100–249 Very great
Over 250 Extreme

0   50   100   150 Miles

tants), compared with only fourteen such centres in central Spain. These contrasts reflect on the geographical resources and their utilisation. The abundant rainfall of the north coast and the use of irrigation water in

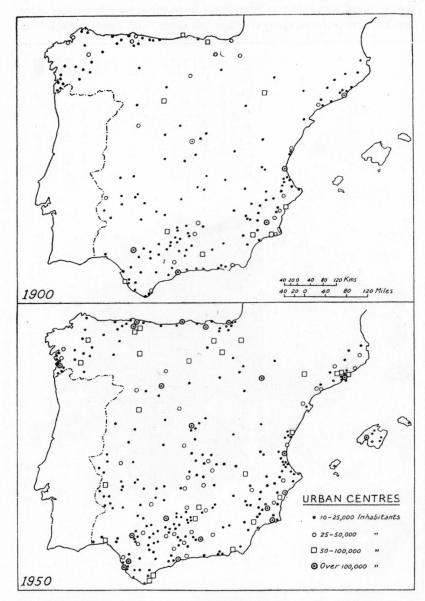

FIG. 95. Distribution of urban centres, 1900 and 1950. Note the concentration of such centres in the southern half of Spain

the eastern *huertas* have attracted high rural densities. The coalfields of the Asturias, the iron mines of the Basque lands, the great industrial resources of Catalonia, and the many ports and industrial cities have been the loci of a great influx of population since the nineteenth century. Galicia has also high densities but its lack of industrial development makes it a notable exception in terms of population change. In the last fifty years it has lost over one million emigrants, providing for South America what Old Castile and Aragon have done for the industrial areas of northern Spain.[8] Andalusia is also distinct demographically, with a slight overseas emigration to North Africa, of Almerians to Catalonia, and some internal changes resulting from mountain depopulation and the uncertainty of mineral exploitation (Fig. 94).

Portugal, although included broadly within the peripheral area of the Peninsula, comprises within it elements of the Castilian centre. This is closely reflected in its population distribution. Comparison with the first reasonably reliable census of 1527 shows that the interior of the country has continued to decline in importance.[9] At that date the northeast province of Trás-os-Montes had 12·2 per cent of the total population; today it has only 8 per cent. Elsewhere the population distribution has kept remarkably constant. Then, as now, the great bulk of the population has been in the 'core-region' of the nation, between the Minho and Vouga valleys, which had almost a fifth of the total population in the sixteenth century and still has the same. Apart from Lisbon, the Algarve has shown the highest rise of population, increasing ten times since 1523, in consequence of its favoured coastal towns and rich agricultural wealth.[10] During the last few centuries the great mass of the population has continued to concentrate on the coastal zone north of the Tagus, where today 4·95 million or 69 per cent of the total are within 32 per cent of the territory, an area which includes 18 out of the 21 urban centres of the nation which have over 10,000 inhabitants.[11] Only since the beginning of this century has there been a marked shift of population southwards, to colonise the sparsely settled lands of Alentejo (Fig. 94). In some districts between one-tenth and one-fifth of the present population consist of migrants.

2. *Population Distribution.* The marked dependence of the population upon agriculture (40 per cent of the total labour force in Spain, 32 in Portugal), the extensive uniformity of land utilisation and the physical control, have created paradoxically both 'levels' and 'gradients' of population densities. The former is characteristic of much of the Meseta, whereas the latter is common in the peripheral zones. These have not been smoothed out by the process of natural growth and migration.

The consequences of war, religious expulsion and other upheavals have been to make re-settlement more selective not less, creating greater permanent sparsity in some of the poor regions such as Aragón after the expulsion of the *moriscos*, in 1609–10.[12] The Huerta of Valencia in contrast was little affected, despite a massive exodus at the time, as its rich lands quickly attracted new settlers.[13]

Fig. 96 indicates that the most extensive areas of the Peninsula have between 50 and 100 per sq. mile. This area covers most of Old Castile,

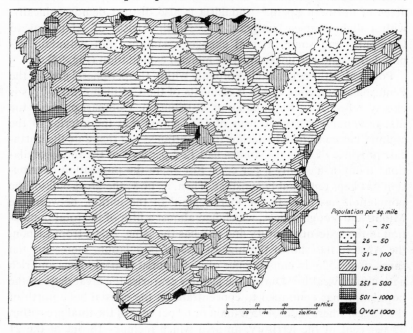

FIG. 96. Density of population in the Iberian Peninsula, 1950. Unit of density is the 'partido'

New Castile, Extremadura and Alentejo. The high mountains, the steppes of Aragón, and the eastern edge of the Meseta, especially in the Iberian mountains and plateau, have all densities below 50 per sq. mile. In all those extensive areas, it is possible to discern the significant levels of population density, as a reflection of the type of agricultural economy practised. Densities of over 100 per sq. mile are characteristic of the peripheral regions of the Peninsula notably west, central and north-western Portugal, Galicia, the Cantabrian and Basque coasts, Catalonia and the irrigated areas of the Levante and the south-east. Similar densities are characteristic of Andalusia, on the better soils of Extremadura, on the alluvial and piedmont fans on the south side of the central Cordillera, benefiting from irrigation, and in the valleys of Old Castile and Aragón for the same reason. As the unit used in Fig. 96 is the district or *partido*, some of the provincial capitals account for the relatively high densities in some isolated areas.

The lowest densities and deserted zones occur in the mountains and 'steppes'. The limit of settlement varies with latitude to some extent, so that whereas it is at 3,600 ft in the Galician mountains of Cebrero and Ancares (lat. 43°), 4,330 ft in León, and 4,600 ft in Albarracín (40·5°), it is at 5,000–5,500 ft in the Sierra Nevada (37°). Aspect too is important, the southern slopes of the Sierra Nevada having 60 per cent of their total population. The physical limitations to settlement tend to be different in the mountains and steppe lands. The former is quantitative, the amount of cultivable land available being the important control in the size and therefore the density of population. In the main valleys of the Spanish Pyrenees densities may be as high as 60 to 70 per sq. mile, with significant groupings of market towns, while the smaller and higher valleys may have 15 to 20 per sq. mile. Remoteness is also a factor in some mountainous areas. For example, Las Hurdes in the western sector of the central Cordillera has densities ranging from 40 per sq. mile on the lower lands to 50 on the higher lands, although the resources are so limited that overpopulation is acute. After the Reconquest, the Alpujarras and Ajarquia in Upper Andalusia were mountain refuges for a relatively dense population, which still persists.[14]

Over the plains and plateaux, the controls of population are less clearly discernible and are more emphatically qualitative. Several levels of density are widespread. Over the true steppes, where aridity, salt accumulation and the effects of soil erosion are apparent, densities are as low as 10 to 20 per sq. mile (for example Los Monegros in Aragón averages 13).[15] The poorest lands of the Sierra Morena where the schistose soils are only skeletal, and the borders of New Castile and Andalusia where Triassic soils are also infertile, have similar densities. An agro-pastoral economy associated either with poor lands for meagre pasturage and some barley cultivation, or with lands only recently colonised, has a second level of density between 20 and 40 per sq. mile. The western borderlands of León, Zamora, Salamanca, Cáceres,[16] Badajoz, Trás-os-Montes and eastern Beira and the eroded limestone *páramos* of Palencia, Soria, Guadalajara and Cuenca belong typically to this group. A third level is apparent in the richer grain lands of Old Castile, La Mancha and Alentejo where densities of 40 to 75 per sq. mile are usually associated with a virtual monoculture of wheat or rotation cereals. The richer lands have a comparatively high density, such as Tierra de Campos (75 per sq. mile) in Zamora, Campo de Montiel (78) in New Castile, and La Sagra (76) in the Tagus valley and Évora (79). Wherever vines are cultivated in addition to cereals, the densities of population become greater. Thus the northern sector of La Mancha has 68 per sq. mile compared with 30 to 55 in the southern half, the valley of the Douro has 100 and Tierra del Vino in Zamora 120. The added association of olives further increases densities. The Tierra de Barros in Extremadura has 125 per sq. mile, south-western La Mancha 130[17] and much of lower Andalusia has over 130. In the watered valleys of the Meseta, the highest densities and some of the most ancient settlements occur. Thus along the Ebro there are densities of 150 to 200 per sq. mile, whereas beyond the first terrace the densities rapidly decrease to 50–80 per sq. mile in the wheatlands.[18] Fruit-growing on an intensive scale produces very high densities, for example 280 per sq. mile on the lower Tagus terraces of Ribatejo.

The concept of 'levels' of population densities tends to break down in Peripheral Spain. Instead the concept of population 'gradients' becomes more significant. Thus in the irrigated lands of the Vega of Murcia there are densities of 500–1,000 per sq. mile, whereas in the un-irrigated lands of neighbouring districts densities may be 10–20 per sq. mile. Similarly, in Valencia, within twenty-five miles of the Huerta, densities drop from 1,200 to 45 per sq. mile.[19] The coastal plains generally have much higher densities than the interior because of their agricultural possibilities, their accessibility, the consequent growth of urban centres and the development of ports and manufacturing industries. Thus the Cantabrian coast has over 250 per sq. mile compared with 5 to 10 in the high interior mountains. Even in Galicia, which has some of the most densely populated rural areas of Spain, the density is 330 per sq. mile on the coast of Pontevedra compared with 120 in the interior of Lugo.[20] There is a sharp contrast between the densities of 300–400 per sq. mile in the maize and potato districts of Braga and Viana do Castelo and 85 per sq. mile in the rye and oats districts of Braganza in the rain-shadow area to the north-east. Fishing is here an additional factor for the dense concentration along the coast. Similarly in the Basque province, the density of 490 per sq. mile on the coast and only 86 per sq. mile in the interior is largely explained by the location of the largest industrial centres. There are, of course, some coastal areas with very sparse population, notably the *Marismas* or salt marshes of the mouth of the Guadalquivir. Others, such as the Ebro delta, have only been colonised recently; in 1857 it had less than 5 per sq. mile, today it has 75. In the steppes of Almería and south-east Murcia, the population would be naturally very sparse but for the presence of mining communities, raising the average to about 100 per sq. mile in several districts.

The industrial activities of certain favoured regions provide the climax to population densities. The provinces which have the highest densities are also the most industrialised (Barcelona 740 per sq. mile, Viscaya 680, Madrid 620 and Guipuzcoa 500). The greatest industrial region of Spain, in Catalonia, has over two and a half million concentrated into little more than 800 sq. miles. The absolute maximum is in Madrid with 4,500 per sq. mile. Similarly in Portugal, the industrial conurbation of Oporto has 623,000 concentrated into 162 sq. miles, with the highest density of the country 2,160 per sq. mile. Excluding Oporto and its four urban centres this is still a density of 1,090 per sq. mile in a region where only 10 per cent of the working population are engaged in agriculture. The Lisbon district has almost three times the total population (1,222,471) of the Oporto district, and twice as many suburban and satellite centres, but it lacks the high rural densities in the countryside which is so characteristic of its northern rival.

THE TOWNS

1. *Urban Origins.* Nearly all the important towns of the Peninsula have had ancient origins. Cadiz for example is reputed to date from the second millennium B.C. But they have been heirs of diverse cultures. The predominance of town life in Andalusia is perhaps traceable to the Tartessian civilisation which exploited the mineral wealth of the Morena and made Tarshish famous.[21] Lusitania and especially the east coast were influenced by Phoenician and Greek commerce, and important emporia were created, such as Ampurias Tarragona, Denia and Malaga. In the north-west, the Celts developed the *castros*, defended hill-top settlements, from which are originated many towns of northern Portugal, such as Coimbra, Oporto and Braga[22] (Fig. 97). On the Meseta, the Vetoni lived in fortified centres, and in the Celtiberian territory near Soria the famous ruins of Numantia have been excavated, a town with c. 2000 houses.[23] From such ancient and diverse origins town life has suffered many vicissitudes: decline during the Visigothic era; the struggles of the Reconquest when many new towns were created; the commercial decay of the seventeenth century. But through them all three great periods of urban creation have left their mark upon the Peninsula: the Roman, Hispano-Muslim and Reconquest eras.

Like the Greeks and the Carthaginians before them, the Romans fostered commercial centres along the east and south coasts, facing the Mediterranean. But in the west and north, the few Roman towns that were created were usually military or administrative centres such as Merida, Évora, Beja, Coimbra, Braga, Lugo, León and Saragossa, chosen for their nodality on the road systems.[24] Even so, the *barros* of

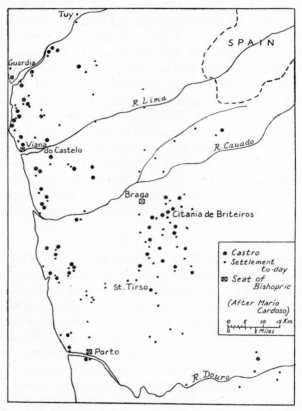

FIG. 97. Distribution of castros in northern Portugal in relation to existing settlement

Évora and the *vegas* of Mérida and Saragossa suggest also the utilisation of rich lands and irrigation. Pliny, a procurator of *Hispania*, noted the irregular distribution and character of these towns.

The small number of Roman towns in the western province of Lusitania, compared with those of the east and south, is striking. Ever since then the Levante and Andalusia have always had the majority of the towns.

In the northern half of the Peninsula, the majority of towns owe their

Towns in the Iberian Peninsula in the Augustan Era

		Tarragona	Baetica	Lusitania	Total
Colonias		12	9	5	26
Municipios		13	18	1	32
„	(with				
	Roman privileges)	18	29	3	50
„	(free)	—	6	—	6
„	(allied)	1	3	—	4
„	(tributary)	135	120	37	291
	Total	179	185	45	409

(From Pliny, Book III, 7, 18 and Book IV, 117.)

origin to the Reconquest. Only a few were created by the Arabs, such as Tudela and Calatayud in Aragonese *huertas*, the majority being established as fortresses by the Christians.[25] In Portugal, nearly all the towns north of the Tagus were built on hills, many influenced by *castro* ancestry (Fig. 97).[26] Aveiro was the outstanding exception of a town built on the plain but protected by its marshes. In Castile the river valleys were the chief routes, so at confluences or bridge-points most towns were built. Burgos,[27] Valladolid, Coca, Segovia,[28] Sepulveda and Arevalo are examples of the former, and among the innumerable examples of the latter are Oporto,[29] Zamora, Tora, Tordesillas, Aranda and Soria[30] on the Douro, Tortosa, Saragossa, Tudela,[31] Miránda, Haro and Logroño[32] on the Ebro.

2. *Types of Town Plan*. The Roman legacy of the gridiron plan has been preserved in several northern towns, notably Braga, Lugo, León, Saragossa and central Barcelona. But it has been obliterated in all the major cities of the south and east and even in smaller centres such as Mérida, Évora and Beja it is not clear. This is because the Muslims, though they did not create new cities, radically transformed the plans of existing cities to meet their own needs. A social balance was achieved between the public life of the market-place and the mosque, and the privacy of the home, that was screened by high walls and courtyards from both public gaze and the hot sun.[33] The mosques or *mesquitas*, formed the focal points for the various quarters of the city with their irregular maze of streets and narrow lanes, often commercially distinct. A description of Valencia in 1762 still enumerated a maze of 428 'streets' and at the fork of two or more alleys some 131 narrow squares. Outside the walled town or medina was often a ghetto (*judería*) as at Toledo, Córdoba and Valencia. Apart from Córdoba which had 100,000 in the

eleventh century, the Muslim city averaged 15,000–25,000 inhabitants: Toledo and Almería 27,000; Granada 26,000; Palma 25,000; and Málaga, Valencia and Seville 15,000–20,000.[34] Each had the appearance of a garden city, surrounded by a dense rural population, scattered in farms, villas and summer residences on irrigated lands.

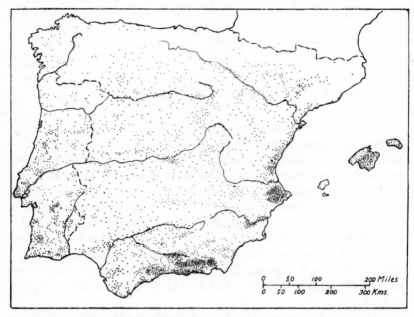

FIG. 98. Moorish place-names in the Iberian Peninsula. Note four areas of major concentration: the Algarve, eastern Andalusia, N. Alicante and Majorca

How different is the urban landscape of the Castilian towns associated with the Christians. The outline of the built-up area suddenly appears in the midst of a wilderness of fallow, a characteristic which even Madrid has not yet lost. The rise of independent municipalities as garrison towns had much to do with Spain's success against Islam.[35] Once a fortress was established or taken, a series of nuclei tended to grow within the walled town. This cellular plan is typical of the older centres such as Pamplona, Burgos, Soria, Valladolid, Salamanca[35] (Fig. 126) and Ségovia. The plan arose from a number of factors: the extent of open land within the walls to impound the stock; the ethnic grouping of distinct migrants into different quarters; and the successive stages of town growth with the fortunes of war and trade. Until the fifteenth and sixteenth centuries, when the central square was created, usually near the cathedral, these towns had no central focus.[36] Once the central square was adopted, new streets were then driven through the old quarters to give more centrality to the layout, and imposing town halls were built.

Other Christian towns were created by the military needs of the Reconquest. These were either street plans, towns aligned along highways notably the Pilgrims' Way from France to Santiago[37] (Fig. 40) or more formal plans for fortresses. One numerous group of new towns was created in the Basque provinces, notably Durango (1180), Tolosa (1286) and Bilbao (1300). Along the Pilgrims' Way are Vitoria (1181), Santo Domingo de la Calzada and Castrojeriz. Briviesca and Foncea are other, later examples. In northern Portugal too are numerous examples: 69 town charters were granted to Trás-os-Montes by the mid-thirteenth century.[38] Thus contemporary or even earlier than the bastides of southern France are numerous examples in northern Spain and Portugal. It is significant that the province of Castellón like south-east France, with which it had cultural links, has examples of more sophisticated town-planning. More geometrical than the Navarrese type, are the rectangular, gridiron plans centred on a central square, such as Almenara (c. 1258), Soneja, Villarreal de Burriana (c. 1273) and Nubes (early fourteenth century), comparable to those of Montauban (1114) or Montpazier (1284) in France.[39] In the case of both Castellón (1272) and Nubes, the original site was on a hill, later transferred with careful planning to the plain.

The later examples of town planning are more sporadic and diversified in character. Santa Fé, near Granda, was built in 1491 on the model of Briviesca, as a garrison town to subdue Upper Andalusia.[40] The establishment of universities in Alcalá de Henares and Coimbra in the same century led to the growth of their towns. Caldas da Rainha developed during the same period as a health resort. At the beginning of the seventeenth century, Lerma was replanned as a ducal seat, its layout being repeated in the creation of El Escorial. Later, the baroque planning of the Bourbons established La Granja (Ségovia) and then Aranjuez (1768).[41] In Portugal, Pombal's schemes created a new centre for Lisbon (Plate 50), the new mineral port of Vila Real de San Antonio, and the redevelopment of Nazaré as a fishing settlement. The naval struggles of the same century saw the development of Gibraltar (after 1704) and Port Mahon (after 1708), when the English built the new town of Fort George in 1711. The latter was used as a model plan for Barceloneta built later in the same century. El Ferrol was created in 1752–70. Plans were also conceived for a major port at San Carlos de La Rapita on the Ebro delta but except for the creation of a small settlement the scheme fell through. It was also the age of colonisation schemes in Andalusia, with the creation of new centres at La Carolina (Jaén), La Carlota (Córdoba), La Luisiana (Seville) to act as foci of settlement; founded in 1768–69.[42] Formal fortresses were built on the Portuguese frontier (Plates 48, 49).

3. *The Function and the Growth of Towns*. It is generally true to say that whereas the towns of the interior have risen and then declined according to changing political circumstances, the coastal cities have remained relatively stable, and the significance of their site and location has been often more permanent. Córdoba and Toledo have had a more brilliant, medieval past; Granada in the twelfth century had over 300,000 inhabitants spread over 420 acres compared with 60,000 in 1800 (154,378 in 1950). The early Christian capitals, such as Jaca and Huesca, though much smaller, also declined with the shift of the frontier. Economic changes explain the decay of others, notably the decline of the Mesta which affected adversely the fortunes of the woollen towns, such as Segovia, Soria and Cuenca. Towns with special functions, which never quite managed to acquire new activities and not all in the interior are common. Such are some of the fortress towns: Fuenterrabía, Lugo, Tuy, Obidos, Elvas, Calatrava and Avila. Ecclesiastical centres, such as the monasteries of Sahagún, Guadalupe, Ripoli and Alcobaça, hostelries like Santo Domingo de la Cazada, and others notably Santiago, Pamplona and Guadaljara, suffered from the Reformation and other religious upheavals. Ducal towns such as Palencia, Ubeda, Baeza, Cabra and Lerma, still reflect their origins in the glories of their buildings, but they have a faded look. The same is true of former University towns such as Oñate and Alcalá de Henares. Thus many of the small market towns of the Peninsula have had proud annals in history, but their present status is circumscribed by the poverty of their environs and the lack of other than agricultural pursuits (Fig. 99).[43]

As the table on p. 238 shows, out of 245 towns and cities in Spain which have over 10,000 inhabitants, only 46 may be classified as manufacturing.

Fig. 99 illustrates the markedly different regional distribution of such centres. In Andalusia there are 65 agricultural centres with 10,000–20,000 inhabitants each, with another 18 such towns having 20,000–50,000 inhabitants. The Levante too has 28 agricultural towns. But in striking contrast, there are no such centres in Old Castile and the Ebro valley, where instead 8 of the 11 urban centres are commercial, wholesale and administrative centres. There instead of the large village, the hamlet is the agricultural unit, and the towns with their medieval municipal privileges are the commercial centres. The towns of New

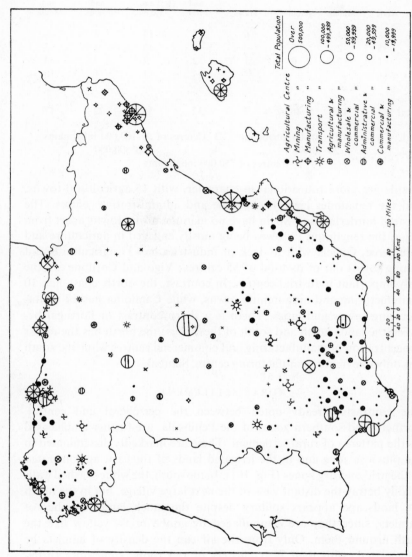

FIG. 99. A functional classification of urban centres in Spain, 1950. The census material is not available for Portugal.

Functional Classification of Towns in Spain, 1950

	Agric.	Mining	Manufac.	Trans.	Agric. and Mfrs.	Wholesale and Comm.	Admin. and Comm.	Comm. and Manu.
1.	148	14	35	6	23	14	3	—
2.	35	2	7	—	7	13	5	1
3.	1	3	3	1	2	7	7	4
4.	—	—	—	—	—	1	6	10
5.	—	—	—	—	—	—	1	2
Total 184		19	46	7	32	35	22	17

1. Centres of 10–20,000 inhabitants   3. Centres of 50–100,000 inhabitants
2.   ,,   ,, 20–50,000   ,,   4.   ,,   ,,   100–500,000   ,,
5. Centres of 750,000 inhabitants

Castile are more transitional in character, with 15 agricultural towns, and the remainder largely wholesale and administrative centres. The western borderlands of Spain have no manufacturing towns apart from Béjar, the remaining 19 towns being mostly engaged in agriculture and commerce. Galicia with its lack of industries has 37 agricultural and fishing towns out of its total of 55 centres; Vigo and Corunna are the only important industrial centres. In contrast, the north coast has 10 manufacturing and nine mining towns, while Catalonia has 17 manufacturing towns and cities. There is a sharp contrast in Portugal between the lands north and south of the Tagus: the north has the major concentration of manufacturing and commercial centres while the south has only one major manufacturing centre, Sétubal.

RURAL SETTLEMENT

The contrasts already noted between the peripheral and central, northern and southern zones of the Peninsula, are further emphasised by the patterns of rural settlement. These are markedly disseminated in the pluviose zone and in the irrigated lands of the east, agglomerated in the arid and dry zones (Fig. 101). In the south, the white-washed walls readily betray the distant view of the next large village, but in the north the landscape appears solitary despite the much larger number of hamlets, since they are camouflaged by adobe brick, yellow like the earth around them. Only from the air can the density of hamlets be appreciated, with their neat clusters of red roofs, sometimes turtle-backed, quite unlike the large rounded plans of the southern villages and towns. The regional patterns of rural settlement may be divided into eight major groups.

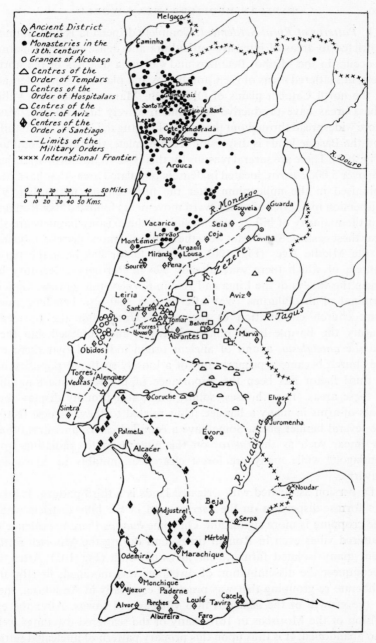

Key:
◊ Ancient District Centres
● Monasteries in the 13th. century
○ Granges of Alcobaça
△ Centres of the Order of Templars
□ Centres of the Order of Hospitalars
⬠ Centres of the Order of Aviz
◈ Centres of the Order of Santiago
--- Limits of the Military Orders
xxxx International Frontier

0 10 20 30 40 50 Miles
0 10 20 30 40 50 Kms.

Melgaço
Caminha
Dume
Guimarais
Santo Tirso
Celorico de Bast
Leça
Cete Pendorada
Paço de Sousa
Arouca
R. Douro
R. Mondego
Gouveia
Guarda
Vacarica
Seia
Coja
Lorvão
Montémor
Arganil
Miranda
Lousa
Covilhã
Soure
Pena
R. Zezere
Leiria
Aviz
Santarém
Fores Novas
Tomar
Belver
R. Tagus
Abrantes
Marva
Óbidos
Torres Vedras
Alenquer
Coruche
Elvas
Sintra
Juromenha
Palmela
Évora
Alcacer
R. Guadiana
Noudar
Adjustrel
Beja
Serpa
Mértola
Odemira
Marachique
Monchique
Paderne
Aljezur
Alvor
Forches
Loulé
Cacela
Tavira
Albufeira
Faro

FIG. 100. The settlement of Portugal during the Middle Ages (after R. de Azevedo and O. Ribeiro). Note the predominance of monastic colonisation in the north and of military settlement in the south

1. *Patterns of Rural Settlement.* Complete dispersion is not common, restricted to areas of intensive agriculture and dense rural population. It occurs in the Minho, Betanzos and Corunna districts of the north-west, in scattered areas of the Cantabrians and plains of Santander, and in the north Catalan plains of Olot, Vich, Maresma and Alto Vallés. These areas have productive soils and relatively high rainfall. Much more widespread throughout the north of Portugal, Galicia, the Asturias and the Basque lands is dispersion from hamlets, the fundamental unit (Fig. 102). There are several reasons for this type. In the north-west there are over 5,000 *castros*, located in densely populated areas that have been colonised in the millennium after the fifth century B.C.[44] (Fig. 97). Dispersion in a series of valley-ward movements followed Pax Romana, but the majority of hill or plateau sites of the existing hamlets are still near these castros. Significant were the number of monasteries established in the Middle Ages (Fig. 100). Another factor has been the parish church, of which there were already 576 in Portuguese territory between the valleys of the Lima and Ave in the eleventh century. Galicia, terminal of the Pilgrims' Way after *c.* A.D. 830 also benefited much from church colonisation of the waste. Until after the thirteenth century the Basque lands remained lawless and unsettled, but there too the *anteiglesia*, a unit of ancient origin indicated that there too the church became a primary unit of a loosely scattered population.[45] A third factor has been the importance of the Reconquest nobility in these areas. Their houses, solidly built, still proudly display their coats-of-arms in many a hamlet. Thus related to these diverse factors are several hamlet plans. Some have a rounded *castro* ancestry, others are linear such as the *rueiros* on the pilgrim routes radiating from Santiago,[46] while many are forest clearances, notably in Álava and Navarre.

Dispersion associated with irrigated lands is a third pattern. It takes two forms: dispersion on the *huertas*, and in the hilly districts where tree cropping is more significant. On some *huertas* there is evidence of scattered villas even in Roman times, and during the Moorish settlement many isolated farms (*alquerías*) were built (Fig. 105). After the Reconquest the dissemination of dwellings was modified, first by the deliberate re-grouping that was practised especially in Andalusia, then by the growth of the *alquerías* into villages and towns. After the expulsion of the Moriscos in 1610 many of the scattered dwellings were also abandoned. It is thus upon this primary pattern of nucleated settlements that there has developed during the last century an intense form of dispersal with the further growth of population.[47] In other areas of

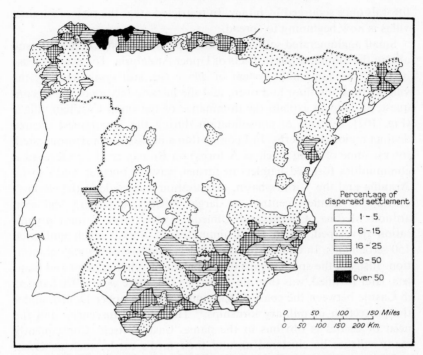

FIG. 101. The dissemination of rural settlement in Spain, 1950 (by *partidos*)

dense Moorish settlement (Fig. 98) such as the lower Algarve, northern Alicante and Majorca, the hilly terrain, the abundance of springs and the importance of tree crops have all favoured a long-established dispersion, aided by the careful use of terraces.

Modern dispersion is often associated with the development of new lands. For example in the Douro valley the spread of vineyards was sponsored by Pombal's protection policy for the district after 1756 (Fig. 141). This has promoted a rash of scattered *quintas*, very different from the hamlet pattern of the surrounding plateaux. Similarly, the reclamation of the Ebro delta after 1850 has resulted in the scatter of *barracas* near the rice fields (Fig. 96). The reclamation of the sandy hills inland from Castellón and south to northern Alicante by pumped irrigation for the orange groves has transformed a sterile area, now dotted with farms. The spread of table-grape cultivation in Malaga and Almería and the sherry districts of Cádiz, are other examples of this type of dispersion. A fifth type is the colonisation of sparsely settled lands, characteristic of south-west Portugal and parts of Spain, notably on the littorals once scourged by piracy. In restricted areas the rash of summer villas is now beginning to spread.

Small agglomerated settlements are typical of León, Old Castile and also in the mountainous districts of Upper Andalusia. The extensive use of land, the communal system of *año y vez*, still symbolised by the village threshing floor and oven, and the historic factors of the Reconquest, all help to explain the dominance of the small Castilian village (Fig. 102). Systems of consolidation during the Reconquest created distinct regional patterns. In León, within a network of numerous small towns, some of them (such as Astorga) on Roman roads, ecclesiastical communities fostered hamlets in former waste.[48] Further south in La Armuña and the Tormes basin, colonisation was made in the eleventh century of hamlets centred on larger villages, a pattern still seen around Medina, Cuellar and Olmedo. Later, more formal organisation developed, as in the Comunidad of Soria, which embraced 150 settlements. In Old Castile there is less evidence of church colonisation. Instead, the spontaneous development of small granges and hamlets, later fortified, was the rule. Thus in 1353, there were 2,070 hamlets in Castile between the coast of Santander and the upper Douro, under the protection of military lordships.[49] The general insecurity and the need of castles is obvious in the name 'Castile' itself. Consequently many villages lie clustered around their lord's castle, such as Coca, Cuellar and Sepulveda. In Trás-os-Montes in north-east Portugal there is a similar pattern, where 80 territorial units of colonisation were granted during the Reconquest, compared with only 50 in the more densely settled lands further west between the Minho and the Douro.[50]

Depopulation is often suggested as a contributory factor in the relatively small size of these Castilian villages. Normally the village has only 100–200 inhabitants in the poorer and higher lands of the *páramos*, whereas the *campiñas* have units that average 500–600. Medieval historians such as Sanchez Albornoz may have exaggerated the extent of depopulation which occurred at the beginning of the Reconquest, since the density of pre-Arab names is high in the rich grain lands of Tierra de Campos, significantly called also 'Campos Goticos'. But certainly in the seventeenth century, there is evidence of marked depopulation. Hergueta has referred to 121 'lost villages' in the old bishopric of Calahorra, and Quelle estimated that 25 per cent of the settlements of Guadalajara were depopulated at this time. Old maps evidence this decline.[50] Coello's map of Palencia lists 39 'lost villages' and Lopez's map of Salamanca (1783) lists 169, especially around Ciudad Rodrigo.[51] One estimate of Old Castile in 1800 lists 22,318 isolated churches, where

FIG. 102. Types of rural settlement in Spain.

presumably hamlets or villages once stood. The freedom of Castilians to emigrate, the municipal and church control over vast territories, epidemics, the paralysis of agriculture by the dominance of pastoralism, notably the Mesta, and the general economic decline from the seventeenth century onwards, may all be listed to explain this depopulation and stunted size of settlements.

Very different are the patterns of large villages and agricultural towns that characterise lower Aragón, New Castile, Extremadura and parts of Alentejo. In Aragón, there is a marked contrast between the high density of hamlets in the Pyrenean valleys which have been remarkably constant ever since the ninth century, and the large villages widely spaced over the 'steppe' lands. The lower lands, more sparsely settled after the Reconquest, were also markedly depopulated after the expulsion of some 70,500 Moriscos in 1610. South of the Tagus, the large village pattern is particularly well developed. Thus the sixteenth-century survey of Philip II indicated that of the 16,000 units of settlement in the Kingdom of Castile, only 600 were in New Castile. A similar contrast occurred in Portugal, both reflecting the radical change in the Reconquest strategy once the Christian armies were across the Modego and Tagus valleys (Fig. 100). Instead of the guerrilla warfare and spontaneous peasant movements of colonisation that occurred in the north; south of the Meseta was more abandoned and reconquered by the military orders. In both countries the king exercised the right of ownership of abandoned or conquered land (*presuria*). Thus in southern Spain four military orders were granted vast territories to defend with great fortresses and to settle with large, widely spaced villages:[52] the Hospitallers in the Campo de Consuegra, the knights of St John in the Campo de San Juan, the order of Santiago in the Campo de Ucles; and the more bellicose order of Calatrava in the southern half of New Castile, in the district named after it.[53] Similarly in Portugal four orders helped to resettle the lands south of the Mondego: the Cistercian abbey of Alcobaca (1153) was given the task of re-colonising some 40,000 ha in Extremadura. The Order of Christ occupying northern Extremadura and lower Beira fortified over 22 towns and villages (Fig. 100). The Hospitallers stretched south of the upper Zezere and controlled an enormous area east of the Guadiana. Further south still the orders of Avis and Santiago settled southern Alentejo.[54] Throughout these districts, large villages have remained the primary pattern, with some dispersion in lands where the vine or the olive have prospered.

Finally, in many parts of Andalusia and Alentejo the pattern of large villages has been modified by the widespread dispersion of large farms, associated with latifundia. In Córdoba, for example, 78 per cent of the population is grouped into large settlements but another 12 per cent are scattered in *cortijos*, or large farms. In the rich plains of the Campiña this dispersion is higher still. In some areas such as around Évora in Alentejo, there is evidence from the sites of Roman villas on or near which *montes* now stand (Fig. 103), that this dispersion is very old. But there are many areas where it appears the Christians deliberately concentrated the local population for easier surveillance. Around the southwestern border of the Baetic redoubt numberous towns and villages have the suffix *de la frontera* in their place-names as evidence of their defensive character during the closing phase of the Reconquest (Fig. 102).[54] Thus it is impossible to consider the varying patterns of settlement in Peninsula, without some reference to the stages and imprints made by the Reconquest, still apparent on the landscapes.[55]

2. *The House Types.* The most primitive dwelling is the troglodyte, found scattered throughout the arid and dry zones of the Peninsula, where rainfall is low and local limestone or other suitable soft rock can be excavated. They occur in the Ebro and Jalón (e.g. Lodosa, Calatayud), the Tierra de Campos (Valladolid and Palencia), the Tagus and Jarama valleys, La Mancha (Villacanas, Chinchilla, Quero), and are particularly abundant in Upper Andalusia where they form suburbs of the towns of Granada, Guadix and Almería.[56] The housing shortage has made them a fashionable solution, for example at Burjasot, Paterna and Godella west of Valencia. An archaic type is the shelter dug in the ground, covered with stones, which is still found in the remote district of Las Hurdes.

The house types of today have developed primarily from two or three early forms: the conical, the rectangular and the square. The conical shelter made of branches and vegetable covering, is still found among pastoralists of the north-west, and in the poorer districts of La Serra in the northern Algarve and the Sierra Morena. The *pallaza* (Fig. 104) of eastern Galicia and northern León, is a more elaborate form, divided into two quarters, for the household and animals respectively. Other humble types are the crude *chozas* of Andalusia, and the temporary shelters built for the seasonal vigilance required at harvest time. The primitive rectangular house was introduced probably by the Celts and from it a great number of variants has developed.[57] The *barraca*, still found between Orihuela and the Ebro delta, but commonest in Valencia is a famous example. Framed with reeds, infilled with adobe and thatched with grasses or straw, it is clearly palludal in origin, still serving as a shelter for the peasants of the *huertas* (Fig. 104).[58] The square house, walled with stone, and covered with a conical or pyramid-like roof of thatch, is another primitive type. It is common in Upper Aragón and parts of northern Portugal, where the harsh climatic conditions of high mountainous districts, demand a steeply pitched roof and strong walls in the minimum of space.[59]

Apart from human influences and traditions, physical factors have influenced the appearance of some house types. Compared with the steeply pitched roofs of the central Pyrenees, the broad, square base of the house plan, and the gentle pitch of the roof help to explain the Catalan *masía* with its narrow, rectangular plan. A common feature of the characteristic *masía* is the appendage of out-houses on either side of the house proper so that the principal facade has three units[60] (Fig. 105). The balcony, gallery and arcaded porch, are characteristic of mountain areas, as in the *casona* of León and Burgos and the *caserío* of the Asturias. The balcony is highly characteristic of the tall blocks of fishing settlements, especially in the Basque provinces. The arcade is found in many parts of the Peninsula, most typically in the house-type of Denia and northern Alicante (*riu-rau*), associated with the raisin drying which is important locally. Where hot summers make ventilation essential the chimneys are large and often are the most elaborate architectural feature of the house, characteristic of Extremadura and the Algarve (Fig. 103). The importance of the interior *patio* or open courtyard in Andalusia is indicative of the need for a cool house during the excessive summer heat. In Old Castile, protection from the cold winters has been devised in the construction of a *gloria* or *trebedes*, a heating system whereby the oven fired with straw and other fuel, heats the stone floor of the sleeping quarters above it.

Fundamentally, however, the house types of the peninsula may be classified according to their plan, reflected by the economy they practise. The distinction made between the multiple storey dwelling and the single storey house is valid and important. The former is associated with a stock-rearing economy where animals are stalled on the ground floor, the living quarters on the first floor, and usually hay and straw lofts above. In Portugal, it lies north of a line drawn between Leiria and Castelo Branco, but in Spain it occurs more diffusely throughout the pluviose zone and the mountains generally. Sometimes the animal quarters form a kind of basement cut into the hillside, as in many Basque *caseríos*, (Fig. 104) and the living quarters will then appear to be at ground floor level from the front of the house.[61] In the Aran valley in the central Pyrenees, the living quarters are apart in an annexe, the main building housing the animals and stores, but this type is not widespread. Generally, the size of the house is greater in areas where cattle are more important than sheep-rearing and grain. Usually, the staircase connecting the living quarters with the ground floor is inside the house, but it is characteristic of the Minho and Galician types for the staircase to be outside and built like the rest of the house, of granite.

The single-storey house is characteristic of the lowlands, or plateaux,

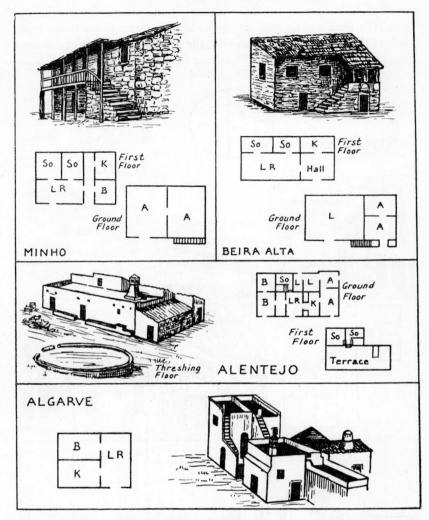

FIG. 103. House-types of Portugal. Abbreviations: A—animal quarters; B—bedroom; K—kitchen; LR—living-room; L—loft for fodder; So—stores

wherever cereal cultivation is important. The size of farms and the volume of production will influence the layout of the house. Generally, the living quarters are on the ground floor and first floor, the granaries above. The courtyards are usually large with a number of outhouses depending on the character of the farm economy. Sometimes the wine cellar is below the house, but it is more characteristic of Castile for caves to be excavated on the outskirts of the village for storing the wine. The wealth of an area may give more character to the house type, such as the *alquerías* of the Levante, the *cortijos* and *quintas* or *montes*

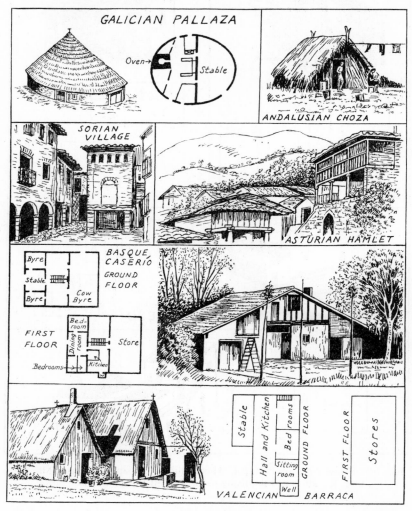

Fig. 104. House-types of Spain

of Andalusia and Alentejo respectively (Fig. 103). Compared with the peasant's *barraca* (Fig. 104), the *alqueriá* is a large stone-built residence of a landed proprietor with a central gateway and passage, through which carts can pass into the enclosed courtyard behind the house. It was sometimes fortified especially when near the coast, and has extensive stores in the upper storeys of the house, for the variety of the irrigated crops grown (Fig. 105). The *cortijo* or *monte* is associated

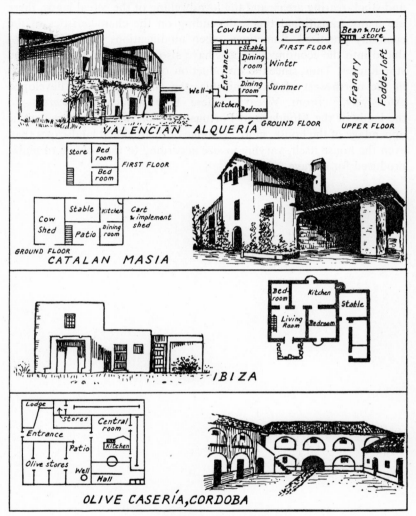

FIG. 105. House-types of Spain

with latifundia and consequently is much the largest house unit, generally with two or more rows of low dwelling houses for the workers employed on the estate. In the Andalusian Campiña, the *cortijo* is often walled into one unit, facing a central courtyard. Most of the *cortijos* have been built since the early seventeenth century, but undoubtedly they have replaced similar units of labour.[62]

Between these two fundamental types, the tall house of the pastoral and stock-rearing areas, and the low dwelling of the cereal lands, there are many transitional types, depending on the characteristics of the economy practised. Sometimes when modifications have been introduced into the economy, changes have also occurred in the associated storehouses. Thus, since the introduction of maize and its importance in the north-west of the Peninsula, the *hórreo* has been developed extensively.[63] From Vizcaya—where they are called *garaixes*—to the lands of the Mondego in Portugal the *hórreo* is the characteristic appendage of the house, more symbolic of the regional landscapes than even the house itself, varying in size according to the volume of maize produced for storage.

CHAPTER 11

THE REGIONS OF SPAIN:
THE PERIPHERAL PROVINCES

'The Spaniards who have written on their own geography and . . . who ought to be supposed to understand their own country and institutions the best have found it advisable to adopt this arrangement of kingdoms, from feeling the utter impossibility of treating Spain (where union is not unity) as a whole.'

(Richard Ford *Gatherings from Spain*).

The Iberian Peninsula is often conceived to be a continent in miniature, and Spain comprises four-fifths of this area. There are several reasons for this impression. The continental area of Spain (190,115 sq. miles) is such that there is a relatively low ratio of coastline to land-surface (1 mile: 95 sq. miles). At the same time, it must be remembered Spain is washed by two seas, with an Atlantic coast of 605 miles and a Mediterranean littoral of 1,712 miles. The dimensions of Spain can be appreciated perhaps by the position of Madrid, only a few miles away from the geometrical centre of the Peninsula (at Cerro de los Angeles); Madrid is 294 miles by rail from its nearest port of Valencia, 302 miles from its traditional outlet of Santander, and 424 miles from Cadiz. A second reason is the distinct physique of the country. The average elevation is 2,000 ft, and so Spain is second only to Switzerland as the highest country in Europe. But unlike the latter, Spain is not the transit centre of a continent but its vast cul-de-sac. The mountainous rim exaggerates to continental dimensions the regional differences within the country. For example, nowhere else in Europe are such contrasts to be seen as on the northern and southern flanks of the Pyrenees. In the south-east also, it is possible to proceed within a distance of 20–30 miles from sub-tropical crops of sugar cane and bananas on the coast to the snows of the Sierra Nevada. At the same time, the dreary monotony of landscape over much of the Meseta with a cloudless sky spreading from horizon to horizon, tend also to exaggerate the dimensions of the Peninsula.

To which continent does this Peninsula belong? Its strange exoticism to European eyes would suggest that it was African. In Castile and along the east coast, it has more steppe-lands than in all the rest of western Europe. The badlands and pediments of Jaca, Cuenca, Murcia and

Andalusia, set in vivid colours that are brightened by the drought, and exposed to the intense luminosity, are comparable to the landforms of eastern Morocco. The vast brown and yellow plateaux of the Meseta have their geographical counterpart in the High Plains of Constantine and a geological connection with Central Morocco. The black soils of the Andalusian Campiña are repeated in the *tirs* of the Gharb. There has also been a similar human response. The marked nucleation of settlement seems to express a universal anxiety to escape from the emptiness of the surrounding spaces—*pueblos* and *ksars* equally beleaguered by the isolation of sun-drenched plains and mountains. Even in the very name of 'Almoravides' (frontier castles) there is the evidence of similar effects of conquest in North Africa, as the Castilians (*castilla* or castles) imposed on Spain. The irrigation systems also, in Valencia, Murcia, and Granada have a common ancestry with those of Marrakech, Meknes and Fès. Schraeder's statement, therefore, has some truth, 'Africa begins at the Pyrenees.'

It is equally necessary, however, to point out the European affinities of Spain. The *bocage* landscapes of much of the north coast are Atlantic European in appearance and in origins, while the Galician rias are almost Scandinavian. The Reconquest which has left an indelible imprint on the land, was a European crusade and colonisation movement, for the apparent 'deserts' of Spain are full of Christian churches. Widespread deforestation which created its 'African' steppes, was encouraged by the Meseta, in the interests of the European wool trade. In consequence of this paradox, Spain has many facades. Its south is more truly African, its north Atlantic, its east coast Mediterranean, and its centre indigenous and continental.

In Spanish history there has never been a king of *Spain*. His title has always been *Rex Hispaniarum* (king of the Spains), not only in view of the New Spain overseas but because the home country itself was a political mosaic. The kingdoms of Castile, Navarre and Aragón, the county of Catalonia, the lordship of the Basque lands, and the Principality of the Asturias are a reminder of political hegemony rather than the organic unity of one state (Fig. 106). This political fragmentation, engendered by the Reconquest, has been the basis of the provincial framework of Spain. The usage of the Roman term *provincia* is first seen in documents of the sixteenth century, at first vaguely welding together areas which according to medieval custom had been variously termed dukedoms, counties, marquesates, communities, valleys, councils and lands. A few provinces, such as Navarre correspond roughly to former political units. Others are subdivisions of a kingdom, such as the Castilian units

FIG. 106 (above). The kingdoms of Spain
FIG. 107 (below). The existing provinces of Spain

of Salamanca, Segovia, Soria and Burgos, entities of Reconquest
settlement. Some even mark stages of the military frontier in the
Reconquest, notably Huesca, Saragossa, and Teruel. During the
Napoleonic occupation a framework of *préfectures* was imposed (in
1811). Names were taken from physical features with a bias towards the
unity derived from drainage basins. As a reaction to this imposition, fifty
two provinces were created in 1822 but annulled by further changes in
1823 and 1833 to the present division into forty-eight provinces
(Fig. 107). Within this administrative framework, there are the district
units and parishes.

The strong sense of Spanish localism has also fostered other regions,
the *comarcas* (Fig. 108). With their close intimacy of land utilisation and
peasant societies, these are comparable to the French *pays*. These

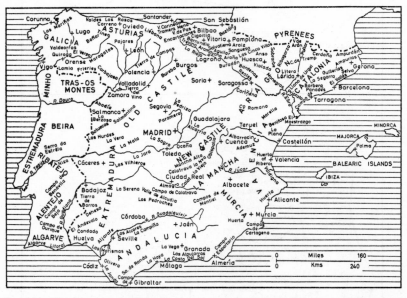

FIG. 108. The 'comarcas' of the Iberian Peninsula. Only the best recognised natural
regions are shown. The Spanish Institute of Statistics lists 280 comarcas and other
agricultural zones in its publication, *Ensayo de division de las provincias Españolas
en comarcas agrícolas homogeeneas*, Madrid, 1949

comarcas are of variable size, ranging from La Mancha with 10,900 sq.
miles, through intermediate units such as La Alcárria (1,660 sq. miles)
to small units such as the Val d'Aran (18 sq. miles). They have both
physical and historical connotations preserved by their historical role,
their economic utilisation, and their consequent communal organisa-

tion or feeling. In some of them, the land utilisation is paramount, as in the Tierra del Pan (260 sq. miles) and Tierra del Vino (255 sq. miles) in Western Castile. The rich plain of La Campiña in Andalusia and the numerous *Vegas* or valley lands and *huertas* or irrigated lowlands, are similar. In some cases, the predominant vegetation cover gives its character to the comarca, for example La Jara (890 sq. miles) referring to its dense cover of gum cistus. Others are physical units, such as the recognition of three zones in the Asturias: Las Rasas or coastal abrasion platforms, La Montaña the interior mountains, and La Peña the summits. Isolated mountain communities explain the distinctive traits of La Alpujarra in Upper Andalusia, and Las Hurdes (124 sq. miles) west of the Sa de Gredos. In the Pyrenees, valley communities which formed medieval counties explain regional terms such as, Conflent Cerdaña, Urgel, Pallars, Ribagorza, Sobrarbe, etc. More negative areas with sparse population such as Los Monegros in the Aragonese steppes, or the Maestrazgo (620 sq. miles) in northern Castellón may also be distinct units. Thus localism engendered by poor communications, provincialism coming from a pride in diverse origins, and regionalism fostered by political and economic conditions, have all emphasised the conservatism and individualism of Spain's diverse regions.

THE NORTHERN REGIONS

To the Spaniard, the North has a distinct connotation, associated with the three elements of the Atlantic Ocean, the mountains and a humid climate. Its palette is restricted to vivid greens, symbolic of lush and simple resources to the pastoralist, but appearing somewhat harsh and vulgar to the Castilian painter, accustomed to reflect on the sad and subtle hues of the Meseta. This is pre-Christian Spain, where the peasantry are Celtic and Basque and where the family life is still based on ancient traditions. Indeed, this is part of Atlantic Europe, with a common civilisation that once ranged some two thousand miles from the Mondego to the Scandinavian fiords, having similar deciduous flora and a comparable folk lore. Its life has focused on the ways of the sea, partaking in the trade of the Cassiterides, as later in the travels of the Celtic saints. It was only in the ninth century that the long sea route of St James terminated symbolically in Santiago de Compostela, and the Pilgrims' Way along the borders of Humid and Arid Spain opened up the possibilities of continental connections with Western Europe. Since then its outlook has been ambivalent, in part towards the centre but more naturally still towards the sea. Nowhere else in Spain do geographical and cultural features sharpen more distinctly the character of all things regional than those termed *norteño*. Yet within this climatic and cultural zone are four regional units: Galicia, Cantabrians, La Montaña and the Basque lands.

1. *Galicia*. This is one of the most distinctive regions of the Peninsula. Its broad expanse of 7,345 sq. miles, its double coast line of nearly 300 miles, and its structural uniformity of granite and schist have helped to create its marked individuality. Its dense population which totals 2·7 million inhabitants and its ancient cultures have left their imprint upon humanised landscapes whose regions are innumerable, distinguished by subtle differences rather than violent contrasts. It is difficult to generalise about Galicia. It may be likened to a wild garden with an endless variety of components: coastal rias, broad plateaux, scarped hills, deep valleys, cascades and springs, over which spread broad expanses of heath, scattered pine-woods, and a fragmented mosaic of maize fields and garden plots. Rosalia de Castro has vividly described the poetic elements of its landscape moods. Generally they are sad, reflective landscapes in autumn veiled by the soft white mists, in winter weeping through the long, wet season of 135 to 180 rain-days darkened by grey skies when the south or west winds blow. Everywhere there is the fresh Atlantic atmosphere, expressively termed *marinan*, which means that rarely does the evaporation exceed the precipitation in the north-west in Finisterre an annual maximum of 95 inches occurs. Gales along the exposed coasts make coastal navigation dangerous in winter, and bend the trees and bushes at a permanent angle, while the constant winds sway the pines in a continual sigh.

The granite landscape is everywhere apparent. In the hills the lichen cover cannot disguise its great domed masses breaking skyward out of gentle contours. On the plains, centuries of manuring and spreads of shelly sea-sand carried inland up to 20–25 miles, cushion it in small garden plots. But on every hand it crops out, in desultory rubble walls making their way over the skyline, in squat, quadrangular cottages, in storehouses or sieved by the wind, or just in the waste of stony tors, grotesquely shaped and engendering legends of the past.

It is a Celtic landscape, of small churches rising isolated on knolls, serving a wide scatter of small hamlets, which number more than 32,700 units of settlement, half at least having fewer than 50 inhabitants. (Fig. 110). In a document of 1587, the Church authorities wondered how effective was their influence when there were no less than 2,445 rural parishes for a scattered population of 120,229 families. In the old settled lands of the south-west and west, the hamlet is the unit, going back perhaps to a tribal aristocracy, with the parish forming an ancient, collec-

45 Burgos, northern gateway to Old Castile, with its cathedral on the right

46 The walled town of Ávila

47 Torrevieja, a planned town of S. Alicante

TOWN PLANNING IN PORTUGAL

48 Elvas, border town of Alentejo and Badajoz

49 Valença, another fortress town on border with Galicia across the R. Minho

50 Central Lisbon, planned by Pombal

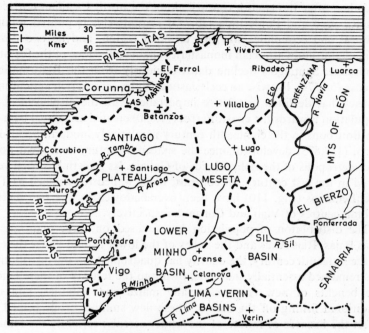

FIG. 109. The regional divisions of Galicia

tive unit. Rounded hamlets are the oldest form, linked frequently with the pre-historic *castros*, of which there are over eight hundred identifiable and some 440 as place-names. The primitive rounded dwellings of the eastern mountains of Lugo and Orense, are a reminder of the Celtic dwellings formerly associated with these *castros* (Fig. 97). The ruined mansions of noble families indicate, however, the former strength of feudalism, and the long periods of insecurity from which the countryside suffered in the middle ages.

Nowhere is the power of the church seen more strongly than in the growth of the towns. Only two, Corunna (133,844) and Betanzos (10,827) were not originally sees. Lugo (53,743) Orense and especially Santiago (55,553) owe much to ecclesiastical influence. Lugo is the oldest town, a fortress since Roman times placed as the interior capital to subjugate the north. From the sixteenth century, the regime of security saw its decline though its Roman walls still indicate its former function. Santiago, established in the ninth century round the shrine of the apostle, linked the coastal rias and the interior, and became the great terminal of the pilgrims route, first along the Cantabrian coast and then after the twelfth century along the north Castilian corridor, via Ribadeo and Ponferrada (23,773) respectively. It poured wealth, cultural and economic, into this terminal region, and its two dozen Benedictine and Cistercian monasteries changed the face of the forested landscape. Santiago's decline dates obviously from the Reformation. Orense (55,574), likewise an ecclesiastical centre set in a rich agricultural district, has declined in relative importance with the displacement of population towards the coast. Ferrol (77,030) created as a naval base by the Bourbons in the eighteenth century is relatively modern. So also is Vigo, (137,873) developed since the sixteenth century as a great port, and metropolis of the richest lands of Galicia. Its growth has been very rapid in the last century. In contrast, older walled towns such as Tuy and Betanzos (Fig. 110) have been overshadowed by the two metropolitan centres of Vigo and Corunna respectively.

The distribution of population has focused on three main areas: Rias Bajas, Rias Altas and the valley of the lower Minho. Since the end of the sixteenth century, the density has quadrupled but the distribution has remained essentially the same, owing to the fertility of these lands, the benefits of new crops especially maize and potatoes, and the traditional fishing off the coasts. These new summer crops helped to offset the hazards of failure of the winter cereals; certainly the famine of 1768 stimulated the rapid spread of the potato. They also help to explain the small size of holdings, fragmented by the population pressure into minute plots so that the common unit is the *ferrada* of 440–640 sq. metres with the *cupelo* in Orense measuring five sq. metres and the *pasta* in Pontevedra only one sq. metre. 75 per cent of all the plots in Galicia are less than one hectare in size.

Only the exuberant growth, under mild and moist climate, and the intensive polyculture of its peasant cultivators, permit such pulverisation of the land to be an economic proposition. Distinction is general between the lands below 1,300 feet where maize, other cereals, potatoes and beans are the chief crops, together with some vines, and the uplands above this, given over largely to stock rearing. In contrast with the Asturias, there are few meadows except some fields of trefoil in the western districts. Instead, the dark brown earth, enclosed in stone walls or hedgerows abuts suddenly upon heathlands, as expansive as those of Wales or Limousin. Everywhere in the interior of Galicia, are great spreads of yellow gorse, green erica (*E. umbellata and E. tetralix*) or sullen peat bogs in the depressions with the smell of the heaths mingling with the resin of the maritime pines and the smell of manure spread over leached, acidic soils. Gorse (*Ulex Europaea*) might well be con-

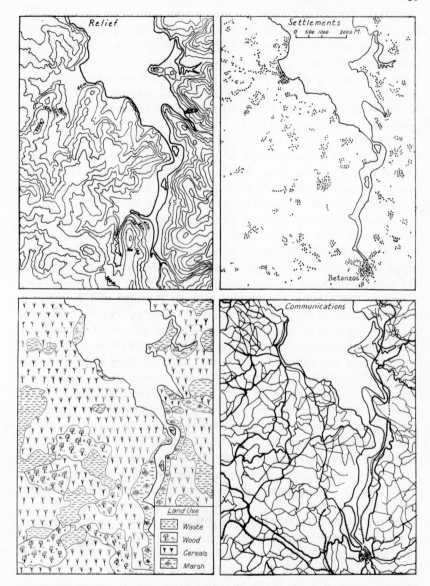

FIG. 110. Relief, land utilisation, settlements and communication in the district of
Betanzos (Corunna)

sidered the symbol of Galicia, for after a poor crop of cereals on heathy lands, the traditional rotation has followed with eight to twelve or more years of gorse, first grown as a fodder and bedding for the cattle, then as a source of charcoal fuel. Many communes still cast lots for the communal cutting of the gorse. As the cultivated lands represent only 27 per cent of the total, and one third of all Spanish cattle are concentrated in Galicia, the full utilisation of the hill lands is the major challenge of modern agriculture.

But Galicia appears still fossilised in its past traditions. It is remote and insular and its ports are all of local importance apart from Vigo, Ferrol and Corunna. The express from Corunna takes nineteen hours to reach Madrid 527 miles away; and the train to Catalonia is scheduled to take thirty-six hours if it runs to time! Within Galicia is the most northerly point of the Peninsula (Estaca de Vares) and Finisterre is one of the capes flung furthest west from Europe into the Atlantic. Galicia is a world apart, and perhaps never more so than today. Its past seems by comparison more glorious; the mineral objective of the ancient navigators to the Cassiterides; a link in the Atlantic community between Portugal and Norway; a great terminus of medieval pilgrimage. As long as Galicia could look seawards turning its back on the poverty of its own hinterland, it could find recompense in its fishing and mercantile interests; first as a whaling and cod-fishing base for the Atlantic, then as a sharer in colonial emigration and trade. But in the modern world, its premier status of fish producer, employing 140,000 in the trade, and now as exporter of hydro-electric power to Madrid, is but a poor compensation for its illustrious past. Over-population has been the curse of Galicia, and its principal export has been humanity, losing in the last century alone 1·3 million Gallegans, chiefly to South America. The nostalgia of the exile, distinctively called *morrina* is sharpened by the remembrance of the features which make the regional landscapes of this Atlantic region so distinctive.

Within Galicia, Dantín has distinguished no less than fifty different *comarcas*. These comprise mostly valley units, nodes of early colonisation, comparable perhaps to the English vales. As three-quarters of Galicia lies below 1,500 ft and most of the interior is an undulating plateau of about 1,200 ft the term mountain usually means no more than a marked ridge separating the broad swell of plateaux and river basins. The upper basin of the Minho, centred on Lugo, and the series of fertile basins, laced together by the Lower Sil and Minho form the nuclei of interior Galicia for population and communications. In the south-east of Orense and the east of Lugo province, the mountains are higher, still largely covered with forests of pedunculate and toza oaks.

The great wealth of the country lies along the west coast, where the majority of Galicia's eighty-seven ports are concentrated. Craggy, mountainous peninsulas effectively cut off the rias of Muros, Arosa, Pontevedra and Vigo from each other, favouring this multiplicity of small ports, while seawards offshore islets make navigation dangerous. At the head of each ria, some 30 miles inland, a small market town is sited characteristically where landward communications are significant, as in the notable example of Pontevedra (43,221). At the seaward arms of each peninsula are two or more fishing ports, such as Marín (17,592), and notably Vigo. Compared with the distinct isolation of the Rias Bajos, the Rias Atlas further north are shallower, smaller, and focus on the three regions of Corunna, Betanzos (Fig. 110) and Mondonedo (8,533) each an ancient centre. But the coasts are rocky, cliffed steeply, and the incised valleys recently elevated by Quaternary movements are less suitable for inland communications and so remain largely forested. Widespread heathlands and a stock-rearing economy also predominate along the north coast, which conserves some of the most lively traces of the ancient past.

2. *The Asturias.* This is a compact landscape that boasts some of the most mountainous and deserted, and yet also some of the most long settled and now industrialised countrysides, in the Peninsula. Exposed coastal plateaux, narrow green valleys, filled with soft blue-gray mist, thickly wooded slopes of deciduous oaks and maritime pines, high mountain cornfields, scattered red-tiled farmhouses, tiny Visigothic churches, industrial plants and coalmines—such are the elements that make up the Asturias. The mountain framework clearly defines the bounds of this region to the south and east, and the steep cliffs, which rebuff the long fetch of the Atlantic rollers, are no less definite. Only in the north-west does the Asturias merge more transitionally with Galicia, approximately along the Eo valley. The Asturias looks neither seaward like Galicia nor inland towards Castile like La Montaña, but centres its interests within its own longitudinal depression behind the coastal ranges, the most extensive of all the Cantabrian corridors.

The southern mountain rampart of the Asturias extends some 180 miles from west to east, the most effective barrier to communications in northern Spain. In the south-west, separating León from the Asturias, the massive mountains of Cabrera rise to over 6,000 ft, a wild country of peneplaned surfaces, covered with immense areas of gorse and heath, and of dreary tablelands. The *brañas*, especially between the headstreams of the Navia and the Nalon, are still frequented by transhumant *vaquieros*, primitive pastoralists that spend their year between the lower settlements and the summer upland huts. To the north-west, the folded mountains, trending north to south, comprise poor country. Depopulation has been marked, although sheltering in the fertile basin of the Narcea, is a more productive countryside of maize fields and vineyards around Cangas de Tineo (21,143). Despite the north–south trends followed by the valleys, there are no significant mountain passes leading southwards, apart from the Col of Leitariegos (4,990 feet). East of these mountains, Palaeozoic schists and limestones are carved into impressive peaks such as Peñas Urbina (7,930 feet), heavily forested on the northern slopes but bare and denuded on the Castilian flanks. The Pájares Pass (4,470 feet) the chief one of the Cantabrians is still a difficult route, only eased by the recent electrification of the railway which links Palencia and Gijón. To the east, in the Picos de Europa is the most impressive scenery of all, a mountain redoubt of glaciated limestones that now comprises a national park. Here in the gorges of Covadonga, the Asturian king Pelayo first took a stand against the Muslims, the thickly forested valleys and bare peaks that rise to over 7,000 feet providing ideal conditions for the inception of the Reconquest. It is still a wild, heavily wooded country.

Because of the steep cliffs along most of the coast, settlements tend to avoid the shore, except where rias have favoured sheltered harbours, some of them still surrounded with their medieval town walls. Coastal platforms hang suspended from the coastal ranges, notched like a natural stairway that is, however, inadequate for communication with the shore (Fig. 72). Ports are therefore small, though picturesque, at Castropol (6,752), Luarca (24,730) (Fig. 102) and Cudillero (10,520), and the exploitation of timber from the interior is an alternative occupation to fishing. A sequence of bays and headlands follows the erosion of the Silurian slates and quartzites, culminating in the Cabo de Peñas with its magnificent sea views and sunsets. On either side of it lie sheltered the two chief ports of Asturias, Gijón (110,985), and Avilés (21,270). Gijón, a walled town built on a small coastal promontory has been the traditional outlet for the Central Depression, exporting in the middle ages chestnuts, cheese and other land products as it now exports coal. Traditional glass and ceramic factories are now overshadowed by the great metallurgical furnaces whose industries have fostered the spread of the city eastwards along the beach of San Lorenzo and west of the old port. Avilés is now witnessing a more rapid growth, doubling its population since 1950 with the construction of a new port, giant steel-strip mills and coking plants, all added within a decade, a formidable future rival for Bilbao. The fretted coastline continues eastwards, favouring the sites of Villaviciosa (20,348), Colunga and Ribadesella, formerly whaling ports, now engaged in fishing and tourism. Pastures and apple orchards form a friendly hinterland to this coast. In contrast, the linear and karstic coast east of Ribadesilla backed by the Sa de Cuera (4,300 feet) is a poor region. Only the floors of the polja are sheltered enough for the orange and lemon gardens to ripen. But along this whole coast, Llanes (20,107) is the only port worthy of the name.

Between the coast and the mountains of the interior, is the historic and economic hearth of Asturias, the longitudinal depression between the two Visigothic capitals of Cangas de Onis (10,713) in the east and Oviedo (106,002) in the west. It is not a continuous plain, but a hilly, rolling country rising to 1,000–1,200 feet in parts, with bocage features of high hedgerows and pastures. The eastern valley of the Cores is a pastoral landscape with heavily forested slopes but westwards the broader basin of Oviedo is more intensely cultivated under a succession of beans, maize, vegetables and orchards, especially in the Vega de Grado to the west of Oviedo. This is a neighbourly countryside with densely scattered hamlets and small fields. Oviedo, the great capital, is sited where the anticlinal ridge of the Monte del Naranco overlooks the valley. Nearby are the Visigothic churches of Santa Maria de Naranco and San Miguel de Lillo, and from the shelter of an eighth century monastery, Oviedo has itself grown. In 1857, its walls still enclosed many gardens and its population was only 14,157. It was the railway (built in 1886) that helped to create a new industrial city, which now spreads along the roads leading out towards Gijón, Santander and Castile. Its factories are chiefly engaged in the demands of the coal industry, armaments and heavy chemicals. Following up the valleys of the Nalón and the Caudal are the coalfields, which have revolutionised the traditional mode of life since the end of the last century. There, in deeply incised valleys, great mining centres such as Langreo (50,000) and Mieres (60,000 including suburbs) have grown rapidly (Fig. 125).

3. *La Montaña of Santander.* The province of Santander corresponds loosely to the region between Asturias and Biscay, called 'La Montaña'. It is linked by the Pas and Besaya valleys with Burgos and Plasencia respectively. Its Castilian overlords found in this deeply dissected relief, a mountainous country compared with their own tableland, even though much of it is considerably lower in elevation than Castile. The name is thus a feudal relic of Castilian rule—'Lords of the mountain'— and its economic ties with the Meseta further distinguished it from the

lands to the east and west. The climate is transitional, showing more markedly than Viscaya the influence of southerly air-streams, and a generally lower rainfall. But Santander is typically Cantabrian in its fundamental distinction between the coastal lands, *La Costa* and the interior higher lands, *La Montaña* proper.

The coastal zone presents a series of docile landscapes, in which the majority of the total population is concentrated (Fig. 125). It boasts evidence in the upper Palaeolithic caves of Altamira, Castillos, etc. and in its Iron Age *castros*, of a long continued settlement. The very high density of population, and the tradition of peasant ownership (two-thirds of the holdings are owner occupied) have created a marked fragmentation of holdings. Some 84 per cent of all holdings average less than one acre, and at least ten to twelve parcels of land constitute the average holding. Everywhere there is the dominance of meadow land, one third of the total area being grazed in this form, and another third used as mountain pasture. The deciduous oak forests have disappeared and even the chestnut groves are being often replaced by thick stands of eucalyptus. Agricultural land is limited to less than one-tenth of the area, so that intensive polyculture of beans, maize and potatoes tends to be concentrated in the valley lands. Although surrounded by hedgerows, the landscape appears more open than that of Biscay. The two-storeyed dwellings, with their four sided roofs, stone walls and more open balconies because of the drier atmosphere, are all features different from the Basque *caserío* (Fig. 104). But dissemination of houses is intense, especially in the lower valleys of the Pas and Besaya.

Traditionally, the coast was governed by the 'Four Towns': Castro-Urdiales (11,646) and Laredo (6,866) in the eastern region of Trasmiera, Santander (102,462) and San Vicente de la Barquera (3,313) in Ribamontana al Mar. All, except Santander, are moribund ports, where modern seaside resorts are more important than their fishing harbours. Santander, situated on a magnificent ria excavated in a breached anticline, was first established as a port in the eleventh century. After the thirteenth century, it became the chief outlet of wool from the Meseta to Flanders. After the railway connected it with Valladolid (in 1866), it became the outlet of Castilian flour to the Antilles. Santander, which still had under 50,000 inhabitants a century ago, reached its present growth by the development of metallurgical industries, milk-processing plants and chemical factories. Torrelavega (23,728) the focus of the rich dairy lands of Asturias de Santillana, shares in similar activities. The coastal lands of Santander are the dairy of Spain, concentrating on its pastures three quarters of all its milch cows.

In the interior, there is a sharp contrast between the east and the west. In the south-east, karstic plateaux merge into the Castilian tablelands, a poor and sparsely settled land of fortified villages. In the south-west, the ranges of *montaña* limestones rise steeply and enclose fertile basins with considerable densities of population. Liebana is the most distinctive *comarca*, a tectonic trough in which shelter vines and even olives. The Valle de Campóo, centred on Reinosa is less clearly defined, a high transition area, forming a traditional pastoral community. Meadows and pastures are the main features but forests of pedunculate oak are still preserved, reaching an optimum development at between 1200 and 2600 ft and then succeeded by beech forests. But on the poorer soils of the Triassic and Wealden sandstones and marls, deforestation has left open vast tracts of erica heath (*Erica cinerea, E. vagans* and *Calluna vulgaris*) and gorse (*Ulex europeus*). Only local breeds of poor stock graze on these lands, compared with the commercial grazing of Dutch cattle in the north.

4. *The Basque Lands.* Las Vascongadas are a unique region of some 2,740 sq. miles, because of its unique people, now numbering 1,063,000. Composed of three of the smallest provinces in Spain together with northern Navarre, it is a linguistic expression. In Roman times probably most of the people of the western Pyrenees spoke Euskaria but since the eighteenth century the language has been in full retreat: first from Roncal and the Ribera of Navarre, then through central Navarre and eventually it has settled along the main watershed between the drainage of the Ebro and the Atlantic streams. Within its two northern provinces of Viscaya and Guipùzcoa, Euskaria is disappearing also in the industrial centres which have drawn on alien immigrants. In the countryside however, the Basque people, of unknown origin, have maintained their identity and have even talked of the idea of a separate state, 'Euzkadi'. Geographical conditions have aided such an independence of outlook for the region belongs to a Cantabrian rather than a Pyrenean context. The Pyrenean valleys unite and lead inland, the Basque valleys divide and look seawards. The Basques have lived, therefore, in more isolation than the Aragonese. Each valley is a human region, formerly a tribal unit of pastoralism. Thick forests and to the north, the marshes of the Landes, provided effective frontiers. Thus the political units of the county of Guipúzcoa (728 sq. miles), the lordship of Viscaya or Biscay (663 sq. miles) and Alava 'the land between the mountains' (1,176 sq. miles) suggest in their juridical peculiarities the difficulties that the Spanish crown had in governing these unruly territories from the fourteenth century onwards. The tripar-

tite division also reflects, however, underlying geographical differences.

Biscay has a corrugated relief, structurally controlled by the gently folded Mesozoic rocks, that are orientated west-north-west to east-south-east. A few rivers, such as the upper Nervión follow denuded anticlinal folds, but the lower course of this river, and indeed the great majority of the longitudinal rivers, follow synclinal depressions. The fishermen of Biscay have given their name to the whole of the great oceanic bay. Yet the valley trends provide some shelter from the northerly and westerly winds, so that the orographic rainfall is less generous than in Guipúzcoa. At the same time, the province is exposed to southerly air-streams from the Meseta. The climate is consequently a mild oceanic, Mediterranean type, whose moods vary between the transparency and red sunsets and grey skies. Evergreen forest on calcareous stands mingles with the dominant deciduous species, especially the pedunculate oak. Pastures tend to burn out in summer, cereals are important in the rotation, and vineyards have more significance than is usual in the north.

In Guipúzcoa the west-north-west to east-south-east trends in relief are still marked but the relief is more markedly erosional consequent on its uplift nearer the Pyrenees, with intensive differential erosion which has etched out transverse corridors. The grille pattern of relief induces easier communications between land and sea. The oceanic air streams penetrate deeply, encouraged by the coastal trend of the Bay of Biscay which funnels upon eastern Guipúzcoa. Rainfall reaches a maximum of over 120 inches annually. On the coastal ranges is thus heard the resonance of water in a lush Atlantic selva of deciduous oaks and chestnuts or in the rapidly established plantations of *Pinus insignis*, that are favoured by the paper mills. In the Pyrenean inliers of Cinco Villas and Rhune across the border in Navarre, the Palaeozoic shales and slates break down into deep soils with dense forests which often cover 80–90 per cent of the slopes, notably in the Valle de Santestéban. The high mountain framework to the south of Guipúzcoa, excluding southern influences more effectively than in Vizcaya, explains the dramatic contrast of the Atlantic facade and the Mediterranean landscapes that begin at Alsasua for example, south of the Sa de Aralar (Fig. 75). Everywhere in Guipúzcoa the landscape is green, the shrill green of the maize fields, the pastel or darker shades of the orchards, the sombre green of the occasional *chacolí* vineyard, all set in a sea of pasture and forest. Only the broad, red tiled roofs and the whitewashed walls of the *caseríos* relieve this monotony of colour.

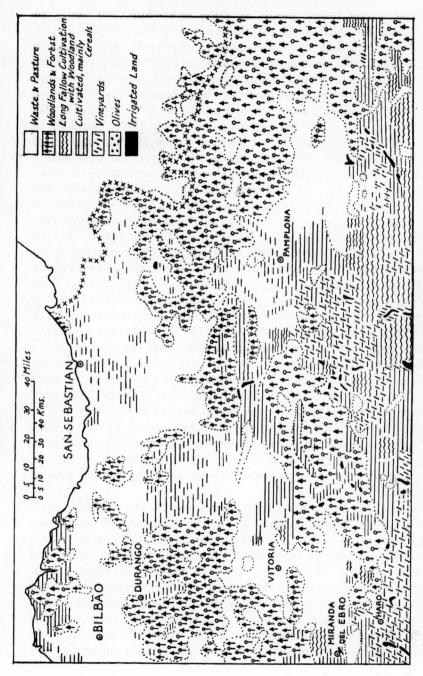

FIG. 111. Land utilisation in the Basque lands

The market towns, mostly at valley cross-roads, are nearly all medieval foundations of the thirteenth and fourteenth centuries. Historic towns with noble buildings, they are generally small, averaging only 1,000–5,000 inhabitants, such as Oñate and Guernica. Like South Wales, the green valleys of Guipúzcoa and Viscaya have been smudged with industry. Mineralised limestones have been sources of iron and copper from ancient times, smelted primitively in hollowed-out oaks lined with clay. Such *ferrerías* existed until the 1880s, especially in Guipúzcoa and skilled crafts developed, notably the manufacture of arms at Placencia, Eibar, Mondragón and Tolosa. The high quality ores of Viscaya attracted modern industrialism, however, to the lower Nervion valley between 1841 and 1892. Bilbao, which had been carefully planned in 1300 as a Castilian port, still had only 9,500 inhabitants at the end of the eighteenth century and 17,870 in 1860. As a consequence of the steel industry and the creation of a new port in 1883, its population from 83,306 in 1900 to 229,334 in 1950, supporting about 400,000 in its conurbation. During the last half-century, the economic pendulum had therefore swung from Guipúzcoa to Viscaya but there are now signs of the possible reversal of this trend with the growth of the industrial towns in the former province. Such towns are: Irun (19,956), Pasajes (11,773), Rentería (12,784) and Tolosa (14,971). Even more so, the new phenomenon of tourism has encouraged the expansion of San Sebastian from a medieval fortress and an eighteenth century centre, trading in Venezuelan cocoa, to a summer resort. Prior to the advent of the railway in 1864, it had only *c.* 9,000 inhabitants, but when the summer palace of the Regent Maria Christina was built in 1893, the population had risen to over 30,000, reaching 113,776 in 1950. Tourism is now transforming the economy of some coastal settlements such as Fuenterrabia and Cestona, but fishing is still important, especially at the Viscayan ports of Ondarroa, Lequeitio and Bermeo (12,460).

Alava is more Castilian in its aspect than its two northern neighbours. As its Basque name implies (*araiiar*, set among the mountains), the core region is an intermontane basin, the Llanada de Vitoria (*c.* 1500 feet). Its physical setting is thus comparable to Navarre and ancient Aragón, whose centres are both placed in a similar tectonic corridor. Situated between the ravined valleys of the northern Basque lands and the east-to-west folded ranges in the south, (Sierras de Codés, Toloño and Cantabria) Alava is aligned along the broad corridor, which is traceable in Pamplona and Jaca. More than them, however, Alava shares the continental cold and the summer drought of the

Meseta. Apart from oak and beech forests on its higher northern slopes, Alava is an open landscape, with bare contours and cereal-covered plains. Maize is grown only on the northern borders. Vineyards became famous in the Alavese Rioja in the south. Large farms are common in central Alava and modernised farming of sugar beet and fodder crops is noteworthy. Compared with the dissemination of settlement to the north, there is here a marked grouping of hamlets with 50–200 inhabitants. But unlike the high densities of 660–750 per sq. mile averaged in the two northern provinces, the population is only 97 per sq. mile. In the whole province Vitoria is the only town with more than 3,500 inhabitants. Built in 1256, near the site of an ancient hamlet, its medieval oval plan had little subsequent growth until the coming of the railway. Since the mid-nineteenth century when it was a market town of 15,000 inhabitants, it has tripled in size (46,940 in 1950) with the establishment of new factories utilising the region's agricultural and timber resources.

EASTERN SPAIN

Compared with the North, Eastern Spain appears to have less geographical unity and yet, perhaps, it has more cultural uniformity. Here the northern distinction between pluviose and arid conditions is replaced by the contrast between irrigated and non-irrigated land. There are no impressive ranges such as the Cantabrians to demarcate it from the interior. For the edge of the Meseta, although mountainous, has notable corridors, such as those of Teruel-Liria, Játiva-Almansa and the Segura valley—which have incorporated in the past Valencia within the Aragónese realm, and made Murcia a Castilian province. The length of the east coast, running some 600 miles from Cape Creus to Cape Gata through more than four degrees of latitude, embraces all the Mediterranean climatic transitions from sub-humid type in north-east Catalonia to a xero-Mediterranean type in Murcia. Geologically, three styles of relief are represented: the Catalan (Hercynian units), the Iberian (Saxonian massifs) and the Sub-Baetic (Jurassic folded ranges). The vegetation cover gives more uniformity to the landscape. Along the coast, the zone of *Quercete-Lentiscetum* and the cultivated *Oleo-Ceratonion* rises from sea-level to about 1,150 ft in Catalonia, higher still to the south. The enormous tracts of garrigue and degraded forms, in which species of *Brachypodium* predominate, present much similarity, varying according to the basic climaxes of the calciphyte *Rosmarin-Ericion* and the calcifuge *Cistion-ladaniferi*.

South of the Llobregat forests are sparse with a total area of 334 sq. miles.

There is also a remarkable linguistic uniformity, with six of its seven provinces bound by the common roots of originally Provençal dialect (though any self-respecting Catalan will protest at this view of his language). A common outlook on the Mediterranean, with its mercantile and political opportunities unified eastern Spain still further. Why then was a nation not forged here comparable to Portugal on the west coast? The absence of any natural harbour on the east coast, apart from Cartagena which faces a barren hinterland, has resulted in the rise and fall of many ports. Catalonia has not enjoyed the splendid isolation of the Minho. Neither was history favourable when Aragón was united to Castile in 1471, and when oceanic discovery deprived the Western Mediterranean of its international leadership during the sixteenth century. Despite this, the individualism of Catalonia and the three Levante regions is marked. For in this environment man has clearly been the measure of things.

1. *Eastern Catalonia.* Triangular in shape, its base running along the Pyrenees and its sides flanked by the Mediterranean sea and the Segre valley, Catalonia has its apex beyond the Ebro delta. Thus, while it extends some 112 miles from Cape Sebastian via Vich to the headwaters of the Noguera Pallaresa and its coast runs sinuously for 258 miles, Catalonia is only 18 miles wide in the southern district of Reus. Within Catalonia, with its three and a quarter million people, there are sharp contrasts in density. Its name is derived from the small feudal counties (*catalonya*) which developed after the decline of the Carolingian empire on the frontiers of the eastern Pyrenees. 'Old Catalonia' was constituted when the counts of Barcelona gained supremacy of the northern counties, roughly to the north of the Llobregat valley. In the Reconquest, the capture of the lands between the Segre and Tarragona constituted 'New Catalonia'. This historic distinction coincides roughly between the more pluviose northern sector and the drier western and southern lands, so that it is a fundamental divide. Catalonia is also shared by three physiographic regions: the Pyrenees, the Ebro valley and the Mediterranean mountains and littoral. Consequently, only the last of these is treated here (see pp. 290–6) coinciding approximately with the province of Tarragona and also most of Barcelona and Gerona. The diversity of landforms, the duality of 'Old' and 'New' Catalonia, and the strongly developed regionalist feelings of this proud and incendiary land, are the major characteristics.

From the top of Montserrat (4,350 ft) the sacred mountain of Cata-

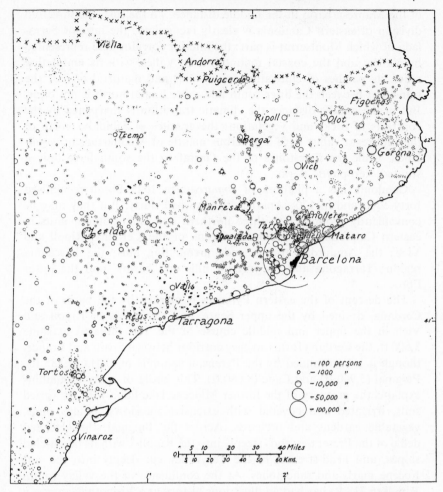

FIG. 112. Distribution of population in N.E. Spain. Note the marked industrial concentration around Barcelona, the dispersed character of settlement in the Ampurdan trough, and the nucleated nature of settlement in the Ebro plain and northern Castillon. What the map fails to show is the pronounced change from dispersed rural settlement in Old Catalonia, north of the Llobregat and the nucleated units south of the river that is south of Barcelona.

Ionia, it is possible to view these features. Ascending the funicular, grotesquely eroded conglomerates rise sheer for several hundreds of feet in great vertical columns, chimneys and serrated summits (Fig. 21). To the west, the view of the arid Eocene scarplands of the Sagarra and the Llanos de Urgell on the horizon is only relieved by the greenery of the Manresa basin in the middle distance. To the east, the threefold division of eastern Catalonia is clearly recognised: the interior Serralada of which Montserrat is part; the interior corridor here represented by Vallés; and the coastal mountains. In Vallés, with its undulating relief, its patches of cultivation, pinewoods and matorral of ilex, the transition between the drier south and more humid north is not clear. But in the middle distance the climatic transition is sharpened by the contrasts of rocks and vegetation; the granites of Tibidabo north of the Llobregat valley have a generous mantle of Mediterranean woodlands, while the limestones of the Garraf to the south have only a stunted, xerophytic flora.

Catalonia has a plethora of *comarcas*; in 1628 Bosch recognised forty-eight and in 1708 Aparici distinguished thirty. But they may be conveniently grouped into three northern and two southern units in eastern Catalonia: the mountain basins of the Cerdaña, Ripoll and Vich; the Ampurdán trough and surrounding hills; the Barcelona region; Tarragona and the interior hills and basins; and the lower Ebro.

The descent of the eastern Pyrenees is marked by the basin of the Cerdaña, drained by the upper Segre, and the plains of Ripoll and Vich in the upper and middle course of the Ter. Situated at some 3,500 ft, the Cerdaña forms an easy corridor between Spain and France, though it is surrounded by the Pyrenean summits of Carlit (9,585 ft), Puigmal (5,960 ft) and Cadé (8,680 ft). This girdle of rainy mountains explains the greenery of the former Miocene lake floor with its varied soils, irrigated and covered with extensive meadows, potato plots, vegetable gardens and orchards. Across the Puigmal, the glaciated defile of the Freser descends steeply into the Ripolles with its beech-clad slopes, and head-streams of the Ter valley cut deeply into the soft Eocene marls and sandstones. At the confluence of the valley routes Ripoll (6,718 ft) has had an illustrious history as a Visigothic county, a medieval monastery that initiated the Catalan Reconquest, and today a tourist and market centre. Downstream the Ter valley widens into the Vich basin, with its borders of Eo-Oligocene badlands and granitic mountains.

The folded relief of the Guillerías and the wooded mountains of Montseny form the western edge of the tectonic basin of the Ampurdán. But the Olot plain with 30–40 in is climatically more associated with the humid zone of north central Catalonia. Its lush cultivation of maize, beans, forage and other crops, and its intensive stock-raising makes it a rich *comarca*, eulogised in the poems of Maragall.

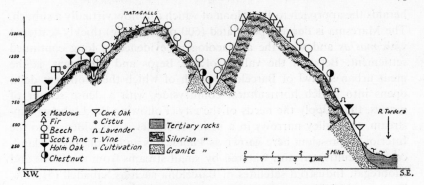

FIG. 113. Geological cross-section and vegetation of Montseny

As a local saying puts it, 'when Olot gets no rain, nowhere else will'. Montseny (5,615 ft) the highest range in eastern Catalonia is clothed in extensive forests of both central European and Mediterranean species, although the ilex predominates (Fig. 113). The wild region, the medieval redoubt of Catalonia, evokes in its environs such regional names as *La Selva*, still covered thickly with cork oak woodlands and *Garrotxa*, that is, matorral. East of Garrotxa and Montseny, the valleys of the Fluvia and Ter open respectively into the undulating plains of Upper and Lower Ampurdán. At once, the drier, more Mediterranean aspect becomes apparent, with vines, olives and *huertas*, the latter screened by reed fences against the cold winds that blow from the Pyrenees. Figueras (15,624) and Gerona (27,414) are the market centres of these plains, fortresses of early origin; in the Gerona district there are numerous examples of Catalan farms (*masías*) occupying the sites of Roman villas. On the coast at Ampurias where there are the ruins side by side of Greek and Iberian towns (Plate 21), the sense of continuity is still felt in the charming fishing villages that lie secreted in the inlets of the indented Rosas coast and the more popularised tourist centres of the southern Costa Brava. The latter, backed by the granitic hills of the Gavarras, are deeply weathered by chemical action and clothed in dense woodlands of pines, ilex and cork oaks, on the southern border of pluviose Catalonia.

From the mouth of the river Toreda near Blanes, the cliffed coast of the Costa Brava terminates and the narrow plain of Maresma or the Costa del Levante scintillates with granitic sands washed down from the interior of the Serralada de la Marina. It is a lowland of intensive market gardening and of numerous industrial, especially textile, centres, notably Mataró (29,424) and Badalona (41,454). The latter heralds the approach to Barcelona of which it is now virtually a suburb. The Maresma is densely populated (600 per sq. mile) thickly scattered with *masías* and with the archaeological evidence of long continued settlement. Between the valleys of the Besós and Llobregat, is the great urban sprawl of Barcelona, south of which the Llobregat delta opens into a rich horticultural countryside, with a dense scatter of *masías*, that supply the needs of the city. Following the Llobregat upstream, the valley narrows in a series of defiles, then widens into the Interior Depression, here known as *Vallés*. It is an undulating lowland, carefully cultivated and watered by small streams from the Besós and Llobregat. Industrial satellites of Barcelona such as Sabadell (51,727), Tarrasa (56,738) and Granollers (14,573) are now much more important than the old centres, such as the monastery of San Cugat.

The site of Barcelona has the features typical of a Mediterranean port. Situated on the coastal plain between the deltas of the Besós and the Llobregat, the coastline has changed considerably since its foundation. An open roadstead, it was sheltered by the isolated hill of Montjuich (568 ft) from the prevailing northerly and easterly winds and protected by its fortress. The Carthaginian and Greek city of *Barcino* was built on an island, Taber (39 ft above sea-level). The ancient harbour lay to the south of Montjuich probably when this hill was still an island, but which gradually was united to the coast with the growth of the Llobregat delta. By Roman times, Taber was linked with the Besós delta and the Romans built their port at the mouth of the Jonquere torrent nearby. Now the site of the cathedral (1298–1438), Taber was formerly the nucleus of the merchant quarters. The old harbour gradually silted with the expansion of the Besós delta, and it was virtually useless in the fifteenth century. But Barcelona, now at the apogee of its Mediterranean trade rivalling Venice and Genoa, could afford to surmount natural disadvantages. Two islets offshore, which aligned the growth of the Besós sand dunes were linked to form a jetty and enclose an artificial harbour after 1447. The bar continued to grow and it had virtually blocked the narrow entrance between it and Montjuich during the seventeenth and eighteenth centuries. In the nineteenth century, the mole following the trend of coastal evolution was extended and new docks excavated under the Rafo plan (1859), not completed until 1926.

The plan of Barcelona shows a medieval layout grafted upon a modern creation (Fig. 114). This is explained by the two great periods of Barcelona's growth, the Middle Ages and the nineteenth century. Barcelona focused on its harbour, grew out from Taber between the

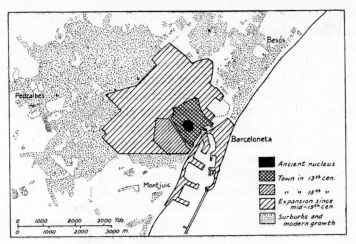

FIG. 114. The growth of Barcelona

two torrent beds of the Malla and Jonquere, now the alignment of the Ramblas. A local Visigothic capital, Barcelona became the capital of the Catalan kingdom in 1137 and henceforth its growth was intimately linked with the brilliant expansion of the Catalan empire and its rich Mediterranean trade. A wall was built around the growing town in the thirteenth century and a hundred years later the population was estimated at 35,000. Another wall was added to contain the south-eastern suburbs in the fifteenth century. These medieval walls sufficed to surround the city until the nineteenth century because of the commercial decay consequent on debarring the Catalan ports from free trade with the Americas during the period 1492–1778. Thus the city lay-out and the construction of its main buildings date roughly from the two main periods: 1300–1500, when the city was a great commercial capital, and 1850–1900, when it regained supremacy as the economic and industrial capital of Spain.

The nodality of Barcelona has best been realised in the nineteenth century expansion. The through valleys of the Besós and Llobregat, that focus on Barcelona, enabled the capital to command all Catalonia in the Middle Ages by use of the Interior Depression. These same valleys provided water power for its textile industries, first for its water-mills after 1778. Then, by the generation of hydro-electric power, Catalonia built up the densest rail network in Spain, and the same valleys gave Barcelona trans-Pyrenean and Aragonese connections. all focused on its four terminal stations. The discovery and exploitation of the Suria potash field, accessible via the Llobregat valley, stimulated the chemical industry in the environs of Barcelona. Thus the growth of the city was consequent on this industrial expansion: in 1850 175,000 and in 1950 1,278,999 (Fig. 114). The gridiron of the Cerda plan has been the expression of this phase and also of Castilian autocracy, since Barcelona was never consulted! First the medieval walls were pulled down (1854), then began (in 1860) the most systematic planning of a European city up to that time. Unfortunately little attempt was made to integrate the new city with the old, nor were grafted the suburbs within the new city which had already developed at the foot of Tibidabo (1,680 ft) such as Sarria, Sant Gervasi and Gracia. After half a century of intense rivalry with Madrid, Barcelona now seems to be settling down to the role of the second city of Spain, still growing, but less explosively so.

Following the alignment of the Via Augusta across the old Roman bridge of Martorell, over the ravine of the Llobregat, the dry karstic landscape of the coastal mountains (Garraf) with a thin cover of pine woods and garrique plants, announces the realm of 'dry' or 'new' Catalonia. Between the tourist beaches of Castell de Fels and Sitges, the coast truncates the limestone hills in cliffs. Inland, the smooth features of Vallés are superseded south of the Llobregat by the more varied relief of Penedes. Soft marls are dissected into badlands while hard conglomerates form hills, such as Pacs and Velobi, 300–400 ft above the corridor. From the stoney Pliocene soils, vineyarded terraces produce champagne wines whose profits have enriched the mansions of Villafranca del Penedes the regional centre. Southwards the Interior Depression widens, to merge with the rolling coastal hills and plains of the Campo de Tarragona, a fruity landscape of olives, hazels, almonds, vines and carobs. Densely populated since Roman times (250 per sq. miles today), the region is divided into the following districts: the Upper Campo centred on picturesque, walled Valls its land less intensely utilised (160 sq. mile); Lower Campo with its prosperous market and industrial town of Reus, backed by the poorer lands of Priorate; all focused on the great historic centre of Tarragona (36,000) near the mouth of the R. Francoli. Perched magnificently on a coastal hill (226 ft) the Iberian, Carthaginian and Roman stronghold of *Tarraco* was the site of the medieval walled town. Separated sharply from the new town or 'Marina' at the port, it has preserved its old character, crowned by its great Romanesque cathedral. Tarragona is still essentially the commercial outlet for its wine and olive-grown hinterland.

South of the fertile Campo de Tarragona, the country grows barer, a dusty olive country with white limestone hills and patches of terra rossa, backed by the great sweep of Jurassic style mountains. Through the latter, the Ebro cuts its way sinuously in impressive gorges to flow turbulently past Tortosa perched on a rocky ledge. Its Lonja indicates its share in medieval trade, now restricted to some river traffic. About nine miles downstream from Tortosa, the Ebro leaves its gorge at Amposta and enters the marshy, partially cultivated ricefields of the delta. Two-thirds of this lagoon-strewn, gley land, has been converted to rice cultivation during the last hundred years, formerly a malarial-infested waste and haunt of wild fowl. Distinction is now made between the *huerta* land of the upper delta, from La Cava via Amposta to Tortosa, with its scatter of cottages, and the more extensive spread of ricefields in the lower delta, dotted only with the towers of the pumping stations. South of the delta, the sandy hook of the Punta del Calacho curls protectingly around the almost enclosed natural harbour of Alfaques. But San Carlos, which Carlos III dreamt of making into a great eighteenth-century port, is still a modest fishing village. Across the dry *rambla* of the Cenia one has left Catalonia and crossed into the next kingdom of Valencia.

2. *The Valencian Levante*. The two provinces of Castellón and Valencia have comparable features, unlike Alicante, which was formerly the third unit of the kingdom of Valencia. The most striking feature of this region is the concentration of almost nine-tenths of the population within one-tenth of the area, along the littoral (Fig. 116). The transformation of these semi-arid plains into *huertas* reaches its climax in the Vega of Valencia with almost oriental densities of population, and a commercial opportunism unique among the rural communities of the Peninsula. The envy of all its conquerors, the Valencian region has an ancient continuity of settlement, traceable through its Iberian towns, Roman villas and Moorish *alquerías*. More important than the diversity of landforms has always been the contrast between the poor lands of the interior and the fecund coastal plain.

From the Maestrazgo and Javalambre massifs rising to over 6,000 ft in the north, to the heights of Chinchilla in the south, the interior of the Levante is wild, mountainous country, carved out of folded Mesozoic limestones, Triassic sandstones and marls, and down-faulted in a series of dissected plateaux. The rivers Mijares, Turia and notably the Júcar and its Cabriel tributary, are deeply incised. Apart from pastoralism, exploiting the extensive range lands of Mediterranean shrubs and plants, some seventy-five *vegas* have attracted settlement since ancient times. Springs are a noticeable feature in this karstic region, determining the sites of at least one hundred and eighteen villages. There is a marked difference between the mountainous areas with a sparse population of 20 to 40 per sq. mile, and some of the lower plateaux and basins with

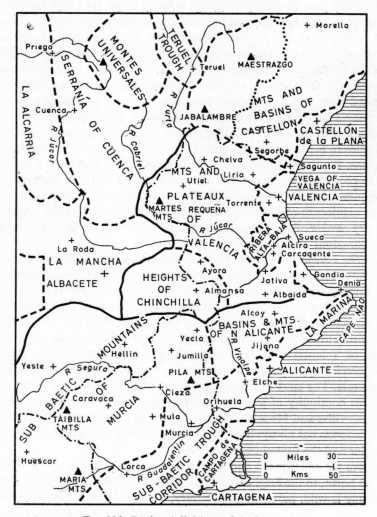

FIG. 115. Regional divisions of the Levante

densities of 150 to 250 per sq. mile (Fig. 116). Examples are notably the vineyards of Requeña and Utiel (10,269) which have doubled their area since the end of the last century; the olive, carob and soft fruits of Segorbe; and the peach and apricot orchards of Liria.

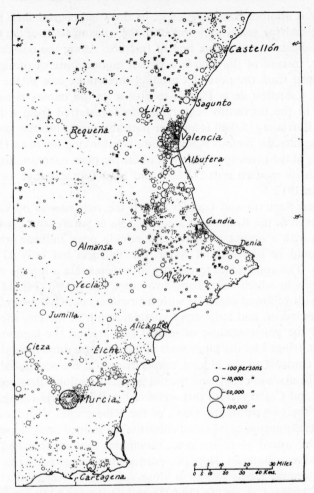

FIG. 116. Population distribution in the Levante. Note the marked contrast between the concentration of large centres and densely dispersed population on the coastal huertas and the sparse but nucleated settlement of the interior. Northern Alicante with its denser population is exceptional, having both marked dispersal and numerous centres

In northern Castellón, after the picturesque fishing settlements of Vinatoz, Benicarlo and Peniscola perched on its tombola, the coast is broken by the foothills of the Maestrazgo with their arid cover of dwarf palms and garrigue, aptly called 'the Desert of Palms'. But south of Benicasim the irrigated plain of La Plana, five to seven miles wide, is seen, stretching for nearly thirty miles to the hills of Almeniara in the south. It is another Bas-Languedoc, its drowned coastal shelf like the Planasse shelving gently seawards until the volcanic islets of the Columbretes indicate a submarine line of fracture. Along the coastal plain, however, instead of the vine is a virtual monoculture of oranges that are shipped from the port of Castellón three miles east of the capital (45,528). Castellón de la Plana—to give it its full name—is so called because in the thirteenth century it was transferred from a hill site nearby. Burriana (15,000) is another port also created in the same century. Sagunto, the famous Roman ruins overlooking the town (12,093), is already at the gateway to Valencia where the plain narrows. Separated from it is its modern port (13,800) and blast furnaces that were only erected in 1917.

Between Sagunto and Gandía stretch the rich *huertas* of Valencia, known even to the Romans as a cornucopia of nature. But the interior foothills with a scatter of agave and prickly pear, indicate what this plain would be like without water, for Valencia has only 17 inches annually. The approaches to the city of Valencia are a mosaic of vegetable lands in which some forty-two crops are grown (Fig. 117). It is dotted with yellowed *alquerías* with their stately date palms and whitewashed *barracas*, and long street villages. South of the city there is in summer, the green expanse of tassled rice around the lagoon of the Albufera, fringed by the pinewoods along the sand dune littoral. It is a striking contrast to the Huerta, empty except for the occasional sailing boat in the maze of canals and the tall pumping stations. Between Sueca (17,605) and Carlet (7,926) this scene of the Ribera baja changes once more to the polychromatic views of the Ribera alta, with its *huertas* and especially orange groves, that climb the red stained talus slopes at the foot of the jagged white limestone mountains that are trenched by the Júcar and its tributaries. Here prosperous towns known internationally by their orange labels follow in close succession: Algemesí (15,727), Alcira (20,648), Carcagente (14,628) and Jativa (17,422). Back to the coast of Cullera, the plain narrows but it is intensely utilised by the *huerta* of Gandía (15,713) that repeats in miniature the same features of the Valencian plain: ricefields near the coast, then vegetable gardens, orange groves and eventually vineyards on the foothills of the interior. Made famous in the paintings of Sorolla and in the novels of Blasco Ibañez, these Valencian landscapes, so humanised and utilitarian, are a Mediterranean paradise of luminous light and colours. Here it is easy to appreciate the local saying that 'man is of vegetation and vegetable life is of water' (see plate 39).

From the cathedral tower of the Miguelete, it is not difficult to see

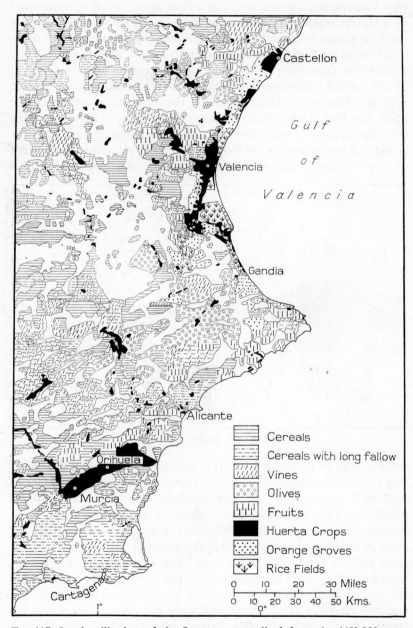

FIG. 117. Land utilisation of the Levante, generalised from the 1/50,000 topographic maps

why Valencia has become the third city of Spain, for it is surrounded by a Huerta supporting densities of 500 to 1,100 per sq. mile. The city itself has spread over a fifth of its traditional Vega, watered by its seven canals from the Turia, thus threatening to destroy its very *raison d'être* in its urban expansion. As the early site of Valencia was not favoured by any marked advantage of nodality or defence, it had little importance until the Moors developed markedly the agricultural wealth of the plain. The Moorish layout is still clearly recognisable in the centre of the city, though some of its narrow streets have been opened up in post-war changes. Rapid growth in the fourteenth century led to the construction of a new enceinte which sufficed until the walls were destroyed in 1865

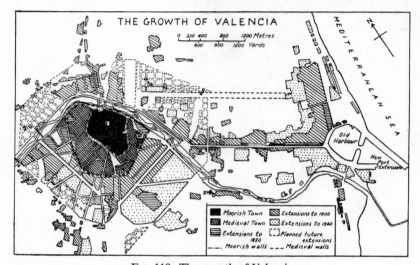

FIG. 118. The growth of Valencia

and replaced by the boulevards. It is only since the nineteenth century that Valencia has developed rapidly from a *Huerta* city of 82,000 in 1800 to a great commercial and industrial capital of some 500,000 inhabitants (Fig. 118). The first significant factor was the gradual development of its port after 1792, followed by the construction of the main railway lines and narrow-gauge regional network during the latter half of the nineteenth century. The latter creates a problem, since some forty level-crossings around the city suburbs interfere with the flow of traffic along the roads. On the periphery of the city, the gridiron planning is discontinuous with the absorption of former Huerta villages, such as Ruzafa, Patraix, Mislata and Nazaret. Beyond the Huerta, new suburbs are now being grafted upon the old peripheral centres such as Torrente (15,545), Paterna (10,787) and Burjasot (12,134), situated between the irrigated plain and the dry hills of the interior. From the city to the port of El Grao, a ribbon development of working-class dwellings and factories continue to thicken outwards into the Huerta, with shipyards south of the port, timber yards and box factories near the port, and textile and chemical plants to the north.

3. *The Alicante Levante.* Unlike Valencia, this region has neither high mountains, extensive plains nor rivers worth the name. It is a rolling, tangled country, in a series of folded ranges that run *en echelon*, enclosing many basins and limiting the coastal plains to discontinuous beachheads, except south of Alicante city. The sheltered, southerly aspect and karstic supplies of irrigation together with the legacy of Berber settlement and careful terracing, have favoured the intensive cultivation of fruit trees that support a densely scattered rural population, averaging 100 to 300 per sq. mile. Despite the rugged relief of limestone crests and marly basins, one-fifth of the total area of the province is irrigated. The interior basins of Cocentaina, Alcoy (40,748) and Villena (15,612) are clothed in olive groves, with busy regional centres engaged in traditional Moorish crafts such as paper making and textiles (Fig. 116). Jijona combines its local almonds and honey from the scented garrigue into a delicious sweetmeat called *turrón*. In the coastal district of La Marina, between the ancient port of Denia (7,818) and Villajoyosa (6,817), a dense population of 250 per sq. mile cultivates the thousands of miles of terraces for muscatels, almonds and some carobs and olives. In early spring the almond blossom suggests a Japanese landscape, but the place-names, the people and the palms indicate more definitely that this is a favoured corner of Africa. This impression is most convincing in the date palm oasis of Elche (34,717), athwart the cactus-grown rambla of the Vinalapó. Terraced roofs, minaretted churches, sun-drenched plains and dusty roads add to this allusion. In contrast, the red-brown earth of the vega of Alicante, with its luxuriant growth of gardens, vineyards and numerous white farms is perhaps more Valencian in appearance.

Alicante (90,770) is obviously placed at the first break south of the *calas* coast of the Marina, where the plain is extensive and routes to the south-eastern Meseta are easy via the Vinalapó valley. Protected by the fortresses of Sta Bárbara and San Fernando to north and west, the town grew up between them and the port at the head of an extensive bay. It is doubtful if it was the Greek *Leuka Akra*, whose site is more likely to have been at Beniform. It was not important as a Moorish port, and indeed it is only in the last century that the port was enlarged to deal with the trade of its agricultural hinterland. Consequently Alicante has a modern appearance of gridiron streets and a smart palm-fringed promenade.

4. *The Murcian Levante.* The valley of the Segura introduces a new style of landscape, so that southern Alicante is best included in this region. This valley forms a corridor with Castile, and unites its tri-partite areas of Sub-Baetic mountains, irrigated *vegas* and the coastal plain. Most of Murcia is a tawny wilderness of bare hills and steppe lowlands, dust-filmed, shimmering with heat and so dry that even the hedgerows of prickly pears seem to wilt under the cobalt sky. The early morning queues of women waiting with their waterpots at the village fountains, indicate that here water is at a premium, for the annual rainfall is 15 to 10 inches, even less towards the south-east coast.

The western basins centred on Yecla (21,040) and Jumilla (16,101) are clothed in vines and olives, overlooked by the high esparto-covered plateaux of Castile. Eastwards there is the dissected monotonous landscape of the Pila mountains (4,140 ft) that are sparsely inhabited. The southern border of Murcia has more impressive relief in the high upthrusts of limestone and red sandstones that form the mountains of Espuña (5,200 ft) and Taibilla (6,565 ft) along the Andalusian border. In the south-east, the Carrascoy mountains (2,123 ft) though lower, are even more dismally barren. Across these ranges that follow the Sub-Baetic trends, east-north-east to west-north-west the Segura has cut a transverse course, joined by subsequent tributaries especially on its right bank, where the higher relief ensures more water supply. Large villages of 10,000–13,000 inhabitants control the lonely routes between the barley fields of the plateaux and the irrigated valleys, such as Cara-vaca, Mula and Totana (Fig. 116). Lorca (20,990) is a more important agricultural centre, favoured by the Guadelentín that waters 11,000 ha of its cereal lands and by the minerals exploited in the vicinity.

But the life of Murcia largely depends upon the waters of the Segura. Twelve great dams conserve upstream some 782 million cubic metres of water annually to supply the 75,000 ha of traditional *huertas*. New projects such as the Taibilla Canal now under construction, will lead water for 125 miles to supplement well irrigation in the plains of Cartagena (50,000 ha irrigable), and another will run to Alicante. The westernmost of the important *huertas* is around Cieza (20,848) but the richest is that of Murcia which stretches 15 miles along the Segura valley near the confluence with the Guadalentín, and some 4 miles wide. Watered by two canals, whose laws date back to 1277, it provides a collective system of distribution to sixty settlements of *heredamientos*.

The huerta specialises in vegetable crops notably peppers, melons, tomatoes, together with apricots, lemons and oranges, though the list of crops grown is almost as varied as that of Valencia. In the midst of a densely scattered population of 270,000 living in some 400 small settlements, Murcia itself is not a large town (57,640). It first appeared as a small Moorish settlement on the north bank of the Segura in the ninth century, and it is still an agricultural centre, though its baroque, architectural embellishments give it an urban atmosphere. Now almost continuous, the Huerta merges into the irrigated lands of Orihuela, with its hemp and lucerne fields, its mulberries and fruit trees, interlaced with vegetable plots, and dotted with the white *barracas* of the cultivators. An old town, probably founded by the Romans, it has suffered severely from floods on the Segura, and has remained more than a rich local centre (14,408).

The coastal plain south of the Segura is dull country, with few settlements and much halophyte steppe, only enlivened by the windmills that pump water for scattered gardens, and the pinewoods of the Manga, a sand bar that runs for 12 miles to enclose the lagoon of Mar Menor. Cartagena nestles at the head of a *calanque* inlet sheltered offshore by the volcanic islet of Escombrera and the hills of Galeras and S Julian. Since *Carthago Nova* was built by Hasdrubal about 243 B.C., it has been a naval base, and important outlet of mineral wealth. But its layout dates chiefly from the sixteenth century when it was virtually rebuilt by Philip II, and in 1733–82, when its naval arsenal was constructed. By 1820, however, it was still only a small town of 26,000 inhabitants. Its modern growth to 41,763 is the result of the revival of the naval arsenal and the expansion of its mining, metallurgical and related industries. South and west of Cartagena, the landscape becomes increasingly arid, with desolate roads frequented only by flocks of goats or an occasional donkey piled with esparto grass, with here and there the clay-coloured peasant dwelling surrounded by beehive-shaped ricks of barley straw. Rose Macaulay has described it as 'a menacing landscape, a heave of burnt hills, quite dry and bare . . . shadowless and treeless, choked with dust, scorched with sun.' The Celtic, green landscapes of Galicia appear as far off here as the Scandinavian fiords appear to the traveller in Arabia.

CHAPTER 12

THE REGIONS OF SPAIN: THE CENTRAL
AND SOUTHERN PROVINCES

'L'Espagne par excellence.' (E. Reclus)

Central Spain is both the geographical and the historical heart of the
Peninsula; it is the essential Spain of Castile, Aragón and Extremadura.
At first sight it appears to be a desert, empty and barren. Certainly
it is a vast ensemble that stretches 500 miles from the central Pyrenees
to the Sa Morena, whose 9·3 million inhabitants (1950) represent
a third of the nation on half of its total area. Hilaire Belloc has
vividly described this first impression to the northerner who descends to it over the Pyrenees. 'That immeasurable sweep of yellow-
brown bare earth fills up whatever is not sky and is contained or framed
upon its final limits by mountains as severe as its own empty surface.
Those far and dreadful hills are unrelieved by crag, or wood, or mist;
they are a mere height, naked and unfruitful running along wall-like
and cutting off Aragón from the south and the old from the new
Castile.' It is, however, false to speak of these wastes as deserts or even
steppes (see p. 205), for in spring their void is filled with waving
cornfields. Medieval towns, Gothic churches, and much of what we call
Christian civilisation has sprung from this land. Mystics like Santa
Teresa, painters like Goya, writers like Cervantes have lived there. Why
then is there this optical delusion about the Meseta? A sympathy with
its geographical features will help to explain.

Central Spain is essentially the Meseta and its piedmont plains.
Tertiary cycles of erosion have sculptured vast plateaux, and exaggerate
the monotony of their expanse. The skeletal siliceous soils of the western
plateaux discourage cultivation, while the deeper, richer calcareous
lands to the east are dusty and appear even emptier. From the surrounding rim of highlands, or from the central ranges, the whole of this
Meseta world may be grasped in only a few views, each wider than any
in most parts of Europe, for dusty plains meet cloudless skies, fore-
shortened in the heat haze. Then too the continental climate, sun-
drenched for nine months of the year, shivering cold for three months,
emphasises the dominance of nature, austere and severe in all its

seasonal moods. Most of it is treeless, except where a line of plane trees edges the roads, or poplars follow the larger rivers. Only an occasional woodland of holm or pine betrays how naked man has made this dust-filmed landscape. Human habitation lies camouflaged, rising from its earth in adobe brick. Only the air view seems to check the accuracy of the map, which reveals the blots of numerous villages, betrayed by their red roofs. But from the ground branch roads seem to lead no-where, the straight highway creates the atmosphere of deadly boredom, dulling the senses of the traveller who fails to observe the mosaics of colour produced by soil and slope. But this is not a dead world, for the solemn grandeur of its tragic plains and castled villages is rich in history. It is a world deeply humanised despite nature's aggressive expanse.

ARAGÓN AND NEIGHBOURING PROVINCES

1. *The Pyrenees.* At first it may seem strange to place the Spanish Pyrenees within Central Spain. But in good measure, the centrality of the Meseta, with its Aragonese borderland is effectively created by the massive and compact ranges of the Pyrenees, which screen off outside influences. Although averaging some 8,000 ft in its central mountains—almost half the altitude of the Alps—there is no other mountain ram-part in Europe which more impressively divides two climatic zones from each other. On the western and the eastern extremities, more open to Atlantic and Mediterranean influences respectively, there is little contrast between the Spanish and French borders. But in the central Pyrenees, the contrast is most dramatic, between the thick forests of deciduous oaks and lush green pastures on the northern flank, and the gaunt pinewoods and evergreen scrub on the south. The great wealth of data written about the Pyrenees may be summarised as exemplifying three basic geographical principles. Although the Pyrenees may claim to be a major physiographic region, they have neither had geographical nor political unity. Bioclimatic stratification of life is the dominant feature of their landscapes and societies. Isolation has long been, and now is even more so, an essential factor in the Spanish Pyrenees, because of both transverse valleys and customs posts.

The Spanish Pyrenees have not provided a uniform barrier throughout their length of 260 miles and area of some 15,000 sq. miles. Whereas their ranges are 15–18 miles wide in the west and only 6 miles in the east, the central sector widens to nearly 80 miles. From the Pico di Ori facing the Roncal valley, the western Pyrenees descend gently in massive outlines of flysch and limestones to the Pass of Roncesvalles (3,468 ft) and the terminal gateway of Velata. In the eastern Pyrenees roughly from the upper Segre valley eastwards, the descent is more abrupt to the coast of Ampurdán, and traverse is also easy over six cols of which Puymorens and Perthus are the most significant. Astride these two zones of passage, the political frontier is only one of diplomatic compromise, finally settled in the Treaty of the Pyrenees (1659) and eventually demarcated in 1856–68. But indifferent to this frontier are the areas of Basque and Catalan culture. Today, their Pyrenean valleys are patinated with modern industries, whose economic importance makes their regionalism even more vocal. Very different are the Central Pyrenees, the true rampart of central Spain, where for some 170 miles from the Maladeta with the highest summit of the range (Pic d'Aneto, 11,169 ft) to Carlit the frontier follows the watershed except in the valley of Arán. There are only three international passes, Bonaigua, Portalet (6,000 ft) and Somport (5,349 ft) and the newly-constructed road tunnel of Viella (in 1948). Along this watershed, the frontier was first a tribal boundary convenient for Roman administration then imitated more seriously by seventeenth-century politicians. Essentially a world apart, nature dominates here and nurtures its own pastoral societies.

Reference has already been made to the geological, zonal arrangement of the Pyrenees (see pp. 186–7). The broad masses of granite and schist have been corroded into sharp alpine summits by Quaternary glaciers. Strewn over the high surfaces are some 1,070 glacial lakes (430 only on the Spanish side) of which the granite country of the Encantats is a notable example. Bordering this serrated wall is the spectacular limestone scenery of the Interior Pre-Pyrenees with the 3,000 ft canyon of Oropesa and the arched, rugged sierras of the Exterior Pre-Pyrenees, separated by the tamed landscapes of soft, marly depressions, cultivated and settled (Fig. 120).

These differences of scenery portrayed on the geological map, are overlain, however, by the bioclimatic zones, induced by longitude and altitude. Between 5,500 and 6,200 ft the tree-line begins to disappear, first the fir, then the mountain pine, giving place to alpine pastures. But whereas there are 605,880 ha of natural meadows in Navarre, in Catalonia there are only 10,000 ha of artificial meadows; such is the climatic difference. Eastwards then the pastures decrease, though the upper slopes of the valley of Arán are exceptional with 80 per cent under meadows (Plate 4). These alpine pastures are occupied in summer by transhumant flocks of sheep. The more limited pastures of the Interior Pre-Pyrenees support only local flocks, while the Exterior Pre-Pyrenees have restricted normal transhumance from the plains of the Ebro.

The second or forest zone is also variable in altitude and character from east to west. In the Navarrese forests mixed deciduous oaks and beeches are characteristic between 3,000 and 5,000 ft. But in the central Pyrenees, magnificent stands of fir descend from 6,500 to 2,500 ft and the Scots pine invades aggressively into lands now abandoned through depopulation. Only in the valley of the Arán do the low clouds of Atlantic air-masses favour the beech forests. Eastwards the Mediterranean influence encourages the *Pinus laricio* and especially the evergreen oak, which climbs the sunny slopes of the upper Segre valley to 5,000 ft (Fig. 34). Despite the meagreness of forests on the Spanish Pyrenees, isolation has preserved more of the original cover than on the French side. The northern forests though impressive are nearly all of secondary growth or new plantations. Thus Arthur Young noted in 1789 how Spanish forests were being exploited for French interests.

The third zone, that of mountain agriculture, is important particularly in the broad longitudinal depressions of the Pre-Pyrenees, such as the basin of Pamplona, Canal de Berdun, Tremp and the Upper Segre. The Atlantic west is favoured as far as Pamplona by maize fields and apple orchards. Wheat and oats on the lower and higher lands respectively become more significant in Aragón, while the vine reaching Pamplona at 2,000–2,250 ft, attains to 3,100 ft in the Cerdaña. The less hardy olive, reaches west to the Cinca valley, at 1,300–1,900 ft but averaging 2,300–2,600 ft in Catalonia. In the lower Ribagorzana, Tremp and the middle Segre, olive groves become more conspicuous. But these crops, together with the ubiquitous potato, occupy only 10 to 40 per cent of the land of the communes, the rest lying waste in a vast sea of Mediterranean scrub, where thyme, kermes oak and other shrubs evidence the degradation of the former Mediterranean woodlands.

Isolation has been a transcendent control in the Pyrenean regions. The accumulation of early Tertiary flysch, covering the flanks of the Pyrenees to an average depth of 2,600 ft explains the superimposed courses of the transverse drainage. Each major valley, a rosary of shallow basins and narrow defiles strung together, is its own independent unit. Thus it is not surprising that the province of Lérida is the basin of the Segre, Huesca of the Cinca and Saragossa of the Gállego. Earlier still, the regions of Roncal (Esca), Hecho (Subordán), Canfranc (Aragón), Tena (Gállego), Broto (Ara), Bielsa (Cinca), Benasque (Ésera), Barrabes (Noguera Ribagorzana), Fosca (Flamisell) Pallars Sobirá (Noguera Pallaresa), Andorra (Valira) and Barida (upper Segre) were the pastoral communities of their isolated mountain valleys (Fig. 108). Where the longitudinal corridors of the Pre-Pyrenean Depression permitted some linkage, political unification was also possible as in Alto Aragón (Canal de Berdún), Sobrarbe (Cinca), Ribagorzana (Noguera R.), Pallars (Noguera Pallaresa) and Ribera del Segre (Fig. 119). Thus too, the population distribution has reflected this evolution, with dissemination in the upper valleys, concentration in the interior basins and an empty belt along the outer Pre-Pyrenees which had served as a no-man's-land prior to the Reconquest (Fig. 120). Historic capitals such as Jaca, Tremp and Seo de Urgel, serve now as markets as once they played a more political role, because they have always been route centres.

2. *The Ebro Valley*. From the summit of San Juan de la Peña (4,100 ft), the Aragonese shrine of the Reconquest, not only is there a wondrous panorama of the successive ranges of the Pyrenees, but to the south is seen unrolled like a map, the chaotic badlands of the Pyrenean foot-hills, merging expansively with the Ebro plain in low, rolling, shadeless hills. Seventy miles across the flat open space which is the Ebro trough, towers on the skyline the Sa de Moncayo overlooking westernmost Aragón. North-westwards, the Aragonese trough may be said to start with the Ribera of Navarre. Long, straight roads and distant shepherd towns show no life apart from the pall of dust rising behind the isolated traveller. It is a silent world, birdless and treeless, muffled in a veil of dryness that stretches from hills to plain. Like a painted desert, its soils are coloured with ochreous, yellow and grey hues, lustreless and dirty. It is a vast scene, for the Ebro valley, 576 miles in length and collecting 222 tributaries, represents one-sixth of the drainage of the Peninsula, and boasts the largest basin. But the distant view rarely shows the glint of water, revealing only the green ribbons of the major valley floors. Yet surely the view of sameness must be a mirage, for the map shows many regions, and not all this world is void of life. Perhaps its geographical secrets are best revealed in describing it as a piedmont, an asymmetrical valley, continental in climate, whose chief resource is living water, and in which communications are easy.

Across this piedmont valley, covered thickly with sediments, the superimposed tributaries, 100 to 150 miles in length, follow independent courses, sometimes cutting deeply in broad valleys. Between them, tabular plateaux of intercalated limestones, sandstones and gypseous marls, or gently folded hills, form broad interfluves, like miniature doabs. To the east, however, the confluence of the Cinca, Noguera Ribagorzana and Noguera Pallaresa with the Segre, reveals the ancient alignment of the geological basin north-eastwards, now reversed by the new base-level of the Ebro, which has successfully breached the Catalan mountains in the gorges below Mequinenza. Folded sierras like

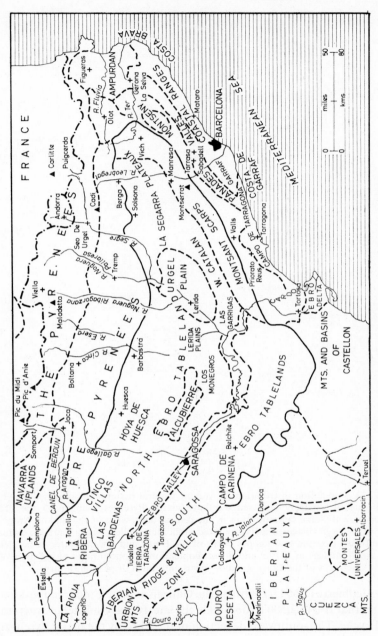

Fig. 119. Regional divisions of Aragón and Catalonia

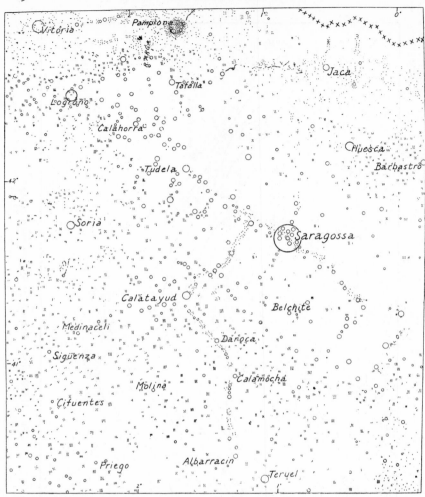

FIG. 120. Population distribution in Aragón. Several patterns of settlement can be distinguished: sparsely scattered dwellings in the Pyrenees; hamlets in the Pre-Pyrenees with some concentration in the central depression of the middle Aragón and Arga; large villages, widely separated in the Ebro valley, with a marked absence of settlement on the low steppes north of the Ebro; and a thin scatter of hamlets and small villages in Teruel and Soria. Population is concentrated along the river terraces of the Ebro in major towns and much dispersion of farms

the Alcubierre (2,664 ft) between the Gállego and the Cinca, and residual buttes that rise to 2,500 ft, dominate the late Tertiary surfaces, structural and cyclic. The southward deflection of the Ebro by the major Pyrenean rivers (only the Jalón in the south has comparable length) and the intensity of their erosion under semi-arid conditions, has created numerous interfluvial regions. Some of these are white marly tabular steppes such as Las Bardenas, Los Monegros and La Litera with a sparse density of population 20–25 per sq. mile, huddled in nucleated villages (Fig. 120). Others are more fertile basins favoured by seepage water and usually centred on a larger town, such as Cinco Villas (Sos), Hoya de Huesca (Huesca), Somontanos (Sariñena), Hoya de Barbastro (Barbastro) and Solsonés (Solsona). On the south side of the Ebro trough, the smaller streams, less capable of intense erosion, cut through a broad belt of glacis, fronting the Iberian ranges. There, regional units are less

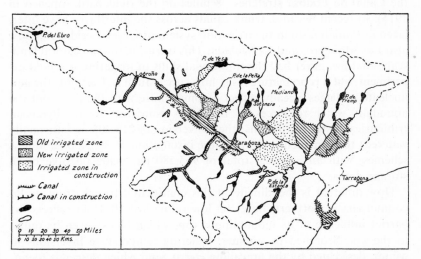

Fig. 121. Irrigation, actual and potential, in the Ebro basin. Reservoirs are shown in enclosed areas: black, already developed; open, under construction

obvious, apart from the sphere of influence of the larger centres, such as Tarazona, and Cariñena. These rolling, hilly tablelands, comprising most of the area, were until the nineteenth century, empty spaces of pastoralism, divided into huge communal tracts, crossed by the *cañadas*. Now *secano* cultivation has taken over these lands for cereals, especially along the *vals* or small valleys that notch the tableland where the soil is deeper. But with variable soils, the percentage cultivated varies from 10 to 70 per cent. Below the white *mesas* are a flight of red-coloured terraces generally at 400–425, 114, 65–72, 32–40 and 10–16 ft above the rivers. These are devoted especially to vineyards and some olives.

In the broad green floor of the Ebro and its major tributaries, the rivers meander widely, intersected by hundreds of veins injecting water everywhere. This domain of the *huertas* is in sharp contrast to the Tertiary steppes, for irrigation, cash crops, communications and the sustenance of a dense population, varying from 100 to even 500 per sq. mile, are its pre-occupation (Fig. 120). From at least Moorish times, the numerous riverine settlements have practised irrigation in private holdings. The Canal Imperial on the right bank of the Ebro, running 60 miles between Tudela and Saragossa to water twenty-four communes, was begun in 1521 and eventually completed in 1796 (Fig. 121). On the left bank, the Tauste canal, watering twelve communes, goes back to the thirteenth century, though only completed in 1775. More ambitiously the Canal de Lodosa stretches 78 miles on the right bank (opened in 1915). In recent decades, trunk canals across the interfluves have interlaced in Punjab fashion the irrigation system of Urgel, Lérida, and now also Los Monegros and La Violada, This intrusion into a pastoral landscape that has never had the traditional skills of irrigation is a bold experiment, but it is premature it say how successful it is. Certainly the new nucleated villages already reflect a compromise with the past. But the abundant water resources of the Ebro nourished by its Pyrenean tributaries, foster big dreams: the conversion of 215,205 ha (seasonally watered) to permanent irrigation, the installation of 305,400 ha in new schemes, with an eventual total of 965,580 ha, made possible by 76 storage dams.

How different is the climate of this continental trough from its Po counterpart in northern Italy! Its low rainfall of 10–15 in reflects the barrier influence of its mountainous rim, which blocks even its outlet to the sea. Scorched in summer, suffering temperature inversions in winter, desiccated by the prevailing *cierzo* wind which descends foehn-like from the north, the climate and its inhabitants are alike austere.

The straight alignment of the Pyrenees and the transverse parallelism of its valleys are also contrasted with the arcuate Alpine ranges, that focus on more than one major centre in the Po basin. Here the nodality of Saragossa is unrivalled, central to the plain. It is aided by the Gállego, concentrating all the communications that use the central Pyrenean passes, and by the Jálon and Ágreda passages the routes from Castile and Valencia follow. At the junction of these routes with the ancient road between Calahorra and Caspe, Saragossa is situated. A city of brick in an environment of lacustrine clays, it has grown up as a religious and university metropolis, a military and economic centre, and the administrative capital. Here the Iberians sited *Salduba*, the Romans built their colonia of *Caesarea Augusta*, the Moors created Mudejon with its towers and gardens, and the Aragonese built the

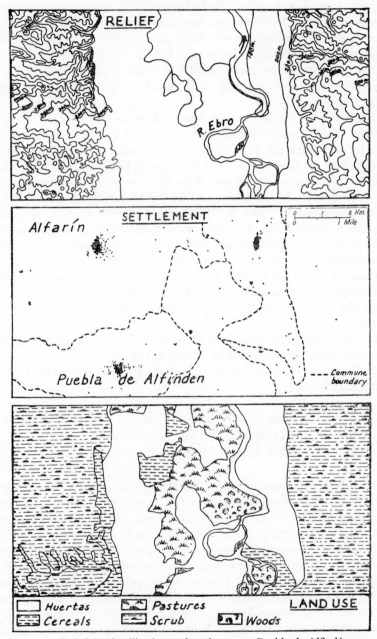

Fig. 122. Relief, land utilisation and settlement at Puebla de Alfindén, near
Saragossa

massive stone bridge across the turbulent Ebro, and created the great shrine of El Pilar. Saragossa has been compared to Toulouse; certainly their situation and historic role have been similar, and both are still sensitive to trans-Pyrenean influences. But the relatively slow growth of Saragossa until modern times (235,450 in 1950) despite its incomparable nodality in the country, is only a reflection of the general backwardness of the nation.

3. *The Iberian Cordillera.* For nearly 300 miles from Burgos towards Valencia, the Iberian ranges form a common frontier with Aragón, Castile and Valencia. It is high, difficult country, snowy and wind-swept, with an average width of 60 miles. It falls naturally into three regions. The north-western mountain block is grouped around the Sa de la Demanda, Sa Cebollera, and Sa del Moncayo, all over 7,000 ft and culminating at 7,600 ft. This is the Castilian redoubt of Soria, with its plateau of Agreda, overlooking Aragón as from a balcony. The central ridge and basin relief, which centres on Calatayud, is more transitional in character because more accessible, on the routeway between Aragón and Castile. The south-eastern mountain group of the Albarracín and Maestrazgo, lower (*c.* 5,000 ft) but markedly broader than the northern mountains, is an Aragónese province, centred on Teruel.

In Soria, the landscape is rounded and tabular, with wide undulating plateaux lying between 3,500 and 5,000 ft, cold for nine months of the year (Plate 37). The poet Antonio Machado grimly describes the typical scene near Moncayo,

'Soria country, arid and cold,
Among bare hills and mountains
Small green fields, ashen ridges . . .'

But the higher, heath-clad slopes reach up to the clear air of the high mountains, whose extensive forests of Scots pine have largely displaced the original cover of oaks (*Q. Lusitanica* and *Q. toza*). It is glaciated country, with pastures noted for their stock in the mountains of Urbión and Cebollera, and with a distinctive house-type, reminiscent of the Basque *caserío*. Eastwards the pinewoods disappear and the *matorral* is only cleared in patches for cereals as in the Campo de Gomara. Soria is the successor of Celtiberian *Numancia*. It is situated on the medieval *cañada*, follows down the upper Douro valley, leaving it at Soria to avoid the gorge below. Situated between the forested and pastoral mountains, and the cereal plains of the Douro, Soria once flourished as a regional market, but today it is the smallest provincial capital of Spain (16,878).

The central tablelands of Medinaceli, treeless and covered with the sombre scrub of thyme and other plants, have a desolate appearance. On the south side, the deeply trenched valleys, tributary to the Tagus, add to the gloom. Although this routeway has witnessed the march of armies since Roman times, a sad air of remoteness and poverty is apparent in its villages, such as Siguenza and Medinaceli. But further east, in the fertile basins of Calatayud and Daroca, careful irrigation and horticulture create a marked change in the landscape, bordered by the vivid magenta and yellow rocks of the folded ranges. Variety in the eroded details of relief, with switch back-curves along the mountain roads, become a welcome change.

Following the Jiloca tributary of the Jalón, the basin of Teruel is entered, surrounded by its high mountains of forests and extensive pastures, blessed by their heavy rainfall. Scots pines on the higher slopes, *Pinus pinaster* below, and scrub of *Cistus Laurifolius* on the schistose rocks are typical. Cultivated terraces on the glacis debris and wider fields in the Triassic marls, supplement the main resources of stock and pastures. The Albarracín mountains is still the communal preserve of its twenty-two villages. But the towns are small (Teruel) and life is hard; population densities average 20–40 per sq. mile (Fig. 120). To the north-east, the Maestrazgo is even more repulsive, barren limestone mountains deeply dissected and isolated. From a series of high plateaux, descent is made north-west into the 'Tierra Baja' of Alcañiz, where springs attract large villages and the milder climate permits olive groves and vineyards to sprawl expansively over the warm, marly soils. Numerous small towns such as Alcañiz, Caspe and Belchite ive off their more favoured lands.

THE MESETA

The term 'Castilian Meseta', often used to designate the heart of the Peninsula, has geographical but not geological significance. It refers to the two vast tablelands: the northern 140 miles from north to south, 110 miles from east to west and the southern 150 by some 300 miles. The division between them is essentially climatic, the southern table-land being lower and with a milder climate. Between them the Central Cordillera makes an effective divide. Two further divisions, termed 'Siliceous' and 'Calcareous' Spain by Hernández Pacheco, are conse-quent on the rock structures. The siliceous rocks to the west of the Meseta are widest in the south-west, and so it has been designated

'Extremadura', though this Reconquest term was formerly used of all lands south of the Douro. But the personality of the Meseta with its fourfold division springs from its Castilian unity, consequent on its Reconquest history, and evolving in common one language and one literature. The name 'Castile' was first applied during the ninth century to the castles that guarded the small eastern front of Santander, within the Asturian kingdom. This was the natural route to follow south-wards from the humid zone. Despite the poverty of the Meseta, the centrality of Castile enabled it to dominate the Peninsula, especially in the critical half century 1050–1100, when it was uncertain whether Navarre, Aragón, or even León might have ruled instead. Today, the yellow, open plains of Castile may be likened to a medieval manuscript, dotted generously with decrepit towns, like emblazoned capitals, recording the glorious history of a former age.

1. *The Northern Tableland.* The cold, continental climate of Old Castile and León is consequent on the high position of the tableland, 3,500–2,000 ft in the western valley of the Douro, and surrounded by high mountains. In this land where climate is harsh and rainfall is meagre, it is the soil that creates the changes of the landscape. The Palaeozoic peneplain to the west, with its smooth skyline, varied by the outcrops of granite, slate and quartzite, has vast areas of matorral and oak forests. The eastern and central plains are more varied in aspect, according to the grey, yellow and white hues of limestones, sands and marls. But the Douro unites all relief so that within this piedmont basin three concentric zones are recognisable: the mountain borders and their passageways; the piedmont zone with its broad, deserted *páramos*; and the central valley of the Douro, with the *campiñas* of its tributaries near their confluence with the trunk valley (Fig. 65). Another charac-teristic of the tableland is its rural aspect, having 3,500 rural settlements chiefly hamlets, with a total of 1·8 million inhabitants, but only seven-teen towns with over 10,000 inhabitants (Fig. 125). Yet most of the towns have great antiquity, with thirty-one centres on or near Roman roads. Thus it is a vista of endless plains, parched open fields, with vast areas of fallow, occasional rows of poplars along green valleys, and scattered small villages that huddle in the shelter of a castle or fortified church.

The north-east consists of several transitional regions. The first of these is La Rioja, the threshold of Aragón, aligned along the valley of the upper Ebro. Climatically, its mild climate associates it with the northern zone, geologically it is part of the Ebro trough, and historically it is linked with Old Castile. Between Logroño (52,000) and

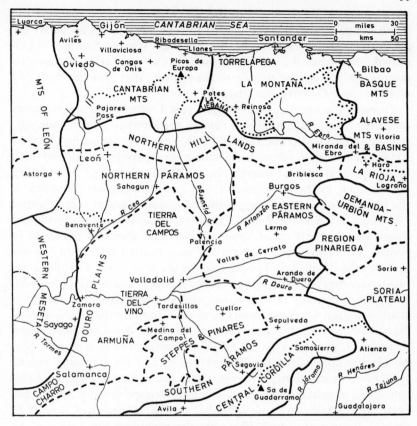

FIG. 123. Regional divisions of the north of Spain

Calahorra (14,000), however, the Rioja has rich, irrigated lands, watered by the Canal of Lodosa to produce a variety of crops and fruits. Here is an ancient focus of population which today has a high density of population. The upper Rioja, beyond Logroño, is more varied in appearance ranging from the sea of vinyards around Haro and Najera, which cover 32,000 ha, to the stock-rearing country in the hills above the narrow depression. Varied and prosperous, the food industries support the relatively large towns. Bounded to the north by the folds of the Montes Obarenes, southwards the Bureba region consists of dissected tablelands, cereal lands with densities of 50–80 per sq. mile. To the north is the dissected tableland of La Lora, a folded synclinorium in Cretaceous limestones, whose basins are exploited by the devious courses of Ebro headstreams. A cold, humid region, it is devoted to pastoralism.

At the confluence of routes in this gateway is Burgos, guarding the Arlanzon pass (Fig. 123). Founded in A.D. 884, it was an early Reconquest capital, benefiting by the Pilgrims' Way to Santiago which passed here. After the Middle Ages it was an important commercial centre. Revived by the coming of the railway, it is now the third city of Old Castile (74,061). See Plate 45.

Towards the south-east of Burgos, past Lerma, once the Versailles of Castile when Valladolid was capital, the *páramos* stretch endlessly, passing from a Miocene surface to an early Tertiary surface at over 3,000 ft. The borders of this Soria country are sparsely settled with small hamlets of 100–400 inhabitants, in a bleak landscape of some cereal lands, much matorral of juniper and some pinewoods. Southwards the plateaux of Sa Pela merge with the eastern border of the Central Cordillera in the Sa de Ayllon. Palaeozoic slates succeed the secondary limestones. In the Pass of Somosierra, a fault displaces the slates in contact with gneiss, and then further west in the Guadarrama mountains, gneiss dominates. The *páramos* at the foot of the Cordillera are much narrower, but west of the Duraton valley, and north of Segovia, extensive pinewoods of P. *pinaster* and P. *pinea* cover the piedmont sands, supplied by Guadarrama streams. Guarding the approaches to New Castile, over the gently rising ramp of the Cordillera, stand Segovia (29,586) and Ávila (22,577) both military towns, as the Alcazar of Segovia dominating the Eresma valley, and the imposing granite walls of Ávila still testify (Plate 46). Both had extensive communal pastutes in the mountains, though the commercial importance of Segovia has been more significant, now enhanced by the tourist attraction of its famous Roman aqueduct. Close by, the royal summer palace of La Granja is a picturesque tourist attraction. In the folds of the Guadarrama mountains and more so in the rugged Gredos ranges, sheltered basins form pockets of rich cultivation, attracting a marked density of scattered dwellings and villages (Fig. 125). The landscape near Ávila has been expressively described by G. Santayana: 'too austere to be beautiful, too dry and barren, yet it reveals eloquently the stone skeleton of the earth; not a dead skeleton like the mountains of the moon but like the mountains of Greece, vivified at least by the atmosphere and still rich in fountains and in hidden fields' (*Persons and Places*, p. 105).

In the south-west and west of Castile, in the lands bordering Portugal, Extremadura and León, there is a marked change in the landscape. The milder and moister climate favours thick forests of mixed oaks and chestnuts, which replace the pinewoods common in the eastern sierras. Climbing the slopes of the Peña de Francia and Sa de Béjar, viewpoints

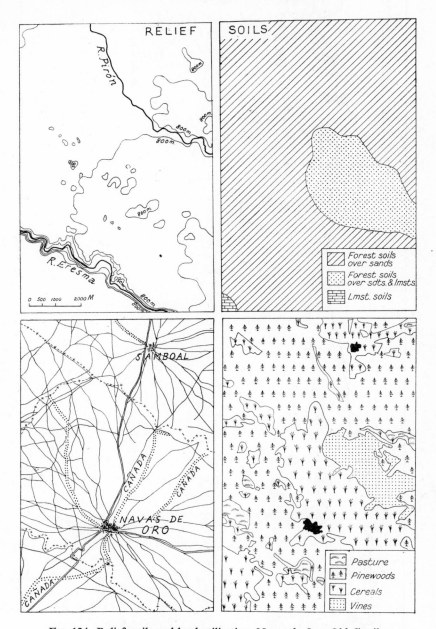

FIG. 124. Relief, soils and land utilisation, Navas de Oro, Old Castile

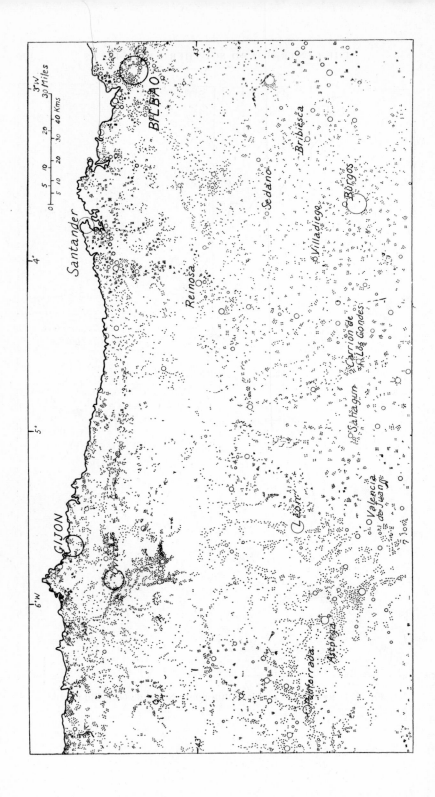

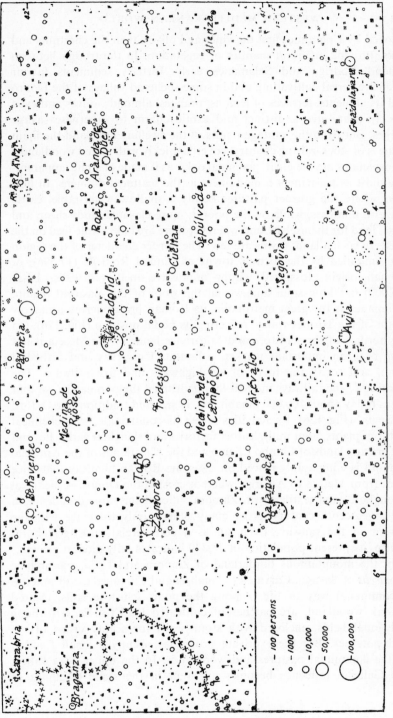

Fig. 125. Distribution of population in north central Spain. Note the industrial concentrations around Bilbao, Gijón, Oviedo and its southern coal-mining valleys. Although dispersed in the pluviose zone, settlement is rightly influenced by the relief. Towards the arid interior of Castile, settlement is much more nucleated in hamlets and villages

beloved by Unamuno, first the vines and olives, then the chestnuts and oaks, provide luxuriant mantles of vegetation. In the trough between Ciudad Rodrigo and Salamanca early Tertiary sediments favour extensive cereal cultivation, and in some sheltered valleys of the Douro and its affluents, terraces of lemons, oranges, almonds, olives and even prickly pear, give a distinct and exotic charm to otherwise savage gorges. But from the vantage points of the swelling tableland the main scene is of stock-raising country, covered thickly with mixed woodlands. Conspicuous are the great, perennial oaks, as if made of stone, apparently almost as permanent a monument as the scattered dolmens. In hollows where the greener pastures betray a shallow water-table, cattle graze in numbers, while on the poorer, more elevated lands sheep and goats fend for themselves, and wherever there are oaks swine feed on the mast. In such a land, towns are few. The border character of the region is exemplified by the fortress towns of Ciudad Rodrigo (12,596), of Roman origin, fossilised within impressive medieval walls. Béjar (15,000) has long spun and woven the wool of this pastoral region. Salamanca is the great metropolis, its Roman bridge across a narrow sector of the Tormes valley, reflecting its nodal position (Fig. 126). On the borders of the schistose and calcareous lands of the Meseta it has long been an important market, a famous University and cathedral town, and today the focus of six highways and five railways. The creation of the railways in 1880–90 quadrupled the population, so that it has today about 100,000 inhabitants, in size and tradition 'the Oxford of Spain' (Fig. 126). Its activities reflect its countryside, with chemical fertiliser plants, flour mills, leather factories and slaughter yards. Beyond the grazing lands of Campo Charro and the wheatlands of the Armuña, Zamora is comparably placed on the same Roman highway that once went from Merida to Astorga, where it crossed the Douro. A medieval stronghold, and textile town, Zamora suffered the same decadence in the seventeenth century as so many others, only to revive with the advent of the railway. Even so, as a commercial and agricultural centre, its present population of 38,320 indicates only modest growth.

In the mountainous borderland of Zamora and León, the archaic *comarcas* of Sayago, Carvajales, Sanabria and Carvalleda, still practise a communal way of life. Among the poor, schistose soils, cleared of oak woodland, are patches of cultivated land (*cortinas*) forming polygonal fields, enclosed with stone walls for scanty crops of rye and potatoes. But these private properties occupy a small fraction of the communal pastures and woodlands. In the upper Tera valley, the Galician influence becomes apparent in the stone dwellings of

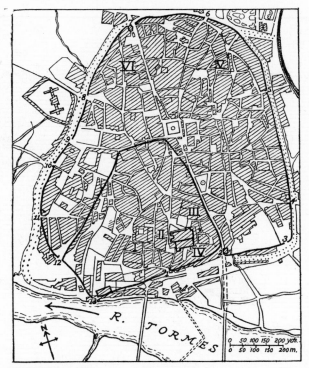

FIG. 126. The growth of Salamanca. Inner wall of 11th century contained quarters of the '*Serranos*' (i), *Francos* (ii), Portuguese (iii) and Mazarabes (iv). Outer wall of the 13th century defended quarters of *Toros* (v) and Castilians (vi)

Sanabria, while the charming, glacial lake of Castañeda is a reminder of its Atlantic borderland. In the mountainous regions of Cepeda and the Maragatería are an ancient people, that have distinguished themselves as the muleteers of Spain, because of the poverty of their valleys. Astorga (10,000) was a Roman town and halt on the Pilgrims' Way. Further east, the mountains of León stand out boldly in folded ranges running north-west to south-east, whose subsequent headstreams comprise a multiplicity of *comarcas*. The exploitation of the scattered coal mines earlier this century and the construction of the railway that runs along the foot of the mountain fault scarp, to connect them with Oviedo and Bilbao, have modified the way of life. South of the scarp, the *páramos* extend widely, poor pastures with scattered fields of rye and potatoes deeply dissected by the numerous consequents that descend in asymmetrical valleys towards the Douro trough. Their ribbons of meadow land and gardens, bordered by poplars and ash, are in marked contrast,

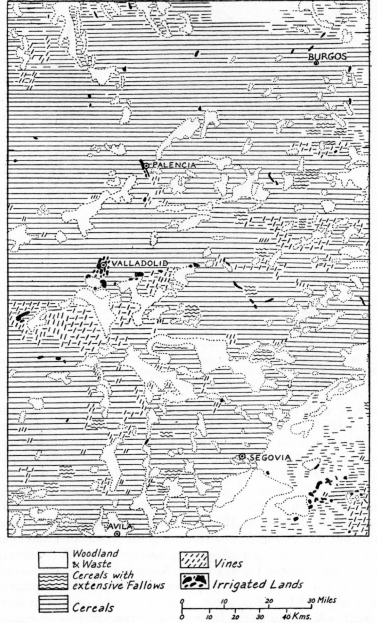

FIG. 127. Land utilisation in Old Castile (generalised from the 1/50,000 topographic maps)

the site of most of the settlements and the chief market towns, such as Benavente and Sahagun. On the northern borders of the tableland the Romans built their camp town of León, to guard the approaches to the Pass of Pajares across the Cantabrians. Although a medieval capital, its slow growth has preserved its central Roman plan. Only with modern communications has León jumped from 15,000 in 1900 to 59,549 inhabitants in 1950, creating a new town with its industrial and commercial enterprise.

The central plains of Old Castile lie about 300 ft below the limestone tablelands (at 2,200–2,500 ft above sea-level) cut into broad valleys festooned by occasional buttes. These rich lands covered with clayey limon, are more densely settled with the population living in larger villages (500–1,000 inhabitants) (Fig. 125). The adobe dwellings contrast with the stone dwellings of the mountain borders, and their more lavish use of timber, or the brick houses of southern Castile where the sandy pediments are too friable for building use. Most of the central plains comprise the Tierra de Campos, that ancient foyer of the Vacci and area of dense Visigothic settlement, from whose name of 'Campos de Godos' it is derived. This is a well-defined region, lying between the lower courses of the Pisuerga and Cea, though merging westwards into the similar wheatlands of Zamora, the Tierra del Pan (Fig. 123). This is the great breadbasket of Castile, where wheat, barley and also chick-peas are so important (Fig. 90). Irrigation is now being energetically developed on the main rivers, except the Cea, with the aid of some fourteen dams in the mountain valleys. This is a more realistic development than the original Utopian scheme of the Canal de Castilla (1842–49) built as a projected waterway to connect eventually Castile with the Atlantic, down the Besaya valley. Sited to the east of the region, ancient *Pallantia* was an important Roman and later medieval town, on the frontier between León and Castile. Today, as the commercial centre of a rich agricultural region, Palencia (41,769) boasts both gothic monuments and modern town planning.

Between Aranda de Duero and Roa, the Douro valley widens into a broad trough, bordered profusely by vineyards as far as Penafiel, with its enchanting castle backed by pinewoods. Wheat lands and vineyards alternate downstream in the regions of Valladolid, Tordesillas and Zamora. Valladolid is the great metropolis of the northern Meseta, but, unlike many other towns of great antiquity, nothing is known of it prior to its arab name. In the eleventh century, it was merely a small fortress at the crossing of the lower Pisuerga. Later, royal patronage gave it magnificent buildings, enclosed in a second wall in the fourteenth century. For a brief period (1600–1606) it was even the capital of Spain. But the seeds of its decay had already manifested themselves in the sixteenth century and it remained moribund until the revival of Castillian trade in the eighteenth century. Then with the advent of the railway its population jumped from 40,000 in 1857 to over 150,000 today. It is now a great industrial city, at least by Spanish standards.

2. *The Central Cordillera.* Dominating the southern horizon of Old Castile are the snowy ranges of the Central Cordillera, which run from

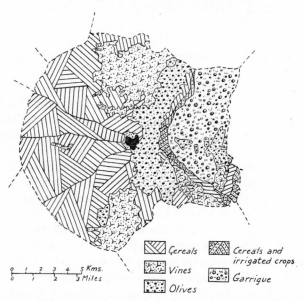

Fig. 128. Land utilisation of the commune of Horche, Guadalajara (from Garcia Fernandez)

north-east to south-west for nearly 250 miles. First the Sa de Ocejon rises above the Soria tableland, then Ayllon, Somosierra Guadarrama, Gredos and Peña de Francia succeed in turn (Fig. 130). From the Tagus trough they appear more impressive, as the tableland of New Castile is some 300 ft below that of Old Castile and the Tagus trough is well below that of the Douro. The rock scenery is very varied, from the sombre slates of Somosierra to the high gneiss summits of the Guadarrama, reaching 8,100 ft in the high peak of Peñalara, and the more uniformly granitic and more intensely glaciated slopes of the Gredos. After the Sa Nevada and Pyrenees, the Sa de Gredos comprise the highest mountains of Spain, their naked summits towering to a maximum of 8,727 ft in Almanzor.

The mountains are a climatic divide between the harsher continental conditions to the north, and the milder climate to the south. Thus in the northern valleys, the holm oak climbs alone, but on the southern flanks, it mingles with the cork oak and gum cistus, the latter filling the air with its distinctive scent. In the sheltered southern basins, there are mimosa, magnolias, tamarisks and eucalyptus, flora quite different from the Central European species to the north. As a climatic and botanic island, the central Cordillera has been the refuge of plant migrations since the cold Quaternary phases; this explains the curious occurrence of the beechwoods in the Somosierra valley of Montejo. There is however a transition from east to west. In the Somosierra and Guadarrama mountains, the Scots pine rising from 4,000 to c. 6,000 ft has successfully ousted the deciduous oak (*Q. toza*). But in the Gredos where the rainfall is higher and the winter temperatures less severe the *Quercus toza* mingled with *Pinus Pinaster* is still the prevailing cover of woodland. Above the tree-line the gentler slopes are extensively covered by the purple and golden blooms of summer, provided by heather (*Calluna vulgaris*) and the Genista or *Spartium purgans*. Interior basins (*navas*) add a colour contrast with their vivid green meadows and humus-darkened soils of cultivation.

As the population map indicates (Fig. 131) the region is a poor world, sparsely settled with 10 to 20 per sq. mile, largely supported by forest resources and pastoralism. Primitive conditions and isolation have preserved archaic modes of life, as in the Batuecas and Alberca. The poverty, inbreeding and overpopulation of the Hurdes has been well described by Legendre, as an economic and social squalor unequalled in the Peninsula. In contrast, the kindly granite valleys of the southern Gredos, the deeper soils, milder climate and easier access promote the high density of population in the Alberche and Tiétar valleys with their lemons, figs, olives, vines and vegetable gardens. In Hemingway's novel *For Whom the Bell Tolls* the strategic importance of these mountains has been graphically described. The passes are few and elevated: the easy crossing of the Somosierra (4,687 ft) is used by the direct highway from Madrid to Burgos; the Alto de León is on the route to Corunna; the col of Navacerrada is snowbound for half the year and less important. They all attract *Madrileños* to the winter sports on the high *parameras*. Along these routes, a rash of summer chalets has sprung up among the fragrant pinewoods, especially along the railway line to the Escorial, that monastic retreat of Philip II that symbolises Spain's golden century. Arenas de San Pedro and other small market towns are also becoming popular as cool retreats in summer.

3. *The Tagus Valley and Madrid.* At the foot of the Cordillera, stretching to the skyline of the Montes de Toledo, the piedmont consists of undulating plains and broad interfluves that decrease gently in height from north-east to south-west. The axis of the trough is followed by the rivers Henares, lower Jarama and from Toledo westwards by the Tagus. This tectonic trough, known as the Campiña de Henares, the Tierra de Toledo and the Campo Aranuelo, is infilled by a wide range of late Tertiary and Quaternary sediments, coarse in the mountain fans, fine sands towards the south-east where they merge with the Miocene lake marls. River terraces renowned for their hidden stores of Palaeolithic artefacts, valley floors watered generously by the snows of the Cordillera, and famous towns of noble history, are features of this interesting region, which at first sight seems to comprise merely dull and monotonous cereal lands, reduced to the same tonality by the devouring heat and light.

The rich, irrigated lands of the Campiña de Henares (canal built in 1859) are shared between Guadalajara (19,000) the old administrative centre, and Alcalá de Henares (20,000) a medieval bishopric and a University seat (1509–1836). Between the productive vegas of the Henares, Járama, Guadarrama and Alberche that help to feed Madrid, stretch a series of broad interfluves that were once covered with pine woods, now used for grazing and cereals. They merge south into the heavier soils of La Sagra, famed for its cereals and olives. Contrasted with the desolate tablelands is the *huerta* of Aranjuez (25,000) which once belonged to the Order of St James and was then a royal estate with its capriciously designed palace and exotic gardens. Downstream, the Tagus narrows its valley, permitting only limited gardens in the concave meander spurs at Toledo, but widening again at the Alberche confluence, to give Talavera (22,500) a fecund *huerta* and a promising future for irrigation in the plain between the Alberche and the Tiétar, The site of Puente del Arzobispo, like Talavera, was characterised by the river crossing of a *cañada* over the Tagus. Toledo has long been the capital of this varied region. As a Celtiberian and Roman fortress on a meander spur of the Tagus, and at the contact of two economies between the pastoral mountains and agricultural plains, Toledo has had a long and illustrious history. It was a Visigothic and then an Arab capital, with some 60,000 inhabitants in the sixteenth century, when Madrid was still a mere township. Its later decadence has preserved its medieval appearance so that together with the legacy of its luxury industries, tourism has helped to revive it once more (23,717 inhabitants in 1900, 40,243 in 1950).

Much nonsense has been taught about the artificial site of Madrid. Situated between the borders of the piedmont and the compact soils of La Sagra, it was until the mid-nineteenth century well provided by seepage water in shallow wells in the Quaternary granite catchment areas of the Guadarrama adequately supply this vast city. Its food supplies have been locally assured: vegetables from the bread basket of La Sagra; fruit from the orchards of La Vera; beef from Avila and the Járama; and the wheatlands and vineyards of Castile add to the bounty. The variety of building materials, Miocene brick and tile clays, limestones and granites have aided the growth of the city. Since its Arab fortress of Magerit was captured in 1085, its location and site were recognised to be of first-class importance; lying on the major routes of the Peninsula that utilise the passes of the Central Cordillera and the Tagus valley. True, Madrid was inferior to many provincial capitals when it was selected as the royal capital in 1561: it did not have the long history of Cádiz, the opulence of Seville, the military prestige of Toledo, the mercantile importance of Valladolid, the culture of Salamanca, nor the foreign contacts of Barcelona and Valencia. But in the interests of federal unity, Madrid was an ideal choice, costly though it was to maintain because of long inland communications.

Seen from the air the face of Madrid today reflects five major stages of growth. These are: the medieval, the sixteenth and seventeenth centuries, the eighteenth to mid-nineteenth centuries, the mid-nineteenth century to the Civil War, and the recent growth. Medieval Madrid is still discernible in the old quarter near the royal palace, overlooking the valley of the Manzanares. Where a small side stream isolates a hill 125 ft high, the Alcazar of Magerit was built to defend a river crossing. East of the fortress was established the Almedina or settlement, protected on its exposed flanks by the ravine of the Castellana stream to the east, another to the south (Calle Segovia) and a third to the north (Calle Arenal). Moorish and Jewish suburbs grew up outside the enlarged post-conquest town. Extramural settlements later grew up around the Benedictine monastery of San Martin to the north, San Francisco to the east, and the hermitage of Atocha to the southeast. A new wall was built in the thirteenth century to protect these suburbs which sufficed for the next three centuries. Growth persisted towards the north and east where the terrain was more suitable. Meanwhile Madrid had become the habitual residence of some Castilian kings and the population is reputed to have doubled between 1513 and 1546. By 1560 Madrid had 25,000–30,000 inhabitants.

The second stage commenced in 1561 when Philip II decided to move

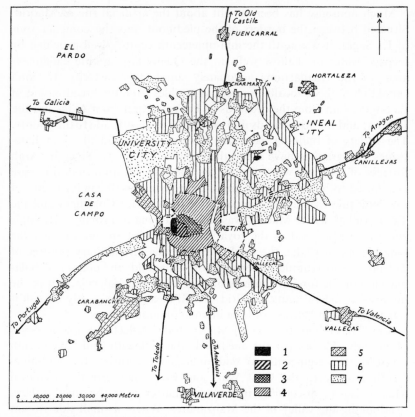

FIG. 129. The growth of Madrid. Legend: 1. Alcázar; 2. Medieval town; 3. City in
late 18th century; 4. in 1857; 5. in 1896; 6. in 1928; 7. in 1950

the court permanently to Madrid. In consequence of its royal patronage, a third wall was made in 1625, with an imposing Plaza Mayor
(built in 1623), a Bohemian quarter south-east of the Puerta del Sol,
and to the east the houses and palaces of the nobility along the Castellana. The latter was the 'West End' of Madrid, built however on the
east side of the city as a protection against the prevailing cold winter
winds, off the Guadarrama. The Retiro or royal summer palace, likewise was built in the east, a more comfortable and popular residence
than the draughty palace on the site of the Moorish fort. By the end of
the seventeenth century, Madrid had over 100,000 inhabitants. Then
followed the monumental buildings created by the Bourbons so that
there were some 150 public buildings by the early nineteenth century.

But the mid-nineteenth century view of Madrid could not have been altogether attractive, since the city was surrounded until 1868 by mud walls, while outside deforestation of the environs had produced its toll of choking summer dust and cold winter winds, with a scarcity of fuel and limited water supplies.

During the fourth stage, the capital was assured the amenities of a great city. The advent of the railway (1851, Madrid-Aranjuez line), the use of gas-lighting (1847), piped water supplemented by the Lozoya Canal (1855) and the Plan of Castro for a new town (1857), helped to revolutionise the face of the city. Castro's plan was, however, put into execution only in 1891, three years before the project of the 'Lineal City' was begun, to link the eastern suburbs between Chamartín and Argüelles. Thus between 1900 and 1920, Madrid had grown from 540,000 to 750,000 people (Fig. 129). Since the Civil War, Madrid has faced not only the problem of devastation wrought during the prolonged siege of the city but also the inadequate solutions of its previous phase of development. Castro had assumed for his plan a city of only 450,000 in the mid-twentieth century. Today, Madrid has over two million inhabitants and the city has grown with no strong guidance. Industry sprawls over one-third of its area, mixed indiscriminately with residential areas; most are small workshops in the basements of private dwellings. Zonification has begun notably in the magnificent lay-out of the University city, and in such post-war developments as the political centre of Nuevos Ministerios, the new transport schemes, and the industrial growth of such suburbs as Carabanchel and Vallecas. The spread of the residential suburbs, northwards towards the Guadarrama mountains, is rapidly opening up new districts. Thus Madrid no longer looks like an urban oasis in an open landscape of *año y vez*. Its approach is heralded by ever widening links of ribbon development, for it has become the energetic primate city of the Peninsula.

4. *The Tablelands of New Castile*. East of Madrid, beyond the Henares valley, the Miocene tabular relief becomes more marked, the coloured mosaics of truncated soil horizons revealing the rapidity of vertical erosion. This region is the Alcarria, stretching towards the headwaters of the Tagus and its tributaries. In the west, lower Alcarria (3000 ft) is a cultivated landscape, Castilian in aspect, with large villages and their numerous satellites of hamlets (Fig. 64). But west of the Sa de Altomira, Upper Alcarria rises above 3,400 ft with higher tablelands deeply trenched by the valleys and all smothered in a vast sweep of matorral, except around the cleared patches round the small hamlets with their rows of beehives. Between the two areas, the Tagus and Guadiela cut

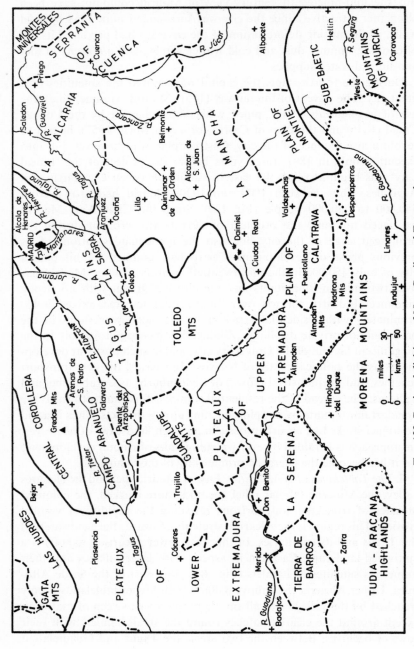

Fig. 130. Regional divisions of New Castile and Extremadura

magnificent defiles where the dams of Entrepeñas and Buendia create artificial lakes for several miles upstream. The linear landscape of high limestone tablelands, folded ranges and deep gorges becomes more exaggerated in the Serranía of Cuenca and in the Paramera de Molina. There the Karstic feature of the Ciudad Encantada is a famous example of the effects of solution creating a limestone 'city' of grotesque forms, floored with *terra rossa* (Fig. 21). This is *par excellence* a forested landscape famed since antiquity for its pine timber, floated down the affluents of the Tagus and Júcar by the *gaucheros*. The altitudinal range is well recognised by the levels of vegetation. From 2,500 to 3,000 ft, where the climate is warmer thrive vast areas of rosemary and kermes oak scrub and where the fractures in the limestone provide abundant sources of sub-surface water are stands of black pine (*P. laricio*). Above 11,000 ft the Scots pine is dominant with dense *matorral* of *Genista scorpius* and lavender. Between 4,000 and 5,000 ft box is the prevailing shrub and above this the juniper (*J. sabina*). Cuenca (24,800) is the capital of this wild country, suitably located between the southern plains and the fault scarp of the Serranía. Its castle dominates the picturesque gorge of the Júcar-Hueca confluence, controlling the routes north of Albarracín and east towards Valencia.

South of the Alcarria are the plains of La Mancha (2,300 ft) immortalised by Cervantes. Known as the 'Esparto country' by the Romans and 'the waterless land' by the Arabs, it is the widest stretch of pseudo-steppe in the Peninsula. On its sunburnt earth of pale reddish-yellow hues appear here and there white-washed, compact villages that appear from the air like scattered bird-droppings (Fig. 131). The borders of La Mancha have never been clear: forming a small community that centred on Campo de Criptana under the patronage of the military order of St James in the fourteenth century, it was created a province in the next century and was enlarged in the seventeenth century. Vaguely it stretches to the lilac horizon of the Montes deToledo in the west, to the white limestone hills of Cuenca in the north, and the grey foothills of the Sa Morena in the south, smeared with yellow broom. The *genius loci* of this simple region has been preserved in the *comarcas*, created as spheres of influence by the military orders, with their fortress towns (Fig. 108). The windmills, a less obvious element of the landscape today, than when Don Quixote tilted at them, were first introduced in the early sixteenth century during a series of severe droughts.

Ocaña stands at the threshold of Upper Mancha to the south of the Tagus valley. Stretching as far as Alcazar de San Juan (25,139) was formerly the domain of the order of St James, with its large settlements, several of which today have over 10,000 inhabitants. Further south is Lower Mancha, more uniformly flat, richer and more densely populated, with a spread of vineyards that supports larger centres such as Daimiel (20,204). Here the water-table is near the surface, exploited in the province of Ciudad Real by over 21,000 water-wheels to water as many or more hectares of vegetable gardens, anis, maize and alfalfa fields. In the Campo de Montiel, the landscape changes to the Triassic limestones, with their reddish soils and karstic features, such as the lagoons of Riudera, associated with the legend of Merlin, and the grotto of Montesinos. In the south-west is the Campo de Calatrava, more mountainous and surmounted by the series of volcanic cones. All these regions have numerous lakes (over 40), some fed by springs in Pontian limestones, others parts of disrupted drainage systems now desiccated by drought, and a few in volcanic craters. Finally to the east, rises the Mancha of Albacete or Montearagon with more rolling relief, isolated windmills on the cuesta skyline, and scattered clumps of Aleppo pines amidst medium-sized properties of cereals and vines. In this land of historic towns, it is a sign of the times that Albacete (71,900) only a small village a century ago, should now be a great centre of routes and commerce, while Chinchilla slumbers beneath its old fortress.

5. *Extremadura.* Unlike the northern tableland, where the Tertiary plains merge with the western Palaeozoic plateaux, the south-western block of Extremadura turns its back on New Castile in a series of naked quartzite ridges and bare basalt or slate mountains. Administratively, it may be said roughly to consist of the provinces of Cáceres and Badajoz, though geographically its landscapes overlap into the provinces of Toledo, Ciudad Real and Huelva. Extremadura is rather a historic term, referring to the Reconquest, where for several centuries, it was a no-man's-land, fought over and desolate. This feature is still apparent in the large agglomerated settlements widely spaced, in what may be termed 'the empty quarter of the Peninsula' (Fig. 131). Only within the last century has closer colonisation been active. Extremadura slopes and faces towards the Atlantic, and because its pastures are greener than elsewhere on the Meseta, this has been terminus of *cañadas* and the domain of pastoralism (Fig. 51). Southern, milder influences are also apparent in the appearance of the wild olive, the silver almond, and other plants more characteristic of Andalusia. The hard-coloured residual relief, the endless rolling peneplains, the constant shade of the ilex and the scent of the gum-cistus are the motif of Extremadura. G. Brenan has well captured its atmosphere in his description of the road towards Cáceres: 'rolling hills thinly scattered with ilex trees, open spaces

of green corn or stubble, then more ilexes. Every tree had the same shape, every shape cast the same shadows, every shadow revolved round its trunk in an identical way. We were in a country of sun clocks, but why so much chronometry when nothing but the shadows ever moved, and nothing recordable ever happened? Except for the occasional chatter of a magpie there was complete silence.' Seasonally, the landscape is whitened by vast stretches of gum-cistus like snow showers in spring, bluish-green in winter and brown foliage in summer. The subdivisions of this monotonous region are the continuations of the Meseta, the western mountains and basins of the central Cordillera, the peneplains of Upper Estremadura, the central mountains of Guadalupe and Montánches, the plains of the Guadiana basin, and the southern plateaux and mountains.

The forested slopes of the Sas of Béjar and Gata, rising gently from the Salamanca tableland plunge steeply to the southern troughs of Aranuelo and Alagon on the northern borders of Estremadura. It is a poor country, apart fron the gardens and orchards of the Alagon and Tiétar valleys, but the picturesque towns, medieval in aspect, such as Oropesa, Palencia and Coria. The gorges of the Tagus and the Salar plunge below the slate peneplains in vertical walls of 600–700 ft. Southwards, the monotonous peneplains of Cáceres and Trujillo marked with a veneer of pediments (*rañas*) rise gradually to the central backbone of Estremadura, the mountains of San Pedro and Montánchez. Easily penetrated by routes, they focus on Cáceres (45,300) a Roman and medieval fortress which is today the regional capital of the north. To the east, the ranges of the Villuercas, Guadalupe and Toledo comprise another desolate landscape widely covered with *matorral* and ilex woodlands, in which lies isolated the charming monastic town of Guadalupe. The *comarca* of La Jara, though now cleared for cultivation, is a reminder of the former extent of the gum-cistus, now more restricted to the mountain slopes.

South of these mountains, beyond the pediments of Albuquerque, the recent valley of the Guadiana links a chain of Tertiary basins. The defile of Cíjara lies upstream, and in contrast to the Tagus which repels settlement in its gorges, the Guadiana attracts the major centres on its vegas. Between the upper and lower vegas, one of the largest Roman colonies of the Peninsula was located, *Emrita Augusta*. Today, Mérida (23,900) is again an active, prosperous centre. Badajoz (79,291) has also a long history as a military centre, but its population has grown rapidly only in the last fifty years. The completion of the Cíjara dam, the key to the Badajoz Plan, will now permit the extension of some

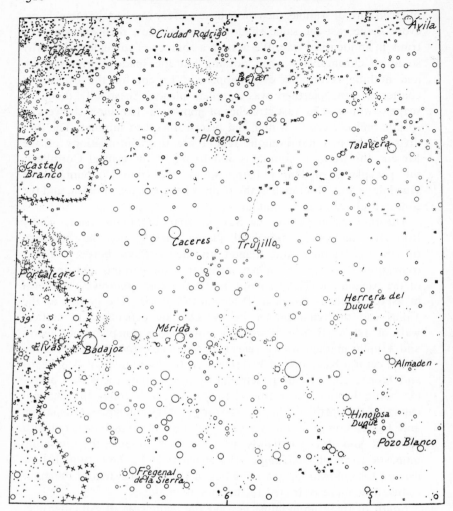

FIG. 131. Distribution of population in New Castile and Extremadura. Note the much higher densities in Portugal compared with the Spanish borders. Other marked differences are the hamlets and small villages of the Alcarria and Guadalajara, the

100,000 hectares in these valley lands, allow the creation of 21 new villages and towns, and radically change the life of this region. Two other *comarcas* deserve special mention in the Guadiana basin. The pastoral region of La Serena (Fig. 130), once the property of the Knights of Alcántara, was one of the richest medieval pasturages of Spain. Forming a sea of spring flowers, it is still the winter grazing lands of

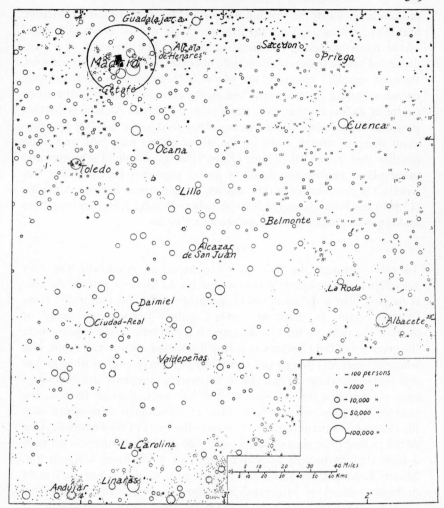

larger villages of upper La Mancha, the large, agglomerated pattern south of Lillo—
many of military origin—and the sparse distribution in the Montes de Toledo
compared with either the Tagus valley of the plains of Mérida and Badajoz

transhumant flocks. Further west, the rich Quaternary soils of Los
Barros have a more polychromatic landscape of olives, vines, cereals
and gardens, centred on the market town of Almendralejo (21,400).

In southern Extremadura, the thin soils of the slate and other
hardened rocks, support only poor cereal lands, woodlands of holm
oak and vast areas of *matorral*. But on the western slopes of the Jeréz

mountains towards the Portuguese border, the penetration of Atlantic humidity is recognisable in the extensive cork woods. The rolling relief of the lands bordering the Sa Morena looks like the swell of a vast, darkened ocean, frozen in the mantle of cistus, heath and other *matorral*. Between desolate plateaux, the plains of Llerena provide a strategic corridor linking Extremadura and Andalusia, controlled by the route centre of Zafra. Further east, the synclinal valley of Alcudia is another pastoral Serena. On its flat, grassy floor feed some 500,000 transhumant sheep in winter, while on the slopes ablaze with pink and white heather that grows 10 ft high (*Erica ciliaris*), shepherd's broom and other plants browse the herds of goats; pigs also fatten in the ilex woods. On the borders of this district, mining towns such as Almadén (13,000) and Puertollano (25,000) are ugly and sordid, fortunately without making much impression on nature's vast vistas.

ANDALUSIA

To cross through the Pass of Despeñaperros, practically the only breach in the three hundred mile wall of the Sa Morena, into Andalusia, is to pass into a different world, geographically and culturally, from Central Spain. In place of harsh Castilian landscapes, rugged or austere, the valley of the Guadalquivir is a rich humanised region where the greenery of the Campiña in spring has varied commercial crops, and where geometrical design and symmetry of form in endless olive groves and scattered white *cortijos* (Plate 38) among vineyards, are characteristic. Al-Andalus the Arabian land of the west, Roman Baetica, the land of Tartessos, of the Hesperides, of Phoenician settlements, stirs the imagination perhaps more than any other part of the Peninsula. One of the richest provinces of Rome, its trade in oil and wine was on such a scale that its broken amphora helped to build Rome's eighth hill, Monte Testaccio. Its arabicised culture gave it one of Europe's most brilliant civilisations. Mineral exploitation has always enriched it with a sophisticated, urban life. Even the villagers think of themselves more as townsfolk than peasants. Everywhere there is a light-heartedness that contrasts with Castilian melancholy. Despite the desperate poverty the dwellings gleam with whitewash, pots of geraniums hang from iron grilled windows, artistic tiles cover cool patios.

The individuality of Andalusia is sharpened if the troughs of the Guadalquivir and the Ebro are compared. The Plain of Andalusia opens widely to the moist Atlantic influences, the Ebro is screened in by continental harshness. Where the steppes occur they consist of alfa and dwarf palm, not the ashen juniper. The soils too are more varied, the

Andalusian trough forming an active marine gulf into the Quaternary. The sunken piedmont plain is still being reclaimed in the Marismas. Although dry farming is as widespread in Andalusia as in Aragón the pattern is different. The grain lands of the Ebro cover the broad interfluves, but in Andalusia these are widely clothed with olives and vines; the *secano* occupies the lower plains where the shallow water-table enables crops like alfalfa, cotton and even tobacco to be grown as well as cereals. It is curious that despite all the rich heritage, little of the irrigation potential of Andalusia outside of the ancient *huertas* has been developed until the modern schemes. Both are asymmetrical valleys, dominated on one side by the great ranges of the Sa Nevada and the Pyrenees respectively. But while the former has garden cities living in a sub-tropical Arcadia, the latter has a simple, pastoral endowment. It is, therefore, not perhaps remarkable that history destined Seville and Cádix to rule the Indies.

The limits of Andalusia are clearly defined by the arid mountains that border Murcia, less so by the borderland of the Sa Morena. The contrasts between the plain of the Guadalquivir and the Baetic mountains, popularly explain the distinctions between Lower and Upper Andalusia. But geographically it is more satisfactory to make a six-fold division: the Sierra Morena, the Plain of Andalusia, the Southern hills and plateaux, the Interior Depressions, Mediterranean Andalusia and the Steppes in the north east (Fig. 132).

1. *The Sierra Morena.* As it has already been emphasised, the Sa Morena is not a mountain chain but the edge of the Meseta, deeply trenched by the right bank tributaries of the Guadalquivir, together with the minor clefts of the rivers Tinto and Odiel (see p. 175). From the high summits of the Madrona (3,800 feet) in the north, this wild landscape appears like a sea petrified in slate, with the infinite rolling relief of ridges. Its narrow valleys, thickly covered with the greatest expanse of matorral in the Peninsula have always been a refuge for saint and sinner. The Sa de Los Santos behind Córdoba is reminiscent of the Christian hermitages set up during the Muslim occupation; some still there. But in such phrases as *esto es Sierra Morena* ('this is Sa Morena') to describe some nefarious deed, the identification with banditry has been more emphatic. La Carolina (1768) was built near the villainous pass of Despeñaperros to stamp out its lawlessness, though it has made more success of mining. Minerals are the *raison d'être* of all the larger centres, portrayed on the map by railway lines, linking Linares (43,900), Peñarroya, Guadalcanal, Pedroso and Riotinto. Side by side with modern techniques in mines, some worked

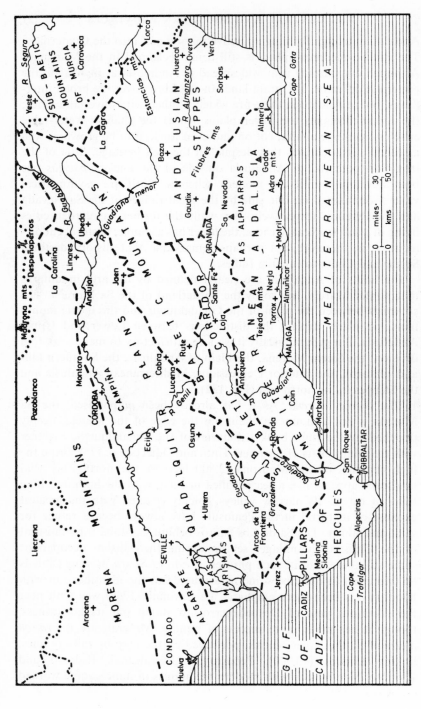

Fig. 132. Regional divisions of Andalusia

continuously from antiquity, the primitive occupations of the charcoal burner and shepherd remain. Only rarely, as in the rich *vegas* of Cazalla is more intensive use made of the land.

This great dreary sweep of the Morena is divided into broad segments: the Sa of Córdoba, the Sa of Cazalla, the Sa Alta of Huelva, and the western ranges of Andevalo. The peneplaned plateaux with their hard slates and limestones decomposed only slowly into thin soil cover, are mantled with a vast cover of gum-cistus and related species. On the higher lands with more generous rainfall, there are extensive woodlands of ilex, cork and chestnut, especially in the Sa Alta of Aracena, which has 30–40 in. Here in Huelva province, almost three-quarters of the total surface is forested, with stone pine and eucalyptus on the lower slopes, deciduous and evergreen woodland above.

2. *The Plain of Andalusia.* The Guadalquivir, 'the great river' of the Arabs flows 423 miles and receives 806 affluents, several of them 100 miles long. Essentially its region has four characteristics. Fed by the melt water and vauclusian springs of the Baetic ranges, the left bank tributaries are the main sources of flow, particularly the Genil. This explains the asymmetry of the Plain, a narrow zone fronting the Sa Morena but a broad sweep of 25–35 miles in the eastern Campiña. A second contrast is the siting and density of settlement; a long line of large villages and towns border the Sub-Baetic mountains between Jaén and Osuña, fed by springs, whereas there is no such long line at the foot of the Sa Morena (Fig. 133). A third feature is the antiquity of settlement everywhere in the Plain. Of the forty-two centres which today have over 8,000 inhabitants, thirty-eight are Roman in origin. Although most of the large farmsteads, *cortijos*, were built in the last two centuries, there are many on or near the sites of Roman villas, dating from the time when Hadrian, Trajan and Seneca were themselves absentee landlords. Finally, the varied character of the soils explains the chief regional features. Under a hot metallic sky the minerals in the soils sharply define their character, so that the variable sediments of this marine trough are major differentials. On the eastern borders of the Sub-Baetic mountains, the Triassic rocks glistening with saline deposits are virtually a red desert, presenting a lunar landscape of deep erosion and a human solitude only for the charcoal-burner. The gently folded Eocene and Miocene limestones, marls and sandstones, produce rolling or hilly relief, whose yellow or white stoney soils are covered for enormous distances with olives, a crop ideally suited to the large estates of absentee owners, since they require the minimum of attention to

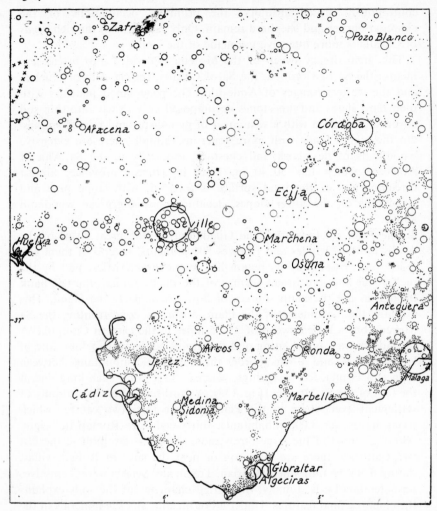

FIG. 133. Distribution of population in Andalusia. Note the markedly nucleated pattern of settlement, with some dispersion in favoured areas, especially Jerez, Malaga, Granada, and the Campina of Cordoba. The sub-Baetic and Baetic moun-

produce a cash crop. Then comes the tabular relief of the *campiña*, with its hard surfaces of rich, loamy soils over the Miocene, less rich over the Pliocene beds, and most productive when the dark chocolate coloured *tirs* cover the plain. Seawards, the Marismas, those salt marshes that resemble the Camargue in landscape and economy are themselves variable according to their position from the river. In all

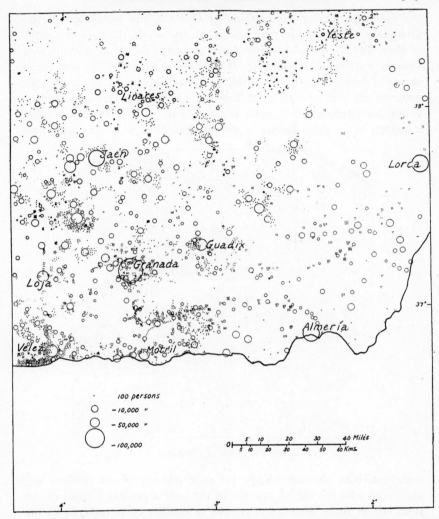

tainous areas however have more dispersion generally than the lands west of the
Guadalquivir. Note the very sparse population of the south-east steppes

this diversity of the Plain, five subdivisions may be broadly recognised:
Jaén and the Sub-Baetic Mountains; the *campiñas* of Córdoba and
Seville, the Huelva lowland and the Jeréz district.

From the Loma de Úbeda, whose Miocene marls provide rich olive
groves and vineyards, there is a diverse vista of Jáen. On its slopes are
the fortress towns of Úbeda and Baeza, adorned with their palaces. To

the east are the high mountains of Cazorla, the watershed of the Guadalquivir, clothed in pine forests. To the south, the narrow valleys of the Guadalquivir and its tributaries converge on the Jaén basin, that historic battleground, Jaén (63,000) itself is sheltered by the steep slopes of Jabalcruz (4,068) ft a dull town with a wonderful aspect, that controls the north-south route between Castile and Granada. It is a rolling landscape of olives as far as the eye can see, 340,000 ha, covering a quarter of the total surface of the province (Fig. 91). They symbolise

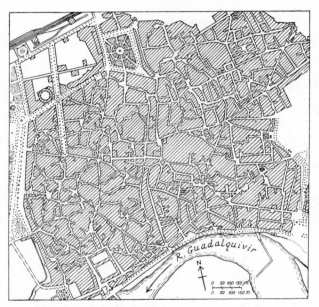

FIG. 134. Plan of Córdoba

such wealth in absentee hands, yet such poverty of the resident un-employed who for eleven months of the year represent a third of the total labour force. Severe soil erosion is another curse inflicted by the olive groves in this province of headstreams.

Towards Andújar, a pre-Roman town, blackened with the smoke of its potteries, the Guadalquivir begins to widen, but even as far as Córdoba it is only about a mile wide, choked with gravels. Built on the right bank of the river, Córdoba with its Roman bridge was the head of ancient navigation. Its etymology suggests that it had a Phoenician oil-press (*corteb*). Certainly it was a rich Roman colony, and later the capital of the Ommeyad Caliphate. In the tenth century, it was probably twice the size of the present town (141,580) on rather less than the existing area (Fig. 134). But hydro-electric power developments are aiding its food processing and agricultural industries, ensuring its growth as an important regional capital. Downstream the right bank is irrigated, benefited by the Guadalmellato dam. But the vista on the left bank is a desolate sweep of open cereal lands, dotted with scattered *cortijos*. Towards the eastern hills, the early Tertiary sandstones and limestones are covered with vineyards, most famous being those of Montilla and Los Moriles. Along the borders of the Sub-Baetic mountains are vast areas of olives and vines, supporting large agricultural centres such as Cabra, Lucena and Puente Genil, with wool centres such as Priego and Rute.

The Genil valley introduces a marked change with its fertile *huertas*, especially around Écija (41,621) that 'frying pan of Spain' that has sizzling temperatures of 110 or 116°F in summer (Fig. 135). Beyond it, the *campina* is less bare, covered more frequently with olives, especially between Carmona and Seville and around Marchena and the ducal town of Osuña. In the east, Triassic marls create a desolate land with salt lakes and saline streams. Between the plains of Alcor and Aljarafe, foci of ancient settlement, is situated Seville, the fourth city of Spain (324,550). Built on the left bank of the Guadalquivir, *Hispalis* was the Roman capital of southern Spain, then later in the twelfth century, capital of the Almohades. It still preserves some monuments of the later period, notably the Giralda, the Alcázar and the palace of Yeso. Then in the late fifteenth to mid-sixteenth centuries, its great commercial prosperity endowed it with many Renaissance palaces. Since then the city has changed little, still roughly contained by the boulevards that mark the alignment of the walls, pulled down in the nineteenth century. In the heart of the city, the quarter of Santa Cruz formerly the Jewish suburb of the Muslim town, still reflects in its narrow streets and vignettes of *plazas* and *patios* the Mudéjar and Arabesque architecture. The culture of this proud city, birthplace of Velasquez and Murillo, its cathedral, and great religious processions, its Archives of the Indies, all give it an old-world atmosphere that charms the tourists. But in the suburbs, especially of Triana there are the textile, ceramic and chemical industries and along the river the quays that ship the products of the region, of mineral ores, cork, olive-oil, oranges and wines.

To the south-west, beyond the holm oak parklands of Aljarafe, the renowned country of Niebla announces a change of landscape in its eucalyptus forests. Along this coast are a series of zones, changing towards the interior: first the sand dunes of Arenas Gordas with their stone pines and eucalyptus woods; then a pleasing landscape of vines,

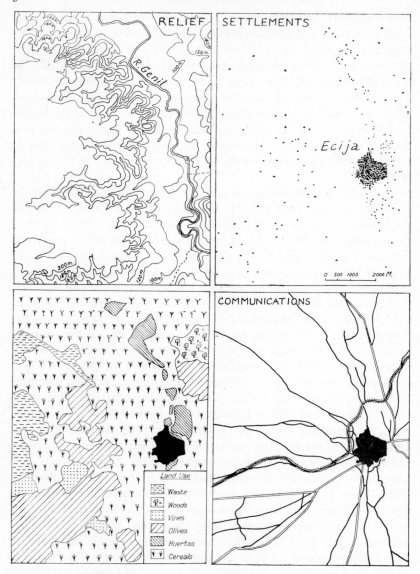

Fig. 135. Relief, settlement, land utilisation and communications in Ecija (lower Genil valley)

figs, almonds and other crops incorporated in the woodlands; and towards the interior as the clay soils diminish a xerophytic flora called *monte blanco* associated with the white flowers of the *Halimium hali-*

folium. Numerous fishing settlements occur along the coast, Palos, Aya-
monte and Isla Cristina having historic associations with the Atlantic
explorers. The site of Huelva (65,000) is probably traceable to the
Phoenician quest for those same ores that enrich it today. A cosmopolitan port, there is seen today in the outskirts the English influence
of bungalow suburbia.

Downstream from Seville, the Guadalquivir only falls 30 ft to the
sea, 88 miles away. Forming a lake in classical times, *Lacus Ligustinus*,
the salt marshes of Las Marismas are the haunt of wild fowl and bull
pastures. Since 1945 three polders of reclamation have been created,
two in the Isla Menor and another upstream, for various cash crops
such as sugar beet, chick peas, cotton and rice. Utrera with its vineyards
and pinewoods, and San Lúcar the fishing port, are the chief settlements on the borders of this dreary, mosquito country. Rising towards
the south-east is the more accidented relief where the Tertiary rocks
outcrop above the Quaternary sands, an opulent landscape of famous
vineyards and olive groves. It boasts the famous cognac town of
Jeréz (80,160), with its great houses of Domecq, Gonzalez Byass,
Terry and Osborne, founded in the nineteenth century. But like its
famous sherries, the houses of this ancient town are of all dates, an
elegant, spacious town, built of local apricot sandstone.

3. *The Southern Plains and Mountains of Cádiz.* From the massif of
Aljibe (3,580 feet) there is a magnificent panorama of this region,
subdivided into the northern mountains, the desolate Campo de
Gibraltar and the south-west populated plains. Eighteen miles to the
north are the rugged, limestone summits of the Serranía of Grazalema
(5,420 ft) with their great forests of holm and deciduous oaks and
large isolated villages. To the east, the gorges of the Guadiaro plunge
1,000 feet towards the Campo de Gibraltar. Below Aljibe stretches a
lonely, swelling relief of Oligocene flysch with deeply trenched interfluves, covered uniformly in a calcifuge mantle of cork woodlands or
invaded by gum-cistus *matorral.* To the south stretches the coastlands
for some 106 miles along the Straits of Gibraltar, dotted with woodlands of stone pine among the sand dunes. Here and there are patches
of cultivation protected by reeds or agave fences against the encroaching
sands, while towards Cádiz the white salt mounds glisten in the green
expanses of salt marsh, with their cover of halophytes (salicornia,
atriplex and tamarix). In the swampy outlets of the Barbate (Janda
lagoon) and Guadalete valleys there are extensive, seasonal marshes.
Compared with the two-thirds of the region thus described, a waste of
matorral and woodland, most of it in pastoral latifundia, for example

W.M.W.—12*

those of the Duke of Medina Sidonia, the south-west presents a different vista. Drained by the Guadalete, it is a wooded, cultivated landscape of vineyards and olive groves, around historic centres such as Arcos, Chiclana and others with the suffix 'de la frontera', reminiscent of the former frontier with the Muslim kingdom of Granada.

Coastal settlement in this strategic region of the Pillars of Hercules is very ancient. Palaeolithic cave drawings, Neolithic flints, Phoenician pearls, Greek pottery and Roman coins have been found in the same vicinity, for example Gorham's Cove at Gibraltar, indicating the long continuity of human occupance. The Moorish name of Gibraltar (Djebel al Tarik) alludes to the arrival there of the Berber leader Tarik in 711. But apart from the Moorish Castle and baths, little remains of this occupance. Only a remnant even of the sixteenth century wall is seen at South Gate. Since the seizure of Gibraltar in 1704 it has remained a British Crown Colony, in which over 25,000 inhabitants live in the narrow compass of 4,800 metres by 1,400 metres most of which is occupied by a hard limestone ridge rising to 1,404 feet. A faulted anticline to north and east bounded by faults, it plunges steeply to the coast. La Linea outside the neutral zone is a larger centre of 72,000 though commercially dependent on Gibraltar. Across the bay, Algeciras (43,100) described by the Moors as 'the isle' (Al Djezira) is a fishing and ferry port, largely rebuilt since the eighteenth century. Tarifa at the southern-most point of Europe, now a small fishing port, also takes its name from a Berber conqueror of A.D. 711. Cádiz, the city of Hercules and the inheritor of the lost city of *Tartessos* is one of the world's oldest ports, probably where the Phoenicians and certainly, the Carthaginians created a rich entrepôt in a sheltered inlet drowned in the vicissitudes of late Quaternary sea-levels. Built on a rocky outcrop at the tip of a series of sandspits, this 'siren of the Atlantic' as Byron called it, has attracted many peoples, reflected in its Punic cemetery, its Roman causeways and its Moriscan character of narrow streets and small market places. Imprisoned behind the massive fortifications of the seventeenth century, Cádiz has altered little in appearance, though its fortunes have fluctuated widely, from the heyday of the American monopoly trading (1720–1765) to nineteenth-century stagnation. Today, with 100,250 inhabitants, the prospects of increased Atlantic trade and the creation in 1948 of a free port, Cádiz shows that, like Marseilles, its vitality is still great. The town of San Fernando (30,000) surrounded by salt pans that date from antiquity, Puerto Real, and Santa María the outport of Jeréz, have been fishing ports at least since Roman times.

4. *The Interior Depressions.* This region may be said to commence in the

upper valleys of the Guadiaro and Guadalete. There, enclosed by the sombre folds of the Grazalema, Bermya and Nieve mountains, the desolate tableland of Ronda (*c.* 2,500 ft) has been deeply dissected. The upper Guadiaro (Guadaleven) has cut through the carapace of Miocene sandstones into the soft, underlying marls, to form a gorge falling sheer for 400 ft. Like Constantine, Ronda is divided by the gorge into the Moorish town of La Ciudad with narrow, crooked lanes, and El Mercadillo, the modern town to the north, which has developed since a bridge was built in 1761. Capital of a mountainous region, Ronda (17,500) is the centre of much contraband trade through Gibraltar and a tourist attraction. From Ronda, the road and railway follow beside rocky gorges and stony *huertas*, flanked by pine-covered mountains and much *ilex matorral*. Numerous scattered dolmens on the high pastures, ancient Berber villages perched precariously on limestone ridges and *villanuevas* of the sixteenth and seventeenth centuries in the more open, marly plateaux, reflect the vicissitudes of settlement. Antequera (29,670) overlooking the poplar-lined valley of the Guadalhorce and its *vega*, has been a stronghold since Roman times and is still dominated by the ruins of its Moorish castle. This limestone district has two large karstic lakes to the north-west of Antequera, while the towering mountains to the south-east supply a rich vauclusian wealth to the fertile *vega* of Loja.

Beyond lies the great depression of Granada, a Miocene trough with its original floor now at 2,600–3,600 ft on the mountain slopes, cut by the Genil valley and its terraces (190–210, 65–80, six to ten ft). From the Sa Elvira (3,590 ft) north of the city, there is a splendid view of the brilliant greenery of the *Vega*, with a multiplicity of crops set in a maze of irrigation channels, and dotted with the tall chimneys of the sugar-beet factories and some tobacco drying sheds. To the east of the Vega, Granada descends the reddish slopes of the Alhambra in a series of quarters, overlooked by the Arabian fairy land of the famous palace and its exotic gardens. Known to its Arab settlers as the Damascus of the west, Granada has always been the focal centre that joined the two Andalusias, of the Mediterranean and of the Atlantic. But in the precocious advancement of this Arab capital, it is only today that the population of some 200,000 has once more regained the size it had reached in the fifteenth century.

5. *Mediterranean Andalusia.* Between the western borders of Málaga, through southern Granada to the city of Almería, the Mediterranean coastlands of Andalusia run for about 185 miles in a sequence of coastal ranges with narrow beaches, cliffs and headlands, interrupted

by broader valleys and Tertiary depressions that give access to the mountainous interior (Fig. 83). This is a Riviera region, dominated by the mountains and the sea. Facing south, sheltered by the continuous sequence of ranges, it has on the lower slopes a temperate Mediterranean climate, while the semi-arid plains are compensated by irrigation, supplied by perennial, snow-fed and karstic streams. The character of the coastal deltas which attract the chief settlements, has changed within historic times, as the ports were relatively more important in the past than now. Roman galleys reached Vélez de Málaga and Adra now situated in their deltas. Phoenician *Malaca* (Málaga) Greek *Mainake* (Torre del Mar) and Roman Almuñecar and Purchena (Almería) were all important ports in classical times. But recent uplift of the coast together with mountain erosion and coastal deposition consequent on deforestation, have built up the alluvial cones and coastal deltas. Most marked has been the creation of the Motril (R. Guadalfeo) and Adra (R. Grande) deltas since the Castilian colonisation of the Alpujarras began in the sixteenth century, clearing the slopes for their traditional *secano* cultivation, in an unsuitable terrain. Thus the agricultural wealth of the coastlands has accrued at the expense of the mountain slopes. Sea trade, which brought exotics such as sugar-cane, bananas, oranges, citron and a wide variety of vegetables, has intensified since the last century the commercial production of Málaga wines and Almerian grapes. The Mediterranean sea, everywhere a tourist attraction, is here greatly enhanced by the mountain views, the varied colours of the flora, and the old towns. The regional landscapes may be grouped conveniently into the following divisions: the mountains, the Serranía and Hoya of Málaga, the Costa del Sol, and the Alpujarra (Fig. 132).

Dominating the mountain borders of Andalusia is the great schistose barrier of the Sa Nevada, running east-west for some 60 miles. Above its basal platform, deeply trenched by the rivers, the summits rise in alpine grandeur to altitudes of over 10,000 ft notably Mulhacen (11,420 ft) the highest peak in the Peninsula, Cerro Pelado (10,700 ft) and Veleta (11,125 ft). Between November and May snow above 6,000 ft creates an impassable barrier, except for the unique breach of the valley of Lecrin, that links Granada with Motril. Nearer the coast, the Sierras of Cazulas and Guajaras, a wild country of banditry is cut off from the plains by precipitous slopes. To the west, the mountains of Almijara (6,010 ft) and Tejeda (6,759 ft) merge with the Penibaetic rampart that borders Antequera and Ronda. Here however there are the most numerous cols to facilitate transmontone communications. But a mountain economy only truly exists in the Sa Nevada, with permanent pastures at 4,600–5,250 ft and small patches of potatoes or rye up to 7,800–8,200 ft. It is the domain of chestnuts, mixed oaks, the black pine and fir (to 5,900 ft). Below this, the temperate Mediterranean zone to 5,500 ft has a rapid succession of plants and crops: ilex woods and associated *matorral* (below 4,200 ft), Aleppo pines and red juniper (below 3,500 ft) vineyards (below 2,600 ft), then cork woods, interspersed in succession with olives, almonds, figs and carob down the terraced slopes.

Between Estepona and Marbella is an indented coastline with narrow plains whose black, marly soils grow cotton. Settlement is in ancient villages and walled towns like Marbella. To the east the Guadalhorce valley widens inland into a broad Tertiary basin, the Hoya of Málaga, which once formed a gulf into the Guadalquivir trough. It is, therefore, an important passageway with fortified hill villages of remote origin. The waters of the Guadalhorce with karstic sources, irrigate orange groves and *huertas*, while on the terraced hills climb a vast sequence of vineyards, among which are dotted the white *cortijos*. The vine-clothed landscape sweeps eastwards beyond Málaga, famed for its Málaga muscatel and Pedro Ximenes wines. The capital (240,500), obviously located at the seaward exit of the mountainous depression has a cramped site between the flood plain of the Guadalmedina torrent and the two hills of Gibralfaro (433 ft) and Alcazaba (150 ft). A Phoenician rival of Cádiz, the Carthaginians endowed it with an artificial harbour and its Punic plan was preserved even in the Roman colony. The Moorish town centre is still recognisable, together with the ruins of the fortified palace of the Alcazaba and the castle of Gibralfaro. Until the eighteenth century, the town walls were washed by the sea, then with the reclamation of the foreshore the new suburb of Malagueta was built there. In the nineteenth century with African trade and the patronage of winter visitors, it grew rapidly, creating the luxurious châteaux and gardens of La Caleta, Miramar and El Limonar, the hotels of Pedragalejo and also the industrial suburbs south-west of the harbour, with their sugar refineries, cotton mills and smelting plants. In the last three decades, another 100,000 residents have been added, housed in garden suburbs that climb the valley slopes of the Guadalmedina.

East of the Málaga mountains with their rugged relief, there is the smaller basin fertilised by the river Vélez and its principal centre of Vélez Málaga. It is surrounded by the rich sub-tropical vegetation of palms, oranges, bananas, sugar cane, indigo and other crops. This coast is known as the Costa del Sol, sheltered from the cold blasts of

the northern *terral*, and facing towards the African sun. All this sub-
tropical Arcadia is however a human achievement, created since the
Moors of the terraced slopes of the Ajarquia first evolved the careful
use of water. But between the rich vegas in the valley exits, at Nerja,
Almuñecar, Motril, Adra and Almería, are rocky cliffs overlooked by
corniche roads, and broad expanses of dwarf palm steppe, notably in
the Campo de Dalías to the east, Almería (the Moorish 'mirror of the
sea') was developed as a great port in the eleventh century, still looking
like a Moorish stronghold, walled and dominated by the Alcazaba.
Shaken, however, by numerous earthquakes, it only revived in the last
century with the shipment of ores from the Sa de Gádor and other
mountains, and the trade in Almerian grapes.

Inland from the coastal ranges of Gádor and Contraviesa and south
of the Sa Nevada, is the longitudinal depression of Alpujarra. Its
Triassic rocks have been deeply trenched by the river gorges of the
Guadalfeo and its central depression has been fragmented into numerous
cantons. The numerous Moorish place-names notably with the prefix
Ben- a tribal unit, or Alijar (*Djar*) a fortified house, indicate its slow
invasion by the Berbers. After the conquest of this Moorish redoubt in
1482 parts of it were re-settled with Galician and other Christian
colonists. A Spanish 'Kabylia', it depends on the water resources
of the Sa Nevada to feed its overpopulated settlements of some
100,000 inhabitants, concentrated on the south facing slopes up to
5,400 ft. Since the end of the last century, the cultivation of olives,
almonds and especially vines has eased the rigours of this poor region.
Towns are small, such as Lanjaron, a mineral spa, and Ugiyar the capital and silk centre.

6. *The Andalusian Steppes.* To cross over the mountains of Tocon,
Nevada and Filabres is to enter a rose-pink landscape with the wild,
desolate decor of a western film. The Atlantic humidity, penetrating
through the Interior Depressions to Granada (24 in rainfall), is checked
eastwards by the high mountains, while along the coast, Almería is
the last Andalusian outpost to benefit from the perennial water supply
of the mountains. Occupying two-thirds of the province of Almería
and northern Granada the steppes are a desolate region with a population of ten to 50 per sq. mile (Fig. 133) gorges, badlands, heaving plateaux,
all burnt by the sun and sometimes by bush fires. Ochre villages burrow
into the hillsides, with cave dwellings such as the colonies of Guadix.
Human action must share some blame for this naked, treeless landscape, as the relic oak forests of the Filabres testify.

Water and minerals explain the distribution of settlement in this region. Thus at the northern foot of the Sa Nevada, the fertile Vega of Guadix is supplied by numerous streams that fan out into the basin to water the fields of sugar beet and maize. Guadix (22,496) was already a vega settlement in Roman times and its river of *Acci* has given the town its name and prosperity ever since. The basin of Baza and the valley of Almanzora to the north repeat the same features of location and water supply. But eastwards the badlands of the Marquesado and those between the southern flanks of the Filabres and the steppes of Níjar become increasingly dry, until in the coastlands of Gata northwards to the Murcian border, only mineral exploitation explains the size of the settlements, such as Cuevas de Almanzora, Vera and Garrucha.

CHAPTER 13

THE REGIONS OF PORTUGAL

'A nation is not only a product of history . . . but an original and
fecund combination of two elements: land and civilisation. Portugal,
studied in this light, is singularly rich in aspects and lessons.'

(Orlando Ribeiro)

The state of Portugal is one of the smallest in Europe with an area of
34,254 sq. miles, containing in 1950 a population of 7,856,913. Yet it
has preserved its independence from its powerful neighbour, Spain,
which has three times the population and almost six times its area. Its
frontiers are the oldest in Europe, established by 1297. It has built up
its national spirit in the successful fusion of its contrasted regions, the
Atlantic North and the Mediterranean South, recognised in the title
of the former kings of Portugal, 'king of Portugal and of the Algarve'.
The historical evolution of Portugal may be compared with that of the
Catalan thalassocracy in the Levante. Both commenced in the north as
feudal counties, and both were aided by sea-power. But the gorges of
the Douro, Tagus and Guadiana were more effective barriers for
Portuguese independence, aided by the military orders which had
reconquered central and southern Portugal from the Moors (Fig. 100).
The short period 1580–1640 when Portugal was united with Spain came
too late for absorption. Portuguese, a language originating in Galicia,
had become more strongly entrenched than its Provençal counterpart
on the eastern littoral. Since 1661 and especially after the famous
Methuen Treaty of 1703 with Britain, Portuguese independence has
been finally guaranteed by the strategic interests of both allies. Nor
must it be forgotten that the treaty of Tordesillas in 1494 had irrevocably provided Portugal with an empire and colonial wealth of its own.

Throughout its national history the regional divisions of Portugal
have been clearly recognised, and from the middle ages six provinces
have divided the country (Fig. 136). In the north is Minho, or 'between
the Minho and the Douro' to give its full title. This was the location
of the original nucleus and feudal county from which the nation expanded. Trás-os-montes, as its name implies, is the leeward area to the
north-east, which is fundamentally a contrasted region with poor
resources and a primitive economy. Beira is a large and varied province

between the Douro and the middle Tagus, comprising Maritime Beira with its broad plain, Upper Beira with the great mountain range of Estrêla, Trasmontane Beira and Lower Beira in the southern interior, transitional to Castile and Alentejo. Estremadura, like its Spanish namesake, was created during the Reconquest as no-man's-land between the military fronts of the lower Mondego and Tagus. Its maritime position contrasts in every other way with the poor Spanish province of the same name. Ribatejo lies, as its name suggests, on the banks of the Tagus flood plain, whereas the name 'Alentejo' indicates it is on the other side of the Tagus. Finally, in the extreme south, Algarve indicates its affinity with its Moroccan counterpart of 'Al Gharb'. Its monarchs were entitled 'King of the Algarves, on this and on the other side of the sea'. It is significant that this is the only region of Portugal which has maintained its frontiers unaltered from the time of the Reconquest.

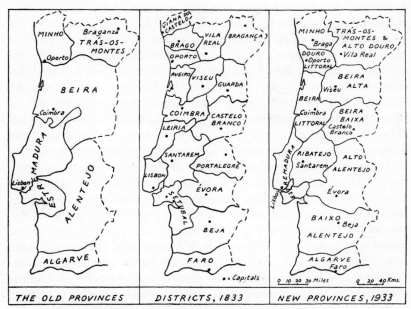

Fig. 136. The provinces and districts of Portugal

These six ancient provinces remained as the framework of administration until 1833 when seventeen districts, analogous to the French departments, were created (Fig. 136). Each of the provinces was divided into two or three districts except Beira which was made into five districts and the Algarve which has never been sub-divided.

During the 1920s the district of Setúbal was added. The geometrical areas of these districts were not homogeneous geographical units. Exactly a hundred years after their introduction, the Salazar government regrouped some of the regions into eleven provinces. They were defined as 'an association of municipalities with geographic, economic and social affinities, endowed with their own organs for the prosecution of their common interests'. The dissatisfaction felt about these new provinces is that they co-exist with the old districts. There is however one advantage. Few south European countries have better statistical sources of data within the wide range of the province, the district, the commune and the parish.

The landscapes of Portugal are more diverse than the regional divisions would suggest. The granite country of the Minho with its misty skies and green *bocage*, the terraced vineyards of the Douro valley baked in the heat, the treeless plateaux of Trás-os-Montes, the mountain splendour of Beira, the lush pastures of the Tagus valley, the monotonous cereal lands of Alentejo and the dusty orchards of the Algarve are a few of its varied vignettes. In its structural features it has been called a geologist's paradise, and for the botanist it is truly the Garden of Europe. Relief and climate divide its diverse features into three fundamental units: the North, the Northern Interior and the South. Along the Tagus valley, relief divides Portugal neatly into a mountainous north with more energetic erosion, and a lowland south (Fig. 69). Of the land above 1,300 ft, 95 per cent lies to the north of the Tagus and the south represents 63 per cent of the land lying below 650 ft. However, whether on the high levels of the north or on the complex lower surfaces of the South, the same even skyline indicates the importance of peneplanation. This Atlantic chara teristic feature is emphasised also by the ubiquitous view of the sea which blends the westward panorama. Climatic and vegetation changes add their nuances to the varied landscapes. The north-west is sufficiently mild and rainy to have mixed Atlantic flora in the same latitude as Rome. Further east, however, the summer drought of one month in the Minho mountains lengthens and becomes severe. Thus the olive which is limited to 1,200 ft in the north-western mountains climbs to above 2,200 ft on the north-eastern plateaux. In the Mediterranean zones of the south everywhere there are at least two months of summer drought and the plants are more typical of their latitude. Thus, whereas north of the Mondego valley 57 per cent of the flora are European species and 26 per cent Mediterranean species, the ratios alter radically to the south. Between the Mondego and the Tagus they are 38 and 42 per cent respectively,

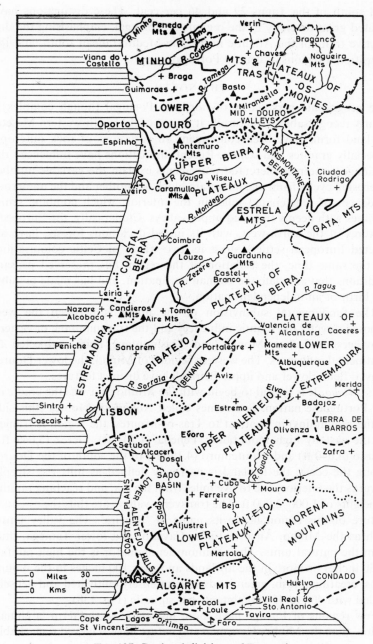

Fig. 137. Regional divisions of Portugal

and south of the Tagus 29 and 46 per cent. These distinctions have created great diversity in the regions of Portugal, emphasising the distinctive traits of the Atlantic north, the Mediterranean south, and the transitional regions of central Portugal.

THE NORTH

The geographic personality of northern Portugal though complex is clearly recognisable. Structurally it is part of the north-western Meseta. Its land forms have been consequent on variations of rock outcrops, especially granites and schists. Recent dislocations have influenced the drainage pattern. Differential movements explain the variable number of erosion cycles from one mountain block to another and the numerous evidences of rejuvenated relief in the interior, which combine senile skylines with deeply trenched upper valleys. Climatically, the European features of the north-west, with its mixed deciduous forests, have attracted European settlers since its two waves of Celtic colonisation. At the same time, the isolation of the region has preserved peasant traditions that antedate the Roman occupation, and has made possible the birth of an independent nation.

The fundamental subdivision of the north is between the west exposed directly to Atlantic influences and the transmontane or eastern provinces of Trás-os-Montes and Trasmontane Beira, subjected to continental influences. The western regions of Minho, the lower Douro, coastal Beira, lower and upper Beira all have distinct features.

1. *Minho*. It is logical to begin with the Minho as it was the cradle of the Portuguese nation. Sometimes called Aquem-os-Montes (this side of the mountains) in contrast to Trás-os-Montes, the region is framed on the east by high mountains: Peneda (4,503 ft), Gerez (5,040 ft), Marão (4,640 ft) and Montemuro (4,190 ft) to the south of the Douro. Along the coast, the lowland is narrowly defined as hills rise steeply towards the interior, one to five miles from the sea, and reaching rapidly to heights of 1,000–2,000 ft. The transverse valleys are thus the essential feature of this region hence its name of 'Ribeira'. The valley units, such as the Minho, Âncora, Lima, Cavado, and lower Tamega, thus form the natural units. The common denominator is the high rainfall of 50 inches or more in the lowlands and over 100 inches in the mountains, creating a lush, green landscape, intensely cultivated and densely settled with 400 to 450 inhabitants per sq. mile (Fig. 138).

Few regions of Europe have more just claim to the term 'a climax region' than the Minho. Here man and nature have achieved remarkable harmony within a closed economy of peasant farming. Four characteris-

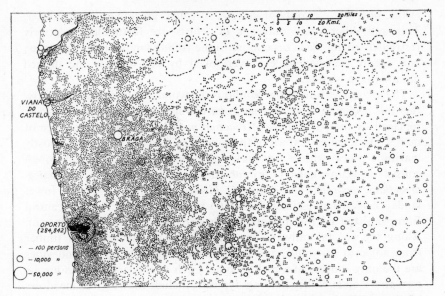

FIG. 138. Distribution of population in northern Portugal. Three features stand out:
the concentration of population around Oporto which is much more a regional
capital than Lisbon; the dense, highly dispersed settlement in the Minho district,
throughout the granitic areas—though densities fall abruptly over the schistose
relief; and the markedly nucleated settlement pattern of Trás-os-Montes, which is
more Castilian than northern Portuguese in character.

tics stand out: the prevalence of granite, the wooded appearance of all
the landscape, the polyculture and the long-preserved traditions of its
peasantry. Granite is symbolic of the natural endowments of the
Minho. The rotten granite screes on the slopes and the loose gravel
sands on the plains provide the local reservoirs for domestic water
supply and the irrigation needs of its summer crop, maize. The massive
two-storey dwellings with their outside staircase (Fig. 103), the *hórreos*:
used for the storage of crops, and the vine stone supports (*estilos*), give
character to this granite country. Terraces climb spectacularly up the
mountain slopes supported by high granite walls cut in the rotten screes.
Aqueducts of the same material traverse the slopes from springs to the
scattered dwellings. The Minho is truly a landscape tamed by man. But
one sees when other rocks outcrop how dependent man in turn has been
on the primitive terrain. Between Valongo and Barcelhos, the fault
scarp of Cambrian schists produces an abrupt change of scenery.
Immediately, an upland district of poor cultivation is entered, sparsely
populated with extensive areas of heath scrub (*mato*) of erica, heather,

cistus, bracken, etc. only productive of rough grazing and gorse litter. This and other small outcrops of schists are fortunately relatively restricted, giving place once more to the rolling landscapes of plateaux and deeply trenched valleys overlooked by bell-shaped, and domed mountains in granite.

The second feature of the Minho is the wooded landscape. Formerly, this was a climax of *Quercetum roburis* but this has been very largely replaced by the paraclimax of *Pinetum maritimae* as a consequence of man's interference. A third of the total area is under woodland, mostly maritime pines, with a few cork oaks and eucalyptus. Undergrowth consists of yellow gorse (*Ulex europaeus*), heather, erica (*E. lusitanica, umbellata, australis*) and cistus (*C. hissutus, salvifolius*). On the lower lands Daveau has estimated that 60 per cent of the flora is central European, but on the mountains, the percentage rises to 86 per cent. Along the coastal railway, the stations are all stacked with timber from adjacent saw-mills, and in the remote districts timber and vines are the only sources of a cash income. Each of the larger farms has its own pine woods. Valley holdings typically include the irrigated meadows of the valley bottom (*lameiras*), terraced slopes, woodland on the steeper breaks of slope and heath (*mato*) above (see Plate 44).

Throughout the Minho, maize as a summer crop and haricot beans a winter crop, form a marked crop-association region. One-third of the total Portuguese acreage of maize is grown here. The small fields, fragmented and scattered, are continuously worked with a succession of vegetables, potatoes, some cereals and especially maize. Interculture of these crops, with hedgerows of cherry, chestnut, oak, elm, poplar, holly and even olive, and vines trailing in the trees, emphasise the poly-culture and the *bocage* appearance of the landscape. This breathless succession of cropping that permits three, or even four, crops to be grown at the same time, explains how more than one-third of the peasant cultivators live on less than two acres of land (Fig. 139). The agrarian practices are the heritage of several developments: first the introduction of the vine in the twelfth century, the olive in the following century and especially the rapid spread of maize after the late sixteenth century, in place of rye. In the more isolated valleys rye is still grown, but maize has penetrated to its limit at 2,600 ft. Above this, a simpler crop system replaces maize and the vine, consisting of winter rye and summer potatoes, with birch woods and pastures. The highest settle-ment of the Minho, Curral de Gonçalo, reaches 3,860 ft.

The cultural features of the Minhoto landscape are ancient. Between Braga and the valley of the Gerez is probably the richest area of Roman relics in the Peninsula, with sections of Roman roads, numerous Roman bridges and monumental stones. Field boundaries can in places be attributed to the divisions of towns made by the Roman surveyors. Kruger has noted some of the agricultural implements, ploughs, yokes and so on which have a similar ancestry. Earlier still are some of the house-types and the *castro* sites. Vasconcellos has observed that thirty-eight out of the sixty-two romanesque churches of Portugal are found

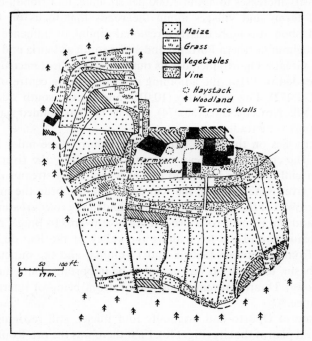

FIG. 139. Vila Verde, a prosperous peasant-holding in the Ancora Valley, Minho

in the Minho. Braga (32,624), ancient capital of the *Callaeci Braca-reuses*, is still the regional centre, and since the middle ages the seat of the Primate of Portugal. The fact that Braga rivalled Santiago helps to explain the ecclesiastical and later political independence of this nucleus of Portugal. Guimarães (11,991) also in the interior plateau country, with its castle, was the early capital and cradle of the Portuguese monarchy. Both are important textile centres today. Smaller market centres are placed in the middle sector of the valleys, such as Ponte do Lima (2,420), Santo Tirso (3,864) and Penafiel (6,016). Along the coast there are a number of small fishing ports, all at river mouths, apart from Póvoa de Varzim (16,994), the chief town. Viana do Castelo (13,131) is a fortress town built by Philip II at the mouth of the Lima, the principal northern market town. Weaving at Viana do Castelo and lace-making at Vila do Conde (11,174) are important. The dense population highly dispersed throughout western Minho, explains this emphasis on handcraft industries.

2. *The Oporto Conurbation.* South of the Sa de Valongo, the population density increases to about 1,000 per sq. mile, in a ribbon-development of farms and villages along the roads that focus on Oporto. Unlike Lisbon, it is more clearly a regional capital, its influence extending throughout northern Portugal and as far south as Leiria and Castelo Branco. Greater Oporto includes its outport of Leixões (erected in 1890 and extended in 1916), the adjoining sardine packing centre of Matosinhos (22,472), Foz do Douro (10,012) and on the south side of the Douro, Vila Nova de Gaia (38,074), with its famous bonded warehouse for the port wine trade.

The city lies on the north bank of the Douro, three miles from its mouth. The crystalline plateau is deeply trenched by the river so that the river cliff has little level land except where small streams debouch into the river. One of these, the Rio de la Vila has been the main axis for the growth of the town, Oporto commanded the river crossing of the Douro and the Roman road proceeding northwards to Braga, reaching the plateau beyond the ferry along the valley of the Rio de la Vila. As the frontier between Galicia and Lusitania, and the outlet for the Douro basin, the location was bound to be important. Only the gorges of the lower Douro prevented navigation from being of international significance.

The site of Oporto had originally four nuclei, still recognisable in the central plan of the city (Fig. 140). First there was the pre-Roman *Cale* or 'Vila Portus' on the Porta de Carros (279 ft) a granitic monadnock close to the Rio de Vila. This was one of several *castros* in the district, such as Gondomar, Campanha, Foz do Douro and Vila Nova de Gaia, whose origins go back to Celtic and even earlier settlements. With the valley-ward movement of settlement in Roman times, a second settlement grew up near the later port, at the mouth of the Vila stream. This was later to be called 'Portucale', a street settlement near the ferry crossing and on the Roman road. It was this settlement which in the later Middle Ages was the centre of the Leónese county (Portucalense) from which the nation took its name. A third nucleus was the Peña Ventosa or Sé built in Visigothic times on the hill of the same name (252 ft), which became the site of the fortified episcopal residence and

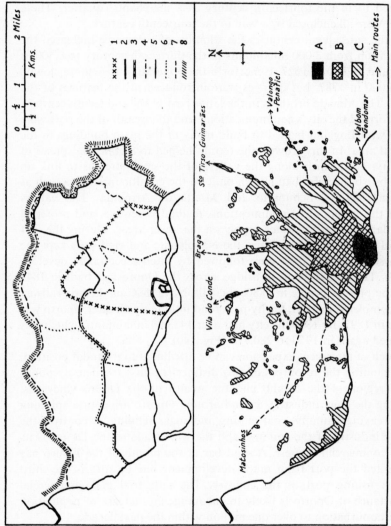

FIG. 140. The growth of Oporto (from data supplied by municipal planning authority). 1. Limit of Conto de D. Tereza. 2. Limit of city in 997 A.D.; 3. ditto in 1374; 4. in 1710; 5. in 1836; 6. in 1837; 7. in 1896; 8. in 1898; A—post-Roman nucleus; B—city in 1813; C—growth since 1892

cathedral. On the slopes of Sé grew up the 'Vila Bayxa', now the oldest quarter of the town, much of its old character still preserved. Finally, on the west side of the Vila valley at Alto da Vitoria a new burg is first referred to in the fourteenth century as a merchants' quarter. These nuclei were all enclosed by a wall in the fourteenth century.

In the subsequent centuries the stimulus of commerce increased the population from 3,000 inhabitants in the thirteenth century to 8,500 in 1417 and 16,000 in 1527. Henceforth the population rose more slowly, to 25,000 in 1787, but changes were introduced in the features of the town. The Almade brothers in the latter part of the eighteenth century, transformed the city's communications, and the wealth of the port wine trade with England helped to build many of the main buildings in the central area. In this growth, the terrain helped to dictate the spread of the city, northwards along the valleys of the small streams to link up and absorb the suburban nuclei, built on the granitic inselbergs such as Areosa (534 ft), Seminario and Monte de Arrábida. The valleys aided the system of communications, facilitated sewage, and provided abundant springs for water supply on the lower areas. During the first half of the nineteenth century, the Napoleonic and civil wars kept the town stagnant but they were followed by intense economic developments. The first suspension bridge across the Douro was built in 1842 and the present bridge in 1886; the Vila Nova de Gaia–Lisbon railway was completed in 1864, the by-pass road linking up Greater Oporto was made in 1897. By 1890 the city had over 143,000 inhabitants, which was doubled again in 1950 to 280,770 (Fig. 140).

Much of the recent expansion can be attributed to its nodal position, commanding the resources of two distinct regions: the densely populated region of the Minho and the wealth of the Douro vineyards. Among the chief industries in and around Oporto are cotton spinning and weaving, tanning, coal mining and sugar refining. It controls the textile industry of the country, and the wine trade of the Douro is its chief commercial interest. A sand bar at the mouth of the Douro has prevented the port from much development but Leixões is the third largest fishing port of the country. The industrial and commercial importance of Oporto is likely to encourage an increase of population in the conurbation to over one million within the next decade.

3. *Trás-os-Montes*. Beyond the Minho mountains of Larouco, Pedrella and especially Marão, the contrasted features of Trás-os-Montes begin to assert themselves. This is well seen on the population map (Fig. 138). The climate and vegetation cover, the rocks and land forms, the settlements and social conditions of life all show

marked changes. This is not surprising as the windward slopes of these mountains, facing the Atlantic, have 100 inches or more annual rainfall. On the leeward slopes it is half the amount, reaching 20 inches in the eastern districts, equalled by the summer evaporation rates. Trás-os-Montes is therefore a parched landscape, reflecting the colours of its pale soils and darkened rock outcrops, which are dominantly schistose. The valley of the Tua is the most significant floristic divide between the Atlantic and Meseta influences. A climax of *Pinetum maritimae* occurs in parts of the Douro tributaries with some woodlands of cork oak in the east and deciduous oaks on the western borders, notably *Quercus toza*. But the latter has usually been cleared for maize cultivation. An important region for early man, nearly all the natural vegetation has been irrevocably destroyed, with vast horizons of cereal lands, extensively cultivated, particularly for rye. Nearly half the total area under rye in Portugal is concentrated here.

Trás-os-Montes is essentially the Portuguese section of the middle Douro basin, divided by its relief into *Terra Fria* and *Terra Quente*. The former, consisting of the higher northern plateaux, north of Chaves and including the lands of Bragança and La Terruca, have continental features, cold and windswept in winter, brown and arid in summer. It is a sad, monotonous and rolling landscape between 2,000–600 ft enriched only by the life that flows through the transverse valleys. These follow the structural fractures north-west to south-east rejuvenated in Pliocene and Quaternary times, notably in the case of the upper Tamega and the Chaves graben. Others such as the basin of Mirandela are less well defined. The Tua, Sabor and Douro itself have cut back to capture interior basins. *Terra Quente* follows these deeply entrenched valleys, importing into the north-east Mediterranean influences of climate and vegetation. The olive groves that replace some of the older vineyards are a sharp contrast to the Castilian elements of wheat and rye fields that cover the plateaux to an altitude of some 3,400 ft.

The collective pastoral rights, first seen in the Barroso in eastern Minho, are typical of Trás-os-Montes. Here and there polyculture is favoured by well irrigation in the sheltered basins of Chaves and Mirandela. But in the large open fields of wheat and rye that cover about half the landscape, communal systems of cultivation comparable to those formerly practised in Castile are still preserved. The population is grouped in villages in contrast to the marked dispersion of the Minho (Fig. 138) and the agricultural population, 63–5 per cent of the total, is excessive. The transverse routes are only of local importance and isolation thus explains the conservatism and backwardness of the region.

Bragança (8,818), the regional capital, is the home of the last Portuguese monarchy, but it is too remote to have economic importance commensurate with its historic dignity.

4. *Upper Douro Valley.* This Portuguese section of the Douro belongs climatically to the *Terra Quente* of Trás-os-Montes, but man has created its distinctive landscape. The monotonous skyline of gently swelling plateaux with their open fields of grain and oak scrub, gives place to the spectacular flights of terraced vineyards (*geios*) that climb the valleys for 1,000–1,300 ft (Plate 43). The densely scattered farmsteads, the river traffic of sailing boats (*barcos rabelos*), the advertisements along the roads to names such as Gonzalez, Cockburn and Sandeman, the bustling market towns of Regoa, Tua and Vila Real all betray the same interest in one commodity, port wine. It is this which explains the much higher density of population compared with that in Tras-os-Montes (Fig. 138).

This human region begins 55 miles upstream from Oporto and stretches along the Douro for nearly 60 miles between Barqueitos and the frontier at Barca d'Alava. It also extends up the tributary valleys of the Corgo and the Varosa. In these valleys, the summer heat is intense, the rock surfaces of the schists trapping air temperatures of 100°F or even more. Formerly they were widely covered with juniper scrub (*Juniperus oxycedrus*), but the Methuen Treaty with England in 1703, and the legally demarcated district of the Marquis de Pombal in 1756, helped to transform the region into an English vineyard. It was considerably expanded during the nineteenth century, new limits being recognised in 1910 and modified since 1931 (Fig. 141). The distribution of soil types roughly divides the district into an upper portion along the Douro and its tributaries which give some of the best quality red port at the junction of the schists and granites, whereas the fertile and friable brown schists in the lower district around Regoa produce quantity rather than quality. The upper limit of the port wine vineyards is about 1,800 ft above sea-level but ordinary stock extends to 2,700 ft. Changing social habits have modified the Douro landscape, the lower demand for port wine versus sherry, resulting in many of the high terraces being replaced with olives. The one untamed element of the region is the river Douro, plunging at the rate of 16 ft a mile, often in vertical gorges 90 to 160 ft deep.

5. *Trasmontane Beira.* South of the Douro is the ancient province of Beira, whose varied regions have been vividly described in the regional novels of Aquilino Ribeiro. Beira is so extensive that the division into Trasmontane, High, Low and Maritime Beira is more realistic. The

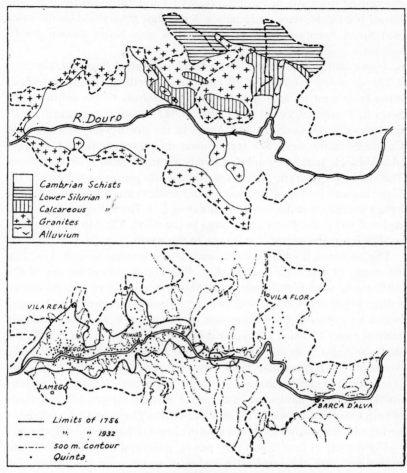

Cambrian Schists
Lower Silurian "
Calcareous "
Granites
Alluvium

Limits of 1756
" " 1932
500 m. contour
Quinta

FIG. 141. Evolution of the Port-Wine district

name Trasmontane Beira indicates that it is a continuation of Trás-os-Montes with the same continental influences from Castile. The only difference is the higher elevation (2,200–3,000 ft) and the predominance of granitic landforms. It drains into the Douro through the Coa basin. Extensive rye cultivation, often in large estates, woodlands of evergreen oak and maritime pines on the valley slopes and vast areas of maquis and other communal waste termed *charneca*, prevail. Towards the south, the nucleated villages become larger in units of 600–1,200 inhabitants. The capital of the region is Guarda (11,586), situated on the highest town site in Portugal (3,585 ft) and aptly described as *fria, forte e feia* ('cold, strong and ugly'). A strategic stronghold on the route into Spain twenty-eight miles away, it is now better known for its sanatoria.

6. *Upper Beira.* This mountainous block of central Portugal, covering 2,200 sq. miles, extends for 70 miles from north to south, and 35–45 miles from west to east. It is framed impressively to the south by the Serra da Estrêla (6,530 ft) and Louza (3,942 ft) and conveniently so, by the Serras de Montemuro and Arada in the north-west, and Serra do Caramulo in the west. The region owes its impressive relief to a pene-planed block flanked by uplifted horsts. Granitic relief is characteristic. The coarse porphyritic granites weathered into grotesque features on the high tors and inselbergs (*cantoaros* and *penhas*) are silhouetted sharply by the prevailing peneplaned skyline (Fig. 21). The valleys comprise the regional units, the Paiva and Vouga in the north, the Mondego and its tributaries in the centre, the Zezere in the south.

The region is thickly forested, and only a quarter to even less than one-tenth of the area is cultivated. Pinewoods prevail in the north, with more mixed deciduous and chestnut woods in the Mondego valley. From about Viseu southwards, a thick undergrowth of labiatae begins to appear in the *Castanetum* on the granites, and also extensive maquis cover of *Erica cinerea* and broom. In the Serra da Estrêla the stages of vegetation are clear. The basal zone to 2,500 ft has a mixed woodland of pedunculate oaks, chestnuts and pines. The black oak (*Q. pyrenaica*) climbs further to 5,500 ft but, more extensive, especially on the southern flanks are widespread maquis covers of rock roses (*Cistus Crispus, C. ladaniferus*) and tree-heath. The slopes are covered in spring with the yellow bloom of a kind of cistus (*Helianthemum alyssoides*).

The density of population (300 per sq. mile) and the intensity of land utilisation, with the impressive flights of terraces up the valleys, are reminiscent of the Minho region. But there are distinct differences. The summer cropping of maize alternates with winter vegetables for first place in the rotation, for here the staple peasant diet is *caldo*, the cabbage soup. Cropped lands are more selective, concentrated on the alluvial lands and lower terraces of the valleys, whereas the higher slopes and older piedmont fans tend to remain under a cover of pine woods or eucalyptus groves. Nowhere in the north are vineyards more extensive than in the valley of the Dáo. Flocks of sheep are also important, encouraged by the facilities for summer pasturage in the Serra da Estrêla, long noted for its transhumance. Around Vizeu (13,190) the regional capital and market town, the densely dispersed settlement is

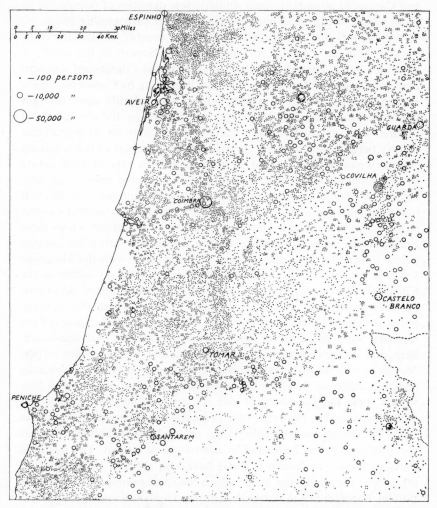

Fig. 142. Distribution of population in central Portugal. Note the high densities of the Mondego basin and the coastal plain. The Serra da Estrêla stands out as an area of very sparse population. Note also the marked dispersion in northern Estremadura

comparable to that of the Minho, but downstream the Mondego basin, subject to more intense erosion, has more agglomerated settlements, confined to the divides in order to use all available level land for cultivation. A series of settlements, with woollen mills flank the northern piedmont of the Estrêla. To the west, the schistose outcrops of the Avada and Caramulo mountains have similarly low densities of population as those of the Minho, a striking contrast to their surrounding plains.

7. *Maritime Beira*. The northern half of the coastal, Tertiary lowlands running between Espinho in the north and Nazaré in the south, is Maritime Beira. The valley of the Mondego forms a significant southern limit, the beauties of whose valley have been sung by Camóens. Like a French Lande, the plain has been infilled with infertile sands brought down by the Vouga and Mondego, and fringed by the coastal ria of Aveiro, with its salt marshes. Although the contrast in population density between this region and the south-western part of the adjoining Minho region is still marked, it must have been very striking before the reclamation which has transformed it in recent times. For here began the zone termed *descampos* during the Reconquest, a political if not a physical no-man's land. Today, the region has several distinct *pays*. In the interior, the Triassic and Miocene limestone scarps form the *Bairrada*, with its vineyards on the slopes and spring-line villages below Caramulo. Near the junction of this district with the Mondego valley is the forested mountain of Bussaco (1,795 ft), an outlier of the Canaris-Lusitanian flora and famous state forest of mixed deciduous and evergreen oaks, cedars, elms and cypresses. From this vantage point, the coastal plain unfolds below, the extensive sandy wastes of the *Gandara* with its cover of strawberry tree, broom and tree-heath, Beira-Ria further north and near the sea, the smiling valley of the Mondego with its olive groves, maize fields and even oranges (especially around Condeixa). Much of the sandy plain has been covered with pine woods since the last century, and the encroachment of sand dunes along the coast has been checked. These dunes explain the salt marshes of the Aveiro lagoon, where the Vouga mouth has been choked, whereas the Mondego is less hampered by a sand bar at its exit. The medieval ports of Ovar and Aveiro (17,107) have also suffered from the shifting sands, especially the latter which was the premier ocean fishing port of Portugal in the sixteenth century. The landscape of the Aveiro Ria, which as its name implies (*Averetum*), is still a bird haunt, is now a maze of drainage canals, with salt pans and flooded ricefields in summer, earning itself another title, 'Little Holland'.

From the University balconies that jut from the limestone hill of Coimbra one can understand why the Roman town of *Aeminium* and the Lusitanian citadel of *Conimbriga*, should always have commanded such nodal importance. At the lowest bridging point of the Mondego, a secure river port, and controlling the main highway to the north and the entrance to Upper Beira, Coimbra was destined to be the major

51 Vouga Valley, Sever, Beira

52 Sajambre Valley, León

53 Dried torrent bed, S.E. Spain

54 Tagus Valley near Aranjuez

EROSION IN ITALY

55 *Frane* in S. Apennines
—a river of liquid mud

56 Pliocene clay lands, Crotone, Calabria

57 Badlands overlooking Metaponto Plain, Basilicata

regional centre. The twin town has remained essentially the same in its layout since the Middle Ages: an upper town crowning the hill with a castle, later a royal palace, and the University after 1537; the lower town, built on a dejection cone with its market place, cathedral and ecclesiastical suburbs. When the capital was transferred to Lisbon in the thirteenth century, it decayed and only revived in the nineteenth century. With the improvement of communications, some woollen, leather and food industries stimulated an increase of population, rising from 12,000 inhabitants in 1864 to 41,977 in 1950.

THE TRANSITIONAL REGIONS

Between the lower Mondego and the Tagus is a transitional zone where Atlantic and Mediterranean influences intermingle. The widespread occurrence of limestone in Estremadura accentuates the southern influences so that whereas Mediterranean plants represent only 36 per cent on the silicious soils, the limestones have 56 per cent. Deciduous oaks now begin to disappear and are replaced by the Portuguese oak (*Q. lusitanica*). Maritime and the heat-loving stone pines intermingle, and the citrus fruits appear for the first time. Vines are no longer supported on fences but trail low on the ground. Olive groves become economical and widespread, and the dry farming system of cereals is important. The field units are larger than in the north-west, and the mingling of fields and woodlands, so characteristic of the Minho and Upper Beira, gives place to separate stands of timber and to cultivated lands. The house-types are also different. The one-storey dwelling with separate outhouses for the storage of crops, replaces the northern two-storey house. Consequently, the store-houses which are small in the north because of the small-holdings and the granaries in the lofts, now become bigger. Even the fishing villages along the coast are distinct. Unlike the Minhoto villagers who combine fishing with agricultural activities the fishermen at Nazaré, Peniche and the smaller centres are a separate society with no land interests.

1. *Estremadura.* These features are not immediately appreciated in Leiria, which is a continuation of the features of the Tertiary plain, sandy soils planted in extensive pine forests and covering some 60 sq. miles, or 55 per cent of the district. This is a tribute to the royal interest in the forest since the fourteenth century. South and east of Leiria the southern aspect of Estremadura begins, aided by the dry and porous limestones and sandy soils. With the dominance of the Jurassic and Cretaceous rocks, four types of landscape result. To the south-west, there are the low undulating hills of sands and clays, deeply dissected

with a dense network of small valleys. Such are the hills of Alcobaça, Cadaval, Torres Vedras and Mafra. Denuded anticlines, notably those of Torres Vedras and Alcobaça form longitudinal valleys, and the north-south Nabáo depressions at the junction of the schistose massifs of Lower Beira in the east, provide a second type of landscape. In these valley lands, the abundance of springs permit an extension of Minhoto polyculture with areas of dispersed settlement. The third and dominant element of the Estremadura landscape is the presence of the calcareous massifs which form the backbone of the province. These stretch from the Caldeiros (2,062 ft) and Fátima-Aire plateau to the north, to the Monte Junto (2,130 ft) and lower surfaces immediately north of Lisbon. The higher plateaux have true karstic features, such as the polje of Mira-Minde, and their dry aspect emphasised by the degraded xerophytic scrub and patches of sclerophyllous woodland, give them Mediterranean features. South of the Tagus, the sheltered peninsula of the Sa de Arrábida facing south, has a true Mediterranean flora, the mild and sufficiently humid climate permitting an exceptionally luxuriant maquis, which has been admirably described by the botanist Chodat (1909). In sharp contrast, as a fifth element which may be added, are the rich soils derived from the weathered syenite of the plutonic massifs and with generous rainfall. The profuse mantle of Lusitanian flora in Sintra is like a naturalised botanic garden, with luxuriant tree-ferns, magnolias, palms, camelias, rhododendrons and other exotics, grouped in the lovely parks of Peña and Montserrate.

If the southern aspect and the varied natural landscapes are characteristic of Estremadura, so too is the series of changes which man has imposed on the region since the Middle Ages. The foundation of the Cistercian abbey of Alcobaça had a profound influence in converting the waste into cultivation. Fruit cultivation is still a speciality of Alcobaça and Caldas da Rinaha, and the best oranges come from some of the sites of the former granges of this rich abbey. Since the seventeenth century, olive groves have been systematically planted, notably on the slopes of the Serra de Caldeiros. Pombal's decree that the flat lands should be devoted to cereals encouraged hill lands to be extensively planted with vines and olives in the latter part of the eighteenth century. In the last hundred years, many of the waste lands of the limestone hills have been cleared, most spectacularly in the district of Setúbal. Viticulture especially, has increased notably, even within the last three decades, in the Colares districts famous for their table wines—Mafra, Torres Vedras and Batalha.

The recolonisation of Estremadura after the Reconquest and the subsequent intensification of land use explains the medieval and even later foundation of its chief settlements (Fig. 100). Some of the old ports have arisen and disappeared, such as Atonguia da Baleia founded in 1167 and sanded up in the late fourteenth century. The existing fishing towns are recent foundations—Peniche (10,057) in the sixteenth century, Figueira (10,486) and Nazaré (9,241) in the nineteenth century. Some of the medieval settlements are villages which have originated from the Cistercian granges, such as Alvominha, Cos, Turquel, Maiorga and Salir do Marto. Alcobaça (4,483) has grown alongside its famous abbey, Caldas da Rainha (10,039) developed after the fifteenth century near its mineral springs, and Leiria (7,123) was created below its castle in the following century.

2. *The Lisbon Region.* Unlike the north-east to south-west trend of Estremadura which engenders its character as a passage-way between the north and south, the lower Tagus enters a synclinal basin between Miocene cuestas, orientated east to west. This forms the drowned estuary of Mar da Palha, an excellent natural harbour of over 97 sq. miles, whose extent helps to regularise the water level of the Tagus floods. Its regular tides, sheltered position and ease of access through a channel one and a half miles wide, give Lisbon an incomparable natural harbour. While the longitudinal routes following the depressions of Estremadura and the Tagus highway all focus on the site of the city. It is not surprising that here should be concentrated within an area of only 24,500 hectares, a tenth of the Portuguese people and an even greater concentration of its wealth.

On the north bank of the Tagus, where spring sapping has fretted the Miocene outcrop of hard limestone (*molasse*), a small marshy plain was built up by the confluence of two small streams. Above it on the outlier of San Jorge the pre-Roman settlement was established. This commanded a defile to the plateau and protected the small Carthaginian harbour of *Olisipo* ('beautiful harbour'). The strategic value of the site was recognised by the Romans who enlarged it into a municipality and situated on the main highway to Mérida and Seville it became the chief town of Lusitania. It remained a stronghold of the Visigoths, and the Arabs extended the town from the *Castelo* and *Alfama* across the lower ground to the western hill of the *Mouraría*, separated by a marshy inlet now drained. The Miocene clays and decomposed basalt lavas on the plateau north of the town provided rich wheat soils. The Arab legacy of irrigation and polyculture in the neighbourhood, fish plentiful in the estuary, and abundant spring water, assured the needs of the growing town. At the Reconquest in 1147, the Christians found it a flourishing and strongly fortified town. The Moorish population was re-settled in the *Mouraría* and the growth of the town continued in a series of scattered hill-sites, each the nucleus of urban quarters, separated by gardens on the low lands and orchards on the steep slopes. Dominating each quarter were built the churches and convents. Lisbon thus had the medieval appearance of a garden city loosely encircled to the north by the city wall. During the fifteenth century, the low ground by the river became the focus of the commercial quarter on land which had been reclaimed. A large square was built on the water-front beside the royal palace whose basements served as the royal warehouses. In the period between 1640 and 1755, when the Brazilian trade was at its height, the shift to this low land near the jetties represented a new phase of growth. This was momentarily set back in the disastrous earthquake of 1755, which destroyed the lower city but preserved the ancient hill quarters of San Jorge and *Mouraría*. This gave Pombal and his architect Eugenio dos Santos the opportunity to create a gridiron plan centred on the Rocio (Plate 50). Along the two valleys that bifurcate north of the Rocio, intensive horticulture had preserved them from being built up, to provide the modern boulevards of the nineteenth century, urban growth taking place on the higher ground.

The great growth of the city has occurred with the development of industries and the improvement of port and rail communications. In 1855, Oporto and Lisbon were linked by railway. Elaborate improvements of the foreshore for new docks and jetties were begun in 1887 and the port authority was taken over by the state in 1907 to push forward its industrial and commercial expansion. Thus the population has risen from 198,000 in 1864 to 790,434 in 1960. With its seaside resorts of Cascais (7,887) and Estoril (5,545) and Almada (11,995) on the south bank of the Tagus, Greater Lisbon (1·3 million) is now embracing both banks of the estuary within its suburban spread.

Sheltered behind the limestone range of Arrábida is the third port of the country, Setúbal (44,235). Chief sardine port and a busy canning centre, its urban functions have been somewhat restricted by its proximity to the capital. Founded in the twelfth century, near the mouth of the river Sado, it has always been handicapped by relatively poor communications, and a sparsely populated hinterland scourged by malaria. Despite this Setúbal succeeded to Aveiro's premier position after the sixteenth century. Since the first cannery was established in the port in 1880, its growth has been rapid, aided also by the agricultural transformation of its immediate environs.

3. *Ribatejo*. Compared with other regions, the structural unity of

Ribatejo is expressed clearly in the tectonic trough of the lower Tagus. On the north side of the Tagus the edge of the Tertiary basin is followed neatly by the regional boundary. To the east, it begins where the Tagus leaves the defile near Abrantes and changes its westward flow to a south-westerly direction. Only on the south border does Ribatejo merge imperceptibly with Alentejo. Separated from the sea, the region contrasts with Estremadura in a number of ways. It is drier and essentially transitional to Lower Beira. Consequently, it tends to show greater uniformity of land utilisation. Stock rearing is more important, with sheep and goats in the drier hill lands to the north, bulls and horses on the rich alluvial pastures of the Tagus. Compared with Estremadura, the population is also more grouped in villages, although intensive polyculture in favoured areas, as in the environs of Santarém and the alluvial terraces of the Tagus, accounts for scattered dwellings.

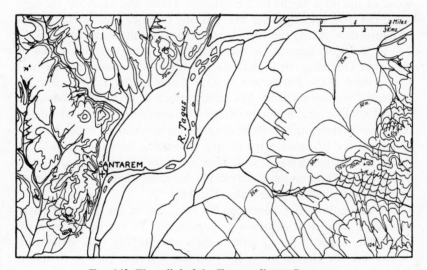

FIG. 143. The relief of the Tagus valley at Santarem

The asymmetrical character of the Tagus trough explains the sharper contrasts between the landforms, land utilisation and population on the two sides of the valley. The complicated relief of the Tertiary hills to the north, ranging from Eocene to Pleistocene rocks, contrast with the simple sequence of Plio-Pleistocene terraces on the south side. It is this structural and morphological asymmetry which presents two distinct geographical facades to Ribatejo, heightening the importance of the Tagus as a boundary and the province as a transitional region. On the north side of the Tagus diversity is the characteristic of its land-scapes. On the higher lands of the Mio-Pliocene surface (900–1,000 ft) carved from the older Tertiaries, there are still extensive *charnecas*, maquis and garrigue lands of cistus and tree-heath with woodlands of stone pines, and groves of eucalyptus. On the lower hills, the *bairros* are characterised by vines, olives and cereals. The vineyards such as the famous district of Cartaxo, have been largely reclaimed from waste since the mid-nineteenth century. In the plains of Torres the vine is a monoculture, a rare feature in Portugal. The olive groves are an older tradition, flourishing on the undulating hill lands of the lower Zezere since remote times, and covering an area of over 185,000 acres in the district of Santarem. A third landscape is encountered along the Tagus valley, the *campo* which is two to five miles wide and partially dyked against the winter floods. The annual renewal of silt makes these lands some of the most fertile in the country. Maize and vines on the light soils, rice and wheat on the heavy lands, produce a perennial mosaic of cultivation. Along the river banks, the water meadows extend over 230 sq. miles, as famous for their bulls and horses as those reared on the lower Guadalquivir in Andalusia. Rice, too, is grown, representing over a third of the Portuguese acreage. South of the Tagus valley, the landscape is more uniform, less tamed, much of it still unreclaimed in the last century, and formerly cursed with endemic malaria. The major difference in the district is the sharp contrast between the valley bottoms reclaimed for irrigated crops of rice and maize, and the sandy inter-fluves and higher terraces with their cover of stone pines and oaks. The economic interest lies chiefly in the *montados*, that is the light wood-lands of cork and evergreen oaks (Fig. 145).

The dramatic contrast between the two sides of the Tagus are sum-marised by the rival densities of population: 75 per sq. mile on the north side, under 25 per sq. mile on the south side (Fig. 144). Settlements of any size are aligned along the northern terraces, such as Santarem (13,114), Cartaxo (5,920) and Vila Franca de Xira (8,296). Almeirim (7,104) is the only settlement of any importance on the opposite bank. Santarem, the regional capital, is perched well above the flood waters on the edge of the Tertiary plateau (Fig. 143). Its historic role as a fortress controlling the main route of the valley is maintained by its modern role as a rail and road junction. Tomar (8,034) on the river Nabão occupies a comparable site to Alcobaça. Within its fertile basin and surrounded by olive groves it has been a centre since prehistoric times. It is better known for its castle, built by the Templars, and later as the head-quarters of the feudal Order of Christ (Fig. 100).

4. *Lower Beira*. This eastern region is transitional not only between Trás-os-Montes and Alentejo, but it is also a continuation of the great Extremadura peneplain. The sharp contrasts which exist between the two flanks of the central Cordillera in Spain here disappear, for the Beira block although fractured is not uplifted and tilted as in the Sierras de Guadarrama and Gredos. Framed by the Serra de las Mesas (over 1,500 ft) in the north-east, the Serra da Estrêla (6,370 ft) and Serra da Gardunha (3,920 ft) in the north-west, it consists essentially of two drainage basins, the smaller, northern one of the Upper Zezere called *Cova de Beira*, and the Ponsul and other smaller tributaries of the Tagus to the south. The pediments or *rañas*, the inselbergs, some rising 500 ft above the plateau, the quartzitic ridges and the valleys following lines of fracture reveal the same essentials as in Spanish Extremadura.

The Cova de Beira in the north-west is a piedmont zone between the two mountain horsts of Estrêla and Gardunha blessed by the seepage water which permits irrigation and intensive land use. The ceinture of its small towns and villages on the fans at the mountain foot is influenced by the flourishing woollen industry, harnessing local water-power and formerly using the wool supplies of the Estrêla pastures. Covilha (21,385) the local capital is the chief textile centre and also winter resort.

In the south-west, the deeply trenched course of the Zezere, with incised meanders in rugged schistose country, follows a poor, austere region that forms an effective southern limit to the more docile granite landscapes of upper Beira. The economic significance of the Zezere lies in the hydro-electric power potential of its gorges, which plunge some 5,000 ft and are in part utilised, notably by the dam of Castelo do Bode.

Also contrasted with the verdant diversity of Cova de Beira with its pinewoods, orchards, vineyards and meadows, the severity of Castelo Branco introduces a third landscape. Only the hill foot zone of the Serra de las Mesas repeats on a more limited scale the productivity which seepage water permits for irrigation. Large estates (*monte*), originally established by the military orders on the plateau, and to the west the waste lands of the *charneca* are the main features of much of this poor land. Extensive open fields of wheat, and communal pastures are the rule, apart from the small enclaves of enclosed holdings around the large villages. Like the Badajoz scheme, much optimism is directed to the completion of the Idanha scheme, which will make possible the irrigation of 35,000 acres from the Carmona dam, on the river Ponsul. The strategic importance of Castelo Branco district in the past explains the medieval atmosphere of its market centres, all fortified strongholds.

Such are Abrantes (11,339) the western gateway to Beira, overlooking the Tagus; Castelo Branco (14,865) the walled capital of the region; and picturesque Monsanto (3,846) perched on one of the granitic inselbergs.

THE SOUTH

The rolling, low plateaux of much of Alentejo and the plains of the Sado introduce an abrupt change of landscape compared with Estremadura, although more gradually to the east. This is explained by the Tagus trough already mentioned. Just as the north has a duality the polyculture of the Minho and the open fields of Trás-os-Montes so too the south has two comparable facades, represented respectively by the Algarve and Alentejo. But their contrasts are as great as their similarities. The Mediterranean tree cultures play a dominant rôle in the south, whether they be almonds, figs and olives of the Algarve or the oaks of Alentejo. The cereal lands of Alentejo do not strictly have the true open field system which characterises Trás-os-Montes, since the exploitation of the cork and evergreen woodland is associated with them. Moreover, there is a marked climatic difference, with more drought in the south. Thus, whereas there is fallow one to two years in the north-east, as much as five to six years fallow is practised in the south. Such a system has long lent itself, therefore, to an agro-pastoral economy. Finally, the communal or collective system of village organisation traditional in the north-east, is replaced by a feudal society in the south, the *monte* estate with its barrack-like dwellings taking the place of the north-eastern village. Much capital has, however, been invested in the south, especially in the cork estates and in recent decades in the modernisation of many estates. Thus the south does not have the political overtones of depression and neglect in Portugal to the extent that it has in Spain or Italy.

1. *Upper Alentejo.* Unlike the Tagus, the Guadiana does not separate contrasted landforms. Upper Alentejo is thus the westward continuation of the Spanish Guadalupe mountains, with the same appalachian relief, *rasas* and soil types. Covering some 5,260 sq. miles, it comprises a series of plateaux elevated at 600–1 300 ft forming the watershed area between the Tagus and Guadiana drainage. It is naturally divided into four regions. First from the Sa de S Mamade (3,350 ft) in the northeast, can be seen the Elvas-Estremoz plateau, to the south and southeast, forming a ramp at the mountain base. To the west and south-west stretches the Campo de Benavila, drained by the river Seda, a tributary of the Sorraia. South of the Sa d'Ossa is the plain of Évora.

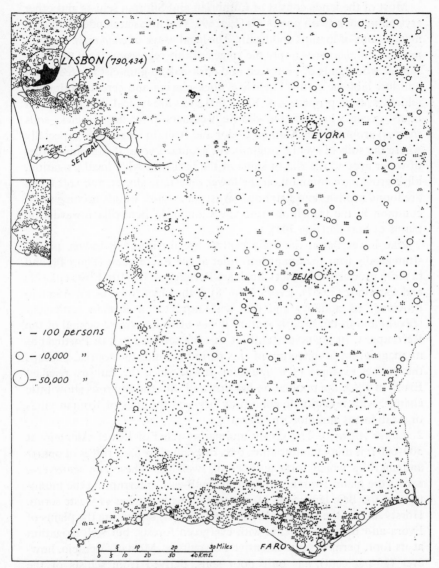

Fig. 144. Distribution of population in southern Portugal. Three zones of settlement stand out: the large agglomerated villages of Alentejo, with some dispersion around Évora and Beja; the sparse, scattered settlement of the Serra; and west coast; and the marked concentration of towns and dispersed farms in southern Algarve

Most of the lands consist of Cambrian and Silurian schists and other crystalline rocks with poor soils (Fig. 69). Vast areas are under degraded associations of maquis and heath. The local usage of *chaparals, boussas, mattos* and *charnecas* imply the stages of this regression from Mediterranean woodlands of evergreen and cork-oak to gum-cistus, tree-heath and low labiatae scrub. Extensive stock-rearing and cereal production (chiefly rye) on properties of 100–1,000 acres are typical. But rich wheat lands occur wherever the diorite weathers into deep, black soils (*barros*) around Elvas, Campo Maior and Ater do Chaio, and especially where the soils of syenite origin occur around Évora. Piedmont sources of water around the rim of some of the basins provide local irrigation, olive groves are common on the lower limestone slopes, and soft fruits are found at Elvas and Estremoz. Westwards, cork woods become more common in the transition from the Campo de Benavilla towards the plains of Sorraia (Fig. 145).

Like lower Beira, the main centres are fortified hill towns, placed strategically near the Spanish frontier at the Reconquest (Plate 48) and in more productive districts. Such are Portalegre (10,510), Elvas (10,821) and Estremoz (7,057). Évora (25,678) is the chief town of all Alentejo province; its nodality and rich soils attracted a Roman settlement (*Ebora*) and in the twelfth century it was made a forward capital of the Reconquest. In the seventeenth, it was the second town of Portugal as its magnificent architecture of this period reminds the tourist, perhaps the perfect example of a 'museum' town. Since the railway reached Évora in 1863, the population has doubled. But the environs show little change, with remarkable continuity between the sites of Roman villas or Arab farms and modern *quintas*.

2. *Lower Alentejo.* The gently undulating relief of Lower Alentejo at 300–600 ft is more monotonous, only diversified by hard ridges of quartz and marbles which form a series of swellings. These run transverse across the plains from north-west to south-east, interrupting the monotony of the Beja landscape of wheatfields with patches of waste scrub. Horsts such as the Serra de Vidigueira (1,300 ft) separating the plains of Évora and Beja are covered with evergreen forests, but well irrigation at its foot, permits some intensive polyculture. Most of Alentejo, however (85 per cent), has only poor soils, derived from schists or the 800,000 acres of Pliocene debris that floor the Sorraia and Sado basins.

The vegetation provides the main regional divisions, especially woodlands in the western and eastern sections, which cover a quarter of the total area. In the western districts there are over half a million acres of cork oak managed in *montado* estates, and it is not hard to realise that this represents one-third of the world acreage and 44 per cent of the global production of cork (Fig. 145). In the central plains there has always been more cereal cultivation but eastwards the evergreen oak comprises a vast domain of three-quarters of a million acres of *montados*.

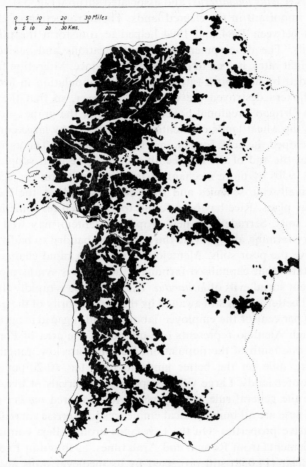

FIG. 145. Distribution of cork oak woodlands in southern Portugal (after air survey, undertaken for Estacao Agronomica Nacional)

This is a traditional system of pig-rearing, common also to Spanish Extremadura. Reclus mentions the big transhumance of pigs that formerly took place each summer from here to the mountains of Beira. An agro-pastoral economy explains too the curious frontier demarcation in Além-Guadiana where the former communal pasturage of the

Contenda de Moura between Spanish and Portuguese shepherds was eventually divided in 1893.

Until the end of the last century, between 80 and 90 per cent of Alentejo was still classified as waste (*charneca*) much of it a vast sea of gum cistus (*Cistus ladaniferus*) and associated shrubs (Fig. 53). Only the vine was important in the cleared lands. The introduction of chemical fertilisers between 1884 and 1894 helped to transform the poor, sili-ceous soils. The development of communications and subsidies for cheap freight rates, helped to open up the province. Migration from the north, aided by high birth-rates doubled the population in a century. The phylloxera destroyed the vineyards however, so that the title of Ramalho Ortigao's regional novel, 'The land of the grape', no longer describes the wheat lands of Alentejo. Investments by large companies have developed the cork forests on a systematic basis. The agricultural changes at the end of the nineteenth century have been supplemented since the 1930s by more mechanised farming, irrigation projects, both private small-scale schemes and state projects such as the Sado and Campilhas plans. Rice has been found to grow well on some irrigated schistose soils. Serradella, a new crop for Alentejo may well revolu-tionise dry farming and provide the animal husbandry so badly needed to improve the poor soils. Alentejo is a region in rapid change, which demonstrates that capitalised farming is not always synonymous with the inherent social evils of *latifundia*. The landscape is rapidly changing, but social betterment is still awaited by the vast majority of the peasants, where 70 per cent of the employed labour is still engaged in agriculture.

Although Alentejo represents one-quarter of the area of Portugal it has only one-tenth of the population. Densities are low, ranging from 70 per sq. mile on the better lands to only ten 10-20 per sq. mile on the poorer lands. Large villages spaced at intervals of five to eight miles are the general rule, interspersed with scattered *montes* or farm estates. These are all built on local eminences to exercise surveillance of the extensive properties. On the rich lands around Beja continuity of rival settlements from Roman and Arab times, as found in Évora, also occurs. Béjar (14,058) still protected by its medieval walls and castle, is the chief market of lower Alentejo.

3. *Algarve*. The southern region is so contrasted with its neighbour that it may be called 'the Riviera of Alentejo'. Sheltered from Meseta influences by the schistose dorsal of the Serra do Caldeirão and the batholith of Monchique (2,886 ft), Algarve repeats on a grander scale the Mediterranean tree crops of the coast of Arrábida, on the north side of the Sado estuary. Its dense population and its coastal concentration

of small ports, make it sharply distinct from its northern neighbour. In early spring, the countryside is flushed pink in a sea of almond blossom, growing above the brightly stained *terra rossa*, and framed by the dark green olive and carob groves. The low plains near the coast are a patchwork of colours, the vivid greens of the *hortas*, irrigated gardens producing early vegetables, the brown earths bearing crops of cereals under dry farming and the white-washed farm cottages. It must be

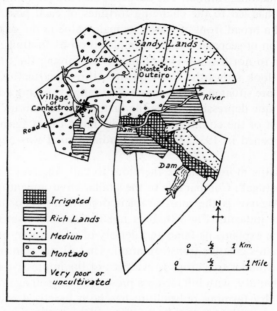

FIG. 146. Land utilisation on a large estate near Beja

remembered, however, that there are two Algarves: the waste lands and cork plantations of *La Serra* in the mountains to the north, and the *Barrocal* whose stoney calcareous plateaux produce the groves of almonds, figs, olives and carobs so characteristic of the Algarve landscape. The break between the folded Jurassic and Cretaceous limestones and the Plio-Pleistocene shoreline and dejection cones of the coastal plains is also distinct. There is a difference also between the predominantly sandy coasts east of Faro, the *Sotavento*, the leeward coast, and the limestone coast to the west, the more humid *Barlovento*, exposed to the Atlantic winds. The low, windswept platform which is cut by the headlands of Cape St Vincent and Sagres is also distinct, for it is the westward end of the Mediterranean world.

The Algarve is not a garden of Eden. Its rainfall is less and its summer drought is more prolonged than that of Alentejo. It is relieved only by the greater air moisture coming from the sea, which even permits the cultivation of maize under dry farming methods. The cultivation of cereals is limited, however, by the stony soils of the *Barrocal*, so that arboriculture is a more natural use of land. Water resources are not plentiful, with no rivers of any consequence apart from the Guadiana at the international frontier. The harbours also are poor and the successive silting has led to the changing fortunes of each port. The *Serra* has formed a broad front of waste, its main value in the past being the accumulation of seepage water accumulated on its foothills. The *Serra* is a barrier to north-south communications, forcing the towns of the Algarve to look seawards. Consequently, three-quarters of the urban population are situated on the coasts. The railway, taking advantage of the Monchique depression made the first, albeit circuitous, land route with the rest of the country in 1889. The more direct Faro-Beja road was only opened in 1932, and the Guadiana road was completed as late as 1947.

It is perhaps more accurate therefore to call Algarve 'the Barbary coast of Portugal'. Comparable to the similar environment of northern Alicante, Algarve is the most arabicised portion of Portugal, as its place-names indicate (Fig. 98). It is not the natural resources of the region which explains its fame and density of population, but the long legacy of man's creative transformation. That 41 per cent of the cultivated area is under tree crops is evidence of the impressive heritage of careful husbandry, with hill terraces preserving the soil against erosion. A form of dry farming polyculture has been practised ever since its Berber population settled there, and the diet of the people has been sustained by figs and olive oil, like its counterpart on the Algerian coast of Kabylia. The isolation of the region which has retained a distinctive culture, its own dialect and mode of life, has also handicapped its progress. Only 7 per cent of the population are engaged in industry, chiefly cork manufactures, flour milling and mining. The fishing activities (sardine and tunny) only employ 3·5 per cent of the population, chiefly at Faro, Olhão, Vila Nova de Portimão and Vila Real de Santo Antonio. High freight rates which until now have discouraged the industrial exploitation of the natural resources, including the mineral mines of Alentejo, will doubtless be reduced as inland communications are improved.

Compared with a low density of 10–20 per sq. mile in the Serra, the *Barrocal* supports densities of 200–400 rising to over 500 per sq. mile around the towns. High densities occur in the rich agricultural belt in which Loule is situated or around the coastal towns. Apart from the Serra, lowest densities are found over the higher areas of the Barrocal, the littoral sands of the east coast and the waterless peninsula of Cape St Vincent. Dispersion of rural settlement is very characteristic. The gleaming white farm cottages are rectangular buildings, with a flat roof that serves as a terrace. The spacious drying yard for the figs and the water-wheel alongside the house, surrounded by cactus hedges in the eastern zone, or limestone walls in the west, are other characteristic features. Of the towns, Olhão is the most typical, perched on the coastal terrace, its flat-roofed houses rising like an urban staircase in flights from the harbour (Fig. 103). The town however, is relatively modern, settled by Aveiro fishermen in the eighteenth century. Faro (17,631) is the present capital, surpassing its former rivals of Tavira (7,496), Silves (4,361) and Lagos (7,143). Olhão (16,592), Portimao (12,066) and Vila Real de Santo Antonio (6,086) complete the list of ports.

THE UNITY OF PORTUGAL

This summary of the regions of Portugal indicates their diversity. Between the two extremes of Minhoto and Algarvian polyculture are fundamental differences. The ambivalent character of Portugal, facing the Atlantic ocean and standing in the vestibule of the Mediterranean world has created marked contrasts which are partly European, partly African. In detail, its landforms are complex, its climate transitional, its vegetation diverse. But the broad contrasts are always between its Atlantic and Mediterranean components.

As Ribeiro has shown, the geographical contrasts between the north and south were once greater than they are now. Before the Roman occupation, the hill-top *castros*, the pastoral mode of life, the chestnut, cider and milk diet, characteristic of the north, must have been in striking contrast to the town life, and the bread, wine and oil diet of the south. The deciduous trees of the north, especially the chestnut, valued for its food, must have encountered the Mediterranean sclerophyllous woodland more abruptly. The Romans spread the olive northwards, and the pines, both the southerly stone pine and the maritime pine more characteristic of the north, have tended to fuse the diverse forest elements together. The eucalyptus introduced since the end of the nineteenth century is rapidly doing the same thing. Since the Middle Ages, the expansion of the vine northwards, the spectacular development of the American plant maize during the sixteenth century, and more recently root and vegetable crops, have softened the dividing zone between the two facades. It has been with such cultivated plants that man has conquered Portugal and unified it into one nation.

The wealth of Portuguese culture is however, more the result of the diversity of the country. The Minhoto-Galician cultural region was the birthplace of the nation and, ever since, its expansion southwards has been the great stimulus of Portuguese life. In a more intangible manner, the Lusitanian culture of its central region has played its rôle, the central position of this transitional region a challenge to leadership. The arabicised south, distinct in its heritage, has added enrichment by careful husbandry. Man may have unified the country, but his character is as diverse as the regions themselves. The pious and taciturn Minhoto, the conservative and superstitious mountain folk of Trás-os-Montes, the mystical and courageous Beirão, the progressive and energetic Estremaduréno, the melancholy and proud Alentejano and the talkative Algarvio, are like so many characters in the same masquerade.

Nature has aided man in his attempt to unify its landscapes. The interpenetration of valleys and mountains in the north, the broad sweep of the plains in the south demonstrates this. But the great achievement which has forged the cultural and economic unity of the country, within its independent political unity, has been the basis of Portuguese nationalism. Having conquered itself, this small nation then grasped and still maintains an empire overseas, which in area equals two-thirds of Europe.

PART III

ITALY

CHAPTER 14

STRUCTURE AND LANDFORMS
OF ITALY

'Italy is essentially a youthful land and one of those countries in
which the incessant task of transformation of outline and relief can
best be observed.' (T. Fischer)

Italy, the central peninsula of the Mediterranean, has neither the square
solidarity of the Iberian peninsula nor the extreme dissected outline of
Greece. It is a simple but narrow peninsula which thrusts 730 miles
south into the sea; no part of the country is more than 150 miles from
the sea, and its average width is about 100–130 miles. Simply on the outline of the country there is a clear distinction between Continental Italy
in the north, which is broadly rooted within the trunk of Europe, having
an Alpine frontier of 1,167 miles, and the Peninsula proper south of the
gulfs of Genoa and Venice. The north includes the clearly distinct Alps
and Northern Plain. The Italian Alps are excluded from this study as
they are but part of the whole Alpine area and entirely within central
Europe; though it is true that one cannot properly envisage the Plain
without its bordering Alpine rim. The Northern Plain, continental though
it is both in position and even partly in climate, must be included for its
immense economic importance within Italy and because even its climate
is, after all, transitional. Peninsular Italy, cut off from the north by the
Apennines, though a land of harsh contrasts, is less distinctly sub-
divisible into regions than the north. Sicily is in so many respects a
continuation of the peninsula that it can be treated here in conjunction
with it, but Sardinia, more remote and vastly different is treated along
with the other Mediterranean islands in Chapter 20.

Italy resembles both Greece and Spain in being a mountainous
country: 78 per cent of its area is classified as hilly or rugged, and 39
per cent of the total as mountainous. The Continental North of Italy
includes not only the highest and most impressive mountains but also
the only extensive plain. In the Peninsula the mountainous backbone,
the Apennines, flanked by hills on either side ensure that mountain,
hill and plain are uniformly distributed and some 70 per cent of each
major region is of hilly or rugged relief.

The physical landscape of Italy derives startling contrasts from its diverse rock types. Three of these are of especial importance and extent in the Peninsula limestones, sands and clays, volcanics. The limestones

FIG. 147. Distribution of karstic areas in Italy

are of varying age, though chiefly Mesozoic. The sands and clays are Tertiary, although there is a marked distinction between those of pre- and post-Pliocene age. The volcanics, most of them very recent, are of Quaternary origin, except for a few Tertiary volcanics in the north.

During the long period of the Secondary and early Tertiary, the location of Italy was marked by transgressive seas, favouring the accumulation of limestones. Such calcareous rocks are now best developed in the pre-Alpine zone, and in the central Apennines notably in the Gran Sasso and Sibilline Mountains, and stretching southwards in the Apennines as far as Calabria and Madonna in Sicily. Distinctive limestone peninsulas are Istria, Gargano, and Salerno. Karstic relief is evident in all three areas, its nature varying with the type of limestone and especially with the intensity of fissures (Fig. 147). In the Abruzzi, the high, massive Mesozoic limestones have been fractured into a series of polja, separated by mountain blocks, but inter-connected by the drainage. Everywhere, they are pitted with dolines.[1] In the southern Apennines, the high, rugged white-faced coral limestones have a more vigorous and picturesque relief than the northern Apennines.[2] In the north, the mountains have only monotonous shaly or sandy ridges intercalated with some limestones, so that their outline is smooth and characterless.[3] In Apulia, the limestone relief is again different, with a gently swelling tabular relief, stained red by a mantle of *terra rossa* or covered with later Tertiary sands.[4] Only the higher relief of the Murge has more of that bleached, rugged aspect typical of coral limestones. The calcareous molasse of Miocene age, *tufo*, has formed an important medium of the arts both in the classical architecture of Sicily and in the late medieval rococo of Lecce.

After the Cretaceous and throughout the Tertiary there was a thick accumulation of gravels, sands and clays around the Alps, Apennines and the Sicilian mountains. They provide some of the most distinctive scenery in Italy. The most comprehensive and extensive in the northern Apennines, is the famous formation of *scagliose* clay, a thick series of clayey shales that include Jurassic, Cretaceous and Tertiary rocks, crushed and laminated. In the Apennines of Umbria and Marche, it is associated with red and gray soft chalky facies (*Scaglia*), and in the northern Apennines with compact, calcareous sandstones (*macigno*) that form the highest ridges of the Tuscan Apennines. Even on gentle slopes, the *scagliose* clay can break away in great scales and produce gigantic landslides called *frane* (Fig. 156). The intercalation of sands and clays foster the lubricating action of sub-surface water at the junction of these porous and non-porous rocks. These slides will occur especially when the dip of the bed follows the relief.[5] When the removal of the underlying clays causes the downfall of the overlying more resistant sands or limestones, creating steep, eroded, clay slopes, the top strata will appear crowned by escarpments (*balza*) of limestone or sandstone. Differential erosion creates the *calanche*, comparable to the badlands of North America, especially in Basilicata along the edges of its Pliocene plateau. Figure 160 indicates the distribution of these landforms, whose variations of relief ranges from the deeply indented badlands of southern Italy and Sicily, under a more torrential regime of erosion, to the more modulated, indeterminate relief of the north and centre of the Peninsula.[6] In the latter, there are gradations of relief, from the tangled, folded structures of the Emilian Apennines with great *frane* scars on their slopes, to the rolling, lunar landscapes of deeply dissected lake beds, as in the middle Tiber valley.

Volcanic rocks are the *alter ego* of western Italy, associated with the subsidence of the Tyrrhenian basin and its lines of fracture.[7] Monte Vulture and Etna are the only exceptions to this general rule. A few volcanoes are still active, notably Vesuvius, Etna, and in the Lipari islands, Stromboli and Vulcano. The volcanic landforms are diverse, reflecting distinct types of vulcanicity and a variety of rock-types. Most of the volcanoes were submerged and their explosive character is associated with the intrusion of sea water into the magmatic vents. Vesuvius is the best known (Plate 1). Its prehistoric crater rim, Monte Somma, forms a vast amphitheatre of 25 miles at its base and rises to 3,713 ft in Monte Nasone.[8] Within this crater wall is the modern active cone of Vesuvius (3,894 ft), its slopes streaked by the series of basaltic lava flows that have been dated since 1714 on the geological maps[9] (Fig. 166). Etna is greater still, an irregular ellipse of 93 miles circumference and of variable altitude (10,740 ft). A central cone rises steeply above a high plateau at *c.* 2,000 ft, pitted with smaller craters; some 260 eruption vents have been identified (Plate 2). In the Lipari islands, Stromboli has perhaps the most remarkably uniformly shaped cone. Monte Vulture, isolated in the interior of the southern Apennines, rises abruptly to 4,354 ft in a basaltic cone, and its extinct crater is filled by the picturesque lake of Monticchio. Older, and more explosive forms of vulcanicity are concentrated on the central Tyrrhenian coast between the Phlegrean Fields and southern Tuscany. Each area has its distinctive landforms. In the Phlegrean Fields, dented with numerous shallow craters, vulcanicity is most recent;[10] the gaseous vents of Solfatara and the heaving coastline of Pozzuoli indicate complete inactivity is not yet reached (Fig. 166). This is the classical world of the inferno. Passing by the crater of Roccamonfina the Alban Hills comprise a second distinct volcanic area. An outer, caldera rim with a diameter of 7 miles, culminates in Monte Peschio (3,081 ft) in the south-east. The high, central cone of M. Faete (3,136 ft) overlooks several craters, two of which are occupied by lakes Albano and Nemo[11] (Fig. 148). North of Rome, the Sabatine volcanics are less resistant to erosion, with undulating, less impressive relief. There are a few cones, however, such as Rocca Romana (1,969 ft), Cimino (3,455 ft) and Vulsinio (2,297 ft) but they are poorly conserved because of the abundance of soft tuffs (or ash beds) and only a few basaltic lavas. The trachytic cone of M. Amiata (5,690 ft) is better preserved although much older. Bolsena is an extensive, well-shaped crater lake, but Bracciano appears the fusion of several craters of an explosive type.

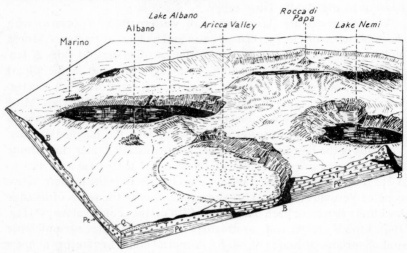

Fig. 148. Block—diagram of the Alban Hills, looking. north Pl—Pliocene; B—Basalt lava; T—Tuffs; P—'Peperina' tuff; Q—Quaternay fluvio-lacustrine deposits

Geologically, Italy is thus a young country, owing its present shape and structure to the recent periods of the late Tertiary and the Quaternary. The oldest rocks represent stumps of Carbo-Permian mountain chains. Some are the faulted fragments of former land masses, notably the granites and schists of Calabria and north-eastern Sicily.[12] Others were involved in later mountain building movements such as the Permian sandstones of Tuscany, and the primary limestones of the Alps. After these rocks had been folded into the Carbo-Permian chains, a second stage ensued when these rocks were worn down and a precursor of the Mediterranean Sea covered the position of Italy. This prolonged submergence favoured the formation of limestones: those of Triassic age scattered throughout the Pre-Apennines, southern Apennines and Sicily; Jurassic and Cretaceous limestones in the Alpine Foreland and the backbone of the Apennines, the Gargano Peninsula, eastern Apulia and Istria; and Tertiary limestones in the same areas and in Sicily. In the Cretaceous rocks of the Abruzzi, eastern Apulia and Istria, periods of emergence of land are marked by irregular deposits of bauxite. Towards the end of the Eocene and Oligocene, the land arose again and the formation of lake-basins began in Sicily and the Apennines, although in the Northern Plain subsidence commenced in early Oligocene times and continued until the upper Miocene. Volcanoes were active in what are now the Euganean hills, north west of Padua. Mountain building movements, mainly of Miocene times, raised the Alps and Apennines, to fashion the central Mediterranean roughly to its present outline. Superimposed over Tertiary flysch the northern Apennines are particularly complicated. Some geologists (Sacco, for example)[13] explain their structure by recumbent folds, while others such as Staub[14] and the Dutch school envisage an immense nappe (the Ligurides) which were thrust 300 miles long over the autochthonous Apennines. The trend of the fold lines was much influenced by the ancient blocks, so that the Alps and Apennines formed great arcs. The simple arrangement of upfold and mountain chain, downfold and longitudinal valley is partially seen in the Apennines, whereas the folding was much more complex in the Alps.

Three distinctive, longitudinal belts can be distinguished in the Peninsula (Fig. 151). The most westerly consists of ancient rocks discontinuously distributed, such as the crystalline rocks of Mi. Peloritani in Sicily, and in Calabria, and the Permo-Triassic limestones and sandstones found in the same areas; and also in the Pre-Apennine region of the Apuan Alps and the *Catena Metallifera* west of Siena. It is uncertain whether the rocks of Elba, Corsica and Sardinia belong to the same mountain system or to an independent one. To the east, the main part of the Apennines occupies the second mountain system, with marked differences in lithology and structures between the north and south, the east and west, The third belt consists of the Jurassic and Cretaceous limestones of the Gargano and eastern Apulia. It is a littoral platform structure whose almost horizontal limestones are in marked contrast to the thick series and steeply folded geosynclinal structure of the second belt. The troughs formed by the subsidence of the Tyrrhenian and Po-Adriatic basins are also markedly different. The Tyrrhenian sea is associated with more localised and irregular subsidence confined to semi-circular, small areas, whereas the long, faulted troughs of the Po-Adriatic have a rectangular configuration.

By Pliocene times, the violence of the Alpine earth movements had died down. As Fig. 149 indicates, there was a marked difference between the present shoreline and the Pliocene configuration.[15] Only the central dorsal of the Apennines, the islands of the south-west and northern

Sicily had comparable shorelines to the present day. But the Pre-Apennines, the Northern Plain, and all the eastern third of Italy was covered by the Pliocene seas. While their deposits of clays and some sands and gravels, were being laid down, lakes were formed in troughs within the Apennines, especially in the Arno, Tiber and Lucanian basins, now represented by wide dissected plains[16] (Fig. 164). As the sea-level dropped in Pleistocene times, enormous spreads of detritus were swept

FIG. 149. Italy in Pliocene times (other dotted line suggests theoretical reconstruction of Pliocene coast)

down from the mountains, especially from the Alps. It is astonishing, however, how fine the Quaternary materials are that cover the N. Italian Plain. It suggests the influence of material carried down in suspension by the rains and supplied by the products of the Pliocene tropical weathering and the chemical products of the Mindel-Riss interglacial. The rapid changes of land and sea over the N. Italian Plains in the Quaternary are, however, the direct consequence of subsidence rather than of the alluviation (Fig. 150). These Pleistocene plains are usually arranged with a clay base, capped by sands and gravels, and an oc- casional layer of limestone (*tufa*). Volcanoes were active in the Pleistocene, in Latium and Campania.

Glaciation was intense in the Alps, glaciers creating extensive morainic amphitheatres at the mouths of the major valleys in the Northern Plain. There is no evidence of Gunz and Donau glaciers advancing on to the Northern Plain, but Mindal, Riss and Würm glaciations were severe; the Würmian deposits extend without a break for almost 150 miles between the Stura and Adda.[17] As the glaciers did not extend so far south in the Italian Sub-Alps compared to those in the Bavarian Fore-land, the transition between each glacial stage is narrowed and therefore

FIG. 150. Italy in mid-Quaternary times

more complex. Yet the formation of the Italian moraines is remarkably fresh, perhaps consequent on milder temperatures that permitted a vegetation cover to mantle them quickly and so preserve their land forms.[18] Minor glaciers were distributed in three groups in the Apen-nines: one centred on the Apuan Alps (above 4,500 ft);[19] a second more extensive group in the Abruzzi-Matese (above 5,500 ft);[20] and a third, small group centred on M. Pollino (above 6,000 ft) north east of the gulf of Policastro.[21] Final retreat of Würmian glaciation is associated with the Flandrian transgression that has drowned the northern sector of the Adriatic.[22] Recent alluviation has shaped the development of river deltas, notably the Po[23] and smaller ones such as the Tiber, and has produced a succession of beach ridges as the coastline has advanced seawards, especially in Basilicata. Uplift of the western Calabrian coast during the Quaternary has been spectacular, indicative of the tectonic instability still apparent in the southern Tyrrhenian basin.

The landforms of Italy, which are the result of these geological stages and processes, may be grouped simply into the following divisions, excluding the Alps and Pre-Alps: the Northern or Po Plain, with its two eastern appendages of Venetia and Istria; the Apennines, subdivided into the northern, central, southern and Calabrian sectors; Apulia and the Sub-Apennines of the Adriatic coast; the Pre-Apennines of Tuscany, Latium and Campania; and the island of Sicily. Of these divisions, the Apennines is the most extensive zone of Italy with 35 per cent of the total area. The Northern Plain, Venetia and Istria together cover 14·8 per cent and the Pre-Apennines 12 per cent. The Alps, Pre-Alps and Sub-Alpine zone excluded from this study have 19·5 per cent of the national territory.

THE NORTHERN PLAIN

The irregularly shaped triangle of the Northern Plain lies between the Alps, Apennines and Adriatic sea. Extending 260 miles between Rimini and Turin, it has a variable width: 50 miles near Alessandria and Milan, 65 at Verona, but with a coastline along the Adriatic of some 200 miles between Rimini and the R. Isonzo. Bores made by A.G.I.P. geologists have revealed the irregularity of the floor of the trough (Fig. 152). Two major synclines, presumably active from Miocene to Quaternary times, curve between Alessandria and Cuneo, and from west of Pavia to the Po above Turin, separated by an anticlinal axis in the Montferrato Hills, created by positive movements in the upper Miocene.[24] A series of sub-Apennine folds form four or five anticlines beneath the central plain between Parma and Pavia, with a second series running between Rimini and west of Bologna. Bores of over 26,000 ft have been made in the Oligocene, Mio-Pliocene floor of the trough. Subsidence has fashioned the morphology of the Plain, and it has influenced the trend of much of the drainage. The Pliocene transgression invaded a relief that was thus markedly differentiated by numerous troughs, masking them with the products of fine sedimentation. However in Plio-Pleistocene times further subsidence, exaggerated by local faulting, differentiated its structural relief once more. This tectonic activity is still very active. The consequence has been the marked difference between the western Plain, with its numerous,

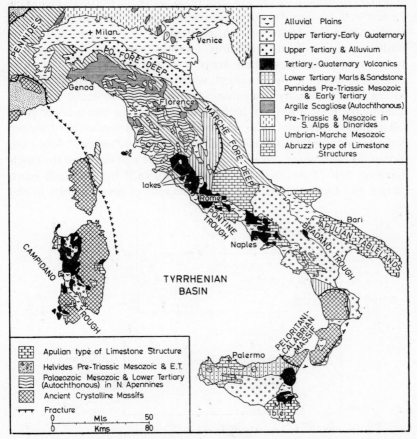

FIG. 151. The structure of Italy (after Fabiani, dal Piaz and Segre)

isolated basins and hills, and the eastern Plain a mere homogeneous lowland.

The geological boundary between the Pleistocene and the older rocks, coincides roughly with the geographical limits of the plain. On the north side, the limit of the plain is generally sharp, sometimes the Alps rising above the plain as in upper Piedmont, though more usually moraines, notably the Serre of Ivrea, and fluvio-glacial cones interpose to form low, dissected hills. On the south side of the plain, the edge is aligned in a less sinuous manner along a post-Pliocene flexure, but the dissected foothills of the northern Apennines with their extensive piedmonts make for a less distinctive border. There is also a contrast between the well-marked belts of distinctive landforms along the northern plain and the less well-developed sequence at the foot of the Emilian plain to the south. Along the Alpine margin, particularly in Piedmont and Lombardy, a series of discontinuous foothills are formed by several morainic amphitheatres. These are of Riss and especially of Würmian age. These front the alpine valleys, which were most heavily fed by ice during the Quaternary glaciations. Between these morainic hills and fronting them are a series of high gravel terraces, the remnants of great fluvio-glacial dejection cones. East of Lake Garda similar but younger deposits continue these so-called high terraces of the *Pianalti*.[25] Along the foot of the Apennines, the absence of impressive moraines and the much narrower belt of fluvio-glacial cones is explained by the much more limited Pleistocene glaciation; the dominance of nival regimes in the

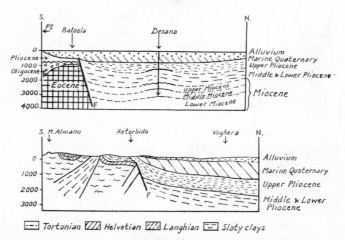

FIG. 152. Cross-sections of the western Po Basin (after AGIP, 1957 and Gabert). A—cross-section between the Plain and the northern border of Monferrat; B—contact between the Po Plain and the Apennines at Voghera

ice ages; the prevailing soft rocks of the Apennines that provide only friable terraces when re-deposited along their foothills, and the effects of later Quaternary subsidence which may be even post-Würmian (Fig. 150).[26] On the north side of the plain, below the high terraces and where these are absent fronting the Alps, are the high (*Alta Pianura*) and low plains (*Basse Pianura*). To the west and in the north, these form the bulk of the plain, distinguished hydrographically between the dry, upper plain, deeply incised by its water courses, with gravelly *ferretto* soils and heath lands, and the wet, lower plain, rich in water and fine alluvial soils. Between them are the famous spring lines the *fontanili*, varying in width from about eight miles in western Lombardy to less than a mile in the east.[27] Their hydrological significance has been somewhat obliterated by the development of irrigation. There is usually a gentle transition from the low plain to the flood plain of the Po valley or to the lagoonal littoral of Venetia. Downstream the Po has raised its bed above the plain, however, and is as much as 20 ft above the delta area. Thus river dikes have been created over many centuries to supplement the natural *levées* and contain the river and the lower courses of its main tributaries. This system of dykes extends up the Po for more than 250 miles, to protect the flood plains which are most extensive south of the Po and towards the delta. Thus although the relief is relatively uniform throughout the plain, the nature of the deposits, the distinction between the upper and lower terraces, and the areas subject to flooding all have contributed very significant contrasts to the regional landscapes, closely reflected in the cultural imprints of husbandry and settlement.

The plain may be broadly divided into four subdivisions: Piedmont, west of the Ticino valley; Lombardy, including that part of Venetia lying west of the Adige; Emilia which embraces nearly all the area south of the Po; and Venetia.

1. *Piedmont*. Only one-fourth of Piedmont consists of the lowlands, which form the ante-chamber of the Northern Plain. The western Alps (Pennine, Graian and Cottian ranges) swing in a semi-circle between the Ticino and Tanaro valleys to the north and south-west of the Piedmontese plain. From the south, the Monferrato Hills push northwards as an extension of the Apennines, to pinch the plain into a narrow corridor, only 1·5 miles wide near Turin, once the gulf of a late Pliocene sea. The Monferrato hills with their northern extension in the Turin hills, break up the plain into three sections. The most extensive is followed by the upper courses of the Po and its tributary the Tanaro, between Cuneo and Turin. More isolated is the lowland of Marengo, centred on Alessandria. Downstream from Chivasso, the Po lowland widens into the broad plains of Vercelli and Novara. There is a marked gradient along the Po valley, descending from 1,752 ft at Cuneo to 830 ft at Turin and 381 ft at Casale Monferrato.

Framed between the Cottian Alps and the early Tertiary hills of the Langhe, the upper Po plain is distinctive. The gneiss and mica schists of the Cottian Alps rise much more immediately from the plain, with no terminal moraines. Compared with the Alps further east, glaciation has been much less intense and solifluction more marked during the Quaternary glaciations. Thus a broad belt of glacis deposits front the

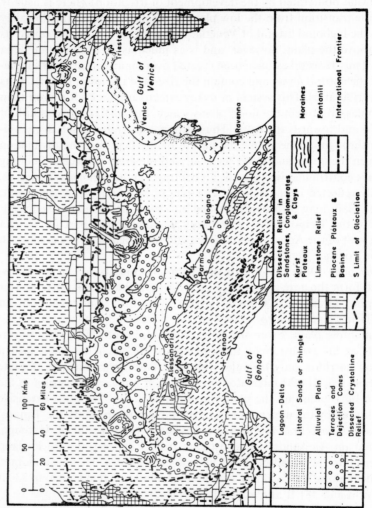

FIG. 153. Landscape types of the North Italian Plain

foot of the mountains, with relative levels at 260, 330 and 425 ft, now dry, heathy terraces (*vaude*). Headward erosion was checked in the western plains during the Quaternary by the encumbrance of so much fluvio-glacial detritus in the lower tributaries of northern and eastern Piedmont, but the Tanaro river system was in sharp contrast. Great spreads of *ferretto* capped terraces of early Pleistocene age, running north–south, indicate the proto-course of the Tanaro between Bra and Turin. Diverted by the fluvio-glacial spreads of the Dora Riparia, across the Turin corridor, the Tanaro was diverted in later Quaternary times to cut across the anticline of Alto Monferrato and the Asti syncline, and flow into the Po at Valenza. Cutting its base-level more vigorously, its upper tributaries now carve deeply into the glacis, creating a dissected lowland relief, backed by the Langhe hills to the south. The basin of Alessandria formed a later Pliocene gulf leading eastwards into the plain of Marengo through which runs the Scrivia valley.

At the foot of the Graian Alps, morainic amphitheatres block the mouths of the valleys of the Dora Riparia, Dora Baltea and Ticino. The first is compact and small, rising to 660 ft above the narrow gap of the Po plain between Rivoli and Turin. The Dora Baltea has a much larger amphitheatre, backed by the Serra, 1,300 ft above the plain. The Ticino group have much less marked features of relief, 660 ft above Lake Orta but rarely above 330 ft south of Lake Maggiore. Between the moraines are extensive areas of high terrace, notably developed around Pinerolo, Lanzotor, Biella and Borgomanero. East of the Dora Baltea, the alluvial plain widens out of the corridor into the main trough of the Northern Plain. Its series of high and low terraces merge eastwards into the Lombard region of Lomellina, drained by the Sesia and Ticino.

2. *Lombardy*. The confused pattern of hills that front the narrow zone of the Pre-Alps in west Lombardy, consists of almost continuous festoons of terminal moraines. These stretch from the amphitheatre of the Ticino, to those of Ceresio, Lake Como and Vallassina. Lake Garda is dammed by the largest of these morainic amphitheatres.[25] There is still no comprehensive authoritative study of the glacial chronology, though it is thought that probably three stages of glaciation may be recognised. Evidence of the oldest, the Gunz, is seen in the cemented conglomerates (*ceppo*) which form a platform for successive stages, notably at the mouth of the Oglio. The Mindel stage is associated with the *ferretto* deposits. The Riss and Würm glaciations are represented in the interior hills of moraines, with massive erratics. The most impressive of these terminal moraines stands 500 ft above Lake Garda, running for 45

miles long and some 8 miles wide. It is only once interrupted in a notch made by the F. Mincio.

South of a line between Mantua and Magenta, formerly stretched the vast gulf of the Pliocene sea. It has been infilled by conglomerates, fluvio-glacial deposits and alluvium, the powerful northern tributaries between the Ticino and the Oglio pushing the Po southwards close to the foot of the Apennines. The high terraces extend continuously in front of the moraines and between them from the Ticino to south of Lake Iseo, but they are absent in eastern Lombardy. The high terraces decrease gently in altitude at *c.* 400 ft to the low terraces, the lowest of which falls 30–40 ft to the flood plain of the Po. The border between the high and low terraces is marked by the zone of springs (*fontanili*). The major rivers, deeply intrenched in the high terraces, widen and meander slowly in the lower flood plains of the Po, Ticino, Adda and Oglio, which have suffered frequent changes of river course, leaving back-waters, meander lakes and marshes. From Piacenza eastwards, the main tributaries flow in courses roughly parallel with the Po, often flowing in much larger courses than the gradients would suggest, such as that of the Oglio. A few hills rise above the plain, notably the Miocene outcrops of the S. Colombano hills (230 ft), an outlier of the Apennines, east of Pavia. Gently rippling the flat relief of the low plain between Lomillina and Pavia are Quaternary sand dunes, gathered by the winds from the vast alluvial deposits, laid down in the recent lateral displacement of the rivers.

3. *Emilia*. Except for the small Lombard triangle of Oltrepo pavese, Emilia comprises all the plain south of the Po, for a distance of 150 miles between Piacenza and the delta. This part of the plain is contrasted sharply with the northern plain, mainly because of the differences between the Alps and the Apennines and the small drainage basins in the latter. Lower and consisting chiefly of soft rocks, the Apennines had little Pleistocene glaciation compared with the Alps. Consequently the Emilian piedmont zone of high terraces is confined to a narrow zone. It is widest between Piacenza and Modena, and east of Forli, associated with more favourable rock types in the upper drainage basins. In the areas where the Pliocene clays form a broad front to the Apennines, especially between Bologna and Forli, the high terraces are little developed.[28] But the absence of lakes, the more markedly seasonal (winter) rainfall, and the prevalence of soft materials explain why the rivers carry down such heavy loads of materials, so that the alluvial plain of recent sediments is wider than it is north of the Po. The Via Emilia, the ancient highway between Rimini and Piacenza, follows

58 Campo Imperatore, a Polje west of Gran Sasso

APENNINE BASINS

59 Diano Valley, a Tertiary basin in the Campanian Apennines

60 *Coltura promiscua* in the hill country near Perugia

61 Cereal lands of the Tavoliere

approximately the lower edge of the older sediments, so that the zone
of fontanile, here much more discontinuous, lies to the north of it. The
low plain is narrow and soon gives way to the featureless, flood plain
of the Po, which gradually widens to over 25 miles by the time it
reaches the delta near Ferrara.

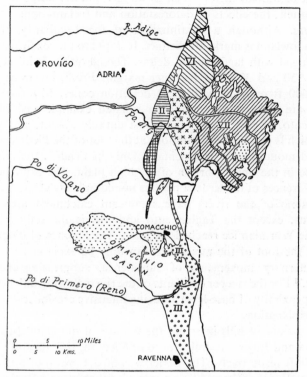

FIG. 154. Evolution of the Po Delta (after Marinelli and Almagia) Deltas I, II, III
are ancient, IV and V are medieval, and VI and VII are modern. Dotted area shows
section of the Valle di Comachio that is now in course of reclamation

According to the Marinelli, the oldest delta of the Po was approximately in the position of the Po di Volano, east of Codigoro, while the
second lay to the north, followed by the actual Po di Goro.[29] (Fig. 154.)
In the Roman era, the third delta was formed to the south in what is now
the Comacchio lagoon, with its outlet along the Po di Primero, flanked
to the south-east by the tombola of the Ravennese Pineta. Two
others are from cartographic evidence of medieval age: the fourth
lying east of the first delta near Pomposa; and the fifth to the north

w.m.w.—14

near Mesola[30]. The sixth delta commenced in the twelfth century near Ficarolo to merge with the waters of the Adige in a man-made outlet (Fig. 154). The latest, or seventh, delta is lobate, fed by the Po Grande, which became the main outlet by the sixteenth and seventeenth centuries aided by the Venetians. The rapid development of this newest delta is a reflection of human factors such as more rapid discharge of water in new channels, the effects of deforestation and reclamation.

4. *Venetia.* Although a continuation of the Lombardy plain, the Venetian lowland is markedly distinct. It slopes to the sea instead of to a river, fringed with lagoons and deltas. The elevation is lower, mainly between 150 and 300 ft at its inner margin. Friuli, however, is much higher, 600 ft or over, with great dejection cones. Morainic amphitheatres are lacking, except for an isolated example east of the F. Tagliamento. High terraces are almost entirely absent, and the hilly zone, which is practically continuous at the foot of the Piedmontese and Lombard mountains, is fragmentary. Only in Friuli is there a similar landscape in the upper portion of the high plain. The explanation for these differences of the eastern plain is not completely clear. East of the Adige, none of the rivers have significant catchment areas in the mountains, except the Tagliamento and this is the only one down which the Würmian ice reached the plain. The absence of older terrace levels at the foot of the mountains can only be explained by possible mid-Quaternary movements of subsidence, suppressing the earlier evidence.[31] For the steeper gradients of the rivers flowing independently, and the proximity of base-level inducing intensive erosion, can only be a partial explanation.

Three groups of hills interrupt the flatness of the plain. In the west, the Berici and Euganean hills, south of Vicenza, rise abruptly to 1,457 and 1,978 ft respectively. The Berici, a compact group of hills of early Tertiary volcanic rocks and limestones, and the volcanic Euganean hills effectively interrupt the spring-line zone and main line of communication. East of these hills, the distinction between the high and low plains becomes sharper, and in the Friulian plain the upper limit of the *fontanili* at about 100 ft is well marked. This eastern lowland forms part of the northern Adriatic syncline, infilled with fluvio-glacial detritus and alluvium. It forms an undulating plain of 160–900 ft backed by the Tagliamento end-moraines which form a three-fold sequence, the outer perimeter extending for nearly 18 miles and rising to 885 ft above the plain. The main rivers, the Piave, Tagliamento and Isonzo, have built up a series of deltas along the coast, separated between lagoons and low, sandy shorelines. East of the lower Isonzo, the coast changes abruptly with the cliffs of the Karst. Planed by marine erosion, with summit levels above 2,000 ft, the Karst proper stretches north-west–south-east from the Gulf of Trieste to Quarnaro isolated to the east and west by two broad, marly synclines in which surface drainage is best developed. To the south and west, is the Istrian Karst now entirely in Yugoslavia (see Chapter 18).

THE APENNINES

The Apennines stretch some 550 miles from Savona on the Ligurian coast to the Calabrian massif of Pollino and form the backbone of the Peninsula. The mountains have a marked variety of scenery. Its major folds are the products of Eo-Miocene orogenesis, subsequently modi-fied by different styles and periods of tectonic uplift and subsidence. There was a long phase of relative stability during the Pliocene trans-gression, so that the Pliocene marine deposits now reach 3,000 to 3,300 ft above sea-level. In the north, the mountain chain is 50 miles wide, composed of weak sandstones and clays, folded into continuous chains (Fig. 155). The main watershed follows approximately the highest ranges[32] and communications are generally difficult because of the height of the passes. South of the F. Tronto in Central Apennines, block fracturing rather than simple folding becomes increasingly important (Fig. 158). The mountains broaden to 60–70 miles wide, and the lime-stone mountains rise in more rugged splendour to the highest summits of the Apennines. Nevertheless, drainage has followed the numerous graben and other interior basins so that lines of communication are easier. The southern Appenines consist of smaller massifs of limestones set in a matrix of clays and marls, and in Calabria these frame the ancient crystalline massifs of the Sila and Aspromonte. Broadly, the Appennines may thus be divided into three major sectors of the north, centre and south.

NORTHERN APENNINES

The border between the Apennines and the Alps is traditionally demarcated at the Cadibone Pass (1,625 ft) though a line between Savona and the Tanaro near Ceva, appears more appropriate.[33] To the west lies the higher calcareous Alps, while eastwards the Ligurian Apennines are lower, with marly, sandstone terrain. A series of short mountain chains, about six in number follow each other *en échelon* along the main trend. Numerous downfolds or troughs run north-west to south-east and contain Pliocene lake-basins. The major watershed between the Tyrrhenian and the Adriatic seas follows generally along the outermost, eastern series of ranges, which have been folded most recently and carry the highest summits. Thus towards the Adriatic the drainage is simple, running transverse in parallel valleys down the slope, creating a dominant linear pattern of relief (Fig. 162). Towards the Tyrrhenian, the drainage is much more complicated, with a marked adjustment to structure. The northern Apennines may be conveniently divided into two regions: The Ligurian mountains, and the Emilian-Tuscan Apennines.

1. *Liguria*. The mountains of Liguria show a distinctive two-fold development, with more of the style of the Alps than the other sectors of the Apennines. Folded along a north–south axis in early Tertiary times, the area was peneplaned by marine abrasion in later Oligocene times, remnants of which are still preserved as a summit level. Then followed east to west folding, which has given birth to the actual relief. Uplift has persisted until recent times, so that the youthful, short, transverse streams plunge steeply to the sea, from heights of about 2,000 ft at less than one mile from the coast. Differential erosion of the hard limestones, gneiss and quartzites, and the softer schists, marls and clays has also been an important feature.[34] In detail, the coast is related to structure, but it is surprising at first sight that the indentations are not more apparent. The explanation lies in the very steep gradients of the short rivers, which carry little detritus on to rocky coasts, with a narrow continental shelf that plunges precipitously. Three morphological subdivisions of Liguria can be recognised: the Alpine sector from the French frontier to Savona; the western Ligurian Apennines from the Cadibona gap to the Genoa Pass; and the eastern Ligurian Apennines from the Genoa Pass to the Magra valley.

The Ligurian Alps have a marked tectonic complexity, as part of the Pennides, but this has no morphological significance. In the western and higher part, the rocks are predominantly Eocene limestones which rise to over 6,500 ft near the French border. The coast is little dented in comparison with the French Riviera, which is rocky and steep. The only sizeable plain is in a synclinal trough at Albenga. Between Albenga and Savona, the effects of differential erosion are much more marked, with varied landscapes of porphyries, gneiss, conglomerates and limestones. The gneisses of Mt Settepani (4,540 ft) and dolomites of Mt Corno (4,558 ft) give diversity to the scenery. Between Savona and Genoa with their respective synclinal axes, followed by the passes of Cadibona (1,505 ft) and Giovi (1,466 ft), *pietre verdi* or secondary calcareous schists predominate. The mountains rise more steeply above the coast, with M. Beigue reaching 4,222 ft within 4 miles of the sea.

In contrast to the Riviera di Ponente with its more rounded, hilly relief, and small alluvial coastal plains, the Riviera di Levante east of Genoa has more complex folded ranges, and more rugged, mountainous relief. Instead of a single series of mountains strung out *en échelon*, there are four parallel series, one behind the other. The first range rises in Eocene marls to M. Becco (2,930 ft) immediately east of Genoa, to die out at Chiavari, fronted by the Oligocene flysch peninsula of S. Margherita. The second chain lies beyond the longitudinal valley of Lavagna that is carved out of *scagliose* clays, and is dominated by M. Ramaceto (4,413 ft). This in turn is joined with the third chain along the Ligurian boundary, traced as far as M. Gottero (5,381 ft), in Eocene sandstones and limestones. The transverse ridge of the Cusna, rising to 5,082 ft in M. Molinatico forms the fourth chain. Behind the abrupt anticlinal limestone cliffs of the Cinqueterre at La Spezia, the Magra and its main tributary the Vara have carved out a second major longitudinal valley, aided by folding and faulting.

2. *The Emilian-Tuscan Apennines.* The Etruscan mountains, as the major portion of the northern Apennines are sometimes called, stretch over two hundred miles from the Trebbia valley to the Trabaria Pass, overlooking the Tiber and Metauro valleys. Compared with the Ligurian mountains (*c.* 25 miles wide), the Etruscan Apennines are uniformly wider (40 miles) and higher (M. Cusna, 6,959 ft and M. Cimone 7,096 ft). South of the Cisa Pass the mountains trend consistently north-west to south-east, the summits exceed 6,000 ft, glacial sculpture is obvious in the limestones and sandstones, and three longitudinal folded zones are apparent as far south as Lucca. But north of the Cisa Pass the relief is very different. Master trend lines are not visible, the mountains are lower, glaciation is less obvious, and soft sediments prevail.

Although the northern Apennines are geologically the best-known structures of the Apennines because of petroleum prospecting, they are still a matter of much debate. Some geologists postulate one or more extensive nappes have been overthrust towards the north-east but as their roots lie below the Gulf of Genoa, their structures still remain hypothetical. What appears certain is that the extensive outcrops of *scagliosa* clays that cover a long period from the Cretaceous and perhaps even the Jurassic to the Tertiary are allochthonous structures, overthrust and orientated by the north-west to south-east folds to lie over the Oligocene flysch. Many geologists consider the Apuan Alps are an anticlinal window, opened by erosion through the overlying nappes, and envisage the Garfagnana depression to the east to be

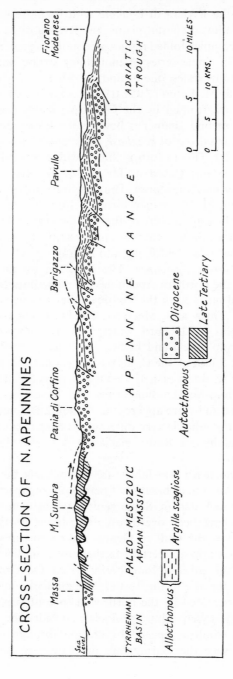

Fig. 155. Geological cross-section of the northern Apennines

caused by a syncline in the nappes. However, the tectonic structure of the Etruscan Apennines is less significant in the relief than the prevalence of soft sediments carved differentially into a veritable museum of erosional landforms, and marked by youthful, linear relief.[35] The marked asymmetry, between the mountain flanks sloping to the Tyrrhenian seas and towards the Po basin, is also striking.

The oldest and most resistant rocks fashion a diverse scenery in the Apuan Alps, a small highland some 40 miles long and 12 miles broad, which overlooks the narrower, coastal plain of Viareggio.

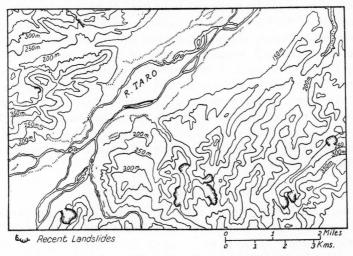

Recent Landslides

0   1   2 Miles
0   1   2   3 Kms.

FIG. 156. Typical clay relief of the northern Apennines, near Salsomaggiore. Note scars of recent landslides

Originally folded north–south, and later uplifted along a north-west to south-east trend, to follow the alignment of M. Gottero, these mountains rise abruptly to over 6,000 ft in rugged, Triassic and other limestones and marbles (M. Pissanino, 6,385 ft). East of the two small Pliocene basins of Castelnuovo and Burgo, laced by the Upper Serchio, in what is termed the Garfagnana, towers the main dorsal of the northern Apennines. Like the Cevennes, these mountains are drenched in rain and in glacial times were the most heavily glaciated section of the Apennines. But unlike the Cevennes, which are mostly crystalline rocks, the Etruscan Apennines are carved out of monotonous spreads of soft sediments. Cretaceous-Eocene clays and marls cover half the area, and even three-quarters in the north-east.[36] Landslides in the unstable *scagliosa* clays are common, notably between the F. Trebbia and F. Sillaro along the northern flanks of the Emilian Apennines. Relief is sharply linear, and so young that erosion has not yet markedly modified the effect of tectonics, notably in the north-west to south-east valley alignments, transverse to the main axes of folding.[37] The central dorsal is associated with the outcrop of anticlinal bosses of Oligocene, micaceous sandstones termed *macigno*, upthrust in the summits of Zuccone, Gottero (5,380 ft), Molinatico and Zatta, flanked by the lower ribbed contours of the more friable sands (*molasse*). Eruptive rocks (*rocce verdi*) associated with ophiolites and serpentines form the three great masses of M. Penna, Maggiorosca (5,840 ft) and Ragde. A variety of more plastic rocks and some local diversity in the prevailing monotony of the broken plateau surfaces. Such are the clayey schists (*galestri*), the calcareous marls (*albarese*) and the occasional banks of serpentine. Although successive cycles of erosion are traceable to stages of uplift, few surfaces are preserved because of the soft sediments. A final feature is the marked asymmetry between the northern and southern slopes of the Apennines. The northern rivers have gentler thalwegs, a marked parallelism of flow guided by tectonic trend lines, and the linear dissection of relief is very marked. To the south, the upper tributaries are very steeply inclined, though the main valleys tend to follow longitudinal corridors.

THE CENTRAL APENNINES

The northern border of the Central Apennines follows approximately between Arezzo and Pesaro, over the Trabaria Pass. South of this, the limestone scenery begins to predominate for some 200 miles as far as the valleys of the Calore and Cervaro. The north-west to south-east trend is marked. Roughly 70 miles wide in the northern and central sectors, the Central Apennines narrow to about 40 miles in the south. Contrasts between the eastern and western flanks of the Apennines now appear more sharply. For nearly 125 miles, the eastern flank terminates abruptly above the coastal hills of Marche in a great fault, forming one of the major tectonic features of the Peninsula, between the Sibilline mountains and the Gran Sasso. Above it, rise abruptly the folded ranges of the Apennines in a series of high mountains roughly parallel with the coast. To the west, the relief is more tabular than folded, with lower ranges that have more uniform plateaus, though again there are significant fault scarps overlooking longitudinal troughs.[38] Highest relief is in the east, especially in the Abruzzi mountains of Corno Grande (9,560 ft) and M. Vettore (8,130 ft). Throughout the Apennines there is the further contrast between the extensive and rugged limestone mountains and the rounded outlines of the clay and sandstone

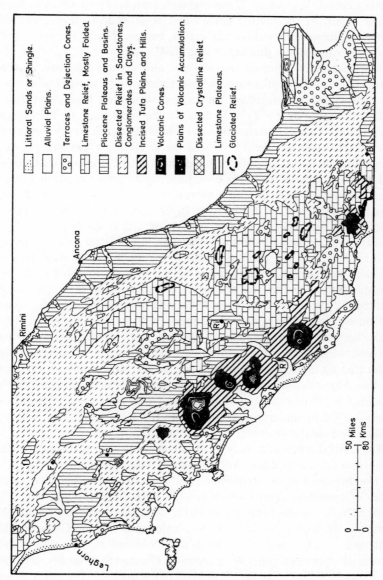

FIG. 157. Landscapes of central Italy. B—Benevento, F—Florence, Ri—Rieti, R—Rome, S—Siena

Legend:
- Littoral Sands or Shingle.
- Alluvial Plains.
- Terraces and Dejection Cones.
- Limestone Relief, Mostly Folded.
- Pliocene Plateaus and Basins.
- Dissected Relief in Sandstones, Conglomerates and Clays.
- Incised Tufa Plains, and Hills.
- Volcanic Cones.
- Plains of Volcanic Accumulation.
- Dissected Crystalline Relief.
- Limestone Plateaus.
- Glaciated Relief.

districts that are commonest in the northern and southern extremities of the Central Apennines. Some eighteen semi-enclosed Pliocene lake basins—many of the faulted graben and polja—add to the variety of scenery in the western and central sectors, and complicate the pattern of markedly longitudinal drainage[39] (Fig. 164).

It appears that whereas the western and central portions of the Apennines are autochthonous, whose resistance to compression has been associated with fracture, the eastern sector has been overthrust, gliding probably over a Triassic base. In the south-east, C. Migliorini has postulated the occurrence of *cunei compositi*, that is to say, resistant blocks overthrust eastward.[40] Where the overlying rocks are plastic, arched anticlinal domes have resulted, such as the central Gran Sasso and Majella. Where the rocks have been rigid, however, parallel fractures, intensified near the point of resistance in the underlying floor, have been important, as in Morrone. In the central Apennines, Demangeot has recognised four major periods of uplift, the Pontian, Mio-Pliocene, Villafranchian and post-Würmian.[41] The latter still continues, as is evidenced in the marked seismicity of much of the zone. In the Majella, Demangeot has recognised evidence of six to seven cycles of erosion, although the widespread Villafranchian level is the most marked.[42] This occurs in a broad belt along the Adriatic coast for some 125 miles, fronted by a belt of 12 miles of Villafranchian glacis. The same surface is represented in the interior basins by lacustrine terraces, which may be correlated with plateau surfaces subsequently dislocated by uplift. Glaciation has eroded the high mountain surfaces of the Abruzzi especially, though its forms have themselves been modified by karstic action which is very widespread. All the major rivers are fed by underground sources, to the accompaniment of polja, dolines and similar features.

The central Apennines may be subdivided into the Roman-Marche, Umbrian, Sabine-Aquilan, Abruzzi and Molise sectors.

1. *The Roman-Marche Apennines.* The Roman Apennines have four series of mountain chains which are 130 miles long, ranging in width from 60 miles in the north to 30 in the centre and south. Limestones comprise the higher portions of the continuations of the Climone and Falterona chains, and the Catria and Sibilline ranges. These are separated from each other by a series of Pliocene lake-basins, the Val di Chiana forming the western boundary of the ranges.[43] The upper Tiber valley links three such basins, with others further east in Gubbio, and Sassoferrato-Camerino. In the west, the lower ranges are of sandstones and marls, but the high central ranges of Nerone, Catria (5,384 ft) and

Pennino are of hard limestones. The final chain to the east is the long, massive wall of Mi Sibillini dropping eastwards in a spectacular fault scarp, and reaching 8,130 ft in the southern peak of M. Vettore. The hilly country to the east, consists of soft, Mio-Pliocene sediments, deeply dissected by the parallel rivers which evolved with the retreating sea-level (Fig. 162).

2. *Umbrian Apennines.* East of the middle Tiber valley lie the Umbrian Apennines, consisting of three parallel blocks of mountains: the Trasi-mene-Narmi ridge, Martano-Torre Maggiore, Catria-Falterona ranges. These are separated from each other by two interconnected depressions, one containing the Todi, Terni and Rieti basins, and the other the Foligno-Spoleto trough.[44] East of Rieti, the massive block of Reatini forms a significant barrier.

3. *Sabine-Aquilan mountains.* Further south, the Sabine, Ernici and Simbruini mountains present a bold, faulted front to the Tiber and Sacco-Liri troughs. These limestone highlands rise to 4,488 feet in the M. Pellechia but many peaks in the south have over 6,500 ft, Mi. Viglio reaching 7,074 ft. Flat-topped summits dip gently into the interior, where the vast Aquila plateau runs for some 70 miles long and 25 wide. A major karst area, it has high *piani* at 3,000–4,000 ft, enclosing further south the Villafranchian basin of Fucino in rocky walls (Fig. 158). To the south and east of the Fucino basin is the wild, mountainous country of Massica, with summits exceeding 6,500 ft. East of it is one of the largest longitudinal depressions of the Apennines, the Aquila corridor which runs for 40 miles and contains the large basins of Aquila and Sulmona.

4. *Abruzzi-Molise.* The Abruzzi Apennines which lie east of the Aquila plateau are the most mountainous block of the Peninsula, massive and compact as well as having the highest elevation (in Corno Grande, 9,560 ft). These mountains comprise a few separate units. To the north is the Mti della Laga, carved out of Tertiary sandstones, and rising in M. Gorzano to 8,054 ft. South of the Vomano gorges is the limestone Gran Sasso, rising from a low platform to a series of peaks each above 8,000 ft, notably M. Intermesole, M. Prena and Corno Grande.[45] Liassic and Cretaceous limestones form the lower slopes, but the rugged upper half of the mountain scenery is carved out of hard, Eocene dolomites, much faulted because of their rigidity, along a west-north-west to east-south-east grain. Evidence of glaciation is seen from the summits to about 8,780 ft. South of the Pescara gorges the Abruzzi are continued by the anticlinal masses of Morrone and Majella, the latter flanked by deep ravines along fault-lines.[46]

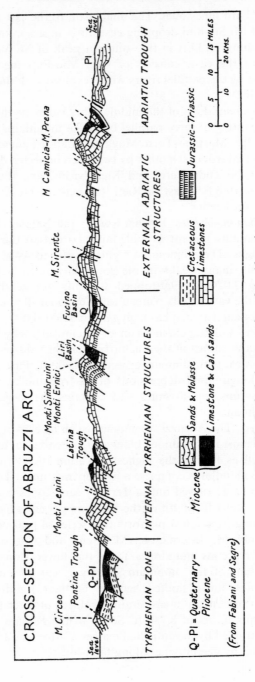

FIG. 158. Geological cross-section of the Abruzzi arc

To the south are the remaining sectors of the central Apennines, the Molise plateau and the massifs of the Meta and Matese. The former is an undulating plateau at 2,000–3,600 ft its sandstones, clays and marls dissected deeply by the eastward flowing consequents. *Calanchi* and *frane* are frequent in the valleys of the Sangro and Biferno, and so the valleys are generally avoided by the main roads. Towards the interior the Mi del Sannio and Mi della Daunia are similar wild hilly country, with landslips widespread. Further west, an erosional flysch depression separates the Sannio from the Matese mountains. The latter is a limestone plateau, a double horst whose central depression is partially occupied by Lake Matese. Marinelli identified erosion surfaces in the Matese but it is more likely these are in part structural levels.[47] Until the position of the Pliocene shoreline has been accurately mapped and the subsequent thalwegs measured, it will not be possible to test accurately the hypothesis of such cyclic relief. Although the western rim of the Matese is lower than that of the east (M. Miletto, 6,726 ft) it is more impressive, rising steeply in white limestone cliffs above the Volturno valley. North of this depression, the Meta massif, also limestone, has a remarkable series of high summits of over 6,500 ft within its small compass.

THE SOUTHERN APENNINES

South of the Benevento Pass with its well-defined route that follows the valleys of the Calore and the Cervaro, the Southern Apennines extend some 120 miles to the Scalone Pass (2,441 ft) in Calabria. They form a broad curve, concave to the Tyrrhenian Sea and approximately 50 miles wide. Lower and less intensely folded than the Central Apennines, they form a mosaic of dissected folds and intermontane basins, fragmented by Pliocene fractures into isolated blocks. In a line drawn roughly between Benevento and Potenza the landforms east of this are carved in Tertiary sands, clays and more recent deposits. But to the west, Cretaceous and Triassic limestones are predominant, the latter forming rugged serrated terrain, carved out of hard dolomites. The stratigraphy of the western portion is very complex and not yet fully understood. Broadly, the zone may be divided into the Campanian and Lucanian Apennines.

1. *Campanian Apennines.* Backing the Campanian plain, the oblong blocks of the Neapolitan or Campanian Apennines are lower and more discontinuous than the mountains further north. Composed of relatively pure Cretaceous limestones, often 3,000 ft thick, they are important for their abundant springs that supply the diverse lowland population

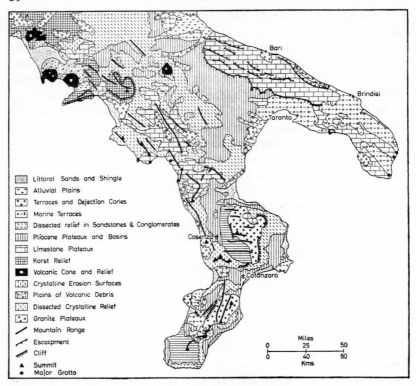

FIG. 159. Landscape types of southern Italy

with water. Some of these massifs have been heavily faulted, such as Taburno and Camposauro in the north. The highest block is Mi Picentini in the south, with a series of summits exceeding 4,000 ft the highest being M. Cervialto (5,930 ft). It is a complex structure of Triassic dolomites and Cretaceous limestones, with well-developed karstic landscapes.[48] It feeds rich springs, some of which supply the source of the Apulian aqueduct at Caposele. Across the depression between Cava dei Tirreni and Nocera, the transverse peninsula of Sorrento has a similar geological structure, a broad plateau ridged by the central, dolomitic dorsal of Mi Lattari, whose axis is continued seawards in the isle of Capri. Isolated by steep cliffs of red Triassic rocks, the southern flank of the peninsula shows clear evidence of marine terraces, but more widespread is the heritage of human effort in terraced vineyards and orange groves, to conserve the thin soils.

As elsewhere in the Apennines, the western calcareous flank is succeeded to the east by the Tertiary sands and clays, folded into rolling relief and dissected deeply by the rivers and *calanchi*.[49] Difficult country to traverse, it is only crossed by the one major and relatively easy route from Benevento along the Cervaro valley. Eocene and Miocene strata, capped by Pliocene clays, comprise a hilly country rarely rising above 2,000 ft but corrugated in gentle folds and valleys.

2. *Lucanian Apennines*. Between the upper courses of the Sele and the Ofanto, runs approximately the border between the Lucanian and the Campanian Apennines. But the landscapes do not alter appreciably (Fig. 157). The rocks and their disposition are similar, though there are more high mountains and the massifs are more fragmented, separated by numerous transverse depressions and valleys. The largest of these is the Vallo di Diano, a Pleistocene lake basin, at about 1,500 ft and 22 miles long, now drained by the F. Tanagro and the upper Agri (Plate 59). Reclamation was commenced in Roman times and has continued intermittently since then. To the west is the massive limestone block of Cilento, built of porous Cretaceous limestones upon a Triassic base, but morphologically little is yet known about it. Cilento has well-developed karstic relief, rising in a number of summits above 4,000 ft (M. Cervati, 6,231 ft). It is continued to the north by the imposing faulted block of M. Alburno that overlooks the Sele plain, a basin of Pleistocene subsidence infilled with Quaternary deposits. To the north of the upper Sele is another broad, tabular limestone block, M. Marzano bordered on the south by two polja, the Alveo del Lago di Palo and the Pantano S. Gregorio.

East of the Vallo di Diano, the Lucanian Apennines have their broadest extent, a tangled highland area of bare, steep-sided limestones such as M. Sierio, Lo Serrone and M. Volturino (6,024 ft) sometimes called collectively the Maddalena mountains. South of the Agri basin, carved out of Eocene flysch, and like the Vallo di Diano a Pleistocene lake-floor, rise steeply the southern highlands. They have the highest summits of the Lucanian Apennines, M. Sirino (6,578 ft) and the Pollino (Serra Dolcedorme, 7,451 ft) forming the watershed between Ionian and Tyrrhenian drainage. The latter also bears traces of glaciation. Confused limestone and dolomite ridges, rocky mountainous masses, high flat basins that are linked by steep, narrow gorges, all contribute to give a desolate, wild landscape.

The eastern Lucanian Apennines are composed largely of Tertiary. laminated clays and sandy marls, which foster *calanchi* (Fig. 206). Ridges of border sandstone are weathered into bizarre shapes, but the general impression is of poor, swelling relief, much of it appearing as

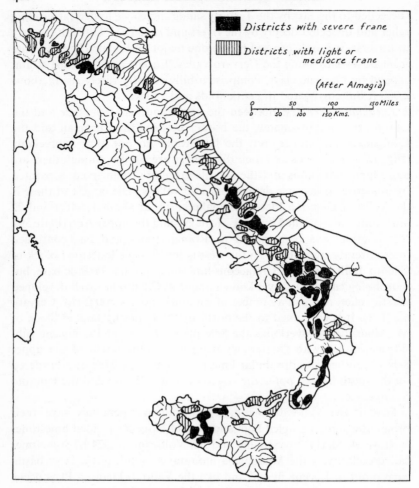

Districts with severe frane

Districts with light or
          mediocre frane

(After Almagià)

FIG. 160. Distribution of *frane* in Italy

dissected, plateau-like country, generally below 3,000 ft.[50] It is bordered
to the east by the broad valley of the Bradano, which occupies the
Plio-Pleistocene trough of the Fossa Bradanica. In the monotony of
these denuded hilly and plateau lands, the Quaternary volcanic cone
of M. Vulture (4,354 ft) is in striking contrast. Tectonically, it occupies
a pivotal position where the Brádano and Ofanto troughs intersect, and
though its crater is now extinct, severe earthquakes still occur (for
example in 1851 and 1930). The outer crater is dissected by streams and
the inner double crater is marked by the two small lakes of Monticchio.

3. *Calabria.* South of the Scalone Pass, the Calabrian mountains form very different structures from the rugged limestone blocks or Tertiary hill country of Lucania and Campania (Fig. 149). Instead, they form a series of impermeable, crystalline massifs of Hercynian age. Their edges bear the marks of intensive stream erosion, but their high central plateaux preserve evidence of peneplains. Between these highlands and more continuously along the east coast, are strips of soft Tertiary sediments carved into basins, plains and dissected hills. As Fig. 159 indicates, there are broadly three types of landscape: ancient massifs, flat-topped and disconnected from the surrounding mountains by steep slopes; surrounding these are Plio-Pleistocene tabular or ridged lands that represent the dissected remains of sand and gravel sheets; and thirdly there are the low-lying Quaternary plains of limited extent, Reference has already been made (see p. 70) to the distinctive type of streams, the *fiumare,* which spread out in wide, braided courses like the north African *wadi* (Fig. 168).

The morphology of Calabria is reasonably well understood, although the stratigraphy is very complex. Quitzow has somewhat dubiously postulated the occurrence of three nappes of Triassic, metamorphic and older crystalline rocks.[51] More relevant, however, in the analysis of the landforms, is the occurrence of a pre-Miocene (pre-Tortonian) erosion surface, magnificently developed on the crystalline massifs, notably in the northern Sila at 2,600–3,600 ft. In Sila only is there evidence of a higher, much older surface. Vertical uplift in post-Miocene times has fractured the blocks into a series of horsts, of which the Catena Costiera of Paola is the clearest example. The relative importance of the pre-Pliocene and Pleistocene movements which have affected the uplift of these mountain blocks is still a challenge to morphological analysis. Gignoux has demonstrated evidence of Pliocene marine terraces on the flanks of Aspromonte, raised to over 3,000 ft above sea-level.[52] But the wide stretches of the Tyrrhenian coast between the Gulf of S. Eufemia and Cilento has no evidence of marine Pliocene, which suggests that here the postulated Tyrrhenides land mass, stretching across to Sardinia and Corsica was only submerged in the Quaternary (Fig. 150).

The disposition of horsts and graben partially fossilised by Pliocene debris and rejuvenated by Pleistocene uplift, explains the disposition of the major landforms.[53] The Catena Costiere of Paola is a narrow chain, stretching forty miles between the Scalone pass (2,441 ft) and the deeply intrenched valley of the F. Savuto. The range rises precipitously from the sea, mostly in smoothly eroded schists, to a remarkably uniform crest line at over 4,250 ft. The eastern slopes are also steep, plunging towards the Crati trough with its highly dissected Pliocene beds, with evidence of discontinuous Plio-Pleistocene surfaces. Below 300 ft, the Crati valley suddenly widens out into the Sibari plain, the largest of the Calabrian lowlands. South of it rises steeply the great crystalline mass of Sila, out of a setting of Tertiary, eroded sediments. The central portion of Sila Grande is a rolling, plateau country, with marked evidence of one or more surfaces of erosion, overlooked by residual summits, the highest of which is Botte Donato (6,332 ft). To the south, the Sila Piccola has been more vigorously attacked by stream erosion, because of the proximity of the Ionian coast. South of the Sila, the Catanzaro trough 19 miles wide, clearly divides Calabria in two, a dissected table-land of Pliocene deposits dipping towards the two coastal plains. South of this depression rises the schistose, broad mass of Serre, with its terraced flanks (notably at 2,000–2,300 ft. on the western side) and rounded summits culminating in M. Pecoraro (4,659) ft. This leads to the Aspromonte, the highest of the crystalline horsts, which rises to 6,418 ft in Monalto. It shows the same features of relief: steep slopes, deeply dissected in Pliocene sediments, terraces which reach up to over 3,300 ft and high plateau surfaces surmounted by slight residual relief. The southern coasts have narrow, discontinuous plains, except for the Mesima-Gioia trough on the west coast.

APULIA AND THE ADRIATIC COAST

The east coast of Italy is markedly longitudinal, stretching some 430 miles from the Murge Salentine in the heel to the Marches in the north-east. It also contains the largest plain in the Peninsula, the Tavoliere, which unites the two distinctive units of the Murge tableland of Apulia and the dissected, rolling hill lands of the Marches. Sometimes termed the Sub-Apennines, the tectonics of this zone comprise two tectonic alignments. From the head of the Gulf of Taranto, along the axis of the Bradano valley is a Pliocene trough, termed the *Fossa Brádanica*.[54] Northwards it forms the western edge of the Tavoliere and continues as the Peri-Apennine trough of the east coast, thus associated with the Po-Adriatic subsidence. The Murge tablelands form a second tectonic unit, subdivided into the Salentine plateau, the Murge proper and the Gargano Peninsula. The Cretaceous-Eocene limestones lying sub-horizontally, have been markedly affected by normal faults, which suggest distension. From the many recent bores made by water concerns and A.G.I.P. there is no evidence that Apulia is a thin secondary cover resting upon an ancient block, as Birot has suggested. The limestones are on the contrary very thick extending over 1,600–3,200 ft. Geo-physical evidence further suggests that the front of the Apennines extends further east under the Plio-Pleistocene deposits of the Brádano trough.

1. *Apulia.* This distinctive region, stretching some 215 miles from Cape S. Maria di Leuca to the F. Fortore, may be subdivided into four areas: the Bradano trough, the Murge, the Tavoliere lowland and the Gargano Peninsula.

The Brádano trough stretches north-westwards for some 70 miles from the Gulf of Taranto to the F. Ofanto, varying from 50 miles wide

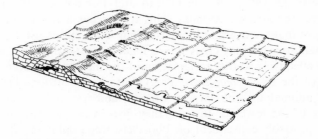

FIG. 161. Schematic block-diagram, typical of the Murge

in the south, to as little as 12 miles in the north. It is defined by a series of faults that follow the Apennine trend, especially in the northern sector where the main axis is maintained by the tributary valley of the F. Basentello.[55] The watershed between Spinazzola and Lavello comprises a dorsal ridge of three horsts, raised above the floor of the trough. The Plio-Pleistocene deposits have been deeply dissected by stream erosion, producing a variety of landforms. In the soft sediments, badlands are developed, notably along the edge of the coastal plains of Metaponto, between S. Bernalda and Ginosa. In the calcareous, organic *tufi* of Matera and Gravina, deep and often dry valleys bite into the edge of the Murge. In the central and northern Brádano trough, the rolling, dissected relief of clays and sands is typical. Along the shore of the Metaponto plain, still in process of reclamation, marine terraces rise in steps towards the edge of the Pliocene tableland (65–100, 160–200 and 330 ft in the east, 50–65, 115 and 230 ft in the west).

The southern part of the Murge or Salentine peninsula is low-lying (659 ft summit). Three types of limestone cover much of this tableland: compact, Cretaceous limestones which form the base of the peninsula and also outcrop in the hilly lands; Miocene, marly limestone, called *pietra leccese*; and Pliocene *tufa*. Unconsolidated, yellow sands and *terra rossa* cover the floors of the depressions. Drainage is markedly absent, since most of it flows underground. North of the Tavoliere di Lecce plain rises the Murge proper, marked by a series of fault-scarps, of varying magnitude, with north-east facing scarps. One of the most impressive is west of the coastal plain between Ostuna and Fasano. The faulted blocks of the Murge average 1,300–1,500 ft but rise to its highest summits north of the Altamura (Torre Disperata, 2,208 ft). Horizontal and deeply fissured, the limestone is favourable for the initiation of a youthful karst, as evidenced by dolines (notably to north of Gravina), dry ravines (*gravine*) and caverns (such as Castellana).

Between the valleys of the Ofanto and Fortore, the plain of the Tavoliere stretches for 60 miles. This trough has a basal structure of limestones that are overlaid by Plaisancian sands and Pleistocene clays. The small streams that cross it are inadequate to dissect it or even drain it effectively so that reclamation of the marshes has been characteristic of the recent *bonificati*. The Ofanto and Fortore valleys both appear anomalous, the largest streams and yet indifferent to the presence of the lowland. Instead, they flow in intrenched, antecedent valleys, probably consequent on Plio-Pleistocene uplift. To the southwest, the Tavoliere rises gently on to the low tableland, a Pliocene outlier, of Cerignola, but further west, the plateau rises more abruptly from some 500 to 1,500 ft in the Mt della Daunia. To the east, the south flank of the Gargano also rises abruptly from the Tavoliere, with a major fault scarp running west–east from S. Severo to the coast, north of Manfredonia. This trough opens easy access through three small basins into the high, Karstic massif of Gargano, flanked impressively by its summits of M. Calvo (3,465 ft) and M. Spigno. Sea cliffs plunge steeply to the east coast, but in the north, the drowned basin of Varano and the lagoon littoral of Lesina have a widening plain.

2. *The Adriatic Coastlands.* North of the F. Fortore, the landforms are youthful in age and simple in structure. For a distance of over 200 miles and some 20 miles in width, the Adriatic shore is bordered by a dissected plain, and crossed by numerous master consequent streams that etch differentially the gently folded Plio-Pleistocene clays and sands[56] (Fig. 162). In a few places, such as M. Canero near Ancona and at San Marino, there are prominent outcrops of limestones. Backing the coast is a well-developed Pliocene surface, generally at 300–400 ft but rising in places above that. As a submerged feature it is also traceable on the continental shelf to the 10 fathom line (Fig. 162). Further west, platforms at the foot of the Apennines occur at about 1,300 ft. In contrast to the low stream density in the high limestone terrain, the Pliocene shows abruptly a

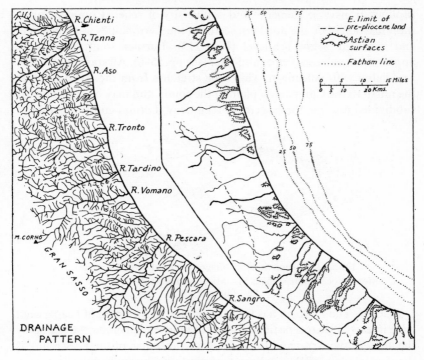

FIG. 162. Drainage evolution of the Sub-Apennines

marked parallelism of the rivers, explained by the relatively small catchment areas, the recent submergence of the coast and the post-glacial erosion of the Pliocene deposits. The valleys are markedly asymmetrical, the folding of the strata possibly throwing the rivers against the steeper sides of the downfolds. Thus the valleys of the Esino, Musone, Potenza, Tronto, Tordino and Pescara all have a ridged southern side, deeply fretted by badlands, and a northern valley slope composed of longitudinal ridges, at right angles to the course of the river. The exposure to storms that prevail from the north-west may also be a partial factor. Significantly, none of the youthful valleys has yet built up a delta along the coast.

THE PRE-APENNINES

The contrasts between the Adriatic and Tyrrhenian coasts are very striking, the latter lacking the simplicity, uniformity and rectilinear features of the former. Instead, the intricate pattern of block mountains and basins, the variety of volcanic landforms and marshy littoral, produce transverse elements and a diversity of relief. Commencing in the Villafranchian, the northern sector of the Tyrrhenides was fractured, and subsided below sea-level (Fig. 213). Further south, subsidence appearsto haveb een deeper and later (see pp. 55–6). All stages have been associated with vulcanism. This zone stretches from the Arno basin in the north to the Campanian plain in the south, and may be conveniently subdivided into the three sectors of Tuscany, Latium and Campania.

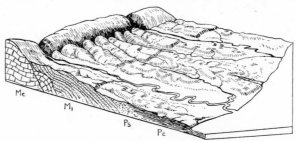

FIG. 163. Schematic block-diagram typical of the Marches
Me—Miocene limestones; M—Miocene marls; Ps—Pliocene sands;
Pc—Pliocene clays

1. *Tuscany*. The R. Arno has linked together, like a string of beads, what were in early Pleistocene times a series of independent units.[58] Built up by the delta of the Arno and the indeterminate course of the F. Serchio, is the coastal plain of Pisa, whose evolution may be studied in the nearby deposits of Versilia. The plain is backed by M. Pisano (2,980 ft) an outlier of the Apuan Alps. Framed by the same massif, the Apennines and the Cerbaie hill terraces is the Lucca basin, which is separated from the Padule di Fucecchio further east by lake terraces. This in turn is backed by M. Albano, a sandstone ridge rising to 2,014 ft which formed the interior barrier to the deep Pliocene gulf now utilised by the lower Arno. Beyond this Plio-Pleistocene shoreline is the Pistoja-Florence basin, the first of a series of Pleistocene lakes that follow the Pre-Tyrrhenian trough between the Apennine and the Pre-Apennine ranges (Fig. 164). In the Pleistocene, the Casentino basin communicated with the Val di Chiana-Trasimene basin, and thence into the Tiber valley. But in historic times the Chiana was diverted by human action into the Arno[59] (Fig. 165). Lake Trasimene, which is the last of these lake relics, has its flood level controlled by an emissarium which was built in the nineteenth century.

South and west of the Arno valley, the confused rolling relief is carved differentially out of Plaisancian clays, capped by Astian sands in the higher areas. The marked parallelism of the Era, Elsa and Pesa

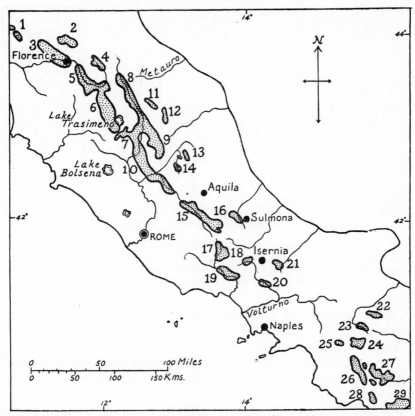

Fig. 164. Quaternary basins of the Italian Peninsula. (After Almagià.) Legend: 1. Garfagnana; 2. Florence; 3. Mugello; 4. Casentino; 5. U. Valdarno; 6. Chiana; 7. Pieve; 8. U. Tiber; 9. Spoleto; 10. Umbria; 11. Gubbio; 12. Gualdo Tadino; 13. Norcia; 14. Rieti; 15. Marsica; 16. Sulmona; 17. Sota; 18. Isernia; 19. Middle Liti; 20. Alife; 21. Boiano; 22. Venosa; 23. Vitalba; 24. Platano; 25. Buccino; 26. Diano; 27. Agri; 28. Noce; 29. Mèrcure

tributaries of the Arno, has resulted from the Pre-Apennine folds which run north-west to south-east. The valleys show much dissection in their youthful headstreams, notably around Volterra. The coastal Maremma is a youthful, ill-drained landscape, much of it added from the sea, only since the Flandrian transgression (Fig. 150). South of the F. Cecina, the Maremma is dominated by the transverse ranges of the Catena Metallifera, chaotic structures of Palaeozoic schists, gneisses and later limestones and sandstones, which have been heavily mineralised.[60] This Hercynian core is linked structurally with the Elba archipelago, now separated by the Piombino strait. The range rises to 3,475 ft in Le

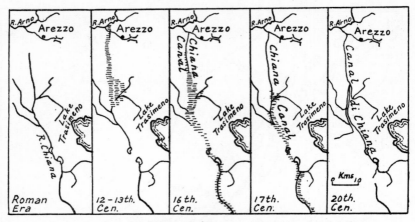

REVERSAL OF DRAINAGE IN CHIANA VALLEY

FIG. 165. Changes of river flow in the Chiana Valley, formerly a tributary of the Tiber that was diverted in Etruscan times into a fertile plain. It became increasingly marshy in subsequent times. Then in the Middle Ages, a canal was cut, and a dam was built across the valley south of the Chiusi lake

Cornate. East of the deeply dissected Elsa trough, rise the Chianti highlands which continue the Apennine trend of M. Albano, along the Plio-Pleistocene shoreline. Composed largely of Tertiary sandstones, they rise to 3,763 ft in Cetona. South of the Ombrone basin, the Tuscan uplands reach their highest elevation in the volcanic region where even the limestone peaks of M. Labro and M. Civitella are dominated by the great trachyte cone of M. Amiata (5,690 ft), rising above a platform of ancient schists and recent basalts.

2. *Latium.* Between the Tiber and M. Civitella, stretches the greatest plateau area of volcanic tuffs in Europe, covering some 2,000 sq. miles.[61] Three longitudinal axes of Pliocene folding occur: one near the present coast; another, along the alignment of the Alban hills, M. Mario (north of Rome) and the medial axis of the Bracciano-Vico-Bolsena craters, a third runs just west of the middle Tiber trough. The vulcanicity commenced in the Villafranchian and ceased in protohistoric times. That of Bracciano and the Alban hills blocked the course of the proto-Tiber, forcing it east and north into its present lower course.[62] For a time, it formed a great lake near Rome, only drained during the Würmian regression when the valley was deeply cut below its present course. Other lake beds further upstream in the Tiber trough have been deeply dissected in detailed relief. West of the Tiber,[63] the volcanic tuff and ash are densely furrowed in shallow but steep-sided valleys, relieved only by

occasional basalt cones and flat-topped relics of more-resistant lavas (Fig. 157). Some fifty-two craters have been identified, five still holding lakes, the largest of which are Bolsena (33·5 sq. miles) and Bracciano (22 sq. miles). The highest parts of the Latium hills, north of Rome, are along the Sabine hills overlooking the Tiber trough, where the crater edge of M. Cimino rises to 3,455 ft.

Along the Tiber, the Roman Campagna runs inland for 33 miles. It is an undulating country of various types of tuffs, exposures of underlying Eocene clays, travertine deposits and alluvium. The Tiber has rapidly built up a delta, which is flecked by a series of fossilised dunes (*tumoleti*).[64] South of Rome, the Alban hills represent a later sequence of vulcanicity (Mindel-Riss) than that to the north and so they stand out more prominently in the relief (see p. 374). To the south-west, the Pontine marshes form a well-defined tectonic trough running for 28 miles along the coast and some 5 miles wide. First formed in the Miocene, it was rejuvenated in the Pliocene by gentle folding, between the limestone anticlines of M. Circeo and M. Ausoni.[65] The basin was finally delimited in the Mindel-Riss interglacial, though its southern coast was later drowned in the Tyrrhenian transgression. The plain has a complex lithology and a sequence of six to seven series of late Quaternary dunes.

3. *Campania.* The Pre-Apennines narrow to the south in Campania, to a belt only ten to twenty miles wide, which show marked evidence of subsidence, so that the coastal plain is discontinuous. Limestones from the northern mountains of Lepini (5,040 ft), Ausoni and Arunci (5,030 ft) were block fractured by the Plio-Pleistocene movements and are separated by transverse, faulted valleys. These blocks, tilted towards the south-west and ridged along a north-west to south-east trend, form massive karstic plateaus. Very different is the volcano of Roccamonfina, which rises steeply to the east of the Garigliano trough. It is thought that it blocked the former course of the upper Volturno, diverting its course from the present valley of the F. Savone. A lake was formed in the middle Volturno valley, which drained eventually through a gorge cut in the low hills south of Alife towards the F. Calore. Between this extension of the Pre-Apennine trough and the sea, are the limestone massifs of M. Massico and Maggiore.

Until the Quaternary, the plain of Campania was below sea-level. Much of it has been built up by the tuffs from submarine eruptions which form now the Phlegrean Field; later alluvial deposits are also present. The plain may be divided into three areas: the lower Volturno basin, the Terra di Lavoro and the Sarno plain. The lower Volturno plain is still in process of being drained, a low-lying area crossed by

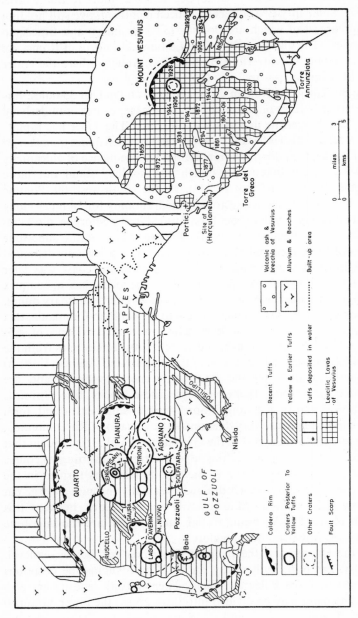

FIG. 166. The landforms of the Phlegrean Fields and Vesuvius

several streams, in addition to the Volturno. The Terra di Lavoro with its thick mantle of tuffs, surrounds the landward flanks of the Phlegrean Fields and Vesuvius, while the Sarno plain is its southern extension, bordered by the Apennine limestone ranges towards the east and south. According to Rittman, two stages of vulcanicity are represented in the Philegrean Fields: an effusive phase, followed by an explosive one.[66] The latter destroyed much of what had been built up by the former, so that the greater part lies below the waters of the Gulf of Naples, although remnants appear in the isles of Procida and Ischia[63] (Fig. 166). The highest crater rim rises to 1,142 ft in Campiglione, but this is dwarfed by the almost perfect cone of Vesuvius to the south-east, which rises steeply to 3,894 ft (see p. 373 and Plate 1).

SICILY

The island of Sicily contains replicas of many of the landform units of the southern Peninsula. The Peloritani mountains repeat the features of Aspromonte, while the Madonie are comparable to the Sub-Apennine calcareous massifs; Etna is a more massive Vesuvius; the plain of Catania is another Tavoliere; and the remainder of the island has the same plastic monotony of Pliocene relief as much of Basilicata. About 40 per cent of Sicily is subject to *frane* and *calanchi*, so significant in the Tertiary sediments of the Peninsula. Unlike Sardinia, Sicily is an appendage of the Peninsula.

The triangular shape of Sicily is explained by the primary east to west axis of the northern mountains, and a secondary transverse axis.[68] The three coasts of the island have been fractured at different stages. The east coast has been affected by fractures since the Cretaceous, cutting deeply into the magma and associated with the volcanics of Etna and earlier eruptions. The north coast, which extends for 175 miles, was fractured in the Plio-Pleistocene subsidence of the Tyrrhenian basin. The south-west coast is relatively young, affected by movements in the early Quaternary when the Tunisian-Sicilian sill was submerged. Geologically, the island may be divided into four major units: the northern mountains, forming the backbone of Sicily; the west; the south central hills; and the distinctive units of the south-east and Etna.

The northern mountains, which run east to west for 100 miles, are diverse in structure and aspect.[69] Overlooking the Straits of Messina, the Palaeozoic granites, gneisses and schists of the Peloritani were violently fractured in klippen faults during the Pliocene and are now deeply cut by short, steep torrent beds or *fiumare* (Fig. 168). Nevertheless, they

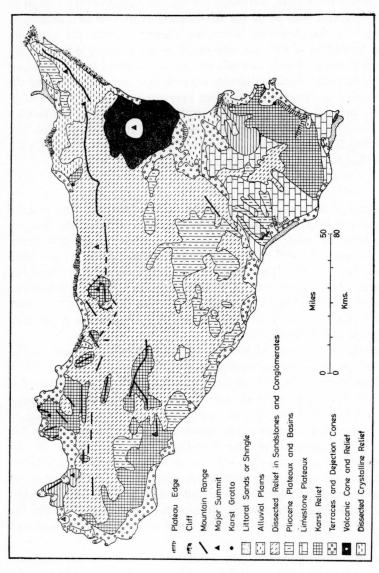

Plateau Edge

Cliff

Mountain Range

Major Summit

Karst Grotto

Littoral Sands or Shingle

Alluvial Plains

Dissected Relief in Sandstones and Conglomerates

Pliocene Plateaux and Basins

Limestone Plateaux

Karst Relief

Terraces and Dejection Cones

Volcanic Cone and Relief

Dissected Crystalline Relief

Miles

Kms.

Fig. 167. Landscape types of Sicily

form a continuous ridge, rising from 3,600 ft to 4,195 ft in Pizzo Poverello. West of these rocks the Nebrodi mountains are very different. Like the northern Apennines, they have been carved out of Eocene-Oligocene flysch, the shales and clays giving rounded profiles subject to landslides. Nevertheless, they rise impressively to over 4,000 ft with the summit of M. Soro reaching 6,060 ft. These mountains fall steeply to the north coast, and the streams have only small catchment basins compared with those on the southern flanks. The third mountain

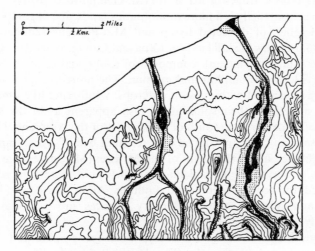

FIG. 168. *Fiumare* in north-east Sicily

group, the Madonie, are also distinct, comprising massive blocks of Triassic and Liassic dolomites, eroded into karstic relief. They have been much less affected by earth movements than the eastern mountains and form the highest relief in the island after Etna (Pizzo Carbonara, 6,993 ft.)

West of the valleys of the F. Torto and Platani, there is considerable diversity of relief (Fig. 167). In the northern sector, Liassic and Jurassic mountains continue the east to west trend, although the ranges are disconnected by numerous small basins, forming the Palermo nappes of Oligocene-Tortonian age, which have had a distinct tectonic style.[70] The mountainous relief is generally above 2,500 ft, bevelled by a Mio-Pliocene erosion cycle. South of Palermo, the highest summits tower above this level (La Pizzota 4,373 ft). Beyond the rocky, north-western peninsulas, the submerged ranges reappear in the Egadi islands. Between the cliffed headlands of the Sicilian coast, in the gulfs of

Palermo, Carini and notably Castellammare, marine terraces of calcareous tufa are well developed; a Tyrrhenian terrace at about 80 ft and Sicilian terraces affected by two cycles of sedimentation at between 100 and 500 ft. The west coast plain from Trapani towards Sciacca is low, rising gently without perceptible terraces to a more dissected low plateau. The interior of western Sicily is a dissected relief of Mio-Pliocene sands and clays, the bolder features standing out as isolated limestone outcrops, such as the precipitous wall of the Rocca Busambra (5,292 ft) and the ridges of Mi Sicani (M. Gennardo, 3,867 ft).

South central Sicily is a more monotonous landscape of gently folded, rounded relief, of dissected flysch and Mio-Pliocene sediments (Fig. 167). As far east as the hill lands of Enna and Caltagirone is the *Altipiano Zolfifero* (Sulphur Plateau), composed of saline and sandy clays, with numerous lenses of sulphur and gypsum. The more abrupt features of relief are associated with gypsum outcrops, weathering like limestones, though sometimes their solubility is also apparent as in the solution hollow of Lake Pergusa, south of Enna. East of the Altipiano Zolfifero, the Plaisancian clays are capped by a resistent bed of Astian sandstone, well developed along the chain of the Mi Erei (M. Contessa, 3,002 ft), where is preserved the planed Pliocene surface of regression, although deformed by gentle folding and faulting. Along the coast, between Licata and Vittoria, the Quaternary terraces are well developed, especially at Gela.

The south-east of Sicily is a distinct palaeogeographic unit, both in tectonic style and stratigraphy (Fig. 167).[71] Before the Pliocene, it was a large island that extended probably to Malta, and only reunited to Sicily after the Calabrian regression. The Pliocene, represented only by marine clays, is tabular and undisturbed in contrast to the rest of Sicily. A complex series of faults is traceable by the basaltic lava flows of Pachino, the Iblei mountains (M. Lauro, 3,232 ft) and of course Etna (10,868 ft). Most of the area between the Gulf of Augusta and the south coast is a bare, karstic tableland of Miocene limestones fretted by canyons of incised meanders (*cave*). The Iblei mountains fall north-wards in a series of steps to the Lentini basin, an annexe of the Plain of Catania. This lowland, the largest in Sicily, is the combined flood plain of the rivers Gornalunga, Dittaino and Simeto, and extends for some 20 miles in length and 8 wide. To the north, Mount Etna towers above its base of clay and sandstone hills; its diameter is about 20 miles.[72] The symmetry of the cone is broken by the deep chasm of the Valle del Bove on its eastern side and by a large number of subsidiary cones on its flanks (see Plate 2).

CHAPTER 15

THE RURAL LANDSCAPES

'This is the secret of Italy . . . Italy is slim and all articulate; her
most characteristic trees are those that are distinct and distinguished,
with lines that suggest the etching-point rather than a brush loaded
with paint. Cypresses shaped like flames, tall pines with the abrupt
flatness of their tops, thin canes in the brake, sharp aloes by the
road-side, and olives with the delicate acuteness of the leaf . . .
these make keen lines of slender vegetation. And they own the
seasons by a gentle confession.'

(Alice Meynell: *Prose and Poetry*, Centenary Volume)

Italy is by no means typical of Mediterranean landscapes. Its relatively
humid climates, its intensive utilisation of land, the high productivity
of its crops, the density of population and the concentration of city life,
are features not found to the same extent anywhere else in the Mediterranean. Yet within Italy there are marked regional contrasts that
suggest Italy is more representative of Europe as a whole, than the
Mediterranean. For the north is continental, the south Mediterranean,
while the influence of altitude explains the varied nuances of
mountain climates and their vegetation cover. Moreover, man has been
so active that physical features alone do not satisfactorily explain the
features of the regional landscapes. Even the fundamental contrast
between the North and the South of the Peninsula has been evaluated
in different ways. In early classical times, it was the South that had the
most humanised landscapes and intensive land use, whereas the North
has been in the lead ever since then. History has been written boldly
on the palimpsest of Italy's countrysides.

ECOLOGICAL CHARACTERISTICS

1. *Climatic Zones.*[1] The climates of Italy comprise a series of sub-
continental and sub-Mediterranean types, usually more humid than
elsewhere in the Mediterranean. Its peninsular character, with a coastline of 3,274 miles or one mile of coast for every 58·7 sq. miles (compare
Spain's 1: 145), its extent through 10° of latitude and its varied relief,
markedly influence the regional climatic features. The two main components, the continental north and the Mediterranean south, are in
strong contrast. But between the insular Mediterranean climate of

Sicily, with its mild winters and single winter maximum of rainfall and the continental north with cold winters and rainy summers, the Peninsula shows a series of transitional regimes. North of Calabria, the winter maximum gradually divides into the two maxima of spring and autumn with a secondary winter minimum. The maritime influence of Tyrrhenian depressions explains the generally heavier rainfall on the west coast than on the east.[2] The Adriatic, more enclosed, shallow and less saline, as well as to the leeward has less influence on the Peninsula. The dominance of the Balkan land mass also explains the more marked continentality of climate in eastern Italy. Relief closely operates with the maritime influence. The Alps are a notable example of orographic control, cutting off the Po valley from the direct influence of Central Europe. The narrower barriers of the Maritime Alps and the Northern Apennines are also effective, while the Carso of Istria has a similar effect. The Central and Southern Apennines which separate the maritime west from the more continental east have their own climate with a rainfall mximum at 2,000–2,600 ft. Relief thus emphasises the continentality of the north and east, and explains the maximum rainfall at an altitude of between 2,000 and 2,600 ft.

Outside of the Alpine zone, which is not included in this work, there are seven broad climatic zones in Italy. These are: the Po, the Eastern, Apennine, Ligurian, Tyrrhenian, Apulian and Calabro-Sicilian. The Po basin has a continental climate with precipitation mostly in spring (in the west) and autumn (in the east); north of the Po, rainfall is less in the winter than in the summer half-year, but towards the Apennines the influence of summer drought becomes appreciable in the floristic associations. Annual isohyets follow the relief, and rainfall is for a Central European agriculture with a modern emphasis on dairying. The Piedmontese zone is more continental, with mean January temperatures 7° to 9°F. lower than in Venetia, while summer temperatures have higher maxima. A sub-type is found around the Lakes, between Como and Maggiore, near which pockets of Mediterranean flora, stranded in the Quaternary hotter and drier phases, now occur in juxtaposition with deciduous plants like beech and chestnut. Here the lakes explain the milder winters, the higher rainfall, and the diurnal changes affected by land and lake breezes. Istria is also distinctive, sometimes grouped with the Alpine zone, because of its winter minimum precipitation, and the control of altitude on the heavy rainfall. But the maritime influence of the Adriatic gives the Istrian coast a reputation as a Riviera climate with mild winters.

The Mediterranean climate of the Peninsula distinguishes it from

62 Large estate and *fattoria*, Torre in Pietro

63 *Trulli* landscape of Valle d'Idria, Martina Franca, Apulia

64 Genoa

65 Naples

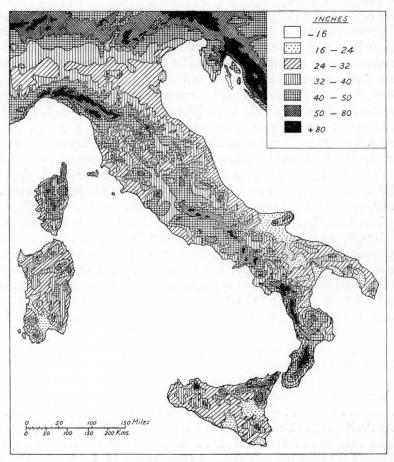

FIG. 169. Distribution of precipitation in Italy

the North Italian Plain. The east coast has relatively uniform climatic and orographic features as far as the Gargano Peninsula which marks a distinct climatic change. North of the Gargano, climatic differences are altitudinal: the mean annual temperature decreases from 57·2° south of Ancona to less than 50° in the mountains; and the rainfall rises from 20–30 in to over 50 in in the interior. Northern Marche is influenced to some extent by the cold, dry *Bora* in winter, developed by Adriatic depressions. Sometimes these bring dry and calm conditions, at others humid, cloudy weather. Rainfall, especially in autumn and winter is associated with the onset of the *scirocco*, blowing when a depression

w.m.w.—15

lies centred over the northern Tyrrhenian sea.[3] Southern Marche and the Abruzzi have colder winters and hotter summers, with weather conditions more dominated by eastern and southern components because of the effective barrier of the Central Apennines. South of the Gargano Peninsula there is a marked change in climate. The Adriatic is deeper and warmer south of the Gargano-Lagosta sill; winter temperatures almost as mild as those of the west coast. This is, however, the hottest part of the Peninsula in summer, and the driest, rainfall reaching the Italian minimum of 7 in in the extreme south-east of Apulia. There is also greater variability of temperature and rainfall; in seventy years Foggia has had a mean monthly range of 36 to 50°F. for the coldest month, and 57 to 77°F. for the hottest month, while annual rainfall has varied from 10 to 34 in.[4]

The Apennines have a mountain climate. Exposure is a significant influence, with most rain falling on the steep Tyrrhenian slopes, exceeding 100 in in the Northern Apennines. The sheltered basins have much lower amounts and tend to be cold in winter, although abnormally hot in summer. Aquila for example, lying at 2,408 ft, has 29 in annually and a July mean of 70·5°F. Above 3,000 ft, snow tends to lie for 10–20 days annually but in the high mountains, even in Calabria, it may lie for three months.

In Liguria where the mountains fall steeply to the Gulf of Genoa in a broad amphitheatre, the tepid waters raise coastal temperatures in January to means of 47–50°F which are only found again south of Naples. The Riviera di Ponente is particularly mild, only occasionally influenced by the irruption of cold *Mistral* air into the Gulf of Lions.[5] But the Riviera de Levante is rather less protected, suffering occasionally from cold jets of Piedmontese air that descends the main valleys. Rainfall is higher towards the east (San Remo, 26, La Spezia, 45 in) because of the configuration of the coast and the paths of depressions.

In the Tyrrhenian climatic type found between Leghorn and the Gulf of Policastro, the irregular physiographic features create climatic individualism especially in the interior basins, such as those of Florence, Perugia, Rieti and Benevento, where the shape and direction of the valleys give varying access to coastal influences.[6] Hilly promontories, notably Sorrento, are markedly humid. The mountains of Corsica deflect the western airstreams towards northern Tuscany, so that it has less rain than the southern part; Sardinia is more distant and less effective as a barrier. South of the Tiber there is a higher proportion of winter rainfall, whereas to the north, autumn and spring have more.

South of the Pollino massif, the climate of the Calabro-Sicilian type

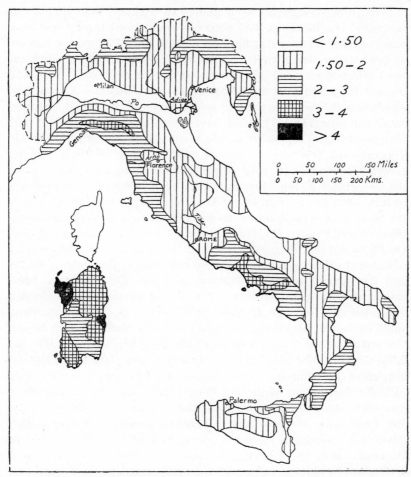

FIG. 170. Annual intensity of rainfall for rain-day in Italy (from Menelli).
Values refer to no. of mm. per rain-day

is more definitely Mediterranean, and less affected by diverse relief features. Even so, the steep rain-drenched slopes of western Sila and Aspromonte (over 100 in) are in marked contrast to the dry east coast.[7] There is a similar contrast between the humid Tyrrhenian slopes of Sicily (Palermo 38 in) and the dry interior, with only 15 in in the extreme south of the island. This aridity is of course accentuated by the high summer temperatures, that reach monthly means of 75–79°F near sea-level. The *scirocco africano*, a blast of hot desert air that descends foehn-like along the north coast, is also characteristic.

Perhaps no country has been studied more closely than Italy for its ecological classifications. Giacobbe has enumerated some twenty-two regional classifications that have been made since 1822 on the basis of altitude, and a further twelve on the basis of plants.[8] Of the latter, the most effective and one of the simplest, is that of Pavari (1916) who divided Italy into four altitudinal zones: the *Lauretum, Castanetum, Fagetum* and *Picetum*, associated respectively with the laurel, chestnut, beech and pine (Fig. 171).[9] Maps have been compiled using the moisture formulae of Lang (1915–20), de Martonne (1926), Emberger (1930–33), Thornthwaite (1948) and Gaussen (1953). Some of these are too complex from which to make simple generalisations, though all assume the importance of humidity. But in the relatively humid environment of Italy, altitude is the fundamental control. Thus Gams (1931), dividing the mean annual precipitation by the altitude, sought to see the altitudinal control.[10] Negri (1934) has also emphasised the same approach.[11] De Philippis (1937)[12] and Giacobbe (1938)[13] emphasise the importance of thermal values as the fundamental reflection of the growing season and the general ecological features of Italy. The *Lauretum* zone, associated with the Eu-Mediterranean flora of evergreens, is subdivided into a hot type found south of Monte Circeo along the west coast and south of the Gargáno in the east, and the milder Mediterranean habitat that covers all the lowlands of Peninsular Italy below 1,600–2,000 and 2,300–2,600 ft. The laurel is certainly a common plant in the coastal districts of the Peninsula, but the limits of the *Lauretum* do not coincide with the distribution of the *ilex* (Fig. 171).[14] This wider transition is dependent upon the distance from the sea, and with differences of 300–700 ft between the western and eastern slopes of the Apennines.[15] Above this, deciduous species dominate to heights of about 6,500 ft. However, while the *Lauretum* is sensitive to winter cold and so is determined by altitude and aspect, the *Castanetum* and the *Fagetum* are controlled more by moisture; they may descend below 1,600 ft wherever abundant rainfall occurs. The Corsican pines—less hydrophytic—can grow below in less favourable circumstances, where the rainfall is under 40 in.[16] The fir (*Picetum*) can endure the least favourable conditions of both drought and winter cold, but its area has been reduced markedly by human action, often replaced by the more aggressive beech.

2. *The Soils.* In contrast to the numerous climatic investigations, of which there are over two hundred dealing with regional studies,[17] pedology has only been pioneered by a few workers, notably Principi. What follows is largely a review of his work.[18] Climatically, three main zonal types may be distinguished: the podsolised soils at the foothills

FIG. 171. Major ecological zones of Italy

of the Alps and the Apennines bordering the Po valley; the brown earth
soils of the Po valley and the higher parts of the Peninsula and islands,
notable the Apennines; and the Mediterranean red earths on the
littorals and the south. Unlike the Iberian Peninsula, however, Italy
has widely varying types; indeed because of the accidented relief and
the active alluviation of the plains most of the soils may be classed as
azonal.[19]

The best soils of Italy are volcanic, but there are widely different
types and not all are good. Italian pedologists usually distinguish between the acid soils derived from rhyolite, trachyte and andesite, and
the alkaline soils weathered from diabase and basalt. Broadly, the

volcanic soils of Tuscany and Latium are from basaltic tuffs, those of Campania are from trachytes, and those of Etna and western Sardinia are basic soils of leucite, diabase and basalt. Thus while the soils of Latium are highly variable in texture within small areas, and the lavas of Etna disintegrate quickly into rich soils rapidly colonised by vegetation, those of Campania are more slowly decomposed and variable in quality. The volcanic relief forms, distance from their eruption, the age of the debris and the influence of drainage, are all factors in the formation of the volcanic soil types. Thus in the Campagna the following variety of types is found.[20] *Cappellacci teneri* is the most widespread in the *Agro Romano*, a granulated tuff with 10–40 per cent clay, suitable for pasture. *Pozzolani* dries out quickly because it is composed chiefly of cinders and with less than 10 per cent clay it becomes almost impossible to cultivate. *Peperino*, on the central slopes, is a gravelly tuff with fragments of rock rich in calcium, forming excellent vineyards around the Alban Hills. Towards Viterbo there is much pumice tuff, while on the gentle slopes distant from the volcanoes of northern Latium, the *terrosi* are clayey tuffs and acid soil. The best soil is derived from *porcino*, in the valleys, where intercalated tuffs, alluvium and much organic material, combine to produce the richest soils of Italy. It is thus impossible to generalise about volcanic soils, especially those of tuff origin.

Alluvial soils rank second best among the Italian soils. They are most widespread in the Po valley where their great diversity is due to varied and changing deposition from the Alpine and Apennine foothills. There is thus a fundamental hydrographic unity of the Alpine and Apennine foothills with the intervening basin. On the high plains to the south of the Po valley, the varied soils reflect a complex fusion of cones and fans. To the north, glaciation has brought more distant influences: calcareous material predominating in western Lombardy, schistose and granitic material towards the east. In central Italy, Quaternary lakes have left a series of clayey soils, cuch as the *pancone* of Florence, and the *cacoro* of the Val di Chiana. Another characteristic is the mingling of calcareous, volcanic and aeolian deposits in rich alluvial soils, such as those of the Pontine marshes and the Volturno plain. In the Tavoliere of Apulia, Quaternary crusts are overlaid by alluvial soils, or ancient alluvium is buried by subsequent coarser soils (*raditi*). In southern Italy, the semi-arid type of erosion encourages a more frequent development of coarse debris, except in plains of marine origin or in former lake floors.

Soils derived from calcareous rocks are common in Italy.[21] They vary from coarse debris, such as the *renaro* of the Apennines resulting from mechanical disintegration, to the fine marly soils of late Cretaceous-Eocene (*scaglia cinerea*) and Eocene-Oligocene limestones (*scaglia rosata*). The coarser types are ideally suited to the olive and the vine where the climate permits, while the finer marly soils are well adapted to cereals. In Apulia, the Pliocene calcareous sands, called *mazzaro* and other names, are often planted with fruit trees. In Central Italy, cemented conglomerates of Neogene-Villafranchian age are common. The most useless skeletal soils are those derived from hard dolomites such as those of the Abruzzi and of the Dolomites. Rendzina soils are common in the Alps, but on the Mediterranean littorals of Liguria, Tuscany and the south *terra rossa*, in the strict sense of the term, is widespread, notably in Apulia, and is ideally suited to interculture of cereals and tree crops.

The commonest soils of the Apennines are those derived from sands and clays of varying Tertiary age. Poor soils generally, they are best wooded, especially as their friable character induces intense erosion (*calanchi*) and their intercalated strata give rise to landslips (*frane* and *lame*) when saturated (Fig. 160). Laminated clays (*argile scagliose*) are particularly common in the Northern and Southern Apennines and also in Sicily. Also widespread in Sicily are Pliocene sands (*tufi*), covering 150,000 ha partly with vines and with cork oak woodland. Other poor soils are those of morainic origin along the northern foothills of the Po Plain. Reflecting the diverse character of their mountain rocks, they also vary appreciably within a small area, from stoney to sandy soils, depending on whether they were formed from frontal or from internal moraines. In such terrain, a sufficiently diverse farm must have soils of different types, and thus farm units tend to be ribbon-shaped or even comprise scattered tracts. Many of these soils of fluvio-glacial origin, are poor, acid and heath covered. *Ferretto* is the common name given to such soils, generally infertile and sometimes dusty if intercalated with loess.

3. *The Vegetation Cover.*[22] In Roman times, the Italian *oecumene* was much more restricted than it is today. The mountains above 1,000–1,300 ft were largely covered in forest. Pliny describes the huge forests mostly under pines that covered nearly all Calabria as far south as Reggio Calabria.[23] Mixed deciduous oaks abounded in the Lucanian Apennines, and between the Volturno basin and Cuma there were many woods of cypress, chestnut and on the higher slopes, firs. The Gran Sasso was almost inaccessible because of the dense forests.[24] In Latium, forests enclosed Bolsena and even vaster forests of corks and oaks covered

much of Tuscany. Liguria was noted for its fine pine forests and great tracts of the Po valley were covered with forests of poplar.[25] Pastoralism was important in Apulia and, to a limited extent, in the Apennines. Extensive tracts of cultivation only occurred in southern Lucania, Sicily and the Sardinian Campidano with specialised viticulture in Campania, and peasant farming in the valleys of Central Italy. It was along the great highways built for their external links, that agriculture spread and new crops were introduced: the *Appia*, with its links at Brindisi with the East; the *Flaminia* in Northern Italy, linking the *Aemilia* and *Aurelia* roads with Western Europe. Today, apart from the mountains, there is little of the original forest cover left. Some patches on the north east slopes of the Gargano, pinewoods near Pisa and Ravenna and secondary ilex and cork oak forests near Monte Circeo, Grosseto, Perugia and Siena are some of the outstanding exceptions.

Woodland and forest today cover one-fifth of the productive area (20·1 per cent) and are situated two-thirds in the mountains (62·4 per cent) and about one-third in the hill lands (31·8 per cent). The best stands of timber are those of Northern Italy (2·5 million ha), then those of Central Italy (1·5 million ha), while those of Southern Italy (1·1 million ha) and the Islands (298,578 ha) are relatively meagre. Unlike the Iberian Peninsula, deciduous species predominate, covering an area of about 4,445,000 ha. Table 11 in Appendix III indicates the relative importance of the chief species.[26]

About ninety per cent of the conifers are located in the Alps, though only the spruce is so restricted. The black pine and the fir are found as far south as the mountains of Sicily. In the Peninsula, however, mixed deciduous species are dominant, with no sharp zonal boundaries between the lower Mediterranean and upper Central European types (Fig. 172). The widespread distribution of beech from the Alps right through the Apennines to the mountains of Sicily is particularly noteworthy, reaching its highest altitude at over 6,000 ft on Etna. Where mature stands occur, a lower tree stratum of mountain ash, lime, aspen, ash, holly, sycamore, hairy oak, etc., is common. Hazel occurs in less dense woods. The sweet chestnut has been extensively induced by man so that its limits are rarely natural. Four species of deciduous oak, pedunculate, sessile, hairy and Turkey oaks, are of varying importance in the peninsula frequently with a fairly dense, shrubby undergrowth. The heavy stands of timber in N.W. Calabria and Sila reflect the marked prcipitation on those mountain slopes (Fig. 172).

The altitudinal limits of the main forest species are shown in Appendix III, table 12. In general, the lower the latitude, the higher is the alti-

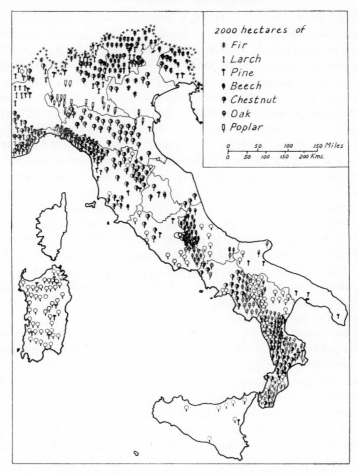

2000 hectares of
* Fir
ı Larch
ı Pine
♦ Beech
♀ Chestnut
♀ Oak
ŋ Poplar

0   50   100   150 Miles
0   50   100   150   200 Kms.

FIG. 172. Distribution of forest types in Italy, 1960

tudinal limit, but the zones also tend to widen with the mass and the altitude of the mountains. The tree-line varies with exposure, usually lower on the northern slopes. There is a difference of 575 ft between longitudes 11° and 17° east of Greenwich. However, the total range of altitudinal difference for the tree-line is only 1,150 ft. This is about half the range found in the Iberian mountains.

Brushwood is a characteristic of the Italian vegetation cover, comprising with coppice 12·5 per cent of the total area, compared with only 8·3 per cent under forest. This is particularly widespread in Central Italy because the forest there has been managed as coppice.[30] Three

W.M.W.—15*

types of brushwood occur: high mountain brushwood, deciduous coppice and the Mediterranean macchia. Alder, juniper, rhododendron and stunted beech comprise the chief species of the high mountain brushwood, restricted chiefly to the high Apennines. In contrast to other Mediterranean countries, *macchia* (only 16·3 per cent of the forested area) and garrigue forms are not very widespread in Italy, except in Sardinia (64 per cent of the island), since the lowland zone where they occur is usually intensely utilised by man. But the deciduous coppice (60 per cent of the forested area) is very characteristic of the Peninsula, and it is frequently an integral feature of individual farm management. Over half the total area under deciduous oaks, half the beech area and some hazel, chestnut and other species are coppiced. Among the numerous factors that favour this feature are private ownership of woodland, the pressure of population in the mountains[31] and the needs of soil conservation. In peasant-owned holdings, the coppice is chiefly chestnut since this, if it is well managed, represents one of the most intensive forms of forest use. Coppice as a source of charcoal fuel, and the forage even of leaves, have also encouraged its development; the rapid regeneration also avoids the worst forms of soil erosion that occur on bared slopes.[32]

Unlike Spain and Portugal, Italy has a predominance of private forests (64 per cent of all timber resources) compared with communal and state-owned forests. In the Alps, wooded areas are mostly communal. In the Northern Apennines, small and fragmented private woods are prevalent, an obstacle to soil conservation. The Central and Southern Apennines have larger woodland properties, but they are menaced by the pressure of population and the consequent tendency to change woodland into coppice and coppice in turn to ploughed land. The modest area of Italian state forests is thus the Achilles' heel of Italian soil conservation, ironical in a country so naturally afflicted by erodable strata. The state plan of 1950–65 is to transform 425,000 ha into forest and improve the quality of 700,000 ha of existing woodland. Vast areas are already being re-afforested in the mountains of the South.

THE RURAL ECONOMY

With 39 per cent classified as mountainous and another 40 per cent as hilly, the Italian terrain does not naturally favour intensive agriculture. Yet the dense rural population has lavished prodigious labour upon the transformation of its countrysides. The peasant toil in the hill lands of Central Italy, the laborious terracing of Liguria, the patient reclamation of the Po valley since the tenth century and the more recent transformation of the hungry, *ferretto* lands of the Alpine foot-hills from Piedmont to Venetia, are all salient features of the Italian landscapes. In 1957, 52·3 per cent of Italy was cultivated chiefly with cereals and tree crops, 19·3 per cent was forest and woodland, 17·1 per cent was pasture land (including forage crops) and 11·3 per cent was unproductive. Of the latter figure, it is estimated that with afforestation and pasture improvements only 7·6 per cent is actually impossible to utilise. Appendix III, table 13, summarises the important features of agricultural land use.[33]

Today, some 16,800,000 inhabitants still depend directly upon agriculture, living on 31 million ha of land, of which only 28·5 million ha are classed as 'productive', although barely 16·5 million ha are really worth cultivating. This intense human pressure on the land heightens the contrasts affected by the socio-historical processes: the pastoralism of the mountains of ancient origin; the extensive *latifundia* associated with the cultivation of cereals and with sheep in the South; the peasant farming of Central Italy with its pictorial motif of inter-culture; and the commercialised farming of North Italy, now focused on cereals, industrial crops and forage. These regional types represent historic legacies which indicate that man more than the land has usually had the last word in the creation of his countryside. Every-where, however, Italy is smothered in wheat lands, almost patho-logically so, for the great macaroni paunches of some Italians, especially in the South, are the sign of well-being.

1. *Pastoralism.* In Peninsular Italy, the lower hill zone has been generally the most productive The mountains have been the domain of forests and pastoralism, while the plains with some exceptions have been generally unproductive for agriculture. As deforestation has pro-gressed in the course of centuries so erosion, the consequent silting until recently, and malaria have sealed off these plains, especially during the summer months. The seasonal use of these lands for raising the animals has therefore been encouraged climatically for feeding on the plains in the winter months, and then ascending into the mountains in summer, from May to September. This has been particularly developed in the Apennines between the Gran Sasso and the mountains of Pollino, accessible because of the longitudinal valleys and yet rising to over 6,000 ft. The winter temperatures of the Gran Sasso average about 41° at 1,600 ft and 32°F. at 4,900 ft. In contrast the Tavoliere has 41–43° in the coldest month. In summer, temperatures which average 64°F at 3,000 ft descend to 48° at 6,500 ft. These favourable features for pastoralism have promoted intercourse between the Southern Apennines

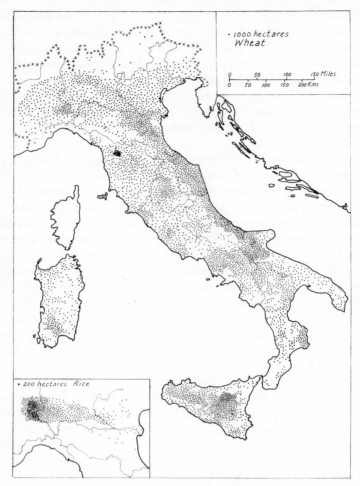

FIG. 173. Distribution of cereals in Italy, 1960–62

and Apulia since Neolithic times,[34] though the organised movement of
stock came later, at the time of the Roman Empire, when much land
of the *Ager Publicus* was taken over by influential citizens to promote
latifundia in the Maremma and the Tavoliere.[35] This was caused by the
Punic Wars, which had accelerated the decay of the South. Emigration
to the Empire created a shortage of peasants to settle the South, so
slave labour and absentee landlords became the rule.[36] This was
resumed by the Normans, especially by their legal privileges granted
in 1155, while the Aragonese, especially Alfonso I, promoted pastoral-

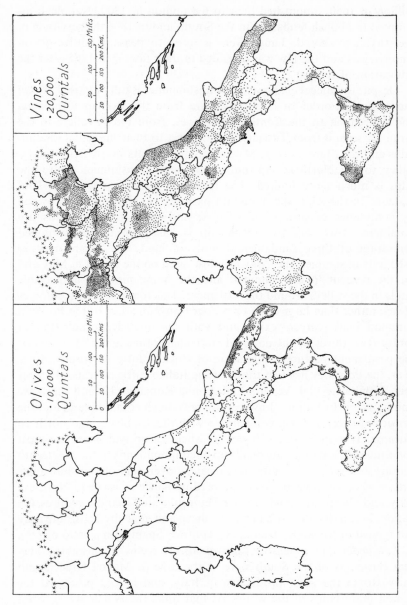

FIG. 174. Distribution of olives and vines in Italy, 1960–62

ism. Transhumant flocks rose from 5·6 million sheep in 1400 to 10 million in 1650, diminished then to 6·8 million in 1800. Napoleon attempted to abolish feudalism in the South, and in 1806 the servitude of the Tavoliere ceased. Lands were granted to peasant cultivators in emphyteusis and the law was extended in their favour in 1865 after the unification of Italy.

Despite these legal changes some transhumance is still practised. These movements in order of importance are from the Roman Campagna and Maremma to the Central Apennines, from the Tavoliere to the Gran Sasso and from Tuscany and Umbria to their immediate mountains and the Marches (Fig. 51). Lesser movements occur from the Po valley to the Northern Apennines, although transhumance into the Alps is much more limited. The reason is bound up with the land systems. In the Alps, the mountain pastures are almost always owned by communes or groups of villages, and here common lands are dominant. This collective ownership is based on the co-ordinated utilisation of three fundamental units of land: the Alpine pasture used only in summer, the 'May meadow' used on the ascent in May and on the descent in late summer, and the home meadow and arable lands in the valleys around the settlement. This forensic system enforces *alpage* rather than large-scale or proper transhumance. In the Po plain common land scarcely exists and with the intensive production of forage (two-thirds of the national cultivated forage and 57 per cent of the permanent pastures), migration of stock is little practised. Moreover, the Po valley has two-thirds of the Italian cattle (Piedmont 15 per cent, Lombardy 19·4, Venetia 12·5, Emilia-Romagna 17) and sheep are unimportant. In Latium, however, there is much common land and the density of sheep is high, comparable with the Tavoliere, and northern Lucania. It is in Sardinia, however, where sheep and goats are most concentrated, although the break-up of common lands in the nineteenth century has reduced greatly the ancient movements of transhumance. The marked contrast between the predominance of cattle in Northern Italy and sheep and goats in the Peninsula and Islands, reduces the national ratio of cattle and horses to sheep and goats by 1:1·2, a feature not typical of Mediterranean lands (contrast Spain with a ratio of 1:5).

2. *Latifundia and Extensive Cultivations.* It seems remarkable today that the lands of the South were at the time of Magna Graecia and early Rome the most productive in Italy, and indeed possessed the richest grain lands of the world. At that time, the North lay in forest and swamp, its Celtic inhabitants engaged in a primitive form of stock-raising. Reference has already been made to the economic decay that

started in the South with the Punic Wars and was later accelerated by other factors.[38] The *villae rusticae*, big agricultural concerns of the factory type and run by slave-labour, were developed by the Romans in Apulia, Calabria, Etruria and Sardinia. But the South became neglected, because the colonisation of the Po valley in the Augustan era was of major political and strategic importance, quite apart from the natural fertility of this region. This contrast set in motion forces that continued to differentiate the North and the South during the Middle Ages and subsequently. The Normans and the Aragonese fostered feudalism in their southern territories to enable them to rule effectively, and it has remained the dominant force in the South for over seven centuries. Fig. 175 reveals the extent of latifundia in Sicily in the nineteenth century. It is a distribution that coincided markedly with the outcrop of Pliocene clays (Fig. 167).

Latifundia in the South has been associated with extensive cereal cultivation and sheep grazing. Compared with the average yields of 20–30 quintals per ha in the Po Plain, yields in the South are still only 10–13. Thus Sicily which has 14 per cent of the total area under wheat, produces only 11 per cent of the total grain crop. A third of Sicily and a quarter of Apulia are under this one crop, although lucerne is a frequent alternative in the rotation. Beans are also an important crop Sicily having about half of the total area. Rotations are variable with a sequence of two to five years generally, though the fallow period varies considerably according to the soil conditions. There is therefore not the rigidity of the Spanish *año y vez*, nor the close relation between cereal cultivation and sheep grazing—except in the Tavoliere. Durum wheat, barley and some oats are the main crops, grown in rotation with pulses (horse beans, lentils and lupins), and alternating with fallow periods. The worst feature of latifundia is the landless class shackled to the large estates. In the high plateaux of Apulia, for example, about 84 per cent of the peasants were landless in 1950.[39] Conditions of poverty are even worse in the clay lands of central Sicily, where yields are scarcely 6 quintals/ha and the intensive summer drought prohibits even the agro-pastoral economy found in Apulian Murge.

3. *Interculture with Tree Crops.* In contrast to the open, cereal landscapes of parts of the South, are the gay countrysides of Central and Northern Italy, crowned with their own fruit and the grapes they support. Trees are a prominent feature of Italian agriculture, growing intermingled with cereals and other crops on almost half the cultivated area (Fig. 177). Specialised tree cultivation occupies only about seven per cent of the total productive surface. It is mostly restricted to the south,

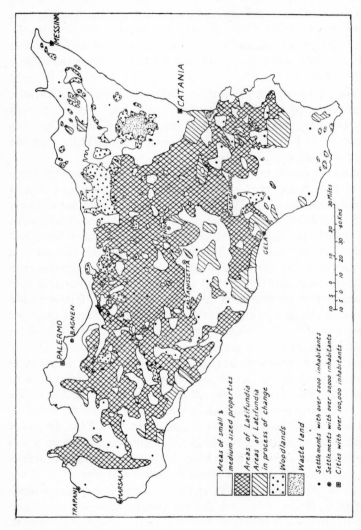

FIG. 175. Latifundia in Sicily in 1929. (From Yolé, *Studio-inchiesta sui latifundia Siciliana.*) Between 1907 and 1927 *latifundia* of over 200 has. fell in number from 1,400 to 1,055 owing to the spread of small-holdings.

notably the olive groves of Apulia (20 per cent of the productive surface) and Liguria (*c.* 8·5 per cent), the citrus gardens of Sicily (*c.* 14 per cent) and Calabria (*c.* 11 per cent). Specialised vineyards are most important in Sicily, Apulia and Piedmont, but 60 per cent of the Italian vines are grown in interculture. Appendix III, table 14, indicates the importance of *coltura promiscua* as interculture is called.[40]

Interculture is the basis of the classical landscape described by the Roman poets. Virgil's Eclogues give a good description of this arcadian scene in Campania, as Herodian gives of Aquileia at the head of the Adriatic.[41] Columella emphasises that the vines and the trees were the farmer's first consideration, the grain an afterthought, designed to use the remaining land.[42] Pliny notes that the vines were generally grown on elms, poplars, or fig-trees, or occasionally on olives; in the North other trees were planted such as the maple, hornbeam, oak, cornel and lime if they were not growing naturally.[43] Columella wrote an important discourse on the virtues of the elm, suitable for the forage of its leaves a good vine supporter and prolific in timber.[44] The poplar is well suited to the damp bottoms of the ill-drained lands, as in Fucino, Ferrara and Lombardy today (Fig. 177). The mulberry has colonised the poor, acid *ferretto* of Lombardy and Venetia. The walnut in Emilia and Campania, the maple in the Central Apennine basins, and the olive in Tuscany and Liguria have a more restricted distribution, in contrast to the ubiquitous maple (Fig. 177). The systems of spacing the trees are very diverse.[45] In Campania, two to four vines are raised 15–25 ft on trees 60–65 ft apart, in hanging canopies above the fields of crops (Fig. 176). In Tuscany, the systems are varied, trees widely spaced in newly drained lands such as the Val di Chiana, closely planted in older lands such as the Val d'Arno. In the Marches and Umbria, the rows of trees called *fulignate,* follow the contours, 25–30 ft apart. Today, the systems of interculture, though now in decline, are still concentrated in Central and North-eastern Italy, with outliers in Campania and in Apulia. They cover 58 per cent of the cultivated lands of Emilia, 44 per cent of Venetia, 40 per cent of Tuscany, 55 per cent of the Marches, 40 per cent of Umbria, 38 per cent of Liguria, 22 per cent of Campania and 18 per cent of Latium.[46] But in some smaller districts more than three-quarters of the total cultivated area is covered in this way.

Desplanques has summarised the reasons for the persistence of this classical landscape.[47] The vine, a wild creeper, is naturally suited to interculture with trees. And as the roots of the vines, the trees and the leguminous crops occupy different soil levels, there is no competition. Interculture is significant in the transitional zone between the Eu-

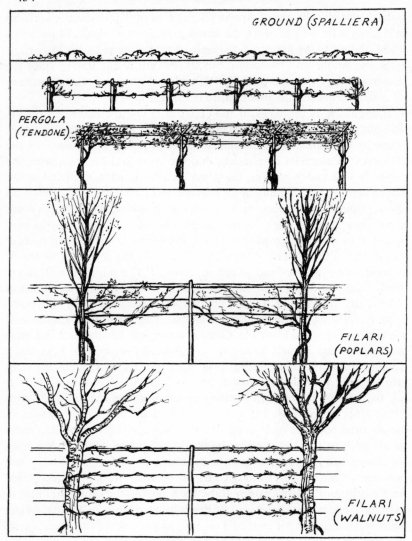

FIG. 176. Types of viticulture in Italy

Mediterranean and Central European climates where summer drought is less marked, but where winter cold is influential. This is especially so in the intermontane basins of Central Italy where inversions of temperature occur in winter, and in the North Italian Plain where winter temperatures are generally low.[48] It is noteworthy that in the Florence basin 84 per cent of the plain is under interculture, whereas

Elm
Maple
Poplar
Mulberry
Ash
Willow
Hazel
Fruit
Olive

FIG. 177. Trees associated with *coltura promiscua* in Italy. (From data of Catastro Rustica, 1929, and after Desplanques)

the surrounding hills have only 58 per cent. It has been estimated that interculture raises the ground temperatures by several degrees in winter, providing a longer growing season and shelter against the excessive heat of summer. Columella long ago recognised that interculture was an excellent protection against soil erosion.[49] But it is only since the end of the eighteenth century that terraced slopes have been vigorously made for the trees in Tuscany. (See Plate 60.)

There are also sound socio-economic reasons for interculture. Soil conservation in the hill lands of the Peninsula is expensive, so while cereals support the peasant family, the wine revenue has been a useful supplement to meet such costs. The landscapes of *coltura promiscua* have been a continuous creation since Roman times, associated especially after the thirteenth and fourteenth centuries with the share-cropping system of *mezzadria*. The plantation of trees, made by the tenant, became a valuable investment to the landowner, at a time when demographic pressure encouraged a more intensive form of land use. The spread of population from the walled towns, after the insecurity of the Middle Ages, was gradual and cautious: first the walled gardens then the suburban expansion and finally venturing out into the country.[50] Transhumance and the use of the stubble after harvest are too extensive forms of providing grazing when the land has to support a dense urbanised population. But the elm, in particular, could provide some of the fodder requirements. Thus interculture, like the cover of coppice, have been expressions of demographic pressure on the land. It is sad to think that farm mechanisation, crop specialisation, the decline of *mezzadria* and the spread of tree diseases, are now all contributing to the steady diminution of this type of landscape, which is characteristically Italian.

4. *Commercial Farming and Industrial Crops.* If *latifundia* are a feature of the South and peasant interculture of the Centre, commercial farming has characterised the Po valley, at least since the eighteenth century. But the roots of this prosperous agriculture may be traced right back to the Augustan era, when some seventy-eight Roman towns flourished in the Po plain. Along the Emilian Way, the centuriated colonisation was achieved by Latin peasants and soldiers (see Fig. 46). Polybius describes in a famous passage the agricultural wealth of the Po valley,[51] while Strabo corroborates this description and makes special reference to the swineherds that fattened in the oak forests, and to the vineyards of the Alpine foothills, producing around Verona the well-known Rhaetic wines.[52] Flax was already an important crop, and locally manufactured into linen cloth. Woollen goods too were important.

The land use organised by a city economy was intensified during the Middle Ages. From the thirteenth century, efforts to abolish feudal ties were vigorous and successful, and it was at that time that the free communes of Lombardy began the large-scale irrigation works that were to transform the lands on the left bank of the Po. Then in the eighteenth century, the enlightened rule of Maria Theresa and Joseph II, enabled Lombardy to push ahead rapidly. A rural *bourgeoisie* successfully integrated agriculture with industry. On the acid, hungry soils of the Alpine foothills, the poor heath lands were converted into mulberry plantations and a flourishing silkworm industry was created, that still supports many peasants. Silk spinning laid the foundations of the modern textile industries, later helping to develop woollen and cotton manufactures, and a dense population of 1,000–1,500 per sq. mile has thus arisen (Fig. 181). This concentrated population stimulated first commercial stock-raising during the eighteenth century, still the basis of the economy of the western regions. Then after the mid-nineteenth century, rice cultivation in Piedmont developed,[53] and later still industrial cropping began on the newly reclaimed lands of the Delta.

Today, three-quarters of the Italian rice crop, three-fifths of the maize, two-thirds of the hemp, three-quarters of the sugar-beet and one-fifth of the tobacco, are produced in the North Italian Plain.[54] Of the 8·2 million people of Italy engaged in agriculture, 2·8 million work on the Plain. Natural conditions have not always been favourable. Centuries of labour have flattened out the sand dune cordons, reclaimed the swamps, utilised the springs, built the irrigation canals, and controlled the rivers. Thus the marked contrasts in the rural landscapes between the west and east betray largely human, not physical differences. The land to the west, reclaimed and developed long ago, bears the imprint of some ten centuries of peasant labour (Fig. 57), while the eastern landscapes betray their youthfulness in numerous ways: concentration of large estates, absence of ancient centres, marked emphasis on industrial cropping, etc. Piedmont, pulverised in peasant holdings, has several distinct economies on the Plain: the permanent meadow—wheat—maize to the west, where abundant water provides much irrigation; the western Po region where 140,000 ha of rice cultivation have spread rapidly since the construction of the Cavour Canal (1866) and the hills of Monferrato, Langhe and Voghera which have been devoted for centuries to vineyards. In Lombardy the vast resources of irrigated land (600,000 ha) are reflected in the great spread of meadows, and the cylindrical silos that dot the landscape. The lands to the south of the Po, in Emilia-Romagna, without water resources that are comparable to those from the Alps, nevertheless support a prosperous peasantry because of the natural fertility of the soils. Large estates intermingle with peasant holdings to produce a variety of cash crops, notably tomatoes, tobacco, hemp and sugar-beet, as well as the usual cereals. In the new lands of the Po Delta, which cover approximately 200,000 ha from the Adige eastwards, in the Polesine and the Ferrarese, holdings are large and capitalised, an open landscape covered with such crops as sugar-beet, hemp, wheat and maize. This area has no legacy of tree cultivation and lacks the intensive animal husbandry of the more urbanised parts of the Plain. Eastwards to Friuli, the Venetian plain is a mosaic of old cereal lands, interrupted by the newly reclaimed lands between the valleys of the Piave and Tagliamento where more intensive farming is gradually being introduced.[55] Altogether about one million hectares are still in process of being reclaimed around the head of the Adriatic. It would be false to suggest, however, that commercial cropping is only concentrated in the Po valley. Ligurian flower cultivation that commenced in the Riviera di Ponente in the mid-nineteenth century (3,900 ha in 1957), the Campanian hemp industry, the tobacco growing of southern Apulia, and Sicilian cotton production are all important, while reference has already been made to the specialised fruit production of the South, especially along the coasts of Apulia, Calabria and Sicily.

5. *Land Improvement*. The reclamation of waste land in Italy is often associated with the political propaganda of Mussolini. But ever since the prehistoric *terramare* settlements of the Po Plain were built above the retreating waters of the north Adriatic gulf, some reclamation has been in progress. Land improvements have, therefore, a long tradition in Italy. The two main developments have been irrigation and land drainage, mostly in the Po valley.

Apart from the Augustan colonisation of the Po valley, land improvement commenced in the eleventh century in Lombardy. This was developed rapidly in the sixteenth century and speeded up again in the eighteenth and nineteenth centuries.[56] Table 15 in Appendix III summarises the main achievements of canal construction.

In this development, first simple canals were built to lead off from the main rivers, and then in the nineteenth century, major schemes were created to water the Upper Plain and cross the rivers, notably the Cavour in Piedmont and the Villoresi in Lombardy. In this progress, the Communes of Lombardy had created some 400,000 ha of irrigated land between 1200 and 1500, while the Piedmontese had transformed some 170,000 ha between 1500 and 1700. Another 300,000 ha have been added since the early nineteenth century in both provinces.[57] Today, in the area between the Po, Dora Baltea and the Oglio, there is almost half (985,000 ha) of the total irrigated area of Italy representing 33 and 28 per cent of the agricultural lands of Lombardy and Piedmont respectively (Fig. 57). Since the latter part of the nineteenth century, 180,000 ha have been irrigated in the eastern Po Plain. In contrast, the irrigated area of the Peninsula is very meagre, estimated at 21,000 ha in Central Italy, 136,000 ha in the South, and 43,000 ha in the islands.[58]

Since the unification of Italy, a second major improvement has been the reclamation of marshland. In the period 1861–1915 attention was almost entirely concentrated on the Po Plain where 330,000 ha were drained compared with only 2,000 ha in the South.[59] Indeed, the first drainage law of 1865 was essentially a Piedmontese measure and the first national law of 1882 was focused on the Po Delta. While, however, the northern marshes were a straightforward problem of drainage, those of the Peninsula were complicated by the general under-development and scourge of malaria; between 1887 and 1920 over two million suffered from malaria, and even in 1928–32, there were some 3,000 victims annually who died from the disease. The Act of 1928 prepared the way for the ambitious Fascist *bonifica* schemes of the Peninsula, notably the Pontine Marshes (75,000 ha), the Maccarese and other parts of the Roman Campagna (200,000 ha), the Sele Plain (41,200 ha) and the Tirso scheme (126,500 ha) in Sardinia, as well as the lower Piave scheme in Venetia.[60] Schemes for some of these areas had been tried abortively in the nineteenth century and few were completed before 1939 (Figs. 58 and 59). But it is to the Fascists' credit that much was achieved in the inter-war period, though the scheme scarcely benefited the peasants. Many of these pre-war *bonifica* have large estates and capitalised farming.

The socio-economic problems of the landless peasant and of latifundia have only been seriously tackled since the various laws of land reform since 1950 (Fig. 60). Already by 1953 8·1 million ha of land had been placed under the jurisdiction of the various reform agencies financed by the *Cassa per il Mezzogiorno*.[61] It is hoped that by 1965 some 130,000–140,000 peasant families will be assigned holdings, with about 360,000 ha under irrigation and over 500,000 ha in tree crops. Already, these *bonifica* landscapes, dotted with closely scattered farmhouses, and with their networks of new roads, canals and their more intensive utilisation of land, are being created out of the wastes of southern Italy and of the Maremma. Such are the plains of the Tavoliere, Metaponto, Crotone, Sele, eastern Sicily, the eastern Campidano, Fucino and Grosseto. Together with the schemes of mountain improvements, these tasks are enormous. In Central Italy alone, 70 per cent of the area of the lowlands needs land improvements, while in the whole of the Italian mountains, 67 per cent of the total area requires some control and improvement.

AGRARIAN STRUCTURES[62]

Size of Holdings.[63] It is foolish to suppose that Southern Italy is dominated by large estates, whereas the Centre and North have smallholdings. There are three fundamental types of rural enterprise, and these are widely distributed: the family farm, which may be either owner- or tenant-operated; the farm run on the *mezzadria* system; and the capitalist holdings of various types. All three systems are more widely practised than is sometimes realised. But before Italian statistics of land holdings are quoted, it is necessary to bear two points in mind: Italian figures refer to 'operating units', not farms; and the system of tenure may or may not exercise a notable influence on the regional type of agriculture. Because of the latter point, Merlini distinguished as many as forty agricultural regions in Italy on the basis of both land use and holdings.[63]

Over half of the total holdings of Italy have less than half a hectare,[64]

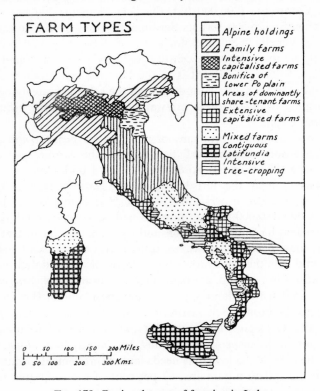

FARM TYPES

Alpine holdings

Family farms

Intensive capitalised farms

Bonifica of Lower Po plain

Areas of dominantly share-tenant farms

Extensive capitalised farms

Mixed farms

Contiguous latifundia

Intensive tree-cropping

FIG. 178. Regional types of farming in Italy

but this does not mean that over half the holders of land cannot feed themselves and families on such diminutive plots. It only indicates the extent of land fragmentation. In the agricultural lands within the Alps, both owner and tenant small-holdings are common. The latter has an ancient origin in the hill lands of Verona, Vicenza and Friuli. In the Piedmontese hills, excessively fragmented holdings are chiefly owner-occupied. This system spreads through the Monferrato, where also population pressure over several centuries has gradually aided the break-up of estates. The same feature is even more exaggerated in Liguria, where the intensive land use and terracing explain why 64 per cent of the holdings have less than five hectares each. Subdivision is characteristic of the poor mountain lands, notably the Northern and Central Apennines (89 per cent under 5 ha) where the use of scattered patches of arable, wood and pasture is important. In the South, where-ever light, productive soils have been converted especially for tree crops, notably along the coasts of Apulia, western Calabria, northern and eastern Sicily, small peasant holdings prevail. Small owner-occupied farms characterise the Campanian plain. In Sardinia, excessive frag-mentation has resulted from the partition of common lands, consequent on the Enclosure Act of 1820 and the Royal Edict of 1839.

The problem of Southern Italy has been popularly connected in the last decade with the extent of large estates. The problem, however, has not merely been the existence of large properties so much as their social and political concentration, tied up with a feudal regime that has ruled the peasantry as serfs until modern times. In 1700 a survey showed that of the 2,000 communes in the Peninsular South, 1,616 were still feudal dependencies, 346 were baronial estates and 38 were the property of the king; in Sicily, of 367 communes 282 were feudal and 85 baronial. Even in 1786 another survey indicated that four-fifths of the population were tied to some form of feudal servitude.[64] The lands immediately ad-jacent to the villages often enjoyed, however, emphyteutic tenures or long contracts, the rent being the equivalent of the value of the annual sowing (*terratica*). There were rights over common grazing and even to making temporary clearings in the woodland. The majority of church lands were conceded in perpetual usufruct on condition their yields were not increased, a favourable factor for the development of tree cropping. But lands owned by the communes themselves were very limited. In the Kingdom of Naples, the *universita*, in part cultivated privately by the peasantry, and the remainder owned communally, represented less than one-twelfth of the total area.[65] The Napoleonic laws of 1806 and 1809 in the South, and of 1812 in Sicily, merely changed the title of the baron to that of landowner. Thus the presence of latifundia and absentee landlordism, have been the main stumbling block to economic progress in the South, although peasant holdings and share-tenancies are numerous, especially wherever tree culture has been the instrument of land reclamations, in areas of light soils. It is indeed wrong to blame history for all the ills of the South. As the latifundia map of Sicily clearly demonstrates (compare Figs. 175 and

167), large estates have persisted wherever the intractable heavy clays (especially Pliocene clays) occur, for these soils are hostile to tree cropping. Irrespective of the past legacies, wherever the lighter soils are capable of growing vines, olives, figs or other fruits, peasant holdings have developed at least since the nineteenth century, if not before.

Why then, it may be asked, have large estates not created economic stagnation in Central Italy, where peasant operators have only 20 per cent of the private lands? Here, however, the estates were managed largely under the contract system of *mezzadria*, which prevails on 49·5 per cent of the area.[66] Most of these tenant holdings occur alongside *podere*, farms somewhat similar to the Catalan *masías* that were built often with impressive buildings during the eighteenth century. Sometimes as many as twenty to fifty farms are organised into a *fattoria*, cultivated by different share-tenants but co-ordinated by the proprietor of them all (see Plate 62). *Mezzadria* is dominant in the Marches, Umbria, the Abruzzi and Tuscany. It is significant also on the oldest colonised lands of Emilia, and in the hills of Piedmont and west Venetia, associated in the latter with the break-up of old estates during the nineteenth century. In Central Italy especially, the system has been a relic of large ecclesiastical estates that have passed into private hands. Traditionally, the dispersion of settlement and the cultivation of tree crops have been associated with this form of tenure. This dispersion of small units under share-tenancy has been idealised in the public image of Italian rural life, so that the same pattern of dispersion has been copied without question as the model for the land reform agencies in the South (see Plate 31).

There are, however, areas of Central Italy where large estates have had similar problems to the latifundia of the South. These have been notably in the Maremma and the northern part of the Roman Campagna. Infertile, tuff soils, irregular drainage, malaria and historical influences have all played their role. Since the devastation of Etruria by the Romans and the creation of the public lands, *Ager Publicus*, in the third century B.C., with a long tradition of agro-pastoralism and seasonal transhumance, this region has been neglected, except in fertile basins and some plains such as Vada. The regular layout of roads and fields in some basins, such as Fallonica, indicate recent reclamation while the small *bonifica* schemes around Grosseto, Orbetello and Volterra are more recent. This region is still, in its economic retardation, part of the South.[67]

In the Po Plain, a different system is found, the capitalised farm, operated with wage-labour, a feature not generally found in the Mediterranean. This system dominates over a million hectares of irrigated lands, forming a quadrilateral marked to the east, west and south by the rivers Mincio, Dora Baltea and Po, and to the north by the line of springs that runs from Turin to Milan and Peschiera (Fig. 178). These relatively level lands, suited to mechanised agriculture, have well-watered pastures to give an intensive livestock economy. In the west, rice cultivation is important. Here are the great barrack-like farms, the *cascina* or *corte* (Fig. 187), where the numerous workers were housed. Very different are the large farms of the eastern Plain, where labour is two-thirds casual, without the solid *cascina*, and where emphasis is on industrial cropping.

In the post-war social struggles of Italy, great prominence has been given to the question of land tenure. This may have been the most urgent and active political problem but it has not been the most important. For small and medium holdings occupy over half of the arable area (56·7 per cent). What will become a greater problem is that greater outlay of effort in utilisation is required in these generally poorer lands than in the rich, highly capitalised farms of the Po Plain. In the 1960s the agrarian scene is in transition once more, because of the effects of rural depopulation in the areas of *mezzadria*, the fiasco of some land reform schemes in Pliocene clay lands, notably in central Sicily, and the consequence of social changes that now disfavour rural dispersion, even in the new schemes less than a decade old!

CHAPTER 16

THE POPULATION AND SETTLEMENTS OF ITALY

'In the earliest time the *landscape-figure alone* dominates man's eyes. . . . The village with its quiet hillocky roofs, its evening smoke, its wells, its hedges and its beasts, lies completely fused and embedded in the landscape. The country town *confirms* the country is an intensification of the picture of the country. It is the late city that first defies the land, contradicts Nature in the lines of its silhouette, denies all Nature.'   (O. Spengler, *The Decline of the West*)

Few areas of the world have been as humanised as Italy, and this has been accomplished largely by an urban mode of life.[1] Indeed, no other country can boast of such a magnificent civic heritage that goes back over more than two and a half millenia. In its peninsula, the chaplet of small, coastal plains, separated by steep-sided mountains and promontories, but laced together by sea trade, explain the origin and the distribution of many of its towns. Italy, like other Mediterranean peninsulas, has found it difficult to establish cultural and political unity; perhaps even more so, because of its mountainous backbone, its central position between the East and the West, and the attraction of its Northern Plain for outside interference. In early times, the mountains of the Peninsula were covered with inaccessible forest, so that the earliest cultures reflect links between the coastal plains. Later, as the stock-raisers conquered the mountains for pasture, economic and social contrasts arose between the herdsmen (*pastores*) and the cultivators (*coloni*). The periodic raids of the mountain folk into the plains led to the establishment of the League of the Latin 'peoples' (sixth to fourth centuries B.C.) on the Latium Plain from which Rome and its subsequent civilisation first arose. The central position of Italy in the Mediterranean helps to explain such centrifugal forces as the dominance of Greeks in the southern peninsula, the rise of Rome as a sea power, the Byzantine influence in the south and east of Italy, and the subsequent international character of its medieval history. Until unification in 1870 the Italian South had been under foreign domination for over seven centuries.[2] Social and regional differences still remain so strong that local patriotism is very marked; the patria of the modern Italian is still his town.

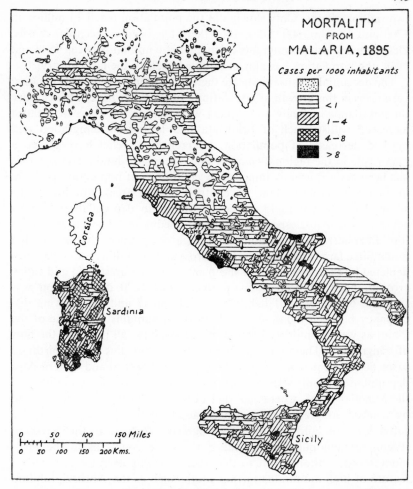

FIG. 179. Incidence of malaria in Italy, 1895 (after Fritche). Blank areas in Italy were free of malaria

POPULATION: ITS CHANGES AND DISTRIBUTION

1. *Population Trends and Changes.* The dynamic power of Italy lies in its population.[3] With one of the greatest population pressures in Europe it had 50·5 million in 1961.[4] At the beginning of the Christian era it is estimated that Italy had about 7 million, rising to 10 or 11 million by the fourteenth century, when the first use of parish registers provided a more precise source of statistics. In 1600 the population had risen to 13 million, but two terrible epidemics (in 1630 and 1657) caused about

two million deaths. Only slowly did the population reach 14 million in 1700 and 18·3 in 1800. Since 1861 there has been a decennial census. Despite a net loss of emigrants calculated at 6 million between 1848 and 1948, the population has almost doubled itself in the last century.

The decennial censuses indicate there have been considerable regional variations in this growth of population.[5] In the latter part of the century the coastlands of Sicily and Apulia were among the areas of greatest increase,[6] whilst much of Basilicata had large-scale emigration and marked decreases of population. Differences of relief have played a major role in the regional changes since then.[7] Mountain depopulation has been severe; usually impelled by conditions of population pressure in an inhospitable habitat. In contrast coastal areas, notably in the south, have shown rapid increases. Mountain depopulation is most acute in the Alps, especially those of Piedmont.[8] The absence of a foothill zone, with an economy that might supplement that of the high mountains, large areas of barren schistose and crystalline rocks, pastures depleted by excessive flocks of sheep and goats, deforestation and valley erosion, have all been unfavourable. Until 1870 depopulation was sporadic but since 1901 it has been widespread and the growing discrepancy between living standards in the mountains and those of the Plain, as well as improved communications, have all hastened the flow of emigration.[9] There has also been a marked decline in the birthrate (over 50 per cent from 1881 to 1936).[10] In the central and eastern Alps depopulation is only serious in the limestone areas of the Dolomites and the Venetian Alps, where the high birth-rates have been accompanied by marked emigration. It has been accelerated recently by excessive subdivision of land and by other agrarian factors. In the Northern Apennines depopulation has taken the same course as in the Piedmontese Alps, though not to the same alarming extent.[11] It is also a feature of high mountains further south, such as the Abruzzi, Sibillini and Pollino, where life is very hard.

Commensurate with this change there has also been the rapid increase of population in some of the lowland areas. Agricultural labour has increased markedly in new settlement districts or irrigation schemes, notably since the Fascist *bonifica* commenced[12]; and this has been accentuated by government policy since 1950. In the plains of Catania, Metaponto[13] and in scattered areas of the Maremma[14], there is now marked increase of new homesteads. All the Adriatic[15] and Tyrrhenian valleys and the Ligurian coast, show a tendency towards growth.[16] Tourism is adding to this development, especially on the coasts of Liguria[17], of northern Tuscany and parts of the Adriatic. Some interior

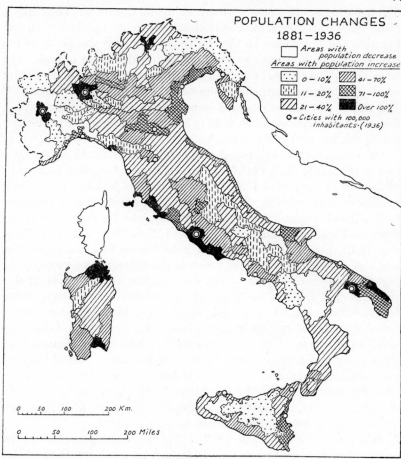

FIG. 180. Population changes in Italy, 1881–1936 (from Guisti)

lowland areas, however, have experienced some rural depopulation, notably areas of share-tenancy in the Veneto[18] and Central Italy. Despite higher standards and a more secure employment than in the South, these areas are now experiencing an exodus from the land. As general standards of education and personal initiative are raised, share-tenancy becomes increasingly unpopular.

Rural migration, however, is much greater in Italy than statistics indicate. This is so quantitatively because communes, especially in the South, are large and movement within the commune is concealed. It is also true qualitatively, since the statistics do not indicate that it is often the best who leave first. Since 1945 large-scale and accelerating migration from the South to the northern industrial centres has been taking place. Some are specialised movements, such as Calabrians to the Ligurian coast, Sicilians to Central Italy, Sardinian shepherds to the Apennines and Venetians to the Lombard-Piedmontese triangle. The large cities, especially Turin and Milan, are acting as depots from which southerners eventually emigrate to other European countries.[19] The effects of these movements is notable in the agricultural labour force[20], which has dropped from 49 to 27 per cent of the active population during the last twenty-five years.[21]

The worst effects of overpopulation in Italy were staved off by emigration in the period 1860–1925.[22] The annual exodus rose from an average of 269,000 in the period 1887–1900, to a peak of 872,598 in 1913 (net outflow of over 580,000). At first, emigration was directed particularly to Brazil and Argentina from the North, but later the main exodus was from the South, especially Sicily, to the U.S.A. Since the First World War restrictions have been imposed, reducing the flow and redirecting much of it to Western Europe, which in the aggregate has received the highest number of migrants. The demographic consequences of this emigration, in terms of age structure and natural increase, have varied widely.[23] Piedmont, with excessive depopulation, has a reproduction rate below the national average because of an ageing population. Lombardy and Tuscany have a high natural increase as well as the advantages of marked industrial development. Venetia and much of central Italy are intermediate in character between the low and high natural increases of the North and South. In the latter, despite heavy emigration and wretched poverty, natural increases are still very high. Mortality rates are remarkably low, although infant mortality is high.

2. *Distribution of Population.*[24] Relief is the major cause of the irregular distribution of population in Italy. Vast areas of the mountains have less than 64 per sq. mile. The climatic zones[25] and steep relief limit agricultural possibilities so that there is a steady decrease of density of population with altitude as table 4 in Appendix IV shows.[26] In the Alps there are 467,000 between 1,640 and 2,590 ft and 55,000 at over 2,590 ft. In the Apennines the comparable figures are 651,000 and 74,000. Increased densities occur in the main Alpine valleys which are comparatively low and have important nodal centres boosting densities to 260–520. The intermentone valleys of the Northern Apennines (Garfagnana, Mugello, Casentino and the upper Valdarno) have similar densities. In the Central Apennines troughs such as Sulmona and Fucino are also examples (Fig. 181). But in the high Alps, the Gran Sasso, Pollino and parts of Sicily densities are less than 64. In the Alpine foothills,

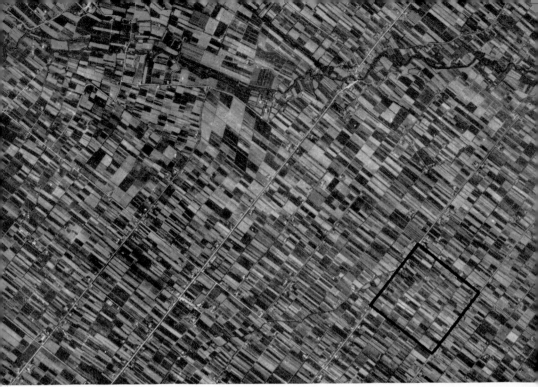

66 Centuriated landscape of the Po Valley near Cesena, showing existing roads which preserve the Roman grid. The original unit was the square of 20 × 20 actus (776 × 776 yards). A specimen is indicated by thickened lines. Contrast the non-centuriated areas at top of photograph

PLANNED LANDSCAPES OF THE N. ITALIAN PLAIN

67 Palma Nova, Veneto, created in 1593

68 The four Romes: classical **Rome** in the foreground with the Capitol hill and statue of Vittorio Emanuele; medieval Rome left of the Corso, the central street; the Vatican City (mostly off the picture) lies beyond the Tiber below the Janiculum ridge; and to the right of the photograph stretches 'Renaissance' Rome with its palaces, squares and in the

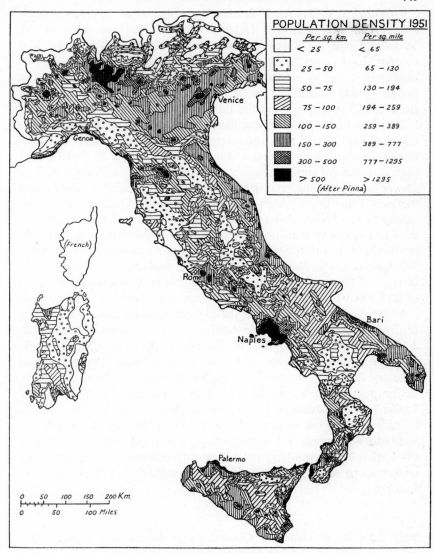

FIG. 181. Density of population in Italy, 1951

the Maritime Alps, Ligurian Apennines, much of the Northern Apennines and the higher ranges of the south, such as Sila, Aspromonte,
Peloritani and Nebrodi, densities rise to 64–130 per sq. mile. In poor
lowland areas, notably the Maremma and interior of the Catanian
Plain, there are similar densities.

w.m.w.—16

Lithological differences,[27] influencing soils, water-supply and agriculture, are also important factors. The poor lowland areas of the Maremma and the lower Volturno have only 64–130 per sq. mile, compared with over 500 in the Neapolitan lowlands, where a series of concentric zones of increasing density focus on Naples; 2,000 on the periphery and over 2,600 per sq. mile in the Phlegrean Fields. Apart from 22,275 per sq. mile in the immediate environs of Naples, where industry and commerce are significant, these high densities are essentially the result of rich soils and intense agriculture on a scale unique in the Peninsula. The north-east and north-west coasts of Sicily have also high densities for similar reasons, reaching 8,000 in the Conca di Oro. Lower but significant rural densities of 900–1,500 occur on the eastern flanks of Etna. Deep pockets of *terra rossa* in the Apulian Murge with shallow water-tables, account for the dense scatter of *trulli* (Plate 63), though the higher densities around Bari and along the coast further north also reflect the commercial activities of its numerous small ports. Widespread in the Northern Plain and the more favoured agricultural districts of Central Italy such as the Valdarno and Chianti, are densities of 200–500, which reflect generally intense forms of agriculture.

Industry, of course, explains the highest densities around the major centres.[28] Notable are the Turin district, and the environs of Milan with 1,300–2,600; the conurbation of Milan averages over 2,600. In these two areas 80–90 per cent of the active population are engaged in industry. Rome is a more isolated nucleus of dense population, while the major ports—Genoa, Naples and Bari—have major concentrations. In the Tuscan districts of Lucca, Pistoja-Florence and the lower Arno, there is growing industry, notably in the compact area of Prato-Sesto, Fiorentino-Florence. Yet apart from the industrial centres themselves, the Italian landscapes have not yet been threatened with the sprawl of conurbations which is annihilating the countryside in parts of Western Europe.

TOWNS

Italy has been described as a country agricultural in occupation but urban in its manner of life. For this reason it is sometimes hard to distinguish between its urban and rural centres. Typical of the South are large villages and towns of 2,000 up to 20,000 or even 40,000 inhabitants. Overcrowded, squalid and desperately poor, these southern towns are a world apart from those of the North, which are comparable in character to those of the more industrialised, Western European cities. Of the 180 towns which had more than 20,000 in 1951, one group only is coincident with much industry in western Lombardy, compared with two other groups associated with the intense agriculture of Campania and around Bari; a looser cluster of other rural centres occurs in west central Sicily (Fig. 183).

1. *Urban Origins.* Compared with the Near East, Italy came late in the field of urban civilisation. Prehistoric and most proto-historic settlements were self-contained, agricultural units. Some of these have been excavated in Apulia,[29] notably the Neolithic village of Passo di Corvo, north-east of Foggia. An oval enclosure 800 by 500 yards contained in one section about one hundred smaller units, making it one of the largest Neolithic villages to have been discovered in Europe. From about the second millennium B.C. appear the *Terramare* settlements in the North Italian Plain, especially between the Oglio and Mella. Their moated, regular plan was once thought to have been the origin of the Roman gridiron, but now it is more certain that the Etruscans and Greeks brought the first urban civilisation into Italy.

It is probable that the Romans first learnt their urban ways from their neighbours the Etruscans, though much has yet to be investigated concerning Etruscan towns (Fig. 182). Their origins were associated with religious and political rites. If the excavated town of Marzabotto is typical—which may be doubtful—the north–south (*cardo*) and the east–west (*decumanus*) streets had a celestial orientation.[30] The subdivisions of the resulting quarters had a religious significance coordinated with the temples. Examples of regular Etruscan towns are Mantua, Spina, Capua Vetere, Acerra and Nola. But in Tuscany, where the Etruscan cities were concentrated, ridge, hill-top or hill-slope sites were common and so discouraged regular plans. Natural defences were used to enclose large areas: Orvieto (260 acres), Veii (nearly 350 acres) and Caere or Cerveteri (370 acres). However, apart from the extensive cemeteries on the adjoining hills, identified from air-photographs (Plate 19), no trace of the plan of these larger towns has yet been made.[31] The grouping of the Seven Hills of Rome (*Septimontium*), at first a series of villages, then grouped around the shrine of the Forum area into the incipient town, owes much to its Etruscan overlords.[32]

Greek influence was limited to Sicily and the South. It has been said that Sicily had more Greek temples than Greece. Certainly the dense Greek settlement on its coasts and the more scattered colonies of *Graeca Magna*, as Calabria and Basilicata became known to the Greeks, has left evidence of many Greek cities[33] (Fig. 182). Although many more towns have been excavated than in Etruria, there are still unsolved major problems of Greek town-planning. It has been thought that

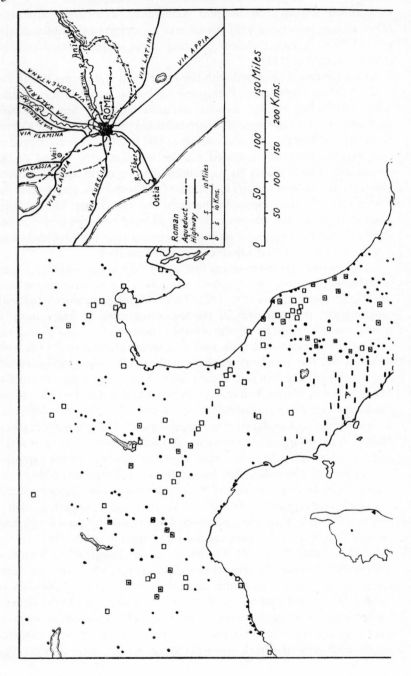

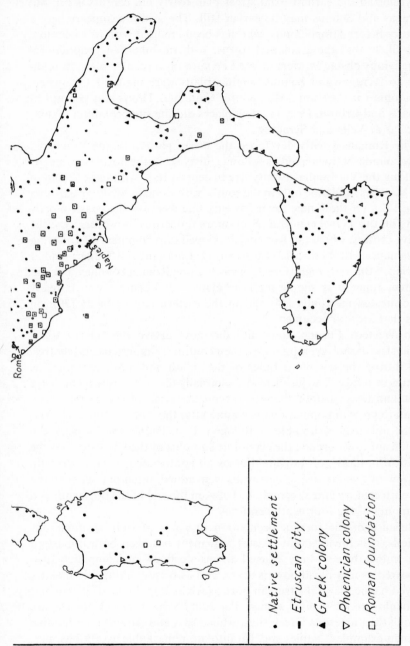

FIG. 182. Origins of Italian settlements (from Touring Club Italiano). Insert shows the Roman aqueducts and the roads that served the imperial city

Smyrna had the earliest axial street plan (early 6th century B.C.), but Acragas and Selinus may be earlier still. The gridiron appears here a century before Hippodamus, who has been credited with its invention. It is likely that these colonial towns, with no inherited proprietorial or religious obstacles, were created *de novo* on a regular plan. In addition to Acragas and Selinus, similar plans were made at Casmenae, Posidonia (or Paestum), Metaponto, Caulonia, Thurii and perhaps at Sybaris and Croton. Only in a few places did the site prohibit a regular plan, as at Velia and Syracuse.

The Romans greatly developed the urban pattern of the Peninsula. New colonies were created as follows: thirty six in the north, particularly along the Via Emilia; twenty five in central Italy with ten of them in the Marches; and nine only in the south, with none in Sicily or Sardinia (Fig. 182). Of these new towns, twenty-one were on the coast, mostly ports on the Tyrrhenian Sea. Even more numerous, however, were the native centres, which the Romans developed into colonies: 42 Umbrian settlements; 10 Latin; 13 Etruscan; 7 Ligurian; 11 Gallic; and 7 Illyrian.[34] But only eight Greek towns became Roman colonies. Even in Roman times it is significant how many tribal centres were already concentrated in Apulia (34) and in the eastern half of Sicily (29), on sites that are still occupied.

In Western Europe, town life did not survive the 'Dark Ages'. Italian towns, however, preserved their continuity as agricultural centres, and during the troublous times of the eighth and ninth centuries, as centres of refuge. The juridical and especially the ecclesiastical character of Italian towns helped them to survive the perils of the period. They began to grow in population once more after the tenth century. The rise of the universities (notably at Bologna, Pisa, Padua and Naples), the mendicant town orders, the economic stimulus of the Crusades and the political initiative of individual cities all contributed to rapid growth. In view of this expansion new walls were added, often one series in the eleventh century and a second one between the end of the thirteenth and beginning of the fourteenth centuries.

Because of the foreign occupation of parts of Italy at numerous periods, it is obvious that coastal settlement has been both important and vulnerable.[35] Many coastal towns declined or completely disappeared as new naval powers arose, and as piracy, silting and malaria played havoc. Several Etruscan ports, such as Populonia, Telaman and Punicum are now only names. Paestum, Sybaris and Heraclea are among the numerous Greek sites, while Ostia and Aquileia are notable Roman examples. Naples and Taranto are remarkable exceptions, persisting from Greek times. However, towns of the interior have also shown a continuity that is perhaps unique in Europe. Many Italian towns were preserved because of their ecclesiastical functions during the critical period of the fifth century. Northern Italy then had 64 bishoprics, Etruria 32, Umbria 30. Altogether Italy had 286 ecclesiastical centres.[36] Agricultural centres—called *borghi* in Tuscany—were walled and acted as 'cities of refuge' during the unrest that characterised the ninth and tenth centuries. The fragmentation of political units, together with the separate overlordship of town and country under the bishops and feudal lords respectively, tended to encourage the growth of numerous regional centres and baronial castles that sheltered villages.[37] During the twelfth and thirteenth centuries numerous planned towns were created *de novo* for purposes of defence, especially on the borders of the northern city-states and by the Normans in the south. Others, with more elaborate forms of defence, were added during the sixteenth and seventeenth centuries in the north. Earthquakes in Sicily especially explain the creation of new towns by local barons during the seventeenth and eighteenth centuries. Such briefly have been the major developments of towns until the modern period of industrialism.

A remarkable feature of Italy between the twelfth and fifteenth centuries was the pre-eminence of a few metropolitan cities. Nowhere else in Europe was the great city so large, dwarfing so effectively all other types of town. This is explained by the Commercial Revolution of the later Middle Ages, the most brilliant in Italy.[38] Venice, unique in its expansion from extra-territorial resources, depended entirely on trade over-seas. Then arose Genoa, Milan and Florence, doubling their population in a century or less. Rome too had unique status as the papal seat. In the south, Naples and Palermo, brilliant as their medieval history was, later had their fortunes too closely tied to Spain. Stagnation followed in the sixteenth century, so that these great cities have preserved their Medieval and Renaissance treasures of architecture remarkably well, though some of the northern cities have been more tarnished by modern industrialism.[39] Thus Italy had a wide choice of potential capitals after the Unification of the country: Turin in 1864, Florence in 1865–70, Rome since 1871. But these capitals were due to the political exigencies of the moment, not to hesitation as to which was appropriate.

2. *Types of Town Plan*. Reflecting the complex vicissitudes of their history, the Italian towns show numerous differences of development, each a human reaction to an ensemble of complicated conditions, some political, others social and economic, and also physical. Markedly

different types of town have developed in Northern, Central and Southern Italy.

The North Italian Plain, so well defined by its mountain frame and its apparent uniformity, has never had a central city. The Po is a divider rather than a unifier, and the drainage generally has partitioned it into sections, each of which has tended to develop its town life independently. Turin and Piacenza are the only notable centres actually on the Po and there are none at the confluences with tributary rivers. There are very few towns on the lower reaches of the rivers, usually strongly fortified as Mantua on the Mincio, Pavia on the Ticino, Padua avoiding the Brenta, and Ferrara two miles from the lower Po. Instead, the towns are commonly located, where the Alps and the Apennines meet the plain. Notable is the string of towns along the Via Emilia: Rimini, Cesena, Forli, Faenza, Imola, Bologna, Modena, Reggio, Parma, controlling the passes through the Apennines. Bologna, the chief town, disputes with Capua in Campania the distinction of being the oldest town in Italy, having had a continuous occupance of almost three millennia. On the northern side of the plain is a row of towns at valley mouths, immediately at the foot of the Alps: Bergamo, Lecco, Como, Varese, Biella, Ivrea, Cuneo (Fig. 190). A second row, roughly between the high and low plain includes the most important cities: Udine, Treviso, Padua, Mantua, Novara, Vercelli, and notably Milan and Turin. Many of the more important centres have had three medieval phases of growth associated with the Lombards, the rise of the communes, and the period of the Visconti or other merchant princes.

Many of the northern towns have a rectangular or quadrilateral plan with wide, spacious streets and a central square. Some had their origin in Roman towns, such as the well-known examples of Turin, Como, Aosta, Verona and notably, along the Via Emilia, Piacenza, Imola, Reggio Emilia and others further east. Of the large towns, Alessandria is exceptional in being erected on a polygonal plan by the Lombard League in 1168. As in Spain, however, there are numerous examples of small defence centres often built by rival city states near their borders, and having suggestive names such as Francavilla, Villafranca, Borgofranco, Castelfranco and Salvaterra (see p. 235).[40] Candelo, Montagnana and Carmagnola have a rectangular plan. The main highway also influences oval plans, such as those of Castel Bolognese and Castelfranco Veneto (1119). The geometric plan is exemplified at Massa Lombarda, Crevalcore and Villafranca Veronese (1185). Cittadella (1220) is a variant of this with circular walls and thirty-one towers. From the fifteenth and sixteenth centuries appear octagonal and polygonal plans such as Urguano, Guastalla, Cologno and Sperano, but the star-shaped Palmanova (1593) (Plate 67) and Forte Urbano are the most striking of these new experiments in defence. In all these types there is the dominance of the central *piazza*, an architectural feature reputedly introduced from the Levant by the Crusaders. Venice (independent until 1797) and Ravenna are unique, the former because of its history and site, the latter because of its role as a Byzantine outpost and capital with its numerous towers and early churches. With their commerce and modern industries, even with a population as small as 5,000, northern towns look entirely urbanised.

In central Italy there are few coastal settlements of any size and only mediocre ports. Some like Pisa, have declined because of silting or are only of secondary importance, such as Ancona and Leghorn. The latter was created in the late sixteenth century by the Medicis with a pentagonal plan. There are numerous medieval *borghi*, many now in ruins such as Monterrioni (1213–19) in the Elsa valley.[41] Hill settlements are characteristic of central Italy. Marche has the most numerous examples of hill-top towns and villages, such as Osimo and Castelfidardo while in Umbria are many on hill slopes such as Assissi, Perugia and Spoleto. In Tuscany and Latium isolated plateaux or ridges are common sites. Star-shaped Urbino, spread-eagled along its ridges, or triangular Siena are distinctive ridge towns. Regular plans are less common than in the north. Notable are Pietrasanta (1255) founded by the Luccese, Villanova d'Asti (1248) and Camaiare. There are a few radial plans developed on hill-tops, such as Sant'Erachio (1300) near Foligno and Lugignano in the Chianti valley.

In Southern Italy the major cities are concentrated on the coast and their origins are usually Graeco-Roman. Such are Naples, Brindisi, Taranto, Messina, Catania, Palermo and Cagliari. Unlike the rest of Italy, Byzantine rule maintained unchanged the classical traditions of its cities, but later in the Middle Ages feudalism was to persist in the South, without the liberating benefits that the northern communes enjoyed from trade and industry. First arose the Tyrrhenian ports of Gaeta, Naples, Sorrento, Amalfi and Salerno. Those with a rich, lowland hinterland prospered most. In the ninth century Amalfi looked as if it might precede Venice as the greatest emporium of the Mediterranean, only to decline in the eleventh century because of its narrow hinterland among other reasons. Palermo, capital of Arab Sicily, expanded on either side of its Graeco-Roman *castrum* in the quarters of *Harat as Sacaliba*, *Harat al Masgid* and *Harat al Calida*, but its irregular plan has been obliterated by subsequent town-planning.[42] Significant has been the

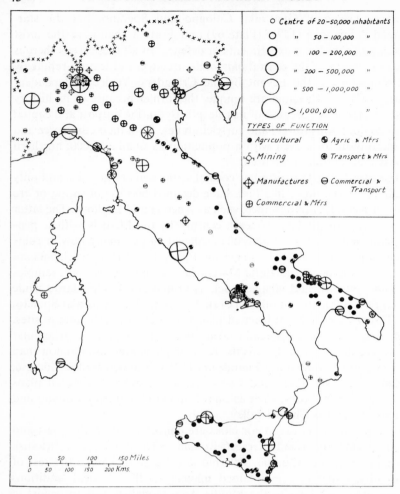

FIG. 183. A functional classification of Italian cities and towns, based on the 1950 census of population

number of towns in Sicily and Apulia of native origin; notable among them is Bari. The Normans were the medieval town-builders of the south, Frederick II founding Augusta in Sicily, Cesarea in the Abruzzi, Montecalone in Calabria and Altamura in Apulia, on the ruins of native towns.[43] After the decline of Siponto on the Apulian coast, Manfredonia was founded (in 1259) as a free port, like Aigues-Mortes in Languedoc; Trani and Barletta were also developed at this time. Fortress towns such as Aversa (1022) north of Naples, Melfi and

Lucera, were also established by the Normans. The most striking examples of regular town plans, however, were created much later as reconstructions after earthquakes or built for other reasons by the large landowners (*feudatori*): in south Apulia east of Gallipoli at Parabita and Aradeo; in Calabria, Filadelfia; in Sicily, Vittoria (1607), Partinico (early seventeenth century), Floridia (1628), Grammichele (1683), Avola (1693), Belpasso (1695) and Pachino (1768).[44] Modern examples of earthquake reconstructions are Messina and Reggio Calabria (since 1908). Bari has a notable modern gridiron, grafted on to the medieval plan. Apart from the major cities of the south, however, many settlements are towns in size but villages in function and appearance. Often they are perched on hill-tops such as Pisticchi in Basilicata (Fig. 206) and Enna and Erice in Sicily.

RURAL SETTLEMENT

Detailed statistics from the 1921 Census onwards make it possible to distinguish three broad categories of rural settlement in Italy. These are: nucleated units such as villages and hamlets, small nuclei or farming units such as the *corte*, *casale* and similar units that house ten to twelve families or more on the same farmyard but without the services that a village community usually enjoys; and the isolated house or farmstead. As in other Mediterranean countries, nucleated settlements predominate, with about 76 per cent (1951) of the Italian rural population living in centres, 7·5 in small agricultural units, and 17·5 dispersed. The majority live in areas where the rural pattern is intermediate in type, that is to say with a mingling of villages, hamlets and dispersed farms.

Unlike Spain, where many of the patterns of settlement are traceable to the conditions of the Reconquest in the Middle Ages, a more complex variety of periods has affected the Italian patterns. Undoubtedly defence against piracy, rival communes and even malaria, were principal causes of concentrated settlement. Nevertheless, isolated, fortified houses in some areas, such as Friuli and the Roman Campagna, suggest that the necessity for defence has not always led to concentration of population in large hill-top villages. Ethnic factors too are not clear, although there is a marked difference between the German areas of Alto Adige or the Slav areas of Istria, where isolated houses and hamlets are frequent, and the Italian parts of both where villages are more typical. Systems of agricultural practice and land tenure, however, are the major influences on the disposition and the size of the Italian settlements.[45]

Two agrarian systems in particular are noteworthy: *mezzadria* and *latifondo*. Under the share-tenancy systems *mezzadria*, the agricultural unit is the *podere* (farm, estate) a family holding usually with mixed cultivation. *Mezzadria* holdings, employing almost exclusively family labour, still cover 60 per cent of Central Italy. In the South they are localised in northern Campania, the south-eastern district of Bari and in northern Calabria. The varied demands for labour among the tree crops implies that the cultivator's home is best located among his fields. As the landlord usually owns a number of farms, worked as one estate, the steward supervises them from his own large farmhouse (*fattoria*) and manufactures the oil and wine from all the holdings. The *latifondo* system in the South and Sicily has resulted in the opposite effect, a marked grouping of tenants into large villages.[46] The monoculture of cereals does not require long residence in the fields, and fearing that peasants might desire their own holdings if resident in the country, the barons (*feudatori*) even founded new towns for their labourers in the grain-growing areas of Sicily (see p. 544). The large village has thus served well the cause of feudalism. Another unit found on large estates under extensive farming is the large farmstead with barrack-like quarters for several families on the centre of the estate. Such are the *casale* in the Roman Campagna, the *masseria* in Apulia and Basilicata, and the *baglio* in Sicily. A similar unit, although under very different commercialised agriculture (*latifondo capitalistico*) is widespread in the Northern Plain and in the lower Arno (*corte*, *cassine*, *bergamine*).

1. *Types of Rural Settlement*.[47] The compact village centrally situated in the cultivated land of the commune is the principal type in southern Italy. It is dominant in the Tavoliere, Murge, Basilicata, eastern and central Calabria, Sicily and in scattered districts of central Campania, Latium and the Abruzzi (Fig. 184). Rural centres average 1,000–4,000 inhabitants but in Sicily and Apulia they may rise from 5,000 to even 40,000.[48] Because of the distances from the village to remote fields, temporary dwellings have tended to become permanent, while re-settlement schemes since 1950 have created new groupings of peasant houses near the limits between communes. Old established secondary centres (*casali*) may number five or more in one large commune, as in western Basilicata, central Calabria, and the Gargano. In the broad lonely belt of country between the Tavoliere, High Murge and eastern Basilicata, and again in the Crotone plain and east central Sicily, large centres with few isolated settlements are the rule (Fig. 184). Other patterns of nucleated villages are common in the lower and middle valleys of the Alps. They originated probably from temporary tent

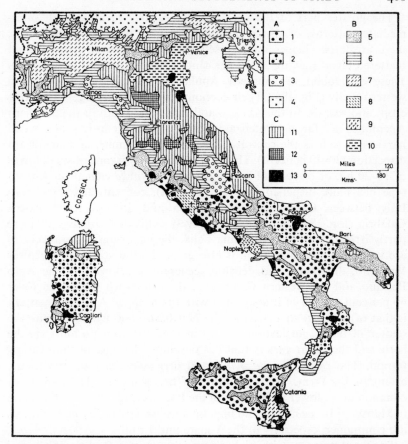

FIG. 184. Types of rural settlement in Italy (based on Biasutti, with modifications by Almagía and Dickinson). Legend: A—Agglomerated types: 1. Large, compact villages and agricultural towns; 2. ditto, but with some dispersed farms; 3. small, compact villages and scattered farms; 4. alpine villages and hamlets. B—Intermediate types: 5. large farms (*masserie* and *cascinali* in zone of large, compact centres (10–15% of population dispersed); 6. mixture of villages, farms and scattered houses; 7. 'corti' of the N. Italian Plain; 8. 'casali' of the Roman Campagna; 9. 'cortile' and large agricultural centres of the Campanian plain; 10. centres, farms and scattered houses aligned along the roads. C—Dispersed types: 11. isolated houses (50–75% dispersion of the population); 12. ditto, with over 75% dispersed; 13. farms and new settlements associated with modern reclamation and land reform schemes

villages that later became permanent. These villages in turn now have a series of temporary shelters at higher levels of the mountain slopes. In northern Istria and in scattered parts of the Apuan and Ligurian Alps, nucleated villages also dominate.

The greater part of the rural population live in areas with intermediate patterns, of which several types may be recognised.[49] First, there are large villages interspersed with medium-sized *masserie* and scattered farms (having 20–30 per cent of the agricultural population). These are found in southern Apulia, north-eastern Calabria and western Sicily (Fig. 184). Their economy is associated largely with tree crops and cereals. In the Abruzzi and stretching south in the Southern Apennines as far as Potenza, another pattern consists of several hamlets as well as the central village in the commune, and significant dispersion (30–40 per cent). This is predominantly a zone of small farms of 10–20 ha, or of peasant-holdings under *latifondo contadino*. A third type has more dispersion (30–60 per cent), concentrated in western Italy between Campania and Calabria and also in south-eastern Calabria (Fig. 184), with tiny, intensively cultivated holdings that are partly irrigated. In the Campania Felix, the major agricultural centres are very large, but dispersion is also great. To the north, in the lower Volturno, dispersion and densities generally are lower. In the Agro Pontino and the western Campagna, there is much dispersion (over 60 per cent), much of it associated with the *bonifica*. A notable pattern is that of the *corte* or *cascine* in the Northern Plain where, despite the scatter of farms, nucleation is very marked.[50] Two main units are the *corte* and the linear variety that has developed because of the swampy terrain. The *corte*, *cascine*, *fenile* and *bergamine* vary in size to the extent of the farms and the nature of the economy. They are most common in the lower lands north of the Po, especially around Milan and in Mantua.[51] In the middle and upper plains hamlets and dispersed farms are commoner, especially in the Veneto and Friuli.

Scattered patterns with high dispersion are characteristic of Central Italy where the tenure system of *mezzadria* is strongly favourable to high dispersion. Until the sixteenth century, tenants were grouped under the shelter of the local stronghold or monastery, but with more peaceful times and active clearance of woodland, scattered farms were developed. In Tuscany dispersion has had a detrimental effect on the hill-towns, often now with only a quarter of the population they had in the Middle Ages. D. H. Lawrence has described them aptly as 'a worn-out little knot of streets shut inside a wall'. Today dispersed farms are densest in the Arno-Chianti valleys, along the Via Emilia from Piacenza towards Rimini and along the coastal belt of the Marches. They are also found in restricted pockets in the South, notably in the districts of Frosinone, Avellino-Benevento and Murgei dei Trulli. With moderately intensive cultivation and small family holdings, these areas appear more densely populated on the map (Figs. 199 and 205) than is in fact the case.

2. *House Types*.[52] As significant symbols of Italy's diverse landscapes are the numerous types of rural dwellings. They have been the subject of intense research by Italian geographers. Briefly, reference may be made to temporary dwellings, transitional types between temporary and permanent houses, the 'Italic' house, the Mediterranean type, farmsteads with numerous outbuildings of which the *corte* is the best example and alpine chalets.

In the mountains, where temporary dwellings are associated with pastoralism, there are diverse types, such as the *grange, baite, malghe, casere* and *alpi*. In the eastern Alps, where winters are severe, the shelters are large, including stalls and dairy. In the western Alps they are much smaller. In the Apennines sheep transhumance has resulted in two distinct types: the winter quarters on the plains, consisting of *capanne*, conical reed shelters found on the Maremma, the Roman Campagna and the Tavoliere; and the summer huts, *stazzi*, with small square base, dry stone walls and thatch roof. The *procoi* of the Roman Campagna and the *caselle* of western Liguria are other types. In the past, charcoal-burners and wood-cutters had similar types of temporary shelters but these are now nearly all abandoned.

A link with the ancient past is seen in the *trullo*, a conical stone house built up as one unit from a cylindrical base to an apex, sometimes ornately designed. This type, popularised in central Apulia, is comparable to the *casite* of Ischia and the *trigor* of Istria (Dignano). All are districts with a plentiful supply of well-fissured, hard limestone. In the north of Apulia an older name used is the *casedda* and in the south, *furneddu*. Especially in the south of Apulia the *trullo* is distinct, having an outside stair, leading to the roof apex. Concentrated in the district between Fasano, Alberobello, Ceglie and Ostuni, most of the *trulli* have been built within the last two hundred years. They reflect the colonisation movement of land-hungry tenants that have occupied and reclaimed common lands and stony wastes of *latifondi* into productive vineyards and olive groves. Cave-dwellings are another feature of southern Italy, notably in the Matera district and south-east Sicily. Troglodytes were once common also in the soft tuffs of southern Etruria. Another and widespread shelter of the Po and Venetian marshes is the *casone*. Of marsh origin, like the Valencian *barraca*, it is a rectangular hut, with reed and clay walls, and a grass-thatched roof. Since the housing regulations of the 1930s it has begun to disappear in the areas between Padua and the lagoonal littoral of the Veneto.

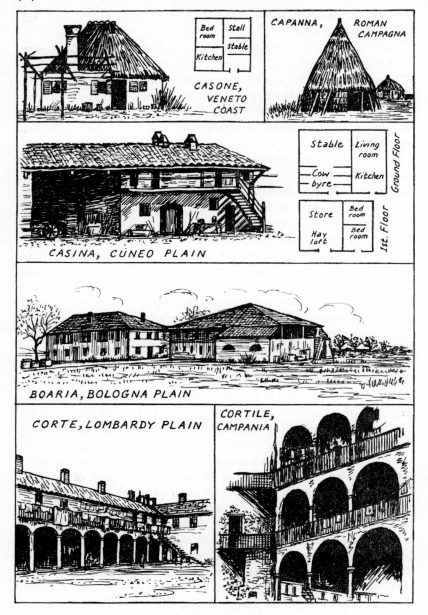

FIG. 185. House-types of Italy

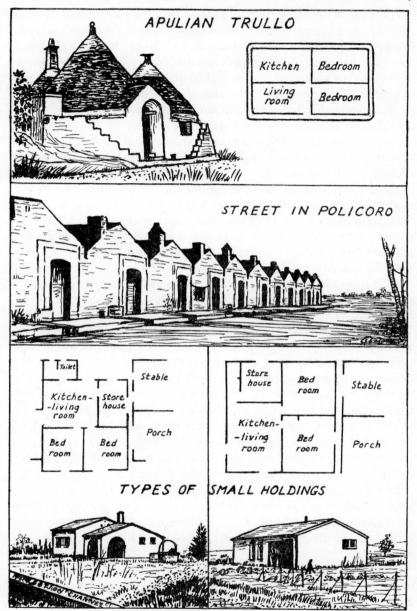

APULIAN TRULLO

| Kitchen | Bedroom |
| Living room | Bedroom |

STREET IN POLICORO

Toilet		Stable
Kitchen-living room	Store house	
Bed room	Bed room	Porch

| Store house | Bed room | Stable |
| Kitchen-living room | Bed room | Porch |

TYPES OF SMALL HOLDINGS

FIG. 186. House-types of Italy

Throughout the whole of the Peninsula with the exception of Apulia, and including Liguria and the eastern plain between the valleys of the Brenta and the Piave, are variants of the 'Italic' house. This basic 'latin' unit has a rectangular plan of two stories. It is usually built of stone with a tiled or slate roof that is pitched gently at 20–30°. Access is by an outside stairway which terminates often in a verandah or balcony. Inside, a vertical wall divides both stories into two halves: on one side a kitchen and a bedroom, on the other animal quarters and agricultural stores. There are numerous variants of this plan, related to climatic and agricultural conditions, and also to local customs. In Liguria restriction on sites because of steep slopes explains the terraced house, usually of three stories. In the chestnut zone in the mountains, a familiar feature is the loft with its grille used as a drier for this fruit (*seccatoio*). In Central Italy there are complex and heterogeneous types. Most of the dispersed dwellings so common in the Marches have evolved from temporary stone huts (*cabreo*) developed after the late Middle Ages. Their successors have usually two stories and tile roofs located up to *c*. 1,500 ft; above that, stone is a commoner roofing material. In some areas, the inside stair is usual, especially in higher and more exposed sites, but nearer the coast as between the Tenna valley and Ancona, the stairway is built outside. In the Marches until about fifty years ago, a small square house, built of adobe was common. Characteristic of all the lands that practise *mezzadria* is the large house of the steward (*fattoria*) with numerous outbuildings, often protected by high walls and perhaps a tower (Plate 62). In Tuscany, another feature of the larger farm-house is the dove-cote. New changes in the Maremma and Pontine districts have caused the removal of the old hovel villages, replaced now with whitewashed houses of two stories, sometimes semi-detached. These dot all areas of modern land reform. In the South two types of dwelling are most common: the densely crowded tenements in the hill-top villages and towns, and the single-storey dwellings of one or two rooms, commonly strung along the road on the outskirts of the settlements. These latter dwellings house the landless day labourers, whose condition of life is still wretched.

In the south-east, Mediterranean house-types are common. Flat or gently sloping roofs often serve as impluvia in an area where water has been at a premium until the construction of the Apulian Aqueduct. The Moorish influence is traceable on the west coast from Ischia and Capri southwards into the coastal districts of Sicily.

Typical of the Northern Plain is the large farmyard with its *corte* type

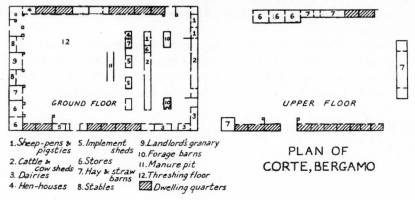

1. *Sheep-pens* & *pigsties*   5. *Implement sheds*   9. *Landlord's granary*
2. *Cattle* & *Cow sheds*   6. *Stores*   10. *Forage barns*
3. *Dairies*   7. *Hay* & *straw barns*   11. *Manure pit*
4. *Hen-houses*   8. *Stables*   12. *Threshing floor*   ▨ *Dwelling quarters*

PLAN OF
CORTE, BERGAMO

Fig. 187. Plan of a *corte*, Bergamo

of buildings. Some *corti* may go back to Roman times, but the names (*corte—cohors*, cattle enclosure; *cascine—casso*, hay loft) and the land use, suggest they were actively spread in the later Middle Ages with the development of cattle raising. Whereas the *cascine* or *corte* is usually built up on three or four sides of the farmyard by the dwellings of the tenants and by the stalls, etc., the *boaria* found in the eastern sector of the Plain is walled and only one side is occupied by the dwelling. In Friuli, where family units tend to prevail, the house type is Italic. In the eastern part of the Plain the Venetian influence is noticeable in the loggia or porch, often flanked with several arches. These are most common in the High Plain where the reclaimed areas of the Middle Ages are oldest in contrast to those nearer the coast. As cultivated land is limited in the Euganian and Berici hills, small dwellings with ample basements to store the wine vats are a distinct type. Throughout the Northern Plain large country houses, sometimes called *palazzi* (in the Veneto) but usually villas, are a common sight.

The *corte* type of dwelling is found in the Campagna, Campania, and on large estates in the south. In Campania Felix the *cortile* has become the unit of numerous overcrowded settlements (Fig. 185). From narrow streets access is gained by a large baroque gateway into a rectangular courtyard that is surrounded on three or four sides by buildings that tower five or six stories high. Outside stairways and arcaded galleries link each floor, so that there may be thirty or fifty families in each *cortile*. At ground level are the stables, stores, communal well and oven. The *masserie* is a common unit on large holdings in the lower Volturno, and along the Ionian lowlands. Near the coast of Basilicata these may be elaborately fortified with a tower and high walls, but in the interior of southern Italy open verandahs and less evidence of defence measures are more typical.

Finally, in the Italian Alps there are the usual types of chalet with scattered outbuildings in some areas to reduce the risk of fire. Ethnic differences are appreciable, especially in the Adige valley, where there are marked contrasts between the Austrian and Italian styles.

CHAPTER 17

THE REGIONS OF NORTHERN ITALY

'Corn heavy with ripeness, the Massic juice of Bacchus, fill the land,—and prosperous cattle abound.—But there are splendid cities, mighty works of men, towns piled laboriously upon precipitous crags, and rivers smoothly underflowing ancient walls. Or shall I name the seas washing both our coasts? the great lakes? you, Como greatest of all, and you, Garda, rising into billows that boom like the sea?'
(Virgil, *The Georgics* 2, 143–4, 155–60, translated by G. Highet)

The name Italy has not always been used to designate the whole of the land now so called. The Greeks first called it *Hesperides*, 'the land to the west'. The name *Italia* 'the land of meat', first appears to have been used in the sixth century B.C. for the small area lying between the F. Sele and the Lao in southern Campania. Then it was applied to all the area south of the Sele and the Ofanto. Roman conquest extended its usage and by A.D. 42 Augustus gave it official sanction for the whole territory north to the Alps. In the time of Diocletian the name was applied by the Church, the *vicarius Italiae* being centred at Milan, in distinction to the *vicarius Urbis* at Rome. The effect was unfortunate, since later in the Barbarian era, only the north was given the name 'Italy'. Apart from its cultural connotation revived by Dante, the political character of the name was lost sight of until modern times. It was revived in the Italian Republic of 1802, the Italian Kingdom of 1805–14, and finally in the united Italian Kingdom, proclaimed in 1861. Then followed the incorporation of Venetia (1866) and of Rome (1870), and the boundary changes of 1918 and 1947.

Within Italy, a three-fold distinction is often made between Continental or Northern Italy beyond the Magra-Rubicon valleys or the 44° parallel, which has 40 per cent of the national territory, and the Peninsula which has 42 per cent. The remaining 18 per cent is Insular Italy, chiefly Sicily and Sardinia. The Peninsula is further divided into Central Italy and the South, lying on either side of the Garigliano-Fortore valleys. The term *Mezzogiorno*, much used since 1950, applies to both the South and the Islands. The first significant division of Italy was that of Augustus when eleven regions were demarcated (Fig.

188), but these were gradually obliterated in the Middle Ages by the political and ecclesiastical fragmentations. Two thousand years later these units are still recognisable, although their delimitation has been upset by many centuries of troubled history. They have been dis-

FIG. 188. The provinces of Italy in the time of Augustus

membered or re-grouped as a conseqence of wars, or political and ecclesiastical events, or even deaths, marriages and frauds. Despite all these changes the wisdom of popular tradition has kept them alive. After the Unification, sixteen *compartimenti* were recognised in 1867, most of them using classical names still in usage (Liguria, Umbria and

Apulia Emilia had fallen into desuetude and was then revived); some were of medieval origin, notably Piedmont, Lombardy, Marche and Basilicata (Fig. 189). These were not judicial units, simply groups of provinces used for statistical and other purposes; after 1913 they were

Fig. 189. The *regioni* of Italy today

designated regions. Two more were added in 1918 with the political annexation of Venezia Tridentina and Venezia Giulia. Other changes since 1945 were the separation of the Val d'Aosta from Piedmont, the creation of the region of Friuli-Venetia and new names given to some of these existing regions. These 19 regions are not comparable in size for whereas the largest are Sicily (25,707 sq. miles) and Piedmont (25,400 sq. miles), the smallest are Liguria (1,716 sq. miles) and the Val d'Aosta (1,298 sq. miles). Nor is their individuality equally marked, Tuscany for example being both a well-defined physical and historical unit, whereas Basilicata is much more indefinite.

There are numerous natural regions within these broad units, comparable to the Spanish *comarcas* and the French *pays*, but without a generic name. Some are valley units, to which the name of their inhabitants is attached, such as Val di Sole (*Solandri*) and the Val di Non (*Nonesi*). Others take the name of an ancient town, such as Lomellina (*Laumellium*) or from a tribe—Sabrina, Fregnano (*Friniates*), Cicolano (*Aequiculi*), etc. Others are descriptive of relief, Campidano, Serra, Aspromonte, or of rivers, Teverina. Some are also associated with the vegetation, such as Castagniccia (chestnut), Ampezzo (*Ampicium*, uncultivated waste), Ogliastra and Sila (*Silva*, forest). To such traditional units, the agricultural economists have created 691 agricultural subregions, which Uge Giusti managed to combine into just over 170. More recently, Sestini distinguished within a geomorphological framework, some 95 landscape types.

Italy is today divided into 92 provinces, and some 8,000 communes. The latter have been developed traditionally as town units. As the cities have grown so the neighbouring communes have been absorbed. But perhaps the event of most regional significance was the granting of the principle of autonomy to some of the Italian *regioni* after the republic was proclaimed in 1946. The State soon recognised the political dangers inherent in the indiscriminate development of such autonomous units so it was subsequently checked, limited autonomy being granted only to the islands of Sicily and Sardinia and to the Alpine units of the Adige and Val d'Alto Aosta with their cultural and irredentist problems. Elsewhere, the development of the Ente or agency, entrusted with the task of land reclamation, and related rural reforms has also promoted indirectly the spirit of regionalism, which has such deep historic roots in many parts of the country. It is realistic, therefore, to accept the *regioni* as the broad geographical divisions of the country (Fig. 189). Only in the north is the regional description somewhat arbitrary, as the Alps and the Pre-Alps are excluded from this book.

THE NORTHERN PLAIN

The human importance of the Northern Plain is out of all proportion to its extent. For while it covers 16 per cent of Italy, it supports about

40 per cent of the total population. In this respect it is interesting to contrast it with the Ebro trough. Both are bordered by mountains, the Alps having about twice the altitude of the Pyrenees, and yet the Pyrenees present a more striking bio-climatic barrier, for reasons already outlined (see p. 13). The arcuate shape of the Italian Alps helps to concentrate the routes focally upon the major cities of Turin and Milan, whereas the straight alignment of the Pyrenees tends to diffuse and isolate the routes crossing them. The water resources of the North Italian Plain, and its significant glacial and fluvio-glacial processes during the Quaternary, also contrast it sharply with the Ebro valley. The Italian Plain has also much more humanised landscapes, with its high densities of population, its numerous cities, its great industries. All these aspects may together explain the utter contrast between the personality of the North Italian Plain throbbing with dynamic energies, and the Ebro trough still shut within an almost medieval atmosphere of dignified poverty and meagre resources. Ultimately, these differences also help to explain why the dichotomy between the North and the South in Italy is so much sharper than it is in Spain.

The Po valley is at first sight remarkably uniform. Alluviation, in this well-developed basin of sedimentation, largely explains this feature, for it has been infilled with fluvio-glacial and fluvial material from the Quaternary to the present, and gradually uplifted. There is a simple sequence of landforms from the foothills towards the Po:

1. A peripheral zone of discontinuous moraines at the outlets of the Alpine valleys and more widespread Plio-Pleistocene *glacis* material associated with solifluction, notably at the foot of the Northern Apennines.
2. The high plain (*alta pianura*) of coarse, porous gravels, dissected by transverse streams.
3. The zone of springs (*fontanili*) thrown out at the contact with the finer alluvium.
4. The low plain (*bassa pianura*), with fine alluvial deposits, abundant streams and marshes.
5. The flood plain of the Po and its major tributaries, protected by dykes, and the reclaimed lands and lagoons of the delta.

Despite the repetition of these features, the Po Plain is also marked by much diversity (Fig. 153). This is explained first by the uncertainty of limit between the Plain and the Alps. The Sub-Alpine lakes may be considered to belong more properly to the Plain, and their distribution and presence create differences of local climate, vegetation and human

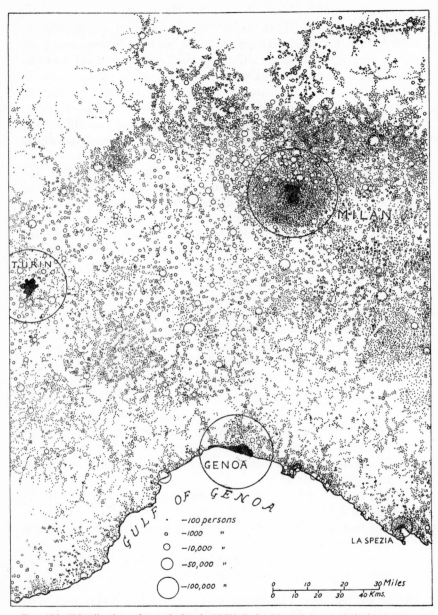

FIG. 190. Distribution of population in N.W. Italy. Note the overwhelming importance of the high terrace densities of population, especially around Milan, and the
other industrial concentrations of Turin and Genoa. High dispersion of settlement
is most marked in Emilia and in southern Lombardy. The Alps and Apennines
stand out as areas of low density

response. The volcanic relief of the Berici and Euganean Hills, the disposition of the moraines, the contrasts between the foothills of the Alps and the Apennines, the Pliocene hills of Monferrato and Asti, and the transition from the Po valley into eastern Venetia, all create distinct differences of landscape. The climate too, subtly changes from the sub-Mediterranean atmosphere around the lakes to the more continental climate of the central plain. Added to these differences is the most fundamental cause of diversity, man himself. For in the historic changes of land reclamation, the patterns of settlement, the social organisations that range from large estates to small-holdings, the multiple uses of land, and now above all in the industrialisation of the so-called 'Industrial Triangle' of Genoa, Turin and Milan, a fundamental contrast is still being deepened between North-Western Italy and North-Eastern Italy. Less noticed than that of the North and the South, nevertheless it is there.

THE NORTH-WEST

In a territory that is only one-fifth of the Italian peninsula there live almost thirteen million inhabitants, that is roughly the same number that are scattered over the enormous area of Fennoscandinavia. The reason for this Italian concentration is basically the Industrial Triangle, which has more than half (53 per cent) of the total industrial population of Italy. Between four and six-tenths of these work in large factory units (employing over 500 workers) so the latter are a prominent feature of the townscapes. Thus this major region of Italy is the most West European in its character. The links between Piedmont and Lombardy are unquestionable in this area, the most prosperous in Italy. Liguria may not seem so obvious at first, as it has links between the Alps and the Apennines, the north and the centre of the Peninsula. Yet Augustus merged it with Piedmont as far as the Po, and in subsequent history it has been politically and economically dependent on Piedmont and its links with the Po valley.

1. *Liguria.* The individuality of Liguria has been markedly emphasised by its maritime façade and its mountainous hinterland. With a coastline of 206 miles, and only 2,085 sq. miles, Liguria has had a close contact with the sea ever since its Pre-Roman inhabitants, the *Ligures*, were pirates. From the Byzantine occupation in the sixth century, the littoral has become well individualised, with the rise of numerous ports, some of them—such as Savona—rivals of Genoa, though none of them surpassing Genoa after the fourteenth century. An important requisite for possible rivalry was the accessibility and control of a

valley pass into the interior, an advantage possessed by Ventimiglia (Roia valley and Tenda Pass), Albenga, Savona (Cadibona Pass) and above all by Genoa (Turchino, Bocchetta, Giovi and Scoffera Passes). Isolation elsewhere has explained the rise of numerous, independent units, such as the 'republic' of Bordighera, and notably the Cinque Terre, a principality of the fifteenth century. Headlands (*punte* and *cale*) separate coastal districts into other numerous distinctive *pays*, while the landward valleys of the Oltregiogo form isolated units. It is not surprising that the *Ligures* were themselves divided into six major tribes.

A second feature of Liguria is the human transformation of its land-scapes since Roman times. Tree crops now dominate the total area cultivated (24 per cent), such as olives (50,000 ha), vines (38,000 ha) and many fruits, were introduced first by the Romans. Liguria, once heavily forested, especially with chestnuts, has been markedly de-forested. Since the nineteenth century, however, there has been more careful forest management so that now Liguria represents one of the most important woodland areas (Fig. 172). Terraces (*piane*) have been created on an impressive scale, many of them stonewalled (*maxere*); horticulture has been expanded (700 ha in 1895, 24,000 ha today); and floriculture (3,000 ha) has created a colourful décor near the French frontier. These terraced flower gardens fetch the highest price for cultivated land in Italy today. Another recent development has been tourism (1,100,000 visitors in 1958), which has transformed numerous fishing centres and other ancient villages into bathing resorts. In-dustrialism at Genoa, La Spezia and Savona has created its own distinctive features and explained the rapid growth of these ports, having about one third of the nation's shipbuilding.

The Ligurian coastlands may be subdivided broadly into two distinc-tive regions, the Riviera di Ponente and the Riviera di Levante, with a transitional unit between them, the Riviera Centrale centred on Genoa, and extending between Portofino in the east and Cape Noli in the west. The Riviera di Levante is more exposed, with a rocky, transverse coast difficult of access and formerly more isolated. It has considerable rain-fall with figures of 60–80 in on the higher slopes, a wide snow mantle in winter, and a lush cover of forests and dense macchia. The Riviera di Ponente is more sheltered, with numerous bays, promontaries less pronounced, and well-developed coastal communications that follow the Roman *Via Aurelia* between the larger ports. It has a drier, milder climate with exotic palms and other subtropical plants, and may deservedly be described as the flower-garden of Liguria. The softer

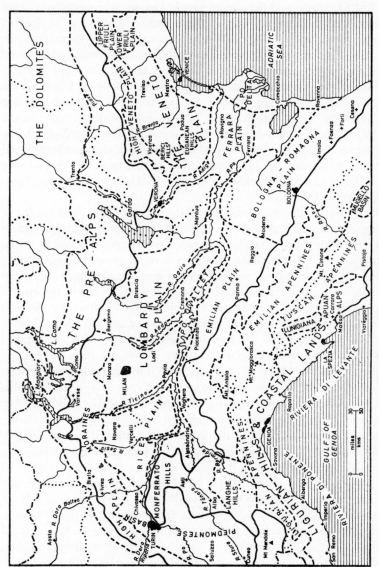

Fig. 191. Regional divisions of the North Italian Plain and Liguria

contours of the calcareous marls west of Albenga, and between Genoa and Sestri Levante, and the schists west of Genoa have a generous cover of woodland. Similar are the *scagliosa* clay slopes in the Riviera di Levante, notable the valley of Fontanalnova and the Vara basin. In contrast, the compact Oligocene sandstones and especially the *pietri verdi*, are rugged and bare. From sea-level to 1,600 ft there is much *macchia* in the Riviera di Levante, composed chiefly of heath (*Erica scoparia* and *E. arborea*), juniper and some cistus. *Garriga* is more typical of the Riviera di Ponente, with oleaster and lentiscus. In the southward facing valleys in the west, the olive ascends to 2,600 ft and the vine to 3,000 ft, the limits also of the ubiquitous chestnut forests and degraded pine forests (*P. maritima*). Above 2,600 to 5,000 ft is the zone of the beech forests, overlooked in the Sub-Alpine zone by the *Pinus laricio* to 6,500 ft.

From Ventimiglia to Alassio is the Riviera dei Fiori, with its flower gardens and horticulture, grown in small fragmented holdings. Ventimiglia (16,000) is the great flower market of Liguria as Sanremo is the tourist capital (40,000). There has been a rapid growth of population in recent decades, notably with Calabrian immigrants. Vines and olives alternate on the gentler slopes with chestnut woods while in the Nervia basin and along the coast there is much terraced cultivation. Behind in the Ligurian Alps, much of the land (65 per cent) is forested or in *macchia*, with medieval villages fortified originally against Saracen piracy and protected by feudal castles. The sandy bays, with their holiday beaches and their small towns, graced by date palms and flowers attract much tourist industry. The narrow Tyrrhenian terraces widen into the Albenga plain, with its orchards and scattered villas. The attraction of alluvial bays (*marine*) and headlands (*capi*) sheltering numerous villages is typical of this coast. At Savona the Riviera centrale has already begun, with the economic pull of Genoa felt by the presence of the large shipyards, blast furnaces and other industrial activities of this port. With two Roman sites, a bishopric from the ninth century and a flourishing port from the twelfth centry, Savona has had an illustrious past, proudly independent for much of it from Genoa. But it is in the last century that tourism and industry have promoted its growth from 19,611 in 1861 to 69,035 in 1961. Varazze is another, smaller resort, while at Voltri, greater Genoa has already begun.

The supremacy of Genoese history has been aided by its position at the head of the Gulf, where the mountains are narrowest and communication is comparatively easy via the Giovi pass to the Northern Plain. Selected by Greek and Phoenician traders, the Romans then enlarged the port and rebuilt the town at the foot of the Sarzano promontory. From three medieval nuclei, which were walled in the tenth century, the town expanded with the growth of the port and a new wall was made in 1155, to enclose the northern suburbs. This was further widened in the fourteenth century to enclose the northern shore, its tenements rising six or seven storeys at the foot of the cliffs and with its fine palaces, many of them along the via Garibaldi, built chiefly in the sixteenth and seventeenth centuries. A series of fortifications and walls were built in the seventeenth century on the high hills around the city at c. 1,200 ft though the town itself was restricted to the lower slopes by the steep relief. Little growth of the city itself occurred during the two subsequent centuries, with c. 60,000 inhabitants at the end of the seventeenth century and 100,000 at the middle of the nineteenth century. With the advent of the railways, the expansion of the port and the rise of modern industries boosted its further growth; 130,000 in 1871, 230,000 in 1901, and 320,000 in 1921. In 1926, Greater Genoa was created, to include 19 communes. The city has pushed out along the coast, especially west of the old harbour where new docks have been built, and to a more limited extent along the lower valleys of the Bisagno and the Polcevera. Much damage was done to Genoa in the last war, so in 1956 a new regional plan was begun to deal with the city's numerous problems, notably those of zoning, the creation of speedy arteries along the coast and up the Bisagno valley, and the reconstruction of the central quarters. Today, this great industrial port and commercial capital has three-quarters of a million people concentrated in a confined location, only eased by the coastwise development at Sampierdarena, Cornigliano and Sestri Ponente, west of the city (see Plate 64).

In the hills behind outer Genoa olive groves, vineyards, orchards and markedly scattered villas and farms, utilise intensively the available terraced slopes. The promontory of Portofino terminates the Riviera centrale, and the Riviera di Levante begins. The coastal cliffs plunge steeply to the sea, except at the head of the Gulf of Rapallo where the resorts of Ste Margherita (8,000), Rapallo (18,000) and Chiavari (20,000) nestle in compact plains. Cypresses and bougainvilleas shelter in luxurious villas, but on the exposed slopes, stone pines are contorted by the wind. Along this coast are concentrated nine of Liguria's twelve fishing ports, excluding the major one at Genoa. On the rocky cliffs of the Cinque Terre the villages of Riomaggiore Manarola, Corniglia, Vernazza and Monterossa, built of the local stone, seem to climb out of the rock face as part of its structure. Their vineyards are celebrated, but because of their isolation, the population of the *pays* has remained stationary, unlike the other coastal districts of Liguria. In the interior valleys of Lamagna, Trebbio and Vara, the rural settlement is markedly dispersed, in contrast to the more nucleated, fortified villages in the Riviera di Ponente (Fig. 190). This is explained partly by the security of the rocky coast, broken only by the Lamogna trough, and the spread of vineyards and olives since the last century. In contrast, such has been the strategic importance of the lower Magra valley to Tuscany, Liguria and Emilia, that its hill flanks have been guarded by large, fortified villages.

Well sheltered at the head of the Gulf of Spezia is an excellent natural harbour, unique on the west coast of Italy. Although a medieval fortress, La Spezia remained undeveloped until Cavour constructed the naval base in 1857–69, with the rectangular arsenal and shipbuilding yards. The population was then only 10,000 but with completion of the naval base it jumped to 65,000 in 1901 and to 112,245 in 1951. It has been laid out on a regular plan (1908–32).

2. *Piedmont*. The term *Pedemontium* was used in medieval documents of several Italian regions, such as Venetia, Tuscany and Campania. It was first used in Piedmont in 1193 and gradually assumed a political as well as physical connotation. As its name suggests, it owes its individuality to the mountains that surround it on three sides. At first, Piedmont comprised the lowland area between the upper Po and the Dora Baltea, hemmed in by alpine valley units and the feudal countries of Monferrato and Saluzzo. Later, it extended its influence notably under the house of Savoy, until by 1748 it comprised all the modern region. As the vestibule of Italy, it is the most westerly and the highest part of the Plain. It is relatively remote from the sea, Turin being 65 miles away, and comparable to Milan (75 miles). This has significant climatic consequences and politically Piedmont has always looked to the Alps rather than to the Mediterranean. Indeed, Piedmont is the most alpine of the northern regions, with 48 per cent of its area within the mountains and only 20 per cent on the Plain. The wide semicircular sweep of the Alps not only dominates the vista, with their forested slopes and snow-capped summits, but furnishes many of the subtle nuances of change to be found in the Plain. For the local *pays* bordering the Plain have their core areas in the alpine valleys. The petrological differences of the soils in the Plain also originate in their bordering mountains. Compared with other Italian regions, Piedmont has not been richly endowed by Nature, yet nevertheless it has some of the highest densities of population in Italy. Irrigation has been one of the most impressive developments man has introduced, the great rivers of the Po, Dora

Riparia, Dora Baltea, Sesia and their tributaries being harnessed to water some 470,000 ha. The rich subsurface supplies of the *fontanili* zone supply another 91,000 ha especially in the lowlands of Vercelli. Half of this total area of irrigated land has been added in the course of the last century, the rest being more slowly acquired since the Middle Ages (Fig. 57). Piedmont is also a strategic centre of communications, having a major hub at Turin for the trans-Alpine routes and a minor one at Alessandria for the trans-Apennine routes.

The Plain makes a wide sweep around the Monferrato Hills, which make a convenient starting point for a traverse of Piedmont (Fig. 191). The Monferrato is divided into upper and lower sections by the intervening hills of the Astigiano, justified on geological and historical considerations but not from the landscape. The whole area is a rolling geometrical pattern of vineyards, guided by the orientation of valleys and gulleys and crowned by badlands and sandstone cuestas. On these terraced hills there are 132,000 ha of specialised vineyards associated with the production of Vermouth and sparkling wines. Small-holdings of about 4 ha are the rule and farmsteads are scattered, often crowning the ridge at 600 to 1,000 ft. In Astigiano, of 103 commune centres, only 15 are located in the valley bottoms. Asti (52,000), capital of the region, is one other exception, overlooking the river Tanaro. It was a Roman creation, but was much more significant as a medieval ducal centre, when its fortunes became bound up with its control of the fruitful and commercially important valley of the Tanaro. Downstream, the Tanaro leads into the basin of Alessandria the chief granary of Piedmont, with market gardening around the city supplied by well irrigation. Protected at the confluence of Tanaro and Bormida by elaborate fortifications, Alessandria has been an important stronghold, and is still a rich market for a fertile region and railway junction. Eastwards, the basin opens into the rich plain of Marengo with its sugar-beet fields and meadows, virtually part of the Lombardy Plain. To the south-west are the green hills of the Langhe, a small region originally a papal domain, where *macchia* is interspersed with cornfields and woods on sandy hills. Nearby is Cuneo (26,000) one of the early free communes of Piedmont, now a market town and silk centre. The Cunese is a pastoral countryside, with meadows liberally fed by the fontanili and where cattle-raising is prominent. Chestnut woods are abundant on the sides of the upper Tanaro valley. Northwards, in the sheltered valleys of the Saluzzese there is a 'riviera' aspect where orchards, vines and gardens of palms and magnolias testify to the mild climate. Downstream the major valleys have much cereal cultivation in a four-year

rotation with hay and root crops. In all this area south of the Dora
Riparia, the Cottian Alps rise suddenly from the Plain, without moraines and practically no high terraces. The rivers run swift and are
deeply incised in their terraces.

Where the Dora Riparia debouches on to the Plain, its morainic
amphitheatre and the westward end of the Monferrato confine the
lowland to a corridor only 8 miles wide. Here Turin (905,000 in 1958)
has been located strategically. From the Maddalena hill (2,345 ft) to
the east of the town it is possible to view all the city. First noted as a
Bronze Age settlement it was later constructed by Augustus as a
Roman *castrum* of 52 ha, its *decumanus* aligned to cross the Dora
Baltea and run parallel with the Po. Throughout the Middle Ages, it
continued to be a great military and commercial centre, controlling
the route of Mt Cenis and others over the Cottian and Graian Alps to
France, as well as the corridors of the Upper Po and Tanaro valleys,
towards the Tyrrhenian Sea. Turin also controlled the main routes in
the Plain. The town charter of 1360 first makes reference to its growing
textile industries based on the local production of flax, hemp and silk,
as well as wool. The Roman plan remained unmodified until 1564-6
when a castle was built to the southwest, followed by two enlargements
of the city on the south and southeast, all enclosed by the wall of 1640.
The construction of a bridge across the Po and the opening of a new
boulevard to it (in 1673) also modified the Roman grid. Further growth
on the south and west was associated with a rapid increase of population
24,000 in 1612 to 56,336 in 1717. Then the city remained relatively
stagnant until the nineteenth century when its growth was further aided
by a series of political events. Chief in importance was the establishment of the royal court of Sardinia in Turin (in 1823) which helped to
double the population. By 1853 had an area of 1,705 ha, a series of plans
helping to maintain the symmetrical growth of the gridiron layout.
When Turin was established as the first capital of the united Kingdom
its population showed another rapid increase (179,635 in 1858, 211,546
in 1865). Henceforth the fortunes of the city have been most closely tied
with the automobile engineering industries, notably of Fiat, which have
some 25 factories and offices scattered around the city and employ
71,000 workers. Together with ancillary industries, they have made
Turin the Detroit of Italy, manufacturing 92 per cent of all the Italian
automobiles. Since the beginning of this century, the population has
tripled and very rapid immigration has taken place especially in the last
decade with the influx of southerners seeking work. Today, it may seem
a far cry from the Roman centre and the palaces of the seventeenth and

eighteenth centuries, to the great industrial sprawl of suburbia, steel-works and engineering shops that are found to the west and south of the city. Nevertheless, the Roman gridiron favoured the orientation of the medieval squares and the symmetry of the later growth. It has given

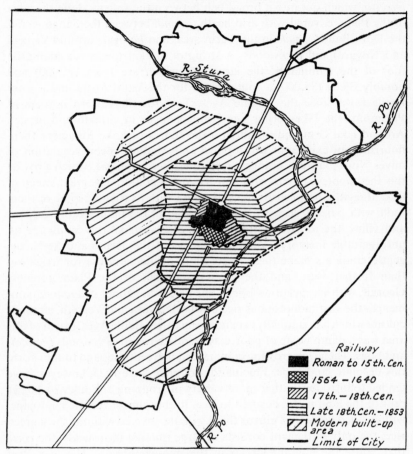

Railway
Roman to 15th. Cen.
1564 – 1640
17th. – 18th.Cen.
Late 18th.Cen.–1853
Modern built-up area
Limit of City

Fig. 192. The growth of Turin

Turin a compactness which is unrivalled among the other millionaire cities of Europe. Indeed, it may have been Turin's plan that inspired Colonel Light to create a comparable design in the Antipodes, at Adelaide.

North of Turin, the plain once more widens, flanked by the foothills of Canavese, centred on the morainic arc of Ivrea. Above, the mountains are densely forested, with many orchards in the lower valleys. High rainfall (over 40 in), balconied farmhouses, and green pastures on the slopes, and valley orchards blossomed by the accelerated temperatures of föhn winds, indicate the importance of the valley outlets from the Alps. The high gravel terraces with their impermeable surface layer of *ferretto*, widen out into a broad belt between the valleys along the edge of the Plain, covered with arid heath (*gerbidi* between the Sangone and the Dora Baltea, *vaude* in the Turin area, and *baraggie* around Vercelli and Novara) and pinewoods. A string of market towns run along the foot of the mountains, the largest of which are Ivrea (11,000) and notably Biella (35,000) a route centre for the Val d'Aosta and a wool textile town since the Middle Ages. Towards the eastern borders of Piedmont, the lakes bring significant changes in climate and aspect. Around lake Orta and notably on the shores of Lake Maggiore there flourishes an exuberant subtropical and Mediterranean vegetation of olives, vines, laurels, oranges, magnolias and camelias, which provide this Piedmontese riviera with a profusion of colour. The great sweep of lake Maggiore between Arona and Stresa with its islands, some of them built with palaces such as Bella and Madre, the innumerable gardens and villas, the tourist centres notably Stresa, make this landscape an unforgettable memory. Along the valleys of the Ticino and Sesia, the gentle gradients make these rivers more docile to utilise for irrigation than further west, and the green panorama of the Plain, serenely Georgic with its meadows opens up. Below the zone of *fontanili* commences the vast monotonous rice bowl of Novara and Vercelli, a monoculture which has gradually expanded since the Middle Ages. Much of this area was a damp waste of poor, clayey soils, covered with woods (*gerbidi*) and bogs. Then rice-growing commenced five centuries ago to transform this desolate landscape. Fluctuations of price since 1925, however, have tended to introduce rather more variety of cropping although 70–80 per cent of the land is still devoted to rice. In this almost Asiatic landscape, with flooded fields that mirror the sky or are covered with the shrill green rice, the only settlement consists of large isolated farmsteads, the *corte* that house the migrant labour in the summer season. The two great centres of this region are Novara (60,000) and Vercelli (39,000), the former situated between the high and low terraces on the Cavour canal, and the latter at an easy crossing point of the F. Sesia. Both were Roman forts and medieval ducal capitals, and are now important agricultural markets and textile centres. Vercelli, especially, is the great rice market of Europe.

3. *Lombardy*. The name *Langobardi* was first applied in 629 to a local tribal group and used in Carolingian times of all Italy. In 888 it was

restricted to the Milanese area and it has subsequently been applied to
the region between the Alps, the Po, and its two tributaries the Ticino
and Mincio. The Alpine border was defined politically in 1797. Lombardy is not a natural region, nevertheless it has developed marked
characteristics, largely as a result of human efforts, and its landscapes
have been radically modified by man. It is a region of superlatives
—the most densely populated and industrialised and the richest agricultural area in all Italy. There are perhaps four chief characteristics
of Lombardy: the economic importance of the Plain; the abundance of
water for irrigation, navigation and power, the creation of distinct
agricultural regions and the number of its towns (18 have over 20,000
inhabitants).

The Plain comprises 47 per cent of Lombardy. When viewed from
such a distance as the Brianza hills, the uniformity of the Plain is
deceptive. Sloping gently from the Sub-Alpine lakes towards the Po,
more important than the gradient is the diversity of water and soil
conditions. They reveal the fundamental distinction between the high
plains bordering the moraines (*Pianalti*), the upper plain (*Alta Pianura*),
the *Fontanili* and the lower plain (*Bassa Pianura*) (Fig. 191). Until the
late Middle Ages these distinctions were largely smothered in the dense
forests that covered much of the Plain. Even so, there appear to have
been differences between the damper oak forests of *Q. cerris* and *Q.
pedunculata* and of poplar on the lower plain, the elms (*Ulmus campe-
stris*) towards the high plain, and the mixed beech, chestnut and pubescent oak forests on the morainic hills and Sub-Alps. A climax of evergreen oak, with undergrowth of box, tree heath and associated shrubs,
creepers, etc., was found around the lake-shores. After the first development of *marcite* meadows in the twelfth century when the Roman
hydraulic system was again put into use, the colonisation of the lower
Plain was most favoured because of its water supply and alluvial soils.
Here were established the numerous *corte* estates and the richly monu-
mented cities of Pavia, Cremona and Mantua. In this areas the monks
of Chiaravalle Abbey first made progress with the cultivation of water
meadows after 1138. On the dry, upper plains, especially in the west,
acid heathy lands long lay unused, two-thirds of them still owned by the
church and aristocrats in the early eighteenth century. Then followed a
rapid development of mulberry cultivation on these poor soils, with the
growth of the textile industry in the nineteenth century. Since about
1880, the rapid industrialization of the high plain has completely
reversed the importance of the two zones. With its industries and
numerous towns, it is the Alta Pianura which has densities of 500 to

12,000 per sq. mile, whereas the Bassa Pianura remains composed essentially of rural landscapes, with 300–500 per sq. mile. Between these two contrasted zones stretches out the great metropolis of Milan with its 1,600,000 inhabitants, 24 per cent of the total population.

The cities have dominated the countryside, ever since the communes arose in revolt in the twelfth and thirteenth centuries. Consequently, the subdivisions of Lombardy are the traditional territories of the larger centres, based on historical rather than geographical considerations. In the foothill zone and extending into the Alps these are: the Comasco, Brianza, Bergamasco and Bresciano. On the Plain, these are: the Milanese, Lodigiano, Pavese, Lomellina Oltrepo, Cremonese, Cremasco and Mantovano.

The edge of the Plain lies at 850–1,000 ft in the west and 500 ft near Brescia. It is backed by the morainic hills that have dammed the seven Sub-Alpine lakes, six of them in Lombardy (Maggiore, Lugano, Como, Iseo, Idro and Garda). The lakes follow a series of pre-glacial valleys along lines of fracture and weakness, which some 5,000 ft of ice was able to sculpture in the Quaternary. Overlooked by the morainic hills, c. 500–650 ft above the lakes, and the Sub-Alpine mountains to the north, the endless vistas, mild climate and flowers attract wealthy residents and tourists to such centres as Bellagio, Cadenabbia Menaggio (Como) and Gardone (Garda). In the Brianza Hills especially, the cultivation of vines and mulberries is noted. High terraces extend continuously in front and on either side of the horseshoe moraines from the Ticino to Lake Iseo, at 50 to 100 ft above the Plain. On the *ceppo* pebble beds (Gunz) and the *ferretto* gravels (Mindel), as well as on the interior morainic hills (Riss and Würm) there are still large areas of heath and brushwood, especially in the west. But where the land has been cleared, wheat and maize fields dominate, with a scatter of small farms and orchards. Three historic cities are located in the Sub-Alpine foothills. Como (57,000) occupying the low terraces and delta south of its lake, retains the rectangular layout of the Roman city, and is still enclosed by the remains of medieval walls. It is the centre of the Italian silk industry. Another important route centre is Bergamo (94,000) with the medieval walls of the Citta Alta (at 1,201 ft), overlooking the new city, spread over the plain below. It is also a noted textile centre. Brescia (110,000) has a similar position and history, with the remains of a rectangular layout and walls, reminiscent of its Roman creation and medieval function as a great fortress. Modern armament and engineering works, as well as textile mills have diversified its functions and greatly promoted its growth in this century.

Milan, 'the central point', or *Mediolanum* of Roman times, still indicates in its circular plan that it is the pivot of Lombardy, with its routes radiating across the Plain. It lies at the cross-roads of three highways: between Turin and Venice; from the Alps, via Lake Maggiore to Piacenza, Bologna, the Apennines and the Adriatic; and from Lake Como to Pavia and Genoa. Situated on sloping ground between the Alta and Bassa Pianura, Milan was formerly bounded by the Po

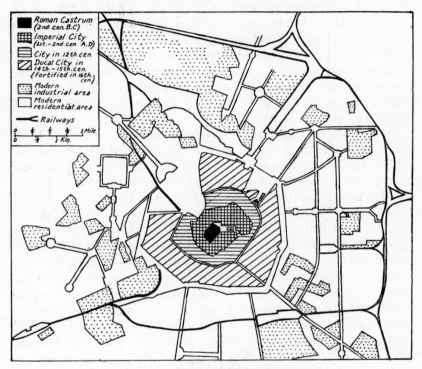

Fig. 193. The growth of Milan (after Pecora)

tributaries, the F. Olona and F. Lambro. It is also linked with the F. Ticino by the Naviglio Grande and Pavia canals, and with the F. Adda by the Martesana canal. Its location has made Milan the industrial and communications capital of Italy, as well as a great marketing centre for the richest agricultural region.

From the Duomo roof, it is possible to visualise the successive stages of growth in the layout of Milan. The site of the first Celtic settlement and Roman *castrum* (7 ha) is under the Piazza del Duomo in the centre of the modern city. Augustus expanded the town, and from the fourth century A.D., use was first made of streams from the Alta Pianura, diverted into the *navigli* (a system of canals) to protect the town and to prevent floods; today, its network extends over 90 miles. The radial plan of the walled *navigli*, rebuilt after 1162, was further protected by the Castle of Porto Giovia (1358). But with the rapid growth of the city—there were some 130,000 inhabitants by the mid-fifteenth century—a new radial wall was added in 1547–8, by the Spaniards (Fig. 193). These served to contain the city until the nineteenth century; in 1801, of the 7,000 ha enclosed by the walls, only 300 were actually built-up, housing 115,000. The Union of Italy initiated a period of rapid expansion; in 1873 inner and outer ring-roads were started, the piazza del Duomo was redesigned after 1877, and much of the old centre was demolished to make room for improvements. Then followed the railway era, with industrial expansion and the built-up area covered 10,000 ha, with 490,000 inhabitants in 1901.

After 1918, the rapid sprawl of the city engulfed a number of out-lying centres, such as Baggio, Trenno, Musocco, Niguarda, Precotto, Greco, Lambrate, Chira valle, etc. As in all large cities, there has been a commensurate decline of population from the centre; the Cerchia Dei Navigli decreasing from 113,000 in 1901 to 61,000 in 1951. But the rapid rates of overall immigration have pushed up the metropolitan total from 720,000 in 1921 to some 1,260,000 in 1951. Meanwhile, there have been marked shifts in the location of Milanese industry. In 1881, textile mills were most numerous, concentrated especially on the south side of the old centre. Three decades later, engineering and metallurgical plants were more numerous especially along the railways to the north, south-west and south-east of the radial city. Since then these loci have been expanded into larger plant sites, while the chemical factories have become more concentrated in the south-west along the Naviglio Grande and Naviglio Pavese.

The industrial expansion of Milan is related to the rapid rise of other satellite towns situated along the Alta Pianura, Notable are Rho (18,381) with its oil refineries; Monza (63,625) with its textile and engineering plants, which has tripled its population in less than a century; and Sesto Giovanni (41,941). Legnano (38,003), Gallerate (30,000) and Saronno (20,000) are other industrial towns. The country-side is marked by fragmented holdings, a mixture of villages and dispersed farms, and rotations that favour maize, wheat, potatoes and trefoil (Fig. 194).

The springline zone of the *risorgivo* varies in width from 15–20 miles towards the Ticino valley to only three to six miles towards the F.

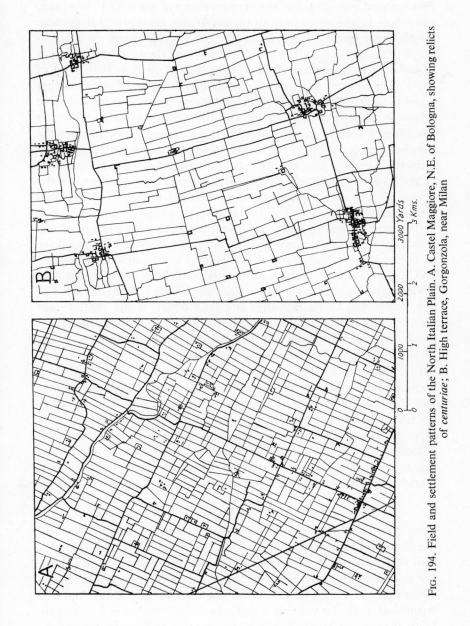

Fig. 194. Field and settlement patterns of the North Italian Plain. A. Castel Maggiore, N.E. of Bologna, showing relicts of *centuriae*; B. High terrace, Gorgonzola, near Milan

Chiese and Mincio. Its copious water supplies 22,000 ha of permanent meadowland (*marcite*). The even temperatures of some 55°F. in winter, contribute to the misty haze so typical of this green, rural landscape. South of the *fontanili* is the Bassa Pianura, a vaster, more varied landscape of several distinctive agricultural regions. Here the fragmentation of holdings is more marked than in the high plain (Fig. 194). West of the F. Lambro are the great rice-fields of Pavese and Lomellina that cover some 50,000 ha each year, in a rotation with grass crops and some wheat or maize. Favoured by the nobility, the introduction of rice in the fifteenth century quickly spread in this area and it has remained the dominant crop. Pavia (57,000) is the most prosperous agricultural and industrial centre, a historic city that has been famed as an early capital of the Lombards and for its University. Situated on the left bank of the lower Ticino, it has preserved the rectangular plan of its Roman foundation. In the centre of the Lombardy plain, astride the Adda valley, *marcite* became more important, but fields of maize and wheat, grown in rotation with hay, are the chief crops. This district, noted for its horses, with its scatter of fortified villages and moated *corte*, centres on Cremona (56,000), which stands on the north bank of the Po at a convenient crossing that avoids the wide sweep of the river meanders. The city, dominated by its cathedral and lofty tower, is still partially enclosed by its walls and moat, and noted for its food industries. Eastwards towards the Oglio, the flood plain is more ill-drained, recent reclamation schemes only being made possible by the control of Garda's lake-level. This dairying country, home of Vergil and sung about in the *Georgics*, is still a green, pastoral scene of water meadows; and the large farmsteads (*bergamine*) with their capacious cowsheds are silhouetted by the circular silos. Surrounded by its lakes, remnants of an old meander of the Po, is the aquatic site of Mantua (47,000), well protected to act as the medieval buffer state between Venice and Milan. Today it is somewhat remote from the main lines of communications, a market town whose rich buildings denote a more illustrious past.

THE NORTH-EAST

Even after crossing the Oglio one is aware that the industrialism and the density of settlement is much less than in the 'Industrial Triangle'. East of Lombardy in the territory of the 'Three Venetias' and Emilia, the rural character of the landscape becomes pronounced. This northeastern part of the Po Plain with its mountain borders of the Alps and Apennines, is the largest major region in Italy. Population densities are lower than in the North West but they are also more uniform. But the

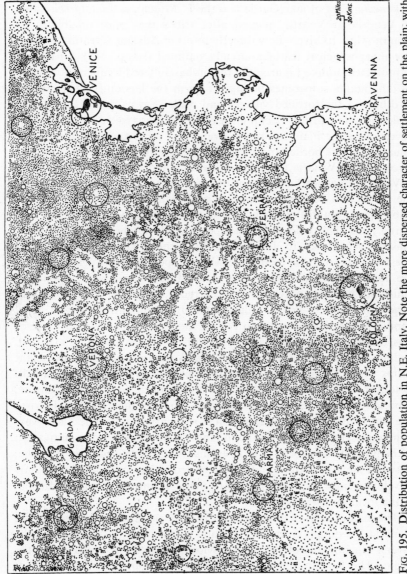

FIG. 195. Distribution of population in N.E. Italy. Note the more dispersed character of settlement on the plain, with lower densities and fewer large cities, compared with the N.W. The influence of centuriation can be recognised in Romagna

landscapes are as diverse as those to the west, for the Alps with their varied scenery dominate the whole northern border.

1. *Venezia*. East of lake Garda and the F. Mincio, is the imprecise area of Venezia or Venetia, named after tribes that once inhabited the eastern Alps. Its rivers flow directly into the Adriatic, creating distinctive morphological features already outlined (see p. 386). Open and unprotected, unlike Liguria, the region has suffered frequent invasions, its inhabitants sometimes taking refuge in the lagoon-fringed littoral, at others in the fortified villages and walled towns at the foot of the Dolomites and Friuli. Lacking the high terraces typical of Lombardy, nevertheless the Plain has more diversity of relief and land utilisation. Since 1918, this borderland of Italy has been divided officially into the three *regioni*, Venezia Euganea, Tridentina and Giulia.

Venezia Euganea has perhaps the most varied landscapes. Elsewhere the distinction between mountains and plain is abrupt, but here the Sub-Alpine foothills are extended on to the Plain in the Euganean and Berici Hills. This volcanic landscape of single sombre cones and more massive relief rises to 1,978 ft in M. Venda. Thickly wooded with chestnuts and oaks on their upper slopes especially the Euganean Hills, the lower southern slopes have a Mediterranean flora of *macchia* which has been partially cleared for terraced vineyards, olive groves and peach orchards. Perched villages, dating from antiquity with Este, capital of the Venetes prior to Padua, indicate the early importance of this district. From Garda and the Mincio to the coast, is a varied, rolling countryside of wheat, maize and rotation meadow, in tenant farms which range from medium-sized properties in the west, to small-holdings in the east. Vineyards are on the decrease but fruit culture, especially of peaches in the coastal area, is increasing. South of Treviso, the plain is poorer and the conquest of the marsh has been less achieved. Where reclaimed, the lower-lying land is important for the cultivation of hemp and sugar-beet in large farms. A distinctive *pays* is Polesine, between the lower Adige and the Po, ceded to Venice in 1484, but only developed since the reclamations of the last century. Rovigno (18,000) is the local industrial centre.

The major towns of western Venezia are located on the margins of the Plain at the outlets from the Alps and in defensive positions along the rivers. The nodality of Verona is obvious, where the F. Adige enters the Plain. The Roman site is protected by the meanders of the river. It flourished under the Scaligeri (*c.* 40,000 in the late thirteenth century), only to decline later for political reasons, and because of the pestilence in 1630–1. Its function as a fortress was perpetuated by the defences built in the eighteenth century, becoming the chief bulwark of the 'Austrian Quadrilateral' (together with the other fortresses of Mantua, Peschiera and Legnago) after 1815. A silk and agricultural centre, Verona has now a population of 135,000. Vicenza, at the confluence of the F. Bacchiglione and Retrone, guards the passage between the limestone hills of M. Lessini and Mi Berici, along an ancient trade route between the Alps, Padua and Venice. It is also an agricultural and silk centre, with historic buildings designed by its citizen Palladio. Recent, diversified industries have promoted its growth to 61,000 inhabitants. Downstream the Bacchiglione valley, Padua is another route centre of the Plain. Its stages of growth are traceable in the walls and moats which formed its defences: a central oval of 1195–1210, a triangular addition in the fourteenth century, and a rectangular appendage two centuries later. A commercial centre and famous University town, Padua has grown rapidly in the last fifty years and now has 140,000. Treviso (53,000) has a more central position on the Venetian plain than those already mentioned, at the cross-roads of routes crossing the Plain and following the Piave valley into the Alps. It has long remained stagnant (14,000 in 1563, 17,000 in 1873) and only silk and other industries have developed it recently to 53,000.

Dominating the Venetian Plain is the unique city of Venice, created by thirteen centuries of human ingenuity, and built on piles over some 120 islands in the middle of the large, shallow Laguna Veneta. These islands are divided into two unequal groups by the Grand Canal, which curves through the city with its approximately 450 small branch canals (*rii* or *rielli*). Some 400 bridges link up the countless little alleys (*calli*), which unite the larger squares (*campi*) and smaller courtyards (*campielli*). To the south is the isle of Giudecca, an industrial suburb (formerly a ghetto); to the north is Murano, famous for its glassware; and to the east are the residential suburbs of the Lido, with its beaches, villas and hotels. The history of Venice has been well described by Molmenti and other historians. Founded by refugees from the mainland during the barbarian invasion, aided by the Byzantines and, after the ninth century, established as a flourishing mercantile republic, Venice was long mistress of the Adriatic and even of the Levant. Its cargoes made Venice the emporium of the world's merchandise, and the city reached its apogee in the fifteenth century when it numbered 200,000 inhabitants, a figure only reached again in 1951 (203,000). It now remains essentially a tourist centre, apart from the industrial suburb of Mestre (73,000) which has metallurgical industries and shipyards. The whole conurbation numbers some 350,000 inhabitants.

East of the Piave, the division between the high and low plain becomes most marked. The high plain rises as much as 800 feet above the low plain, porous and a practically waterless waste of heathlands (*magredi*) and thin pasture (*prateria*). It is sparsely populated (Fig. 195). Even the Alpine streams lose their water as they flow across these dejection cones, and the Tagliamento and Isonzo have been known to dry up in this section of their courses. At about 100 ft above sea-level, the upper limit of the *fontanili* occurs, its presence marked by green fields of maize, wheat, and leguminous meadows, and orchards and the immediate crowding of settlement. These contrast with the mulberries, vines and heaths of the upper plain. Towards the sea, recently reclaimed lands are divided into large farms where cereals dominate, especially maize. But in Friuli generally, holdings are fragmented and small because of inheritance laws, notably towards the east. This region is noted for its emigration, its remoteness, conservatism and limited resources that discourage full employment. The frontier character of Friuli is seen in its numerous fortresses, with elaborate defences in centres such as Pordenone (22,000), Palma Nova and Gorizia (34,600), aligned along the *fontanili* zone, while Monfalcone (24,000) guards the road into Istria. Udine (65,000) is another stronghold, but its textile and chemical industries have created its modern appearance and importance. The narrow corridor between the Karst plateau (800–1,000 ft) and the coast, had no great strategic significance in the past, and the small port of Trieste still only had *c.* 5,000 in the eighteenth century, largely because of its unsuccessful rivalry to Venice. It was developed as an Austrian outlet, with a new port constructed in 1869–93 and its population rising from 38,000 in 1810 to 135,000 in 1900. Restored to Italy in 1918, it was further developed as the third port of Italy, with shipbuilding yards, metallurgical and food industries. It has expanded southwards along the Bay of Muggia where its industrial zone has developed. From Montebello (879 ft) the growth of the city can be traced. The Roman and medieval plain, grafted into the gridiron of the new eighteenth-century city, lies alongside the port. Behind is the nineteenth-century development, the later growth sprawling along the coast and on the hill slopes. Today, it is a city of 272,000.

2. *Emilia-Romagna.* Emilia-Romagna covers barely half of the area of Venezia, but it has more evident unity along the axis of the Po and the Apennines. Between them is the great Roman highway of via Aemilia that gave Emilia its name. Built in 187 B.C., it was associated with a major scheme of Roman colonisation which had some 40–50,000 holdings surveyed in centuriated fashion, the evidence of which is still

apparent in the graticule of minor roads, field patterns and the town plans (Fig. 194). Not surprisingly, it was identified as a distinct region (VII, or *Regio Aemiliae Viae*) in Augustan times (Fig. 188). It is probable that even in Etruscan times some effort to drain the foot of

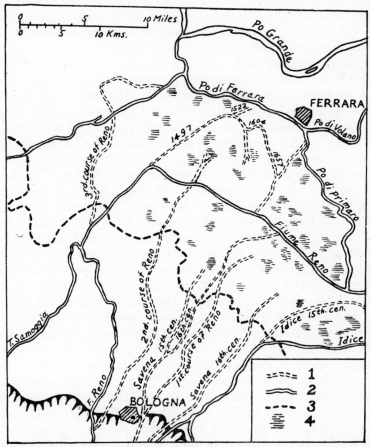

FIG. 196. Colonisation and reclamation in Emilia: 1. ancient courses of rivers; 2. actual river courses; 3. lower limit on the plain of Roman colonisation; 4. marshy areas of the sixteenth and seventeenth centuries. Jagged line in the south represents N. edge of the Apennines

hills had been made. Such long continuity of settlement and man's intensive tillage of the soil have made this one of the richest regions of Italy, with the greatest agricultural income. The other name 'Romagna' refers to an eastern district indistinct geographically from the rest of the region, but having political significance in 1859. There is a clear threefold division of Emilia-Romagna into the Apennines, the Hills and the Plain.

Backed by the Etruscan Apennines that run uniformly for some 40 miles wide and 250 miles in length, Emilia has a clearly developed mountainous backbone. Its chains run parallel to one another and to the direction of the range as a whole, with its components arranged in echelon, but so spaced out that there are not more than two parallel chains in any cross-section. Great rounded masses of Eocene sandstones comprise the higher lands, and only the highest summit of Cimone (7,096 feet) is distinctive, snow-clad for most of the year. Wide valleys such as Secchia with their pronounced terraces lead gently over the numerous passes between the Bratello and the Trabaria gaps, so that transverse routes are easy, and have favoured the growth of its cities on the Plain. More resistant masses of limestone and volcanics stand out from the sandstones, sometimes as isolated cliffs, gigantic steps, or more often as wide tablelands aligned in long narrow bands. In Romagna, sharp crests and pinnacles of limestone thrust through more swelling, plastic relief of clays and sandstones. These rocky outcrops in Emilia and Romagna are favoured as sites for medieval castles, built to defend the routes and the surrounding countryside. It is a poor, bare landscape of little value to man. Some 200,000 hectares are miserably cultivated, in excessively fragmented holdings, that are no inducement to prevent rural depopulation. More than a third of the mountain area is devoid of vegetation, except for some poor pasture, and between half and a third of the productive area is covered with woods, mostly coppiced mixed oak scrub and chestnuts, with some beech woods above.

A broad belt of hills front the highlands, deeply eroded and continually scarred by the *frane*, which frequently dam the valley floors. This terrain of *argile scagliose*, and of Pliocene blue clays and yellow sands, presents a contrasted picture of wooded or unproductive slopes on the former and of smiling, vine-clad, orchard country on the latter. This alternation of dantesque and buccolic scenes, discriminated by tenant farmers, is reflected in the population map (Fig. 195). The limited glaciation of the northern Apennines, compared with the Alps is evidenced by the small patches of debris that are scarcely distinguishable from the hills against which they rest.

The High Plain forms a narrow belt of transition between the huis and the Po valley, widening at the valley mouths, where the rivers constantly choked by the *frane* have changed their courses many times (Fig. 196). Cereal lands alternate with vineyards, mulberries, orchards, tomatoes and forage crops in a rich profusion of polyculture. Holdings, though small, are not fragmented, and are of a size which can give the highest profits to its rich peasantry. Population is grouped in small nucleated villages. The lower edge of the High Plain is neatly followed by the Emilian highway, with its string of small market towns between Piacenza and Rimini. From these Roman towns, centres of valley cantons, traditional *pays* strike into the mountains valleys, such as Piacentino, Parmense, Reggiano, Modenese, Bolognese, Imolese, Faentino, Forlivese, Cesenate and Riminses. The largest centres, notably Piacenza (60,000) Parma (85,000), Reggio (50,000), Modena (75,000) Bologna (316,000) and Rimini (50,000) are all industrial cities with a long history, associated in the Middle Ages with the rivalry of Guelphs and Ghibellines, and aided by their independent transverse lines of communication.

Situated on the via Aemilia, between the valleys of the Reno and the Savena, the importance of Bologna as a route centre has been ensured since Roman times. In Celtic times it already occupied 8 hectares, and from its Etruscan centre it was enlarged by the Romans (after 189 B.C.) In Byzantine times it was overshadowed by Ravenna, so its real importance dates from the twelfth century, when the University was founded and its communal liberties were developed. It was then that its second set of walls were built in 1139, with a third set in 1330, whose circumference is still marked by the existing gates. It became known as 'Rossa Bologna' because of its great red sandstone palaces, built between the thirteenth and sixteenth centuries. Today, it is the junction of five main railway lines and a great food processing centre.

Between the High Plain and the Po, the land drops gently about a hundred feet. The limit of Roman colonisation was along the 50–60 feet contours approximately, while the area below 45 feet still had much marsh (*valli*) in the sixteenth to eighteenth centuries (Fig. 196), despite the efforts of Benedictine monasteries during the ninth and tenth centuries. Drainage was undertaken, notably in Ferrara (1564–80) by the Este family and in Reggiano (1567). But the subsequent relapse of some 40,000 hectares to waterlogging and desolation around Ferrara showed the need of constant vigilance, and this area was only restored again for human use during the last eighty years. The hydraulic achievements of Emilia have been immense, with about 250,000 hectares reclaimed since 1835, with notable schemes in 1872, 1882 and 1933. By 1950, 64 per cent of all Emilia had been improved by hydraulic and mountain conservation works, of which 400,000 hectares had been put into cultivation. This man-made landscape of the Low Plain has an open appearance, flat, vast, and uniform. Away from the hills, the rows of vines thin out, to be replaced by industrial crops, grain and forage. Here in large farms (Fig. 185) are concentrated half of the total sugar beet and hemp production of Italy, and with the abundance of forage crops, livestock, notably dairy cattle, are as numerous as in all of Lombardy. Ferrara (70,000), retaining the pentagonal outline of its medieval walls, has long been a fortress among the Po marshes, still silhouetted by the towers of the Castello. Further east, the sandy coastal plain of Romagna is better suited to vegetable crops, notably tomatoes; and small-holdings again prevail as in the High Plain. Along the sand dune littoral, dotted with its groves of maritime pines and swamps, life is again stirring. Alongside somnolent, Byzantine Ravenna (35,000) there are signs of a new era, evidenced by pipe-lines, a major refinery and the great new oil port of Ravenna.

CHAPTER 18

THE REGIONS OF PENINSULAR
ITALY AND SICILY

'Among variegated pillars, woods are planted;
the most admired mansions command huge landscapes:
toss Nature out with a pitch fork, still she will return,
And conquer unobserved your false fastidiousness.'

Horace (Ep. I. 10)

Peninsular Italy is very different from the North Italian Plain in its landforms, climate, features of settlement and economic background. Less tangible, though no less real in the life of its people, are different evaluations made of resources. In the North they are to procure more money, and instincts are like those of Western Europe. In the South, money is desired for other objectives; status, power over others, these count for much more than the accumulation of wealth for its own sake. Thus the two extremities of Italy are worlds apart in environment, standards of living and the psychological evaluation of resources. Despite extensive coastal plains, the whole Peninsula is dominated by the mountain ranges of the Apennines. Compared with the North Italian Plain there is therefore much more variety of agrarian conditions and rural landscapes. As its history has also been associated with political fragmentation this too has created much regional diversity. However, three broad distinctions are clear in this land: the Centre, the South and Insular Italy. The Centre is the traditional 'heartland' of the country, with its traditions of the Church, a cultural heritage of many ancient towns, and a sturdy peasantry that has been reasonably prosperous and has left an imprint on numerous tamed landscapes. Central Italy has a temperate air for a Mediterranean habitat, with rich moist plains, much ploughland, and various trees clothed in vines. Different again is the south, scene of chronic poverty that is in part the result of historical conditions, but afflicted also by poor water resources, much limestone, erodible lands and the curse of malaria that prevailed until very recently. Sicily is more comparable with the southern mainland than with Sardinia, except that both express the poverty of the South in superlatives.

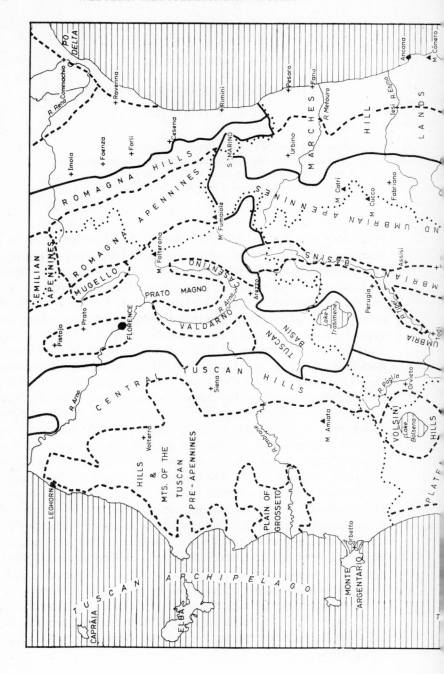

Fig. 197. Regional divisions of central Italy

1. *The Adriatic Coastlands of the Marches, Abruzzi and Molise*. Stretched for over two hundred miles along the Adriatic coast, between the valleys of the Foglia and the Fortore, is the region of the Marches, Abruzzi and Molise. As the former name implies, this area once comprised a series of marchlands that included in the Middle Ages the marks of Ancona, Fermo and Camerino. Earlier still, part of the region was called 'Piceno', a tribal territory traceable back to the Bronze Age when much of the area—as its name suggests—was still covered in pine forests. On the geological map the Marches appear deceptively simple, as if a Tertiary tempest had been fossilised into the mobile relief of Mio-Pliocene folds that rise gently in swells towards the interior. Certainly the relations of geology and relief are simple, but the short consequent rivers that fall steeply to the coast from the Sub-Apennines form transverse, small basins that segment the life of each district. What unity there is has been forged by the Adriatic littoral, never more than 15 to 25 miles away. There are several significant elements in the landscape; a threefold zonation of landforms from the coast to the interior; the features of monotonous relief only relieved occasionally by badlands and landslides; the dominance of interculture; excessive fragmentation of holdings with the tenure system of *mezzadria* and the high dispersion of isolated farms; and the frequent occurrence of hill-top villages (Fig. 199). These features are particularly characteristic of the Marches countryside. In the Molise, the land-use is poorer, the holdings are larger, and there is more woodland and waste. Lens-shaped beds of gypsum and sulphur, together with severe badlands and formerly much malaria made this a more desolate area.

About one-third of the Adriatic coastlands are mountainous, half are hilly and the lowlands are limited therefore to about one-tenth of the total area. Sympathetic with the geology there is a three-fold zonation of relief (Fig. 163). Along the coast there is normally a narrow plain carved out of Pliocene clays, and backed by the dissected remnants of Pliocene sandy plateaux. These rise gently inland from 300 to about 1,100 ft. A more pronounced rise to 1,300–2,000 ft on Miocene sandstones, clays and marls, is associated with more deeply dissected relief, especially along the twenty or so major consequent valleys that rise within the Apennines. Their lower tributaries are fed by springs in the Miocene limestones. Beyond, there is much steeper ascent to the wall-like barrier of Mesozoic limestones that form the Apennines of the Marches, the Gran Sasso and other mountains of the Abruzzi, and the

Molise Apennines. This alternation of mountains and hills, small asymmetrical valleys and narrow plains, with wild abrupt scenery in the west, more docile, more monotonous relief in the east, produce an endless variety of components, many of them of feudal usage. It is best, therefore, to describe these three zones of the coast, the interior hills and the western mountains, rather than attempt a detailed, regional subdivision.

The narrow coastal plain is divided unequally in two by the flat-topped limestone headland of M. Cònero (1,877 ft). Its steep seaward slopes are covered in *macchia*. To the north, the coastal plain is interrupted by low, broken cliffs, especially between Pesaro and Cattolica. Valleys are broad, though deltas are imperceptible. Much of the lowland is intensively cultivated with vegetables and fruit trees, while the lower slopes are mantled under an interculture of vines, mulberries, elms, walnuts, cereals, maize and a variety of other crops. It is a landscape reminiscent of Romagna. Pesaro (35,000) a walled town of the Sforzas, and laid out in a pentagonal plan in the eighteenth century, is now being expanded as a fashionable seaside resort. Passing by Fano, another fortress town, we come to Ancona (62,000) the capital of the Marches. As a free city in the Middle Ages, Ancona has passed through many vicissitudes, reflected in its medieval hill town to the east of the artificial harbour, its sixteenth-century citadel to the west, and its rapid post-war expansion to the south-east, now stimulated by its industrial development.

South of M. Cònero, longshore drift is less significant and the coast is more cliffed, with the sea eroding into the typically flattened edges of the Pliocene plateaux. Cultivation is still intense with much interculture and irrigation along the broad, lower valleys (*cerretano*) of the Potenza, Chieti, Tenna, Aso, Tronto, Vomano and Pescara. The population is dense (500 per sq. mile), concentrated on the clay ridges and on the recent coastal plains. Between the Tronto and Pescara valleys this area of the Abruzzi Sub-Apennines is very similar to the Marches, with the same rounded and monotonous relief of clay lands, finely dissected by the close drainage pattern, and mantled in mixed cropping. But between the Pescara and Trigno valleys to the south, there is a marked change in the region known as the Frentane Sub-Apennines. Here the Upper Pliocene sands (Astian) form a cover over the dull coloured clays, and the land-use is different, gaily garlanded in more specialised tree cropping, notably vines, olives and some mulberries. Pescara (48,000), situated between the Aprutine and Frentane Sub-Apennines, is the regional capital. Terminus of the Via Valeria and medieval fortress, it is today a flourishing agricultural centre and fishing port. South of Vasto, between the Trigno and Fortore valleys, there is an abrupt change in the countryside. The valleys are waste, malaria has been a severe limitation on population densities (100–250 per sq. mile) and except for the olive groves around the hill villages, there is a dreary expanse of cornlands and fallow. It is also a land of sheep walks leading to the Tavoliere.

Inland from these coastal lands is a similar landscape of swelling relief of hills, more broken by Miocene limestones that thrust through the clay mantle, and scarred by fresh landslides (*ripe* and *scrollani*). Vines and olives alternate with cereals and fodder crops, though cereals occupy over half the cultivated area, with a preference for the broad plateau interfluves, such as those of Foglia, Metauro, Cesano, Misi, Tronto Teramo and Chieti. There are two lines of towns running through the interior. One series runs some six miles from the coast, such as Chieti (26,000), Atri, Fermo and Chiaravalle, often paralleled by new *marine* along the coast. Another line of towns lies 15–20 miles from the coast, near the foot of the Apennines. These include Teramo, the granary of the Abruzzi, Ascoli (25,500) on the Via Salaria, Piceno, Macerata (20,000), Iesi (21,500), Urbino and San Marino. All are market towns, most of them walled medieval fortresses and Renaissance ducal towns, and several are still bishoprics. San Marino, nestling beneath the rugged limestone crags of M. Titano (2,480 ft) has been effectively defended by its castle 125 ft above the town, and is the one extant city republic of numerous other historic examples. In Molise, where the population is much sparser (Fig. 198), the only sizeable town is Campobasso (21,000) clustered loosely around its Lombard castle. Today it is an important agricultural centre.

From the vantage point of Cingoli (2,093 ft) the rugged limestone flanks of the Apennines are seen to rise abruptly in the west. Further south in the Abruzzi there are bold fault scarps but in the north, the Montefeltro forming a great palaeogene island enveloped in gently folded Miocene strata, is a squalid, desolate landscape of *argile scagliose*. The basin of Camerino is a softer, more fertile country with its marls under cultivation and its sandy, acid soils covered in woodland or *macchia*. Rising above such synclinal troughs is the rugged outcrop of thick Mesozoic limestones, broken into deep gorges that are bare of vegetation and flanked by enormous screes of debris. Only a few towns are found in this sparsely populated area (less than 250 per sq. mile). They are of ancient Umbrian-Roman origin located on strategic valley routes, such as at Fabriano (10,500), Camerino, Aquila (24,850) and

Sulmona (17,700). Aquila, the chief town, is laid out formally in a regular plan that dates from the thirteenth century. Other centres are smaller, usually fortified villages that formerly protected groups of mountain hamlets. The lower mountain slopes have small, scattered fields of grain and pasture, followed upwards by great forests of beech and mixed oaks, particularly notable on the flanks of the Maiella, Gran Sasso and Laga. Over the craggy, glaciated summits are the broad pastures, notable in the polje of the Campo Imperatore, a silent world filled only with the legends of the pastoralists (Plate 58).

2. *Umbria.* Between the Sub-Apennines and the Ante-Apennines lies the historic region of Umbria. In morphology it is complex and in shape disorderly. First vaguely defined as an ancient tribal territory of the north-central Apennines, Augustus recognised it as his seventh region (Fig. 188). During the Middle Ages it disappeared, being replaced by the Duchy of Spoleto at the time of the Lombards, and having a somewhat different area. Nevertheless, its focal area has always been the interior basins of the Upper Tiber. Umbria is the only major region of Italy without direct access to the sea, yet it has been the major artery of communications between the Tyrrhenian and Adriatic coasts. Bordered on the east and north by the high ramparts of the Apennines, it opens on to the hills of Tuscany on the west; thus in Etruscan times Perugia was not an Umbrian city but Etruscan. The distinctive geographic features of Umbria are its intermontane basins, its routeways and nodal centres, and an abundant water supply utilised now for its modern industrial growth. Like the neighbouring regions of the Marches and Tuscany, Umbria has markedly dispersed rural settlements, much interculture and the *mezzadria* tenure system.

Rough and melancholy, Umbria includes three types of landscape: the Central Apennines to the east, the central basins of the upper and middle Tiber and its tributaries, and the lower mountain and hill country to the west (Fig. 157). In the Umbrian Apennines, there is a prevailing northwest to south-east trend of anticlinal ranges, complicated by faults. In the north the Falterona range divides in two to enclose the small, faulted basin of Gubbio. Rounded forms in sandstones predominate with much forest cover, but rising above them are the highest summits such as Catria (5,384 ft), Pennino (5,158 ft) and to the west, M. Subasio (4,232 ft) a bare, rugged scenery of grey, steep-sided limestones. South of Foligno limestones predominate and give the highest relief of Umbria in the Reatine Highlands (7,261 ft). It is a deserted country, with much depopulation, so densities are less than 50 per sq. mile. Stone-built villages huddle around miserable

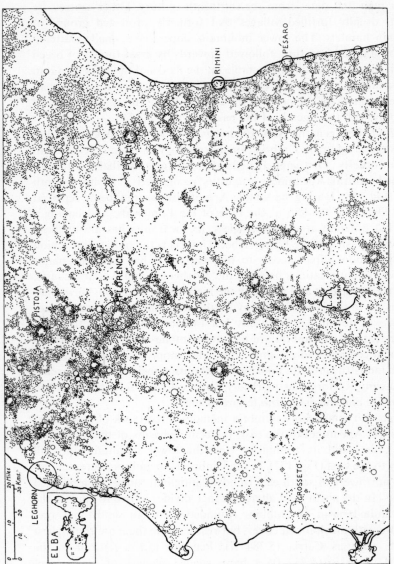

FIG. 198. Distribution of population in north-central Italy. (Same key as in Fig. 196.) Note the distinct patterns of settlement: the marked concentration of population in the Arno basin; the stellar pattern of market centres and road-side farms radiating along the ridges in the Marches; the dispersal of settlement in the Tuscan and Umbrian basins; the sparsity of settlement in the Maremma and parts of the Roman Campagna; the marked dispersion in the Frosinone basin; and the planned distribution of scattered farms and towns, notably in the Agro Pontino

holdings of two to three hectares, with every evidence of a decaying rural life.

Very different is the network of interior basins and valleys laced together by the Tiber system (Fig. 197). This has long been the hub of Umbrian life, as centres of cultivation and of communication. In the north, extending into Tuscany is the Val Tiberina, the *pays* of the upper Tiber, narrowing into the meandering valley of the Tiber below Citta di Castello. A second Pliocene lake-floor extends from there to Umbertide and a third from Umbertide to Perugia (Plate 60). The floors of these basins are intensely cultivated, and the slopes are forested. The Umbrian Valley or basin of the Clitumni is one of the richest, its pastures being renowned from antiquity. Maize, tobacco, fodder crops, sugar-beet are also important. Though less extensive than the vine, it is the olive that lends colour to Umbria. Between Perugia and Todi, the Tiber drains another basin, whose floor is also intensely cultivated, but its dry sandy slopes are left in scrub. The Nera, the most important tributary of the Tiber, drains the Terni, Rieti and other basins which are also well cultivated. Between the Terni and Rieti basins are the travertine falls of the Nera, cascading for some 825 ft and now partially utilised for hydro-electric power. These basins are the orchards and gardens of Umbria with high densities of population. There is much dissemination of farms, though the fortress character of the old towns gives a medieval atmosphere. Perched on ridges above the basins, the towns are even reminiscent of the Algerian *ksours*. Many, such as Orvieto and Assisi, live in the past, and there are only four that have more than 12,000 inhabitants. Terni, the industrial capital is atypical, only revived in modern times with the harnessing of the Velino falls for hydro-electricity (in 1875–85). With its satellites engaged in metallurgical and electro-chemical industries, it has over 75,000 inhabitants. Perugia, magnificently situated 1,000 ft above the Tiber valley, is a famous Etruscan, Roman and medieval city, owing its importance as a route centre to an impregnable site. For several centuries it remained stagnant but today it has 40,000 inhabitants. Foligno (20,000) and Spoleto (14,000) are other route and fortress towns of antiquity, now agricultural centres.

To the west of Umbria are two highland blocks, the M. Martano-M. Toore Maggiore and the Trasimeno-Narni ridge. The former rise in sandstone hills to about 1,300 ft although in the south they reach over 3,500 ft. In the latter there is a rolling dissected relief of 1,000–2,300 ft. Much of it is grainland, with scrub on the higher slopes.

3. *Tuscany.* Etruria or Tuscany, perhaps the oldest and most civilised region, was in classical times also one of the richest regions in the

central Mediterranean. Much of it was cultivated, and the Maremma was an important granary until the Barbarian invasions when it relapsed into a malarial swamp and *macchia*. Etruria contained nearly the entire mineral wealth of classical Italy and unlike the isolated Greek colonies in southern Italy, the Etruscans formed a great continental confederacy of twelve city states, based largely on the intense metallurgical exploitation. Etruria has been a variable unit, extending in Etruscan times even into the North Italian Plain. Under the Lombards it shrank to the Arno basin with Lucca as its capital, only later expanding once more to include the Principality of Piombino and other units in the seventeenth and eighteenth centuries. Tuscany is therefore more a cultural than a natural region, only roughly defined by the northern Apennines, the Tyrrhenian Sea and the Volsini mountains just north of lake Bolsena. Tuscany is indeed one of the most varied areas of Italy, both because of its diversified relief, soils and land use, and also because of man's imprint upon its landscapes.

If the theory of a Levantine origin for the Etruscans is true then it is probable they were first attracted here because of the mineral wealth: iron in Elba, lead and zinc in Campiglia, marble in the Apuan Apennines, manganese in Argentario and copper pyrites in several localities. Since antiquity it is estimated that 30 million tons of iron ore have been extracted from Elba. In modern times great scars of marble quarries have been made in the Apuan mountains and vast depressions excavated in the lignite beds of the upper Valdarno and in the Maremma. There has been extensive clearance of forest for the smelters; some 800 sq. miles between the fourteenth and the nineteenth centuries. The cypress, typical as a silhouette of the Tuscan landscape, was probably introduced from Asia Minor by the Etruscans. There has been much transformation of the indigenous beech forest in the Apennines to firs, favoured for their naval timber, and the extent of 160,000 ha of chestnuts (out of a total forest cover of 813,000 ha in Tuscany today) also shows the influence of man. Impressive too has been man's reclamation in a region once noted for its numerous Plio-Pleistocene lakes and marshes. This started when the Etruscans built their *cuniculi* (pp. 123–4, 514). After the Goletti of Chiana was built in 1342 the flow of the Chiana was completely reversed (Fig. 165). During the following centuries the Florentines straightened the Arno and embanked its lower course, conquering the Pisan plain. Since A.D. 1000, reclamation of the Maremma has proceeded slowly. Modern schemes have speeded up the changes so that in the period 1928–40 alone, over 200 miles of canals were constructed in Tuscany. Since 1951 about 35,000 ha have been converted from waste for cultivation in the Maremma, and another 28,000 are in process of development. The scatter of numerous new farms over the Maremma is only the latest evidence of man's intense imprint on the Tuscan landscapes.

Along a bold front of forty miles, the Apuan Alps rise steeply from the densely populated littoral of Massa, with its holiday resorts, largest of which is Viareggio (37,500). Above its schistose base, densely covered with chestnut forests, rises the dolomitic range in all its rugged splendour, to heights of 6,000 ft. Narrow terraces climb steeply, but the depopulation of the hamlets explains the decline of the chestnut woods and the relapse of the small pockets of cultivation into waste. The high levels support extensive pastures, and watered generously, the summits are draped in winter snow. From the highest summit of Pisanino (6,383 ft) there are wonderful vistas across the island-dotted Tyrrhenian sea. To the east of the Apuan Alps, a series of depressions are exploited by the rivers Magra (Lunigiana) and upper Serchio (Garfagnana). There, abundant karstic springs support intense interculture and closely scattered farms.

Very different in character are the Etruscan Apennines, which form the northern border of Tuscany for 250 miles in a series of ranges about 40 miles broad. Bare-topped and rounded with a marked accordance of level between 3,000 and 5,000 ft above sea-level, their relief appears much drearier and monotonous. These mountains only differentiate the schistose clays (*argile scagliose*) and marls with landslides and softer contours, from the more resistant sandstones. Everywhere the scenery is softened by a thick covering of coppiced mixed woodland and scrub, very different from the bare cereal lands of the Romagna slopes of these same mountains. The watershed is continuously high and the high summits such as M. Cimone (7,096 ft) do not stand out so conspicuously as in other ranges. East of Cimone, the Apennines are interrupted by a long depression, itself broken up by transverse ridges into short, isolated basins. Notable are the former lake-basins of the Mugello, the Casentino and the Val Tiberina (see p. 406), all clothed in vines, fruit trees and cereals. Compared with the old villages and the predominance of peasant cultivators in the basins of Garfagnana and Luinignana, these eastern basins have more the stamp of a feudal regime, with a dispersed population sheltered by cypress and umbrella pines, practising *mezzadria* under the surveillance of large country houses (Plate 62). These were built after the mid-sixteenth century when, as the principality of the Medicis, the economic centre of gravity moved from town to country, and agriculture flourished at the expense of the urban interests. Apart from these cultivated basins and the coppiced slopes, there are few other distinguishing features of these mountains. Only a few forests have survived, usually under monastic protection, as at Boscolungo near the Abbetone pass, Vallombrosa on the western Prato-magno, and la Verna and Camaldoli on the south-eastern and north-eastern slopes of the Casentino.

South of the Apuan Alps and backed steeply by their outlier of M. Pisano (2,980 ft) is the plain of Pisa along the lower Arno. The lower slopes of Pisano are covered with orchards and higher up with chestnut woods. On the plain south of Pisa water meadows reflect the difficulties of drainage, which were initiated in the Middle Ages when silting of the port of Pisa spelled the decline of this Italian Bruges; until 1284 Pisa had been of at least equal status to Florence. Malaria, silting, the constant floods, have all hindered this plain, and Pisa has only revived since the advent of the railway; today it has 62,500. By comparison, Leghorn is modern, created on a pentagonal plan in 1571–1618, and now a busy port and industrial centre (131,000). Between these two cities there is a graticule of drainage ditches, fronted near the coast by mixed coppiced woodlands, and pines.

Apart from the Maremma, the rest of lowland Tuscany may be grouped under the general context of the Tuscan Hill and Basin region (Fig. 197). On the east of Pisano is the rich basin of Lucca, flanked to the north by the famous olive groves along the foothills of the Apennines. Interculture and irrigation (around Lucca) provide intensive use of the plain. Lucca (43,000), still encased in its city walls (1560–1645), is an agricultural centre for a densely populated region. Beyond Montecatini, over the chestnut wooded slopes of M. Albano, is the fertile plain of the middle Arno, stretching between Pistoja and Florence. The Pistoja district, drained by the Ombrone, a tributary of the Arno, is enveloped in orchards, and flanked by olives, scattered in disorderly array, on the foothills of the basin. Pistoja (33,500), still enclosed by its hexagonal walls, and Prato (44,600) are both ancient centres of some note, but southwards the increasing density of population heralds approach to the great tourist mecca of Florence. The city (342,500) is best seen from the slopes south of the Arno at the Piazzale Michelangelo, with its numerous towers, the seven bridges across the muddy river, and the great domed cathedral dominating all. Medieval suburbs near the modern centre still preserve their narrow streets, only to exit suddenly on to spacious squares, gardens or wider streets that were redeveloped during the seventeenth and eighteenth centuries. From Fiesole, a wider view of a gracious countryside of olives and vines, undulating over rolling hills, is to be seen. Past the wooded defile west of Signa the Arno valley opens widely into a vast garden of interculture, with large agricultural villages such as Empoli and Fucecchio and a dense scatter of small farms. South towards Casciana vineyards become prominent and towards Poggibonsi olives silhouette the hills. Similar landscapes sweep south along the Elsa, upper Arno and the Chianti valleys. Geological outcrops are significant: erosion has exposed the Plaisancian clays in the valleys, while the Astian sandstones generally form rolling plateaux, whose edges have often small scarps. Cereals and tree crops tend to respond according to the two types of relief. Isolated outcrops of Eocene rocks and various limestones have a cover of garrigue, often with villages at their foot surrounded by olive groves.

Towards Siena and especially to the south-east of the town, the bare, clay *crete*, with grainlands and pastures are a desolate contrast to the rest of this type of country. Densities of population fall to 70–80 per sq. mile compared with 500 or more in the Valdarno and Chianti. Badlands are a marked feature of the Siennese country. Nevertheless, the nodality of the district at the cross-roads between the ancient Maremma towns and the Apennines, and on the great north-south highway gave Siena an important role in the Middle Ages, rivalling Florence. Built on three converging ridges, which divide the town into distinct quarters (*terzi*), the town has a star-shaped plan. In its medieval glory, Siena had double its present population (40,000) and the town has preserved its medieval atmosphere. Indeed, decadence from a glorious past seems characteristic of many small Tuscan towns such as Certaldo, San Gimignano, Poggibonsi, Montepulciano, Pienza and Chiusi. Of this list only Volterra is the exception, with over 10,000 inhabitants. Arezzo, like Siena, has a pivotal position, between the Casentino, Valdarno and the Chianti valley. It has been a market centre since pre-Roman times.

Apart from the smooth, parallel ridges of Chianti (2,930 ft) and Cetona (1,118 ft), the highest relief of the Pre-Apennines lies west of the Elsa-Paglia valleys. Tertiary sandstones and a complex of hard old rocks provide a variety of colours and forms in the highlands of the Catena Metallifera, while the steam emissions at Lardarello present a miniature Yellowstone. South of the marshy floor of the Ombrone valley, the volcanic cone of Amiata rises spectacularly to 5,690 ft from a schistose base thickly clothed in chestnut woods, with beech forests above. Settlement is grouped in villages of ancient origin at the foot of these uplands favoured by generous springs of water (Fig. 199). The westward view is dreary, a rolling expanse of cornlands or coppice,

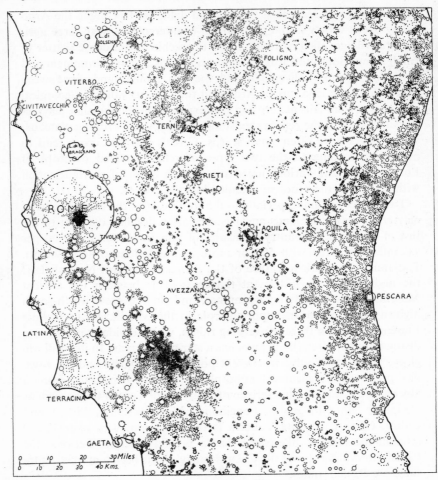

FIG. 199. Distribution of population in central Italy. (Same key as in Fig. 196.) Note the unevenness of settlement concentration, with a marked absence of population in the Maremma and parts of the Roman Campagna, and a general sparsity along the coast. The Abbruzzi mountains are among the most deserted of Italy's ranges. Distinct is the intense dispersion of settlement in the Frosinone basin, the planned distribution of isolated farms and new towns, notably in the Pontine lowland, and the pattern of settlement along the Adriatic coast

with small oases of olives and other fruit trees around the sparsely scattered villages. Yet from Grosetto (25,000) brave efforts of reclamation have been made, and the new lands of the *bonificati*, now dotted with newly built farms, give promise to this formerly malarial and forsaken region. Along the coast is a series of wooded headlands and low-lying cornlands. Off the coast are the seven isles of the Tuscan archipelago, of which Elba is the largest, with its windswept *garrigue*. Small clearances for cereals and vines centre around its small mineral port, significantly named Portoferrajo.

4. *Latium.* As a region, Latium has never had the same significance as other historic regions such as Tuscany. Excluding Rome and its immediate environs, it is still one of the least-populated regions of Italy. In early Roman times, the lands north of the Tiber were considered to be Etruscan, and in the Middle Ages the name 'Latium' was not used. Nevertheless, the volcanic relief of the Latium hills and the dominance of Rome over this area make its distinctive context. Framed by the Volsini uplands in the north and the Central Apennines in the east, only its southern border is more arbitrarily drawn across the Liri corridor to the lower Garigliano. As one of the largest volcanic regions of Europe, it is a sequence of crater lakes, tuff plateaux and lava hills, giving a great variety of soils and therefore of land use, that make the geographic personality of Latium. Lakes, plateaux, tufaceous and Plio-cene hills, the limestone mountains and the coastal plains are the varied regional ingredients.

The central plateaux of Latium are dotted with crater lakes and many more now drained in shallow basins. Highest relief occurs on the volcanic rims, notably above Bolsensa (Mi Volsini, 2,096 ft), Vico (Mi Cimini, 3,455 ft), Bracciano (Mi Sabitini, 2,300 ft) and Albano (M. Cavo, 2,736 ft). Viewed aerially, these hill lands north of Rome are a monotonous landscape, poorly cultivated, with vast expanses of *macchia*, especially in the 500 sq. miles between Orbettello and Tarquinia where Etruscan tombs have lain undisturbed (Plate 19). The district of Vico is exceptional, with its north-western flank covered with olives and beech forests higher up. Here is situated the old walled, market town of Viterbo (26,000). The whole plateau area is deeply scoured by a myriad of small-scale ravines (*fossi*) readily eroded in the soft tuffs, except where hard beds stand out as cliffs or where the valleys have been drained by *cuniculi* (Fig. 200). Roads and villages therefore keep to the ridges. Very different are the Alban Hills south of Rome, where much richer soils, weathered from basaltic lavas support a dense population in large, picturesque villages between Frascati and Velletri, many of Volscian origin, and collectively known as the *Castelli Romani*. Their terraced slopes are one vast vineyard, whose vintage has been re-nowned since Roman times. East of the twin crater lakes of Albano and Nemi (Fig. 148) the scene changes dramatically on the tuffs to extensive and silent forests of beech.

The broad saddle of plains between the Alban Hills and the northern plateaux centred on the broad valley of the Tiber is the heart of the Roman Campagna. Poor tuff soils with untillable crusts (*caffellaccio*),

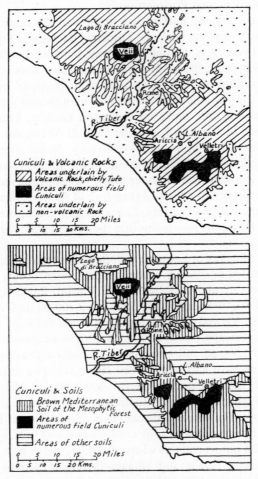

FIG. 200. Distribution of *cuniculi* in southern Etruria. These drainage channels are concentrated in the soft tuffs which could be cut easily, and associated with clastic, ill-drained soils. See also plates 22 and 23

ill-drained alluvium and clays present a melancholy view, half of which is uncultivated and the rest pasturage or cereal lands only extensively cropped, with fallows of one to two years (*terziera* and *quatiera*). The neglect of the hydraulic systems after the collapse of the Roman empire, the recrudescence of malaria, particularly during the seventeenth and eighteenth centuries, created a waste of latifundia and ruined settlements. The modern villages have evolved around the old country houses (*casali*). The Via Appia, of which 800 acres have been recently declared a national park, expresses well the sad elegance of old villas, ruined tombs and clumps of oleander bushes, cypresses and pines that characterise the Campagna landscape. Along the Aniene valley and the coast north of the Tiber delta the *bonifica* laws of 1878–83 and 1903–10, have borne successful results in the reclamation of some 100 sq. miles.

Rome appears like an oasis of civilisation in this wilderness that has survived many vicissitudes. Of the three great cross-roads of the Peninsula (middle Arno, lower Tiber and the Neapolitan lowland) Rome is the most advantageously placed at the central one. It controls six major natural routes, which the Romans developed into the highways of Appia, Casilina, Tibertina, Salaria, Flamina and Aurelia (Fig. 182). For the initial growth of a town, the site of Rome was a good defensive position, with its famous hills eroded in volcanic tuffs (Fig. 201 A), namely the Palatine (167 ft), Capitoline (194), Aventine (150), Caelian (165), Esquilino (195), Viminal (180) and Quirinal (170). Of these, those nearer the river were first occupied, but only the Palatine combined steep slopes, adequate space for a town and a link to the north-east with lands above the flood plain. Near this site was the lowest bridge-point on the largest river of the Peninsula, the head of estuarine navigation in a sea which the Romans created as their *mare clausum*.

The wide sweeping meanders of the Tiber through the city, the irregular relief within Rome (with other hills as well as the Septimontium, viz. Pincius (213 ft), Monte Vaticano (263) and the Janiculum (289)), and the complex history of Rome, all make it difficult at first to understand the urban landscape. The city is best viewed from the Janiculum, where the four central sectors can be distinguished. First, across the Tiber lies classical Rome, to the south of Piazza Venezia, between the ruins of the Colosseum, the baths of Caracalla and the former rubbish dump of Monte Testacchio. Secondly, there is medieval Rome, between the Corso and the Tiber, in the former Campus Martius, a gloomy, squalid part of the city, only in part rebuilt. On the opposite side of the Tiber has been laid out the Vatican city with the suburbs of the Trastevere, contained in the west wall of Urban VIII, and on the north side by the former marshy valley floor of the Inferno. Fourthly, what may be termed sistine Rome, east of the Corso, was laid out formally in the Renaissance. It was begun by Sixtus V (1585–90) who constructed the Via Sistina and the general street plan between the

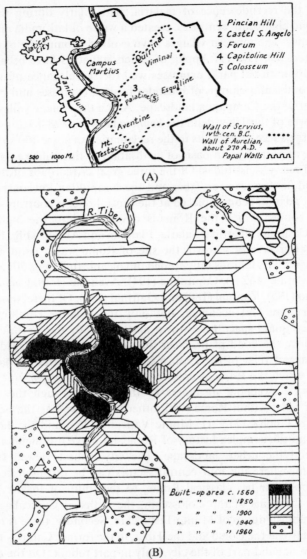

FIG. 201. The walls and the growth of Rome

Pincio and S. Maria Maggiore. This explains why the city centre has shifted several times in the course of its history, creating a number of focal points (see Plate 68).

The first great period of Rome was between the second century B.C. and the third century A.D. when the town spread out from the Palatine

(16 ha) to occupy the Septimontium (*c.* 156 ha) and then to be enclosed by the great wall of Aurelius (*c.* A.D. 270). The latter covered more than double the city in the sixteenth century (Fig. 201 B). The second great period of Rome was the Renaissance and Baroque (1450–1750) during which the many famous churches, palaces and squares were constructed; of the 450 churches in Rome, only one is Gothic. The tardy unification of Italy slowed down Rome's growth until after 1870 (135,000 inhabitants at the end of the seventeenth century), 147,000 in 1799, 230,000 in 1870). But after this expansion began rapidly, first on the Esquiline-Caelian hills (in 1874), then along the main roads out of Rome. The construction of new bridges over the Tiber (20 road bridges) opened up new quarters and a new garden city at Montesacro was built in the Aniene valley. Testaccio, the commercial sector of classical Rome, has become an industrial area, after the plan of 1883 had been put into effect. The Fascist plan of 1925 promoted development between the Via Ostia and the Via Cristoforo Colombo. South of Laurentina, Rome's newest garden city has developed since the 1936 plan, stimulated by the 1960 Olympiad. Apart from these historic stages of Rome's townscape, a further element of diversity is the varied building materials. Bricks made from the lacustrine sediments of the Tiber valley have always been the material for the humble dwellings. Tuffs, ugly and weathering badly, are seen on some of the older buildings; greyish from the Mamertine, yellowish-grey from Grotta Oscura, near Veii; brown from Monte Verde. A harder tuff, the *peperino*, is found on more recent buildings. Travertine from Tivoli, pozzolana, a local volcanic sand, add further variety, while the decorative marbles reflect the great periods of Rome's expansion. 'A city set on a hill cannot be hid' is certainly true of Rome, one of man's finest creations in the Mediterranean world.

Fifteen miles to the east of Rome, is the walled front of the Abruzzi Apennines, a distinctive region but here grouped with Latium for convenience. It rises steeply above olive-covered foothills, and small towns of which Tivoli (20,000) is best known. It is a high, craggy landscape of block mountains and intervening polja, of which the Fucino basin is one of the best examples. The greyish-white limestones form craggy summits, clothed below by some woods and scrub but it is only in the wilder scenery of the Abruzzi national park to the south that forests are extensive. In contrast to the open cereal lands of Fucino, the longitudinal corridor of the Ciociaria or Sacco valley is much more densely populated, with intensive tree cropping.

Along the coast south of Rome extends the Pontine marshes for a distance of 35 miles, between the fishing ports of Anzio and Terracina.

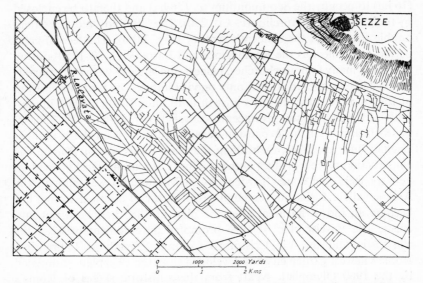

FIG. 202. Relief, drainage and field patterns in the north-east of the Pontine plain. Note the abrupt edge of the limestone block in the north-east, whose karstic supplies of water long made drainage on the plain very difficult. The contrast between the older, piecemeal reclamation and the regular, planned reclamation of the Fascist period is clearly shown

At first sight it appears a uniform plain, with its graticule of drainage ditches and new roads. But in the more undulating northern section reclamation is older and holdings are large (Fig. 202). Around the new town of Latina (14,600) and north of it there is extensive irrigation for maize, fodder and other crops. The sand dune and lagoonal littoral is fringed by pine woods, and at M. Circeo woods of cork oak have been preserved in their natural state. Elsewhere, however, there has been a remarkable transformation of the scrub cover into some 3,000 holdings, settled mostly by Venetians who favour dispersed dwellings.

SOUTHERN ITALY

Although the distinction between Continental and Peninsular Italy is the clearest, the North and South, buffered by the transition of the Centre are also regional realities. What makes the South distinct is, above all, the threat of seasonal drought, in a land far more dependent for its livelihood upon agriculture than the North. The hardness and loneliness of life, the inferior standards of husbandry, the historic insecurity and therefore the concentration of settlement, and the social problems of rich, powerful, absentee landlords, have all left their imprint on its landscapes.

1. *Campania*. Like Latium, which was originally associated with the plain of the lower Tiber, Campania derives its name from the lowland centred on the ancient town of Capua (*Samnites Campani*), which has become known as *Campania Felix* because of its fertility (Fig. 204). Later its connotation was extended to include all the plains between the Sele and the Sacco rivers, a distance of some 95 miles along the Tyrrhenian coast. The variety of rocks, including limestones, volcanic ash, lavas and alluvium, is reflected in diverse landscapes of mountains, plains and islands. As this is one of the most productive regions of Italy, the density of population is very high (Fig. 205), making it unique in the South in its variety of scenery and intensity of agriculture. Its major sub-divisions consist of the Pre-Apennines in the north, the Latin valley to the north-east, the plain of Campania, the Sorrentine peninsula and in the south the Sele basin.

Limestone block mountains form the northern border of Campania, with typical karstic features. From north to south they consist of: the Lepini (5,040 ft), Ausoni and Aurunci (3,576 ft) highlands, and east of the Garigliano valley, the mountains of Maggiore (3,402) and Massico (2,661). Rising abruptly between the Aurunci and the Maggiore mountains is the perfect volcanic cone of Roccamonfina, thickly covered with chestnut woods. Beech forests are widespread in the Lepini range, but the Aurunci are a solitary waste of macchia, except where scattered villages have created olive groves and patches of grainland. Very different is the prospect towards the Latin valley, occupied by the Sacco and Liri rivers. Interculture has made this district densely populated, with a high dispersion of settlement centred on the market town of Frosinone (14,000). Eastwards towards Cassino the relief is more broken and agriculture is less intense as far as the middle Volturno valley. Population is concentrated along the foothills of the Matese and the north-east edge of the Maggiore, where lines of towns indicate the position of springs.

Immediately east of the Volturno valley is the mountain barrier of the Southern Apennines, cut into four main blocks of hills by important gaps followed by lines of communications. These are the Avella-Taburno Highlands, composed of rugged limestones, flanked by Pliocene clay lands, bared for grain cultivation. In Taburno thickets of hazel lead into the Benevento Basin, with the important route centre of that name perched on a hill overlooking the confluence of the Calore

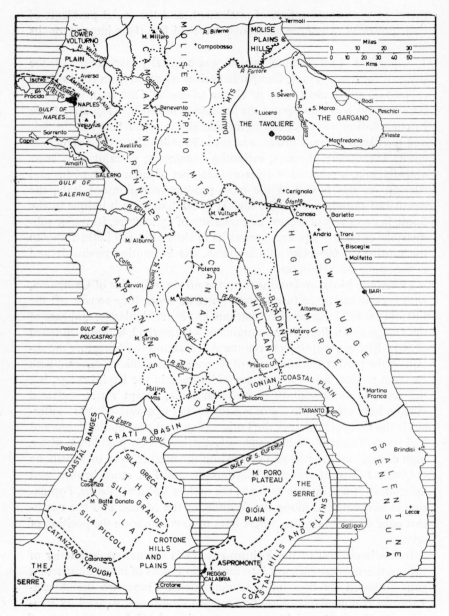

FIG. 203. Regional divisions of southern Italy

and Sabato valleys. This merges southwards into the rich Avellino Basin with its dense population, interculture and higher slopes under oaks, beeches and Judas trees. A ring of large villages surrounds the floor of the basin, which is hemmed in by mountains that tower to over 4,600 ft. To the south-east of Avellino the Mi Picentini extend as far as the Sele valley. Beechwoods cover much of the mountains, and with the absence of water on these inhospitable limestones, the whole area is practically deserted. East of the Sele, the Marzano Plateau forms a smaller waste of pasture, scrub and beech. The Apennines reach the west coast in the rugged mass of Cilento, limestone mountains that rise to 6,230 ft. It is set in poor rolling hills of high relief, flanked to the east by the trough of the Val di Diano, and seawards it divides the gulfs of Salerno and Policastro. Large areas of olives on the western flanks support a stable population, with a mixed flora of broom, mastic and other macchia on the higher hills.

Everything about the Campanian Plain, which extends from the lower Garigliano to the southern, Sarno lowland, may be described in superlatives. Its opulence is such that with an extraordinary variety of crops that give a constant lush cover on the fields throughout the year, yields are three to six times the national average. It has also the most diverse sequence of landscapes on the Tyrrhenian coast. Large, overcrowded villages, thickly scattered farms (*masserie*) as well as deserted marshy districts occur. Dominating the plain in more ways than one, is the volcanic cone of Vesuvius, with its elegant curves. Its foothills and those parts of the plain which have benefited from its fertile volcanic soils are the most densely populated, with numerous villages, vineyards, many vegetable crops and a wide range of fruit trees. To about 650 ft there are densities of over 1,300 per sq. mile. Above this zone to about 1,300 ft densities thin out to 250, and the hedges of prickly pear have on occasion not prevented the lava flows from invading into the vineyards in tongues of brute matter. Higher still, the mountain slopes become a desert of ash and lava, rimmed on the eastern flank by the older, more extensive crater of the Somma, within which rises steeply the crater of A.D. 78. This is a primeval landscape, littered with formless chunks of lava and ash slopes. It is difficult to believe that, given time, out of this primal matter is created gardens like those of the lower slopes. West of Vesuvius, the Phlegrean Fields present another, lower type of volcanic scenery (Fig. 166). With numerous crater hollows and cones still well preserved, this has been described as a lunar landscape. But this is inaccurate, for it is garlanded with vines; so that its features are as much those of man's handiwork as a volcanic creation. Beech

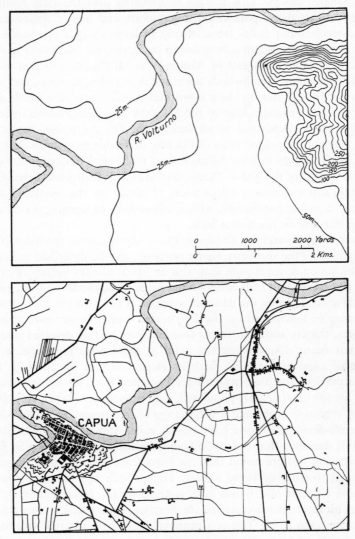

FIG. 204. Relief and settlement in the middle Volturno plain, north of the Terra di Lavoro. Note the faulted outlier of limestone in the east, the marshy floor of the Volturno, with an old meander core, and the intensely cultivated plain to the south with its large farms. Capua, a Samnite capital (Casilinum) was strategically perched where the Via Appia crossed the Volturno, and finally re-fortified in the seventeenth century

woods rim the higher craters. Nevertheless nature still asserts itself in a region whose solfatara the Romans conceived to be the entrance to the underworld. Gunther's researches have shown that this coastland was at least 17 ft higher in Roman times, then sank to 18–20 ft below present sea-level, to be heaved up again in the sixteenth century when the crater of M. Nuovo (1538) appeared. Ancient ports such as Cuma, Baia and Bagnoli took advantage of drowned craters to have sheltered havens. The population is very dense along the south coast, in contrast to the deserted, dune-fringed west coast. The steep isles of Ischia and Procida off the coast are flanked by vineyards that support densities of 2,000 per sq. mile below 600 ft.

To the north, the Campanian plain *par excellence* is termed Terra di Lavoro, the most intensively cultivated district of Campania. It has three types of landscape. To the west, the plain is covered with fruit orchards and settlements are more sparsely scattered. To the east, a maze of irrigation canals water the fields of cereals and fodder crops. The central portion is a garden of interculture, with rows of elms, walnuts and other trees laced by vines 15 to 20 ft long, and with a great variety of vegetables, cereals and other crops between them. In the richest parts, it is possible to find four layers of cultivation: vegetables; vines; low fruit trees such as apricot, cherry, apple and pear trees; and towering overhead, magnificent walnut trees. No wonder population densities exceed 2,500 per sq. mile with large agricultural centres; most important of which is Aversa (35,000). Very different is the sparsely populated lowland of the lower Volturno, with its malarial marshes only now being reclaimed, and much of it still pasture for the herds of buffalo (Fig. 205). Settlement is concentrated around the lower slopes of Roccamonfina, nestling among olive groves. But the treeless pastures of the lower Volturno (Fig. 204) and Garigliano valleys are shrinking as reclamation proceeds, with its introduction of a more intensive cropping of grain, potatoes, fodder and some hemp. The plain of Minturno is exceptional, the northern outpost of orange groves along this coast. Finally, south and west of Vesuvius is the lowland of Sarno another district of intensive cultivation, with orange groves and orchards on the lower slopes and irrigated market gardens in the valley. Most holdings are less than one hectare in size. A ribbon development of towns follows the coast road south of Naples (Portici, Torre del Greco, Torre Annunziata).

The Sorrento peninsula has its own individuality, stretching almost 25 miles into the Gulf of Naples. Block mountains with summit levels (*piani*) rise to over 2,000 ft, overlooked by the summit of M. San Angelo (4,734 ft). The higher parts are bare, rocky limestones, with woods of

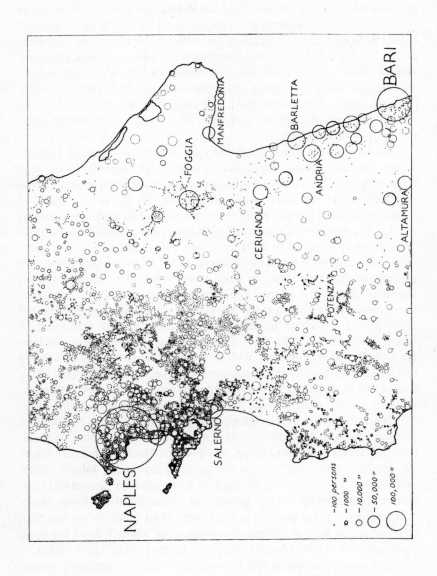

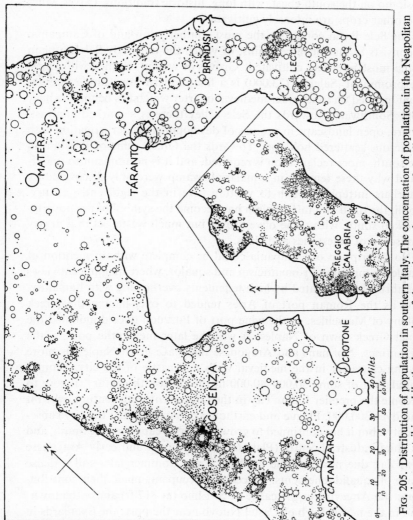

Fig. 205. Distribution of population in southern Italy. The concentration of population in the Neapolitan area is most striking, while the large size of the agricultural centres of Apulia is also significant. Note the low densities of the High Murge, central Basilicata, and the mountains of Calabria. The Crotone valley and the coastal areas of southern Calabria show marked densities

chestnut and beech. Spring-line villages mark the lower slopes on the borders of the Sarno plain, and along the cliffed coasts are numerous small towns such as Sorrento on the north coast and Amalfi and Positano on the south coast, with long, historic traditions. Olives, vines and other crops are intensely cultivated.

The Sele Basin comprises the most southerly lowland of Campania. It consists in fact of three plains, of which the northerly Salerno plain is the most intensely cultivated. Groves of walnut, clothed with vines, are prominent. Salerno (73,000) is a fine modern town along the sea-front, grafted on to its older medieval quarter which lies behind its busy port. Southwards towards the Sele valley there is a marked contrast, a bare, open landscape in process of development under irrigation with numerous scattered holdings. Towards the Greek ruins of Paestum in the south, more reclamation is required, and it is not difficult to under-stand why these temples in a malarial swamp were only discovered by travellers intrepid enough to venture here in the eighteenth century. Eboli, the third and inland plain has become the symbol of the poverty-stricken south, with some olive groves but much waste, set in a dreary landscape of limestones and clays.

No description of Campania could be complete without mention of Naples, a mixture of romanticism and squalor, where magnificent views are abruptly terminated by high tenements overflowing with humanity. Just as the Roman port of Arles tended to overshadow the Greek colony of Marseilles, so the wine port of Pozzuoli once dominated the small Greek town of Naples. It was the later mercantile powers, the Byzantines, Normans and Aragonese that have given Naples its more lasting character in the medieval walls and castle of the city. From a population of some 30,000–40,000 in the thirteenth century, it rose to become the premier Italian city in the mid-seventeenth century, when it had over 300,000. Plague and earthquakes have afflicted the city subse-quently, but it has continued to grow rapidly as capital of the South, and its chief industrial centre (Plate 65). The Roman and early Aragonese town lay due north of the modern Porto Commerciale, still a dense maze of squalid tenements. Succeeding occupants made their contribu-tion: the Angevins in the castle of S. Elmo (at 817 ft) above the town; and in the new suburb of Castel Nuovo near the port; the Spaniards in the quarter of Mont Calvo on the slopes of M. Elmo. Despite its subse-quent palaces and fine buildings, little or no coherent plan for the city as a whole was made until the present century. Hindered inland by the steep relief, modern Naples and its suburbs have expanded along the coast, leaving the steep inland stopes for the more luxurious villas and modern flats. Modern suburbs such as Vomero have been made possible by the construction of two tunnel roads through the hill, north of Naples. 2. *Basilicata*. Unlike the other historic regions of the peninsula, Basilicata has little individuality. It is a region of transition between Apulia and Calabria. Its name is derived from the Byzantine term for a district governor. Its classical name 'Lucania', revived since 1932 is also inappropriate (*Lucus*, woodland) for it is a bare, desolate landscape for the most part. Its most distinguishing feature is its drainage into the Ionian Sea. The sites of many ruined villages reflect the frequent incidence of earthquakes, while their perched location above the valley floors indicate the prevalence of malaria in the past, as well as the insecurity of this isolated region. Since Greek colonisation on its coast-lands, deforestation has paid its toll in severe erosion (Fig. 160) and alluviation on the plains, so that even the site of Sybaris, once the acme of classical urban life, remained unknown until 1962. Deforestation in modern times has been particularly severe in the period 1808–80, when cereal cultivation was widely spread. Since then, emigration overseas has been another characteristic of Basilicata.

Three longitudinal belts of rocks parallel with the north-west to south-east trend of the Apennines dominate the relief: the hard, dolomitic limestones to the west that make up the dorsal of the Southern Apennines; the early Tertiary sandstones and marls, forming the rolling mountainous plateaux in the centre; and the soft, severely eroded relief of the Pliocene clays in the east, overlooking the Brádano trough (Fig. 158). The traditional division of Basilicata, however, is that of the districts dominated by the chief towns: Vulture, Potentino, Materano, Lagonegrese and Maratea. Of these districts Vulture is the most distinct, the flat volcanic cone of M. Vulture (4,354 ft) dominating the scene for miles around, and its slopes richly clad in beech and oak forests, notably at Monticchio. Settlement is relatively dense, lands parcellated with small vineyards and cornfields, and with old historic centres such as Melfi (18,000) and Venosa. South-west of Vulture are the Lucanian Apennines, rising steeply in the west like a well-filled denture of high and rugged limestones to over 4,000 ft (Sierio, Lo Serrone) above a soft base of younger rocks. Bare and karstic, their scenery is very different from the Vallo di Diano which forms the western border, a productive district, exploiting a former lake floor, now drained by the Tanagro, a tributary of the Sele. The broader, eastern part of the region is broken into narrow and more scattered limestone ridges surrounded by sand-stone plateaux and clay lands, a poor, monotonous country that is thinly populated, with fewer forests and much bare cereal land fragmented into small-holdings. Potenza (32,560), built on a walled spur, has been a local capital since pre-Roman times. There are other ancient fortresses in the region, such as Acerenza and Brienza.

Eastwards, as the relief descends from 2,000–3,000 to 1,000–1,500 ft, Pliocene clays become widespread, deeply dissected into badlands and pock-marked by landslides showing up as bare patches in winter surrounded by the green of growing corn. This region of Materano is one of the poorest in Italy, exemplified by the cave-dwellings (*sassi*) of Matera (30,000) where more than half its population lived until 1952. Large estates, difficulty of water-supply and malaria explain the con-

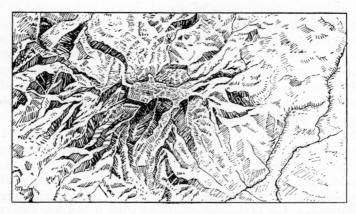

Fig. 206. Block-diagram of plastic relief in the Pliocene clay lands of Pisticci, Basilicata. Slumping of the clays in periods of heavy rains leave scars that pock-mark the landscape

centration of population in large agglomerated villages well above the valleys. The Brádano valley especially is a deserted district, though recent measures include major dams on the Brádano and the Agri, and gradually land reform is breaking down the pattern of large estates, with their isolated *masserie*, to enlarge the size of the small-holdings (*versurieri*) around the villages. Most marked are the changes on the plain of Metaponto, where much resettlement has taken place since 1951. It is on this lowland near the Ionian coast that there are most possibilities for Basilicata's 57,000 ha of irrigable land. Already, it is very different from the days when Gissing saw it in 1905, then so mournfully desolate and 'in winter a wilderness of mud'. Climbing west into the upper basin of the Sinni is the region of the Lagonegro, a similar landscape of much eroded clay lands, except in the south where the limestone mountains of the Pollino rise steeply in forested slopes. These boast of their own native pine forests (*Pinus leucodermis*), and have below a thin mixture of oaks and chestnuts. Westwards the settlements, hitherto agglomerated, become more dispersed with small-holdings and some interculture. On the Sirino range are to be seen the first views of both seas, so typical of much of central Calabria. West to the Maratea coast, is a potential tourist littoral of numerous small headlands and bays covered in Mediterranean scrub.

3. *Apulia*. In classical times 'Apulia' applied to the tribal territory of the 'Apuli' centred on the Murge. The Salentine heel went by the name of 'Calabria', and was distinct ethnically. For long there has persisted a difference of dialects, the former related more with Neapolitan, the latter more like that of Calabria proper. Only after the seventh century A.D. was the name 'Apulia' applied to all the region between the Gargano and the Salentine peninsulas. Controlled in turn by Byzantines, Normans and Spaniards, this strategic area was generally divided into the three areas of the northern marchlands of the Capitanata or Tavoliere, the central Terra di Bari, and the southern Terra d'Otranto. These divisions were only obliterated in the creation of the provinces in 1861. The rectangular shape of Apulia is pronounced, stretching for 225 miles, or the equivalent of the distance between Turin and Venice. Its total area is 7,470 sq. miles. It is sharply defined on the population map (Fig. 205) and its western border coincides with the structural trough of the Brádano, extending northwards along the sharp rise of the Daunia mountains to the Fortore valley.

Three traits give distinctive character to Apulia: its long sea-coast, its ecological features as a 'kingdom of drought and stone', and the remarkable human modifications of its landscapes. Malaria has been the scourge of its 510 miles of coast, especially in the Tavoliere and in the hinterland of Brindisi (Fig. 179), so that settlement has been remarkably concentrated between Barletta and Monopoli where the limestone littoral is well drained, yet masked by Pliocene water-holding deposits. Apulia is the driest region of Italy, with much of it having less than 20 in and concentrated into some 65 days annually. Aquifers are normally deep and uncertain, apart from the rather saline and shallow water-table of the littorals. As much of Apulia is composed of limestones, stone walls are prominent, and especially in the southern Murge the *trulli* appear like conical mounds of stone that make full use of the litter of fissured limestone (Fig. 186). Yet man has transformed this poorly endowed country on an impressive scale. Today the High Murge is a windswept moorland of pasture, scrub and fields of asphodels, crisscrossed by some 930 miles of sheep-walks. But the thick forests of beech and mixed deciduous oaks still preserved in the Gargano reveal the nature of the extensive cover of much of Apulia in the past. The reason is that until 1865 pastoralism had prior claim on the use of the land. Revolutionary was the construction of the Apulian aqueduct (in 1905–39), diverting the waters of the Sele from the Tyrrhenian slopes to supply drinking water to some 400 centres in a pipe 150 miles long and with 1,500 miles of subsidiary channels; this services even the tip of the Salentine peninsula. The reclamation of some 30,000 ha in the Tavoliere has been achieved since 1882. Another 25,000 ha under irrigation has been completed since the post-war period. Such is the scale of transformation envisaged that the completed works in 1956 were still only six per cent of those planned or under construction. Nor must it be forgotten that since the eighteenth century there has been a remarkable spread of vast olive groves and vineyards, especially in the Lower Murge so that Apulia today is Italy's leading producer of olive oil and has the highest area of specialised vineyards.

The Gargano peninsula is a clearly distinct region of Apulia, rising like the bow of a ship above the waters of the Adriatic, overlooking the broad valley of the Candelaro to the west. Some 35 miles long and 20 wide, its broad shoulders and rounded plateaux (2,500–3,000 ft) are pitted by innumerable dolines and other karstic landforms. The highest summit of Calvo (3,460 ft) overlooks a series of steep scarps that frame the southern border. This is mostly sheep country with widespread pastures and fields of spring flowers (especially *Papaver rhoesas* and *Chrysantheum mycanis*). The northern and the eastern flanks are more deeply dissected by small valleys that are thickly covered with magnificent stands of beech and mixed oaks; notable is the Foresta Umbra which still has 11,000 ha. Strung along the northern lagoonal littoral are medieval walled towns such as Rodi, Peschici and Vieste, surrounded with olives, peach trees and even oranges. The south-east coast is very different, with steep cliffs plunging into the sea, on which Aleppo pines and *macchia* try bravely to cover the nakedness of limestone slopes. Another series of villages follow along the scarp foot of the southern Gargano, notably S. Marco and S. Giovanni, leading east to the famous centre of medieval pilgrimage at Monte S. Angelo.

Very different is the descent to the lowland of the Tavoliere, the only true plain of Apulia, that stretches for 60 miles from the lower Ofanto to the Fortore and 30 miles westwards towards the Sub-Apennines. The geometrical design of its central, recently reclaimed lands, the deep ditches cut near the coast to drain the stagnant marshes, the monotonous flat landscape of cereal lands and the distant horizons give character to this plain. But the monotony of the Tavoliere is deceptive for there are variants of soil and land use. They range from the dune-fringed littoral and the salt-pans of Margherita di Savoia (the largest in southern Italy), to the dark surfaced wheatlands of the central plains, underlain shallowly by calcareous crusts, and then westwards to low rising platforms of Pliocene sands between Cerignola and Torremaggiore with their cover of specialised cultures of vines, olives and sugar beet, and the highest densities of population. At the extremities of the Tavoliere are medieval fortress towns, Lucera (22,271) now a stagnant agricultural centre, and Manfredonia (27,634) a prosperous fishing port. To the north and south, S. Severo (47,875) and Cerignola (46,977) are more important agricultural towns. All main roads lead to Foggia (84,891) formerly centre of the transhumant system, now the administrative and regional capital. Its formal plan differs from the evolved casualness of the other centres, owing much both to the reconstruction after the earthquake of 1731 and to modern planning.

To the west of the Plio-Pleistocene platforms, the relief ascends gradually into the folds of the Apennines, here known as the Capitanata from its associations with the Byzantine marchland. Oak woods clothe the sharp edge of the Daunia range (3,775 ft) that rises steeply from 500 to 1,500 ft, and the place-names indicate the considerable extent of former forests. Faeto (beech forest) is the highest Apulian village at 2,841 ft. Bovino is the local centre, with lesser villages of 5,000–6,000 inhabitants serving communes of 17–25 sq. miles in area, under a varied production depending on altitude.

From the lower Ofanto valley rises the great limestone tableland of the Murge which extends for 90 miles as the Apulian backbone. Gently folded, its greyish white limestones rise from low coastal cliffs to over 2,000 ft in the north-west (Torre Disperata 2,251 ft) but it is so extensively covered with a veneer of red-brown earth that bare rock is only visible on ravine sides, along the minor scarps and in occasional rock slabs that protrude above the *macchia*. There are however, marked differences in the three zones of the High Murge, the Low Murge and the coastal Murge.

The solitary waste of the High Murge is well seen from the 'Apulian balcony' of Minervino (20,353) perched at 1,460 ft. Treeless rolling relief under *macchia* or grain crops characterises much of this region, held in vast patriarchal states (*masseria*). It is still much as Edward Lear saw it a century ago: 'elevated stony plains—weariest of barren undulations stretching in unbroken ugliness towards Altamura and Gravina. Much of the hideous tract is ploughed earth . . . dismal, shrubless

Murgie.' The few villages are usually sited on the top of dry ravines (*gravine*) that notch the edge of the high plateau only about five miles wide. Altamura (38,231), located on the Via Appia, is the local centre with a long history, around which active clearance of the waste has taken place in recent decades. Three or more discontinuous series of eastwards facing scarps (*gradini*) run through the Low Murge (Fig. 161) with the abrupt appearance of olive groves, vineyards and some interculture in deeper soils and pockets of *terra rossa* that may be 15 ft thick or more. The striking radial pattern of roads around the huge nucleated villages

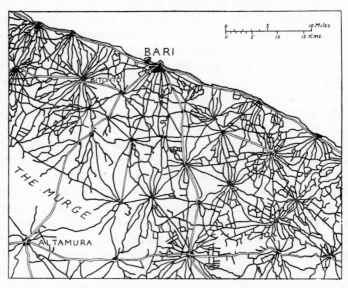

FIG. 207. Road and settlement patterns of central Apulia. The radial pattern of roads define the influence of hinterlands for the coastal ports, and for the large agricultural settlements of the interior

or *città contadini* has already been mentioned (see pp. 457–58). Strips of limestone carry olives, deeper soils have cereals, while vines clothe vast expanses. In the recently settled area of Murgia dei Trulli between Castella, noted for its famous caverns, Fasano and Martina Franca, about half of the population are scattered in *trulli*, looking like a whitewashed apiary dotting the red earth framed by stone walls, figs and olives (see Plate 63). Alberobello, the unique town of *trulli*, only dates from 1635. Towards the north the settlements become more concentrated although the land use is similar. This is the Terra dei Bari, the sheltered hinterland of the chief city of Apulia. Bari is of ancient origin though its medieval town owes much to the Normans who built its castle and cathedral near the old port. But the remarkable concentration of small ports between Barletta (63,398), Molfetta (55,150) and Monopoli (22,269), every six or seven miles along the coast, gave none of them any outstanding advantages until the last century. Then the railway from Bologna was constructed (in 1865) and Bari grew from about 34,000 to 78,000 in 1900, and to 250,189 in 1951. Grafted on to the old medieval plan is thus a modern gridiron plan focused on the new port, and bordered by its oil refineries and other modern industries. Southwards towards Brindisi the littoral of the Murge widens into a less intensely cultivated plain, but which has one of the finest stretches of old olive groves in Italy, growing on the Pliocene sands.

The abrupt edge of the southward facing scarp, running from Altamura, via M. S. Elia (1,477 ft) towards S. Vito, bounds effectively the two southern regions of the Taranto plain and the Salento. Cultivation towards Taranto is more discontinuous, with woods and *macchia* interspersed with olive groves. The Toulon of southern Italy, Taranto has a vast naval anchorage within the lagoon of Mare Piccolo, whose outlet the town guards with medieval bastions, south of which is the new town (begun in 1837). Since 1900, the city has more than doubled its population (147,000 in 1951) and is the premier city of the Ionian coast. Two other southern cities of note are Brindisi (52,000) and Lecce (57,000); both were important Roman towns, but were exposed to Turkish attack and today are still somewhat isolated from the main centres. Although the relief is much lower than in the Murge, the Salento has more variety of rock types, the limestones forming asymmetrical ridges (*serre*) while the tufa, *pietra leccese* and the yellow sands produce a gently swelling relief splashed red with patches of *terra rossa*. The extreme drought is evidenced by hedges of prickly pear. But the same generous mantle of vines, olives, figs and almond groves occurs, though more interspersed with waste on the loose sands that are only suitable for grazing lands. In 1877 Swinburne noted around Lecce 'the prodigious number of stone walls would disfigure a much more fruitful country', and today the peasant's task of de-stoning, *spietramento*, is still as immense. The smaller and more scattered settlements tend to be located in hollows where water supply is more plentiful but the coasts are largely deserted, except at picturesque strongholds such as Otranto and Gallipoli (16,000).

4. *Calabria*. Unlike Basilicata and Apulia, Calabria is a land of water, with heavy rain on its western mountains so that it appears more verdant and fresher in spring than is typical of its southern latitude.

Just as dramatically as the Black Hills of Dakota loom above the American Plains, so the Sila appears in the desolate wastes of southern Italy, as if it belongs to another world. Reference has already been made to the original usage of 'Calabria' for the Italian heel (p. 529) and it is only since the Middle Ages that it has been restricted to the area south of the Pollino mountains. There are several Calabrias however: Calabria Citra to the north, centred on Cosenza; Calabria Ultra or the district of Catanzaro; and the extreme south centred on Reggio Calabria. What gives so much character to Calabria is its mountains and their views towards two seas. The steep valleys (*fiumare*) are readily transformed from placid waterways to what Norman Douglas described as 'living monsters, dragons that roll themselves seawards, out of their dark caverns, in tawny coils of destruction'. The forests are the most extensive in Italy, supplying one-tenth of the total (Fig. 172). Nevertheless, there has been much deforestation and with the torrential rainstorms, it is estimated that two-thirds of the utilised lands above 650 ft are liable to soil erosion. Densities of population are also high, averaging 350 per sq. mile, about the same as Piedmont or Tuscany, absurdly high for the poor economy of Calabria. Holdings are minutely fragmented, and the emancipation from feudalism is recent. Isolated from the rest of Italy, with the faded glory of its classical importance as one of the chief areas of Greek settlement, Calabria is once again awakening from a long period of misery and neglect, as a result of the modern energetic measures of land reform and *bonifica*. Soon too its natural beauty of seascapes, the colours of false broom blazing in the spring, the lush greens of the mountain forests, and the citrus groves on the coast, may be admired more widely by an increasing number of tourists. Until now the lack of a significant town life, so unlike much of the Peninsula, has been a major economic drawback.

Despite its varied districts, Calabrian landscapes may be described under the simple three-fold division of the mountains, the Tyrrhenian coast, and the Ionian hills and plains. The Pollino mountains descend in a precipitous flight of terraces to the plain of Sibari seven thousand feet below. They are an imposing finale to the Apennines that have run without a break from Genoa. To the west and south, are mountains galore, but there are no more craggy limestone ridges; instead the rounded forms of granitic cupolas are now the rule. Pollino, clothed in almost primeval forests, once almost impenetrable with their thick undergrowth and creepers, is thus an effective limit to the north, of a Mediterranean selva. The ponderous, mountainous rectangle of Sila, with its domed summits at 5,000–6,400 ft of granites and gneiss, provides high plateaux of pasture and pines (*Pinus Laricio*). Sila falls steeply towards the south and west into the Crati trough. To the east and north, its descends more gradually through beech and chestnut forests. A girdle of villages at about 2,000–2,500 ft (at the limits of olive and chestnut) rings the Sila. Broken by the isthmus of Catanzaro, the mountains resume in the narrower mountains of Serre and Aspromonte. Their flanks are more deeply dissected by the steep valleys, the mountains descending to the coasts by two to four platforms (*piani, campi*) like gigantic balconies that open out to magnificent views of the sea, and especially southwards towards the Aolian islands and even towards Etna. Formerly described as marine terraces, they are thought to be part of one dislocated platform deformed at various altitudes.

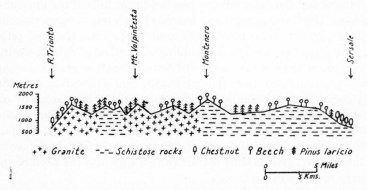

FIG. 208. Profile of vegetation in central Calabria, across the Sila (from Milone)

Serre is more populated than the Sila, so that the forests are less continuous than in Aspromonte, where the vast forest of Montalto is a fine example of beech and mixed deciduous cover. On the lower slopes, enveloped in *macchia*, are patches of cereals, chestnut woods and especially in western Serre there are fields irrigated from springs. Cosenza (45,000) the only major town in the interior, is focally placed in the broad amphitheatre of the Crati valley. It is a densely populated district with its interculture of figs, mulberries, olives and vines. The coast, which is wild and sparsely populated north of Paoli, is more cultivated to the south with tree crops. It widens into the plain of San Eufemia, once a malarial wilderness, now drained (since 1928) for irrigated crops, chiefly sugar beet and maize. The Poro plateau has more of the traditional economy—cereals, olives and stock raising, practised from numerous villages in small-holdings. The Rosarno plain, first drained by the Bourbons, is Calabria's great olive grove, dotted densely with scattered settlements and oil presses. Past the terraced vineyards of Bognara and Scilla, the jasmine fields of Brancaleone, and the lemon and bergamot groves to the south, lies Reggio Calabria (90,000). It has suffered much from earthquakes but because of its strategic position on the Straits of Messina, it has been rebuilt more than once (in 1783 and 1908). It has thus a modern appearance, elongated on a chess-board pattern alongside the busiest port in Calabria.

The Ionian coast is less populated, flanked by hilly, soft Tertiary rocks that are eroded deeply by wild torrents (*marni*) into a desolate, dantesque landscape. Much of it is bared for cereals except around Locri and northwards more discontinuously towards Catanzaro, where olives are extensive. On this coast the twin settlements, the *marine* on the littoral and the older villages perched in the hills of the interior are common. The Crotone plain widens into a hilly lowland which was under large estates for cereal production until 1951, when the land reform began to scatter groups of small-holdings. The plain of Sybari, scourged by the floods of the Crati, was until recently another area of *latifondi*; summer pasture for transhumant flocks, and otherwise, a malarial wilderness. Now it is flanked on the slopes of the Sila Greca by olive groves, so named because of the numerous Albanian colonies established there in the eighteenth century. Orange groves are now expanding on to the plain. Crotone (29,000) and Catanzaro (37,000), both favoured by the railway, are the chief market towns, with also the beginnings of modern industry in the former.

SICILY

Named after its pre-Roman tribes, the *Sicani* and *Siculi*, the island has very varied landscapes. As over three-quarters of Sicily is cultivated and woods comprise only four per cent, there is little natural vegetation cover, although spring flowers carpet the fallow and waste. Until the recent attempts at improvements, Sicily has been described as an 'Eternal Island' where time has stood still: in the interior the hill-top villages go back to remote antiquity, and for millennia, the peasants have trudged out to distant fields; on the coast the silhouette of Greek temples and the monuments of its cities indicate a long occupance. Despite its cultural endowments, Sicilian nature is seen very much in the raw: in the primeval state of Etna's volcanics; in the bare clay hills and the sulphurous plateaux of the interior; in the rocky limestone tablelands of the south-east and west; and in the wild, torrential *fiumare* that thrust out suddenly on to the north and north-east coasts. Although culturally a distinct world, Sicily is geologically a prolongation of southern Italy; the crystalline rocks of Aspromonte reappear across the narrow straits of Messina in the Peloritani; the volcanic chain of the Tyrrhenian re-emerges from a submarine platform where the Lipari islands mark its course like a line of buoys and to the south-east Etna, that monarch of all Europe's volcanoes arises; the limestones of the Apennines are resumed in the Nebrodi mountains; while Basilicata's dreary solitude is repeated in the interior clay lands.

The Arabs divided Sicily into three regions: the Val di Marzora in the west, the Val Demone in the north-east; and the Val di Noto in the south. However, today more fundamental is the brutal contrast between the coasts and the interior. Over half of Sicily's population of 4,700,000 is concentrated round its coasts, where all the major towns are located. On the north and east coasts especially are terraced gardens whose tree crops represent 21 per cent of all Italian vineyards, 12 per cent of its olives, 38 per cent of all its soft fruits and 70 per cent of its citrus fruits. Yet Sicily is also one of Italy's major granaries, represented especially in the bare clay hills of the interior, where cereals are a monoculture. It has an empty forlorn landscape, in which the agglomerated villages are widely separated and the treeless lands exaggerate the silence and monotony of a scenery, almost African in its scale.

The narrow straits of Messina (only 1½–3 miles wide) unite two comparable landscapes. Citrus groves, as in Calabria, form a continuous belt along the lower slopes of the Peloritani between Messina and Taormina, broken only where the torrential *fiumare* gash deeply into the mountain flanks. The groves rise in terraces, whose stone-walls (*saia*) carry the irrigation channels. Higher up, olives and vines take over and climb to 1,600 ft. Messina (168,000), third city of Sicily and the chief ferry port, has grown rapidly since it was destroyed in the eathquake of 1908, now equipped like Reggio Calabria with modern antiseismic buildings. The coast is densely populated. Tourism has been promoted by its scenery, notably at Taormina (since 1874). Narrower than the Aspromonte and without its mountain 'balconies', the Peloritani rise steeply to 3,000–4,250 ft as Sicily's one true range.

South of the Alcantara valley looms the great cone of Etna, bonfire of Europe, and one of the greatest volcanoes on earth, with a girth of 125 miles and a base that covers 600 sq. miles. Viewed from the north, its magnitude of 10,868 ft is belied by its simple form. The cultivated, lower slopes, especially to the east and south, are amongst the most densely populated areas in the world. The ascent of Etna is marked successively by crop changes: orange groves give way reluctantly to a massive sweep of vineyards, and these in turn to more scattered cherry

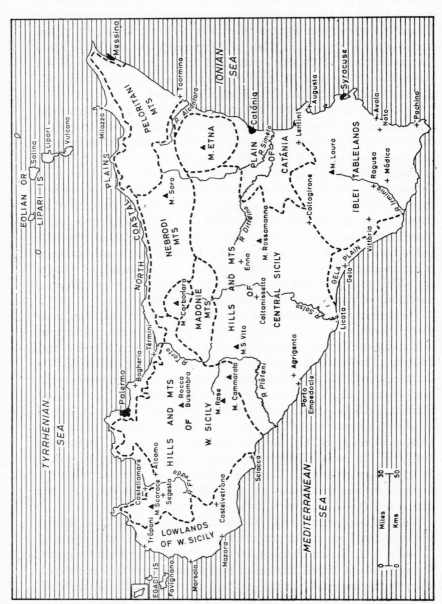

Fig. 209. Regional divisions of Sicily

and apple orchards, and the beautiful pistachio trees. On the south-west slopes, between Paterno (33,000) and Adrano (27,000) are even more expansive orange groves and fruit orchards of pear, peach and pistachio, irrigated from powerful springs that issue from the volcanic ash at 600–1,000 ft. In contrast, the west and north sides of Etna are drier, mainly devoted to cereals and pistachio trees. Higher still between 4,000 and 6,600 ft is a 'forest zone' but it is only on the north and west slopes that beautiful forests of oak, beech and specially larch are still preserved, the remainder having only bracken and a scrubby growth of juniper and other shrubs. Lack of water now prohibits settlement. Above 9,000 ft there lies a grey, lunar desert of brute matter, lava, ash and notably in the Val del Bove dotted with minor volcanoes. Then within the perimeter of the clouds are patches of snow and ice which before the invention of refrigerators provided the Bishop of Catania with his chief source of revenue. From the summit (10,740 ft) are superb views, reputedly as far as 150 miles, and on occasion even to Malta. How quickly this squalid mountain, resembling a rubbish dump, is transformed into one of man's greatest agricultural endowments, may be gauged from the tongues of basaltic lava, the older ones of some decades all transformed into fertile soil, those more recent still streaking the mountain slopes as ugly black masses (Plate 2).

Catania (295,000) the second city of Sicily, is a commercial centre, controlling both the rich agricultural resources of Etna and of the only extensive plain in the island. It has grown rapidly from 45,000 at the end of the eighteenth century, around its impressive Swabian castle. The Catanian plain, traditionally plagued by malaria and the floods of the Simeto river, has an area of 165 sq. miles but as late as 1931 it still had only 700 inhabitants living on the plain; all the villages were located in the surrounding foothills. However, recent works have transformed 40,000 ha for irrigated crops of cotton, citrus fruits, forage, etc. Oranges are grown especially around the ancient centre of Lentini. Along the coast to the south olives, vines and cereals alternate around the Gulf of Augusta. The naval base of Augusta (21,000) is set picturesquely on its tombola. Syracuse (65,000) on a similar site, effectively defended by its isthmus has doubled its size by the development of a new gridiron town on the mainland.

The north coast of Sicily with its belt of olives and vines along the foothills of the Peloritani, is densely settled. A series of fertile plains is strung discontinuously along the coast from Milazzo, with its ferry port, through Patti, Cefalù and Termini (25,000). Behind the latter two rise the Nebrodi mountains (La Caronie) with rounded summits

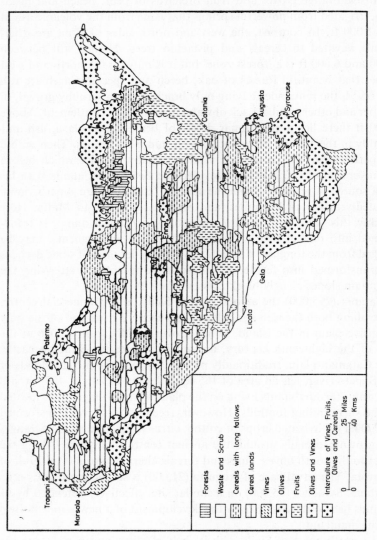

FIG. 210. Land utilisation in Sicily

at 5,000–6,000 ft, except where cappings of hard sandstone outcrop in more rugged relief. But below is a more morbid landscape of clay hills that recall the Northern Apennines and are covered with much scrub and coppice. Settlements are perched on ridges in large, infrequent villages. In the Madonie mountains dolomites, embedded in sandstones and clays, and with karstic limestones, are more reminiscent of the Campanian-Lucanian Apennines. There are beech forests and relics of a native fir (*Abies nebrodensis*) but pastoral lands predominate on the higher lands. At the foot of these broken ranges vauclusian springs generously supply the coastal plains for the irrigation of citrus groves, notably the Conca d'Oro between Baghera and Palermo. From the steeply sided lump of M. Pellegrino (1,988 ft), in process of being planted with eucalyptus and pines, a splendid view of the plain and the city may be had. The broad sweep of orange and lemon groves justifies its golden epithet, for it is among the most beautiful and civilised views in Sicily. Palermo, once the Greek harbour of 'Panormos' (or 'everything'), embraces sea, sky and mountains as well as a harbour for shipping. Palermo (435,000) has long been a major city; in Arab times it is reputed to have had 100,000 inhabitants. As the one major city of Sicily free from earthquakes, its medieval quarters around the old harbour have been preserved and overcrowded on a Neapolitan scale. Palermo is thus a curious combination of a modern commercial city and an oriental bazaar. Set in vineyards west of Palermo are Carini, Alcamo (42,000) and Castellammare.

Very different are the islands off the north coast. The Lipari or Aeolian islands contrast with the north coast like the Exile after the Garden of Eden. Lack of water, meagre soils on painfully terraced slopes and their isolation are only partially compensated by celebrated vineyards, notably on Lipari itself. Treacherous coasts and dangerous currents make fishing precarious and depopulation has made inroads into the economy. The limestone Egadi islands, drowned remnants of the Madonie range, are even poorer. Only Ustica and Favignana have extensive patches of grainland.

Western Sicily has considerable diversity, with small, richly cultivated coastal plains that exploit shelly deposits (*tufo*) and springs that issue from the limestone mountains that back them, set in a matrix of clay hills. Trapani (67,000) like Bari, is a new city grafted on to an old one, growing quickly with the profits of its salt pans (the largest in Italy, with 200,000 tons annually) and the wine trade. Marsala (61,000) has also grown with viticulture, first developed in the eighteenth century by an Englishman, G. Woodhouse. Between the two cities is a sea of vines

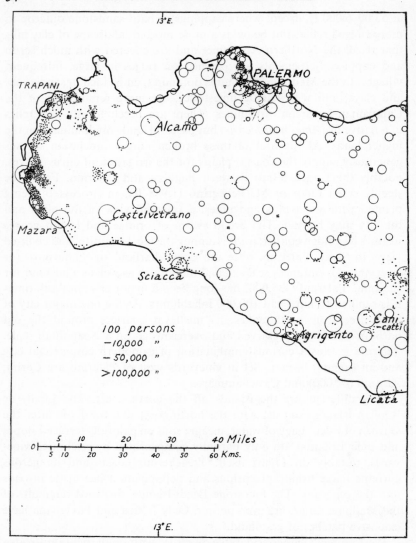

FIG. 211. Distribution of population in Sicily. There is a marked correlation between areas of dispersed settlement, fruit crops (vines, olives and citrus fruit) and the distribution of alluvial and marine terraces and terra rossa. Note the markedly

that stretch south to Mazara and Castelvetrano, interspersed by pockets of well irrigation and disseminated settlements. To the east are bare limestone mountains, where the lonely temple of Segesta and the modern isolated dwellings of the Riforma Agraria tell of efforts long

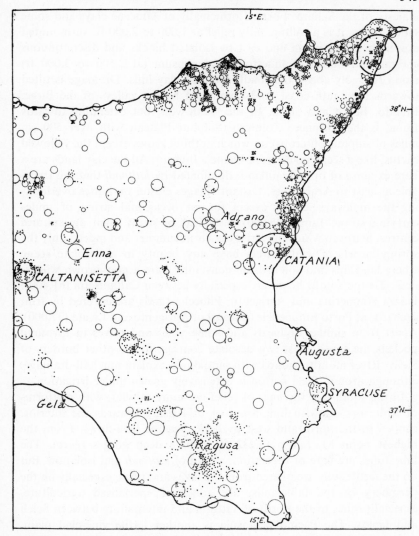

nucleated pattern of large villages over the Pliocene clay lands with their cereal monoculture

separated by time to colonise this difficult waterless country. Rocca Busambra, the highest district in the west (5,290 ft), has one of the few forests of this area.

The interior of Sicily has been described as a desert without the majesty of the Sahara. Formed principally of Miocene clays and some sandy rocks, it is a rolling, hilly relief at 1,000 to 2,000 ft, surmounted especially in the north and east by isolated blocks and discontinuous cuestas and buttes of limestone and gypsum (at 2,500 to 3,000 ft) rising ruggedly above the small, rounded clay hills. Drainage is tilted towards the south coast, and dominated by the valleys of the Birge, Freddo, Belice and Salso. In the south-west, but extending towards Enna, is the Altipiano Zolfifero (Sulphur Plateau with over 500 sq. miles of sulphur outcrops) on which nothing grows except the yellowed cactus, like a scene taken from Dante's Inferno. All the clay lands are a bare expanse of open grainland, dominated by *latifondi* that are traceable at least to Arab times. Distant villages cluster on buttes overlooking the highways, empty except for an occasional string of mules carrying straw. Enna (25,000) is typical of many such agricultural centres. Scirocco winds pulverise the air in summer and indeed only the spring carpets of wild flowers have any beauty in a desolate scene where landslips and soil erosion constantly bare a grey-brown wilderness. To the south, however, especially between Caltanisetta (61,400), Piazza Ammerina and Agrigento, Pliocene sands are covered by fruit orchards at Porto Empococle (outport of Agrigento and Licata (37,000). Apart from similar orchards and some vines and olives in favoured pockets the south coast is a desolate contrast to the other borders of Sicily. River mouths choked with sand dunes explain much ill-drainage, although around Gela cotton is extensively grown under irrigation.

In the south-east the lines of relief are more tabular, with platforms of white or yellowish limestones or tufa rising towards the interior, capped in the north and west by dark, basaltic lava-flows. From the highest point M. Lauro (3,232 ft) radiate deep gorges (*cave*). The limestones are bare of vegetation, a land of *latifondi* and isolation. But on the fertile soils, weathered from the lavas and tufas, especially on the periphery of the tablelands, are zones of specialised agriculture, especially vines to the north of Vittoria and interculture between Scicli and Ispica. The Pacino peninsula is another fertile vine-clad plain, connected along the coast with the orchards of Noto and Avola. As in Apulia, this district of south-east Sicily has large over-crowded agricultural villages, such as Vittoria (40,000) Modica (28,000) and Avola (22,000). Many of these centres have been laid out formally because of earthquakes in the seventeenth century. This is also true of the regional capital, Ragusa (41,000), whose old centre (Ragusa Ibla) was largely destroyed in 1693 and a new town was built below it.

PART IV

PERIPHERAL LANDS OF THE NORTHERN MEDITERRANEAN AND THE MEDITERRANEAN ISLANDS

CHAPTER 19

THE YUGOSLAV LITTORAL

by Professor J. Roglić, Zagreb University

The boundaries of the Mediterranean region of Yugoslavia are clearly defined, both with the neighbouring countries of Italy and Albania and with other parts of Yugoslavia. From the North Italian Plain to the coastal marshes of Albania, the mountain belt exhibits the 'Dinaric' trend, i.e. north-west to south-east, and there are many offshore islands. This is the type-example in the world of a 'Dalmatian' coast, so-called after the historic region of Dalmatia* which occupies the greater part of the Yugoslav coast. Some parts of the coast which the foreigner thinks of as being Dalmatia, the native recognises as belonging to either Istria, Croatia or Montenegro. In this article 'Dalmatia' will be used only in the broader sense in which it is understood by the foreigner.

INTRODUCTION: ITS LIMITS

The Yugoslav littoral has its own specific natural character. Immediately behind the coast itself rises a high barrier of rugged limestone mountains. Although the maritime slope is very narrow, where the Velebit and Biokovo ranges and the south-eastern coast rise sheer from the sea, the mountains effectively isolate the coast from the interior. In the Istrian peninsula, and between Velebit and the river Krka, there are relatively broad coastal plains; around the lower Neretva river and in southern Hercegovina there are peri-Mediterranean depressions, separated from the coast by coastal mountains. In the coastal plains and the peri-Mediterranean depressions the influence of the rugged mountain interior is small and the proximity of the sea and the protection afforded by the mountains cause the winters to be mild and allow the penetration of Mediterranean cultures. The relations between those regions with mild winters and the heights in the interior were especially close in the period of developed transhumance. The low coastal region of Istria and north-western Dalmatia offered greater possibilities for wintering livestock than the high pastures of the northern interior, and

---

* The name 'Dalmatia' derives from Roman times, from the name of an Illyrian tribe, the *Dalmate*, who inhabited this country.

their historical destinies were closely linked with the coast. By contrast, pastoralism in the peri-Mediterranean depressions of Hercegovina was closely connected with the high mountains, as is reflected in the historical development of Hercegovina where the Turks long reigned and cultural elements from Islam and the East spread almost to the Adriatic.

The boundaries between coastlands (*Primorje*) and the interior are related not only to natural characteristics, but also to historical events

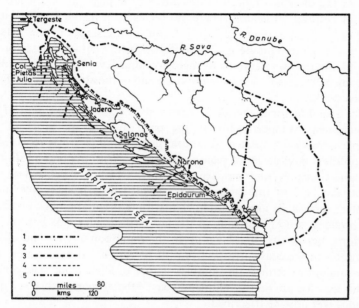

FIG. 212. Significant regional boundaries of Dalmatia, together with the major Roman towns. Legend: 1. the limits of Roman Dalmatia; 2. the limits of Venetian-Austrian Dalmatia; 3. geographic area studied in this chapter; 4. Jan. isotherm of 43° F. (6° C.); 5. boundary between Roman Dalmatia proper and Prevalitania

(Fig. 212). In earlier times, when the economy was centred on livestock, summer pastures in the mountains and wintering grounds in *primorje* were closely related. In later times, with the development of cultivation in the coastal belt and in addition political factors, the name 'Dalmatia' came to be applied only to the narrow coastal belt with its agrarian economy of vines, figs and olives.

After the Turkish defeats in the seventeenth century, Zagora, the ultramontane region, was incorporated in Dalmatia. Until very recently, pastoral Zagora was very isolated, and was more closely related with the highlands than with the coast. By contrast, on the islands and in the coastal belt, Mediterranean agriculture and maritime activities are the main supports of the economy. These parts are traditionally closely related with the sea, and had connections with other coasts of the Mediterranean.

The January isotherm of 43° (6), is not a good boundary. This isotherm does not enclose all of the coast, and in some of the colder parts outside it there are oases of Mediterranean vegetation. The distribution of the olive is a reflection not only of the physical conditions but also of cultural influences. There are olives even in the north-western part of the Yugoslav coastlands, but not on the slopes of the Velebit, where the winter climate is unfavourable. In the climatic oases of the peri-Mediterranean depressions there are some few olives, as a result of the long cultural isolation from the coast and of the absolute dependence on livestock.

The social factor is the most important in defining the extent of the geographical Mediterranean. In the past, the life and work of the people were closely related to natural factors and this was reflected in the political boundaries of regions and states. With the organisation of modern transport and modern economy, which are centred in the coast, the field of influence of the coastal towns has become much greater: ours is an age of stronger maritime orientation. Dalmatia in the broadest sense, especially in the last two decades, has become the maritime façade of Yugoslavia up to the mountain barrier and all life gravitates to the coast, irrespective of federal political boundaries. The only hindering factor is the complex nature of karst relief. The centres of this new life are on the mainland coast—the *primorje*, whose characteristics will now be described.

PHYSICAL BACKGROUND

1. *Relief and morphological regions.* The Dalmatian coastline is the classical example of its kind, by reason of its specific natural traits. The trend, from north-west to south-east, is parallel with that of the mountains, straits and islands (Fig. 212). The most characteristic feature is the parallelism of the main elements of the relief. In spite of the unity given by this parallelism, there are great regional contrasts and characteristic differences of detail. Limestone is the dominant rock; but the life of the people is more closely related to impermeable rocks, such as dolomite and palaeogenic flysch series. The impressiveness of the relief and the interest of some of its details are typical, and exercise a great influence on the life of the Yugoslav coastlands (see Plate 9).

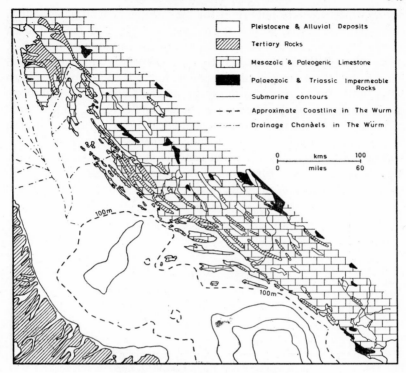

FIG. 213. Geology of the Adriatic area

A thick sequence of Mesozoic and Palaeogenic sediments was folded during the Alpine orogenesis (Fig. 213). In the extreme south-east, impermeable rocks of the lower Trias are characteristic, with dolomite and limestone above them. The Jurassic limestones are generally well stratified, but in Yugoslavia generally a thick series of pure reef lime-stone (Cretaceous) dominates. The Palaeogenic limestones have similar characteristics but with smaller outcrops. The Eocene flysch has special practical value.

During the Alpine orogenesis the thrust came from the north-east and the folds are usually inclined towards the coast. There was some radial movement, that is upward and outward, especially along the longitudinal fault-lines. Examples of imbricate fold structure occur, but without the thrust-sheet structures characteristic of the Alps. As else-where, after the Alpine orogenesis, there was posthumous uplift, followed by the rejuvenation of erosion processes.

At first sight the country appears mountainous. In detail, exceptions occur, which are very important for life and the general geographical character. The karst, with a subterranean world that has not been adequately explored, has been developed by the sinking and flowing of water through thick limestones. Beside the surface and underground karst forms, there are typical peneplains, for instance in south-western Istria, northern Dalmatia, around the middle Cetina river and along the lower course of the Neretva. These erosion surfaces, which are in contradiction to the recent geomorphological history of the karst, find their parallel in the karst of warm, moist climates. They were developed during the Upper Pliocene, when tectonic stability and climate were more suitable for the corrosion of the limestone at its contact with impermeable rocks, from which came streams charged with alluvial

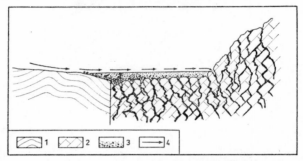

FIG. 214. The process of marginal corrosion. Legend: 1. impermeable rock; 2. limestone; 3. alluvial deposits; 4. direction of drainage

detritus. The limestones were pushed back by corrosion from the zone of contact (Fig. 213).

As a result of tectonic movements in the Plio-Pleistocene, the karstification of limestones and the differential erosion of impermeable rocks were intensified: by these processes greater differences in relief between limestone and impermeable rocks were elaborated. By the erosion of the impermeable rocks and corrosion of limestone *polja* were carved out (Kninsko polje, Petrovo polje, Sinjsko polje, Imotsko polje and others). Allogenous rivers (Raša, Zrmanja, Krka, Cetina and Neretva) cut deep canyons in the limestone.

Differential erosion and the carving out of karst features were further intensified by the glacio-eustatic lowering of sea-level, but the changed climate was a new morphogenetic factor. At the height of the last glaciation, when sea-level stood about 300 ft lower than at present, the part of the Adriatic Sea, north of a line joining Biograd on the Yugoslav coast and San Benedetto on the Italian coast, was dry land, and almost all of the Dalmatian islands were connected with the mainland. Traces of submerged valleys are discernible on hydrographic charts (Fig. 213).

In cold periods of the Pleistocene this region was under the strong meteorological influence of the sub-Polar front and the ice cap of the Alps. Cyclones from the sea brought great quantities of moisture, especially to the mountain slopes; in the winter, enormous quantities of snow fell, from which glaciers developed in the highest part of Orjen (6,220 ft) and Prokletije (8,840 ft). The greater part of the snow melted in summer, feeding streams which accumulated quantities of fluvio-glacial material (Morača, Kiri and Neretva rivers). Quantities of material were deposited also in the *polja*, and many *ponori* (swallow-holes) were choked. This caused temporary flooding, which was the result of the disequilibrium between the volume of water and the capacity of the *ponori*. The same process is seen even today in the periodic flooding of many of the *polja*.

Dry winds carried fine sand and dust from the outwash plain of the north Italian rivers and deposited it upon meeting the barriers of the Dalmatian islands off the coast. These aeolian deposits are found on the coasts of the northern Dalmatian islands (Susak and Unije), in the neighbourhood of Zadar and elsewhere.

Large areas of the mainland were flooded by the sea in post-glacial times. Where in the past was a great plain, today is the shallow north Adriatic sea (Fig. 213). Limestone ridges became islands, and the eroded flysch zones between them are now straits (kanali) of the sea. Where the Adriatic ran up the lower ends of the canyon-like valleys, are now the long narrow gulfs (for example on the Istrian coast). The flooding of a complex system of longitudinal valleys in the zone of Palaeogenic flysch and of the narrow troughs in the limestone, created the scenic gulfs of the Dalmatian coast (see Plate 70), among which the best known is Boka Kotorska (Bay of Kotor). In some places the sea penetrated underground into isolated karst depressions.

The trend of the Dalmatian coast is closely related to the Alpine orogenesis but the most complex features are the effects of petro-graphical differences, and the present features date from the post-glacial rise in sea-level. The submergence of the Dalmatian coast is of post-glacial (Flandrian) date and the more recent processes of accumulation and abrasion have not yet substantially altered it. Few rivers come from the karst and none brings a large quantity of sediment. In contrast to the Italian and Albanian rivers, they do not have deltas. The only exception is the Neretva, which comes partly from regions of impermeable rocks and carries a quantity of detritus. The cliffs are abraded where the limestone is exposed to the dominant winds.

Although the Dalmatian coast is geologically young, there is no evidence of general changes of level in historic times. Besides the generally established evidence of glacio-eustatic change, there are some traces of local landslides and collapse that are due to the petrographic differences and the great development of karst underground features.

In addition to well-marked characteristics which occur throughout, the Dalmatian littoral exhibits regional differences which make it possible to subdivide morphologically.

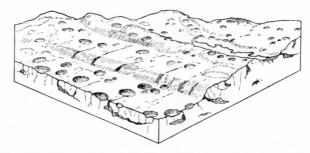

FIG. 215. Schematic block-diagram of karstic relief (after Sestini)

In the north-west, the peninsula of Istria abuts on the sea by a large peneplain on limestone, with depressions cut in flysch and backed by the limestone ridge of Ćićarija. The relief of Istria permits the economic development of the littoral.

The Kvarner region to the south-east is characterised by some morphological peculiarities which contrast with those of Istria. A wall of limestone mountains (Učka, 4,580 ft, Risnjak, 5,010 ft and Velebit, 5,760 ft) rises abruptly immediately behind the coastline. In the bay there are hilly limestone islands, linked with, rather than separated from, the mainland by the sea. The mainland, here ill-endowed and karstic in character, affords only a poor living, and since the days of the ancient *Liburnia* the scanty population has followed maritime pursuits.

Like Istria, northern Dalmatia consists of a limestone coastal plain, Kotari, and from early pastoral times its people were more closely linked with the mountainous hinterland.

The middle Dalmatian region includes several elements: islands, coastal flysch zone, and limestone coast ranges (Kozjak, 2,559 ft, Mosor, 4,396 ft and Biokovo, 5,790 ft). Passes over the coastal mountains link the littoral with the peri-Mediterranean Zagora. The differences in the relief and landscape of the various subdivisions are reflected by differences in their historico-social development.

The long and narrow coastal belt, south-east of the Neretva estuary, fronts the open sea and immediately behind the coastline there are high limestone mountains (Orjen, 6,220 ft and Lovčen, 5,730 ft). The nature of this very narrow coastal belt made it necessary for the inhabitants to organize trade connections with the interior and across the sea; witness the commercial republic of Dubrovnik and the sailors of Boka Kotorska.

2. *Climate and hydrology.* In the Yugoslav littoral climate is under the influence of the relief and of the geographical position. The barrier of the Alps and the Dinaric mountains enhance the importance of the geographical position. In winter, these mountain chains defend the coastlands from invasion by cold polar and continental air, whilst in summer they form the poleward limit of the warm and dry sub-tropical airmass. There are, in addition, contrasts between the northern and southern coastlands, and each of the smaller subdivisions has its individual characteristics (Fig. 214).

During the winter months, there is a tendency for the Alpine anticyclone to join up with the polar 'High', so that travelling depressions are deflected to a track south of the Alps. The indraft into these depressions from the south and south-east comes from the warm humid airmass of the subtropics, and the scirocco or *jugo* then brings to the coastal mountains great quantities of moisture: 18 inches of rain has been known to fall in one day. The rainfall maximum for the year occurs in late autumn (at Ulcinj and Hvar in December; at Dubrovnik, Split and Rijeka in October). In contrast to the dry summers with rare thunderstorms, the autumns and winters have many days with continuous rain. Then the coastal karst gets an abundance of water, many springs break out in full strength, and the *polja* are flooded. In the rainy season too the humid airmass crosses the mountain barrier to the interior, to give a secondary rainfall maximum in autumn, superimposed on the primary maximum in summer.

The cloudiness of autumn reduces the temperature and snow comes rather early to the coastal ranges, often in October. A cap of cold air forms above the orographic barrier and streams down into the coastland. Such irruptions of cold air are known as the bora or *bura* (a cold and dry wind). As the temperature falls in the Pannonian basin, a 'High' forms which from time to time may unite with the east European winter anticyclone, and the bora then becomes part of the broad strong airstream setting from the cool eastern part of Europe to the warm

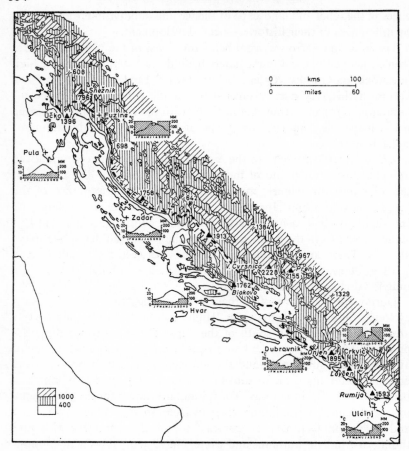

FIG. 216. Distribution of precipitation in Dalmatia. The influence of relief is notice-able. Fužine (2,506 ft.) receives 112 in. and Crikvice (3,900 ft.) even 203 in. annually. (Note use of metres and mms. on map)

Mediterranean. The cold continental airstream is most frequently set up in late January and February, which is why the lowest temperatures come in the second part of the winter. The bora brings with it dry air, bright skies and windy weather, but does not last long. Streaming down the mountain sides, the gusty wind blows intermittently, and even though it may not raise mountainous waves at sea, it is a danger to navigation. The bora is strongest below mountain defiles, through which the cold air pours with concentrated violence, as for example, at Trieste, Senj and Vrulja north-west of Makarska.

Spring, the transitional season, is less marked. The temperature rises rapidly, the pressure conditions which cause the bora disappear, and the Polar Front with its travelling depressions withdraws to a position north of the Alps. For this reason, there is no noticeable spring rainfall maximum.

Summer is an important season in the climate of the Yugoslav coastlands. The rocky land heats more rapidly than the sea and at mid-day a pleasant breeze, *zmorac* or *maestral*, blows from the sea to the land. Water-vapour is carried inland and the littoral may be without rain for months. The aridity is enhanced by the karstic character of the land. Most of the springs dry up, with the result that summer becomes the most difficult season of the year. Rainstorms are rare, occurring in the mountainous parts only, and tend to be followed by short but dis-agreeable outbreaks of the bora.

The long duration of the summer drought, and of the periods in winter when the bora is accompanied by bright and cloudless skies, mean that the Yugoslav littoral enjoys a maximum of sunshine; on average, 2,500 to 2,700 hours per year (Ulcinj, 2,530 hours, Dubrovnik, 2,584 hours, Hvar, 2,715 hours, Šibenik, 2,572 hours, Lošinj, 2,454 hours). In the mountainous interior, the number of hours with sunshine decreases (Senj, 2,142, Bjelašnica 1,521 hours). The total of insolation in summer is well known to be one of the highest in Europe.

In addition to the general climatic characteristics already outlined, there are considerable differences from one part to another of the coastal belt. The outer islands such as Hvar and Lošinj are less exposed to the continental bora, the range of temperature is less, and the annual rainfall varies between 24 and 32 inches. The mainland coast is more exposed to the cold waves associated with the bora, the range of temper-ature is greater, and the annual rainfall usually exceeds 40 inches. The range of temperature as well as the rainfall increase with altitude on the slopes of the coast mountains: at a height of about 3,000 ft the annual rainfall may surpass 120 inches (Crkvice, 3,900 ft gets 203 inches annually—the highest rainfall in Europe). The considerable extent of the Pleistocene glaciers, especially on Mt Orjen, is accounted for by this exceptionally heavy precipitation.

Very important is local mildness of winter, related to the exposure to the open sea or to the protection from severe continental influences. The mild winter climate of the outer islands is well known (January mean, Vis 49°F, Hvar 47°F, Lošinj 45°F). Similar mild winters charac-terise the south-east coastal belt (January mean, Dubrovnik 48°F, Budva 47°F). Some sheltered places on the inner coast also have mild winters (January mean, Rab, 43°F, Opatija, 42°F, Split, 45°F).

The general Mediterranean features—winter rain, summer drought and high insolation—characterise the north-east Adriatic coastlands. These Mediterranean features with longer drought and higher temperatures throughout the year, are more pronounced in the south-east. In the north-west, due to an earlier autumn and the passage of depressions until later in spring, the summer dry season is shorter and the Mediterranean characteristics are less pronounced. The differences in relief are reflected by differences in climate and vegetation. The karstic character of the coastland accentuates the defects of the Mediterranean climate and the summer drought presents difficulties to all forms of life.

Although the coast ranges receive enormous quantities of rain, the water quickly disappears underground. Hence the surface is dry. The water circulates underground under pressure, and some of it escapes by submarine springs *vrulje*. This loss of water is tragic for the inhabitants and for all forms of life. A few rivers (Raša, Zrmanja, Krka, Cetina and Neretva) rise in regions of impermeable rocks and traverse the limestone in narrow gorges. Some of them (Reka, Vrlika in Imotsko polje and Trebišnjica) sink underground by *ponori* (swallow-holes) and are called *ponornice* (disappearing rivers). These rivers near the sea emerge as strong springs, or follow courses under the floor of the sea.

The season of rainfall is the most important factor in the regime of the rivers. High water in winter is followed by very low water in summer, and many of the smaller rivers become dry. During the rainy season many springs break out and the volume of water in the streams increases, with the result that the capacity of the *ponori* is exceeded and the *polja* are flooded. Atmospheric humidity is high on account of the scirocco and nearness to the sea. In the dry summer, the crops wilt and even drought-resistant vegetation suffers. Supplies of water are conserved in artificial cisterns. The islands suffer most, being built almost entirely of limestone, and without springs. During the summer drought, water is very often transported by ship to many of the islands. The struggle against the shortage of water in summer and the need to satisfy the demands of people and crops is the dominant problem of the coastlands. In spite of the quantity of rain that falls, its seasonal regime is unfavourable.

3. *Vegetation.* A continuous belt of evergreen Mediterranean vegetation (*Quercetum ilicis*) stretches north-west to the neighbourhood of Zadar. Evergreen vegetation is found further to the north-west on the outer islands and down to the southern part of Cres island; also on the outer coasts of Pag and Rab. Isolated areas of evergreen vegetation may

also be found on the south-eastern coast of Istria; such areas are relics, formerly more widespread, from the time when the evergreen vegetation was a continuous belt. The distribution of the olive, the type species of the Mediterranean cultivation, has been extended outside the evergreen vegetation belt, for example in western Istria; but sudden cold in winter does it great damage. In the higher parts of the littoral and in the interior of the evergreen vegetation belt there are oak and hornbeam (*Caprinetum orientalis*), which are well adapted to karst conditions. The mountainous country above 3,000 ft (Učka, Velebit, Mosor, Biokovo, Orjen, Lovćen) is covered by beech forests (*F. sylvaticae*).

Although the extent of a species indicates the natural conditions obtaining, the forms and distribution of the vegetation are the results also of long-enduring social influences. The vegetation on the karst, once destroyed, cannot easily be restored. A degraded form of undergrowth predominates. Forests survive only in privately enclosed and protected areas (*ograde*). In areas where reafforestation has been carried out pine (*Pinus spp*) predominates. Communal pastures have however been despoiled of their vegetation. The reafforestation of these naked limestones (*kamenjari*) is a difficult and perhaps an insoluble problem. The naturally well-conditioned coastlands have, from early times, attracted people by whom they were quickly devastated.

THE ECONOMY OF THE RURAL LANDSCAPES

Although the karstic base and the summer drought are unfavourable factors, agriculture is the economic mainstay and is all-important to an understanding of the character and evolution of the country in the past. The poor shallow soils are not suited to arable agriculture, especially not for grain, which suffers badly in the summer drought. The country is better suited for tree crops such as olives, vines, figs and almonds, but orchards had little importance in the past in Zagora, where self-sufficient subsistence stock-farming was the rule.

1. *The Crops.* The cultivation of the olive was one of the first agricultural activities, particularly in the south-east; the Yugoslav coastlands as a whole are marginal to this culture. Spells of severe cold during the winter do great damage to these trees, especially to the isolated groves on the west coast of Istria. For historic and social reasons the olive did not penetrate up the Neretva valley. Olives grow very successfully in the south and on the islands, where the climatic conditions are the most suitable. The olive could not be made a satisfactory basis of a trading economy as the yield is erratic, from one year to another, and in some years there is none. The trees are not well

cared for, being of subordinate importance. The olive groves were used for winter pasturage and olive cultivation was not given the advantage of specialist labour. Everybody helped with the harvest. The oil was nevertheless an important item of trade with the interior, and was encouraged by the church for use instead of animal fats in Lent, etc. The importance of the olive groves declined with the spread of the vineyards. At the end of the eighteenth century the olive trees in Venetian Dalmatia numbered 25 million; at the end of the nineteenth century there were only four million.

The cultivation of the vine is as old as that of the olive, but the commercial rise of the vine is comparatively recent, although Dalmatian wines were known to be of high quality in ancient times. Its cultivation declined in the Dark Ages. To transport wine without its deteriorating is difficult, and later the spread of Islam under the Turks made it impossible to carry on the wine trade. The re-establishment of routes after the Turkish period made possible its renaissance in the eighteenth century. It blossomed with the growth of towns, the building of railways and the organisation of wine markets such as Trieste and Rijeka (Fiume). The crisis in France with phylloxera and in Italy with mildew, opened the market to Dalmatian wines. Vineyards were extended and often replaced olive groves. The profits from the sale of wine financed the planting of new areas. Vines became the main landscape element, and on the islands and mainland coast were almost a monoculture by the end of the last century. This was a dynamic period in agriculture, although less so in the south-east, where the olive maintained its importance, because this area is too distant from leading wine markets.

The greatest expansion of the vineyards took place in the second half of the nineteenth century. The railway was built through the vineyard country from Trieste through western Istria, and fleets of sailing boats transported Dalmatian wine to the ports of Trieste and Rijeka. From there, the wine went to interior markets in Austria-Hungary. This was a period of prosperity for Dalmatia, especially for the islands. On the islands, experience of vine cultivation was longest and the wine was the best. The income from the sale of the wine changed the face of the villages and raised the standard of living.

In 1894 phylloxera hit the Dalmatian vineyards, which were rapidly destroyed. Their reconstruction on American stocks was slow. It was impossible to restore the previous number of vines. The cultivators had not the necessary money, and the karstlands are not suitable for the new American stocks which require deeper soils and better cultivation. Besides, the reconstituted French and Italian vineyards were in produc-

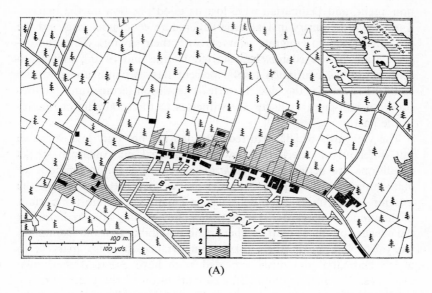

(A)

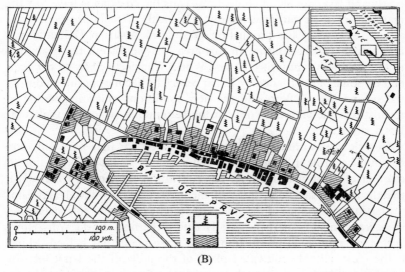

(B)

FIG. 217. The evolution of land utilisation on Prvić Island near Šibenik between 1825 (A) and 1959 (B). Legend: 1. vineyards; 2. pastures; 3. gardens. In 1825, the vineyards dominated the economy and the holdings were larger. The reduction in the size of holdings and the decline of the vineyards, reflect the agrarian impoverishment. In spite of an increase in the number of houses in the village, the population declined from 1,200 (1825) to 66 (1953)

tion again, and Dalmatian wine lost its good position on the market. The vineyard country in Dalmatia suffered an economic crisis and the peasants began to emigrate overseas with their savings. Thus the depopulation of the islands had started by the end of the nineteenth century. It has continued to the present day, because no substitute could be found for the vine. Deserted cultivation terraces and picturesque but half-empty villages are witnesses to the economic prosperity of the past.

The vineyards which were reconstituted are not only less extensive but differently located. For new vines grafted on American stocks conditions are better in the *polja*. The new mechanised methods of cultivating vines and processing the grapes give better results in the interior. Hence Imotski and Benkovac in Zagora are the most important of the modern vineyards. The autarkic policy of Italy favoured grain at the expense of vines in Istria. There is no possibility that the Dalmatian vineyards will regain their former importance, because markets to which Dalmatia previously exported wine have enlarged their own plantings. The new methods of vine cultivation in the karst soils are costly and less capable of competing. Thus the coastlands have lost the mainstay of their earlier economy. The peak of their prosperity was about 1890, when the production of wine in Austrian Dalmatia was about 1,300,000 hectolitres. In this area, the yield from the beginning of the twentieth century to the first World War declined by 42 per cent, and on some of the islands by 75 per cent. The decline continued during the second World War, and the new conditions make it possible to reconstitute the vineyards only in the better soils, which, in the karstlands, are scarce.

Other cultures are of secondary importance, for they have only just begun. Their rôle in the economy is not easy to define. Figs are not an essential element in agriculture. The cultivation of the cherry (*maraska*), pyrethrum and lavender, most of them recently introduced, have not the lasting importance of the vine. Tobacco had a similar rôle, extending its acreage in some parts especially before the first World War. However, the commercial production of all these plants has helped. Maize is the most suitable cultivated plant of the *polja* of the karst interior which are flooded in winter. In pockets of soil on the high karst, potatoes are successful, but there are not enough of them to be a staple food.

The cultivation of winter vegetables and flowers is a relatively new activity, developed only round the towns which have good communications with the interior. The difficulties are the scarcity of good

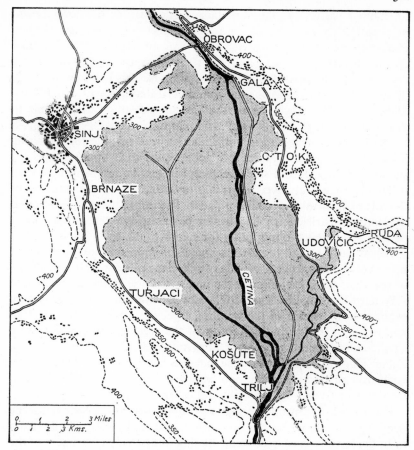

FIG. 218. The situation of the settlements around the margins of the Sinjsko polje

soil and water in the karst. The success of market gardening depends on location relative to the market, and on the standard of living. Arbori-culture exhausts the soil, which needs modern fertilisers. In the periodic-ally flooded fields of the *polja*, only crops sown late in spring can be cultivated. The fragmentation and small size of the holdings (average of 3·7 acres arable land) are additional negative factors in Dalmatian agriculture (Fig. 218).

2. *Pastoralism*. Although stock-raising is of secondary importance today, it has been of such significance in the past that a knowledge of its position is essential to an understanding of the historico-geographical evolution of the country. The proximity of coastal wintering grounds

to summer pastures in the mountains made possible the development of pastoral activities based on transhumance. On the high Dinaric plateaux of central Hercegovina there was an abundance of summer pasture for the livestock, and for the winter the flocks and herds descended to the peri-Mediterranean lowlands. This livestock-breeding hinterland was the basis for the commercial development of medieval Dubrovnik. The stockmen of the interior relied on Dubrovnik to organise and control the long-distance caravan routes.

The lowland of northern Dalmatia also was suitable for wintering livestock, but the mountains behind gave no such opportunities for summer grazing. Hence stock-keeping had less importance there than in Hercegovina, but nevertheless it is essential to an understanding of the role of classical and medieval Zadar. The same applies in the coastal lowlands of Istria which had winter pastures, and the interior karst plateau gave limited opportunity for summer grazing.

Other parts of the coastlands and their mountainous hinterlands, being very karstic, have little value for livestock. Before the ascendancy of the vine, stock-keeping was the major activity. It was a poorer and very hard kind of life. The people moved with the animals and were exposed to the strain of the weather, especially trying to the children and old people. The bigger centres of the stock-keeping period were situated on the mainland coast: Dubrovnik (*Epidaurum*), Split (*Salonae*), Zadar (*Jadera*) and others. The phase which followed, that of the vineyards, made the islands more important, and the ports best suited for the wine trade—Rijeka, Split and others prospered.

In the days of transhumant pastoralism the sheep was dominant. The people got wool and leather for clothes, milk and meat for food, from it. In the second place were goats, finding forage to the detriment of the vegetation, but having no importance for clothes. The spread of the vineyards and agriculture on the coastlands reduced the possibilities for wintering livestock on the littoral. Besides which, factory-made textiles competed with home-grown materials and so the role of the sheep declined. For the sake of the regeneration of the forest vegetation, the keeping of goats was recently forbidden. Besides, few today like the hard life of a herder. These changes have caused the livestock industry to decline. The growing population of the towns supports the development of dairying, but the possibilities for cattle breeding are very limited. Since the decline of extensive livestock (sheep and goats) the natural regeneration of the forest on the karst is noticeable. This process is most important for contemporary changes in the landscape.

3. *Maritime Life*. The poverty of the karstic coastland and the multitude

of islands to which sea transport is traditional, caused an early development of maritime activities. These draw the country into the maritime life of the world. Greek sailors founded colonies at suitable points. They had difficulty with the local pirates, who were reduced only by the Romans after their skilful attacks had troubled trade routes for centuries. The security of the sheltered sailing route between the islands and the inner coast was the main reason why the Venetians needed strategic coastal supporting points (Zadar, Trogir, Split, Hvar and Korčula).

The long maritime tradition and experience of the sea was reflected in the skill of the ancient Liburnian and other Illyrian pirates, and the glorious sailors of Dubrovnik. Their exploits were succeeded in the eighteenth and nineteenth centuries by those of very skilful sailors and merchants from Boka Kotorska, Pelješac, Lošinj, Rovinj, Piran and elsewhere. The prosperity of vine cultivation in the nineteenth century spread trade to the interior, to which wine was exported and whence various goods were imported. The majority of the trade was carried by sailing-vessels and consequently many small harbours arose, each of which was the scene of maritime activities. This was a period of maximum economic activity for the coastlands: the sea was alive with sailing boats, and the land with vineyard workers. A period of prosperity was followed by a complex of crises.

Steamers brought a change, in that trade came to be concentrated in a smaller number of the bigger mainland ports. The older ports on the islands gradually lost their people and their importance. Unwillingly the sailors abandoned their homes and gardens in Boka Kotorska, on the coast of Pelješac, Lošinj and other islands for flats in the new blocks of buildings in Trieste, Rijeka or Split, or went overseas. Money made in the vineyards or in shipping paid for the strong stream of emigration from the Dalmatian littoral in the late nineteenth and early twentieth century.

Many of the older men skilled in traditional sailing found the new techniques beyond them. Some of them, however, adapted themselves, and the maritime tradition of Dubrovnik (Fig. 219) was carried on by the purchase of steamers, which worked not only along the Dalmatian coast but all over the world. Some of those people displaced from Boka Kotorska, Pelješac and particularly Lošinj soon dominated the maritime activities of Trieste and Rijeka. Some of them played an important role in the shipping world of Argentina and Chile, and in the Pacific fisheries of North America. Dalmatian sailors are accepted and well-esteemed by the crews of the ships of all countries. In their native country all opportunity was exploited to renew and to develop further the maritime tradition of the past. The Yugoslav maritime centres between the two wars were especially Dubrovnik (Plate 72), Split, Sušak, and Kotor. After the second World War, the domestic ship-building industry helped the growth of the state-owned fleet.

Fishing is of relatively small importance because the clear blue sea off the karst coast is not too rich biologically, although the species of fish are numerous and of high quality. The seasonal summer fishing (sardines, mackerel and so on) is the most important. The best-known fishing grounds are around the outer islands of Lastovo, Vis, Kornati and others, where the water is shallow. The development of fishing

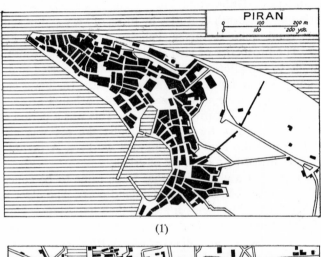

(1)

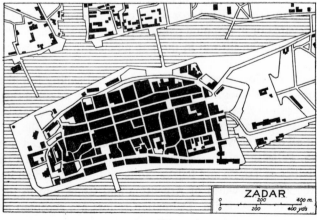

(2)

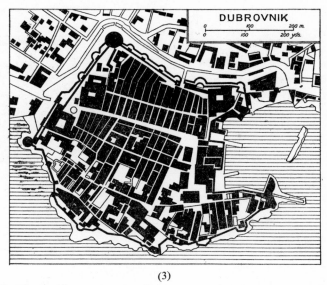

(3)

FIG. 219. The positions and types of old ports: 1. Piran; 2. Zadar; 3. Dubrovnik

depends too on market and social factors. Besides the fishing round the islands, the principal ports aided by new routes, supply the urban demand of the interior (Ljubljana, Zagreb, Belgrade). Fishing is concentrated around Rijeka, Zadar, Split, Pula and other ports. With mechanisation after the second World War it has become more effective. The factor of the urban demand first made itself felt in Italy, for example at Chioggia near Venice and at several fishing centres round Trieste. The fishermen fish all over the Adriatic, and this was one reason for the customary conflicts between the older Italian and the younger Dalmatian fishermen.

The economic evolution caused the concentration of shipping at the best located ports, the improvement of traffic connections with the interior, and the emergence of larger towns. Modern shipyards replaced the numerous and dispersed boat-building yards which had built sailing ships in the past, of which those on Lošinj, Korčula and Trogir were the best known, not only in the Adriatic but outside the Mediterranean. The shipyard in Rijeka, although restricted in area, is well known. The shipyards in Pula developed from an Austro-Hungarian naval base. The shipyards in Split grew slowly between the wars and after the second World War became a big undertaking. The shipyards of Kraljevica and Boka Kotorska have a complementary rôle: while the experience in Lošinj, Korčula and Trogir are perpetuated in the manufacture of

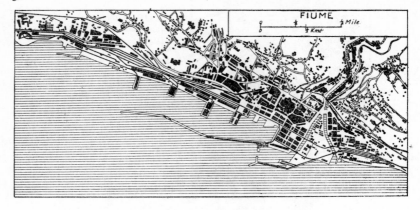

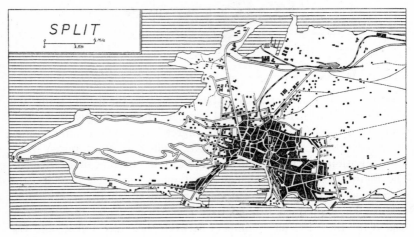

Fig. 220. The two leading Yugoslav ports, Rijeka Fiume and Split

fishing, sports' and other small boats. In all these shipyards the traditional skill of boat-builders is still alive. The Dalmatians built many types of boat, from old times known as the boats of Liburnia and Dubrovnik.

Parallel with ship-building and fish-preserving other industries have developed, mostly after the second World War; the principal centres are: Rijeka, Split, Šibenik, Pula and Zadar. Besides shipbuilding and related industries in Rijeka there are the wood industry, oil-refining, paper-making and others. Split became early a centre of the cement industry using high grade Eocene marine marly limestone. The synthetic plastic industry and others have made Split an important industrial centre. Šibenik is the main centre of the Yugoslav aluminium industry (with two plants). Pula, besides the shipyard, has a textile industry, glass and cement. Zadar, the capital of Dalmatia until 1818, has a famous factory for liqueurs and others for tobacco, fishing equipment and precision instruments. Other industrial centres are of relatively less importance. The concentration of industry differentiates the port-towns and is the dynamic factor in the development of the Yugoslav coastlands.

Besides the labour force, hydro-electric power is an important industrial factor. The steep longitudinal profiles of the rivers and the abundant winter rainfall are suitable for the generation of hydro-electricity. The river regime is complementary to that of the interior rivers. The nature of the karst and the submergence of the limited areas of arable land are specific problems in hydro-electrical installations in the karst. Regional hydro-electric potentials are an essential factor in the development of the Dalmatian industries.

In the new socio-economic and traffic conditions, the Dalmatian coastal belt has a specific value and new possibilities. Its picturesque and contrasting character and abundance of cultural monuments attract many tourists. Tourism began in the north, which was most accessible from the interior, after the construction of the 'Southern Railway' from Vienna to Trieste in 1857. After this, provision made for tourists in Opatija increased rapidly. A specific cultural heritage and the unique beauty of the scenery in the south made Dubrovnik world-famous as a resort. The Brioni islands are well known for their mild climate and dense natural and naturalised vegetation. The island of Lošinj, with a similarly mild climate, is rich in maritime traditions. Its suitable geographical position in the middle Adriatic has made Hvar continuously important. Boka Kotorska is a natural and human contrast, and especially attractive.

The influx of tourists between the wars 'discovered' the Dalmatian coast and soon made popular some of the lesser known and quite unknown places. Tourism brought new life to the country. It is the new factor influencing the whole economy, importance and physiognomy of settlement as well as the way of life.

The tourist traffic was renewed immediately after the second World War but the motor age did not find the roads good enough. With the completion of the motor-road from Zagreb to Rijeka, and the building of the coast road and some lateral connections still in progress, tourism has been stimulated. In the next few years the motor road from the Italian to the Albanian frontier will be finished. In the meantime it is planned to build new motor roads from the interior to open both the mountains and the coastlands as recreation zones. The Dalmatian coast has big possibilities for tourists. Technical developments have strengthened the coastal-interior links, and tourism is more important than agriculture in the economy of the karstland. The change is visible in the physiognomy and functions of many settlements.

SETTLEMENT AND POPULATION

1. *Historical Summary.* The position of the country between the Mediterranean and middle Europe gave it an early importance for human migrations. The country attracted and retained migrating tribes. In many localities traces of a well-developed Neolithic culture have been found, dating from the time when the caves of the karst were inhabited.

About 1000 B.C. the Illyrians were the dominant people. From the seventh century B.C. the Greeks opened commercial relations with the Dalmatian coast and from the beginning of the fourth century the Greeks founded colonies on the Dalmatian coast and islands. Commercial exchanges with the Illyrian pastoralists, and traffic by the Amber Route, brought the Greek argonauts up to the northern coast of the Adriatic sea.

About the middle of the third century B.C. the Illyrians founded their first states along the coast and their piratical attacks disturbed the Roman Empire. After long and hard battles which continued over two centuries the Romans finally subdued the country, imposed the Roman order, and founded the province of Illiricum. From Illiricum, 'Greater Dalmatia' emerged. The Roman Emperor Diocletian divided this province into Dalmatia proper and Prevalitania (Fig. 221). The boundary between them was important for its future influence, since it divided the western from the eastern or Byzantine territories of the Roman Empire.

During their long dominance of the east Adriatic coast, the Romans built several important centres, for example Salonae, Narona, Jadera and Scardona. In the mountainous interior they built a network of garrison towns and successfully controlled the pastoralists. The Latin language in the course of time came to be generally accepted, especially owing to the activity of the Roman Church.

In the fifth century A.D. Dalmatia came under the Byzantine Empire and acted as a bridge connecting metropolitan Byzantium and the Byzantine territories in northern Italy. Soon came the *Völkerwanderung*, which disturbed the established relations of the Byzantine power and reduced its foothold in Dalmatia to several fortified points along the

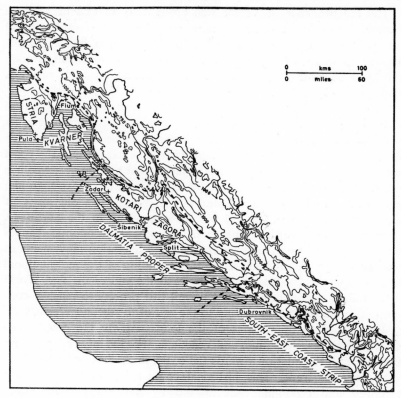

FIG. 221. Regional divisions and drainage features of Dalmatia

coast and on the islands (Trogir, Zadar, Split). After the conflict with the Goths followed the first strong wave of Slavs, which finished with permanent Slavonic settlement of the north-eastern coastlands of the Adriatic. The fortified and ethnically isolated Roman towns had to learn another way of life and ultimately were absorbed by the new Slavonic states: Croatia, Zeta and Rascia.

The decline of the Croatian state about A.D. 1000 helped the rise of Venice, which took by force, first the more important settlements and later the whole of the coastal belt, in order to ensure the security of the important coastwise shipping route between the islands and the mainland of Dalmatia. With great adroitness the Venetians kept their gains, in spite of the opposition from the newly united state of Croatia and Hungary. This period was followed by the strong and long invasion of the Turks (which began in 1499).

The independence of Venice was brought to an end in 1797 by Napoleonic troops, and at the same time Venice lost its territorial possessions along the east Adriatic coast. The brief but important French domination (1805–1815) caused nationalist movements among the local Slavonic peoples, which the succeeding Austrian rule was powerless to annihilate.

In the nineteenth and twentieth centuries, besides the political changes and national evolution, there came technical improvements which brought about changes in the Adriatic. The sailing ships which had literally sailed by the channels between the islands and the coast were replaced by steamships, and the latter kept a more direct course outside the islands. Much more trade now crossed the ocean than had ever been handled by the Mediterranean boats. The old ports of Dalmatia were too small, and new ones grew up in the north-east Adriatic—Trieste, Rijeka and others. Technical and economic changes upset the pre-existing relations, and national liberation movements as well as military defeats caused the disintegration of the multinational and polyglot Austro-Hungarian Empire at the end of the first World War. Italian nationalism did not permit this process to reach a conclusion, and it was prolonged up to the end of the second World War.

The general characteristics of the long past are the conflicts of Greeks, Romans, Byzantines and Venetians, with the local peoples who pressed from the interior towards the coast, in the hope of developing their overseas trade. This historical conflict was ended by recent technical and economic changes and by nationalist stabilisation. In the recent past, after World War I, the internal processes continued to act and relations between the coastlands and the interior improved. The local people have been the authors of these large-scale changes, especially since the last War, since which the political situation is related to the ethnic relations.

2. *Settlement.* In the old pastoral-agrarian economy the villages were the main type of settlement. The siting of the villages was influenced by economic factors and the danger of attacks from the open sea. The villages on the islands were hidden in the interior. On the mainland coast they were situated at the contact of the flysch with the limestone, and in Zagora they stood at the edges of the *polja* or were scattered in the karstland (Fig. 218). The villages in the period of self-sufficient economy were isolated one from another and towns were rare and were fortified. The houses were small and very often with the people and livestock in the same room.

With the increase in security in the eighteenth, and the commercial orientation of the vineyards, maritime development and increase in road traffic in the nineteenth century, the conditions quickly altered. The settlements on the islands and along the coast moved closer to the sea, and on the mainland were attracted by new roads. The attraction of the coast lay in the greater opportunities for sailing and bathing as recreations.

In the villages on the north-eastern coastlands of the Adriatic there are also examples of three phases of development. The old settlements of inner Istria were very often fortified and crowded '*gradine* or *castelieri*' (fortified settlements) having existed since early times. The same type of settlement occurs in the interior of the islands and on the peneplain of north Dalmatia. Many of these out-of-the-way anachronisms are today half-abandoned. Present conditions favour coastal sites, for many of them use of the surrounding land for agricultural purposes is of subordinate importance. Tourism has connected these settlements with the outside world.

After the withdrawal of the Roman peace, a long period of insecurity prevented the evolution of urban life. The few towns were in isolated positions and surrounded by walls, because the need for defence was greater than that of relations with the neighbouring country. The sites were similar to those of the *gradine* of inner Istria and of the fortified settlements of Zagora. The towns along the coast chose peninsular or insular positions, as these were more easily defended from the mainland and at the same time provided useful anchorages (Fig. 219). Among these fortified coastal towns the most important were Dubrovnik, Zadar, and after them numerous smaller centres. Dubrovnik was the organising centre for the caravan routes of the mainland, which it linked with its own shipping and so expanded commercially. Zadar had a more typically peninsular site, which was known as the best supporting point and anchorage of the sailing route along the inner coastal channel. The importance of livestock in the immediate vicinity was the basis of its commercial life. Other fortified centres in analogous sites were of less importance.

The strides made in economic and technical progress did not help the old centres. The livestock economy was superseded by agriculture, the railways did not follow the caravan routes, and the replacement of sail by steam led to the concentration of shipping and mercantile occupations in the bigger ports—Trieste, Rijeka, Split—(Fig. 220), now connected by rail and improved roads with the interior.

The administrative and economic progress of the agriculture-sailing period combined the commercial and handicraft industries with the administrative role of district and communal towns. Each island, as well as the more important parts of the coast and the interior, had its own centres. The mechanisation of trade as well as the concentration of commercial activities and the beginning of industry supported the development of the best-situated centres, such as Rijeka, Split, Šibenik. Dubrovnik stagnated, in spite of its many centuries of experience, likewise Zadar, which lost its function as the administrative centre of the whole of Dalmatia on account of the changed politico-economic conditions. The naval and military importance of Pula is in decline.

Recently, the differentiation of the main centres and the concentration of population in the best localities have become noticeable. Tourism, however, has opposed this trend with its interest in the smaller, quieter and, for its clientèle, more attractive places, such as Dubrovnik, Opatija, Hvar, Makarska and Korčula.

The different phases of development are reflected in the types of settlement. The well-preserved, stone-built fortified towns are the best known: such as Trogir (Plate 71), Korčula and Krk. But they could not retain their importance under present conditions. Many Dalmatian towns have a fortified compact centre with an outer ring of more modern and dispersed buildings (Fig. 219). The features of this new outer part depend on orographical conditions and on the function of the settlement. The insufficiency of level land is the biggest problem at Rijeka, while the position of the existing industrial quarter influences the expansion of Split. The new residential parts of Dubrovnik are expanding into areas of typical Mediterranean vegetation, which gives them the aspect of gardens, as in Opatija and its environs.

3. *Population.* The population of the coastal belt (about 9,836 sq. miles) numbered 1,189,000 in 1953, or 161 per sq. mile. The density is less than the Yugoslav average, which is 172 per sq. mile. The coastal belt represents 7·3 per cent of Yugoslav territory, and about 6·8 per cent of the population of Yugoslavia lives within it.

The number of the population is increasing slowly. From 1910, when it numbered 1,124,550, it had increased in 1953 by only 9·5 per cent. This increase is less than the Yugoslav average, and is a reflection of the economic passivity of the coastlands. The coastlands have been characterised by strong emigration caused by their poor, karstic nature, by economic and political changes, and by their geographical position.

The population of the littoral shows a slow increase, while the population of the islands has decreased very much (from 171,000 in 1910 to 143,000 in 1953, that is a decrease of 16 per cent). The decrease

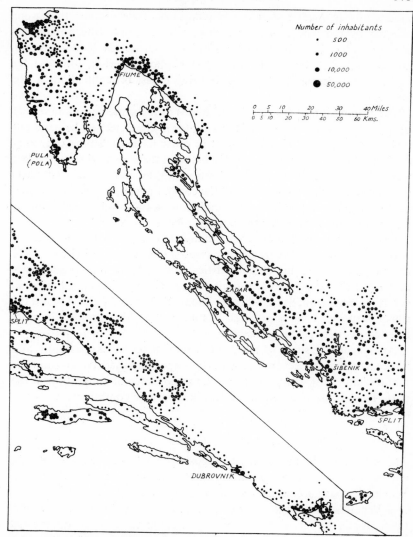

FIG. 222. Distribution of population in Dalmatia. The karstic islands are sparsely settled. The importance of the lowlands in Istria and north Dalmatia is evident; also the role of the principal ports (Fiume, Split, Zadar and Dubrovnik), and the importance of polja in Zagora

was most marked in the outer islands (Silba 51 per cent, Lošinj 45 per cent and Cres 41 per cent). These islands are remote from the new administrative and economic centres on the mainland coast, to which the population from the islands emigrated, as well as overseas. The same thing happened with the populations of the islands that were affected by the new economic changes; for example, the population of the island of Brač between 1910 and 1953 decreased by 36 per cent and that of Krk by 21 per cent. The phylloxera crisis, followed by emigration overseas and to neighbouring cities, brought about a big decrease.

The population of the interior (Zagora) in the same period increased by 18·5 per cent. This part of the country is characterised by seasonal migration in search of employment in other parts of Yugoslavia, particularly the Pannonian plain. Only between the wars and since the last war, permanent colonisation has been important in the Yugoslav parts of Pannonia and in some towns of the coast. Zagora has suffered from a backward economy and a lack of traffic routes. Its population, therefore, had neither the means nor the opportunity to emigrate.

Although the population on the mainland coast as a whole increased between 1910 and 1953 by 8·8 per cent, some of its subdivisions have their own demographic characteristics (Fig. 222). In the coastal strip, centres of the social and economic life are situated in several regional centres, Dubrovnik, Split, Šibenik, Zadar, Rijeka and Pula. Around the towns mentioned the population has increased rather rapidly; in more isolated districts it has decreased.

Apart from the slight increase in the population of the coastlands as a whole, the big decrease in many parts—especially the islands—and the preponderance of women indicate the importance of emigration in the past. This is closely connected with the economic conditions.

THE REGIONS

The several regional units of the Yugoslav coastlands are the result of a combination of natural features and social factors, past and present. When overseas influences were important (in Greek, Roman, Byzantine and Venetian times) the outer coast and islands had particular importance. Now, the active force comes from the mainland—the inner coast and the gulfs have attracted the most important centres. This change is significant for the geographical differentiation of these units (Fig. 212).

1. *Istria*. Istria is an outstanding part of the Yugoslav littoral. The coastal lowlands or plains, in the period of stock-raising, were suitable for wintering livestock. The coastal belt attracted the herdsmen from the Dinaric regions and probably from the Carpathians. The presence of people of Roumanian extraction in Istria is witness to such migrations having taken place in the past. Oak timber, building stone and livestock

products were the principal items of exchange with Venice. The agrarian reorganisation in the eighteenth century re-enforced the Istrian economy and influenced socio-economic evolution. Istria is the most important agricultural region of the Yugoslav coastlands. Its outstanding position gave the peninsula a special importance at some stages in history. From Rome, via Ancona and Istria, was the shortest route to the frontier belt of the Roman Empire in the Mid-Danubian lands. This was the reason for the building of a monumental winter camp, *Colonia Pietas Iulia* (the present Pula or Pola), of which numerous monuments remain, especially the arena for about 24,000 spectators.

Pula, and with it Istria, again assumed importance in the second half of the nineteenth century on account of the strategic balance of the period. The Austro-Hungarian fleet made use of the outstanding position and the bay on the southern extremity of Istria. Much capital was invested in making Pula one of the strongest naval bases in the Mediterranean. This caused the early railway connection (1876) with the interior and the development of the town, which in 1815 had been a small fishing village with a population of 1,104. At the beginning of the first World War Pula housed more than 60,000 inhabitants. The military experience of the first World War exposed the weakness of all fixed and exposed naval bases and Pula accordingly lost its military importance. During the Italian occupation between the two wars it suddenly declined. In this same period, Istria reverted to a self-contained economy.

Relatively rich agricultural yields, particularly of wine, fruit and vegetables, provided the material of commercial exchanges with the interior. Today Istria is well-placed for tourist traffic in virtue of its geographical position and good trunk roads. Freight connections with the interior have made industrial development possible, especially in the coast towns. These social and economic links with the interior increased with the end of Italian occupation after World War II, when sovereignty reverted to Yugoslavia. It must be remarked that the potentially good traffic connections, especially with the eastern Kvarner region, have not been realised.

2. *Kvarner*. The Kvarner region is the triangular territory between the peninsula of Istria on the west and the mainland coast on the east (Fig. 212). The Bay of Kvarner is enclosed by steep mountains, and the islands of Krk, Cres and Lošinji, Rab and Pag are hilly karstlands. The karstic nature of the country made the region unimportant in the live-stock-and-agricultural period. The greater part of the area is sea; the inhabitants are few and poor and since ancient Liburnian times they

have engaged in piracy. Although Senj, Fiume, Bakar and other ports had a long commercial and maritime tradition they could not make closer connection with the interior, and so bring about a higher degree of development.

A turning-point came with the rise of trade in the eighteenth century. In 1719, the Austrian government decided to make Fiume (Rijeka) and others into free ports. Roads were built later, after which Fiume forged ahead. The central Austrian government favoured Trieste, which was connected by rail with the interior in 1857. Fiume was connected by rail sixteen years later. In the development of Trieste and Fiume the conflict of interest between Vienna and Budapest was manifest. The Italian occupation between the wars cut off Fiume from its immediate hinterland, retarding its growth as a port and as a town. A worse blow came at the end of the second World War when the port was almost completely destroyed by German troops.

Since the second World War Fiume and the Kvarner region have experienced a renaissance of their maritime and commerical life. Fiume is again connected with its remoter hinterland; being as well favoured in its position as Trieste in relation to the pass of Postojna (1,998 ft), whilst the best route to the richest and most fully developed southern parts of the Pannonian basin runs through the Gorski Kotar. The Danubian waterway by the river Sava up to Sisak is the nearest inland waterway to Fiume.

The Kvarner region is the natural gateway from overseas to Yugoslavia and the Pannonian basin. This position caused the port installations at Fiume to be rebuilt rapidly after the war (Plate 74). By 1949 the traffic of the port was greater than it had been in 1913. The population since the war has nearly doubled (from 50,000 in 1945 to 80,000 in 1957). Parallel with the rebuilding of the port, other economic activities have developed. Thus Fiume became a symbol of Yugoslav maritime dynamism, and the focus of the Kvarner region, which might well be renamed the Fiume region. Fiume has become the centre of Istria too, which, under the new relations, is to be included as part of the same region.

The picturesque and easily accessible Kvarner region is particularly suited for tourism. Besides the well-known Opatija Riviera on the east coast of Istria, tourism is important on the Vinodol coast, south-east of Fiume. Like a smaller Genoa, Fiume has a double frontage, a Riviera on each side of it. Furthermore, the attractive islands (Rab, Lošinji, Krk and others), as well as the mountains inland, give every possibility of combining the recreations of a seaside with those of a mountain holiday. In no part of the Mediterranean is the life more

69 Rovinj, W. Istria. Built on a peninsula that was formerly made into an island for defence

70 Baška on Krk Island. It is easy to distinguish the greater economic value of the lowland flysch zone from the upper, denuded limestone area

71 Trogir, site of ancient *Tragurion*, and formerly one of the most important places on the Dalmatian coast

COASTAL TOWNS
OF DALMATIA

72 Korčula, once important harbour for sailing vessels at entrance to open sea from a sheltered channel

73 Dubrovnik, medieval fortress, port and terminus of land route. Today it is a popular tourist resort

74 Rijeka, chief port of Yugoslavia. View of section of harbour for coastal passenger boats

strongly influenced by the sea than in the Kvarner region—singled out for full development of the tourist traffic in the near future.

3. *Dalmatia*. Dalmatia proper extends between the Velebit mountains on the north-west and the Pelješac peninsula on the south-east. It is the central and most complex part of the Yugoslav coastlands. Off the coast, there is a line of islands, and inland, between a mountainous ridge and the coast, there extends a relatively wide erosion surface which on the north is open to the sea and on the south is separated from the sea by coastal mountains. The connections and mutual compensations of these inner parts and their separation by a sparsely populated mountainous tract from the deeper interior have led to the survival of the name 'Dalmatia'. The offshore channels, together with the local resources, attracted the old sailing routes, near which the Greeks, Romans, Byzantines and Venetians held their fortresses. Apart from the coastal emporia which were well known to the older civilisations, the whole country has remained ethnically pure. Since the first Slavonic immigration, there have been constant valley-ward movements of the economically more backward hill people, which increased in intensity during the Turkish invasions. During the period of livestock economy, the north-western lowland (Kotari) was the most valuable part, contributing to the importance of Zadar and the situation of the centres of the medieval Croatian state. The economic importance of Kotari explains the longer duration there of the Turkish occupation.

The south-eastern part of Dalmatia proper is characterised by a bigger range of relief. The economically more important settlement-areas are scattered in several *polja* and in the narrow flysch zones. The predominantly karstic nature and the small possibilities of wintering livestock were negative factors in the pastoral phase of history. Part of the region acquired greater significance after the agricultural revolution and the rise of the vineyards. The islands of Vis, Korčula, Hvar and Brač, as well as the neighbouring mainland coast, quickly developed the cultivation of the vine. A cash economy soon predominated and was reflected in the development of market centres and a changing way of life. The better living conditions were reflected also in an increase of population. After the phylloxera crisis, many of these people emigrated; their remittances to relatives remaining in the country have been helpful.

The period of cash economy was reflected in the development of towns, among which Split was soon outstanding (population 27,000 in 1910 and 75,000 in 1953), on account of its central position and good connections with the islands and the interior. The island people provided the money, those of Zagora the labour force. Particular importance attaches to the early development of the cement industry round Split. The lack of rail connection with the interior retarded the rise of Split until 1925. The favourable situation and the hydro-electric power of the neighbourhood helped industry after the second World War. Besides this, Split has many of the functions of a regional centre, competing with Fiume for the leading position of the Yugoslav coastlands. Fiume is characterised by a suitable position for maritime trade, but Split, besides its central position on the nation's coast, has greater regional importance. The geographically central situation has been of particular value in making Split a collecting and distributing centre.

Split has not in Dalmatia proper the dominant regional importance that Fiume has in relation to the Kvarner region. The strong historic tradition and suitable position of Zadar in the north-western part of the region and the completion to it of a railway from Knin will conserve its rôle. Šibenik reinforces its local functions by some industrial development, and in its turn challenges Zadar. The central situation and the growth of Split influence the use made of the Neretva valley. The narrow gauge railway through this valley is to be replaced by one of normal gauge. At the mouth of the Neretva river a new port, Ploče, is being developed.

4. *The South-east Littoral.* To the south-east of the peninsula of Pelješac the coastal tract narrows to a strip between the coast ranges and the sea. At its centre is the Gulf of Kotor, surrounded by high mountains. The local economic possibilities remain as small as in the period of livestock and agriculture. The importance of this strip depended on the organisation of routes into the interior, as well as on maritime activities. In this difficult position, the activities of Dubrovnik were successful in the days of livestock economy. Dubrovnik was the most important point of trans-shipments between overland caravans and sailing ships. Commercial skill was the basis of its prosperity, political reputation and cultural progress. After the agricultural and technical revolution there remained only the business experience, which found expression in successful maritime activities and overseas emigration. Merchant sailors from Boka Kotorska and Pelješac followed those of Dubrovnik. The traditional cash economy was the factor promoting emigration overseas and the growing coastal towns. The population of the coastal strip decreased, particularly that of Boka Kotorska, when it lost its strategic value.

The south-east coastal strip has attractive natural conditions, this is most obvious from the vegetation and the possibilities for growing citrus fruit. The natural beauty (Boka Kotorska, the strait of Korčula and the surroundings of Dubrovnik), the beaches of the far south, and the many historic monuments which bear witness to the cultural heritage (Dubrovnik, Korčula and some of the towns in the Gulf of Kotor) are added attractions. The lack of good routes makes it difficult to develop tourism to the full, and so make tourist traffic a factor in the regeneration of the country. Dubrovnik (population 14,367 in 1910, 19,072 in 1953) is the most important and attractive tourist resort in Yugoslavia (Plate 73).

SUMMARY

The mountainous coastlands of Dalmatia have an attractive individuality. The proximity of sea and mountains provides natural contacts and the karst gives some small economic possibilities, among which the herding of livestock was for long the most important. The hard nature of the life killed the weak, but increased the resistance of those who survived.

In the days of the sailing-ship in the Dalmatian channels there was frequent traffic between the Dalmatian ports and those of the Mediterranean. The importance of these Adriatic routes attracted foreign intervention by Rome, Byzantium and Venice, who built the fortified settlements along the coast.

The rise of the vineyards was a period dominated by agriculture, and the same epoch saw the growth of a commercial cash-economy. Steamers and railways improved the connections with distant countries. Better living conditions caused the population to increase and the central commercial sites to grow. The decline of the vineyards represented the loss of the main activity and caused emigration from the vine-growing districts, particularly from the islands, where there was no alternative and the process of depopulation was long drawn out.

The economic connection with the interior reinforced tourism and after political unification the coastlands became the long façade of the interior. This new function has been reflected in their rapid and complex recent evolution. The progress of social and technical developments in the coastlands is part and parcel of the development of Yugoslavia as a whole. The political problems of the Dalmatian coastlands were the outcome of foreign desire to restore and prolong a historic relationship, the reasons for which have now disappeared. The second World War revealed drastically the real state of this part of Europe and made it possible to achieve a satisfactory socio-political solution. The rôle of the Dalmation coastland is to connect the interior with countries beyond the sea. This country, with its natural beauty and its historic monuments, demands the attention of visitors from far and wide.

CHAPTER 20

MEDITERRANEAN FRANCE

*'En analysant devant vous les paysages de la France Méditerrannée
. . . il n'est pas indispensable d'aller en Espagne, en Italie . . . ou en
Afrique du nord, pour devenir un Méditérranean.'*
(M. Sorre, *Paysages Médit. Français, B.S.G. Lille*, 1928)

Two recurrent homologues of the Mediterranean are Quaternary coastal plains backed by Tertiary plateaux, and the folded relief of mountains and basins with a longer and more complex evolution. They are found in Valencia and Catalonia, and they are repeated in Bas Languedoc and Provence respectively. This Mediterranean façade of France is *le Midi* par excellence. Stretching for 170 miles between the eastern Pyrenees and the southern Alps, its diverse landscapes are bathed in the luminosity and parched in the drought that are so typical of the Mediterranean world. This climatic uniformity is further imprinted in a common mode of life, though the monoculture of the plains to the west of the Rhône and the polyculture of the basins to the east of the Rhône may at first suggest further contrasts. Nevertheless, this Mediterranean region of France is essentially a geographic borderland, and this is exemplified in its structure, relief, climate and even its political evolution. The region stands on the threshold of divergent geological structures, loosely distinguished as Hercynian, Pyrenean and Alpine, whose axes explain the broad geological architecture. In more recent geological times, the region has been hinged along axes of downwarping and uplift and affected by oscillations of sea level. This then is a terrain of classical debate between the hypotheses of eustatic and isostatic changes. Wind, too, is a marked feature of the region, dominated by the *Mistral* from the north, the *Cers* and *Tramontane* from the west. The draughtiness of this climatic threshold between the major meteorological provinces of western and Mediterranean Europe explains the precarious character of its climate. Man has also had an ambivalent outlook on the Midi: inwards via the corridors of the Rhône and Naurouze, seawards towards other Mediterranean lands. The latter outlook in periods of mercantilism has given the Midi its most enriched culture. But the uncertainty of outlook at least partially explains why the political frontiers of the Midi are relatively modern.

A. INTRODUCTION: ITS LIMITS

To define the Midi sharply is to misunderstand the regional concept. Climate is the definitive content of this environment. Azure serenity that sharpens the palette of red-stained earth, white limestone and dull green vegetation are characteristic. The relation between plant associations and climatic zones of altitude, and the rhythm between the plant life cycle and the seasons are clear and close. Summer drought is perhaps the most significant feature but, taken alone, its boundaries would embrace all the Maritime Alps and the eastern Pyrenees, as far as Andorra, within the realm of the Midi. The limit of the olive is therefore to be preferred,[1] which Gaussen has used to define his Eu-Mediterranean zone (see p. 84).[2] This has the convenience of excluding the slopes of the eastern Pyrenees above about 2,000–2,500 ft, crossing the Carcassone gap and skirting the lower slopes of the Cévennes. In the more vaguely defined limit in Provence, the olive reaches Sisteron and Digne, passes the corridor of Draguignan, climbs the Var basin and touches the high corniche above the Nice coast.[3] Botanists however, do not like to accept a plant whose actual distribution is determined by economic considerations and which twice in recent times (1709 and 1956) has been dramatically destroyed by severe winters.[4] Perhaps the most convenient boundary is that of the mean monthly July isotherm of 73·4° (23) (reduced to sea-level) which follows approximately the same boundary as the olive (Fig. 223). But there are in fact two Mediterranean zones in the Midi. Along the warm littoral of the Riviera, sheltered more effectively from the Mistral, and where the barometric pattern is less conducive to continental incursions, the evergreen oak gives place to the Aleppo pine, and the carob is sub-spontaneous. There, garrigue associations of euphorbia, cistus and myrtle, and subtropical exotics introduced by man, thrive. Shelter, too, explains the long growing season of the plains of Roussillon. Elsewhere, the Mediterranean climate is more precarious and its vegetation requires to be more tolerant of winter cold.

The tardy political evolution of the Midi explains some Catalan influences in Roussillon, and Italian affinities in the environs of Nice. The lower Rhône has long served as a barrier, perhaps explaining the distinct dialect of Langue d'Oc west of the delta. Once Roman unity, which had been preserved by its Mediterranean ports, was broken, there followed a long period of disunity in the Midi. Along this zone of passage, between two Mediterranean peninsulas, Visigoths claimed the lands west of the Rhône and Ostrogoths included the lands to the east.

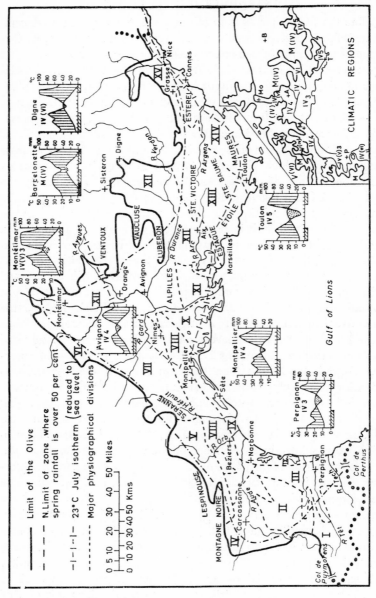

FIG. 223. Climatic boundaries and other features illustrating the limits of the Mediterranean in the French Midi

Provence then became a mere fragment of that Roman 'provincia' which had once extended from Roussillon to Lake Geneva. With the rise of its ports in the eleventh and twelfth centuries, Languedoc became again a Mediterranean society closely associated with the Aragonese-Catalan empire, and later more autonomously under the Counts of Toulouse. Provence, first linked with the Angevin-Sicilian empire, then more realistically with the Pisans, has naturally had close relations with the Ligurian coast. But it was the influence of the Rhône corridor that finally prevailed to incorporate Languedoc (1229) and most of Provence (1486) within the French domains, that is between the Aude and the Var valleys. Roussillon, however, was not taken from Catalonia until 1659 and the county of Nice was only handed over by the house of Savoy in 1860, leaving the tiny principality of Monaco as the legacy of a military stronghold.

PHYSICAL BACKGROUND

1. *Structure and Relief.* The disposition of plains and plateaux in Languedoc, and of basins and mountains in Provence, has had a more complicated history than the relief might at first suggest. But five features of the landscapes may be selected to indicate its evolution. These are: the juxtaposition of ancient and more recent rocks, with their related transverse structures; the widespread importance of limestone terrain; the even skyline of bevelled surfaces and basins, plateaux and ranges alike; the debris of intensive erosion during Plio-Pleistocene times; and the markedly antecedent character of much of the drainage.

In upper Cretaceous times, the Hercynian unit of Maures-Esterel was probably linked with the ancient massifs of Catalonia and the eastern Pyrenees, and perhaps also with the Corso-Sardinian block. But the break-up of the 'Tyrrhenides continent' was already foreseen by the existence of a shallow marine gulf stretching from the basin of Marseilles along the Bas Languedoc coast. A narrow isthmus linked the Maures-Esterel with the Massif Central across eastern Provence.[5] The corrosion of the Urgonian limestones was already leaving a legacy of bauxite that filled the irregular pockets of the karst. To the east of a line linking Gap, Digne, Castellane and Nice, lay the abyssal Alpine zone. Commencing in the Eocene and Oligocene the Pyrenean movements created a series of east-west folds and fractures, most intense in western Provence, where the area between the Maures-Esterel massif and the alpine structures was narrowest. This created, or further developed, basins such as Aix, Apt-Fourcalier and Alès and gave the pronounced east-west folds of its Jurassic and Cretaceous limestones. Hercynian inter-

ference explains the resurrection of Variscan trends, such as the alignment of the Cévennes, the Seranne and Gardiole. Also, the Miocene
and later Pliocene alpine movements explain the further break-up of
blocks by these north-south fractures. Together, like the pattern of a
parquet flooring, the discontinuous east-west alignments, the north-
south fractures and the rejuvenated Hercynian grain, all repeated by
Plio-Pleistocene movements, explain the present mosaic of relief units.

Beginning in the Oligocene and then continued into the Miocene
(Aquitanian), these fractures caused the foundering of the Gulf of Lions
and the opening of the Rhône valley to the sea. The axis of subsidence
is seen today along the edge of the continental shelf of La Planasse
(Fig. 12) which probably joins the structures of the eastern Pyrenees
with those of Maures-Esterel. The Gulf has a gentle gradient of only one
per cent for 60 to 90 miles off the coast, to a shallow depth of about
300 ft; this covers an area of 2,800 sq. miles.[6] Then along the edge of the
shelf there is a steep drop to 6,500 ft below sea-level, trenched by some
eighteen submarine canyons (rechs), all cut since the Miocene.[7] In the
Pliocene (Plaisancian), further subsidence created a deeply fractured
and indented coastline, witnessed in the troughs of the Roussillon plain,
the lower courses of the Aude, Agly, Hérault and Gard, the long sinuous
ria of the Rhône and Durance and farther east of the Gulf of Argens
and the delta of the Var.[8] Thus, during much of their geological history,
marine limestones have been deposited. Upper Jurassic corallian
limestones, often with hard dolomitic facies form the white landscapes
of High Provence. They spread out in great karstic plateaux, between
Grasse and Castellane; they rise 1,400 ft in the vertical canyon walls of
the Verdon gorges; and they dominate the Côte d'Azur between Nice
and Mentone. Lower Cretaceous (Urgonian) limestones give much
character to the landscapes of western Provence. Dazzling white they
rise in rocky ridges such as Ste Baume and Ste Victoire, as well as
forming vast, rocky wastes in the plateaux between Grasse, Nîmes and
Avignon. The calcareous, marly molasse of the Miocene is less massive,
but more capriciously covered by erosion in the plateaux that overlook
the Bas Languedoc plains. As the pierre du Midi, it is much used in the
buildings. Intercalated with these limestones, clays occur. The Oligocene
clays are actively quarried to make the small red tiles (tomettes) that are
so typical of the housetops.

The level horizons of the Midi, made effective by the vertical silhouette of poplar and cypress belong to several Tertiary and Pleistocene
cycles of erosion.[9] They range from the erosional accumulations of the
Quaternary plains, such as the remarkable deltas of the Crau and

Costière and the plateau of Valensole, to the rocky platforms of Grasse and the Garrigues and the bevelled surfaces of the limestone anticlinal folds (Fig. 224). All have been well preserved by their porosity and poor run-off. It is logical that the marked altitudinal differences of these surfaces and terraces should be best seen in western Provence, since it was nearest to the distinct oscillations of the lower Rhône base-levels, since the Mio-Pliocene. Surfaces at 1,300, 900, 600 and 250 ft, and terraces at 450, 250 and 200 ft are well recognised, while on the Hérault, Ob and Aude the terraces at 80 and 50 ft are only modestly distinct.[10] Erosional debris of gravels and sands cover much of the low-lying lands. These are of two types: the *costières* and the piedmont glacis. Isolated by later Tertiary and even Pleistocene faults, the limestone plateaux of the Garrigues are flanked by Pleistocene deltas such as those of the Costière de Saint-Gilles, the Grès near Montpellier and the Aspres of Roussillon.[11] These range in relief from the rolling plateau of the Costière, 20 miles in length between the Rhône and Vidourle valleys, to the dissected hills, trenched deeply by narrow valleys in the Aspres. The second type of erosional relief, the piedmont glacis, is characteristic of the border of the garrigue from the Rhône to the Etang de Thau, the western border of the Gardiole, much of Biterrois along the eastern border of the Montagne Noire, and at the southern foot of the Corbières. Piedmont glacis also fringes the Tertiary basins of Provence, notably at the foot of Ste Victoire in the Aix basin. Deposits indicate the effects of solifluction in pluvial phases of the Quaternary and of frost action in periglacial climates, the study of which is only just beginning to be made. The evidence of these deposits is of a great regression of the sea in Villafranchian times, with intense erosion. At the end of the mid-Quaternary another regressive phase of erosion created some of the major lagoons along the coast, notably Thau and Berre.[12] The Flandrian transgression submerged the river mouths, and the present coastal plains are thus very recent. The channels of the Rhône delta (Camargue) have only been formed during the last 5,000 years.[13] Marked changes have taken place in the coastal drainage of plains such as those of Roussillon, Narbonne and Fréjus.[14] The eighteen lagoons, which cover 1,200 sq. miles along the coast of Bas Languedoc, are the relics of more extensive areas of salt marshes, created behind the post-Würmian sand dunes of the littoral.

Broadly, the drainage appears antecedent to the present relief, presumably developed on the gentler relief of the Pliocene peneplanes. Deep gorges on the upper or middle courses of the rivers cut indifferently into the rocks, although in detail some adjustment to structure

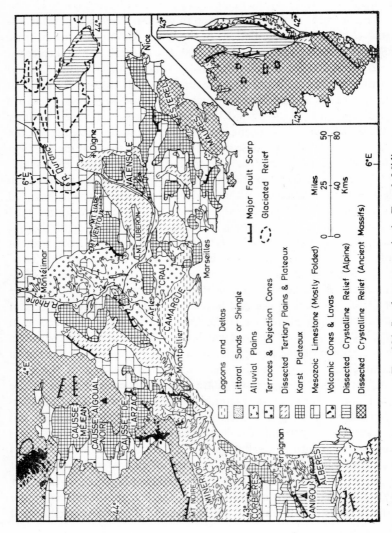

FIG. 224. Landscape types in the French Midi

has modified the drainage pattern. The plain of Roussillon, like its Catalan counterpart of Ampurdán, is divided by a shallow anticline followed by the small Réart valley.[15] The southern trough of Vallespir is occupied by the Tech and the northern one of Conflent by the Tet, flanking the granite horst of Canigou that towers steeply from the coastal plain. Such gradients explain the intense erosional deposition of the plain and the marked dissection of the Aspres glacis at its foot into hilly relief. The Agly valley, trenched into the granites and limestones of the Fenouillèdes, forms approximately the northern border of the province. Despite the apparent simplicity of the lowlands and plateaux of Bas Languedoc, the relief and drainage are complex. The upper Aude, rising in the upper Pyrenees, once flowed through the Col de Naurouze (627 ft) westwards into the proto-Garonne. After the subsidence of the Gulf of Lions, it turned at right angles to the Mediterranean and now cuts a defile through the folded limestone edge of the northern Corbières between the basins of Carcassonne and Lézignan.[16] Torrential tributaries, from the south-east flank of the Montagne Noire, trench the plains and the low terraces of Minervois Narbonnais. The Orb flowing through a tectonic trough, between the Espinouze and Basse Montagne Noire, is like the lower course of the Aude; it is influenced in its lower course by structural features. Between the Hérault and the Vidourle tectonic troughs, lowered between calcareous plateaux, also guide the lines of drainage. Notable is the deep gorge of the Aniane which plunges in a defile 3,300 ft below the high summit of Aiguoual (5,140 ft) on the borders of the Cévennes.[17] Differential erosion has etched out broad basins, where the rivers carve out clay and marl outcrops, while they trench defiles in the limestones. In this wild garrigue country, which falls from about 2,000 ft at the foot of Cévennes, to 350 ft between Montpellier and Nîmes, inversion of relief is marked in the gently folded rocks. The synclines tend to preserve hard carapaces of limestone, jutting out abruptly in ridges, while the heavily eroded anticlines have exposed the soft, underlying marls and clays in broad valleys and basins. Similar features are found in the drainage basins of the Gard and Cèze that join the Rhône valley.

In Provence, the dominances of the Pyreno-Provençal trend lines running east-west have a marked influence on its drainage.[18] The lower Rhône below Donzère asserts its superiority in flowing in antecedent defiles between the plains of Pierrelatte, Orange and Avignon to reach the apex of its delta of the Camargue at Arles. But the Arc and Argens follow intricate courses along to the east-west pattern of Tertiary and Triassic depressions respectively. The Durance is more complicated, a

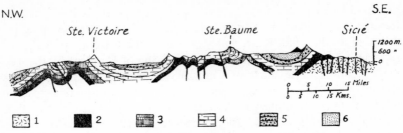

FIG. 225. Geological cross-section of western Province (after Bénévent) 1. Crystalline; 2. Trias; 3. Lias; 4. Jurassic; 5. Cretaceous; 6. Tertiary

rosary of antecedent defiles and basins, resting on a tectonic trough infilled thickly by deposits since mid-Tertiary times. Further east, the gorges of the Verdon, Loup and headstreams of the Var bite savagely into the Alpine limestones. The latter has built a vast, submarine delta since the Pliocene on the steep edge of the continental shelf.[19]

2. *Climate and Vegetation.* The climate contributes effectively in the uniform processes of land sculpture in the Midi. Although the annual precipitation averages 20 to 30 in, four to five in more than some parts of the Paris basin, the 50 to 70 rain-days come brutally and violently (Fig. 223). Sudden, heavy rainstorms fall on the parched earth from September onwards, dry gullies are rapidly filled by tearing torrents and the flood plains become, on occasion, dangerously brim-full of destruction. The following days may reveal bone-dry hill sides, bathed in sunshine. On average the Durance transports, 3,110 tons of sediment per sq. mile and the Hérault 300 to 600 tons each year, but the periodic floods cause enormous destruction.[20] From the steep slopes of the Cévennes, one-third to half of whose catchment slopes are torrential, floods of over 2,500 m³/sec on the Hérault and 7,800 m³/sec on the Ardèche take place. One rainstorm on June 16, 1950, flooded 300,000 ha in the plains of Bas Languedoc.[21] The fall of 37 in of rain within twenty-four hours on the flanks of Aigoual, must be one of the world's records outside the monsoon lands of Asia. Not only is the process of erosion most effective under these rainstorms but it sharpens greatly the differential erosion of the Midi's varied rock types. It is under the influence of the Atlantic depressions passing over the Bay of Biscay, especially when high-pressure conditions are marked over Italy, that violent rainstorms from the Gulf of Lions hit the Midi coast. Thus, as de Martonne has observed, the Mediterranean sea explains more of the climatic accidents than the average conditions.[22] Relief is an inexorable control, explaining the more exposed continental changes of the Rhône

delta, the more uniform conditions of Bas Languedoc and the more varied features of Provence.

The intensity of the hot, dry summer, influenced by the prevailing high-pressure systems, is perhaps *the* Mediterranean trait of the Midi. There is then at least an average of 73° F, although grilling heat that bakes the landscape has sizzled at even 108° F. It is then that the aspect becomes important and, especially on the Côte d' Azur, that the inducement of sea-breezes temper the aridity. Everywhere the formula of aridity (de Martonne) is below ten, and it is this which makes the olive a significant indicator of the Midi—not winter cold. The mild winters of the Midi are emphasised by the low incidence of frost, averaging twenty days on the plains of Roussillon and on the Côte d' Azur; everywhere else, it has still less than forty days. But the snow cover of the surrounding summits of the Alps and Pyrenees, with their high pressures and the frequency of low-pressure systems over the Gulf of Lions, explain the violent and frequent currents of cold winds, blowing from the north and west, especially during winter and early spring. Generally dry, such winds as the *Mistral* in the Rhône valley and Provence, the *Cers* in Bas Languedoc, and the *Tramontane* in Roussillon, disperse the clouds, and create the right conditions in their wake for temperature incursions.

It is thus not to the average conditions of sunny skies and intense luminosity conducive to marked photo-synthesis that the plants have to be adapted, but to the climatic extremes of drought, wind and storm. The plant decor is one of the most marked characteristics of the region.[23] Yet of all the vegetation cover of France, that of the Midi has suffered the most from human interference. In Roussillon, the marked Iberian influence in the flora is still recognisable in the importance of the evergreen oak and especially the dominance of the cork oak on the crystalline rocks, now usually degenerate into a mixed cover of maquis and garrigue.[24] In Bas Languedoc, most of the evergreen oak woodlands, formerly extensive, have been eliminated by the spread of the vine.[25] In the Rhône valley, there is a mingling of northern species of deciduous trees such as the pubescent oak, the elm and poplar, invaders during propitious Quaternary pluvials, and the more Mediterranean species. Provence, however, has the most varied flora, with marked endemism and some evidence of Ligurian species.[26]

Broad altitudinal patterns of flora are evident in the Midi. On the lowlands and in the hills to about 1,000–1,300 ft the Aleppo pine is an aggressive element, marking all the littoral and climbing gracefully on the rocky slopes. It enters the kermes scrub (*garou*) and is often the

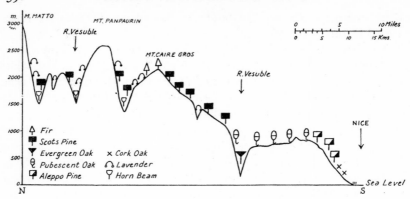

FIG. 226. Vegetation profile of the Maritime Alps north of Nice

avant garde of the evergreen oak in the maquis. Exceptionally it climbs to 2,800 ft in the Maritime Alps (Fig. 226). The cork oak climbs to about 2,100 ft in the Albères and Maures-Esterel, but it is usually loosely scattered in light woodlands associated with pyrophytes of *Cistus lentiscus* and arbutus that make the hazard of fire great. The evergreen oak, an important component of the maquis in the limestone plateaux of Languedoc, climbs to higher altitudes of 1,000–3,250 ft in the eastern Pyrenees where it mingles with the more moisture-loving deciduous oaks. The chestnut forests of the Cévennes and Conflent, found between 650 and 3,000 ft have been seriously ravaged by the ink disease (since 1860 in the Pyrenees, 1871 in the Cévennes), though they still cover over 18,000 ha on the slopes of the Hérault department.[27] The typical mountain zone between 3,000–5,500 ft is one of beech and fir forests.[28] But the beach climax still preserved in the Ste Beaume is rare in Provence, the slopes and erosion surfaces usually laid bare by the ravages of pastoralism; over 20,000 ha of high plateaux in western Provence, once wooded, are now sterile wastes. The higher forests of Scots pine have been much ravaged by pastoralism and new plantations of cedars (introduced *c.* 1861–7) have scarcely compensated for their losses in Provence. But on the Pyrenean slopes of Conflent, Capcir and Cerdagne, mountain pines (*Pinus uncinata*) are still extensive to the tree-line at about 7,500 ft. Above this sub-alpine zone are the high pastures of the alpine vegetation proper.

EVOLUTION OF THE RURAL LANDSCAPES

Two features have characterised the Mediterranean landscapes of the Midi. There is the oasis-like distribution of much of the cultivated land

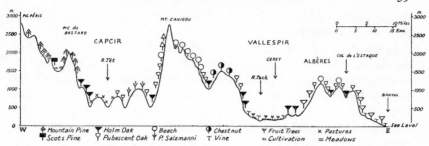

FIG. 227. Vegetation profile in the eastern Pyrenees, between Capcir and Canigou (Roussillon)

in a waste of maquis, garrigue or rocky outcrops, and there are the dramatic changes towards specialised cultures, especially since the mid-nineteenth century. The three-fold distinction of Ager, Saltus and Silva (see pp. 116–17) has been clearly marked, associated respectively with a traditional polyculture, with pastoralism and transhumance, and with much use and misuse of the forests. The ancient biennial rotation derives from the age-long need of cultivation and pasture, so it may well be traceable to the first Neolithic clearings that men made in the Maritime Alps and the Garrigues of Vaucluse and Nîmes. Clearer distinction between cereal lands and pasturage was made in the Iron Age when metal ploughs, brought in from the Swiss villages, permitted the damper basins and plains of the Midi to be cleared for cultivation. But the climatic accidents of the region and the predominance of azonal soils must have early suggested the virtues of polyculture.[29] Because the soils are notably poor in phosphorus and potash they cannot give good yields of cereals.[30] Moreover, the effects of erosion and climate explain the dominance of porous, sandy, gravelly and marly soils. The best cereal soils were associated with the alluvium of the river valleys and basins. The olive was apparently introduced by the Phoenicians, and a pre-Roman oil-press was discovered at Ollioules, near Toulon. From there the olive spread into the surrounding limestone districts and is mentioned by Strabo as being cultivated by the Massaliotes.[31] Although a vine (*vitis vinifera*) was indigenous to the south of France, fossils of it being recognised in the Astian tuffs near Montpellier,[32] imported domesticated stock established viticulture in the first century B.C. Prohibited at first in the interests of the Campanian wine trade, the districts around Narbonne and Béziers later became important for their vineyards.[33] Lands cleared by Gallo-Roman settlers then became consolidated into vast estates (*villae latifundia*), especially in the lower

Rhône plains, one of which, *Aulus Annius Camars*, gave its name to the delta of the Camargue.

In the early Middle Ages, there followed many social changes but the cleared land oscillated only between its abandonment in war and its reoccupation in times of peace. After the eleventh century, deforestation became more active, with the churches taking over large estates that were chiefly *Saltus* and *Silva*.[34] But serfdom was unimportant, so there was much individual initiative, with family holdings and commercial estates intermingled in such lowlands as the plain of Montpellier. There was much prosperity at this time, and immigrants from the surrounding mountains were favoured by the perpetual tenure of *aprisio*, to those who worked the land in Languedoc. In the subsequent religious wars the large estates suffered while the peasantry affirmed their rights. Similarly at the end of the fifteenth century, the mountain immigrants from the Alps and Italy recolonised abandoned lands in Provence under the metayage contracts of *facherie*. Soon all the south of France was entrenched in systems of emphyteusis, helping to create the irregular field systems and their well established polyculture.[35]

Private ownership of the *ager* and the communal use of the garrigue (for pastoralism) and the woodland were the common practice. Enclosure began early (in the sixteenth century) and by the time of the general act of enclosure in 1767, parcellation of land was severe. The Midi turned its back on the sea, largely because of malaria, especially on the marshy littoral of Bas Languedoc, and because of rocky coasts elsewhere, together with the biological poverty of the sea and the age-long fear of piracy. A maze of routes led towards the interior, especially in Provence, where the basin and mountain terrain accentuated the pressure of population upon the fertile pockets of land. In some areas, such as the Montpellier basin, communes were aligned in long strips to take advantage of plain and garrigue.[36] But more generally, the evolution of a radial pattern of fields and roads from a central hill-top village has become the characteristic feature, with irregularly shaped holdings, fragmented into small units.[37]

In contrast, there are often rectangular patterns of fields and roads wherever drainage and land reclamation have taken place. These occur in a variety of circumstances. Oldest are the coastal marshes which have gradually become reclaimed since Roman times, along the littoral of Roussillon, the mouth of the Aude, the Camargue and the Arc deltaic plain; their features are carefully described by Lentheric.[38] River valleys, notably the lower Durance have slowly been reclaimed since the Middle Ages. The earliest canals date from the ninth century and the earthen ditches (*rechs*) of Roussillon were carefully organised by the Aragonese in the fifteenth century. In the Camargue, associations of dyke builders can be traced back to the twelfth century, though reclamation was not active in the Rhône delta until the sea dyke was completed in 1855–70, and three major drainage canals were constructed. There is evidence around Arles of Roman *cuniculi*. From the twelfth century—when the Canal St Julien (1171) was built—until the nineteenth century, some twenty-five major canals have converted the Rhône plains from the Eygens and Durance to the northern Crau[39]. These are now smiling gardens, reticulated in a verdant bocage of strip fields that are closely sheltered by wind breaks of cypresses and reeds. In the *polja* and upper river valleys, where rejuvenation has not yet affected changes of thalweg, minor drainage schemes have also been completed since the thirteenth century, such as the upper Provençal valleys of the Argens, Arc, and Issole.[40]

The traditional equilibrium associated with transhumant flocks[41] on the garrigue lands, wheat and irrigated crops on the plains, olives and vines on the stoney slopes, was shattered in the eighteenth and nineteenth centuries by a number of changes. Instead, the monoculture of vines in Bas Languedoc and parts of Roussillon, and the intensive forms of commercialised polyculture in Provence and Roussillon were introduced. Today, only a few isolated districts in Languedoc still preserve some of the traditional features. In Provence, however, the renovations of landscape have been more limited and much more localised in extent, responding more to internal changes.

The most sensational development has been the spread of the vine in Bas Languedoc. Cassini's map of 1775 showed that for a width of several miles along the littoral between the Rhône and the Hérault, there was then an expanse of garrigue, with some knolls of pine woods among the coastal sand dunes, especially on the edge of the Camargue.[42] Vineyards were widely developed on the first series of escarpments but they were only just beginning to push out on to the plains. Windmills, used as oil and wine presses, dotted the landscape. Mulberries were extensive, especially along the foot of the Cévennes and around silk centres such as Nîmes. The first impetus to the spread of the vine may be dated from the creation of the Port of Sète in 1666 and to the opening of the Canal Royal in 1681, which linked Sète with Toulouse and then via the Garonne to Bordeaux.[43] A century later, Arthur Young was full of praise for the lines of communications in Languedoc which had done so much to stimulate the wine trade.[44] Intense clearing of the woodland in the latter part of the eighteenth century had been made for new vineyards, so that the hill lands and terraces were still the main locus of the vine. Between 1850 and 1860 the railways were constructed and as a result the Languedoc and Roussillon vineyards increased from 238,000 ha in 1828 to 309,000 ha in 1850 and to 430,000 in 1875. [45] Here was concentrated 18 per cent of the French vineyards. Then ruthlessly, between 1863 and 1882, the phylloxera epidemic struck in a disaster which threatened to destroy the whole rural economy of the region. When it was observed that vines planted in the sandy coastal areas remained healthy stock, new vineyards were rapidly created along the littoral and the borders of the Camargue. Meanwhile, the plains were replanted with American stock (*Riparia*). Found to succeed best in the deep water-retaining soils of the plains proper, much of the poorer hill lands were permanently abandoned.

Other disasters after the mid-nineteenth century, and later, the improvement of communications have also changed the *ancien régime* elsewhere, to create several new types of landscape. The olives that had created a Tuscan atmosphere in the countryside of western Provence, receded sharply with the competing trade in oil seeds, imported at Marseilles; only around Salon are the olive groves still extensive. [46] The silk-worm disease ruined agriculture after 1855–65 and the mulberry groves of Comtat and the Cévennes have disappeared. The madder plant grown on the plains of the lower Rhône was ruined by new techniques in the dye industry. Fortunately, at this critical juncture, the construction of the P.L.M. railway and other lines, together with the improvement of roads and the building of new highways such as the Corniche road along the Riviera, began to introduce the possibilities of new markets. First, there has been rapid expansion of horticulture with irrigation in Roussillon (44,000 ha) and the Rhône-Durance plains (69,000 ha) together with smaller, more scattered areas in Vaucluse (44,000, ha), Basses-Alpes (16,000 ha), Var and Gard (10,000 ha). These now produce one-fifth by value of all the market-garden products of France. One third of the cultivated lands of the lower Durance plain is like some horticultural machine producing three to four crops annually by agricultural techniques of the highest intensity. Market specialisation has developed such as the salads and early potatoes of Roussillon, the tomatoes of Carpentras, the melons of Cavaillon and the strawberries of the last two named districts. A second development has been the orchard country created at the foothills of Vaucluse for cherries, and in the Aspres for apricots (two-thirds of French production). A third type of countryside is that specilised in flower growing (4,000 ha). Mimosa, introduced at the end of the last century, flourishes on the siliceous soils around Cannes, Antibes and Cagnes, with carnations, roses, camelias, lilies and other bulbous flowers. Violets are a speciality of Hyères and Vence.[47] Around Grasse, the perfume centre, instead of cut flowers, the demand is for scented species for the distilleries, notably jasmine, violets and roses. Since the first lavender fair was established in 1920, three species of lavender have been grown extensively over the limestone mountains above Digne and over the plateau of Forcalquier.[48] Floral cultures now provide half the revenues of the Martime Alps. Finally, since 1943 the Camargue has become more and more interested in rice cultivation, growing over 24,000 ha in large estates.[49] Thus Mediterranean France has created two worlds, one in which specialised economies have been developed since the nineteenth century, and another whose backward economy is still associated with stock raising as in the Baronnies, or with the traditional polyculture as in the remoter basins of Provence. Further progress is being envisaged by the completion of the Serre-Ponçon dam to enable the Durance to irrigate another 20,000 ha. The dream to convert 160,000 ha in Bas Languedoc between the Rhône and the Aude into irrigated lands under vegetable, fruit and forage crops, is now being conceived by the plan of the Canal du Bas-Rhône.[50]

POPULATION AND SETTLEMENT

1. *Population*. The discontinuous distribution of population has been a characteristic feature of the Mediterranean. It is well exemplified in the Midi, where a desolate silence still reigns over the siliceous maquis, the stoney, limestone garrigue and over the remaining marshes of the Camargue. In the past, malaria and piracy explained the absence of settlement along the littoral of Bas Languedoc or in the Calanques of Provence. But in the last century these areas have become more settled and yet differences of population density have become sharper.[51] Regional economic changes and the growth of towns have been significant causes of this. In 1876, the Midi had just over three million inhabitants or 8·6 per cent of the total population of France. The life of the interior hills and lower mountains was little different for the cultivator than that of the plains. Consequently, there was more homogeneity of population. There was, however, no longer the need for the security of the interior and their hill-top settlements. A series of economic circumstances triggered off a marked emigration from these areas. Thus the maximum population attained by the mountain communes took place between the censuses of 1851 and 1886.

The advent of phylloxera was a primary factor in the depopulation of the hills and its passage may be traced in the sharp fall of population figures. The scourge first appeared in the Nîmes-Lunel district between 1869 and 1870, in the Montpellier plain between 1870 and 1875, and then spread towards Biterrois and Minervois in the following decade. While the coastal areas with their relative immunity showed little variation in the upward trend of their population graphs, the interior showed a sharp drop. Direct emigration either to Algeria, or to the horticultural districts of the Rhône Valley and Roussillon and the return of immigrants to the Massif Central took place. Meanwhile, the silk-worm disease of 1855–65, encouraged the depopulation of the Cévennes, and the subsequent lack of attention to the chestnut forests caused further decline. On the high plateaux and lower mountains of the interior, the population today is only 40 to 50 per cent of that reached in 1876. The hill lands of the Aspres, Corbières, the garrigue lands of Languedoc and the interior hills of Provence are still below the 1876 census with 60 to 95 per cent.

In contrast, the coastal regions have shown marked increases of population, notably the Nice coast (248 per cent since 1876), the Fréjus plain (233), Étang de Berre (288) and the Crau (214). Significantly the plain of Bas Languedoc shows little or no increase with its monoculture of vines. Rapid urban growth around Nice (458), Toulon (200), Marseilles (207), Montpellier (179) and Perpignan (247) explains the very rapid increases in their environs. In the last twenty years the most marked increases have occurred in the horticultural areas of the Lower Rhône, and around the oil refineries of the Étang de Berre. Thus, apart from the plains of Roussillon and Gard, all the marked regional increases of population in the last century have taken place to the east of the Rhône. Bouches-du-Rhône dominates all other departments of the Midi with over 1,200,000, attracting a youthful, immigrant population. The *départements* of Alpes-Maritimes and Pyrénées-Orientales, with less than half this number, receive in contrast a retired and ageing population to their attractive and sheltered coasts. In the *départements* of Aude and Hérault associated with viticulture the alarming decline of the birth rate, the sluggish growth of the towns, and the lower standard of living all express the need to diversify an economy still too precarious on its undue dependence on one crop; hence the significance of the Plan of the Bas-Rhône Canal which interests a population of 600,000.

2. *Rural Settlement.* In the past, the preoccupation of the Midi with the needs of defence explains the widespread distribution of nucleated villages, perched on hilltops or astride the ridges. Effective clearance of the lowland forests began in the periods of Phoenician, Greek and

Roman colonisation. Many of the settlements, dating from the Gallo-Roman colonisation, may be identified by the place-names with suffixes of -ac, -an, as, et, and -argues. Some of these such as those ending in -ac may be older. But the decay of Roman order led to anarchy and unrest that persisted to the seventeenth century, with such threats as the invasion of the Visigoths, in the sixth century. Saracen piracy notably in the eighth to tenth centuries, the Albigensian wars of the thirteenth century, and finally the Huguenot persecution.[52] It is, therefore, understandable that the older villages are still often dominated by the ruins of an old château. Particularly characteristic of Provence is the tight cluster of houses raised in tiers on the rocky slopes of the eyrie site. These are notable in the crystalline rocks of Maures-Esterel, though a classic example is Les Baux on the limestones of the Alpilles. Today such sites are impracticable, with the difficulties of water supply, inaccessibility and the shift of economic interests towards the plains. Many such sites were deserted even before the last century. In Baronnies, for example, of the fifty-three abandoned hill-top villages, thirty-five had already been deserted by the end of the eighteenth century, the rest being abandoned mostly towards the end of the last century. In the plains, especially in Bas Languedoc, eminences for defence are rare, and the fortifications were perforce artificial, often rectangular-shaped ramparts.

The defence factor, however, can be exaggerated.[53] As important was a good water supply, so that the location of springs, or other sub-surface supplies has been significant. Some were also located on the drove roads, acting as toll-gates where fees were charged for the passage of transhumant sheep. Many others were located at a convenient, medial site where geological and soil conditions gave the commune a balanced use of land. In some areas, the village has only slowly evolved and dispersion of settlement has been more characteristic. Such is the case in the foothills of the Cévennes and the Central Massif, more isolated and distant from the coastal invaders. No doubt the importance of sericulture in some districts had the same influence towards dispersion of isolated mas farmsteads. Between 1398 and 1792 there had been some thirty epidemics of malaria, some lasting five to seven years. The recent intensive settlement of the plains now that malaria is no longer a danger, has been stimulated by the development of specialised cropping, notably around Avignon and Hyères. There is also a tendency towards dispersion among the vineyards of Bas Languedoc.

Building stone is abundant, and the patina which comes to the grey-white limestone with age, gives great beauty to the houses. Most house-types have a double storey. They have an economy of ground space which makes them suitable to the tightly nucleated villages of Provence, while the needs of the vine-grower of Languedoc are modest for space. The prevalence of small dwellings is itself a reflection of the small size of the average property either under the traditional Mediterranean polyculture, or the more recent commercialised viticulture and market-gardening. Usually a large doorway gives entrance for the cart, implements, and interior courtyard with perhaps a wine press and vats. A stairway leads to the upstairs quarters where the family live and to the attic where the grain may still be kept and formerly the silk-worms were reared.

Regional differences of course are recognisable. In eastern Provence, big flocks of sheep and extensive cereal lands account for the larger, spacious farms. In western Provence, notably between Aix and Salon, where the old polyculture still persists in some areas, the houses are markedly small, with a rectangular plan scarcely more than 30 to 50 ft in length.[54] In the Camargue, the reed huts (*cabanes*) in which the stock-keepers and fishermen used to live, have largely disappeared. But massive, solitary *mas*, orientated east–west, with no windows on their northern facade because of the *mistral*, stand as lonely sentinels within the large estates. In Languedoc, the wine cellar and wine press are more universal, and the houses tend to form a street-village arrangement along the highways, while in Biterrois large vineyards are reflected in larger farm-houses.[55] A modern feature is the bizarre rash of summer villas that has sprung up along the holiday coasts, notably along the Côte d' Azur.

3. *The Towns.*[56] Urban population in the south of France is above the national average. The numerous small cities and towns, apart from the two great centres of Marseilles and Nice are a Mediterranean characteristic. They indicate a checkered history of urban development, divided broadly into three phases: the classical, medieval and modern periods. In Phoenician and Graeco-Roman times, the creation of a number of small ports and road centres emphasised the rôle played by communications in fostering town life. Early use was made of some natural harbours at Menton, Nice, Villefranche, Monaco, Antibes, Fréjus, Toulon, Ciotat and Marseilles. Classical navigation was further aided by the shelter of fringing islets such as Hyères and in Marseilles bay, and by submerged reefs. The Languedoc coast is less favoured, though classical ports existed at Agde, Narbonne and Collioure. A coastal highway was developed by the Romans, with more strategic

than commercial importance. As the *Via Aurelia* in Provence, it followed in part an older Phoenician road, following the Ligurian coast from Genoa along the east Provençal littoral. At Fréjus, which was for a time the chief port of Roman Gaul, the road then turned into the interior to Aix and then to bifurcate, one branch going to Marseilles but the main highway continuing to Arles, the Roman port that rivalled the Greek colony of Marseilles. Across the Rhône, it continued as the *Via Domitia*, past the Roman town of Nîmes, which commanded valley routes across the Cévennes. It then followed between the Languedoc littoral and garrigue plateaux, to Narbonne, Elne near Perpignan, and then over the Col de Perthus into Spain. The most important Roman towns were Narbonne (*c.* 60,000 at the end of the first century A.D.), Nîmes (*c.* 40–45,000), Arles (*c.* 40,000), Orange and Fréjus (*c.* 20,000). But apart from Roman monuments little of the Roman plan has been preserved in these towns.

The mercantile renaissance of the Midi in the twelfth and thirteenth centuries explains the origin of new towns such as Perpignan, Montpellier and Avignon. Perpignan, first mentioned as a village in 927, had become the capital of the Aragonese kingdom in the thirteenth century. Montpellier, growing out of two villages, was first enclosed in 1150 to protect its mercantile quarters (Plate 78). Sited on a pilgrims' way, the town was located at the nearest point where the garrigue approaches the sea, and with routes to the navigable lagoons. At its apogee, its oriental trade rivalled that of Marseilles. Avignon, also a point of contact between the interior lands and a navigable stretch of the Rhône, grew upon a calcareous promontory that defended the bridge across the Rhône (built in the twelfth century). The installation of the papal court in 1309 further fostered its growth. Similarly, Aix developed after the twelfth century when it was chosen by the counts of Provence as their residence. But the ports of the Rhône delta have had a more transient history. Juvenal and Lattes soon disappeared, Maguelone became the quarry for the construction of the Canal des Étang (in 1708) and only Aigues Mortes, created in 1240–4, remains a museum piece of medieval planning.[57] The creation of the port of Sète in 1666 made it ultimately moribund.

In modern times, agriculture, tourism and industry have promoted three major types of 'urban growth'. Agricultural wealth explains the rapid growth of towns such as Perpignan, Narbonne, Béziers, Montpellier, Nîmes, Avignon, Aix and Grasse. There is a marked cluster of smaller agricultural centres around Avignon where horticulture has been most advanced. Tourism was launched by English patronage in the nineteenth century, notably Lord Brougham who patronised Cannes after 1854. Today, there is a coastal concentration of over half a million people between St Raphaël and Menton, clustered in the seaside resorts that have more than doubled their population in the last fifty years. None has grown more rapidly than Nice. Its old town had 25,000 in 1820 and alongside it a new city has been created, whose population has doubled every thirty years since, to its total of 250,000 today. Tourism has also helped to round off the population growth of the older towns further west, such as Aix, Arles and Nîmes, and to enliven the picturesque ports of Roussillon at Banyuls, Collioure and Port Vendres. Industrial growth has been most marked at Marseilles (see pp. 605–7) and to a lesser extent at the naval base of Toulon, the coalfield town of Alès and the wine ports of Sète. The oil refinery centres around the lagoons of Berre and Thau are a more recent development.

Today there are eighteen towns between 10,000 and 50,000 inhabitants and five from 50,000 to 100,000 (Cannes, Aix, Nîmes, Avignon, Béziers). Four others have over 100,000—Marseilles, Nice Toulon and Montpellier. Of a total of forty-six urban centres, ten may be classified as industrial centres, seven as agricultural towns, six as tourist resorts on the Côte d' Azur, and two are ports (Sète and Toulon). The rest are mostly all commercial towns, all the larger ones having a well developed regional trade such as Prades, Carcassone, Perpignan, Narbonne, Béziers, Montpellier, Nîmes, Avignon and Aix.[58] These centres to some extent make up for a curious deficiency in the Midi, the absence of a true capital. For despite the erroneous prestige and industrial importance of Marseilles, it cannot claim to be the capital of this varied region, stretched so widely along the Gulf of Lions.

THE REGIONS

A land of *pays*, the French Midi may be fragmented into numerous regional units. The Institut Géographique National has recognised primary divisions and subdivisions (Fig. 228).[59] For our purpose these may be arbitrarily grouped into Roussillon, Bas Languedoc, the lower Rhône, western Provence with special reference to the Marseilles conurbation and the Côte d' Azur.

1. *Roussillon*. Roussillon is compact and diverse. Its triangular plain is framed by the eastern Pyrenees or Albères to the south, and by the impressive massif of Canigou in the west.[60] The coastal slopes of the Albères are flanked by terraced vineyards wherever the red Triassic rocks outcrop. At Banyuls, the vineyards rise on the slopes to over

1,500 ft above the sea. It is only on the Côte Vermeille that maritime interests are represented in Roussillon: Collioure (3,200), a sardine fishing port, and Port-Vendres (3,600) with Spanish and Oran trade. A dense scrub of cork oak covers the siliceous foothills of the eastern Pyrenees, succeeded by ilex and chestnut woods and then by mountain pines. The rugged summits culminate in Callitte (9,581 ft). To the north, the Roussillon plain has a three-fold distinction: the saline lands of the coast, the irrigated alluvial plains and the glacis slopes fronting the mountains, with their late Tertiary dissected surfaces. A string of some twenty salt marshes (*salanques*), separated by better drained lands (*salobre*) with some vineyards occur along the coast, with ancient settlements such as Elne. On the plain, there is a marked contrast between the well populated and densely cultivated valleys under a gridiron of irrigated ditches (*rechs*) and red fences for the protection of early vegetations, and the stoney soils of the *aspres* or *glacis* foothills. The former enjoyed a traditional rotation of four to five crops in two years, while the latter had biennial rotation and winter pasture on the stubble. But this contrast has been softened since the period 1830–79, when the area under vines was doubled. Renowned for their coarse vines, centres such as Byrrh have prospered, though orchards of apricots and other fruit trees have more recently displaced the vines on the higher slopes of the Aspres. Towards the interior of the plain, the entrenched valleys of the Tet and Tech widen again into the upper basins of Prades and Céret with their *pays* of Conflent and Vallespir respectively. The heavily forested slopes of chestnuts in the Tet and Tech valleys, the irrigated meadows and market gardens of Prades, and the cherry orchards around Céret create diverse landscapes. Standing guard between these valleys, like some other Olympus is Canigou (9,125 ft), whose forested slopes provides so much of the hydraulic wealth of the plain. Perpignan the regional capital controls much of this wealth, especially since the advent of the railway and more recently with the establishment of refrigeration plants. Throughout the nineteenth century its population was stagnant at 20,000–25,000, but in recent decades it has grown rapidly to 70,000 with high densities scattered in innumerable *mas* farm houses, over its rich *huerta*. To the north, the Agly trenches its way in a series of subsequent valleys within the Fenouillèdes syncline, framed between hard, Aptian limestone folds. Beyond, the Corbières representing a unique structure of the Pre-Pyrenees, deeply dissected and faulted in Tertiary rocks rise in rugged relief to over 4,000 ft, around the schistose nucleus of Mouthoumet. It is a sparsely populated district whose mixed evergreen and deciduous

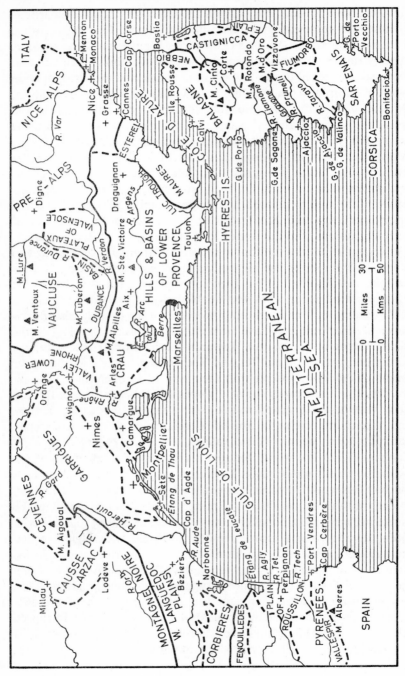

Fig. 228. Regional divisions of the French Midi. Distinction is made between major and minor divisions

oaks and beeches indicate the transitional character of its climate overlooking the climatic threshold of the Sill of Naurouze.

2. *Bas Languedoc*.[61] The variable hills of Narbonne and the deep synclinal trough of the middle Aude open into the broad plains of Biterrois and Narbonnais. Blanketed in vineyards, grouped in large holdings, this prosperous countryside has high densities of population It is in abrupt contact with the ancient rocks of the Montagne Noire and Espinouse with their silent chestnut forests and heaths climbing the slopes to over 4,000 ft. Despite its important port, Narbonne (32,000) has remained a sleepy market town with only a slow growth of population in recent decades. Carcassonne, also on the river Aude, stands guard at the entrance of the corridor into Aquitaine, a picturesque medieval fortress that was re-planned in 1249, and now a show-piece for the tourists. Béziers (64,000) also occupies a defensive site overlooking the Orb Valley. A stronghold from pre-Roman times to guard the routes into the Massif Central, and southwards to Narbonne, it is a port on the Canal du Midi, and above all a regional centre associated with the wine trade.

Between the valleys of the Hérault and the Vidourle the central corridor of Bas Languedoc has more varied relief and intricate structures.[62] Instead of the abrupt juxtaposition of plains and mountains found to the south and west of the Hérault, the limestone plateaux of the Garrigues interpose. A series of anticlinal flexures and synclinal depressions add to the variety of the scenery, such as the depressed basin of the middle Hérault and faulted against the Montagne Noire, and the series of smaller basins and plateaux near the coast, aligned parallel with the littoral.[63] The Quaternary and recent sand dunes and bars are silhouetted with clumps of stone pines and patches of vines. The shimmering surfaces of the lagoons, the largest of which is the Étang de Thau, have gleaming white salt pans, and a profusion of summer villas loosely scattered around large settlements. The oil refinery at Frontignan and the lively bustle at Sète, indicate the economic importance of this district. Sète sheltered by the restricted site of Mont St Clair has now 36,250 inhabitants and is the second largest port of the Midi, actively engaged in the wine trade.

Stoney limestone plateaux such as the Gardiole and the Costière[64] vine-clad scarps, and the terraced coastal plains with their sea of vine-yards, are the characteristic features. Montpellier (91,000) with its cultural prestige as a University town, is the important regional centre. Inland stretch the Garrigues,[65] a broad belt of limestone plateaux that rise from 1,000 to 2,000 ft whose bared slopes have a scanty cover of kermes oak and associated plants. If this pastoral landscape is left un-disturbed, a heath of cistus (*C. albidus*) and euphorbia appears, and a brushwood of ilex and stone pine which prevent soil degradation and so encourage an undergrowth of box and other shrubs to be re-established. In the higher areas such as Pic St Loup (2,077 ft) cedars, Corsican pines and chestnuts occur intermingled with evergreen woodlands. Population is sparse concentrated in small basins of cereal and lucerne cultivation, flanked by scattered orchards of almond, peach and apricot and some vineyards. At the edge of the Garrigues, Nîmes (90,000) is another great viticultural centre, but also a railway junction and manufacturing town.

Towards the interior, between the Seranne and the Tanargue, the Garrigues are overlooked by the abrupt front of the Cévennes. Deeply dissected by erosion into a series of valley cantons and mountain ranges, the life is isolated. This has helped to preserve a subsistence polyculture, though the chestnut has lost much of its former importance. The relatively dense population is also explained by the two industrial zones of the small coalfield around Alès (52,000) with its metallurgical industries and the textile districts of Ganges and Vigan where there is still a silk industry. Serious efforts are being made to revitalise industry in the remote areas.[66] while the afforestation of the Cévennes with pines, firs and cedars among the decaying chestnut forests is also active.

3. *The Lower Rhône Valley*. The lower Rhône Valley may be con-sidered as the chronometer of the Midi. Its terraces reveal the morpho-logical changes of its shorelines and glaciations.[67] The contrasts between the isolated, perched villages with their traditional polyculture, and the modern dispersion associated with market-gardening on the plains, reveal the recent changes of its countrysides. The region is therefore one of marked contrasts. Such are the differences between the stoney lime-stone cuestas of Mondragon, Luberon and Alpilles and the expansive plains of Orange, Avignon, Crau, and Camargue; and between the high karstic plateaux of Lure and Ventoux and the low karsts between the valleys of the Gard and Cèze. The lower Durance feeds three-quarters of the irrigated area and consequently a marked contrast has resulted between the still desolation of much of the landscape west of the Rhône and the fervent town life found on the left bank. Towns are sited notably at the junction of valley routes such as Montélimar (11,000), Bollène (8,312), Orange (17478,), Avignon (62,768), the twin towns of Tarascon-Beaucaire (10,197) and at Arles (17,478). New towns have grown up in the interior of the Provençal plains at Cavaillon (11,740), Chateaurenard and Barbentane. Older centres such as Carpentras (15,076) and Salon are few. Population is now dense,

with over 360 per sq. mile, and is associated with the creation of new landscapes of intensive horticulture, framed in windbreaks of reeds and cypresses (Plate 75). Nevertheless, several of its towns have seen better days. Arles, still a centre of transhumant flocks from the Crau and a commercial town on the Rhône had 20,000 in 1756 and only (21,000) in 1954. Avignon (62,768) perhaps reached 80,000 in the fourteenth century and though it has extensive suburbs today, the intramural population of 32,000 is no more than it was before 1840.

A very distinct landscape is that of the bare and stoney Crau, to the south of the Alpilles.[68] Even here, however, the transformation of 18,500 ha under irrigation on its northern border has created verdant meadows. Contrasted again is the active delta of the Rhône, with its watery fusion of land and sea.[69] Once prosperous in the early Middle Ages, the delta further subsided and has only been resettled since the seventeenth century, especially in the Upper Camargue for wheat growing and cattle rearing.[70] Its wastes are now being further reclaimed under the shrill green of growing rice. The native vegetation reflects closely the morphological features. Below sea-level, the marshes and saline tracts (sansouires) are colonised by atriplex and salicornia. The ancient dunes (montilles) once under stone pines are now frequently cleared for vineyards, and the recent sand dunes have a cover of Ammophila arenaria, tamarisk, cypress and stone pine. Although there is an average diversity of 73 per sq. mile, many tracts are still a desolate waste.

4. Marseilles. From the east bank of the Rhône delta, the first evidence of the industrial expansion of Marseilles is to be seen in the oil refineries around the quiet waters of the Étang de Berre, at Berre, Lavéra and La Midi. Marseilles itself, however, is neatly contained within the limestone ramparts of Nerthe and Étoile in a coastal basin of 86 sq. miles. Because of its importance as the largest Mediterranean seaport the scale of our description therefore changes. Marseilles is also one of the oldest settlements, its offshore islets of Pomegues and Ratonneau being used by Phoenician traders and its hill of Notre Dame de la Garde (531 ft) being settled by Greeks. It is from this hill that the best view of the urban landscape can be studied (Plate 77). At the foot of the northern flank of the hill nestles the Old Port of Marseilles, in the calanque of Lacydon, sheltered from the Mistral and protected from the alluviation of the Rhône delta. The inlet also furnished springs of fresh water. The westward longshore drift has assured Marseilles of a continuity as a port that the more ephemeral port of Arles and those west of the Rhône delta have never had. At the head

of the Lacydon inlet, a small stream, the Jarret, entered a marshy terrain offering natural protection to the ancient port, whose *reed* beds are still reminiscent in the urban quarter named Cannebière. To the southeast of the site, another small stream the Huveaume provided alluvial soils for the food requirements of the small colony. There is little evidence of the Roman occupation visible in the city, as Arles eclipsed it as a port for five centuries.[71] Until the Crusades, it remained a very modest settlement, huddled around the 28 ha of the Lacydon. Then followed a series of developments. First new commercial quarters grew north of the Old Port with small wooden quays built into the sea, though the streets of St Victor, following old stream beds, reverted to torrents during heavy rainstorms. A new and more powerful expansion took place at the time of Colbert, which lasted until the end of the eighteenth century, associated with the imposition of a tax of 20 per cent on all Levantine goods not landed at the port. With the resultant expansion of the port, a new geometrical layout of streets with broad arteries such as the rue de Rome, rue de Noailles and rue de Cannebière, was created. This is now the commercial heart of the city. Then followed until the mid-nineteenth century, urban expansion along three great routes out of the city: to Brignoles, Aix and Cassis. Thus a star-shaped sprawl took shape towards the limiting mountainous edge of the basin.

Greatest growth has taken place since the nineteenth century. The first railway entered the city in 1849, after piercing the Nerthe in a long tunnel. In 1844, the construction of a dock (Joliette) introduced the idea of a new northern port, followed by five others by the end of the century. New suburbs of industry and residential areas followed the northern waterfront, around the railway stations of St Charles and Belle-de-Mai and along the tramways to Aix and Aubagne (developed 1900–14). Later still, the valley breach of the Huveaume became utilised partially in the city's expansion. Along the Durance Canal (1837–48), built to supply Marseilles with water, other suburban growth took place. Population rose rapidly from 195,140 in 1851 to 406,920 in 1891. Further growth has continued.[72] In 1919, the Chamber of Commerce obtained control of the ports of Bouc and of the Berre lagoon, a canal and tunnel were cut to connect them with Marseilles (in 1926). New docks were excavated, first to the north of the port, and subsequently to the south of the Old Port. Marseilles today has a population of (661,492) and has grown too big for the strait jacket of its limestone hills, experimenting in fantasies such as the *Cîté radieuse* of Le Corbusier and spilling along the highways beyond its basins, especially towards Aix. These have helped to lessen slightly the congestion at the centre. With 85 per cent of the port's imports used for local industrial enterprises, the factories of Marseilles are a prominent feature, belching their fumes from the oil refineries, the chemical and cement works, the smelters, the soap, vegetable oil and food factories. The triumph of Marseilles has been the utilisation of an unfavourable industrial site, overcoming its obstacles to communications, to make it the third port of Europe. Nevertheless, Marseilles is introspective and can scarcely claim to be the capital of the Midi.

5. *Hills and Basins of Western Provence.* Between the limestone folds of the Luberon and Estaque to the west, and the Permian depression between Toulon and Draguignan in the east, a great variety of land-forms occur.[73] The most impressive are the structural forms in the centre, where the steeply folded anticlines of Ste Baume[74] (3,786 ft) and Ste Victoire[75] (3,316 ft) rise sharply on either side of the Arc basin, with craggy silhouettes, beloved of painters (Fig. 225). The planed skylines of the Étoile, Estaque, Nerthe, and Alpilles in the west emphasise the dominance of erosional forms. These are also dominant in the basins of the Arc and Beausset where differential erosion has etched out the hard rocks into rolling, hilly relief, trenched in superimposed gorges and linked by broad shallow valleys in the softer rocks.[76] The limestone massifs have been largely denuded of their forest cover so that bare, craggy slopes alternate with a maquis cover over the gentler slopes. Only the beech forest climax of Ste Beaume reveals something of the former high cover, although afforestation in the Luberon under stands of Corsican pine, cedar, and higher up of Scots pine, indicates what can be done more widespread.[77] Over the lower slopes of the basins, poor wheatlands in sandy soils, scattered vineyards and olive groves pimpling the glacis debris, are relics of the traditional polyculture.[78] Only in the well-watered clay plains is there a more intensive and commercialised interculture of varied crops.[79] Aix (54,200) is the natural centre. Built near thermal springs that were frequented by the Romans, it is a spa resort, whose architectural charm as a ducal residence of Provençal nobility is still preserved. Grafted on to the medieval town, the new quarters indicate a resurgence of growth associated with Marseillaise commuters and local industries.

East of Marseilles, the coast is rocky and karstic, associated with pronounced submergence where cliffed calanques project at various angles into the sea.[80] Offshore, a hidden archipelago of submerged reefs and islets is most prominently marked by the islands of Hyères.[81] Ancient settlements,[82] such as Cassis and Ciotat (12,425), now associated with tourism and shipbuilding respectively, lie sheltered in deep inlets. Only the lower course of the river Gapeau opens into the smiling coastal plain of Hyères. Sheltered from the mistral by Mont Fenouillet this rich, almost oriental, garden is landscaped with tropical plants such as Japanese medlars, Barbary figs, agaves, palms and oranges. Nearby is the naval arsenal of Toulon, an ancient port which was only developed after 1514 when it was converted into a naval base and its town area doubled. South of the main boulevard de Strasbourg is the old town and its arsenal, which already had 18,000 inhabitants at the end of the sixteenth century. To the north is the new town with its regular plan enlarged from 60,000 in 1840 to its present total of 133,300 inhabitants.

6. *Maures-Esterel and Côte d'Azur*. The eastern border of the Provençal basins and hills, is the Permian depression, followed by the faulted troughs of the Cuers and Luc, and the middle course of the Argens. Lignite beds and bauxite give it an industrial significance but its landscape is a rolling relief of vineyards and woods. South of it rise the rounded eminences of the Maures, a Hercynian massif with erosion surfaces at 800, 1,300 and 2,000 ft now much fragmented by erosion along lines of structure, and culminating at 2,560 ft in Sauvette.[83] Beyond the lower Argen valley rises a second Permian massif Esterel, more deeply dissected by chemical weathering. Red porphyries, carved into sugar loaves, such as in Cap Roux, and cliffed calanques, glow with colour between an azure sky and a deep blue sea. The fretted coast is such that, though the distance between Cap St Louis and the Gulf of Cannes is only about 26 miles, the shoreline measures possibly 250 miles and the sea boils noisily over hidden reefs. Inland from these two massifs is the third and smaller unit of Tanneron, a raised crystalline dome that slopes steeply in its juxtaposition to the Pre-Alps in the north. Forests cover nearly 120,000 ha of these mountains, especially maritime pines and cork oaks.[84] The latter are widely disseminated in woodlands, notably in the Maures where the chestnut also has an important place in the deep, north-facing ravines. Maquis, the corollary of fire is extensive everywhere, represented by various heaths, cistus, strawberry tree, and lentiscus. It is a wild landscape with few villages and densities of 137–142 per sq. mile including the fertile plains of the Argens.[85] It is there that the only Roman port of Fréjus (5,600) and its outport of St Raphael (6,800) are located, now noted for their market gardening and tourism.

East of the Sigane valley and the Gulf of Napoule, the Pre-Alps come close to the shore, and the Riviera proper begins. Between Cannes and Nice, the coastal hills are etched differentially out of gypsum, marl

75 Market gardens in lower Durance Valley. Note prevalence of shelter belts

TYPICAL LANDSCAPES OF FRENCH MIDI

76 Contact between limestone anticline and Tertiary basin in W. Provence. Ruins of deserted village in foreground

77 Marseilles

78 Montpellier—central *enceinte* was built in 1150 to incorporate three earlier settlements

and marly limestones, backed by the solid buttresses of the Alpine mountains, folded and carved out of Jurassic and Cretaceous limestones. The hills are crowned with umbrella pines, while the plains are covered with citrus trees, and fields of flowers. Luxurious villas dot the coast and hills, flanked by palms and approached by shady avenues of acacia and eucalyptus. A decor of dark pine woods on distant hills, surmounted by the eternal snows that shine from Monte Visco, frame the inland views. Closer inspection will reveal the stages of mountain vegetation: maritime and Aleppo pines on the lower slopes; deciduous oaks above 1,500 ft, then chestnuts, Scots pines and above 3,000 ft beech forests.[86] Between mountainous plateaux and the hills nestles Grasse (21,000), on the edge of its plain where 35,000 ha of flower gardens supply its scent factories. But most population has been

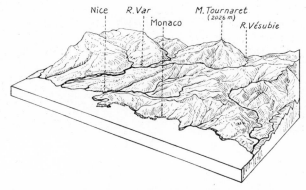

FIG. 229. Block-diagram of the French Riviera, looking westwards (after O. Barré)

attracted to the sea-side resorts where densities of 750 to 1,250 per sq. mile occur continuously along the coast. Ancient settlements, notably Cannes (60,000), Antibes (33,000) and Nice (244,290) have grown rapidly since the mid-nineteenth century as a result of foreign patronage and tourism.[87] Nice, in particular, has had an important history. The old town, rising in tiers above the lower Paillon valley to its chateau (at 308 ft), protected the chief part of Savoy—Piedmont from 1388 to 1860. West of the Paillon, the modern holiday resort has grown orderly over a deltaic plain, overlooked by luxurious villas. Beyond Nice, the Pre-Alps reach the coast in steep limestone cliffs, providing such effective shelter that its coast has been called 'Little Africa'. Here paleolithic man enjoyed a long occupation in caves and grottoes scattered between

W.M.W.—21

Nice and Ventimiglia. And here today, the terraced groves of lemons and oranges above Menton and the exotic flower gardens of Mont Carlo advertise their modern charms as winter resorts. The tiny principality of Monaco with only 150 ha, is divided into three towns: the old fortress of Monaco (2,020), the commercial quarter of La Condanine (10,705) and the luxurious hotels and casino of Monte Carlo (10,830), adjoined by the French resort of Beausoliel (13,050). If the whole Midi is characterised by its borderland features, so too from this edge of the Riviera other lands are to be seen. On a clear day from the col of Turbie, the pale outline of Corsica, the serrated summits of the Apennines, and the great inland chain of the Alps can all be discerned.

CHAPTER 21

THE ISLANDS OF THE WESTERN
MEDITERRANEAN

'Vivere non est necesse,
navigare est necesse.'
(Pompey, *De imperii Cn.* 12, 34)

In the Western Mediterranean, the islands are so numerous and varied
in their size and character that they can scarcely be said to form a coherent milieu. Corsica, Sardinia and Sicily (already treated) have major
dimensions (see especially pp. 536-44). At the other end of the scale
there are islets, notably in bays associated with great ports such as
Marseilles, Venice, Naples and Algiers. Some islands are strung along
the coasts, such as the Pelagii, Egadi and Lipari islands off Sicily, the
Tuscan archipelago with its seven islands, the Hyères near the Provençal
coast, and the Columbretes off Castellón. The larger islands also
have their archipelagos, Corsica with forty-three, Sardinia thirty-five,
the Balearics sixteen. Italy has at least one hundred and seventeen
islands and their enumeration has long intrigued Italian geographers.
Their insular characteristics range from sophisticated Capri, a pleasure
resort since Roman times, to the wild isolation of Sardinia, and from the
domestic landscapes of Majorca to the rugged scenery of Corsica. Some
are gardens created by much human toil such as Djerba, Malta and
Majorca, while others are still poorly developed like Menorca and in
the case of isolated islets, such as Alborán, only an occasional drinking
point for the infrequent visits of fishermen. Galita seems to have even
been a vast Carthaginian leper colony, while several islets have been
prisons, fortresses and even monasteries.

But most of the islands, whether great or small, have been indispensable as stepping stones in the trade routes of the Mediterranean,
recognised as such by Pompey's famous dictum that heads this chapter.
Links between Malta and Sicily and from Sardinia to the Balearics,
can be traced back to Neolithic times. The *sesi* of Gozo and Pantel-
laria, the *nuraghi* of Sardinia and the *talayots* of the Balearics, all
reflect common megalithic links. Later, the north-south axis of Corsica,
Sardinia and Sicily became significant, when Rome sought to be

mistress of the seas. At least from Phoenician times, a wide variety of products has been exchanged, such as the wines of Dalmatian islands, the copper and iron of Elba, the silver and gold of Sardinia, the wheat, oil and silk of Sicily, the salted meat and timber of Corsica, the fruits of Majorca, the salt of Ibiza and the olive oil of Djerba. No wonder that all the important, inhabited islands have been invaded in turn by Phoenicians, Carthaginians, Greeks or Romans and Arabs, and involved later in the rivalries of Tuscans and Genoese, Spaniards, French and English. Some have been fortified at numerous times, such as the Hyères, the Balearics and Malta, while Corsica was strung with about 150 Genoese forts at every vantage point during the sixteenth century. The cosmopolitan character of their inhabitants is obvious, explaining in part the contrasts in their outlook, modes of life and physique. The shepherds of Corsica and Sardinia, and the gardeners of Majorca and Malta, have made pronounced contrasts in the creation of their landscapes. Even in small islands like Elba, the mingling of peoples can be very marked: Tuscan at Porto-Ferrajo, Spanish at Porto-Longone and Rio, Neapolitan at Capoliberi, and Corsican and Genoese at Marciana. The Catalan dialect is still preserved at Alghero in Sardinia, and even Greek at Cargèse in Corsica. Invaders have created much of the urban life and its architecture. The Pisan, simple Romanesque and the Genoese worldly Baroque, are recognisable in many Tyrrhenian churches, while the English influence in Menorca and Malta has radiated from Port Mahon and Valletta.

The islands of Corsica, Sardinia, the Balearics and Malta being the most important are singled out for detailed descriptions. They epitomise the salient contrasts of the Mediterranean islands and illustrate strikingly the regional interactions of man and his landscapes. Table 5 (Appendix IV), summarises their marked differences of area and population. Undoubtedly the physical contrasts of these islands explain much. The average elevation of Corsica is about 1,800 ft, with the highest mountain, Mt Cinto, at 8,891 ft and some forty other peaks rising above 6,500 ft. Ratzel well described it as 'a mountain rising above the sea.' Two-thirds of its surface consists of ancient crystalline rocks, mostly granites, granulites and schists. Its soils are generally poor and the only extensive Quaternary lowland on the east coast has long been malarial. Sardinia has a lower average elevation, consisting of mountainous plateaux, while the high eastern dorsal of the Gennargentu (6,016 ft) turns its back on Italy. Three-fifths of Sardinia consists of impermeable, crystalline and volcanic rocks with rapid run-off. Drought and a thin soil cover impoverish much of the island, and only about a third of the total area has the physico-chemical properties and depth of soil to make agriculture possible, chiefly in the Campidano. This region, unlike the eastern Corsican plain has consistently been the food store of Sardinia since early times, but Quaternary plains only represent 14 per cent of the island. The total area of the Balearics is just under 2,000 sq. miles, Majorca representing 67 per cent. Menorca (293 sq. miles) consists mostly of poor, crystalline rolling relief, apart from the settled limestone plains of Mahón and Ciudadela. But two-thirds of Majorca comprises Tertiary plains and basins, intensively cultivated and densely populated. Geological differences, however, do not explain the great concentration of population in Malta which is the highest in Europe. Indeed the low, tabular, calcareous plateaux are wrinkled with man-made terraces and carefully developed soils.

Compared with other Mediterranean lands, the islands have more humid conditions, orographic influences being particularly marked in Corsica and Sardinia. Mild temperatures favour the intensive agricultural production of Majorca and Malta, wherever the limestone aquifers can be tapped for summer irrigation; the waterwheel (*noria*) is, therefore, a common feature there. Apart from the differences induced by altitude, table 4, Appendix 1 indicates that there are marked similarities of climate. Winds are an important element of the insular climates. In the Balearics, the *Tramontana* is especially a scourge in Menorca, the blow-out of the Mistral from the Gulf of Lions, the south-west wind (*Llebeitx*) is desiccating. The position of Sardinia at the crossroads of cyclonic tracks and trajectories of cold northerly air, explains its violent winds, notably the north-westerly *maestrale* while the island also suffers from the hot, southern *scirocco*. Especially in Corsica, the marked graduation of plant zones and their associated modes of life reflects the climatic changes with altitude.

The spatial relations of the islands are noteworthy. Corsica lies about 105 miles from Provence and 51 miles from Tuscany. It is separated from Sardinia by the straits of Bonifacio, seven miles wide, created in the late Quaternary. The Greeks and Carthaginians occupied the eastern plain around Aleria, and the Romans built a highway down the east coast with a transverse link between Aleria and Ajaccio. But the island remained largely in forest, until the Middle Ages, when the Pisans and, especially the greedy Genoese, wrought much havoc in its forests. It became an established Genoese policy to destroy the chestnut groves, symbol of Corsican resistance, and in areas of Genoese settlement notably the Balagne, olive trees were planted, as evidence of a settled government. Along the coasts the invaders built the urban centres: the Pisans at Bonifacio, the Genoese at Ajaccio, Calvi and Bastia. But the native villages always resistent to conquest have been typically withdrawn, commencing four or five miles from the coast, and concentrated in the interior valleys at 1,200 to 2,600 ft. It is only since 1769 that Corsica has belonged to France, and in a country that needs immigrants and enjoys a higher standard of life, emigration has been a major factor in Corsican life. There is probably more than double the population of Corsica living abroad that come from Corsican stock, and since 1936, the decline in Corsica has been absolute. Neglected and depopulated, the Corsican countryside is strewn with ruined fields, decayed chestnut forests, and shrunken villages, all enveloped in a vast expanse of maquis that bears witness to the constant, pastoral incendiarism.

Sardinia has also been a neglected island, but for different reasons. It lies 115 miles north of Africa but its north-east coast is only 130 miles from the Italian port of Civitavecchia. Yet from 1297 it was claimed by Spain, although only completely conquered in 1478. It remained ruthlessly exploited by Spanish feudalism until 1718, when it was conceded to the House of Savoy, more as a political pawn than as an economic asset. Economic stagnation has persisted until modern times; abolition of feudal rights took place only in 1835 and malaria, which was ubiquitous, has only been stamped out since 1952. Pastoralism is still dominant, pursuing archaic practices. Italian overpopulation and the more immediate 'Southern Problem' of the Peninsula have discouraged Sardinian emigration; as it is, Sardinia is the most thinly populated province of Italy. Like Corsica, Sardinia is a land of villages, 93 per cent of the population (1951) living in 544 nucleated settlements, 279 of which have over a thousand inhabitants. Also like Corsica, 94 per cent of them are sited away from the coast. The two towns, Cagliari and Sassari, fostered by the Spaniards have 17 per cent of the island's population.

How different has been the history of the Balearics which since the thirteenth century have been in the capable hands of Catalans and Valencians, apart from a brief interlude of seventy-two years when Menorca was occupied by the English (1708–56, 1762–82 and 1798–1802). Heirs of Berber settlement (Fig. 98), industrious and enterprising, the Mallorquins in particular have fashioned a rich food base, which impoverished Spain has never cared to neglect. Its flourishing port of Palma (113,844) 125 miles from Barcelona and 160 miles from Valencia, has long been the keystone, with about one-third of the total population. In comparison, the capitals of Ajaccio and Cagliari are provincial. There has been no attraction for the inhabitants of the Balearics to emigrate, except perhaps to the Catalan industrial region. Linked so closely with Barcelona and Valencia, tourism has drawn the bond still closer.

Malta is a world apart, its position, 60 miles from Sicily and 180 miles from North Africa, making it remote. Yet its central location on the threshold between the Western and the Eastern Mediterranean, has long given it a strategic importance that has dominated its human geography. First as the bulwark against the Turks, the Knights of St John held it from 1530 until 1798. After a brief Napoleonic interlude it has been in British hands since 1800, and has more than doubled its population (115,945 in 1841, 245,638 in 1951). Almost half are urban dwellers, one-fifth employed directly in military duties, many more indirectly. Malta is thus a unique community, unless it is compared with the similar naval base of Singapore. At all times it has been the catalyst of the Old World conquests.

The effects of these human contrasts upon the landscapes of the islands are significant. In Corsica about 40 per cent of the total area comprises the spontaneous vegetation of *macchia*, forests cover another 20 per cent and pastures represent 25 per cent. situated chiefly above the tree-line. Only eight per cent is cultivated and there has been a dramatic decline of this area since the mid-nineteenth century. Artificial terracing is seldom seen except in northern Corsica. In Sardinia, mining has added to the havoc of pastoralism so that only 4 per cent of the island has forests. About 67 per cent is in various degraded forms of spontaneous vegetation, chiefly garrigue. Although 18 per cent of Sardinia is classified as plains, only 2·8 per cent is cultivated under arable and tree crops. Majorca, however, is intensely cultivated, notably under tree crops, and garrigue is limited to the north-western sierras and south-east coast. Malta also, despite much thin soil cover has 40 per cent under cultivation. Thus the chestnut groves and maquis of Corsica, the garrigue heaths of Barbagia and openfields of the Campidano, the almond and olive groves of Majorca, and the terraced gardens of Malta, are all symbolic of the varied insular relations between man and nature.

CORSICA

It is impossible to generalise about Corsica, the most mountainous island of the Mediterranean. Its varied landforms combine structures that are analogous to the granites of the Montagne Noire, the *schistes lustrés* of the Piedmontese Alps and the limestone calanques of Provence.

Forests of Corsican pines, stoney deserts and lagoonal plains are enveloped by the scented maquis. Mountain scenery, the widespread cover of spontaneous vegetation (see Plate 12) and the inertia of its rural settlements, summarise the features of its countryside.

1. *The Landforms.* Geologically, Corsica represents two distinct mountain systems along an axis drawn between the valleys of the Ostriconi and the Solenzara (Fig. 224). To the east and north-east, folded structures of alpine origin, most of them in Triassic, meta-morphosed *schistes lustrés*, constitute the overthrust of two nappes detached from the Tuscan archipelago. Dome-shaped mountains, carved deeply out of homogeneous schists, sometimes capped above 3,000–5,000 ft by green serpentines and hard gabbros (for example in the Orezza district) rise to a maximum of 5,683 ft in San Pedrone. These mountains are crossed by relatively low cols (*bocca*, in opposition to the higher ones, *foce* in the western, crystalline mountains). North of the Golo, Corsica's longest river, the nappes are folded into wider, clearer amplitudes, the synclinal basins of Novella and St Florent alternating with the two anticlinal ranges of the Agriates and Cap-Corse (28 miles long). Altitude is lower, the peak of Mt Stello (4,270 ft) in Cap-Corse being the highest summit.

West and south-west of this folded relief, the remaining two thirds of Corsica comprises an upraised remnant of the Tyrrhenides continent that foundered in late Tertiary times, which has been peneplaned and rejuvenated. From the north-west towards the south-east runs the main watershed of the island, bearing the highest summits. These are: Paglia Orba (8,280 ft) a jagged, mountainous tooth; Cinto (8,891 ft) the highest summit of Corsica; Rotondo (8,610 ft) with its glaciated relief; Oro (7,845 ft) in splendid isolation; and Renoso (7,665 ft) and Incudine (6,988 ft). Their axis is only an imaginary line, however, as the short rivers flow westward in deep, mountainous valleys. Hercynian trend-lines, running north-east to south-west, re-emphasised by Plio-Pleisto-cene fractures, are repeated some thirty to forty times by the parallel, high ridges and deep valleys, that isolate all western Corsica. The crenulate, ria coast shows pronounced submergence emphasised by the four great gulfs of Porto, Sagone, Ajaccio and Valinco, followed inland by the valleys of the Liamone, Gravone and Taravo. At the head of the gulfs, Flandrian and Tyrrhenian (50–65 ft and 700–115 ft) terraces are clearly developed, while the marine abrasion of the Sartenais calanques is marked by a flat skyline. The rocky headlands and drowned valleys of the west coast terminate abruptly in a narrow continental shelf that plunges deeply to over 3,500 ft in distances of twelve to eighteen miles offshore (Fig. 13). How different is the appearance of the eastern coastal plains, notably that of Aleria (40 miles long and four to eight miles wide), revealing the emergent features of lagoons and bay bars on a shelving coastline. In the south-east, the structural relief reasserts itself in fault scarps and trellis drainage, following the fractured structure. This is most clearly seen in the area of Porto-Vecchio.

The scenery of Corsica owes much to the diverse morpho-climatic processes that have affected the sculpture of its rock-types. Reference has already been made to the chemical processes of the Quaternary interglacials (see pp. 66–67), weathering the granites to depths of even 100 ft. The curiously hollowed *tuffoni*, in the north-west, are particularly a feature of the deserted region of Agriates (Fig. 21). The hornblende-granite weathers rapidly into softly rounded plateaux, while the hard granulites and rhyolites form the high ridges and rugged pinnacles, notable in the Calanques de Piana on the west coast (Plate 79). Further variety is produced by the chemical weathering of gabbros, diorites, serpentines and eroded brecchias of volcanic origin. Mamillated landscapes of rugged relief predominate in the fine grained granites, such as aplite and granulite. The most widespread partial erosion surfaces are found in the porphyries, with broad valleys and high benches. Widespread pediments associated with late Pliocene sheet-floods occur in the lower valleys and south-western peneplains. Glaciation has been a factor of some importance above 6,000 ft. It is argued by Dresch that there has only been a Würmian glaciation, but Tricart and others think there have been two. Joints have been a major control, and where they are frequent, U-shaped valleys have been created, whereas when joints are scarce, the V-shaped profile is common. As the Corsicans are concentrated in the upper valleys, this can be an important distinction in its human geography. Actual erosion is characterised by intensive mechanical weathering: frost action above 2,000–2,500 ft and exfoliation are common on the granites. The latter has been accentuated by the human action of fire, together with the exposure of bare surfaces by overgrazing and soil erosion.

2. *The Rural Landscapes.* The three altitudinal zones, coastal, mountain and sub-alpine, are basic to the landscapes of Corsica. From sea-level to 1,500–2,000 ft, the Mediterranean maquis is supreme, varying from impenetrable, evergreen thickets of myrtle, strawberry tree, lentisk and tree heath, to a continuous low cover of stunted cistus (*mucchio*) and arid garrigue cover of lavendar, thyme and rosemary. The maquis is most vigorously developed in the broad valley bottoms and intermediate slopes, where deep granitic sands prevail, while on shallow

soils in fissured granites, the evergreen oaks or olives tend to have exclusive occupance. On the schists and especially in the environs of Porto-Vecchio (with 6,500 ha) cork oak woodlands have importance, with degraded associations in the Sartène and Cap Corse. Various species of maritime pines silhouette the coasts and on the marshy plains rustling groves of eucalyptus have been planted since the end of the last century. From 2,000 to 3,250 ft, the mountain zone has changed features. Trees become dominant, the chestnut occurs on the shady valley slopes from 1,300 ft and covers vast areas between 2,250 and 3,000 ft especially in the siliceous lands of the north-east; altogether there are 30,000 ha of chestnut forests. The evergreen oaks and the beech, which comprise 22 and 17 per cent of the Corsican forests, are important, especially over the granites. From 2,800 ft to the upper tree limit, which varies from 5,000 to 6,000 ft, is the zone of pines, representing almost half of the total tree cover (47 per cent). The Corsican pine (*Pinus laricio*) is the chief species, forming magnificent stands of timber that grow to 150 ft. Between the mountain and sub-alpine zones, Corsica has 136 communal forests (of over 500 ha each) some of them of ancient origin, such as Ghisone, Vizzavona, Marmano and Aitone (Fig. 230). In the sub-alpine zone, the fir and beech mingle with thickets of alders. Beyond the tree line are natural pastures (14 per cent of Corsica), wherever the rocky slopes permit.

Since the inventory of 1892, when agriculture covered a quarter of the island, the cultivated area has declined from 200,000 to 12,000 ha. Cereals have slumped from 140,000 ha to about 5,000 ha. The imports of cheap wheat after 1855, the poor yields and rural depopulation have all been attributable. The system of *achère morte*, whereby the land is cultivated for one or two years and then abandoned to fallow waste for ten to twenty years, is still practised in the west coastal areas, and in the mountains. Only on the richer plains of the Balagne, and the alluvial plains, such as the Taravo, Campo di Oro and Liamone, has the tradition been a threefold system of maize, wheat and fallow pasture. Olive groves (11,470 ha) especially in the Balagne and vineyards in Cap Corse, present a more typical Mediterranean landscape, while fruit trees (citrus, citron, almonds and peaches) are cultivated in the low sheltered plains of Nebbio, Balagne, Porto and Ajaccio. *Primeurs* (early vegetable crops) are grown on a small scale in these same plains.

Originally, all the lands were communally owned by the pastoral clans; then they became divided into village lands, fragmented by the families, the communal pastures and the forests. Today, a typical holding of 20–50 ha may possess a small vineyard, an olive grove, valley

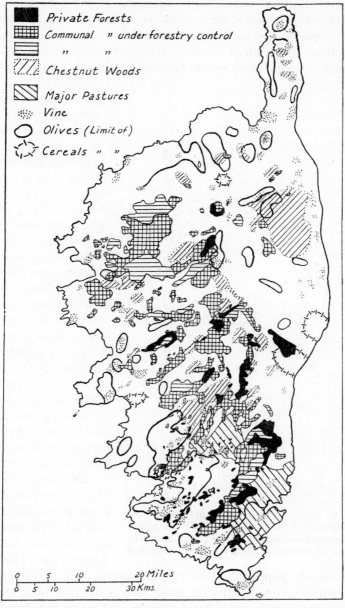

FIG. 230. Land utilisation in Corsica (based on Plan de mise en valeur de la Corse, inventaire, 1949)

land, periodically reclaimed from the maquis or under more intensive utilisation, and a share in the chestnut woods and pastures. In the west, small properties are much fragmented into *lenzi*, sometimes only a sixteenth or eighteenth of a hectare. But on the eastern plain, holdings are large, often including several hundred hec$_t$ares of maquis.

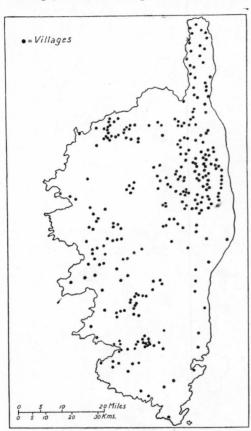

● = Villages

3. *The Regions*. The mountainous terrain has isolated the village communities, especially as the population has always been concentrated on the upper valley slopes (Fig. 231). Originally the valley units comprised clans and derived from this system there were still 66 *pieves* in the nineteenth century. The 62 cantons today are a reminder of this fragmentation. Their small size in the Castagniccia or chestnut region of the north-east, reflects the traditional concentration of settlement in this redoubt, that long resisted the Genoese domination. There are still 114 out of the 204 villages of Corsica in the north-east, chiefly in the Castagniccia. The valleys of the Liamone and Gravone and the Balagne, have also been

FIG. 231. Distribution of villages in Corsica. Note the influence of the chestnut forests of the north-east in concentrating settlement in that area. The absence of settlement along the coasts is marked

more densely populated. The high mountains, that run diagonally from north-west to south-east, have been a deserted tract forming the major regional and cultural division of Corsica into the *Banda di dentro* on the east and the *Banda di fuoro* on the west, with 45 *pieves* in the former and 21 in the latter. This distinction, which roughly coincides with the schistose and granitic landforms, is recognisable also in the dialects of Cismontan and Oltremontan, whose detailed features have been admirably mapped in the monumental atlas of Bottiglioni. With such particularism, regional divisions are legion, so it is only possible to outline briefly the main regions. These are the west coastal regions, the interior mountains and basins, and the east coast.

In the north-west, the Balagne is sharply focused by the stoney deserts of the Agriates and Galeria to the south-east and south respectively. It is the garden of Corsica, with prosperous villages surrounded by olive groves, vines and cereals. Population densities rise to over 500 per sq. mile, especially around the coastal settlements of Calvi a walled Genoese fortress and Ile Rousse founded by Paoli in 1758. Behind the coast there is the spectacular, mountainous backdrop of Cinto rising to 8,890 ft. South towards Piana is the deserted west coast, an enchanted landscape of red porphyritic obelisks that rise tier on tier in Wagnerian splendour, with rugged ridges of hard rhyolite enclosing the deep ria of Porto. Here the past seems more glorious, with the episcopal 'city' of Sagone now a hamlet of fishermen, Cargèse a little corner of Greece, Evisa perched precariously on a rocky site, Vico and other villages, all less important than they once were. Around the villages, orange and citron trees, vegetable gardens and olive groves are characteristic and beyond, the pervading scent of the maquis. At the head of the largest ria, the rich lands of the Camp di Oro and the easy communications of the Gravone valley, help to explain the location of the Corsican capital since French rule began. Ajaccio consists of three nuclei, the fortified chateau, the walled town, and the Borghie or suburb, where rural immigrants settled. Aided first by port facilities (begun in 1810), then by the railway connecting it with Bastia (after 1878), and then by the rural depopulation of the valleys, Ajaccio has grown from 19,000 to 36,000 in 1954. South of Ajaccio, the hard granulites with their rugged decor give place to the rounded relief of softer granites in the Sartenais. It is a countryside of cork oaks, and in the Taravo valley the Megalithic menhirs rise like Picasso statues in the maquis. The deep gulf of Porto-Vecchio, dominated by the granulitic mountains of Cagna and Ospedale is also enveloped in this cork woods, with the most marked dispersion of settlement on the island. To the south, the maquis tends to disappear with the outcrop of the limestone plateau of Bonifacio, and stone walls screen the crops against the prevailing winds. Bonifacio (4,000) stands perched above the sea-cliffs, walled and dominated by its *citadelle* and acting as a small port in the shelter of its faulted 'canal'.

North of the Solenzara valley begins in the region of the Fium-Orbo the zone of interior basins, marking the geological border between the granitic and schistose sectors of Corsica. Over a series of cols, the small basins of Sarba, Vizzani, Venaco and Corte are linked. The heavy rainfall and isolation explain their thickly forested slopes of chestnuts and pines. The mountainous regions of Cinarca, Ornano and Niolo are remote, once the haunt of banditry, and still conserving the traditions of pastoral life. Niolo aptly meaning 'region of the clouds', is the highest plateau of Corsica (2,600–3,600 ft) with its centre of Calacuccia. Another remote plateau Nebbio, 'the black country', opens to the coast at St Florent.

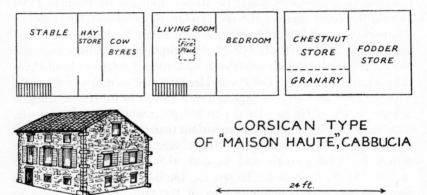

FIG. 232. A typical stone house in Corsica (Cabucchia, Gravone valley). Animal quarters occupy the ground floor, living quarters are on the first floor, with loft, chestnut stores, etc. above. The thick walls insulate against winter cold, as most villages are situated in the chestnut zone at 1,200 to 2,500 ft., and also were once useful for defence

Along the east coast, the extensive plain has been created by the numerous rivers that debouch rapidly, loaded with sediments. Famed for its fertility in classical times and facing the Italian mainland, it was exploited by Carthaginians, Greeks, Romans and later Genoese. But it fell a prey to malaria and until this disease was finally eradicated in 1952 it was desolate and unimportant, cultivated seasonally by the villagers of the surrounding mountains. As in Calabria, each mountain village has tended to develop in recent decades its own *marine* settlement near the coast, notably in the Casinca region. Castagniccia, as its name applies, is dominated in the high basins by chestnut forests. These basins have been the nuclei of several *pieves*, and densely populated (150–200 per sq. mile). The birthplace of the patriot Paoli, this region

experienced the bitter struggles of the Corsicans to achieve their indepe-
dence in the eighteenth century. The chestnuts were the provender of
liberty and, for this reason, the French later (in 1778) prohibited the
planting of chestnuts in agricultural lands. The traditional house-type
of Corsica, built with thick stone walls, usually has a chestnut store in
the upper storey, and kept dry by the smoke from the central fire-
place below (Fig. 232). The impoverishment of the soil, consequent on
the neglect of the chestnut groves and the spread of the ink disease,
has encouraged marked rural depopulation from the high valley
basins. To the north-east, the richly endowed hinterland of Bastia has
favoured its growth from the shelter of its Genoese bastide. It is the
largest town in Corsica, the chief trading outlet and the nearest link to
the French mainland. Further north the anticlinal peninsula of Cap
Corse is dissected deeply by small streams into a series of *conques* or
small regions, with terraced slopes under vines and fruit trees, presenting
a rich landscape with many scattered settlements.

SARDINIA

Also part of the Tertiary continent of Tyrrhenides, Sardinia has many
affinities with Corsica. Like it, Sardinia has two-thirds of its area in
crystalline and granitic rocks. But plateaux and plateau scarps are more
characteristic of the Sardinian relief than mountainous Corsica. Its
culture is also distinct, reflecting mostly African origins in the physique
of its early settlers. The dialect is pure latin, the customs Spanish, but
the pastoral mode of life and the organisation into villages are probably
traceable to the Bronze Age; many of the villages are on or near the site
of the ancient *nuraghi*, of which about 6,500 have been identified (Plate
83). The lack of urban life, outside of the capital Cagliari and Sassari,
is in part consequent on the neglect of the maritime life, as in Corsica.
Indeed, of some 2,400 local proverbs only three make any reference to
the sea, and all terms for fishing are expressed by Catalan or Genoese
words. Thus, aloof from the Mediterranean sea-lanes, Sardinia has only
recently awakened to modern developments. This juxtaposition of
archaic features and recent changes is characteristic of its countryside,
still largely enveloped in a mantle of spontaneous vegetation cover.

1. *The Landforms.* The fracture of the crystalline rocks, marine
transgressions and vulcanicity have created the major landforms of
Sardinia. The backbone of the island is the east central block, composed
chiefly of granites intruded in Carbo-Permian times, carved into erosion
surfaces over wide stretches of Gallura and Gennargentu. Formerly
island units, the granites of Sarrabus and Sulcis are more fragmented.

Less uniform are the Palaeozoic crystalline rocks, especially schists of the Barbagia Iglesiente and the Nurra. Submerged or islanded, these rocks were in part covered by the Mesozoic seas, remnants of whose

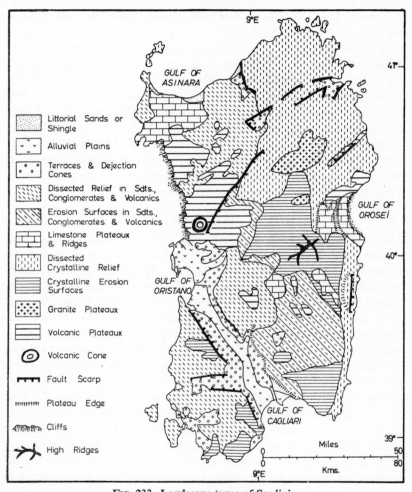

FIG. 233. Landscape types of Sardinia

hard limestones still resist erosion in the Orosei district and also between Laconi and Tertenia. The fracture of the Campidano in the early Tertiary, running diagonally from south-east to north-west, has created a basin infilled with varied Mio-Pliocene sediments and even with Quaternary shorelines (Würm). In the north-west, the varied relief reflects the outcrop of Oligocene trachytes in dissected lava plateaux, overlain by Miocene limestones. At the juncture of the Campidano and the Planargia, where transverse fractures meet, Plio-Pleistocene basic lavas have been outpoured from vents, notably the great cone of Ferru (Fig. 233). The age of these fractured blocks, the phases of uplift and the discordant surfaces are thus the essential morphological problems of Sardinia, only now beginning to be studied. All that can be summarised here are the morphological features of the crystalline, sedimentary and volcanic landscapes.

The rectilinear east coast has been fractured, especially in the southeast where north-south fracture has occurred off-shore, though the borders of the Flumendosa plateaux show erosional relief. The gulf of Orosei had been shaped by arcuate fault scarps, whose downthrow in pre-Eocene times has helped to preserve the Mesozoic limestones, sometimes to depths of 2,500 ft. Hard and resistant to erosion, they have inverted the relief in some areas, standing out as escarpments on the borders of great perched synclines, such as Urzulei. The granites frequently shattered and crushed, form basins such as Ogliastra, which is overlooked by the craggy limestones of Baunei and Lanusei (Fig. 233). In the north-east, the ria and valley of Terranova has been faulted north-east to south-west. The crenulate headlands of north-eastern Gallura run inland, in an Appalachian relief of quartzites which surmount the rolling, pre-Tertiary surfaces of the granites. The rectilineal Gulf of Asinara also is evidence of fracture. In Iglesiente, the fossilised landscape of ancient massifs, fragmented by north to east and east to west faults into horsts, is contrasted with the grabens, infilled by Tertiary sediments, trachytes and Pleistocene alluvium, to form plains and plateaux.

Mesozoic and Tertiary rocks, mostly unfolded, cover wide areas of the southern centre of the island. Jurassic sandstones, covered by limestone in flat-topped masses known as *tacchi*, are characteristic of the peneplaned tableland of Sarcidano, southern Barbagia and Ogliastra. They are bounded by the abrupt fault scarp to the south-west of the Campidano and to the north-west by the deeply dissected valleys of the Flumendosa and its tributaries, cut in the schists. Southern Barbagia is the principal area of Sardinia to suffer from landslips (*lame*) where granites underlie the sedimentary cover at steep angles. The Campidano is the major sedimentary basin, stretching sixty miles from the gulf of Cagliari to that of Oristano. The valley floor is some nine miles wide, rising to an indeterminate watershed of 260 ft near Gavino Monreale. The borders of the plain form a wider, fretted belt of dissected Tertiary hills, with remnants of terraces at about 230, 330 and 660 ft above sea-level. At the seaward ends are lagoons; those around Cagliari are now mostly saltpans, while those in the Oristano plain, aggravated by the floods of the Tirso, are now being reclaimed in an important reclamation scheme (Fig. 238). The western tributary of the Cixerri, follows another graben, dividing the Iglesiente region into two sectors and linking it with the coastal plain of the south-west. In the north-west, the Nurra, once a Tertiary island, is united between the crystalline range of Forte (1,522 ft) and the trachyte plateaux of Planargia, by an undulating lowland that rises from sea-level to about 250 ft. Much of it is the winter grazing lands owned by the commune of Sassari.

From Anglona in the north to the Tirso valley for some fifty miles stretches a series of volcanic landscapes (Fig. 233). Anglona has heterogeneous relief of varying resistance, from hard trachytes and andesites to soft tuffs and ash beds, mixed with lacustrine sandstones, conglomerates and Miocene limestones. These rise to 2,516 ft in a former crater near Osilo but generally the tilted blocks which are fractured by north to south, east to west and south-west to north-east faults, are lower (1,000–1,800 ft). South of Anglona, the region of Logudoro is a region of small plains and hills where marls are interspersed with remnants of lava-flows. The volcanic landforms vary with their age. The Miocene and lower Plocene lavas form basaltic plateaux, such as Monte Santo and Monte Pelao. Later Pliocene volcanic have conserved part of their craters, such as Monte Ruju, while the Quaternary cinder cones such as Monte Annaru are still preserved, especially along a line from Ploaghe to Bonorva. Towards the south and west the lava plateaux become larger and higher but south of Bonorva an east-west escarpment marks the edge of another landscape of broad plateaux and deeply incised valleys. These merge in the south-west with the great volcanic cone of Mt Ferra, dissected by radial streams into separate peaks of which Mt Urtigu (3,445 ft) is the highest. This mountain overlooks the Campidano to the south.

2. *The Rural Landscapes.* Sardinia has three climatic features which are of importance to its vegetation cover. First, from sea-level to about 1,500 ft the island suffers from drought for four or five months of the year, and above 3,000–3,500 ft there are still three dry months. Consequently the beech is absent on the island, and the mountain pines are rarely represented. Secondly, the marginal position of the island in relation to the passage of air masses results in a high variability of rain from year to year; too far south for assured influences from the Gulf of Lions, and north of the central Mediterranean depressions.

Wind is an important element and its dominance over the island helps
to explain the marked absence of dense forest. In the north-west, where
winds (*maestrale*) are very strong, the maquis cover of Nurra seems a
natural adaptation. Thirdly, compared with Corsica, altitudinal zones
are less marked, but three regional divisions can be recognised: the

I. VEGETATION PROFILE TODAY

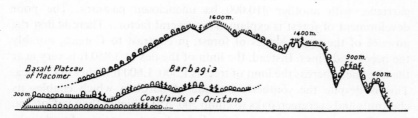

GENNARGENTU

1600m.

1400m.

900m.

Basalt Plateau
of Macomer   Barbagia

600m.

300m.   Coastlands of Oristano

||||||||||| Pastures and rocky waste
ﻌﻌﻌﻌ Thyme garrigue

⚡ ⚡ ⚡ Remnants of beech and coniferous zone

✿✿✿ ✿✿✿ Remnants of mixed deciduous zones (oak. and chestnuts)

✿✿✿ffff Evergreen woods of holmoak and juniper (*J oxycedrus* and *J phoenicea*)

|||||||||||ooooo✦✦✦ Pastures, cereals and vines of the evergreen zone

II. VEGETATION PROFILE IN GLACIAL TIMES

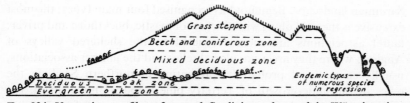

Grass steppes

Beech and coniferous zone

Mixed deciduous zone

Deciduous   oak   zone
Evergreen oak zone

*Endemic types—
of numerous species
in regression*

FIG. 234. Vegetation profiles of central Sardinia to-day and in Würmian times
(after Rikli). The narrow zonation of plant association during glacial times is
obvious

southern Campidano and coastal Sulcis have sub-tropical and semi-
arid features, where the dwarf palm is a characteristic plant; the hot
temperate climate of all western and northern Sardinia is associated
with the evergreen and cork oaks; and in the sub-humid climate of the
eastern highlands above 1,500 ft the colder winters and the short, dry
season favour a few deciduous oaks, especially the sessile variety.
The altitudinal changes of vegetation which have taken place since the
Würm are summarised in Fig. 234. Apart from climatic conditions

soils may cause inversion of flora in some regions. Such cases now are relatively common in the deep basaltic soils of the north-west with deciduous oaks below the ilex, or in the Arborea Marmilla and Trexenta where the limestones carry ilex woods above the acid soils of the schists.

The spontaneous vegetation of Sardinia covers 67 per cent of the island. There is a relatively small area of forest (130,000 ha or only five per cent of the total area), with another 188,000 ha of coppice. The rest or some 1,135,000 ha permit pastures on range lands of maquis and garrigue, with another 410,000 ha unenclosed pastures. The poor development of forest is explained by several factors. There is first the absence of the upper stages of forest, in contrast to Corsica, notably the beech and pines. Instead, the limit of the ilex at 3,850 ft is very near the tree line, whereas the limit of trees is 1,300–1,600 ft higher in Corsica. This is despite the southerly latitude of Sardinia which enables its chestnuts and evergreen oaks to climb 300–650 ft higher than in Corsica. Secondly, some 66 per cent of Sardinian forests consists of cork oaks which rarely form dense stands except for some 12,000 ha in central Gallura. Cork began to be exploited about 1830. The ilex forms only thick woodland in south-eastern Barbagia. Wind and deforestation are other explanations. In the early nineteenth century La Marmora noted that one-fifth of the island was covered in thick woodland but after 1860, when Sardinia came out of its solitude, incendiarism was intensified and much timber was cut for the railway.

Exuberant and varied stretches of maquis are characteristic of the Sardinian landscape. Beguinot has recognised four main types: the most extensive is the wild olive, with thickets of mastic, buckthorn and privet; laurel associations are more restricted to the sheltered valleys of Anglona where they are a pre-glacial relic; and the juniper associations, usually coastal and probably representing in northern Sardinia the relics of the undergrowth of Tertiary pine woods. Unlike Spain, the heathlands and the garrigues do not show extensive areas of one species, the cistus plants for example only forming a discontinuous cover except in the plain of Cixerri the south coast between Pula and Domusdemaria and the regions of Marrubiu and Oziere where cistus has been induced by *écobuage*. Garrigues of dwarf palm in the Nurra and elsewhere on rocky soils of rosemary and juniper are common.

The regional landscapes of Sardinia can only be understood in relation to the influences of their relative isolation, the impact of feudalism, the scourge of piracy which continued until 1815, movements of colonisation and the agrarian laws of the nineteenth century. A glance at the population map (Fig. 236) shows that, apart from the

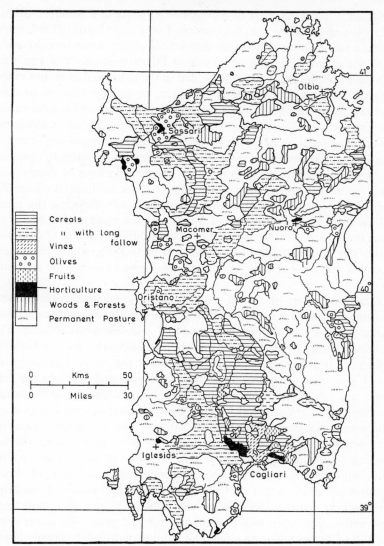

FIG. 235. Land utilisation in Sardinia

two towns of Cagliari and Sassari, the chief concentration of population
is in the villages of the west centre of the island, with blank areas in
the eastern highlands and around the coasts. Only in the interior areas
where soil conditions enable a relatively intensive use of land has
population been traditionally concentrated, namely the Campidano,

Marmilla, Trexenta, part of Sarcidano, Anglona and Sassari. Around the village evolved an openfield system. In the grain lands of the Campidano a two-field system was developed: the *vidazzone* under cultivation and the *contro-vidazzone* or *pabrile* in fallow pasture. New lands reclaimed (*tanche*) from the waste added to the cultivated area. But in the central plateaux, the village lands might be divided into ten or even twenty units, with long fallow periods that emphasised the importance of pastoralism. This evolved the fundamental duality of Sardinia between the lands under cericulture and under stock-raising. Further distinction has developed since the late sixteenth to nineteenth centuries between the peripheral regions, once desolate because of piracy, and later colonised in dispersed settlements and the traditional village life of the interior. The isolated settlements, the *ciuli* of Nurra, the *stazzi* of Gallura, the *furriadroxius* of Sulcis and the more recent *baccili* of Sarrabus are all distinct, according to their different modes of colonisation. The most marked dissemination is in Gallura, which being near Corsica, has been settled very largely by Corsicans since the sixteenth century.

The landscapes of walled fields (*tancas*) so characteristic of west central Sardinia are consequent on the General Enclosure Act of 1820 when lands could be generally enclosed and commons divided. The marked density of the nuraghi, and the volcanic rocks, used as building materials for the field walls, and especially the mixed husbandry of stock and agriculture, facilitated this. In Sassari and Anglona the field units are small with more intensive agriculture, whereas to the south in Planargia, Campeda and Abbasanta where stock-rearing is important the *tancas* are large. Elsewhere in Sardinia, the landscapes remained in open fields, the communities being too poor to renounce the advantages of communal organisation, or were already owned by individual colonists. In 1839 another attempt was made to divide lands among peasants. Again in 1865 lands were expropriated from large landowners, but these 350,000 ha were poor lands, usually remote from the settlements. Thus today, there are still vast properties either common land or belonging to a few rich families, with much fragmentation of peasant holdings. Land reclamation of Sardinia was started late in the Fascist régime and concentrated on the coast and valleys, notably the Flumendosa–Cagliari scheme, which will eventually irrigate 50,000 ha, the lower Tirso scheme and others at Chilivani, Fertilia, Terralba, Sulcis, Orosei and Posada. Slowly the 1933 plan, to benefit 890,000 ha of lowland and another 400,000 ha of the Nuoro mountains, is being completed, though modified by the laws of 1950 and 1952.

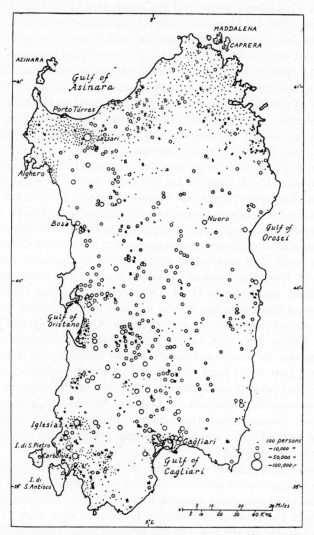

FIG. 236. Distribution of population in Sardinia. Typical of other Mediterranean islands, is the concentration of population in villages in the interior, with recent dispersion in the peripheral areas, notably the Gallura, the Sulcis and Sarrabus

3. *The Regions of Sardinia.* The regional divisions of Sardinia reflect its complex history, with the evolution of pastoral tribalism and the imposition of feudal fiefdoms. Rich in local names, these regional units may be grouped into four divisions: the eastern highlands, the north-

west, the Campidano plain, and the south-west (Fig. 237). From the summit of Punta La Mamora (6,018 ft), the highest in Sardinia, the immense distances across the Gennargentu, with its vast cover of moorland, can be best appreciated: northwards to the serrated ranges of Olierna and rolling plateaux of Gallura, westwards to the Marghine chain and Mt Ferru, southwards to the Pula promontory and the silvery waters of the Gulf of Cagliari, and eastwards to the mountains of Ogliastra that plunge steeply into the Tyrrhenian sea. Such Sardinian views are not desolate but wistful and serene, with that far-off feeling of isolation. On the steep bosky slopes of Gennargentu's massive frame are thin sprinkles of stubby deciduous oaks, lithe chestnuts and red-gashed cork trees. When the high summits are clothed in winter snow, long tresses of waterfalls plunge down the eastern borders. But on the rolling plateaux, myrtle scrub and impenetrable miles of hazel thicket smother all evidence of stock-grazing. Villages are sparsely scattered and their life is primitive. Population is concentrated in the western Gennargentu and the plains and basins that overlook the Campidano. But in the east apart from the Lanusei–Ogliastra district, vast areas are quite uninhabited, described by D. H. Lawrence as 'a savage dark-bushed, sky-exposed land, forsaken to the sea and the sun,' with 'no life in sight: even no ship upon the pale blue sea.' Only the almond blossom around Orosei gives any variety to this solemn landscape of rocky promontaries, bays and moorlands, lost to humanity. Terranova, the busy ferry port at the head of its Gulf, is the only exception, since the disseminated hamlets and farms are swallowed up in the gentle folds of the maquis-covered plateaux of Gallura. Situated in a marshy ria, Terranova Pausania was the ancient Olbia, a colony traditionally founded by the Greeks and with a Roman port; it is the nucleus of the modern harbour works.

Beyond the Coghinas valley, the granitic moorland landscape of Gallura changes to the more varied relief of Anglona, with its Miocene tilted blocks of limestone, volcanic rocks, trachyte lavas and ash beds. Westwards the productive Miocene limestones with their tablelands deeply dissected by the rivers merge into the Sassari district. From the north-west coast up to about 1,300 ft the countryside is thickly dotted with olive groves, protected by stone walls and with a high dispersion of farm houses. Along the coast and bordering the interior plateaux are numerous villages, many of Genoese origin, though the walled part of Alghero is still clearly Spanish in character. Population densities are 150–250 per sq. mile and over, around Sassari (44,000) the northern capital of Sardinia. Medieval in origin, a city of refuge to the coastal

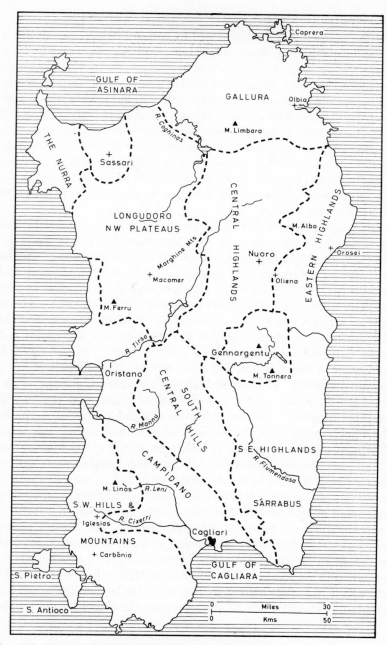

FIG. 237. Regional divisions of Sardinia. The island is like Corsica, rich in natural regions which have had much influence in the cultural fragmentation of its society (N.B. 'Cagliara' should read Cagliari, and 'Longudoro', Logudoro)

settlements when they were harassed by corsairs, Sassari was already a regional capital in the thirteenth century, and today it is an important market centre for a rich agricultural hinterland. Southwards stretches Logudoro, 'the land of gold', a diverse landscape of Tertiary marls, limestones and volcanics, not unlike Anglona, but thickly strewn with *nuraghi* and today with compact villages occupied in cattle-raising and mixed agriculture. South of Logudoro, there is the series of wide lava plateaux such as the higher Campeda and lower Abbasanta, with their squalid villages, and the snake-like trail of *tancas* that enclose the fields of asphodel pastures (Plate 80). Macomer and Bosa are the only sizeable settlements, although the northern and eastern slopes of Mt Ferru have some large villages.

The broad, marshy valley of the Tirso now in process of reclamation marks off the north-west from the Campidano. There are, however, two *Campidani*—the Quaternary plain, the Campidano proper, with its large villages isolated by monotonous lowlands of cultivated land, and the Miocene hill lands to the east, with more varied rolling relief, smaller but more numerous villages (300 villages in Trexenta alone), and not quite so treeless. Both have large estates, big farm houses, and the villages—many of Roman origin—are route-centres with roads and tracks radiating from them like a spider's sweb. Cagliari (78,000), perched on a series of fortified hills, centrals the Campidano at its seaward extremity. It flourished as a Carthaginian, Roman, Pisan and Spanish capital, and it has maintained its lead as the largest, most industrialised and wealthiest commercial centre of Sardinia. The adjoining salt pans, the spacious harbour, and the rich, vine-clad hinterland of the Campidano to which the waters of the Flumendosa will add considerable productivity, all attest the importance of Cagliari. How different is the south-western region of Sulcis, with its deserted mountains of Capoterra, though more populated Sulcis mountains with their small mining centres. Here the hamlet is the rule, the focus of pastoral settlement since the sixteenth century. The coastal plains, linked almost continuously, are treeless and almost deserted. It is the mines that attract settlement on the hill slopes and at the foci of routes, notably so in the local capital of Iglesias (17,000). Here in the island's extremity land and sea both seem to give out. Indeed Sardinia seems lost between Europe and Africa, belonging to no one heritage, to no one people.

THE BALEARIC ISLANDS

The submarine sill which stretches 250 miles north-east of Cape Nao carrying the Balearic archipelago, clearly indicates it belongs to Sub-

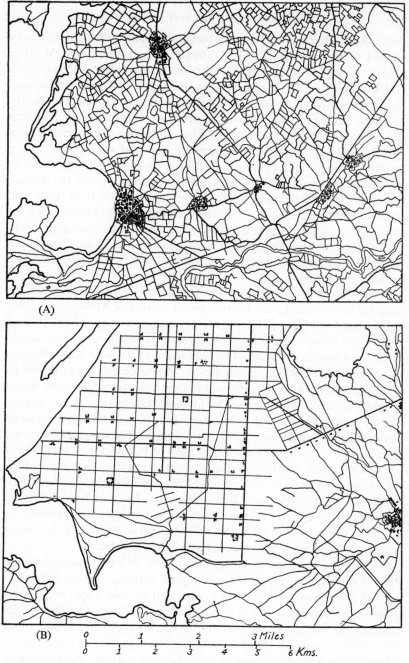

(A)

(B)

| 0 | | 1 | | 2 | | 3 Miles |
| 0 | 1 | 2 | 3 | 4 | 5 | 6 Kms. |

Fɪɢ. 238. Road and settlement patterns in the Oristano plain. Note the contrast between the radial tracks used by the pastoralists in the area of old settlements, north of Arborea (A) here markedly nucleated, and the new colonisation of Terralba (B) where 5,000 hectares of the Sassu lagoon were reclaimed in the 1930's

Baetic Spain (Fig. 81). The islands form two groups: the western one or ancient Gimnesias consists of Majorca (1,325 sq. miles) and Minorca (293 sq. miles), separated from the Pityusae islands of Ibiza (228 sq. miles) and Formentera (37 sq. miles). They exhibit three types of structure: the hercynian remnant of the Catalan continent, represented by the northern sector of Minorca and probably underlying the eastern mountains of Majorca; the alpine folded mountains of western Majorca and the hills of Ibiza; and the tertiary plains of southern Minorca, central Majorca, and Formentera. The north-east–south-west axis of western Majorca and Ibiza follows the geosyncline in which the thickest Mesozoic strata have been accumulated: some 2,200 ft of Trias and nearly 3,200 ft of Jurassic and Cretaceous limestones. These have been moulded by organic movements between late Cretaceous and Burdi-galian times. Subsequent marine transgressions and in the Tyrrhenian phase the disintegration of the sill into islands, have completed this geological evolution.

Structural, erosional and karstic features are all widespread in the Balearic landforms. In the north-western Sierras of Majorca, complex imbricated folding and overthrusts of secondary rocks, have formed some seven series of ranges, closely compressed and four of them reach-ing a considerable elevation. The fault scarp of the west coast trenches the highest relief, which culminates in Monte de Atalayasa (4,986 ft) and Puig Mayor (4,757 ft) only two to four miles from the coast. Relief is youthful on the west coast of Majorca with short obsequent streams, trenching deep gorges, and with subsequent drainage that links up some of the intermontane basins of *polja* and dolines. The range, terminating to the north in the bold headland (or *cala*) of Formentor, is reminiscent of the Dalmatian coast, with similar drowned dolines forming embay-ments such as Soller, with steeply-folded ranges, knife-edged pro-montaries and intermontane basins (Fig. 14). The structure of Ibiza is similar, though the two folded ranges in the north-west and south-east are more open, lower (Atalayasa 1,559 ft) and separated by the broad central plain between San Antonio and Santa Eulabia.

The second morpho-structural unit of the Balearics, comprises the hills of eastern Majorca and north central Minorca. In the latter, the highest relief is carved out of Devonian and Jurassic rocks that culmi-nates in Monte Toro (1,175 ft). In eastern Majorca, the Sierras del Levante which begin in the region of Arta, Manacor and Felanitx and are drowned seawards in the Cabrera archipelago, form a landscape of rolling hills and mountains below 1,500 ft. Their morphological features are similar to those of Ibiza: high Plio-Pontian surfaces, platforms of marine abrasion such as between the Calas of Ratjada and Freu, and Tyrrhenian fossilised sand dunes (*mares*). Extensive karstic plateaux occur, especially around Porto-Cristo with the famous Jurassic caves on the coast at Arta and Drach, probably formed in the Grimaldian.

The third morphological unit of the Balearics is represented chiefly by the central plain of Majorca, composed of Miocene and late Plio-Pliestocene deposits. The undulating relief of basins and plains is only interrupted by two Triassic and Jurassic inliers, represented in the hills of Randa (1,857 ft) and Sineu (1,014 ft). The intense erosion of the north-western mountains under semi-arid cycle has resulted in a piedmont belt of low hills at their eastern border, comprising Würmian cones. These are quite distinct from the Quaternary glacial phases of solifluction seen above 1,500 ft. The plains are deeply covered with a red mantle of *terra rossa*, mostly of Würmian age but probably belonging to several interglacial phases. The southern two-thirds of Minorca forms a rolling tableland of Miocene limestones, at 150–350 ft and broken by deep gorges. Formentera has similar lowland relief, though less dissected. The absence of any perennial streams, and the climatic changes from humid interglacials to the present semi-arid Mediterranean, explain the peculiar features of the micro-relief.

The islands have been largely cleared of their spontaneous vegetation cover, since deforestation has been intensive for a long period. The Aleppo pine giving its name to Ibiza and Formentera ('the pine islands') is still the chief woodland species, still covering about one-third of Formentera and also important in Minorca and the western sierras of Majorca. There are also rarer patches of stone pine and in western Majorca ilex woods climb above the Aleppo pines at 2,200–2,500 ft. The garrigue is much more widespread terminating at about 2,500 ft. Moisture and incendiarism largely determine the garrigue associations: dwarf palm is profuse in north-east and south-west Majorca and central Ibiza, juniper, cistus and rosemary are more widespread, and in western Majorca and north-eastern Ibiza oleander and myrtle follow along the river beds. Asphodels are ubiquitous, a tribute to the over-grazing of the limestone tablelands.

Majorca, favoured by its generous mantle of *terra rossa*, is the most intensively cultivated. But the agriculture of the Balearics only developed significantly after the eighteenth century. Berber settlers had developed dry polyculture, especially in Majorca during the Middle Ages, and from 1229–1232, when the Aragónese Jaime I conquered the islands, until the late fifteenth century Palma gave the islands important trade links. Then agriculture declined with the attacks of the Barbary pirates;

Minorca was largely waste and in Majorca settlements avoided the coasts apart from the redoubt of Palma. All this was changed when the English took possession of Minorca, especially during the governorship of Sir Richard Kane (1712–1736). He reclaimed the marshes around Mahon and elsewhere, introduced the potato, vine and clover, also cattle and sheep from North Africa and pigs from Sardinia, and encouraged the enclosure of land in stone walls to protect the tree-crops from the *Tramontana* winds. New settlements were built, Villa Nuera de San Carlos and San Luis (by the French), and a road was built to connect Mahon with the former capital, Ciudadela. Population rose from 16,082 in 1723 to 20,815 in 1749, excluding the garrison. Today Minorca has 42,500, though the features of the countryside have changed little since Kane's enlightened rule. In Majorca, the change came later in the eighteenth century, from 1778 when a society to improve the economy was founded. Nurseries of young almond, fig and carob trees were set up to distribute freely to the cultivators (1782), while French emigrants planted apricot and peach orchards. Cereal yields had always been very irregular so during the nineteenth century the tree-crops rapidly replaced the wheat fields of the central plain. At the end of the century, foreign exports of almonds began and the area under this crop rose from 6,000 ha in 1880 to 26,500 in 1917. The olive and carob have maintained their importance chiefly in the western sierras, giving place on the plains to the almond, fig, apricot and some vegetable crops, notably tomatoes. In Ibiza, the planting of tree-crops commenced later, at the end of the nineteenth century, though the other agricultural features, the reclaimed foreshore gardens of Ibiza (*feixes*), are traceable to Moorish times. The famous Majorcan terraces at Bañalbufor are also probably Moorish, while the windmilles and water wheels that are so widely dispersed are of similar origin. There is little fragmentation of land, few large estates, and especially in Majorca there is little of that Mediterranean poverty that shocks one; there is rather a charming atmosphere of genial moderation in domesticated landscapes.

The population map (Fig. 239) clearly shows that, grafted upon a primary network of nucleated settlements, usually away from the coast, a secondary dispersion has followed in recent times. Some centres are very ancient, such as Ibiza (12,283) founded by the Carthaginians on a coastal hill rising 200 ft above the sea, still surrounded by its sixteenth century walls. Port Mahon (14,723) was also a Carthaginian foundation, though its development was chiefly in the eighteenth century under the English rule. Palma and Alcudia are Roman in origin. The densely dispersed farm names (notably *Beni-* and *Rafal-* prefixes) indicate the importance of Berber settlement (Fig. 98), while the hamlets and villages, clustered around watch-towers dating from the period of Barbary piracy, indicate that dispersion and nucleation have alternated with the times of peace and insecurity respectively. In 1785 only six per cent of

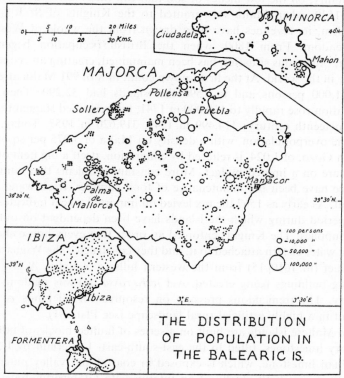

FIG. 239. Distribution of population in the Balearic islands. The central lowland of Majorca and Ibiza have marked dispersion of farms and the major centres. By comparison the density of population in Minorca is sparse

the houses (outside Palma) were dispersed; today over a quarter of the Majorcan dwellings are isolated, aided by agriculture and tourism. Palma (117,000), however, dominates Majorca (350,000), in a way that no other island capital does in the western Mediterranean (Plate 84).

THE MALTESE ISLANDS

Although less than half the size of Ibiza, the Maltese islands (Malta, 92 sq. miles; Gozo, 24) have an importance out of all proportion to their area, because of their strategic position and their dense population. The group is situated almost in the middle of the Mediterranean about 60 miles south of Sicily and 180 north of the African coast. Malta boasts the highest density of population in Europe (2,623 per sq. mile) and for centuries the islands have not been a self-supporting community, on the few inches of soil that cap their barren limestones. Since 1530, when Malta was granted to the Knights of St John of Jerusalem, its revenues have been drawn from the whole of Western Christendom. From 1800, when the British occupation began, a similar, precarious situation has been maintained, creating an economy unique in the world. At the first known count in A.D. 991 Malta already had 21,000 persons and in 1590 the islands had 32,290. Then the population rose rapidly to 110,000 in 1741, but remained stagnant until the nineteenth century; 114,499 in 1842, 319,620 in 1957. Today, the extreme overpopulation, with a density on Malta of 3,075 per sq. mile, and on Gozo, of 1,024, is relieved by emigration, itself a big item of expenditure on a limited budget. More constant problems than military defence have been the maintenance of food supplies, fresh water and the soil. As early as 1567 the tax levied on imported wheat indicates the long period during which the islands have been dependent on outside food supplies. The Knights enforced an order that every house should have a water cistern attached to it, and they constructed the Wignacourt aqueduct (in 1610–15) from the western hills to Valletta. A law forbidding buildings being erected over *terra rossa* soil was made in this century. The tremendous pressure on resources of all kinds is thus evident in a highly artificial rural landscape (see Plate 81).

The Maltese islands are built on a series of faulted blocks of tabular Tertiary limestones, tilted to the east-south-east. Underlain by Lower Corallian limestone, which is exposed in coastal and valley outcrops, the islands are built chiefly of an intermediate Globigerina limestone and the Upper Corallian limestone. Sandwiched layers of blue clays and marls have little significance in the relief except in narrow bands of the hill slopes, but they constitute an impermeable layer which gives rise to springs and the most verdant part of the island. The Globigerina limestone weathers easily in softly undulating and low plateaux, over the southern and eastern half of Malta, where the soil is deeper and agriculture more intensive. Its tawny tone lends colour to every aspect of the countryside: the walled fields, the terraces and the settlements. The soil, rich in phosphates, explains the marked concentration of its population. The Upper Corallian limestone, more resistant to weathering, outcrops to the north and west in plateaux that rise to the highest

79 *Tuffoni* weathering in granite cliffs, Calanques of Piana, W. Corsica

80 Basalt plateau with *tacci*, Barbagia di Belvi, Sardinia

81 Small field in *terra rossa* depression in Upper Coralline Plateau, W. Malta. Note wind pump to raise irrigation water

82 Corsican village of Ocaña in chestnut zone, Col de San Alberto (1,700 ft.)

83 *Nuraghi* in W. Sardinia in typical position at the head of a valley

84 Palma de Mallorca, with castle of Bellver in distance

summit at 845 ft in the Rabat Ridge. This comprises the main water catchment and storage area for the island, with some 26 in of annual rainfall. North of the Grand Fault that transects these Corallian table-lands, the relief is largely controlled by parallel faults. Contrasted with the drowned rias in the east and south, the west coast is tilted steeply with cliffs rising to over 700 ft. Malta has three major

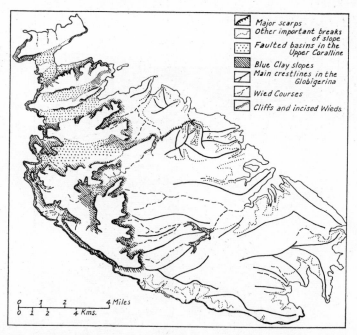

FIG. 240. Physiographic features of Malta. The island falls readily into two parts along the Victoria Lines fault, defined by the major escarpment that runs across the island between Ras-ir-Raheb to north-east of Gharghur. The outcrop of Coralline Limestone explains the high western plateaux at 600–800 ft. in contrast to the valley and basin lands surrounding them. The Globigerina Limestone in the centre and east is generally associated with lower and gentle relief

physiographic units: the western plateau sloping gently eastwards from 850 to 600 ft with an abrupt, scarped edge; the Rabal-Dingli plateau in the south and southeast, an area of subdued relief, with undulating hills and plains incised with water-courses (*widien*); and north of Lija a series of ridges separate wide, flat-bottomed valleys that runs W.S.W.–E.N.E. In Gozo, the same outcrops are more intimately mixed, with the low rolling relief of the Globigerina limestone, over-looked by the cliffed caps of Upper Corallian limestone.

W.M.W.—22

As 40 per cent of the islands is cultivated, the spontaneous vegetation is restricted, consisting chiefly of plants common to Sicily (94 per cent of species). Leguminous plants are the commonest, providing the pasturage of the dissected uplands, while some of the rocky valley slopes of the *widien* are covered in Malta heath (*Erica peduncularis*). Most of the area is bare and windswept, with small fields enclosed by walls,

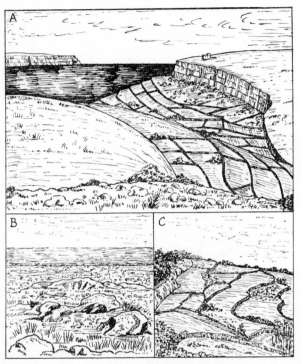

FIG. 241. Features typical of Maltese landscapes. (A) General view of west coast near Dingli Cliffs. (B) Karst surface of Upper Coralline Limestone. (C) terraces under cultivation of cereals, tomatoes and carobs

an occasional olive or carob tree, the frothy outline of prickly pear and the dotted silhouette of the wind pumps (Fig. 241). The landscape is largely the outcome of 'scirocco, sun and sweat', every field a terrace, every declivity a series of *campi artificiali*, and cultivated with the hoe. In the last hundred years, the cultivated land has extended to three times its original area (in 1842, 50,000 acres, in 1957 156,211). Holdings are very small and fragmented, the unit of land, the *tomna*, being equivalent to only 0·278 acre or 0·112 ha, and 82 per cent of all the holdings having less than 40 *tmien*. About half the cultivated area is under cereals (48 per cent in 1957), 38 per cent is vegetable gardens and only 4·8 per cent is irrigated. Because of the small size of the farms, more than half of the farm population is part-time on 25 per cent of the land. The standard of living is low with a third of the dwellings having only one or two rooms.

There is a marked contrast between the rural countryside and the great concentration of suburban population in the conurbation of the Harbours with towns of Three Cities, Valletta and Sliema, in which live 64 per cent of Malta's population (189,436 inhabitants in 1957, of a total of 292,019). This underlines Malta's dependence on its external relations. Valletta, the capital (18,202), with its elaborate fortifications built by the Grand Master La Vallette in the sixteenth century on Mt Sceberras, took the place of the Muslim capital of Medina in the interior of the island. Today, the suburbs of Sliema (23,399) now exceed the fortified city. In the rural areas, the village is the unit of settlement, clustering around the church which seems to have been the main social influence for nucleation. But in Gozo (27,601), where the villages are more a response to the former dangers of piracy, the compact semi-urban features of the Maltese villages are absent, forming instead loose agglomerations with their prickly pear gardens behind the houses. Compared with the other Mediterranean islands, the Maltese islands thus appear to be the most humanised product, as the catalyst of Mediterranean conquest.

PART V

NORTH-WEST AFRICA (THE MAGHREB)

CHAPTER 22

THE MAGHREB—ITS LANDFORMS AND ECOLOGICAL FEATURES

'From the humid Mediterranean to the desert, the Maghreb is a land
of violence and instability in all its nuances of space and time.
It is a marchland, where the structural and climatic influences
belonging to the Mediterranean realm engage in a struggle with the
rigidity and the aridity of the desert.'   (J. Dresch)

Only eight miles from Europe across the Straits of Gibraltar lies the
Maghreb, the most European sector of Africa. It shares with the
Mediterranean world a general architecture of fold mountains, similar
mosaics of landforms, the same temperate and changeable climate, and
a comparable sequence of mountain flora. Despite the cultural contact
of trans-Saharan trade, its population is still non-negroid. Thus the
Maghreb contrasts with the rest of Africa in numerous fundamental
respects. It is unlike the African continent in the absence of vast,
tabular relief and broad ecological zones. Indeed, to the Arab geographers, it was *Djezira el Maghreb*, 'the island of the West', isolated
from the rest of the continent by the greatest desert on earth. The
Sahara covers some four million square miles, and by comparison the
Maghreb's 200,000 sq. miles comprises only a narrow border, some 200
miles broad along the littoral where the Atlantic and Mediterranean
seas meet—a linear distance of some 1,400 miles between southern
Morocco and the Gulf of Gabès. The 'island' of the Maghreb is emphasised by the high relief of the Atlas ranges, which coincide with the areas
of heaviest rainfall and therefore of most luxuriant vegetation cover in
the whole of northern Africa. Like Syria, the Maghreb turns its back
upon the desert, and faces the sea. At least half of its territory may be
described as Mediterranean; the remainder is mostly steppe, ante-
chamber to the southern desert.

The three independent territories that make up the Maghreb today
have not had the long political history of the peninsulas of the Mediterranean. The name 'Africa' was first applied in classical times to
Tunisia and the adjoining High Plains of Constantine. This area has
always been the most exposed to alien influence, whether under the
Carthaginians, Romans, Arabs or Turks. On the contrary, Morocco

has been a most effective redoubt, sheltered from invasion by its formidable mountain ramparts. It still boasts the largest indigenous population (known to the Greeks as barbarians or Berbers), and it was the last of the three territories to submit to European colonialism (Fig. 61). More exposed to the relentless struggle between the desert and the sown, and therefore more disunited, Algeria has been traditionally, perhaps, the poorest realm of the Maghreb. Subjugated after the sixteenth century by the Turks and then by the French, it has gained its first political freedom only since 1961. Despite their uncertain division on socio-political grounds, the three territories have distinct environmental identity, notably in the structural foundations of their diverse and contrasted landscapes.

THE LANDFORMS

1. *The Structural Background.* Like the Iberian Peninsula, the Maghreb is a land of high relief, averaging 2,500–3,500 ft, except in the lowland extremities of the Atlantic littoral and eastern Tunisia. Mountain ranges of roughly parallel trend run from south-west to north-east, with a progressively younger age from the Anti-Atlas in the south to the Rif-Tell mountains in the north. This scheme is upset, however, in central Morocco, where the ancient Meseta block has guided the transverse north to south ranges of the Middle Atlas. Uplift has been the dominant feature in the structure of the Maghreb, reflected both in the variable lithology associated with the marine transgressions, and in the Tertiary mountain movements.

In Hercynian times, the Maghreb was peneplaned extensively.[1] Remnants of this landscape thrust through the surrounding cover of Meso-Tertiary rocks in the High Atlas,[2] and the Anti-Atlas as far as Tafilalet. Smaller outcrops occur in the Djebilet, Rehamna,[3] the northern borders of the Moroccan-Oran tableland, and in discontinuous blocks on the littoral between Ceuta and Edough. The latter are considered to be foreland remnants of the foundered Tyrrhenides continental block.[4] Since Mesozoic times, epicontinental seas have lapped over the borders of the African block shallower towards the Sahara and deepest in the Rif-Tell.[5] As the transgressions in the Tertiary became more limited, there has been a progressive southward retreat of these marine shorelines.[6] There is thus a vast range in the thickness of these sediments from 0 to 20,000 ft. Also, red sandstones, marls and limestones with abundant coral reefs predominate in the southern Maghreb, whereas slates and other schistose rocks, with marls and limestones poor in fossils are characteristic of the Rif-Tell, where bathymal conditions have tended to prevail.[7] The reef limestones in the southern and central mountains tend to produce a more resistant and therefore more simply folded Jurassic style of relief; whereas the generally plastic rocks of the Rif-Tell, associated notably with the saline Triassic clays, have given these northern mountains a more complicated architecture with nappes, and diaperic structures. A third major style of structure is represented by the ancient rocks of the Mesetas and the Anti-Atlas, where fracture rather than folding is responsible for the modern relief forms.

Tertiary orogenic movements have been long and complicated. Geologists divide these into two Pyrenean and three subsequent Alpine phases associated with the following periods: end of middle Eocene, upper Oligocene, mid-Miocene, late Miocene and Pliocene-Quaternary.[8] The first phase appears to have been the most violent, but intense erosion ensued, reflected in thick zones of flysch especially in the Rif-Tell. The first Alpine movements (mid-Miocene) were of major importance in the Rif and were localised in the Tell, when nappe formations developed. There were, however, stable areas in the Maghreb until the end of the Miocene, notably in eastern Tunisia, where the Saharan block approaches into the Mediterranean. There, fracture and subsidence have been characteristic of the Plio-Pleistocene movements[9] (Fig. 17). Troughs of subsidence occur elsewhere, especially along the littoral, such as at Bône, Mitidja, Oran,[10] Rharb[11] and Sous plains. Recent instability is further seen along lines of fracture by the Quaternary volcanics of the Moroccan Meseta, eastern Morocco and Oran. Indeed, it is the structural movements since the Pliocene that have given the Maghreb its actual configuration. Interspersed with these movements, peneplanation has occurred at several Tertiary periods, notably at the end of the Oligocene, in the Pontian,[12] and in Pliocene Villafranchian times.

2. *Climatic Morphology*. The landforms of North Africa have a number of distinctive features because of their location on a structural and climatic borderland. There is a striking contrast between the folded mountains and the more southern, arid and monotonous plateaux. The variety of lithological types in the fold mountains already mentioned emphasises their structural styles of relief, while the altitudinal zonation sharpens in detail the contrasts of glacial, pre-glacial and piedmont systems of erosion.[13] Very different are the landscapes that border the southern Maghreb. There the widespread coherent character of the rocks associated with the Meso-Tertiary transgressions, lying horizontal and undisturbed over the resistant shield, and under semi-arid climates for long geological periods, have combined to discourage active erosion. The Saharan climate border has undoubtedly fluctuated

since the tropical conditions of the Tertiary but it has never been far from its present position.[14] During the Villafranchian, a savannah climate prevailed in the Maghreb, but since then there has been a fluctuating deterioration to the present desiccation.[15] Although less radical than in northern and central Europe, the Quaternary changes of climate in the Maghreb have been no less significant for its landscapes, since even a difference of 5 inches of annual rainfall makes significant changes in the system of erosion.[16]

One of the most distinctive types of landform in North Africa is the pediment, whose origin is still a debated problem.[17] They occur both in the Rif and northern Tunisia—though heavily dissected by the heavier climatic conditions[18] (24–30 in)—and in the steppes of the south, where the annual rainfall is some 4–8 ins.[19] They occur only in areas where soft, homogenous rocks lie at the foot of landforms of hard rocks. Three structural types occur: in synclinal depressions often on a large scale, in anticlinal depressions where the relief has become inverted, and in numerous cases though more limited in scale, in monoclinal depressions. Given these structural conditions, it is understandable they should be associated with a semi-arid climate where the alternation of a dry season with intense evaporation is followed by one of violent rains. But they are fossil landscapes, elaborated during climates more humid than now, when the periglacial slope waste above could be removed downwards by more lateral movements. In ensuing interfluvials, the desiccation restricted downward movements to the well-fed wadi floors, and so linear erosion would predominate. These fragile landscapes have been preserved to a considerable extent by the formation of soil crusts, carbonate crusts under more humid conditions of rain wash and gypseous crusts under more arid conditions.[20] They are a vital document of the bioclimatic habitat, and from them six 'fluvials' have been identified in Morocco: Moulouyan, Saletian, Amitian, Tensiftian, Soltanian and Gharbian [21] (see Fig. 19). Towards the desert border, some of these are missing (for example Saletian in the Saharan foreland of Tunisia)[22] and over the hammadas four cycles or less are found.[23] This suggests that the so-called 'fluvials', cooler and wetter than today, became less marked towards the cooler south where semi-arid conditions still persisted. This has been substantiated by the few palynological studies that have been made (for example at El Guettar, near Gafsa).[24] These piedmont zones called *dir* in Morocco, *tell* in Algeria, are of vital importance to man. Always more favoured by water supply, they represent the main zone of villages and of arboriculture in much of the Maghreb, as well as being in the drier *dirs*, the zones of assembly (*azarar*) for the annual march in summer to the mountain pastures.

The distribution of *terra rossa* is another indicator of climatic significance. Büdel's studies in Algeria[25] and those of Mensching in Morocco,[26] indicate its association with the Mediterranean forests of the Tell and western Morocco. It is limited to areas of 15–20 in[27] and therefore associated with the fluvials which had more summer rainfall. Two of these have been particularly recognised (Würm-Soltanian, and Mindel?-Amirian). This fossil soil covers a wider area of central Morocco than the climatic area now suited to its development, but nowhere in North Africa does it extend as far south as the present Saharan foreland. In the mountains its limits are more difficult to discern (*c.* 6,300 ft in the Middle Atlas) as it is not always possible to determine whether it is a fossil or an active soil.

Evidence of climatic change is also apparent in the drainage systems. Youthful and disrupted, the rivers have irregular profiles,[28] with contrasted sectors of gorges and broad floodplains. More than half of Algeria and two-thirds of Tunisia are not drained to the sea (Fig. 243). Because of its generous water supplies from the mountains, Morocco has the major rivers, notably the Sebou, Oum er Rbia and Tensift. Plio-Pleistocene basins have been opened or captured, such as the basin of Meknes-Fez by tributaries of the Sebou, while the Moulouya, Cheliff and Medjerda have linked rosaries of small longitudinal basins. Further south, however, drainage is disrupted, consequent on the desiccation of the interpluvials. It is associated with such phenomena as the salt lakes of Algeria and Tunisia (*sebkha*) where flood waters evaporate in salt marshes, and rivers such as the O. Draa and O. Za now only occasionally exoreic.[29]

Glaciation has had only very limited importance in the highest mountains of the Maghreb, notably in the Middle Atlas (Bou Iblane) above 9,500–10,000 ft, and in the High Atlas (Ayashi) at 10,500–11,000 ft.[30] Elsewhere in the mountains, fossil forms of a periglacial type descend to as low as 6,000 ft in the High Atlas, 3,000 ft in the Middle Atlas and even lower in the Tell Atlas.[31] This has been fashioned especially in the Tensiftian fluvial (probable Riss equivalent) for the Würmian equivalent (Soltanian) is frequently 1,500 ft above the Tensift limit.[32] During these glacials the importance of aspect was greater than now, with sharp contrasts between the northern and southern flanks of the mountain chains. Below the periglacial zone, there is a broad zone in which pluvial solifluction has been active, checked below by the spread of forests during the last pluvial.

3. *Major Regional Units.* Because of the importance of climate in shaping the landforms of North Africa no structural divisions are an adequate basis for regional differentiation. Happily, the three-fold structural realms of the Rif-Tell, the Atlas and the Anti-Atlas coincide broadly with the climatic zones of the Mediterranean, the semi-arid lands, and the desert borderland, each with its distinctive systems of erosion today. Even where there are common structural, orographic and climatic affinities, the landscapes are very varied, so that it is impossible to deal with these other than in general terms.[33]

The Rif-Tell Mountains. Between Tangiers and Bizerta with a depth behind the coast that varies from forty to almost a hundred miles, are the mountain ranges of the Rif and Tell Atlas. These complex mountain chains have broadly two structural systems: the ancient massifs which occur discontinuously along the coast, and the folded mountains which occur *en echelon* throughout the zone, often separated from each other by major synclinal troughs (Fig. 242). The former has two major units: the western Rif, between Ceuta and Punta Pescadores, and the Great and Lesser Kabylia, together with minor units such as the Edough massif that overlooks Bône. They consist of schists, and other Palaeozoic rocks, deeply dissected, so that they are flanked by flysch beds, inter-penetrated by soft Miocene clays, and associated sometimes with Liassic and Jurassic limestones that stand out boldly in folded arches. These structures are a rugged terrain, with deep gorges, scarped coasts, and a chaos of steep hills which have long sheltered their Berber inhabitants.

The folded chains of the Rif and Tell are very complicated structures. Their Mesozoic rocks were laid down in bathymal conditions, in places interrupted by geanticlinal zones, and the underlying Triassic rocks have favoured nappes. Composed chiefly of soft strata, the zone consists of deeply dissected hills with only occasional mountain ranges. There are three distinct units: the Rif, the Algerian Tell and the Tunisian Tell.

The Rif is a dorsal of Cretaceous and Jurassic rocks where sandstones carry the highest summits (Tidighine, 8,040 ft) above broad plateaux. On their flanks, relief is dissected in a tangle of structures and varied rocks, with numerous Liassic nappes with karstic limestones, and flysch hills.[34] Towards the lower Moulouya trough, relief becomes simpler with plateaux of marly sandstones and limestones.[35] Along the lower Moulouya the presence of pediments, camels and nomadic tents suddenly indicate a small outlier of the Sahara close to the shores of the Mediterranean. Structurally also, it becomes impossible to trace the connection between the Rif and the Algerian Tell. Instead, the Quater-

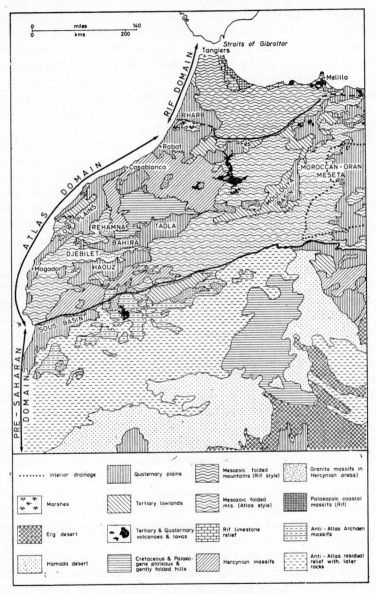

FIG. 242. Landscape types of Morocco

nary volcanoes of Melilla and in the Oujda plains are a dominant element (Fig. 242).

In the Algerian Tell, the striking feature is the longitudinal disposition of the ranges and plains.[36] For over two hundred miles runs the longitudinal trough of the Mleta plains, the Oran sebkha, the Habra-Rilizance plains and the lower Cheliff, tawny steppes similar to the landscapes of Murcia. Bordering them to the north are the discontinuous, complex structures of the Sahel d'Oran hills, the Cretaceous mountains of Miliana (Zaccar, Gharbi, 5,180 ft). South of the trough from west to east are a series of mountains: the Traras and Tessala.[37] Further inland, the plains of Tlemcen, Sidi bel Abbès and Mascara are strung along the foot of high plateaux (3,000–5,000 ft), which are deeply cut by gorges. Despite this, drainage is incomplete and Plio-Pleistocene rejuvenation marked, giving a markedly youthful character to the scenery, not seen in the eastern Tell of Algeria. East of the Cheliff plain, the Moroccan-Oran tableland disappears, and both the coastal and interior Tell ranges become much wider. These are the Dahra hills with their rocky sandstone coast, and the Ouarsenis, the backbone of western Algeria and most impressive mountain range whose crenulated bastion of limestone thrusts upwards to 6,538 ft. Further east, both systems of the Tell are interrupted by the broad synclinal basin of the Sahel of Algiers with its continuation in the Mitidja trough, sunk by Pliocene movements and then deepened by post-Villafranchian erosion.[38] Extending for some sixty miles, this landscape is the showpiece of European colonisation in North Africa. Backed by the mountainous barrier of the Blida Atlas to the south,[39] uplifted by the same movements that lowered the Mitidja, communications north to south are here very difficult. Finally, to the east lies the great limestone range of Djurdjura, whose grandiose scenery is sometimes called 'the little African Switzerland'.[40] This northern Tell range of Kabylia, is continued east of the Soummam valley by the crags and gorges of Lesser Kabylia, and beyond by the limestone hills and their transverse gorges that shut off the gulf of Bougie. Uplift since the Flandrian transgression, more prolonged erosion, and the more mature relief distinguish this eastern sector of the Algerian Tell.

From the vicinity of Bône eastwards, the character of the Tell changes, with the disappearance of the ancient massifs and the backbones of limestone. Instead, thick isoclinal folded sediments with lubricant intrusions of Triassic marls are the rule, and the trend of the ranges becomes more markedly south-west to north-east. Vigorous, structural relief is characteristic of the Algerian border, becoming more gently

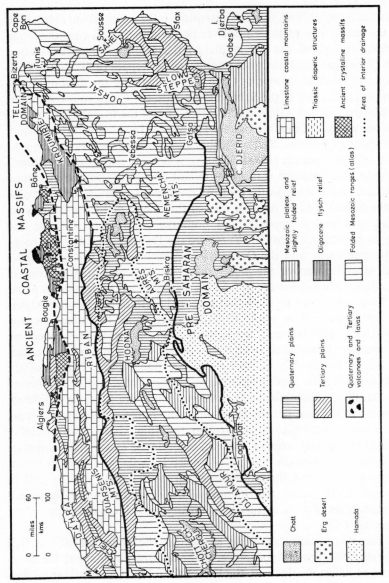

Fig. 243. Landscape types of Algeria and Tunisia

folded in sandstones and clays in the Kroumerie, but everywhere inversion of relief is marked.[41] The Medjerda has captured a series of lacustrine basins in its middle course of tectonic origin, to open up a longitudinal depression and aid intense erosion. Ancient gulfs have been infilled to provide the plains of Mateur, Bizerta and the lower Medjerda.

The Atlas Mountains. For some 1,200 miles from Agadir to Cape Bon, the Atlas system is wider, with generally simpler structures, monoclinal in its style of folding, with limestones and sandstones alternating with marls. The limit of these mountain systems with the Saharan foreland is clear and often abrupt, as the result of a system of fractures that date from the upper Pliocene (Fig. 17). In this realm there are also Hercynian blocks, fossilised and then rejuvenated, surrounded by the Atlas mountains.

The Rharb trough forms the border between the Pre-Rif mountain system and the Moroccan Meseta. These Miocene straits emerged in Pliocene times to isolate lake plains in Fez and Meknès districts, which have subsequently been dissected into a hilly terrain. North of them, the Pre-Rif is a confused relief of badlands and *frane* of early Tertiary clays and marls not dissimilar to the northern Apennines, but with short ranges influenced by underlying blocks.[42] East of Fez this swelling relief disappears, and the abrupt change of mountain trend lines, now aligned north to south, is associated with numerous evidences of recent volcanoes, where the Middle Atlas directly confronts the eastern Rif (Fig. 242). To the west, the Sebou river occupies the low-lying trough of the Gharb, still inundated by floods.

Between the Rif, Middle and High Atlas, is the Moroccan Meseta, with its varied landscapes[43] (Fig. 242). First, from Rabat to Marchand, some 60 miles inland is a low Atlantic plateau gently planed by several surfaces, and mostly cultivated. Inland, above 650 ft, is a series of plateaux (*gaada*), south and east of which abruptly rise a series of fault scarps that mark the rise into the Central Moroccan Plateau, domain of the wild Berber regions of Zemmout, Zaët and Zaïan (4,000–5,000 ft).[44] Its dissected plateaux and appalachian relief have been carved out of two anticlinoria, running south-west to north-east (Khouribga-Oulnès, and Kasba-Tadla-Azrou), separated by a synclinorium (Four-hal-Telt).[45] Dominated by J. Mtourzgane (5,200 ft), its eastern border has the same key-board, faulted front as the Sa Morena (p. 175). To the south, the ancient surface disappears under the mantle of Meso-Tertiary rocks, in the Plateau of Phosphates and in the vast, stoney courses of Upper Chaouïa. In the south-east, the Tadla plains occupy a

Pliocene lake floor, lined with the Srarhna plains by the middle basin of the Oum er Rbia. The Rehamna is a small replica of the central Meseta,[46] flanked by the dissected hercynian relief of the Djebilet. Beyond, lies a synclinal depression stretching from Mogador to the Haouz of Marrakech, an ancient chott now drained by the Tensift. Between Fédala and Mazagan are the rich Quaternary plains (*tirs* and *hamris*) of lower Chaouïa, a monotonous expanse of grainlands.[47] These extend south of the Oum er Rbia, into the even broader plains of the Doukkala, bordered on the coast by widespread fossilised dunes. The former marine gulf of Sous, enclosed by the High Atlas and Anti-Atlas, is a distinctive region.

Separating the Moroccan, western Meseta from the eastern or Oran Meseta, is the complex mountain barrier of the Middle Atlas, some 180 miles in length. Like the French Jura, it has two major features. To the east, run a series of parallel, wide anticlinal folds with the highest relief (D. Bon Naceur, 11,000 ft and D. Bon Iblane, 10,470 ft) separated by broad depressions.[48] To the west, the limestone relief is more tabular, with a sequence of high, karstic plateaux which extend from the borders of the Zaïan plateau to the Taza corridor in the north. They are occasionally capped by small volcanic cones and lava flows, notably at Timhadit and El Hajeb.

To the south lies the greatest mountain range of the Maghreb, the High Atlas, which runs 450 miles from Cape Ghir on the Atlantic coast to the eastern borders of Morocco, separated abruptly from the realm of the Anti-Atlas to the south by a series of faults and flexures.[49] The col of Telouet at the watershed of the Tensift and Dra divides these mountains into two distinct sectors. The western High Atlas rising above the Atlantic, consists of ridged, limestone plateau, with high cliffs above the sea, cuestas and depressions, notably the transverse cut of N' Fis. In the centre of this sector, ancient crystalline rocks rise in tabular ranges of 10,000–13,000 ft, not dissimilar to the central Pyrenees. Very different are the eastern ranges with broad, abruptly folded ranges, often faulted. Perched synclinal summits, bordered by magnificent scarps exceed 11,500 ft, but the highest are anticlinal peaks (Ayachi, 12,300 ft) whose glaciated summits give them a more alpine appearance than those of the western ranges (Plate 5).[50]

Between the High and Middle Atlas to the east lies depressed the Moroccan-Oran Meseta and its continuation in the High Plains of Algeria (Fig. 243). Drained in the west by the Moulouya west-south-west to east-north-east limestone folds isolate small narrow plains such as those of Zelouane and Triffa, near the Mediterranean. Further south, the high plains (*c.* 1,500 ft) of Oujda form an important corridor between Algeria and Morocco, overlooked by recent, dissected volcanoes. Further south and eastwards, the plains widen and rise in the high plateaux of Dahra to 3,600–4,250 ft[51] with enclosed basins occu-

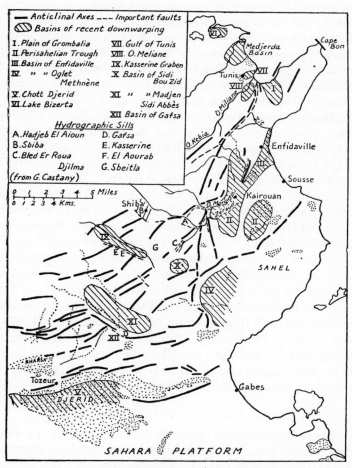

FIG. 244. Basins and sills of Tunisia

pied by chotts (Rhatbi and Chergui).[52] The Moulouya to the west has linked a series of alluvial basins, whose borders have been deeply dissected and flanked by widespread pediments.[53] To the east,[54] the gently undulating relief stretches in a monotonous spread of 500 miles, the ruined remnants of folded structures. More than half of it is the realm of *sebalch* with no drainage outlet to the sea. About one-fifth consists of small massifs that rise 1,000–2,000 ft above the plains. Indications of its folding are seen in the Ksour and Amour and Ouled Nail mountains, also known as the Saharan Atlas, an extension of the eastern High Atlas. These are anticlinal ranges of Jurassic rocks, which in the eastern range of Zab enclose the depression of Hodna (Plate 86).[56] Atlas trend lines meet obliquely the normal south-west to north-east grain, in the upraised Aurès massif which reaches 7,630 ft in Chelia.[57] Although folds influence its mountainous relief, the block has been upraised by Plio-Pleistocene movements, rejuvenating its Oligo-Miocene fossilised relief. Eastwards the southern folds of the Atlas divide central Tunisia into two, between the Dorsal and the Gafsa mountains. Here as Castany has shown a series of grabens have been developed by Plio-Pleistocene faulting (Fig. 244), notably the Kairouan and Grombalia, basins.[58] Here the juxtaposition of the Atlas and Pre-Saharan structures have had striking tectonic and morphological results.

The Anti-Atlas. The realm of the Pre-Sahara commences thus in Tunisia with the shallow waters of the Gulf of Sirte, the islands of Kerkena and Djerba, and the landward continuation in the basins of the Tunisian Sahel.[59] But it is at the other extremity of the Maghreb, where the Anti-Atlas of Morocco, shows most dramatically the edge of the Saharan or African block. Composed of some of the most ancient folded rocks of the earth's crust, these have been raised and levelled many times, until finally uplifted in Pliocene times into a spectacular asymmetric range.[60] Rugged crests of quartzite rise over 6,000 ft (Djebel Akhri, 8,300 ft), with Palaezoic limestones and sandstones providing uniform plateaux overlooking the Sous basin, while to the south the beds (*jebel*) dip steeply to provide a sequence of cuestas (*kreb*) that overlook the desert hamadas (Plate 87).[61]

THE CLIMATE AND WATER RESOURCES

The climate of the Maghreb appears at first glance simply a hotter and generally a drier version of that experienced through the western Mediterranean, because of its southerly latitudes of 37–29°. The influence of the Sahara, the east-west orientation of its relief, and its position along the Mediterranean appear clearly as geographic controls. However, its regional features are much more complex. The Saharan influence almost reaches to the coast in the lower Moulouya valley. But everywhere else, the generally east-west grain of the Maghreb, made emphatic by the mountainous relief, sharpens the contrast between the Mediterranean littoral, with its winter rains and milder temperatures, and the interior with its more brutal, continental regime of spring rains and excessively hot summers. Regional differences are further made by the contrast between the warm waters of the Mediterranean, notably the shallow waters in the Gulf of Gabès that promote secondary cyclonic storms in autumn, and the cold waters off the Atlantic coast of Morocco with its fogs and dew-fall. Morocco benefits from its position to receive rainfall from both south-westerly and westerly air masses, while Tunisia also facing the sea on two flanks has reasonable precipitation. Algeria hemmed in between, sheltered on the leeside of the Moroccan mountains and in Oran also by the plateaux of the Iberian Peninsula, is much more poorly off. Although vitally important to the creation of its landscapes and the welfare of its peoples, these regional differences are not the essential feature of the Maghreb's climate. For the seasonal rhythm of its climate and the weather changes are very largely controlled by the aerological conditions of the upper air above 500 mb. These in turn are conditioned by distant planetary controls which Pédelaborde has discussed.[62] For if the climate of western Europe at ground level may be said to be dependent on extraneous circumstances, the climate of North Africa may be described as dependent at height.[63] Upper air conditions thus play a vital rôle in the ground level variations of weather in the Maghreb.

Briefly the position is that in winter, North-West Africa is dominated by storms associated with the Polar front, whose cold air masses reach the Maghreb from both continental or maritime areas, depending upon the position of the Azores and the Euroasiatic anticyclones.[64] It is then that the Mediterranean may become a cause of enormous vertical instability, but whether this is of widespread or local extent depends upon the incursions of cold air. The fronts affecting the Maghreb however, are less vigorous than those of western Europe, and are much more dependent on conditions in the middle troposphere. This explains why a cyclonic pattern near ground level may not necessarily provoke rainfall. There is thus greater unreliability of both seasonal and total annual precipitation, compared with conditions in the northern Mediterranean. In summer, polar air still prevails over the Maghreb as the tropical front never actually reaches the area, but it is stagnant air, rapidly heated. Any contact with air masses of different origin produces a border not a front. Under these summer conditions, thermal depressions of the Saharan surface air, may cause local convectional storms, but the anticylonic conditions at height quickly redress the situation.[65]

Temperatures are more influenced by the sea along the Maghreb littoral, than by latitude. Winters there are mild, with January means of

51·6° (10·9) at Gabès, 54·1° (12·3) at Tangiers and 53·0° (11·7) at Casablanca, while summers are not too hot: August mean monthly temperatures are 81·5° (27·5), 74·6° (23·7) and 73·0° (22·8) respectively. Mogador
has a notably low mean annual range of only 12·2° (6·8), because of the
efficiency of the cold Canaries current offshore. Inland the range of
temperature increases markedly, with cold winters and very hot summers: Meknes 31·8° (17·3) and Taza 35·7° (19·8). Troughs shut off from
the sea and exposed to the desiccating influence of foehn-like winds, such
as the Medjerda valley, can shiver in winter and sizzle in summer:
Souk el Arba, January mean 48·5° (9·2) and July mean 82·5° (28·1).[66]
When the hot desert winds blow in summer temperatures may even
reach 125° (52). Towards the desert, the dry air exaggerates the diurnal
range of temperature, which is greatest in summer.

Because of orographic controls, the Maghreb is a windy area. Mountain winds (*djebili*) are foehn-like in their desiccating effects, when
depressions pass along the Mediterranean coast. In summer, easterly
winds in Morocco (*Chergui*), southerly elsewhere (*Chehili*) may sweep
the whole of the Maghreb with dry furnace heat and choking dust from
the Sahara or Algerian Plateaux, or may follow restricted gaps through
the Atlas, to affect more localised districts. Such conditions are produced when an anticyclonic ridge is situated north of the Maghreb and
an easterly current of air sweeps over the country.[67]

Drought is the most fundamental character of the Maghreb. The dry
summer begins usually in the first half of June or late May, and lasts
until late September. There is no autumn season, but the spring is
marked in the interior by having the maximum precipitation falling in
spring along the littoral, the interior has 40 per cent or more, notably
in Serson, the High Plains of Constantine,[68] and eastern Morocco,
reaching a maximum of 58 per cent at Outat Oulad El Hadj in the upper
Moulouya.[69] In these sectors, the lee-shadow effect of the mountains of
Oursensis, Kabylia and the Middle Atlas respectively, exaggerates their
continentality so that in winter local anticyclones of thermal origin
minimise precipitation, while in spring and summer ascendant air
currents provoke convectional storms. In these mountain areas, summer storms are particularly common, even with hail in the higher altitudes. Between these two zones of the littoral and the interior, there is a
transitional zone with 30–40 per cent of its precipitation occurring in
spring and summer. Highest amounts of annual precipitation are closely
related to the relief, with over 30 inches in the Rif (Djebala), the northern Middle Atlas, and the Tell between Algiers and Bizerta. Next in
importance are the coastal hills and plains between Mazagan and

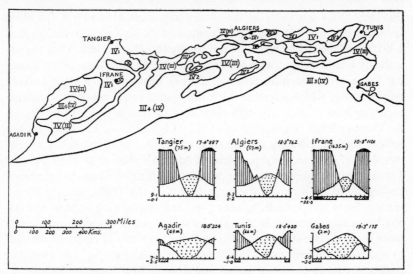

Fig. 245. Climatic regions of the Maghreb (after Walter and Lieth). For explanation of numerals and climatic graphs see Fig. 86 (p. 200)

Nabeul, where the amounts vary between 15 and 27 in. The rest, or two-thirds of the Maghreb, have less than 15 in so that there drought is a constant menace (Fig. 8).

Because of relief, the climatic regions show little zonation, and the area of typical Mediterranean conditions is irregular and discontinuous (Fig. 245). It commences near Tunis, invades deeply into the Tunisian Tell continuing westwards to the borders of the Cheliff basin.[70] There, a more arid type prevails along the coast as far as the western Rif. The Mediterranean type finally disappears on the coast of lower Chaouïa, although inland it comprises much of the higher relief of the Atlas. The transitional, semi-arid climates bordering the deserts show clearly both the effects of a more southerly latitude and more important the leeward influence of the mountains, notably in the Moulouya valley (Fig. 245). True mountain climates are much more limited than a casual inference might suggest. They are restricted to small areas in the northern sector of the Middle Atlas, the south central mountains of the Rif, and the summits of the Ouarsensis (Fig. 245). These have winter snow for four to five months above 8,000 ft and above 10,000 ft frost occurs for eight to nine months of the year.[71] The other mountain areas have a humid Mediterranean climate with seven to nine months with adequate moisture.

Water resources in a land of such uncertain rainfall are at a premium.

But they differ markedly in the three territories. Morocco is the most favoured because of its Atlantic façade and its high mountains, so that it boasts of the major rivers of the Maghreb. The Middle Atlas is particularly well endowed with water resources, its limestone cover allowing for a probable infiltration of 20 per cent of the annual surface precipitation, which together with the winter snow cover in high altitudes, assures a relatively high river flow in summer: 35–45 m³/sec on the Oum er Rbia (greatest river of the Maghreb) and 15 m³/sec on the Sebou. Even a tributary stream such as the O. Fès (Sebou) has a summer flow of 4 m³/sec the equivalent of Algeria's chief river, the Cheliff.[72] These water resources together with over 60 m³/sec recoverable from underground resources in the great basins of the Triffa, Rharb, Tadla, Haouz, Sous and Tafilelt, have encouraged the development of ambitious irrigation schemes. In Algeria, however, water resources are much more limited. The steep gradients and short courses of many of the Tell rivers, result in very rapid discharge, so that the Cheliff for example, discharges seven-tenths of its annual flow in four months. Moreover, the chief utilisable resources lie to the west with its lower rainfall respresenting one-fifth of the Tell discharge.[73] Erosion and consequent silting of the dams constructed is the hydrological problem of Algeria

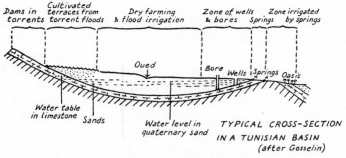

FIG. 246. Typical cross-section of a Tunisian basin

so that the future of major dams is uncertain, especially as the expense of their construction to withstand enormous floods is most uneconomic. In Tunisia, not much reliance can be placed on the rivers as the main source of water. Even the largest river, the Medjerda, has such an irregular outflow that two years' flow has to be stored by its dams. However, the Quaternary basins are extensive and rich in sub-surface water. These are now being investigated and exploited with thoroughness.[74] They already produce over 10 m³/sec. (see pp. 35–6).

SOILS AND VEGETATION

As elsewhere, the classification and nomenclature of soils is in a confused state in the Maghreb.[75] With the sagacity of peasant experience, the native terms are numerous, ranging from the red sandy soils of the *r'mel* to the diversified terra rossa light varieties of *hamri* and the black soils *tirs* and other clayey types *tin*. In the mountains, the skeletal soils are known after the relief, such as *djebel* and *tell*. Soils protected from erosion on plateaux surfaces are called *sra*. Thin, stoney soils *haroucha* cover vast areas of the steppe. Like the saline soils (*chott*) they are virtually useless for agriculture. The geological correlation of soils and of erodibility shows very varied conditions,[76] but climatically the soils may be simplified into three major types. In the Mediterranean zone, where the rainfall is above 15 inches or below 3,000 or 4,000 ft, red soils prevail except in areas of recent alluviation or of marked erosion. In the areas above this altitude, especially where the forest has been preserved, brown soils are common though not always permitted to mature. In the semi-arid lands with under 15 in of annual rainfall, a chernozem type evolves under a rich vegetation of dwarf palm and associated plants, but where the steppes are exposed, with scattered alfa, a variety of arid soils occurs, characterised by marked deposition of calcium carbonate. In the Maghreb, where the gap between the forest and the desert is relatively narrow, especially on the southern flanks of the Atlas mountains, very little disturbance is needed to start a chain of processes that lead to irrevocable degradation of the vegetation cover and therefore to the erosion of the soils.

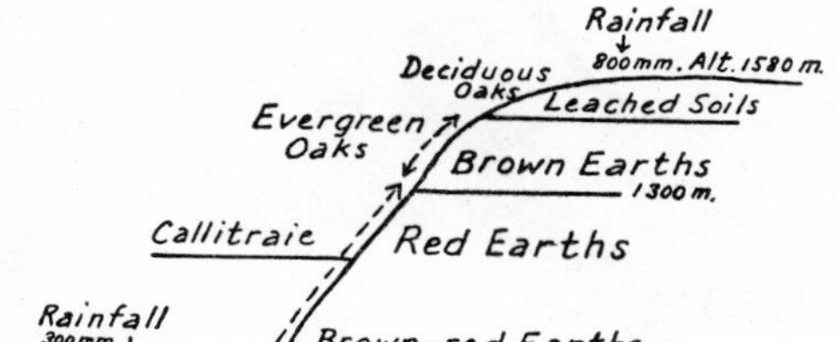

One is accustomed to view the vegetation cover of Mediterranean landscapes in terms of its tree species. This is much less significant in the Maghreb

FIG. 247. Altitudinal sequence of soils and vegetation in the mountains of Oran (from Aubert and Monjauze)

where the destruction of the forest cover has been so extensive.[77] This exaggerates the aspect of aridity in the landscapes. Five biogeographical zones may be distinguished: the mountain or subalpine, the humid and subhumid Mediterranean, the semi-arid, the arid and the Saharan (Fig. 248).[78]

No part of the Rif is above the climatic tree-line which is at 7,050 ft in the Djurdjura,[79] and 9,200 ft or higher in the Middle and High Atlas.[80] But the lower limits of trees have been much interfered with and modified by man. Subalpine conifers, associated with juniper (*J. thurifera*), reach 10,000 ft in the High Atlas, which alone has an alpine plant zone. Relict flora of firs are found on the high Rif summits related to species of Andalusia.[81] On the high slopes, firs are never pure, but mixed with deciduous oaks, maritime pines and notably cedars. The scattered distribution of deciduous oaks is difficult to explain (*Q. tozae, Q. lusitanica*) though both seem calcifuge. They are probably Pleistocene relicts. The cedar forests (*cedrus atlantica*) are North Africa's most valuable source of timber, found chiefly in the Rif, Middle and High Atlas, and more isolated on some of the highest summits in Algeria, especially on the leeward slopes.[82] The cedar is sensitive to the loss by erosion of the detrital mantle, demonstrated in certain areas of the eastern Middle Atlas by the retreat of the cedar with the erosion of the Quaternary covering and the advance of Aleppo pines on the denuded marly schistose slopes.[83] It may be for the same reason that the Aleppo pine is so important a feature of the Tunisian and Algerian Tell,[84] once more restricted to an intermediate zone between cedars

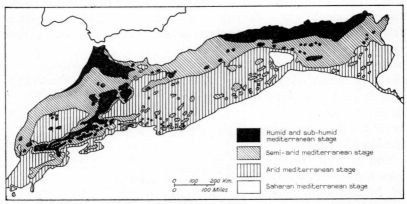

FIG. 248. The bioclimatic stages of vegetation in the Maghreb (from Emberger)

and Mediterranean evergreens. Where the oak (*Quercus faginea = Q. lusitanica*) combines with cedar, in the northern Middle Atlas, are the thickest forests of the Maghreb, quite different from any others.[85]

The Mediterranean flora in the Maghreb is typically associated with the holm oak (*Q. ilex*) though it does not form forests as for example the Aleppo pine or cedar. Emberger estimates it is spread over some

700,000 ha of Morocco, perhaps less than half of its primordial range,[86] but still occupying over one-third of the wooded cover. As such it is the commonest tree of the Maghreb except in Tunisia, with extensive woodlands on the western slopes of the Middle Atlas, the southern border of the central Meseta, on the north and west of the High Atlas, the plateaux of eastern Morocco and Oran, and widespread in the eastern Tell. In the better watered areas, such as the coastal flanks of the Tell, it may be associated with dense undergrowth of pistacia (*P. lenticus*), laurel, *Phillyrea* and *Cistus*,[87] while in the more arid regions such as the mountains of Aurès, Hodna Ksour and southern High Atlas, it is associated with junipers (*J. thurifera*) and alfa (*Stifa terracissima*). The cork oak which is more neatly limited to a minimum of 15 in annual rainfall, appears on schistose and sandy soils. It occurs well preserved in the forest of Tabarka, unique in Tunisia, and notably in the Mamora (137,000 ha) north of Rabat, the largest cork forest in the world.[88]

Below the holm oak in the mountains and in drier situations than the cork oak extends the thuya or sandarac tree (*Callitris articulata*). Thuya formations appear in the highlands of Tunisia and over the Oran province, but Morocco is the chief domain of this tree. There this Tertiary relict tree is important in the western High and Middle Atlas ranges, in the Rif, and even in the Anti-Atlas. But its value as an aromatic timber and its slow growth have made it vulnerable, despite its remarkable powers of survival.

In the semi-arid Mediterranean stage, shrub vegetation is most common, dominated by dwarf palm or palmetto (*Chamaerops humilis*) and the xerophytic camel thorn (*Zizyphus lotus*) which are sometimes divided into two distinct formations. The former is usually associated with the wild olive (*Olea oleaster*) and the Atlantic turpentine tree (*Pistacia atlantica*), to form a dominant plant association of *Oleo-Lentiscetum*. In Oran and much of Morocco, notably the Rif, this *tirs* of Chaouïa and Doukkala, and in much of the Sebou, the *palmetto* is dominant, the source of local fibre, and a distinct trait of landscapes that are ablaze in spring with the colours of herbaceous plants. In eastern Algeria and Tunisia the dwarf palm is less prominent and its associates, the wild olive and turpentine tree, may form dense thickets. The stunted nature of the so-called dwarf palm is probably recent in historic times, since it can grow 15–25 ft high. Another relict tree is the Barbary almond or argan (*Arganier spinosa*), an evergreen, olive-like in appearance that has an average height of 18 to 25 ft (Plate 16). It is concentrated specially in south-western Morocco (over some 400,000 ha). It is the degraded relict of a tropical family (*Sapotaceae*), which formed more extensive and much thicker savannah, associated with the Canaries (Macronesian).[89] Elsewhere in the semi-arid zone, the thorn scrub is dominated by *Zizyphus lotus* where drupe or 'lotus bread' may be an important food when cereal stocks are exhausted.[90]

Steppe formations in the Saharan realm are typified by alfa grass (*Stipa tenacissima*), together with such plants as esparto grass (*Lygeum spartum*) and dwarf sage (*Artemisia herba alba*). Southwards, away from the mountains, the flora become more and more sparse, except along the wadis where gum acacia (*Acacia gummifera*) and other tropical species (*A. seyal, A. tortilis*), worm-wood (*Artemisia*) and a sumac (*Rhus oxyacanatha*) are more common. But perhaps the best indicator of an underlying water-table is invariably *Zizyphus lotus*.[91] In the more humid areas of the steppe the spread of Barbary figs (introduced since the sixteenth century), is as typical in the landscape as the palm trees are in the oasis. However, this is no longer the realm of the Mediterranean but of the desert.

CHAPTER 23

THE MAGHREB—ITS RURAL LANDSCAPES, POPULATION AND SETTLEMENT

by John I. Clarke

The rural economies of the Maghreb do not present simple adaptations to environment. Their complex patterns are explicable only with reference to the varied succession of external forces which have so greatly influenced the economic evolution of the Maghreb. Nevertheless, the climatic transition from the Mediterranean to the Sahara has undoubtedly conditioned the distribution of rural economies. The gradual transition between a zone of winter rainfall and one of almost total drought cannot be classified easily into east–west zones, partly because of the interference to the gradation wrought by the east–west orientation of mountain ranges, and partly because of maritime conditions affecting Atlantic Morocco and eastern Tunisia. And yet the north–south transition has been a vital concept to North Africans, especially Algerians, who have long distinguished between *tell* and *sahara*. The *tell* corresponded with those heavy well-watered soils giving fairly regular harvests of cereals, pastures which are not entirely scorched in summer, and tree crops which can be grown without irrigation. In Algeria, at least, all that is not *tell* was considered *sahara*: the parched light sandy soils which give very unreliable harvests, which cannot sustain summer crops without irrigation, and which are the scene of pastoral nomadism. In Tunisia, a modification to this contrast is apparent; the eastern low steppe behind Sousse and Sfax supports large areas of olive plantations, as a result of humid maritime conditions and dry farming techniques. At the other extremity of the Maghreb in Morocco, the interdigitation of plains, plateaux and mountain massifs disrupts simple climatic transitions, so traditional regionalism results more from political conditions than climatic criteria: the *Bled es siba* was the land of dissidence and independence in the plateaux, and contrasted with the *Bled el makhzen*, the plains which were under the domination of the reigning sovereign.

Although the contrast between *tell* and *sahara* is too simple on morphological and ecological grounds (see pp. 648–9), the broad concept of Mediterranean and steppe domains[1] throws light on many aspects of the social, economic and political evolution of the Maghreb: the close juxtaposition of nomadic and sedentary societies and their inter-dependence for pastures and products; the varied forms of pastoral nomadism; the limited extent of stable cultivation except in mountain massifs; the south–north orientation of tribal movements; the political domination of the Maghreb by nomadic groups; the resulting political instability and lack of unity; the fluctuating fortunes of towns; the inadequate security for the prolonged extension of irrigation systems ... The persistence of pastoral nomadism owes much to the fact that four-fifths of the Maghreb lie outside the Mediterranean climatic zone.

CHANGING PATTERNS OF LAND-USE

One remarkable feature of the Maghreb is the survival of diverse forms of rural economy representing distinct phases of historical evolution. The past of rural Maghreb is recorded to some extent more as an anth-ology than as a palimpsest. Traditional modes of life and modern commercial economies form intricate patterns. Anachronistic forms of semi-nomadism brush shoulders with extensive arboriculture, subsist-ence cropping adjoins intensive viticulture, densely populated mountain massifs overlook sparsely populated plains.

No understanding of the patterns of land-use is possible without analysis of historical phases and the perception and utilization of the North African environment by its divers invaders. Greeks, Phoenicians, Romans, Berbers, Arabs, Turks, Spaniards, Portuguese, Frenchmen and Italians all viewed the economic possibilities of the Maghreb differently, according to their separate cultural traditions and political and economic aims. They came as cultivators and colonists, traders and town-dwellers, nomads and proselytisers, rulers and tax-collectors, conquerors and devastators, pillagers and pirates ..., and influenced the rural landscapes of the Maghreb in different ways. Some trans-formed entire regions; some left scant visible traces. Few extended uniform dominion or influence over the whole of the Maghreb. There were always pockets of resistance: cultivators to nomads, nomads to colonizers, ports to pirates. Some areas, towns or tribes were able to retain their identity midst a turmoil of changes. Mountain massifs and offshore islands, in particular, have assisted conservation of modes of life and have given refuge to the oppressed and the weak; plains, on the other hand, have witnessed much more movement and change.

Recent changes in the perception and utilization of the environment have resulted from the termination of French and Spanish rule. The independence gained by Morocco and Tunisia in 1956 and Algeria in 1962 has enabled governments to re-assess environments and economies in a new light and to propose important modifications. Rarely before have North Africans been masters of their own destiny.

1. *The Berbers.* The Berbers offer one of the best examples of the persistence of modes of life. Displacing the earliest inhabitants of the Maghreb in pre-classical times, the Berbers were the first to cultivate cereals, and bred domestic animals, notably sheep, horses and dogs. In Neolithic times they were probably more mobile than today, still engaging in pastoralism as well as hunting; large fauna were more

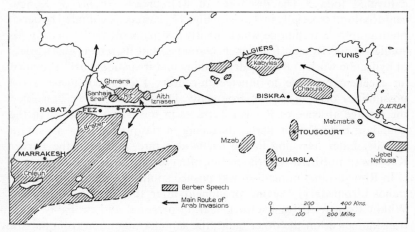

FIG. 249. The areas of Berber speech in the Maghreb (mainly after M. W. Mikesell)

numerous than now, as suggested by archaeological discoveries, especially of rupestrian art. Although there are many Berber nomads in the Sahara, the vast majority of Berbers in the Maghreb are now sedentary and have retained the customs and traditions of a rural society. They have conserved their traditions, despite ethnic mixtures with invading peoples particularly Arabs, largely because of their isolation and concentration in the more mountainous parts of the Maghreb (Fig. 249). Many of their agricultural techniques have not advanced much since antiquity,[2] since they were taught the principles of arboriculture by the Carthaginians: how to care for the vine, fig and olive. Tools, terracing, irrigation, house-types and fortified granaries have changed little. Only those Berbers living on the plains or within easy access of the towns have accepted the Arab and Andalusian introductions of new crops and later arrivals of American plants. As for Berber pastoralists, they have conserved their old techniques, but have adopted the fat-tailed sheep, brought by the Arabs, as well as the hair tent.

2. *Rural Maghreb under Rome.* The Roman occupation of the Maghreb was slow (146 B.C.–A.D. 40) and, as indicated by the *limes*, extended over only one-half of the total area. Agricultural and urban developments within this zone diminished in intensity from east to west, from the province of Proconsular Africa through Numidia and Caesarian Mauritania to Tingitanian Mauritania. By dry farming methods olive cultivation spread over vast areas of steppe (Fig. 44), some of which lies uncultivated today.[3] The discovery of widespread remains of Roman centuriation,[4] especially in Tunisia (Fig. 47), has been facilitated by aerial photography, a technique which greatly assisted Colonel Baradez in his studies of the Roman frontier in Numidia, and its remarkable variety of hydraulic works.[5] Roman dry farming and irrigation works provided an excellent example to nineteenth-century French colonists of the possibilities of semi-arid environments. Despois,[6] however, has noted the strange absence of Roman Terraces in the *tell*, in contrast to the abundant examples of Berber terracing in the pre-Saharan mountain massifs. Later terracing in the *tell* is also rare, and even the Berber Kabyles of northern Algeria do not often terrace their slopes.

In Roman times nomadism was pushed south of the *limes*, where the camel (dromedary) became prominent after the third century A.D.[7] Within Roman Africa livestock rearing persisted and probably some transhumance; on the other hand, the summer migration from Sahara to *tell* was made difficult by the *fossatum*.

3. *Arab invasions and Islam.* The next historical phase to leave a permanent mark on the landscapes of the Maghreb was the Arab conquest of the seventh century. About 150,000 men were involved, who started a rapid process of islamisation but much slower arabisation. A century and a half of troubles ensued, but in Ifrikiya, the eastern Maghreb, there was a revival of agriculture and urban life. The olive and the vine flourished. New crops of oriental and tropical origin were introduced: mulberry, rice, sugar cane, cotton, apricots, bitter oranges, artichokes, spinach, henna, indigo and saffron—crops which require watering. Irrigation techniques were developed, and many systems once thought to be Roman have been shown to date from the Aghlabite and Fatimite dynasties. In particular, the gardens of Kairouan, the prosperous capital of the Aghlabites and later the Zirids, benefited from hydraulic works constructed at this time. Unfortunately the Maghreb never

experienced irrigated agriculture comparable with that which flourished in Spain. In the central Maghreb, nomadism was more persistent and urban life more restricted. In Morocco, however, dynasties established their capitals on the plains; the Almoravids built Marrakesh in 1062 and introduced *foggara* (*rhettara*) to the Maghreb.

Though rooted in the towns, Islam permeates most aspects of rural life. It has meant, for example, the absence of the pig (and, indirectly, the prevalence of the goat) and the restricted use of oak forests. However, it did not entirely prevent the cultivation of the vine,[8] nor did it extinguish maraboutism, the belief in saints. Many tribes in the Maghreb have enjoyed the benevolence of neighbours through claiming to be maraboutic, or descended from a holy man.

One of the most significant aspects of islamisation in rural Maghreb was the spread of a tenurial system sufficiently supple to adapt itself to local environments, as well as to incorporate many Berber customs and even Roman rules. Moslem law recognises as 'live' those lands which are occupied and worked, and as 'dead' those which belong to no one and are considered as waste. Four main types of tenure are recognized:–

- (a) *Melk* or *mulk* is private property of individuals or families— freehold land or trees growing on the land—and is common only near towns and in certain mountain areas such as Kabylia and the Aurès. Unfortunately, the lack of written records causes confusion over titles.

- (b) *Arch* or *sabega* lands belong to tribes or groups in communal tenure, and prevail in the steppe zone. They are inalienable, but members of the tribe pay a special tax as rent (*hokkor* in E. Algeria, *gherrama* in W. Algeria, *karadj* in Tunisia).

- (c) *Habous*, known as *waqf* in the Middle East, also became widespread in the Maghreb. It is the institution of Muslim endowments; all or part of the revenue is devoted to religious and charitable purposes, such as the construction and upkeep of mosques, schools, clinics and wells. Private *habous* are entails, administered by *mokkadem* or trustees, and only become public *habous* on the death of the last heir. Public *habous* are administered by the *djemaa*, or meeting of family chiefs, and are worked by officials called *oukils*. In Morocco, public *habous* were often called *naïba* lands, as *naïbs* were the representatives of the *djemaa* charged with supervising the *oukils*.

- (d) *Beylik* or *makhzen* lands are domains of the state or the ruler. These forms of land tenure have experienced substantial modifications only during the last decade.

The invasions from Egypt in the eleventh century by the nomadic tribes Beni Hillal and Beni Solaym were much less profitable to the Maghreb than the earlier Arab invasions. The immigrants came, as Ibn Khaldun the Berber historian relates, like a 'wave of locusts'. Their violence and destruction denuded the countryside, confined cultivation to isolated localities, especially in the overpopulated mountains, and ensured the predominance of pastoral nomadism on the plains. Wheeled transport disappeared, except in the Sahel of eastern Tunisia, a rare example of the survival of a sedentary peasant community in the lowlands.

Towns grew and flourished in the eastern and western parts of the Maghreb as the temporary capitals of changing dynasties. But the rift between town and country was marked, and the economic basis for stable monarchy was flimsy. This was specially true for the central Maghreb where nomadism was dominant and towns few; facts which undoubtedly caused the continued political fragmentation of the Maghreb as well as its economic backwardness. Indeed, one of the principal objects of the numerous subsequent kingdoms in the Maghreb, and later of the Turkish rulers, was to keep the nomads at bay; this task was only partially achieved but some measure of economic balance was established between nomads and cultivators.

No further invasion transformed the Maghreb before the nineteenth-century, but piracy and perpetual internecine struggles prevented a revival in rural life. Little agricultural expansion took place, except under the stimulus of the 'Andalusians' who left Spain after the re-conquest. In north-east Tunisia they brought about a renaissance of village life, introducing crops, arts and crafts. Artisanal crafts also prospered in the Moroccan cities of Fez, Tetuan and Rabat.

4. *European Colonisation*. The capture of Algiers in 1830 and the establishment of French protectorates over Tunisia in 1881 and Morocco in 1912 were followed by European rural colonisation. Never were the rural colonists as numerous as the European town-dwellers; by the early 1950s the proportion of active male Europeans living from agriculture was only 13·7 per cent in Algeria, 12·8 in Tunisia and 7·5 in Morocco.[9] Nevertheless, of the cultivated areas of the various countries, European colonists occupied about two-fifths in Algeria, one-fifth in Tunisia and one-thirteenth in French Morocco. In Spanish Morocco, however, rural colonisation was discouraged and only a very small pro-portion of the zone was allocated to Spaniards.[10]

Many rural landscapes of the Maghreb were completely transformed, especially in the lowlands of the Mediterranean zone (Fig. 250), where

85 Folded shale and marl relief in the High Atlas gorges of the M'Goun

86 Sandstone ranges of the Hodna, south of Sétif

87 Dissected pediments in desert between Missour and Midelt

88 A ksour in Fezouata, Drâ Valley

89 Casablanca—Kasbah and modern city

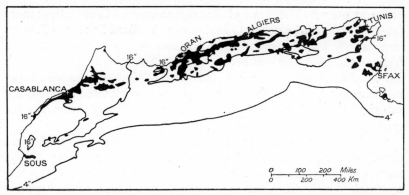

Fig. 250. Areas of dense European colonisation in the Maghreb. Note the significance of the 16-in. isohyet

marshes were drained, and agricultural villages and an ordered pattern of development—formerly alien to the Maghreb—were established.

Official and private colonisation both experienced fluctuating fortunes. Introduced in Algeria in 1838, official colonisation was subsequently fostered to boost French numbers vis-à-vis not merely the Muslims but also the Spaniards in Oran and the Italians in Tunisia. In the early years of the two protectorates official colonisation proceeded more cautiously than previously in Algeria, where many of the poorer peasant colonists had relied excessively on the state and had failed. Private colonisation, particularly large concessions, played a more important role in the protectorates than it did in Algeria. Unlike official colonisation, which usually took place on lands confiscated after revolts, on domain and on *habous*, private colonisation generally occurred on *melk* land purchased from the owners. The private colonist was normally wealthier and more independent than the official colonist, and he effected more technical improvements in agriculture. In French Morocco, however, the area available for European settlement was much more limited than in Algeria, because of the greater density of the Muslim rural population.

Rural colonisation in the Maghreb slowed down after 1930, and in the two succeeding decades many colonists suffered losses through drought, phylloxera or war. The approximate areas of land (in acres) under colonisation in the late 1940s are shown in table 8 Appendix III.[11]

A marked contrast existed between European and Muslim holdings. In 1954, about 22,000 European settlers farmed 5·9 million acres with an average annual revenue of £2,800 per farm, while 6,300,000 Muslim peasants had about 615,000 farms totalling only 11·9 million acres and giving an average annual revenue of about £100 per farm. One French company owned 155,000 acres in the *département* of Constantine; more than 600,000 Muslim peasant families were landless. European farmers have largely been interested in cash crops—soft wheat, wines, citrus fruits, *primeurs*, olives—in contrast to Muslim subsistence cultivation and livestock farming. The excessive extent of vineyards caused embarrassment to the French government, who were committed to importing substantial quantities of North African wines. Indeed, wine was for many years Algeria's major export.

Europeans have farmed more intensively and more successfully than native farmers, because of their larger properties, more efficient methods, more abundant machinery, better credit facilities, more up-to-date approach to agriculture, and higher quality land mainly in the Mediterranean zone.[12] Yields are therefore higher and more reliable. There are local exceptions to these generalisations; some Muslim farmers have emulated and exceeded the standards of Europeans, as in olive production in Tunisia. Date and fig production have remained almost entirely in the hands of Muslims; the marketing of dates, however, was a European monopoly. Unfortunately, some 70 per cent of Muslim properties are too small to be viable. Many Muslim peasants lost or sold their lands to Europeans, and joined the ranks of the unemployed or partially employed who constitute an important proportion of the flood of migrants to the towns. By 1950 about one-half of the Muslim rural population suffered from partial unemployment, and it was estimated that if mechanisation of European farms continued the proportion would rise to two-thirds.[13]

It is difficult to account for the general lack of interest in livestock production shown by European farmers. Cattle were introduced, but few Europeans have kept sheep or goats, the main livestock of Muslims. In consequence, traditional livestock farming methods were not greatly improved during European rule.

In the Mediterranean zone, the increase of cultivation at the expense of pastures strangled the traditional stock-breeding and cereal-growing economy of the plains. The mountain massifs were scarcely encroached upon by colonists, and retained their traditional tree-crops-with-livestock economies. Their population growth became the main problem, relieved only by migration to the towns; the remittances of the migrants made the subsistence economy bearable.

In the steppe zone, the presence of nomadic pastoralists undoubtedly restrained European expansion southwards in Algeria, but it was less restrictive in the eastern and western extremities of the Maghreb. In the Sfaxian region, for example, a few European landlords (often absentees) acquired immense territories which they devoted to olive plantations, established by using Sfaxian labour under the contract of *mgharsa*. The tenant or *mgharsi* leased a plot, cleared and planted it with olives and grew cereals on it until the trees bore fruit, when he received half the trees. This system was also used on the peninsula of Zarzis in southern Tunisia and on the High Steppe of central Tunisia. Elsewhere in the steppe zone some colonists used dry farming techniques, especially after about 1925 when mechanisation increased; but preparatory spring ploughing and cultivated fallow reduced the organic matter content of the soils and made them prone to exhaustion and erosion. Some sporadic attempts were made to settle nomads. The measure of success varied because of difficulties of water supplies, soil fertility, land tenure and the attitude of the nomads themselves. One example of the problems involved is the settlement of the Ouled Sidi Ali ben Aoun in central Tunisia.[14] On the other hand, summer transhumance[15] to the *tell* persisted despite increasing difficulties for the nomads to find pastures for their flocks and work as harvesters. In years of drought, when hundreds of thousands of nomads moved northward, the suffering was great, and some nomads moved into the towns to find work or beg in the streets. The problem of the nomads was further aggravated by the decline of camel caravans and the abolition of raiding and 'protection'. Only the provision of a more even scatter of wells and the control of epizootic diseases have seriously improved livestock farming. The crucial matter of forage reserves never received adequate attention. Fortunately nomads have found some supplementary revenue from cultivation, esparto grass gathering, work in phosphate or iron mines or with oil companies, harvesting of olives, dates or cereals of sedentary farmers, smuggling and migration.

Major French efforts to solve the eternal problems of water supply and irrigation were directed to the provision of dams and reservoirs in Algeria, but advances were delayed until the widespread use of reinforced concrete. Similar works came later in Morocco, although her irrigable area is $2\frac{1}{2}$ million acres compared with 750,000–875,000 acres in Algeria and 250,000 acres in Tunisia.[16] The improvement of the Medjerda, the only river in Tunisia capable of important hydraulic works, was not started until 1946.[17] Hydraulic works in the Maghreb pose special problems of irregular rainfall, rapid run-off and silting as well as those of water-use, land ownership and settlement, so progress in irrigation under French rule was not rapid. Yet considerable success was achieved in locating artesian aquifers in the semi-arid zone.

In general, the most unfortunate rural legacy of European rule was a marked contrast between the prosperous modernity of the populous Mediterranean zone and the backwardness and poverty of the steppe zone.

5. *Decolonisation.* The independent governments of the Maghreb have shown a new appreciation of environments and economies. The neglected southern territories of Tunisia, for example, have become the object of a special national fund: to settle semi-nomads, improve livestock farming, extend the area of olive cultivation, increase the production of *degla* dates, irrigate certain localities along the foothills of the High Tell and control the esparto grass industry. The last has been made a government monopoly. The 3,950,000 acres of *habous* land in Tunisia have been transformed: private *habous* to the benefit of the occupants, and public *habous* to become domains. Like communal lands, domains are destined to be settled by individuals.

The struggle for independence, particularly in Algeria, led to considerable movements of population, as well as the departure of tens of thousands of European settlers to Europe and the flight of European private capital. Departures are likely to continue during the next few years. The successful take-over of European farms is no simple task for North African governments; one obvious difficulty is the future of the vineyards. So far, agricultural progress has been slow in the areas of subsistence farming. It may be decades before regional disparities are smoothed away, but at least the countries are now regarded as wholes for purposes of economic development.

AGRARIAN SYSTEMS

The complexity of environments and historical influences has resulted in a wide variety of agrarian systems, most difficult to classify. The categories noted below, derived largely from Despois[18] and Dresch,[19] should be regarded as arbitrary.

1. *Steppe Nomadism.* Pastoral nomadism is still the most extensive rural economy in the Maghreb and the cause of many of its bare and monotonous landscapes (see Fig. 251). The limits of nomadism are both dynamic and vague, and in no sense is there a frontier between nomadism and cultivation. 'The clash of the desert and the sown' has often been exaggerated; a notable measure of interdependence and reciprocity between nomad and cultivator has existed in the Maghreb, and each has practised something of the other's economy. All shades of activity exist between true nomadism and a completely sedentary economy. Most cultivators possess some livestock, and nomadism rarely

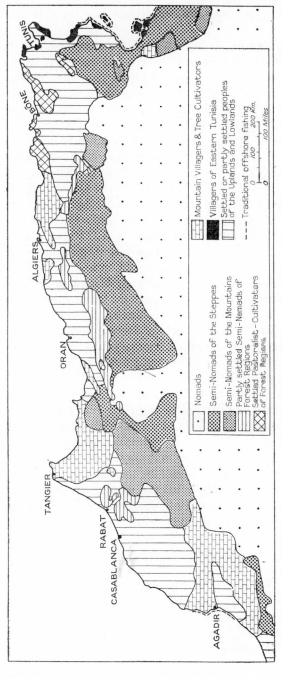

FIG. 251. Rural modes of life of the Moslems (after Despois)

exists without some cultivation of cereals or ownership of trees and gardens.

The most pure form of nomadism in the steppe zone is represented by the Beni Guil of eastern Morocco, but even this tribe possesses palms and gardens in the oasis of Figuig near the Algerian border. Other true nomads travel every summer from winter pastures in the desert to the steppe and Mediterranean zones in search of pastures and work as harvesters; they include the El Arbaa of Laghouat and the Arab Gheraba of Touggourt. Their difficulties have increased with the development of northern Algeria. Some nomads who winter in the desert migrate no farther north than the massifs of the Saharan Atlas or the High Atlas: the Aït Atta of Morocco,[20] the Ouled Sidi Cheikh, the southern Ouled Naïl[21] and the Nemencha of Algeria. They follow traditional routes and often employ share-croppers (*khammes*) in both desert oases and mountain villages to tend their trees and gardens.

The pastoralists of the steppe zone proper are generally semi-nomads; they spend only part of the year (especially springtime) with their flocks, have a fixed abode and engage in shifting cultivation.[22] Some call this mode of life semi-sedentary, and reserve the term semi-nomadic to those tribal groups whose migrations are limited by the majority of sheep over camels. This distinction is unnecessarily subtle for the Maghreb. Each tribe has its own sort of semi-nomadism, which reflects not merely the environmental conditions but human factors such as the size of the tribe, its traditions, its neighbours, as well as the wealth, attitude and stability of the government. Semi-nomads live in a zone of flux. At the present time sedentarisation is taking place gradually on the plains of central and southern Tunisia and on the high plateaux of Algeria and eastern Morocco; cultivation is increasing, summer transhumance to the *tell* is diminishing, huts (*gourbis*) are replacing tents for at least part of the year, encampments are smaller and land ownership is becoming less communal. Loosening tribal ties may be partly attributed to the growing numbers seeking work in the towns. Sedentarisation, however, leaves few physical signs on the landscape as livestock continue to play an important role. The process is less advanced among the semi-nomads of the southern slopes of the Anti-Atlas, the only steppe semi-nomads of western Morocco.

2. *Mountain Nomadism.* In Morocco, semi-nomadism is mostly confined to the mountains of the Middle Atlas, the eastern High Atlas and the eastern Rif. For centuries Berber peoples have lived here in hill-top villages for part of the year, practised irrigated cultivation of cereals, olives, figs and vegetables in valley bottoms or plains, and migrated in

summer to mountain pastures. Modifications are now taking place. The summer movement of flocks to the mountains and the winter movement to the plains are becoming more like transhumance than nomadism, and hill-top villages and their fortified granaries are being abandoned for more convenient valley sites. The annual cycle varies in detail from tribe to tribe, according to such factors as the height of the mountains and the types of tree crops. In essence, the cycle is similar to that practised by three other Berber groups: part of the Chaouïa of the Aurès mountains, the Djebalia (hill-dwellers) east of Gafsa[23] and the Djebalia of southern Tunisia.

In some of the forested mountains along the southern margins of the Mediterranean zone, certain arabised peoples combine pastoralism and cultivation in a different manner, though no more profitably. Summer and winter transhumance, cultivation on unwooded slopes and plains, orchards around villages, lumbering, charcoal burning, harvest migrations and emigration provide varied returns, but the people are poor. Although the tent is still common, many are settling. Examples can be found in the mountains of Tlemçen, Daya, Saïda, Frenda, the Ouarsenis and the Hodna[24] in Algeria, as well as in the western part of the central plateau of Morocco, where the Zaïr and Zemmour gain much of their livelihood from cattle.

3. *Mountain Villagers.* Not all peoples living in forested mountains are semi-nomadic; those of the more humid parts of the north-eastern Maghreb have long been sedentary. In Kroumirie and the mountains of the Mogods in northern Tunisia, in parts of the Tunisian High Tell and in the Algerian massifs of the Edough and little Kabylia, population densities are higher and arboriculture more important than in the semi-nomadic forested areas. Land fragmentation and primitive arboricultural techniques unfortunately hinder progress. The forests provide winter pastures for cattle and sheep as well as wealth from cork-cutting. Hamlets are more common than villages.

These techniques of land utilisation are less specialised than those employed by other groups of mountain villagers found along the Mediterranean coast and the Saharan fringe. Along the Mediterranean Littoral are the Djebala and Rifians of northern Morocco, as well as the peoples of the Trara, the massif of Miliana and the Kabyles of the Djurdjura and the Babor in Algeria. Along the Saharan fringe peasant societies are found among the Chleuh of the western High Atlas[25] and Anti-Atlas, some of Chaouïa of the western Aurès and the Matmata of southern Tunisia. Most of the peoples of these widely scattered regions are Berbers, except the arabised Djebala and some Rifians. Other common characteristics are: village habitats; long traditions of sedentary life; geographical distinctiveness of the tribe; delimitation, fragmentation and private ownership of property; dominance of cultivation over livestock; importance of tree crops; over-population; and outward migration of craftsmen and traders. The systems employed by the northern and southern peoples differ in detail. Irrigation, terrace cultivation and transhumance occur in the south but not in the north, where population densities are higher and tree crops and vegetables are more varied. Apart from olives and figs, the two main crops, grenadines, peaches, pears, apricots, cherries, almonds and plums are all grown.

4. *Villagers of Eastern Tunisia.* The only lowlands in the Maghreb where village life has persisted for centuries are in eastern Tunisia.[26] The large villages of the Sahel (Fig. 260) are surrounded by traditional olive groves, which are gradually expanding on to the steppes, where the Sahelians grow cereals and pasture their flocks. The low rainfall of the Sahel (about 13 in per annum) and its mediocre soils enforce careful cultivation and conservation of moisture.

Arboriculture and village habitats are also traditional in north-east Tunisia, especially along the southern shores of the Cape Bon peninsula. Andalusian immigrants in the seventeenth century helped to sustain this mode of life, which depends less on the olive than on other fruits and market garden products.

On the low sandy islands of Kerkenna off Sfax, village life is supported more by fishing for sponges and sardines than by the prevalent palm, which is a poor date producer. Djerba is more densely populated (63,200 in 1956), is one-quarter Berber speaking, and, apart from two Jewish villages, has dispersed settlement. Palms and olives are numerous, and properties small. Other fruits are grown, but all cultivation suffers from inadequate or saline water.

All these over-populated regions of eastern Tunisia are sources of migrants, from whom remittances are received. Many of the middle classes of Tunisian towns come from the villages of these regions.

5. *Sedentary Peoples of the Uplands and Lowlands.* Before the advent of Europeans in the Maghreb, most of the moister uplands and lowlands knew neither stable cultivation nor security, because of the dominance of pastoralism and tribalism. The ebb and flow of nomads left mixed populations with less stability than either Berber groups or Arab nomadic tribes. Most of the pastures were communally owned. Enclosures were lacking, as the sporadic cultivation was confined to winter cereals. The tent and the *gourbi* prevailed.

Since the arrival of Europeans there has been a complete revaluation of these lands. They have become the most important agricultural areas and the scene of widespread colonisation. Many of the tribes in these areas are now settled or in the process of settling down. Livestock numbers have decreased and cereals have increased. Gardens have been created, permanent dwellings constructed and field boundaries established. The evolution has been most complete on the uplands and lowlands of Algeria and Tunisia. Here many peoples are now almost entirely sedentary; the Hanencha of the Tunisian-Algerian frontier zone and the peoples of the Tell of Oran are notable examples. Over much of northern Tunisia nomadism had never existed, so agricultural improvements came more easily. Emphasis is placed on cereal production, and many Muslim farmers, as for example around Beja, now grow soft wheat and employ techniques introduced by Europeans, such as cultivated fallow and grain selection. Numerous Muslims have been more or less constrained to settle through lack of pastures, because of the spread of colonisation. Many have become agricultural workers, living in *gourbis*, either alongside the villages or near the European farms.

In Atlantic Morocco sedentarisation is less marked. Although the peoples of the coastal zone (for example Doukkala, Abda and Chiadma) and of the mountain foothills are mainly settled, those of the intervening plains and plateaux (for example Rehamna, Segharna and Beni Meskin) are only partially settled, despite a great increase in cereal cultivation.

6. *Types of European Colonisation.* The various types of European colonisation have reflected the dominant cash crops. Cereals, especially soft wheat, have been the main crop over much of the Maghreb. In the zone with less than 20 in of rainfall dry farming and mechanisation moved Europeans to acquire large properties employing few Muslim labourers, especially in southern Constantine and the Sersou. In moister areas, such as the plains of the middle and lower Medjerda, Sebou and Cheliff, mixed farming was possible on smaller properties with more labourers.

In northern Algeria the vine became the basis of European agriculture, occupying up to one million acres. Viticulture enabled much denser European settlement than either cereal cultivation or mixed farming. In the main areas of viticulture—the plains of the Mitidja of Philippeville and Bône, along with the hills around Oran, Mostaganem and Algiers—few Muslims acquired or retained lands, but many worked in the vineyards, where the labour requirements are high. In more restricted areas of north-eastern Tunisia, around Tunis and in the Cape Bon peninsula, vineyards of French and Italian settlers have transformed the landscapes. Viticulture in Morocco is now more extensive than in Tunisia. The main localities are near Meknès and Fez, where the proportion of Muslim vine-growers is higher than elsewhere in the Maghreb.

Market-gardening around the major cities permitted an even closer concentration of Europeans, especially Italians and Spaniards, as well as a greater demand for Muslim workers. Its progress was partly due to better irrigation facilities. Morocco and Algeria have developed exports of *primeurs* to European markets.

Until the Second World War, arboriculture was generally less attractive to Europeans in the Maghreb. Only in parts of eastern Tunisia had it been the dominant activity. Developed by French capital and Sfaxian labour, the immense olive plantations in the environs of Sfax became a monoculture. Until recently about 50 Europeans owned one-seventh of the trees, but many lived outside the region. Few nucleated settlements disturb the regularity of the plantations; the majority of people live in or around Sfax. Similar but smaller examples of European/Tunisian olive plantations are found on the steppes and on the peninsula of Zarzis south of Djerba.

Since the second World War, citrus fruit production has increased substantially with the growth of irrigated agriculture. Oranges, mandarines, clementines and lemons are now important crops in the Gharb and the Sous in Morocco, in northern Algeria and to a much smaller extent in northern Tunisia. During the last two decades Europeans also took greater interest in other tree crops, especially apricots and almonds.

POPULATION STRUCTURE, TRENDS AND DISTRIBUTION

The population of the Maghreb in 1960 was nearly 26 million: 11,598,700 in Morocco (census May 1960), about 10,200,000 in Algeria (excluding the Sahara) and nearly 4 million in Tunisia. The lack of censuses in French Morocco before 1921 and in Spanish Morocco before 1945, as well as the doubtful validity of all census data in the Maghreb, makes it impossible to calculate precise rates of growth, but it seems that the total population of the Maghreb multiplied three times during the first 60 years of this century. At present, the population is increasing by more than two per cent per annum, i.e. by more than half a million every year. By 1970 Algeria should have a population of 13 million, Tunisia over 5 million[27] and Morocco 14–15 million. This fast rate of growth has not been everywhere equal (Fig. 252)—it has probably been most rapid in Morocco—but everywhere it is the result of the impact of European civilisation.[28]

1. *Muslim Population.* Muslims constitute over 95 per cent of the

total population of the Maghreb; and their proportion is increasing as
Europeans and Jews depart. Muslim numbers at the beginning of European rule were small—about 2 million in Algeria in 1830, 1 million
in Tunisia in 1881 and 3 million in Morocco in 1912—and the
population regime was primitive: high fertility, high mortality and low
population growth. Numbers fluctuated according to the prevalence of

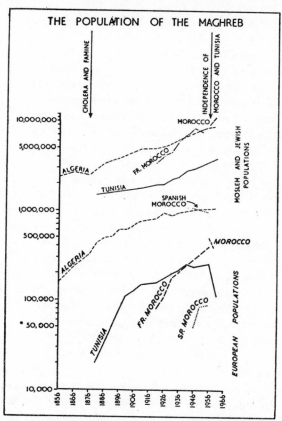

FIG. 252. Semi-logarithmic graph of population growth in the Maghreb. Upper
curves refer to Moslem and Jewish populations, and lower curves to Europeans

diseases and the vagaries of climate. Years of prosperity and years of
disaster were accepted as the will of Allah.

Among the most significant effects of the European impact have been
the reduction of mortality and the subsequent rapid population growth.
'Death control' has achieved this transformation largely through the
elimination or reduction of the major killing diseases of the Maghreb:

cholera, typhus, smallpox, bubonic and pneumonic plague, malaria and venereal diseases. Their influence has been diminished only gradually; in 1928 and 1936, for example, malaria epidemics caused appalling mortality in Morocco. Death rates are now of the order of 10 to 15 per thousand in the three countries, and are naturally reduced by the youthfulness of the population. Expectation of life has also risen to about 45. Nevertheless, because of insufficient ante-natal care and hygiene, infant mortality may be as high as 200 per thousand. Maternal mortality rates are also high, and raise female mortality above male mortality for persons aged 20 to 30, although the war in Algeria has caused the death of tens of thousands of male Muslims.

Morbidity rates are still elevated by continuing poverty and malnutrition. The Maspétiol report[29] of 1955 stated that the average yearly income per head of rural Muslims in Algeria was about £16, while for urban Muslims it was £45. Similar figures are available for Morocco and Tunisia; in 1958 it was estimated that the national revenue per inhabitant in Tunisia was 5·4 times lower than in France, the average annual revenue being only 52 dinars (approximately £52).[30] In Morocco, it was sixteen times lower among Muslims than among the French population. These are merely averages; the bulk of the population have much less. They are clearly undernourished, and studies have shown that over half of the population may receive less than 2,000 calories a day. Summer transhumants have been recorded with daily caloric intakes as low as 190.[31] Starvation is no stranger, especially in the steppe zone.

There is evidence to suggest that malnutrition may be a contributary factor to the prevailing high fertility among Muslims. Birth-rates are still 40–47 per thousand, as there are still early marriage, easy divorce and great pride in family size. Polygamy is not an important factor; probably no more than five per cent of the men are polygamous, and many of those are aged. Birth control has little effect on fertility, although it has been practised for centuries by some peoples of the Maghreb.[32] In independent Tunisia, however, there has been a recent effort to increase birth control, and to raise the status of women by revision of the marriage and divorce laws as well as by the lowering of the veil.

Natural increase rates of 25–35 per thousand are regarded as excessive by the governments of the Maghreb, who are anxious to reduce fertility by social and economic advances. Despite heavy war losses of about 150,000 men the Muslim population of Algeria rose substantially during the period 1955–60. By 1960 Muslims in Algeria had reached 9·3 million, in Tunisia 3·9 million and in Morocco 11 million. It is not surprising that the Muslim populations are young: 50–55 per cent under 20 years, 40–44 per cent between 20 and 59 and 5–7 per cent 60 and over. Population pyramids (Fig. 253) show no signs of ageing.

One factor which has tended to diminish fertility has been the growth of male migration from the overpopulated mountain massifs, the southern oases and the offshore islands to the cities and to France.[33] In the mid-fifties, about 95 per cent of the 130,000 North Africans in

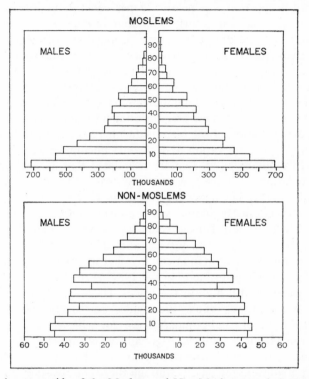

Fig. 253. Age pyramids of the Moslem and Non-Moslem populations of Algeria, 1954. (Five-year age groups)

Paris were males, but the proportion of female migrants is growing. Behr[34] cites an example of a village in Kabylia with no males aged between 18 and 60; one-third were in France, one-third with the F.L.N. and one-third 'disappeared'. Male migration is not a recent phenomenon; it has existed for decades in various forms: temporary, seasonal, periodic and permanent. The Djerbian grocer, the Mozabite shop-keeper and the Moroccan miner are some of the well-known examples of the specialisations adopted by migrant villagers of over-populated areas. Other examples are the Chleuh of southern Morocco, the Dje-balia of southern Tunisia and above all the Kabyles, who provide a large proportion of the North Africans in France.

The influx of Muslims into the towns is one of the most remarkable features of recent decades. Before the second World War only a small proportion of the Muslim population lived in towns: 9 per cent in Algeria, 17 per cent in Tunisia and 16 per cent in Morocco. By 1960 the overall proportion was nearly 25 per cent: 2 million in Algeria, 900,000 in Tunisia and nearly 3 million in Morocco. Tunisia and Morocco have appropriately larger proportions of Muslim town-dwellers than Algeria, as they have much longer traditions of urban life. The stimuli for this massive rural-urban movement have been varied: the concentration of Europeans within the towns; the availability of employment in industries, communications, construction and services; the desire for independence and freedom from the patriarchal family system; the attraction of the blandishments of the large towns; loss of land or livestock; starvation and chronic unemployment. The last is undoubtedly instrumental. Lépidi[35] calculated that 38 per cent of the male population of active age in Tunisia were unemployed or under-employed in 1956. The figure for Algeria in 1955 was 30 per cent. The working man in the Maghreb has to support about five people. In inde-pendent Morocco and Tunisia some reduction in unemployment has occurred through national service and increased opportunities in administration. Reduction in unemployment was also one of the princi-pal aims of the Constantine Plan for 1959–63 in Algeria. Regrettably, unemployment is still high in the towns, because of their inability to absorb the continuous influx. 'Bidonvilles' persist in the large cities.

Redistribution of rural population did not achieve important dimen-sions in the Maghreb until the Algerian war of independence. There is little evidence for recent attraction of population to the richer and more modern agricultural regions,[36] although there has always been sporadic settlement of transhumants in the *tell*. The population map of the Maghreb has not been entirely changed by European impact (Figs. 254 and 255). Mountain massifs, such as the Rif, the Anti-Atlas, the western High Atlas and Kabylie, are still overpopulated; so are the plains of the Doukkala in Morocco and the Sahel in Tunisia, as well as the island of Djerba. These high densities reflect historical conditions, which must be invoked in any consideration of present population densities. Another important factor is the cohesiveness of the tribe. There is consequently no simple gradation of population densities from the Mediterranean to the Sahara. High densities are always associated with sedentary cultiva-

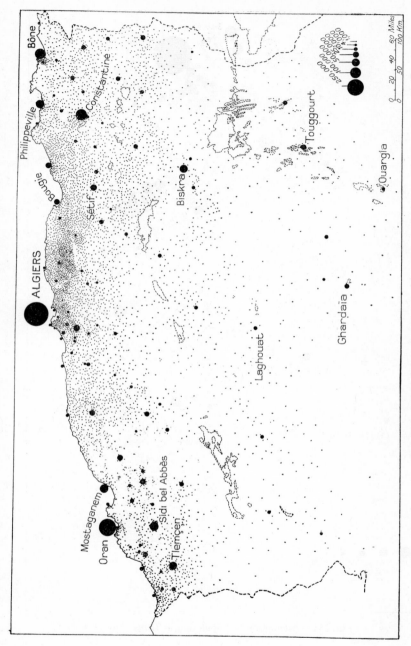

Fig. 254. Distribution of population in Algeria, in 1956

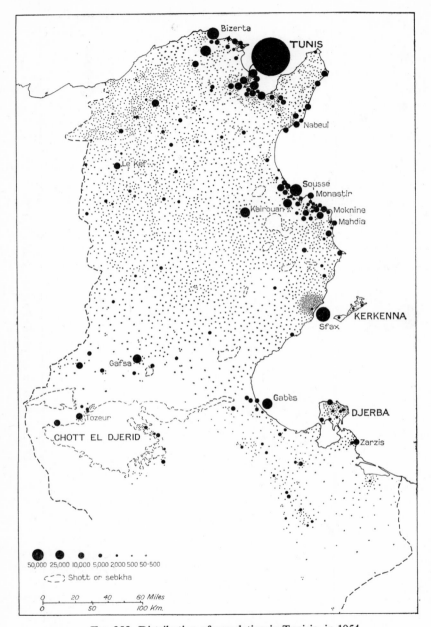

FIG. 255. Distribution of population in Tunisia, in 1954

tion, especially irrigated agriculture, whether in *tell*, steppe or desert. Low densities are associated with pastoral nomadism, but considerable variations exist, according to the availability of supplementary revenue.

The Muslim population of the Maghreb is largely derived from Berber and Arab stocks, but neither of these terms infers ethnic unity; there has been considerable intermixture. The Berbers are the autochthonous peoples of North Africa. On the whole, they have remained rural and particularist, conserving their language, local dialects and traditional customs in the refuge of their mountain fastnesses. The coherence of their family system and the fragmentation of their tribal structure have militated against the formation of stable states. Berber is not a literary language, but it is spoken by about 8 million people, including 40–45 per cent of the population of Morocco, 30 per cent of Algeria and 2 per cent of Tunisia.[37] The numerical strength of Berbers in Morocco has given power to their confederations and enabled spirited defence of their small republics.[38] Of the five main Berber groups in the Maghreb—Rifians, Braber, Chleuh, Kabyles and Chaouïa (Fig. 249)—only the Braber are nomadic.

The purity of Arab blood has been greatly reduced. Probably no more than one-tenth of the people of Morocco can claim to be of pure Arab descent.[39] Arab dialects predominate today in the towns of the Maghreb, and on the lowlands where pastoralism and tribal organisation have long prevailed. Whereas Tunisia has been thoroughly arabised, the Arabic-speakers of Moroccan towns were for centuries surrounded by Berber-speakers. Arabisation has gradually progressed at the expense of the Berber language, especially during European rule, which reduced rural isolation and increased the mobility of population.

2. *Jews in the Maghreb*. Arabic is the main language of the Jews of the Maghreb,[40] with the exception of some in Morocco. They number only 160,000 in Morocco, 140,000 in Algeria and 58,000 in Tunisia; since 1947 their numbers have diminished, as many have departed to Israel. Formerly more scattered, Jews are now rare in rural areas. During European rule they became almost exclusively town-dwellers. adopted European languages and frequently became naturalised French subjects. They were no longer confined to their ghettos (*hara, chara, mellah*) in the old cities and bought houses in the newer residential quarters. They are generally shopkeepers, traders or artisans, especially jewellers. Not all are wealthy; the majority are working-class. Their present situation is delicate in view of Arab-Jewish tensions.

3. *Europeans*. The European population of the Maghreb reached its maximum about 1956 when there were more than 1,775,000: about

1,000,000 in Algeria (excluding the French army), 255,300 in Tunisia, about 380,000 in French Morocco, 90,000 in Spanish Morocco and 50,000 in Tangier, which was abolished as an international zone in that year. Europeans then comprised approximately $7\frac{1}{2}$ per cent of the total population of the Maghreb: 11 per cent of Algeria, 7 per cent of Tunisia, 5 per cent of Morocco and 29 per cent of Tangier.

Between 1956 and 1960 the European populations of Tunisia and Morocco were reduced by nearly half. The departure of Europeans from Algeria has since been even more rapid; about 600,000 left between March and November 1962, causing economic chaos. Further reductions in European populations should be expected during the present decade.

By West European standards, the age composition of the Europeans in the Maghreb has always been young: 36–9 per cent under 20 years, 52–6 per cent aged between 20 and 59, and 7–11 per cent 60 and over (Fig. 253). The age composition has been influenced by immigration as well as by higher marriage and birth rates and lower death rates than are common in Europe. Natural increase has therefore been higher. In 1953 it was about 1 per cent per annum in Algeria, 1·6 per cent in Tunisia and 1·7 per cent in Morocco.[41] The rate of growth of the European population in Morocco during the period 1921–56 was particularly rapid, especially because of the large immigrations of the 1920s (Fig. 252).

In 1956, four-fifths of the Europeans were living in towns: 79 per cent in Algeria, 80 per cent in Morocco and 84 per cent in Tunisia. As administrators, skilled workers and traders they were localised in the larger cities of the coast, which were transfigured by their presence. Many Algerian cities (Algiers, Oran, Bône, Philippeville) had substantial European majorities before the second World War.

The small European rural population has always been mainly concentrated in the *tell* of Algeria and Tunisia, in the basin of the Oued Sebou and the coastal plains of Morocco. Its density has been closely related to the type of agriculture; vineyards and market gardens mean higher densities than aboriculture or cereal farming. The highest densities were found among the Italian peasant farmers of north-east Tunisia and the Spaniards of Oran.

The majority of Europeans in the Maghreb are French, yet in 1948 no more than one in nine of the Frenchmen living in Algeria had been born in France; the rest were either descendants of French settlers, who had come mainly from southern France and Corsica, or naturalised Spaniards, Italians or other Europeans. Although by 1960 94 per cent of the

European population of Algeria were of French nationality, no more than half could claim to be of French stock, as naturalisation had greatly reduced the numbers of non-French Europeans. In the last decade of the nineteenth century, the Spanish population, mostly in Oran, accounted for nearly 30 per cent of the total European population of Algeria.

During the inter-war years a more pressing political problem to the French authorities was the numerical superiority of Italians over French in Tunisia. Not until after 1932 was the balance altered, by naturalisation, limited Italian immigration, and wartime expulsions and departures (Table 6, Appendix IV). The Italians have been mainly localised in north-east Tunisia, especially in the Cape Bon peninsula and in distinct quarters of the city of Tunis, where, in general, they have been employed in more manual activities than the French.

In 1951, the non-French population of Morocco included 111,000 Spaniards (85,000 in the northern and 26,000 in the southern zone) and 13,550 Italians, but their numbers have since diminished.

Apart from French, Spanish and Italian minorities, Maltese and Greeks have always been numerous in the ports of the Maghreb, where they are traders, shopkeepers and fishermen. In other words, the Europeans of the Maghreb have been largely Mediterranean in origin, a fact reflected in their character and customs. Though a small minority of the population of the Maghreb, the Europeans have had an immense influence upon economic development, the growth of towns and communications, as well as the rise in the Muslim population. Most modern developments in the Maghreb have been the result of European initiative and capital, which enabled French administrations to build up colonial-type economies modifying large areas of the Maghreb, without raising substantially the prosperity of its inhabitants. Europeans have enjoyed a much higher standard of living than Muslims, and have lived apart. Intermarriage has occurred between French women and Muslim men[42] but on the whole, religion, customs, traditions, occupations and incomes have impeded close ties. Nevertheless, the massive departures of Europeans will have social and economic consequences as momentous as the initial impact of European civilisation upon the Maghreb.

THE TOWNS OF THE MAGHREB

Three main phases of urban evolution can be distinguished in the Maghreb: the ancient cities; the period of medieval foundation by the Arabs; and the modern extension and creation of cities under European impetus. Although the first phase has left its mark by numerous ruins, the remains and morphology of ancient cities are rarely distinguishable within the present cities of the Maghreb. Far more significant are the second and third phases.

1. *Evolution.* The tradition of urban life is much richer in the eastern and western extremities of the Maghreb than in Algeria. Many Tunisian towns vaunt Phoenician and Roman sites, Turkish and European forts as well as walled Arab *medinas*, but the latter constituted the main form element before European rule. Kairouan, the first camp site of the Arabs in the Maghreb in A.D. 670, became one of the great capitals of the Maghreb under the Aghlabites. It was temporarily replaced by Mahdia, founded by the early Fatimites in A.D. 916, but enjoyed

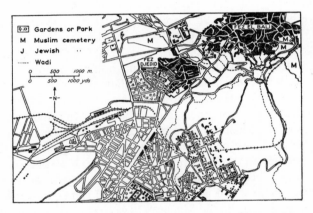

FIG. 256. Fez, Morocco. The old medina, Fez el Bali, is inhabited by merchants, craftsmen and students, and is the cultural centre. It contrasts with the newer Fez Djedid, now a tightly packed suburb. The old sultan's palace (diagonal shading, and the Jewish mellah are in Fez Djedid. The European town lies to the south

considerable prosperity until its destruction by the Beni Hillal and Beni Solaym in 1052. Subsequently Tunis, a former Punic suburb of Carthage, grew rapidly as the capital of the Zirids and the Hafsites. In 1517 it had about 200,000 inhabitants, but by 1881–5 the number had declined to 100–120,000. By this time the ports of Bizerta, Sousse and Sfax had considerable regional significance.

In Morocco, cities were established by the Arabs in the lowlands. The most noble were the religious and intellectual centres, known as *hadriya*, and the capitals, termed *makhzeniya*, where the sultan had a palace. *Hadriya* cities included Fez, Rabat-Salé and Tetuan, to which Tunis, Tlemçen and Kairouan were similar in character; Fez, Rabat,

Marrakesh and Meknès were *makhzeniya* cities, to which Algiers and Tunis could be likened. Fez was the most famous. Founded in 806 by the Idrissites, Old Fez (Fez el Bali) was joined by New Fez (Fez Djedid) in 1276 (Fig. 256). Under the Almohads in the twelfth and thirteenth centuries it attained 400,000 inhabitants.[43] Marrakesh was created in 1062 by the Almoravids (Fig. 257). They fortified Meknès, which much later (1672–1727) became the famous capital of the terrible Moulay Ismail. Rabat, on the other hand, was established by the Almohads in 1150. All these cities bear the imprint of past glories in their layout, gardens and palaces. Yet at the beginning of the French protectorate the urban population numbered no more than half a million, of whom nearly 100,000 were living in Fez.[44]

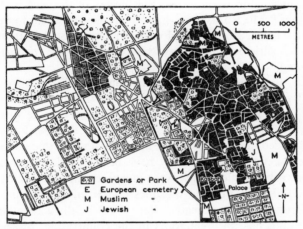

Fig. 257. The plan of Marrakesh, illustrating the contrast between the European and Moslem quarters and the profusion of gardens established by former sultans

Tangier, Ceuta, Melilla, Larache and Arzila all have longer histories, as Phoenician trading stations, Carthaginian camps and Roman towns. They were subsequently occupied by Vandals, Byzantines and Visigoths before the arrival of the Arabs. Later, like so many other ports of Morocco (for example Mogador, Safi, Mazagan, Azzemour, Casablanca, Fedala, Mehdia), they were occupied by Portugal or Spain, and also frequently harboured pirates.

Many of the ports of Algeria also had ancient origins, turbulent histories and long contact with Europeans; Mers el Kebir, Oran, Mostaganem, Algiers, Bougie and Bône are notable examples. But when the French arrived in 1830 only Algiers was more than a miserable village; it had 30,000 inhabitants. In the Algerian interior, towns were few and small before French rule, partly because of the prevalence of pastoral nomadism; with the exception of the former capital Tlemçen, which belongs culturally to Morocco, they scarcely dated back to the Ottoman domination. Miliana and Medea are examples. Constantine was little more than a large Berber village.

2. *The Traditional City.* Distinction between villages, towns and cities in the Maghreb is not easy in terms of mere size.[45] All may have close connections with the surrounding countrysides, which are often farmed by the inhabitants. Some permanent settlements arose from the weekly tribal market or *souk*, often located in a strategic position along a route, at the foot of a mountain range, or on the margins of the desert. But permanent markets are frequently a recent development; in isolated and self-subsistence areas the success of the *souk* may impede urbanisation.[46] The word 'town' has no Arabic equivalent in the Maghreb, because before European colonisation there existed no intermediate stage in the settlement hierarchy between the village (*douar*) and the city (*medina*).

Medinas are almost entirely foreign entities. Created by invaders and by dynasties, they have known neither tranquillity nor stability. Alien to tribal life, they have been the necessary bases for political confederations of tribes as well as the cause of their decline. *Medinas* only maintained their vitality where they had more permanent social and economic functions. Always they have been significant as centres of Islam, the visible sign of which is the great mosque at the heart of every city. At Tunis and Fez the mosques contained Islamic universities. Though propagated by nomads, Islam is essentially a religion of city-dwellers,[47] and has no great roots in the countryside. Moreover, the city-dwellers (*beldi*), who were split into a complicated hierarchy based on origin, culture, occupations and wealth, scorned the countrymen (*berrani*) who invaded the towns from time to time.

Apart from the great mosque, the form of the traditional Muslim city was also characterised by high embattled walls, often adapted to the relief of the site. They contained a compressed complex of dwellings, white from a distance and separated by an intricate maze of narrow, winding streets, which reflected the absence of wheeled vehicles. The *kasba* or fort dominated the city from the highest point, and adjacent were usually a palace and the Jewish quarter. The segregation of the Jews was not unusual; 'Andalusians', Turks (*Kologli*), European and tribal groups also inhabited particular quarters. In the *souks* there were further examples of segregation; trades and guilds were localised in different streets, the cleaner and quieter trades (perfume and incense merchants, bookbinders, jewellers, tailors, etc.) along the vaulted streets near the great mosque, while the dirtier and noisier trades (carpenters, blacksmiths, tanners, dyers, potters) were further away. In cities like Fez, Marrakesh and Tunis the craft guilds occupied up to one-third of the total area. Daily vegetable markets were held near the gates. A city was generally divided into wards, each with a mosque silhouetting the city from afar. The houses were not always crammed within the walls, but, except in the Turkish quarters, they invariably presented a bare exterior concealing closed courtyards.

3. *European Extensions and Creations*. The concentration of Europeans in towns, especially the main ports, has greatly stimulated urban growth. Ports have controlled the colonial trade, exporting raw materials and foodstuffs (phosphate, iron ore, esparto grass, grain, wine, olive oil, dates) and importing manufactured goods, coal and oil. The large ports have become capitals or important administrative centres and have outstripped interior rivals. Some have stifled smaller ports; Casablanca and Safi have killed Mazagan, and Mina Hassan Tani (formerly known as Kenitra and Port Lyautey) has gained over Larache.

Nowhere has the impact of European civilisation been absent. In the heart of the old *medinas* many of the crafts have suffered from the competition of European and oriental mass production. Some crafts have remained active, especially rug-making, weaving and leatherwork, and in Fez many continue to thrive[48]; but the new quarters of the growing cities have a new commercial class dealing with imported goods and considering wider markets than the passer-by.

Urban growth has not proceeded in the same way everywhere in the Maghreb. Not only have policies for urban growth differed in time and place, but so have the rates of growth. Too many towns have become swollen and anguished.

In Algeria, the French initially lived in the original *medinas*, building new dwellings for their needs. But the paucity of towns in Algeria soon induced them to create new ones: Philippeville (1838), Sidi-bel-Abbès (1843), Tiaret (1843) and Sétif (1846). Later, they developed extensions to the old cities in the manner of the period.[49] Layouts are therefore confused. Planning, introduced in 1919, came too late. The main towns have grown up on the coast, where port development exacted important works and numerous extensions. In Algiers, Oran, Bougie and Bône the old *medinas* have been inundated by the new European towns. As for the old cities of the interior, Constantine (223,000) has grown as a market centre, but Tlemçen, Guelma, Saïda and others are still small in comparison with the ports. On the other hand, many old villages in the interior became flourishing small towns following the establishment of a barracks, camp or colonisation centre.

The urban population of Algeria has grown steadily during the century, and in 1960 it was nearly 30 per cent of the total population. Greater Algiers has about 900,000 people and has grown very rapidly since the beginning of the Algerian war. Because of the massive influx of Muslims, Europeans are now outnumbered in all towns save Oran (393,000) and Philippeville (88,000). The old urban elements, the Arab *hadri* and Turkish *kologli*, have been submerged.

In Tunisia, the French established their new quarters alongside the old *medinas*, and have not transformed the form of the latter. The walls of Sousse and Sfax, for example, are still intact, and the *medina* of Tunis is one of the finest in North Africa. Again urban growth has been largely dependent upon the presence of Europeans, and therefore the ports of Tunis, Bizerta, Sousse and Sfax have expanded more quickly than the old centres, like Kairouan, Monastir, Mahdia and Gabès. Furthermore, the new agricultural centres of the Tell are more dynamic than the old villages of the Sahel and the south. The quarters of the major towns tend to be distinct: the *medina* including the *hara* or Jewish quarter,[50] the early European town rectilinear in plan, the new European residential suburbs, the upper-class Muslim residential areas and the 'bidonvilles' (Fig. 258). The squalor of the 'bidonvilles' exists in all large cities of the Maghreb; it is symptomatic of the dangerous disparities of economic and social development.[51]

Between 1921 and 1956 the urban population of Tunisia rose from 23 to 32 per cent, and Tunis itself from 171,700 to 410,000 inhabitants. By 1961, Tunis and its suburbs contained 680,000 people. The recent departure of many Europeans from Bizerta (45,000), Sousse (48,000) and Sfax (66,000) may arrest the growth of these towns.

In Morocco, Marshal Lyautey's policy was to establish European towns away from the sites of the *medinas*, to form twin-cities which should not invade each other. A similar though less enlightened policy was adopted by the Spaniards in their zone.[52] The *medinas* are consequently much as they were before European intervention, with the addition of better lighting and sanitation. Where urban growth has been mercurial a more complex pattern has evolved. In Casablanca, old and new *medinas* are surrounded by new European and Muslim quarters, the proximity of skyscrapers and 'bidonvilles' witnessing to the social and economic contrasts (Plate 89). The growth of Casablanca is the most rapid of all towns in Africa. At the end of the nineteenth century it had about 20,000 people; in 1960, there were 965,000. Morocco

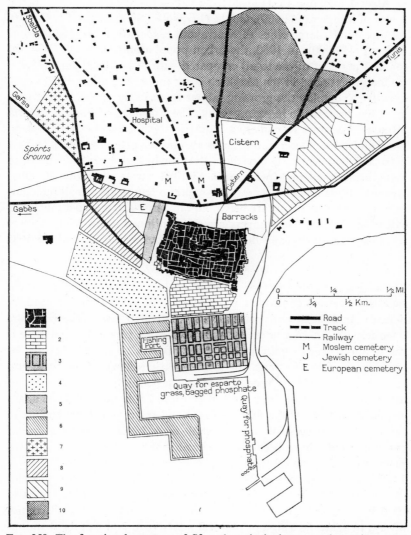

Fig. 258. The functional quarters of Sfax, the principal town and port in central and southern Tunisia: 1. Medina; 2. modern shopping area; 3. modern commercial area; 4. new apartments area; 5. Arab houses and shops; 6. fish and sponge markets; 7. new housing estate; 8. European-style suburb (Pioville); 9. ditto (Moulinville); 10. Arab suburb of R'bat Gouabsia

has seven other towns with more than 100,000 people (compare four in Algeria and one in Tunisia); the capital Rabat (227,000) and the towns of Tangier (142,000), Oujda (127,000) and Tetuan (101,000) are gaining on the large cities of Marrakesh (243,000), Fez (216,000) and Meknès (177,000). In 1960, the urban population numbered 3,404,000 (or 29·3 per cent of the total) compared with only 471,000 in 1926.

One urgent need in the Maghreb is for industrialisation of all types, in order to employ the growing labour force in the towns. Great progress has been made in recent years. The Constantine Plan in Algeria attracted investors to construct industries on the outskirts of Algiers, Oran and Bône. Decentralisation is also taking place: Arzew is to be a petrochemical centre, Duzerville a steel town, and other industries are being established in Mostaganem, Sidi-bel-Abbès, Relizane, Rouïba, Reghaïa, Blida and elsewhere. Although too late to absorb all the manpower, many new plants are being built in Morocco, and to a much less extent in Tunisia. The dangers are the continued drain of manpower from the countryside and the growing gulf between town and country.

RURAL SETTLEMENT

The varied patterns and types of rural settlement in the Maghreb are a reflection of many controls: the rural economy, water supplies, need for defence, traditions, and proximity of cultivated land. These factors operate with differing intensity from one region to another, so there is rarely uniformity of patterns and types of settlement.[53] Stress must be given to the fear of attack, for it has greatly influenced the form and grouping of dwellings used by sedentary peoples. Reduced fears of attack during part of the period of European rule provoked the abandonment of some of the more isolated and fortress-like settlements in favour of more accessible and agreeable ones. Indeed, many features of rural settlement have been modified as a result of the impact of European civilisation, and further modifications may be expected.

1. *The Tent.* The tent is the main dwelling of the nomadic peoples of the Maghreb, but may be used for only part of the year. It is also used by peoples who are no longer nomadic, and therefore it cannot always be taken as a sign of pastoral nomadism. Nor can its abandonment be assumed to indicate social and economic progress; it may result from loss of livestock and impoverishment. The North African tent is probably of Arabic origin, and comprises long strips (*flidj*) made of wool, camel hair or goat hair.[54] Nomads formerly camped only in groups of 40 to 60 tents arranged in a circle (*douar*), in which the livestock were kept at night (Fig. 259). With improved security smaller

Fig. 259. A few traditional types of rural settlement in the Maghreb. The actual
variety is much greater, and is supplemented by European rural settlements

groups are more frequent, but the size of the group varies according to
the seasons, the state of the pastures and the length of the migrations.
Tents prevail in the steppe zone and invade the Mediterranean zone in
summer, including the outskirts of cities.

2. *Temporary Dwellings.* Among many semi-nomads a temporary
dwelling or shelter, known as *gourbi,* is common in winter encampments. Sometimes the *gourbi* is an indication of the poverty of a
pastoralist who has no longer enough livestock to supply material for a
tent. It is in no sense an evolutionary stage between the tent and the
house; rich semi-nomads usually prefer houses for their winter dwellings.
The *gourbi* is a simple construction. Windowless, it has walls of branches

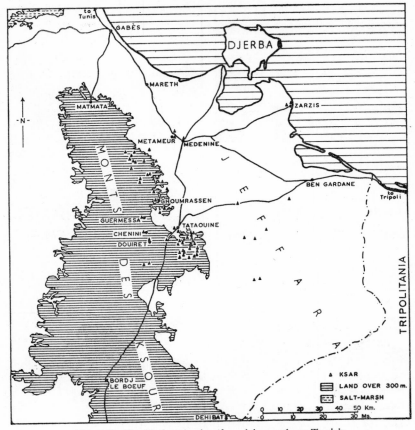

FIG. 260. Fortified granaries (*ksour*) in southern Tunisia

stones or earth, and a ridge roof of straw, diss grass or reeds. The whole is easily demolished and rebuilt elsewhere.

A variety of other temporary dwellings exist in the Maghreb. In Atlantic Morocco the bottle-shaped straw hut (*nouala*) (Fig. 259), reminiscent of West Africa, is found in Rehamna villages. In southern Tunisia semi-nomads construct dwellings of palm trunks (*zeriba*), of branches and straw (*kib*) and of stone or earth (*maamra*). In summer they are located near oases or fortified granaries (*ksour*) (Fig. 260 and Plate 88).

3. *The Traditional House.* Houses are used by some semi-nomads for part of the year, as well as by sedentary peoples. The traditional house (*dar* in Arabic; *tiguemmi, taddert* or *tazekka* in Berber dialects) does not differ greatly from the *gourbi.* Built of earth or stone without windows

or chimney, it has only one room often divided by a low stone wall so that one part may be used as a living-room and the other as a stable. Above the stable may be a little loft where the women and children sleep. The fire place (*kanoun*) is in the centre of the living room. A wall, thorn or cactus fence often forms a courtyard to ensure privacy.

Roof-forms vary. Flat roofs are most typical of the Saharan fringe, the eastern Maghreb and the eastern Rif. Ridge roofs are more common in the north: red tiles in Kabylian and Andalusian villages, and straw in the western Rif. Vaulted rooms (*ghorfa*) are frequent in parts of southern Tunisia, where, in the Monts des Ksour they are often grouped with cave-dwellings. The latter may be carved either vertically or horizontally (from a cliff edge) out of soft marls, and they have the property of mitigating summer heat and winter cold.

4. *Fortified Granaries*. A special feature of the Maghreb are the forti-fied granaries of sedentary and semi-nomadic Berbers of the desert margins. Known as *agadir, igherm* or *tirremt* by the Chleuh of southern Morocco, *guelaa* in the Aurès, and *ksar* in southern Tunisia,[55] the forti-fied granary occurs in a variety of sites, sizes and forms. Many dominate villages from hill-top sites; many are alone on plains. They are usually large square or rectangular constructions, composed of more than a hundred store-rooms arranged in several stories around a central court-yard. Store-rooms are privately constructed and owned, and are often only accessible by use of the various sticks and ledges jutting out from the walls. Constructed as defensive strongholds against nomadic or military attack, many were destroyed by tax-collecting sorties. Some of the hill-top granaries have been deserted for more accessible sites on the plain. In southern Tunisia, many *ksour* of semi-nomadic fractions are found on the Jeffara, or coastal plain (Figs. 259 and 260); they are com-posed of vaulted rooms (*ghorfa*). Granaries are not only vital for survi-val in areas of unreliable rainfall, they are important as social centres, especially for tent-dwelling tribes without any other permanent building. In Morocco, the *tirremt* is not always a granary; the term sometimes applies to the castle or *kasba* of a Berber caïd or chief.

5. *Villages and Dispersed Settlements*. Most sedentary peoples in the Maghreb live in villages. A common type is the village composed of flat-roofed houses on a hill slope, giving the appearance of a flight of terraces. The village normally overlooks the cultivations. In the southern Maghreb, such villages often cling to summits for defence and surround their fortified granaries. Villages of oases, however, are agglomerated partly for purposes of irrigation. In the Sahel and parts of north-east Tunisia, large agglomerated villages are located on the plain, and have

a semi-urban aspect. A large mosque, market and baths are normal amenities. The villages of the western foothills of the Middle Atlas are also impressive in size.

Villages are not always compact. Those in Kabylia, called *taddert*, are usually split into small hamlets, each with a marked defensive look. Hamlets composed of the dwellings of extended families also predominate in north-west Morocco where ridge roofs prevail. In contrast, the flat-roofed houses of the eastern Rif are dispersed.

Since the arrival of Europeans in the Maghreb many rural *souks* have become small administrative and commercial centres, often bearing a name indicating the day of the market, such as Souk el Arba (Wednesday) and Souk el Khemis (Thursday) in northern Tunisia. Such centres frequently have European bars, banks and garages.

Improvements in security have caused a dispersal of rural settlement on plains. Scattered houses and *gourbis* are proliferating in areas of arboriculture, cereal cultivation and even of semi-nomadism.

6. *European Rural Settlements*. The character of European rural settlement has been mainly determined by the type of cultivation and the type of colonisation. It is generally dispersed; with a wide scatter in the case of cereal cultivation, and a close pattern in areas of viticulture and market gardening. Official colonisation is associated with regular patterns of uniformly styled farmsteads with rectilinear villages containing churches and public buildings. Private colonisation brought more varied patterns and types, ranging from small congested farms, such as would be found in parts of southern France or Italy, to magnificent mansions midst vast estates. Mining centres established by Europeans have always had distinct European and Muslim quarters, and the latter have frequently been subdivided into tribal quarters.

The departure of large numbers of settlers will undoubtedly affect settlement types and patterns, but many transformations and influences brought by the Europeans are likely to persist and to be more widely disseminated. This may apply also to the new villages established recently by the French in northern Algeria. These villages, rectilinear in plan, are located in piedmont zones and are designed to re-house people from mountain villages which have been abandoned because of the Algerian war.[56] The present tendency is for the native villages to be recolonised while the regrouped units on being gradually depopulated.

REGIONAL DIVISIONS

In the Maghreb broad relationships are discernible between environment, man and his activities, but it is apparent that human groups and modes of life do not precisely coincide with physical regions. The incessant interplay of diverse human societies in intricate physical environments has produced complex social and economic patterns, which prohibit a simple regional analysis of the whole of the Maghreb based upon any one physical, cultural or economic criterion.[57] The relative influence of different physical factors upon social and economic divisions has varied from one part of the Maghreb to another. In Morocco and eastern Algeria, relief plays an instrumental role; in western Algeria, the climatic transition from the Mediterranean to the Sahara is most influential; in Tunisia, relief and climate have a complementary influence, but there no regional differentiation should ignore the significance of maritime influences (climatic and human) and the existence of coastal zones with human characteristics distinct from those in the interior.

The political division of the Maghreb into three countries broadly reflects fundamental geographical differences recognised by many foreign invaders. The political division does not entirely conform with a geographical division of the Maghreb into western, central and eastern sectors, as Morocco is larger than the western Maghreb while Tunisia is smaller than the eastern Maghreb. However, the political boundaries established by the Turks and fixed by the French are constantly gaining significance as national boundaries, especially since the achievement of independence. Distinctiveness of environment, economy and cultural traditions is now supplemented by separate national consciousness.

The western Maghreb owes its individuality to its amplitude of relief, more abundant rainfall and Atlantic façade, as well as to its contrasts between mountain and plain, semi-nomadic mountain Berbers and sedentary Arab plainsmen, and between remote Berber stronghold and mundane Arab city.[58] Morocco is richer than Algeria and Tunisia in men, minerals, water and beauty, and, though deprived of a Saharan sector, it appears more viable. It has been the source of powerful empires which have extended far beyond the present political boundaries. Roman, Arab and French invaders and pastoral nomads have penetrated with greater difficulty and less effect. A French Protectorate for only 44 years, Morocco is less Europeanised than the other two countries of the Maghreb. It has retained its own positive personality, derived from centuries of international isolation. Recent events have shown that Morocco now feels herself deprived by French delineation from her so-called 'source zone' in the western Sahara.

The central Maghreb has been in many ways the least favoured sector. Aridity and nomadism are prominent. Its Mediterranean zone is low, narrow and fragmented, while its steppe zone is largely coincident with the vast and dreary high plateaux, where drainage is intermittent and centripetal, and cultivation is irregular. The low, dissected chains of the Saharan Atlas have permitted the northward penetration of Saharan influences. Pastoral nomadism has been able to reach almost to the shores of the Mediterranean, with drastic effects upon internal political stability, agricultural development and urban growth. Empires have been fewer, less extensive and less stable than in Morocco; sedentary societies have survived only in isolated mountain massifs; towns were smaller and cultural life more restricted than to the east or west. Roman and French colonisations respected climatic zonation and more or less confined themselves to the *tell*; elsewhere, the nomad has long wandered at will. Algeria experienced more prolonged European occupation than either Morocco or Tunisia, and endured a more bitter struggle for independence. Long considered politically part of France, Algeria was developed by Europeans largely for Europeans. But Algeria has gained in one sense, for a huge area of the Sahara was attached to it by France. Six-sevenths of Algeria is desert, whose newly discovered mineral resources, so jealously eyed by Morocco, will greatly assist economic development.

The eastern Maghreb includes much of eastern Algeria as well as Tunisia. It is the sector of convergence of the Tellian and Saharan Atlas, and is dominated by a broken mountainous relief, without the majesty of Moroccan mountains and never too rugged to impede movement. Rainfall is greater than in the central Maghreb, especially in *friguia*, the local term for the Mediterranean zone. A double maritime façade has contributed greatly to Tunisia's traditions and has modified climatic zonation. On the lowlands south of its mountain backbone is a broad steppe zone where pastoralism predominates. But large-scale pure nomadism is rare in the eastern Maghreb, and Tunisia possesses only a small slice of the Sahara, partly clad with the chaotic dunes of the Great Eastern Erg. North of this *erg*, along the coastal plain known as the Jefara, was the route of entry into the Maghreb taken by Arab invaders. Tunisia has been almost completely arabised, and its cities have sustained Islamic culture throughout the centuries. Village life has also persisted remarkably in coastal localities. Little Tunisia, about the size of England with only one-tenth of the population, seems softer, less contrasted, more cultured and more sympathic to Western ideas than either Morocco or Algeria. Tunisia is extremely conscious of its individuality, a fact respected by France, but suffers from problems of viability.[59]

Regional consciousness is not only national. Traditional tribal divisions are still significant, though tribal cohesion has relaxed as a result of several forces: sedentarisation, improved internal security, the drain of young males to the cities, the growth of nationalism, and the loss of political power by the chief. In Algeria the French administrative framework frequently neglected tribal divisions, but in the two protectorates these divisions were acknowledged and the administrative units established have been largely adopted by the independent governments.

As sedentarisation and urbanisation proceed and administrative services are extended, city regions may be expected to develop. Several cities are already important regional nuclei, but the evolution of city regions in the Maghreb is impeded by two tendencies: the localisation of major cities at the coasts, where invaders have been able to establish administrative, commercial and defensive centres, and, secondly, the excessive big-headedness of urban growth in the three countries. Casablanca, Algiers and Tunis each account for one-quarter to one-third of the urban populations of their respective countries, and are several times larger than their nearest rivals. Their magnetic attractions are detrimental to the emergence of true regional nuclei.

With rapid social and economic progress in the Maghreb, new regions may be expected to evolve, especially if plans for decentralisation and development of steppe zones are successful.

CONCLUSION

'All countries are henceforth accessible, all regions are known . . .
cultivated fields have overcome the forests. . . . The sands are being
planted, the rocks hewn, the swamps drained . . . there are more
cities today than there were cabins some time ago.'

(Tertullian, *De Anima*, 30, 3)

By many a northerner, poet, painter, historian and geographer, the
Mediterranean has been loved passionately, and presumably will
always be so. The poet has been inspired by its life so rooted in the soil.
The painter has been challenged by its colours and varied forms. The
historian has recognised that its civilisations have been fundamental
to the history of mankind. The geographer has found the clearest links
between civilised man, soil and climate. All have been attracted by the
warmth and beauty of its landscapes. Creative of so much, students of
the Mediterranean recognise that in their enthusiasm for this unique
habitat lies the secret of any achievements that they may have accomplished. Here were made the first observations in climatology and
oceanography, here the impressive nature of folded relief was recognised, here ecology and the first steps in Quaternary studies were taken,
here the significance of historical geography was first appreciated by
classical scholars. Is it possible that regional geography, whose image is
apparently bruised in contemporary thought, may be reshaped in this
stimulating environment? If this is to be done, then the geographer
will have to recognise, like the painter, that he cannot depict all the
minutiae he sees before him, but must choose only what is most significant for his purpose.

It must be confessed that in the attempt to paint such a view of the
landscape which this book represents, it has not been possible to integrate in detail even such obviously interrelated matters as tectonics and
landforms, dynamic and regional climatology. It would be foolish to
pretend, therefore, that a complete geographical synthesis had been
attained by the methods used here. Yet some geographers maintain
that this is possible on a regional basis, even if on no other. But the
recourse to the idea of regional synthesis is often confused and may even
represent only a meaningless mystique. If synthesis simply means the
general method of deductive reasoning which proceeds from the simple
to the complex, or from the large-scale view of the beholder to the small
scale of regional generalisation, or from a principle to its application,

it is a general system common to all forms of knowledge. If synthesis represents the third phase in the dialectical process popularised by Hegel, arising from the combination of the thesis and the antithesis to a new level of truth, it belongs more properly to philosophy and logic. If it suggests a unification of knowledge drawn from various sciences, as we might create a new science of landscape out of geomorphology, climatology, pedology, ecology, environmental archaeology and cultural history, on this more limited basis it may have some intrinsic unity, derived from the unity of the landscape itself. Even here the geographer must recognise that distinct, often contrasted, models of thought remain uncoordinated. Then all the geographer can hope to do is to emphasise their inter-relatedness in area.

Perhaps a better term than synthesis would be 'syncretism', a word first used by Plutarch to describe the combination of incompatible elements, specifically theology and philosophy. Geographic method has this essential problem of dealing in particular with two particularly intractable components, man and land, each lending itself to especially divergent models of thought. Yet it is nature herself that provides us with the 'syncretic' result in the very landscape. John Ruskin, writing *Of the Novelty of Landscape*, claims that mankind acquired a new sense when he discovered the art of painting the landscape. Significantly, this art was first acquired in medieval Italy and then later practised in Provence. Perhaps it is no exaggeration to suggest that regional geography could develop a similar experience if the analysis and the description of landscape were made focal to the whole subject.

Although nature herself shows us the link between man and land in the landscape, it would be an arbitrary and false distinction to speak of 'natural' and 'cultural' landscapes as though they were separate portions of the environment. A territory may be more or less endowed with the heritage of man, or damaged by his destructive thoughtlessness. This stamp of human activity on the landscape may be more or less profound, depending on how intensive and advanced the exploitation of resources may be, and how numerous the population is. A comparison of the maps of landform types and of population distribution will help to keep a balanced perspective to both aspects of study, even if the book fails at times to do so. In the classical world of Tertullian's day, quoted at the head of this conclusion, the Western Mediterranean had 15–20 million inhabitants. In the late sixteenth century Braudel estimated the figure at 25 million. Today, it has over 118 million. Their impact is therefore very much greater than Tertullian could ever have foreseen. It would be a fascinating investigation to measure and attempt to map the growth of this human impact on the landscapes of this Mediterranean world.

It is particularly difficult in the Mediterranean to separate or even to distinguish between the natural and the cultural features of the landscape because it has been so long and continuously operated upon by man. We cannot say, for example, for how much of the erosion processes man is himself responsible, directly or indirectly; nor exactly how he has accentuated them; nor how they can effectively be controlled. Studies such as Almagia pioneered half a century ago, and others which Kayser in Basilicata and Poncet in Tunisia have recently initiated, show the way for further investigations. Again, in ecological studies, pioneer work is being done by Bordas, Pujol and others to measure man's impact upon the vegetation cover. Increasingly, the pastoralist is being squeezed out by both the forester and the cultivator. More knowledge of the regressive processes and the proportion of human responsibility for them will aid future policy in land management. Nevertheless, human evaluations of land resources, so contrasted in the past, still leave their imprint in today's landscape. National policies remain distinct; study of their past origins may be of great aid to more objective planning for the future. Ever since man commenced agriculture, re-adjustments of cropped land have been very varied, and there is still much to learn about the interactions of ecology, economy and society in the present patterns of fields and land use. Even the perspective gained from the evolution of the Western Mediterranean cities may aid urban planning in the future. From the Romans we can still learn how to make our new cities function more efficiently. From the Muslims we can re-establish the qualities of neighbourliness, to counteract modern mass-mindedness. From the medieval Christians we can recognise again the values of local initiative through strong municipal government, and so avoid over-centralisation.

In the Mediterranean, strategic pivot of the Old World, political power has played a vital role in the fortunes of its landscapes. Periods of glory have been followed by a swift decline. And what of the future, with man's dangerous and naïve faith in material progress and his temptation to live beyond his means? Yet among the simple Mediterranean peasantry, balance and restraint have been the wise directives in the quest for *Bios*, 'life according to reason'. Prudence and moderation are still needed for posterity. In teaching many lessons, the landscape remains the home of mankind, the nursery of his early experimentation and the schoolroom of his continued understanding of nature. 'He that has eyes to see, let him see.'

APPENDIXES

CLIMATIC AVERAGES

TABLE 1

Littoral Stations

	Mean Monthly Temperatures^T		Mean Annual Range of Temp.	Mean Annual Precipitation in inches	No. of Rain-days
	Jan.	Aug.			
Bilbao	47·6 (8·7)	70·3 (21·3)	22·7 (12·6)	47·4	164
Corunna	48·5 (9·2)	64·4 (18·0)	15·9 (8·8)	30·0	131
Oporto	48·7 (9·3)	69·2 (20·7)	10·5 (11·4)	47·3	113
Lisbon	50·5 (10·3)	71·7 (22·1)	21·2 (11·8)	29·7	116
Gibraltar	55·0 (12·8)	75·0 (23·9)	20·0 (11·1)	35·7	84
Cartagena	50·9 (10·5)	76·0 (24·4)	25·1 (13·9)	13·3	42
Valencia	49·8 (9·9)	76·6 (24·8)	26·8 (14·9)	18·5	56
Barcelona	47·6 (8·7)	75·3 (24·1)	27·7 (15·4)	20·6	72
Palma	50·3 (10·7)	78·4 (25·8)	27·9 (15·1)	17·9	73
Perpignan	44·0 (6·7)	72·0 (22·2)*	28·8 (16·0)	21·9	86
Marseilles	43·3 (6·3)	71·0 (21·7)*	29·0 (16·1)	14·5	81
Nice	43·7 (6·5)	71·4 (21·9)	27·7 (15·4)	21·0	81
Genoa	45·5 (7·5)	75·4 (24·1)	29·9 (16·6)	52·8	119
Naples	46·7 (8·2)	75·2 (24·0)*	28·8 (16·0)	21·6	116
Palermo	50·5 (10·3)	76·9 (24·9)	26·4 (14·6)	29·5	113
Cagliari	48·9 (9·4)	76·2 (24·6)*	27·7 (13·4)	19·0	89
Malta (Valletta)	53·0 (11·7)	77·0 (25·0)	24·0 (13·3)	19·8	77
Bari	46·4 (8·0)	75·2 (24·0)*	29·0 (16·1)	23·2	104
Venice	36·6 (2·6)	73·7 (23·2)*	38·7 (21·5)	26·1	98
Trieste	39·3 (4·1)	71·6 (22·0)*	34·8 (18·3)	26·9	125
Split	44·6 (7·0)	76·6 (24·8)*	33·1 (18·4)	34·5	102
Hvar	47·1 (8·4)	75·9 (24·4)*	29·5 (16·4)	31·3	104
Kotor	44·9 (7·2)	76·1 (24·5)*	33·0 (18·3)		122
Gabès	50·9 (10·5)	81·4 (27·4)	30·5 (16·9)	7·1	41
Bizerta	51·9 (11·1)	78·1 (25·6)	26·2 (14·5)	25·2	101
Algiers	55·6 (13·1)	78·7 (25·9)	23·1 (12·8)	30·0	120
Oran	53·1 (11·7)	75·1 (23·9)	22·0 (12·2)	22·5	67
Tangier	51·8 (11·0)	73·6 (23·1)	21·8 (12·1)	32·9	98
Casablanca	53·5 (11·9)	73·3 (22·9)	19·8 (11·0)	16·6	45
Mogador	56·0 (13·3)	68·2 (20·1)	12·2 (6·8)	13·0	40

T = Degrees Fahrenheit with Centigrade values in brackets.
* = Monthly maximum in July.

TABLE 2

Inland Stations

	Mean Monthly Temperatures		Mean Annual Range of Temp.	Mean Annual Precipitation in inches	No. of Rain-days	No. of Snow-days
	Jan.	Aug.				
Saragossa	41·9 (5·5)	76·4 (24·7)	34·5 (19·2)	22·0	66	2·1
Burgos	36·0 (2·2)	66·0 (18·9)	30·0 (16·7)	21·7	103	—
Madrid	40·1 (5·0)	76·2 (25·0)	37·0 (20·0)	16·5	95	4·0
Badajoz	45·0 (7·2)	79·0 (26·1)	34·0 (18·9)	15·1	65	0·4
Seville	52·0 (11·1)	85·0 (29·4)	33.0 (18·3)	19·4	69	—
Milan	33·8 (+0·9)	73·8 (23·2)*	42·1 (23·4)	42·2	121	9·1
Florence	40·5 (4·7)	74·8 (23·8)*	35·8 (19·9)	33·0	117	2·3
Urbino	36·5 (2·5)	72·0 (22·2)*	36·7 (19·4)	39·6	92	8·7
Caltanisetta	43·3 (6·3)	75.7 (24·3)*	32·8 (18·2)	24·1	80	1·2
Gafsa	(9·1)	(29·6)	(20·5)	8·3	33	—
Biskra	51·6 (10·9)	88·8 (31·6)*	39·0 (21·7)	6·9	49	
Touggourt	51·0 (5·9)	92·9 (25·9)	41·0 (20·0)	2·8	20	
Laghoat	44·6 (7·0)	81·6 (27·6)*	40·4 (21·3)	7·3	25	
Marrakech	51·2 (10·7)	82·5 (28·1)	31·3 (17·4)	9·3	50	

TABLE 3

Mountain Stations

	Alt. in feet	Mean Monthly Temperatures		Mean Annual Range of Temp.	Mean Annual Precipitation in inches	No. of Rain-days	No. of Snow-days
		Jan.	Aug.				
Pic du Midi	2,895	+7·0 (−7·9)	43·7 (6·5)	26·7 (12·6)	63·0	181	118
Penhas Douradas	4,560	36·5 (2·5)	60·5 (15·9)*	24·6 (14·5)	92·5		
Aquila	2,408	34·3 (+1·3)	69·6 (20·9)*	36·2 (20·1)	27·3	116	17

TABLE 4

Climatic Stations of the Islands

Station	Mean Monthly Temperature	Mean Annual Range	Mean Annual Precipitation in inches	Rainfall in June, July, September
Ajaccio	60·0 (16·1)	26·0 (14·4)	29·3	5·0
Cagliari	56·0 (13·4)	(15·9)	19·0	1·2
Palma	63·0 (17·7)	27·0 (15·1)	19·0	1·8
Valletta	64·0 (17·8)	24·0 (13·0)	20·5	0·3

CHRONOLOGICAL TABLE OF THE SEDIMENTARY ROCKS OF THE WESTERN MEDITERRANEAN

		Alpine Glaciations	Mediterranean Raised Beaches
Neo-gene	Pleistocene — Upper {	Würm Riss/Würm Interglacial	Flandrian Tyrrhenian
	Middle {	Riss Mindel/Riss Interglacial	Tyrrhenian
	Lower {	Mindel Gunz/Mindel Interglacial Gunz *Villafranchian/Calabrian continental marine	Sicilian

Full table:

		Alpine Glaciations	Mediterranean Raised Beaches
		Upper { Würm	Flandrian
		Riss/Würm Interglacial	Tyrrhenian
	Pleistocene	Middle { Riss	
		Mindel/Riss Interglacial	Tyrrhenian
		Mindel	
		Gunz/Mindel Interglacial	
		Lower Gunz	
		*Villafranchian/Calabrian	Sicilian
		continental marine	
Neo-gene		*Continental Strata*	*British equivalents*
		Astian	
	Pliocene	Plaisantian	Lenhamian
		Pontian	
		Sarmatian	
		Tortonian	
	Miocene	Helvetian	—
		Burdigalian	—
		Aquitanian	—
Palaeo-gene	Oligocene	Stampian }	Upper Tertiaries of
		Sannoisian }	Hampshire Basin
		Ludian	
		Ledian }	{ Bagshot Beds
	Eocene	Lutetian |	{ London Clay
		Ypresian {	{ Reading Beds and
		Landenian }	{ Thanet Sands
		{ Danian	—
		Senonian	Upper Chalk
		Turonian	Middle Chalk
		Cenomanian	Lower Chalk
	Cretaceous {	Albian	Upper G'sand and Gault
		Aptian	Lower G'sand and Gault
		Barremian	—
		{ Neocomian	—
		Portlandian	Portland and Purbeck
		Kimeridgian	Kimmeridge Clay
		Sequanian	—

* These phases were usually thought to be included in the Pliocene but since 1948 are considered to be the earliest phases of the Pleistocene.

Jurassic   Oxfordian   Corallian
                 Callovian   Oxford Clay
                 Bathonian   Great Oolite
                 Bajocian   Inferior Oolite
                       Liassic Series

Trias

CULTURE TYPES (*Based on Castillo cave, Northern Spain. Approximate*)

Moroccan Chronology	Alpine Chronology	
Gharbian	Post-Glacial	Mesolithic
Ouljian		Magdalenian
		Solutrian
Soltanian	Würm	Gravettian
		Aurignacian
Tyrrhenian III?		Late Mousterian
Tyrrhenian II	Riss/Würm Interglacial	Mousterian
Tensiftian	Riss	Late Acheulian
Tyrrhenian I	Mindel/Riss Interglacial	Middle Acheulian
Amirian?	Mindel	Lower Acheulian
Sicilian	Gunz/Mindel Interglacial	Clacto-Abbevillian
Saletian?	Gunz	
Calabrian		
Moulouyan	*Villafranchian	Clacto-Abbevillian? in Morocco

APPENDIX III

STATISTICS OF LAND UTILISATION

TABLE 1

Land Utilisation, in Thousands of Hectares, 1956–8

Country	Land Area	Cultivated Area Arable	Permanent Pasture	Forested Land	Unused Land	Waste Land
Italy	30,123	15,781	5,124	5,781	1,123	2,314
Spain	50,349	19,986	9,563	13,813	—	6,987
Portugal	8,862	3,380	1,484	2,467	1,191	384
Morocco	39,080	7,770	9,780	3,900	7,580	10,050
Algeria	220,486	6,878	40,176	3,070	—	170,362
Tunisia	12,500	4,265	105	900	3,730	3,500

1. Includes fallow land.
2. Includes 2,200,000 ha of alfa.
3. Comprises 32,000 ha of natural grasslands and 40,144,000 of rough grazings.
4. Includes rough grazings.

TABLE 2

Intensity of Land Utilisation, in Thousands of Hectares

Country	Unproductive Area % of Total Area	Area Cultivated Yearly	Percentage of cultivated area under Cereals	Fallow	Area Irrigated Yearly	Estimated Area Suitable for Irrigation
Italy	3·4	15,750	32·8	—	2,100	?
Spain	10·0	19,986	34·3	26	1,752	3,500
Portugal	16·0	3,380	40·0	25	33	106
Morocco	45·0	7,770	47·5	45	220	500
Algeria	48·0	6,900	51·0	46	250	500
Tunisia	28·0	3,300	57·0	39	50	173

TABLE 3

Cereals in the Western Mediterranean, in Thousands of Hectares, 1960/61

Country	Total Cropland	Wheat	Barley	Fallow(1)
Italy	15,833	4,556	216	—
Spain	20,523	4,244	1,428	5,350
Portugal	4,130	738	120	850
Morocco	8,564	1,645	1,860	2,900
Algeria	6,819	1,920	1,164	2,700
Tunisia	4,912	1,354	688	1,700

1. 1956/7.

TABLE 4

Area of Tree Crops, in Thousands of Hectares, 1960/61

	Italy	Spain	Portugal	Morocco	Algeria	Tunisia
Olives	2,242(1)	2,140	*	*	*	700
Vines	1,143(2)	1,726	323	72	368	47
Citrus fruit	167(3)	110	*	*	*	*
Chestnuts	532	112	70	—	—	—
Cork Oaks	106	504	690	400	430	99
Holm Oaks	986(4)	2,892	?	1,310	?	?

1. Includes 1,353,000 ha in mixed cultivation.
2. Excludes 2,579,000 ha in mixed cultivation.
3. Includes 76,000 ha in mixed cultivation.
4. Includes also *Q. cerris*, *Q. suber* and *Q. robur*.

* National statistics only give production in quintals or metric tons.

TABLE 5

Irrigation in Spain, 1956

Catchment Area	Irrigated Area (in thousands of ha)		No. of Dams in Use	Storage Capacity (in millions of cu. metres)
	Exploited	In Construction		
Northern rivers	0·7	4·2	17	948·2
Ebro	372·0	137·0	35	1,673·6
E. Pyrenees	20·0	0·5	5	21·9
Levante	131·0	23·0	20	1,427·4
Segura	104·0	23·8	8	344·0
Southern rivers	9·7	0·6	3	91·5
Guadalquivir	132·5	43·7	17	1,993·0
Guadiana	6·6	15·5	4	1,017.0
Tagus	27·9	9·0	19	3,011·0
Douro	39·7	40·4	14	1,978·5
Total	845·4	298·5	89	12,506·0

TABLE 6

Irrigation in Italy

	Irrigated Area	
	1952 (in ha)	1962 (in ha)
Northern Italy	184,500	335,000
Central Italy	29,600	40,000
Southern Italy	117,000	186,000
The Islands	11,800	12,000

TABLE 7

Land Reform Progress, 1950–60

Authority	Total Area (ha)	Lands Ex-propriated (ha)	Average Size of family holding (ha)	Irrigated Area (ha)	New Villages Constructed	Other Farms
Po delta	47,497	44,200	6·0	2,549	7	—
Maremma	179,044	177,500	8·0	2,604	5	88
Fucino	15,980	15,900	1·4	2,500	4	—
Sele-Garigliano	15,073	—	—	1,400	—	—
Apulia–Lucania	196,709	189,400	5·4	3,571	41	82
Sila	84,865	74,800	4·0	4,802	12	22
Sardinia	96,908	47,400	13·0	525	8	—
,, (Flumendosa)	4,653	2,500		22	—	2
Sicily	108,253	80,000	4·4	—	15	—

TABLE 8

European Colonisation in North Africa prior to 1958/60

Territory	European Lands*	Percentage of Total Area	Colonisation Official*	Private
Algeria	2,703	37·9	1,700	1,000
Tunisia	758	27·6	399	371
Morocco	1,085	14·5	275	575

* In thousands of hectares.

TABLE 9

Irrigation in North Africa, 1958–60

	Total Irrigated Area*	Percentage of Cropland Irrigated	Area of Large Perimeters Potentially Irrigable*	Actually Irrigated*
Algeria	130	3·5	95·4	41·8
Tunisia	50	0·7	23·0	?
Morocco	180	2·8	143·0	60·2

* In thousands of hectares.

TABLE 10

Iberian Forests and Woodlands, in Hectares, 1956

Portugal		Spain	
Pines	1,151,000	Pines	4,207,700
Oaks	1,158,000		
		P. halepensis	1,242,900
Q. suber	690,000	P. pinaster	1,224,400
Chestnuts	108,000	Fir	72,100
		Oaks	5,286,700
		Q. ilex	3,037,700
		Q. suber	530,300
		Q. robur	340,000
		Beech	577,500
		Poplar	146,400
		Eucalyptus	110,300
		Chestnut	90,800

TABLE 11

Italian Forests and Woodlands in Hectares, 1957

High Forest	2,180,154	*Coppiced Woodlands*	5,617,213
Conifers	1,049,000	*Deciduous*	4,445,000
Scots Pine	224,617	Oaks	751,244
Spruce	182,233	Beech	449,939
Larch	106,430	Chestnut	453,246
Other Woodlands	1,144,682	*Mixed coppice*	1,868,841
Evergreens		*Mediterranean Macchia*	943,000
Ilex		*Other Mediterranean Scrub*	2,542,000
Cork Oak	106,073 (of which 59,656 are in pure stands)		

TABLE 12

Approximate Limits of Forest Trees (in Feet)

	Alps	Etruscan Apennines	Central Apennines	South Apennines	Sicily
Upper Montane Zone					
White Fir	2,600–4,900	2,950–5,000		2,950–5,830	
Scots Pine	1,000–4,300	1,000–4,300			
Black Pine	1,300–3,300	1,500–4,500	3,000–5,000	3,300–5,250	4,300–4,800
Beech	2,300–5,250	2,950–5,250	3,300–5,900	3,300–6,600	4,300–6,600
Lower Montane Zone					
Sweet Chestnut	1,000–2,950	1,000–2,950	1,300–3,300	1,300–3,300	1,600–4,900
Pedunculate Oak	1,000–2,950	330–2,950	1,300–3,600	1,300–3,600	2,160–5,900
Turkey Oak	1,000–3,300	1,000–3,600	1,000–4,300	1,000–4,300	2,160–4,900

	Liguria	Tuscany	Latium	Lucania	Sicily
Mediterranean Zone					
Evergreen Oak	1,600	3,200–3,770	3,440–3,900	3,280	4,260
Cork Oak	1,200	1,600	1,600	2,000	2,000

TABLE 13

Chief Crops of Italy, 1961 (in thousands of hectares)

Total Cereals	5,551	*Vines*	3,693
Wheat	4,339	Mixed cropping	2,538
Maize	1,199		
Rice	123	*Olives*	2,255[1]
		Mixed cropping	1,356[1]
Leguminous Crops	1,070		
Fodder Crops	10,217	*Fruits*	517
Rotation meadows	3,757	Almond	168
Rough grazing	3,814	Citrus	86
Industrial Crops	332	Soft Fruits	188

[1] Figures for 1958.

	%Total Agric. Production	%Total Area
Northern Italy	44·0	27·0
Central Italy	22·6	23·5
Southern Italy	23·0	29·8
Insular Italy	10·4	19·7
	100·0	100·0

TABLE 14

Tree Crops in Thousands of Hectares, 1957

	Vines	Olives	Soft Fruits	Citrus Fruits	Others
Interculture	2,723	1,365	7,581	380	1,258
Specialised cropping	1,088	880	380	86	10

TABLE 15

Development of Canals in the Western Po Plain

Canal	Date of Construction	River Source	Length of Main Canal in Miles
Lombardy			
Naviglio Grande	*c.* 1177–8	Ticino	49·9
Naviglio della Martesana	1457	Adda	
Canal de Pavia Muzza	1223	Adda	43·5
Naviglio Civico di Cremona	14th cen.	Oglio	
Clisio	*c.* 1300		45·0
Piedmont			
Ivrea	1468	Dora Baltea	45·0
Cigliano (Depretis)	1785 (enlarged 1858)	Dora Baltea	19·3
Naviletto	15th cen.	Mandria	
Canal de Rotto	14th cen.	Dora Baltea	11·9
Busca	1380	Sesia	36·0
Rezzo-Biraga	1488	Sesia	35·0
Cavour	1863–6	Po–Dora Baltea–Sesia–Ticino	51·0

TABLE 16

European Farms in the Maghreb

	Official	Private	Total	No. of Farms
Algeria	4,250,000	2,500,000	6,750,000	26,000
Tunisia	998,750	927,500	1,926,250	6,000
French Morocco	687,500	1,437,500	2,125,000	4,000
	5,936,250	4,865,000	10,801,250	36,000

APPENDIX IV

POPULATION STATISTICS

TABLE 1

Population of the Iberian Peninsula

The Kingdoms and Their Regions	Area in Thousands of sq. miles	Population in Millions (and Percentage of Total)		Density per sq. mile		Percentage Increase 1594–1950
		c. 1594	1950	*c.* 1594	1950	
Castile						
Northern Zone (1)	19·3	1·4 (12·9)	3.49 (11·0)	72	170	149
Central Zone (2)	52·0	3·4 (31·0)	5·75 (14·8)	65	110	69
Intermediate Zone (3)	34·7	1·3 (12·1)	2·66 (8·0)	34	76	104
Southern Zone (4)	38·6	1·8 (16·5)	6·36 (19·6)	46	165	247
Navarre	4·0	0·2 (1·9)	0·38 (1·9)	50	95	90
Aragón						
Aragón	18·3	0·4 (3·6)	1·15 (3·7)	21	63	187
Catalonia	12·4	0·4 (3·6)	3·24 (9·3)	32	253	701
Valencia (5)	9·0	0·6 (5·55)	2·73 (7·6)	66	303	355
Portugal	34·2	1·5 (12·9)	7·92 (24·1)	44	231	428
Total of the Iberian Peninsula	222·5	11·0 (100·0)	33·68 (100·0)	49	123	212

1. Basque, Cantabrian and Galician provinces.
2. Old Castile, León and southern provinces of Guadalajara, Madrid and Toledo.
3. New Castile and Extremadura.
4. Andalusia and Murcia.
5. Castellon, Valencia, Alicante and the Balearic Islands.

TABLE 2

Population Changes in the Iberian Peninsula, 1900–50

	Population 1950	Percentage Increase 1900–1950	Percentage of National Total	Percentage born in other Communes	Density per sq. mile
Peripheral Zones and Regions					
The North	*4,840,498*	*43.0*	*17·8*	*33*	*243*
The North-west	2,604,200	31·5	9·6	17	233
The North	2,236,298	58·5	8·2	68	259
The Levante	*5,969,470*	*54·5*	*21·9*	*40*	*240*
Catalonia	3,240,313	64·7	11·9	48	280
Valencia (including Balearic Is.)	2,729,157	41·7	10·0	37	251
Andalusia	*6,362,578*	*54·4*	*23·4*	*23*	*168*
Upper Andalusia	2,647,190	36·4	9·7	18	170
Lower Andalusia	3,715,388	70·0	13·7	26	163
Portugal	*7,921,913*	*63·2*	—	—	*209*
The North	6,813,072	63·0	86·0	—	296
The South	1,108,841	64·9	14.0	—	93
Central Zones and Regions					
Old Castile and Aragón	*4,164,545*	*22.0*	*15·4*	*24*	*67*
Old Castile and León	2,339,808	22·7	8·6	11	62
The Ebro Valley	1,824,737	22·1	6·8	32	69
Extremadura	*5,846,336*	*69·5*	*21·5*	*31*	*108*
The Western Borderlands	2,092,705	41·5	7·9	21	80
New Castile	3,753,631	91·4	13·6	35	129
National Total	*27,183,427*	*45·6*	*100·0*		*145*

TABLE 3

Population Changes in Italy, 1881–1961

	Population (in Thousands) 1881	Percentage of Total	Population (in Thousands) 1961	Percentage of Total
The North	11,841	39	22,566	45
Centre	7,353	28	9,325	18
South	6,893	23	11,443	23
Islands	3,610	10	6,125	14
Total	29,697	100	50,463	100

TABLE 4

Percentage of Total Population in Italy by Altitude

	0–100 m (328 ft)	100–500 m (328–1,640 ft)	500–1,000 m (1,640–3,280 ft)	Over 1,000 m (3,280 ft)
1931	42·0	44·3	12·7	1·0
1951	44·2	43·0	11·9	0·9

TABLE 5

The Western Mediterranean Islands

Islands	Area in sq. miles	Population in 1950–51	Density per sq. mile	Percentage Employed in Agriculture	Percentage of Total Area Cultivated
Corsica	3,367	360,000	106	48·6	2·5
Sardinia	9,301	1,276,023	137	41·6	2·8
The Balearics	1,883	422,089	224	38·0	57·1
Maltese Islands	117	245,638	2,016	1·80	40·0

TABLE 6

Settlers in Tunisia

	French	Italians
1896	17,000	60,000
1916	51,000	87,000
1936	108,000	94,000
1956	180,450	66,900
Early 1961	65,000	40,000

BIBLIOGRAPHY

BIBLIOGRAPHY

ABBREVIATIONS

A.	Academy, Academie, etc.
A.A.A.G.	Annals of the Association of American Geographers
A.E.S.C.	Annales, Economies, Societés, Civilisations (Paris)
A.H.E.S.	Annales d'Histoire, Économique et Social (Paris)
A. de G.	Annales de Géographie (Paris)
Al-And.	Al-Andalus (Seville)
Ant.	Antiquity (London)
A.M.	Annales de Midi
A.H.D.Esp.	Anuario de Historia del Derecho Español (Madrid)
B.A.A.P.G.	Bulletin of the Association of American Petrologists
B.A.G.F.	Bulletin de l'Association Géographes Français (Paris)
B.S.	Boletim, Bollettino, Bulletin—de Sociedad, Societé, Society, etc.
B.E.S.T.	Bulletin Économique et Sociale de la Tunisie (Tunis)
B.S.B.F.	Bulletin de la Societé Botanique Français (Paris)
B.S.G.I.	Bollettino della Società Geografía Italia (Rome)
B.S.G.F.	Bulletin de la Societé Geologique de la France (Paris)
C.R.	Comptes Rendus
C.T.	Cahiers de Tunisie (Tunis)
Celt.	Celtiberia (Soria)
Class. Journ.	Classical Journal
Coll.	Colloque, Colloquium
Com.	Communications, Comunication, etc.
Cuad. Est. Gall.	Cuadernos de Estudios Gallegos (Santiago de Compostella)
E.G.	Estudios Geográficos (Madrid)
Econ. Geog.	Economic Geography
Erdk.	Erdkunde
Est. Seg.	Estudios Segovianos (Segovia)
Et. Rhod.	Études Rhodaniennes (Lyon)
G.	Geography (Sheffield)
G.J.	Geographical Journal (London)
G.R.	Geographical Review (New York)
Geogr.	Geografía (Zaragoza)
Ges.	Gesellschaft
Hesp.	Hesperis (Rabat)
Hisp.	Hispania (Madrid)
I.	International
INQUA	International Association on Quaternary Research
J.G.	Journal of Geography
J.R.S.	Journal of Roman Studies (London)
La Géog.	La Géographie (Paris)
La Met.	a La Méteorologie (Paris)
Landesk.	Landeskunde
L'Univ.	L'Universo (Florence)
M.	Magazine
Médit.	Méditerranée (Montpellier)
Mem.	Memoirs, Memoires, Memoria, etc.

Met.	Metorology, Météorologie, etc.
Mit.	Miteilungen
Proc.	Proceedings
Q.J.G.S.	Quarterly Journal of the Geological Society (London
Quat.	Quaternary (Rome)
R.	Royal, Royale, Real, etc.
R.G.A.	Revue de Géographie Alpine (Grenoble)
R.G.I.	Rivista Geografica Italiana (Florence)
R.G.M.	Revue Géographique Marocaine (Rabat)
R.G.P.G.D.	Revue de Géographie physique et Geologie dynamique (Paris)
R.G.P.S.O.	Revue de Géographie des Pyrenées et de Sud-Ouest (Toulouse)
R.I.S.	Revista del Instituto de Sociología (Madrid)
R.M.	Revue de la Méditerranée
R.T.	Revue Tunisienne
Rec.	Records
Rev. Afr.	Revue Africaine (Paris)
Ric.	Ricerche
S.	Society, Société, Sociedad, etc.
Sc.	Science

CHAPTER 1

INTRODUCTION

Of the numerous works on the Mediterranean, the standard textbooks are as follows:

BIROT, P. and DRESCH, J. *La Méditerranée et le Moyen-Orient*: Tome I, *La Méditerranée Occidentale*. Paris, 1953. 552 pp.

FISCHER, T. *Mittelmeer-Bilder. Gesammelte Abhandlungen zur kunde der Mittelmeer-Lander*. Leipzig und Berlin, 1906. 480 pp.

MAULL, O. *Landerkunde von Sudeuropa*. Leipzig und Wien, 1929. 550 pp.

NEWBIGIN, M. *Southern Europe*. London, 1932, 3rd edn. revised 1952. 428 pp.

PHILIPPSON, A. *Das Mittelmeergebiet. Seine geographische und kulturelle Eigenatt*. Leipzig, 1904. 266 pp.

SEMPLE, E. C. *The Geography of the Mediterranean Region. Its relation to ancient history*. London, 1932. 737 pp.

SION, J. *Méditerranée Peninsules méditerranéennes* (*Géog. Universelle*, tome VII), 1934. Part 1, 234 pp.; part 2, 597 pp.

Other lighter works are:

POUNDS, N. J. *Europe and the Mediterranean*. New York, 1953. 437 pp.

SIEGFRIED, A. *The Mediterranean*, translated by Doris Hemming. London, 1948. 221 pp.

WALKER, D. S. *The Mediterranean Lands*. London, 1960. 524 pp.

REFERENCES

1. BOBEK, H. and SCHMITHUSEN, J. 'Die Landschaft im logischen System der Geographie', *Erd*. 3, 1949, pp. 112–20.
   See also: CAROL, H. 'Zur diskussion um Landschaft und Geographie', *Helv*. XI, 1956, pp. 111–33; and BOESCH, H. H., 'Zur Stellung der modernen Geographie', *Helv*. XVII, 1962, pp. 288–93.
2. HUGGINS, K. H. 'Landscape and Landschaft', *G.*, 1936. pp. 225–6.

3. CROWE, P. R. 'On progress in Geography', *S.G.M.* 54, 1938. pp. 1–18. See reply by R. E. DICKINSON, 'Landscape and society', *S.G.M.* 55, 1938. pp. 1–13.
4. KIMBLE, G. H. T. 'The inadequacy of the regional concept', in *London Essays in Geography*, ed. S. W. Wooldridge and L. D. Stamp. London, 1951. pp. 151–74.
5. MACKINDER, H. J., Journ. Royal Artillery, vol. 39, 1912-13, pp. 195-6.
6. BIROT, P., PEDELABORDE, P., *et alii*. 'Problèmes climatiques sur la bordure nord du monde méd900téranéen', *A. de G.* LXV, 1956. pp. 15–39.
7. BUTZER, K. W. 'Remarks on soil erosion in Spain', MS communicated at the Association of American Geographers' meeting, East Lancing, Aug. 1961.
8. Personal communication of 17 July 1961 from Professor G. E. HUTCHINSON of Yale, who organised the research programme at Lago di Monterosi.
9. BORDAS, J. *Essai d'agronomie méditerranéenne*. Avignon, 1946.
10. LOPEZ, R. S. 'The Trade of Medieval Europe: the South' in *The Cambridge Economic History of Europe*, planned by the late J. Clapham and E. Power. Cambridge, 1952. Vol. 2, pp. 257–354. [A brilliant study.]
11. SCULLY, V. *The Earth, the Temple and the Gods*. Yale, 1962.

PART I: LANDSCAPES OF THE WESTERN MEDITERRANEAN WORLD

CHAPTER 2

THE CLIMATIC SCENE

Useful bibliography contained in:
GLEESON, T. A. *Bibliography of the Meteorology of the Mediterranean, Middle East, and South Asia areas*. Florida Dept. of Met. AF 19 (122), 466 Sc. Rept. No. 1. 1952.

BASIC SOURCES

ALT, E. *Handbuch der Klimatologie*, Tome III: *Mittel-und Sud-Europa*. Berlin, 1932. 288 pp.

BIEL, E. R. *Climatology of the Mediterranean Area*. Chicago, 1944. 180 pp. [Contains useful bibliography.]

BÉRENGER, M. *Essai d'étude méteorologique du bassin méditerranéen*. Paris, 1955. Memorial de la Méteorologie Nationale, No. 40.

BYERS, H. R. *General Meteorology*, 3rd edn. New York, 1959. 282 pp.

Chicago University Institute of Meteorology. *A Report on Synoptic Conditions in the Mediterranean Area*. Misc. rept. No. 14. Chicago, 1944.

CONRAD, V. 'The Climate of the Mediterranean Region', *Bull. Am. Met. Soc.*, 1943.

HARE, F. K. *The Restless Atmosphere*, 2nd. edn. London, 1960. 192 pp. [An excellent summary.]

Meteorological Office. *Weather in the Mediterranean*, revised edn. 1957 (MS); also, *Weather in the Mediterranean*, vol. 1, 2nd edn. *General Meteorology*, 1962. 362 pp. [Important section on upper winds.]

ROUCH, M. J. 'Le climat de la Méditerranée', Comm. Internat. pour l'Exploration Scient. de la Mer Medit. *Rapports*, Vol. XI, Paris, 1938.

TREWARTHA, G. T. *The Earth's Problem Climates*. London, 1962.

World Met. Organisation. 'Seminar in Rome: Synoptic Meteorology in the Mediterranean', *W.M.O. Bull.*, April, 1959, pp. 68–73.

REGIONAL STUDIES

Touring Club Italiano. *L'Italia Fisica*. Milan, 1957. pp. 21–63.
LORENTES, J. M. 'Climas españoles', Inst. Nac. Geof. *Rev. Geof.*, 5, 1946, pp. 204–31.
MASACHS ALAVEDRA, V. 'El Clima' in *Geografía de España y Portugal*, ed. by M. Téran, Tome II. Madrid, 1954, pp. 9–79.
PINNAR, M. *Il Clima della Sardegna*. dell 'Ist. di Geog. Pisa, 1955.
SELTZER, P. *Le climat de l'Algérie*. Algiers, 1946, 219 pp.

REFERENCES

1. THEOPHRASTUS OF ERESUS, *On Winds and on Weather Signs*, translated by J. G. Wood and edited by G. J. Symons. London, 1894.
2. HARE, F. K. 'The Westerlies', *G.R.* 1960, pp. 345–67.
3. PEDELABORDE, P. and DELANNOY, H. 'Recherches sur les types de temps et le mecanisme des pluies en Algérie', *A. de G.* LXVII, 1958, pp. 216–44.
4. PETTERSSEN, S. *Weather Analysing and Forecasting*, 2nd. edn. New York.
5. Personal communication with Dr D. Houghton. Meteorological Office, London.
6. HARE, F. K. 'The causation of the arid zone', in *History of Land Use in the Arid Regions*, ed. by L. D. Stamp, U.N.E.S.C.O. Paris, 1961, pp. 25–30.
7. BIROT, P., PEDELABORDE, P. *et alii*. 'Problèmes climatiques sur la bordure nord du monde méditerranéen', *A. de G.* LXV. 1956, pp. 15–39.
8. AUSTIN, E. E. and DEWAR, D. *Upper Winds over the Mediterranean and Middle East*. Met. Office, M.R.P. No. 811, 1953.
9. For details see SERRA, A. 'Sulle caratteristiche fisiche delle principali masse d'aria nel Mediterraneo Occidentale'. *Riv. di Meteorol. Aeron.*, IX, 1949.
10. LANDI, A. 'Le fronte tropicale sul Mediterraneo', *Riv. Met. Aer.* III. 1939, pp. 3–35.
11. QUENEY, P. 'Types de temps en Afrique du Nord et en Sahara', Sept. *Inst. Météorol. Phys. Globe*, fasc. 3. Algiers, 1943, pp. 7–41.
12. FONTAINE, P. 'Les gouttes d'air froid sur l'Europe, la Méditerranée et l'Atlantique', *La. Met.* 10, pp. 98–112.
13. JAUSA, J. M. 'La masa de aire mediterranea', *Madrid Inst. Nac. Geof. Rev. Geof.* 18, 1959, pp. 35–50.
14. SUTCLIFFE R. C. in 'W.M.O. Seminar in Rome' (as above), p. 71.
15. HARE, F. K. *The Restless Atmosphere* (as above), p. 180.
16. BENEVENT, E. 'Bora et Mistral', *A. de G.* 1930, p. 286.
17. also GALZI, I. 'Contribution à l'étude du mistral', *La Met.*, 1952, p. 7; and MENGEL, O. 'Extension du Mistral en Méditerrannée', *La Met.* 10, 1934, pp. 482–5.
18. BAND, G. 'Die Bora der Adria', *Geof. Pura App.* 19, 1951, pp. 186–219; also DEFANT, F. 'Local Winds' in *Compendium of Meteorology*. Toronto, 1953. pp. 655–72; and PEPPLER, W. *Beitrage zur geophysisk*. Köppen-Band. pp. 223–31.
19. GOREZNOSKI, W. 'Sunshine and cloudiness in the Mediterranean basin', *Bull. Amer. Met. Soc.* 24. 1943. pp. 183–93.
20. HARE, F. K. *Atlas Lee-depressions and their Significance for Sciroccos*. Met Office, London S.D.T.M. 43.
21. BOSSOLASCO, M. 'Lo spostamento dei cicloni nel Mediterraneo' *Geofisica pura e appl.* 22. 1942.
22. BLECKER, W. 'Some climatological remarks about the field of flow and temperature over the Mediterranean sea', *Inst. Met. Geophy. Abh.* 9, III. Berlin, 1960, pp. 51–76.
23. BENDER, K. 'Computation of 5-day temperature normals in W. Europe and the Mediterranean area', *Geof. Pura Appli.* Milan 38. 1957, pp. 265–85.

24. EREDIA, F. *La Temperatura media dell'aria in Italia nel decennio 1926–35.* Rome, 1st. Poligr. dello Stato, 1942.

25. LAUTENSACH, H.; also SEMMELHACK, W. 'Temporaturkartun der Iberischen Halbinsel', *Annalen der Hydr. und Marit. Met. Gotha, 60.* 1932, pp. 327–33.

26. Numerous rainfall maps have been compiled. For Italy, see MINISTERO DEI LAVORI PUBBLICI, *Il servicio idrográfico italiano,* Rome, 1931; also rainfall map published in 1958. For Portugal, see VEIGA GARCIA, A. N., *Carta pluviométrica de Portugal,* 1/1 million. *Observations do Infante D. Luiz.* Lisbon, 1943. For Spain, see MIN. DE OBRAS PUBLICAS, *Mapa pluviométrico de España y Portugal,* Madrid, 1942; also LAUTENSACH, H. 'Die niederschlagshohen auf der Iberischen Halbinsel', *Pet. Geog. Mitt.* XCV, 1951, pp. 145–60. For N. Africa see GAUSSEN, H. et VERNET, A. *La carte des precipitations de l'Afrique du Nord.* Scale 1/500,000.

27. BALDACCI, O. 'Le intensita medie dei piogge in Italia', *B.S.G.I.* 1952, pp. 185–213.

28. GONZALEZ, QUIJANO, P. M. *Mapa pluviometrico de España.* Madrid, 1946, 574 pp.

29. See studies by ISARD, H. 'La répartition saisonnière des pluies en Algerie', *A. de G.* LIX, 1950, pp. 354–61; 'La répartition saisonnière des pluies en Tunisie', *A. de G.* LXI, 1952, pp. 357–62. 'La répartition saisonnière des pluies en Maroc', *A. de G.* L, 1958. pp. 39–42.

30. YEH TU-CHENG, DAO SHIH-YEN and MEI-TS'UN. 'The abrupt change of circulation over the northern hemisphere during June and October', in *The Atmosphere and the Sea in Motion,* ed. B. Bolin. New York, 1959, pp. 249–67; See also SUTCLIFFE, R. C. and BANNON, J. K., 'Seasonal changes in upper air conditions in the Mediterranean–Middle East Asia', *Sci. Proc. Internat. Assoc. of Met.* Rome, 1954, pp. 322–34.

31. PARANT, J. 'Essai sur la pluviometrie du littoral Méditerranée', *Travan.* Paris, 1949, pp. 597–602.

32. GONZALEZ, A. R. 'Fechas de primeros y ultimos helados en España', *Calend. Met. Fen.* 1956, pp. 129–40.

33. OTTMAR, D. *Beiträge zur Phänologie Spaniens auf Grund der Phänologischen Beobachtungen.* . . . 1943–45. Stuttgart. 1959.

34. PETER, A. Das Klima Westspaniens. Doctorate thss. Stuttgart. 1955. 1943–55.

35. LAUTENSACH, H. 'Die temperaturrerhältnisse der Iberischen Halbinsel und ihr Jahresgang. *Die Erde,* XCI, 1960. pp. 86–114 [contains full bibliography].

36. LAUTENSACH, H. 'El ritmo de las estaciones en la Peninsula Iberica', *E.G.* XVII. 1956, pp. 443–60.

37. SCULLY, E. C. 'Notes on synoptic analysis and forecasting of Mediterranean summer weather', *Bull. Amer. Met. Soc.* 32. 1951, pp. 163–5.

38. See ARQUE, P. 'Aridité et Endoreisme en Espagne', *R.G.P.S.O.,* 17. 1946, pp. 233–43.

39. JAEGER, FR. *Trockengrenzen in Algerien.* Pet. Mitt. 1936.

40. de MARTONNE, E. 'Une nouvelle fonction climatologique: l'indice d'aridité', *La Met.* 19. 1926. See also PINNA, M. 'La carte dell' indice di aridità per l'Italia', *Atti XVII Cong. Geog. Ital.,* vol. 3. Bari, 1957, pp. 96–107.

41. BIROT, P. 'Sur une nouvelle fonction d'aridité appliquée on Portugal', *Ann. Fac. Sciences,* Oporto, XXX. 1945, pp. 90–101.

42. BAGNOULS, F. and GAUSSEN, H. 'Les limites biologiques et leur classification', *A. de G.,* LXVI. 1957, pp. 194–220.

43. Among others reference should be made to:
DANTÍN CERECEDA, J. and REVENGA CARBONELL, A. 'Las lineas y zonas

isoxeras de España . . . avance al estudio de la aridez en Espãna', *E.G.* 1941, pp. 35–91.

EMBERGER, L. 'Nouvelle contribution a l'étude de la classification des groupements vegetaux', *Rev. gen. Bot.* 45. 1933, pp. 473–86.

DE PHILIPPIS, A. *Classificazioni ed indice del clima in rapporto alla vegetazione forstale italiana.* Florence, 1937. 169 pp. [Extensive bibliography.]

WATER RESOURCES

BASIC SOURCES

Italy: M. DEI LAVORI PUBLICI, SERVIZIO IDROGRAFICO. *Dati caratteriot dei corsa d'acqua italiani.* Publ. No. 17. Rome, 1939. 433 pp.

Spain: M. DE OBRAS PÜBLICAS. Servicio Central Hidráulico. Aforos. *Regimen de los ríos españoles,* vols. 1911–31, and others since.

Portugal: DIRECÇÁO GERAL DOS SERVIÇOS HIDRÁULICOS E ELÉCTRICOS. *Anuario dos serviços hidraulicos,* since 1932.

Morocco: TRAVAUX PUBLICS. *Mission Hydrologique,* 1937 and subsequent years; also *Carte du Ruissellement,* scale 1/500,000.

Algeria: DIRECTION DU SERVICE DE LE COLONISATION ET DE L'HYDRAULIQUE. *Hydrologie algérienne.*

Tunisia: PUBLIC. MINST. des T.P. Hydraulique et hydrologie. *Rapports.*

REFERENCES

44. CAPELLO, C. F. *et alii.* 'Les phénomènes karstiques et l'hydrologie souterraine dans certaines regions d'Italie', *Assoc. Internat. d'Hydrol. Sc.* 2, pub. 37. pp. 408–37.

45. ROEDERER, H. 'Reflexions sur les relations: precipitations ecoulement', *Hydrogéologie du Maroc.* 1952, pp. 21–31.

46. MASACH ALAVEDRA, V. 'Aportación al conocimiento del regimen fluvial mediterráneo', *C.R. XVI Congrès Internat. Géog.* Lisbon, 1949, Tome 2. pp. 358–90.

47. PARDÉ, M. 'Sur les régimes fluviaux méditerranéens, *ibid.* pp. 391–420.

48. ALMAGIA, R. *L'Italia.* Turin, 1959. Tome 1. p. 441.

49. TONIOLO, A. R. 'I regimi dei corsi d'acqua nella Penisola Italiana', *C.R. Congrès Internat. Géog.* Lisbon, 1949. Tome 2. pp. 435–54.

50. MASACH ALAVEDRA, V. *El régimen de los ríos peninsulares.* Inst. 'Lucas Mallada' de Invest. Géolog. Barcelona, 1948. 511 pp.

51. FEIO, M. and MARTINS RAPOSO, A. 'Contribution à la connaissance du régime des fleuves portugais et de leur action morphologique'. *C.R. Congrès Internat. Géog.* Lisbon, 1949. Tome 2. pp. 334–57.

52. DROUHIN, G. 'Les problèmes de l'eau en Afrique du nordouest' in *C.R. Recherches effectuées sur l'hydrologie de la zone aride.* U.N.E.S.C.O. Paris, 1952. pp. 9–41.

53. MOHRMANN, I. J. C. J. and KESSLER, I. J. *Water Deficiencies in European Agriculture; a climatological survey.* Internat. Inst. Land Reclamation. 1959, No. 5. 60 pp.

54. DROUHIN, G. 'The possibility of utilising minor water resources in Algeria', in *The Problems of the Arid Zone,* Proc. of Paris Symposium. U.N.E.S.C.O. 1962. pp. 371–80.

CHAPTER 3

THE MEDITERRANEAN SEA:
THE INVISIBLE LANDSCAPE

ATLASES AND MAPS

Bureau Hydrographique International.
Hydrographic Dept. British Admiralty. Chart 2158B covers W. Mediterranean.
Instituto Idrografico della Matina. *Carta Batimetrica del Mediterraneo Centrale.*
Genova, 1960 (1/750,000) sheets 1250, 1253.
Soviet Atlas. *MOPKON ATAAC*, vol. 11. Moscow, 1953, 76 sheets.
U.S. Navy. *Marine Climatic Atlas of the World*, 4 vols. 1957–8.

GENERAL WORKS

BOURCART, J. *Les frontières de l'Océan.* Paris, 1952. 317 pp.
KING, C. A. M. *Oceanography for Geographers.* London, 1962. 337 pp.
Hydrographic Dept. British Admiralty. *The Mediterranean Pilot*, vols. 1–3. 1925–9.
ROUCH, J. *La Méditerranée.* Paris, 1946, 241 pp.; also *Rapports de la Comm. Internat.
Explor. Sc. Méditerranée.* Paris 11, 1938. pp. 218–82.
SVERDRUP, H. U. *Oceanography for Meteorologists.* New York, 1942. pp. 177–80.
There is also much scattered material in the publication of:
Annales de l'Institut Oceanográphie, Monaco; and Rapports de la Comm. Internat.
Explor. Sc. Médit.

REFERENCES

1. PETTERSSON, H. 'Oceanographic work in the Mediterranean', *G.J.* 107. 1946, pp. 163–6. See also EWING, M., ERICSON, D. B., BALLY, A. W., and WOLLIN, G. 'The deep sea and early man', *Quat.* I. 1954, pp. 17–28.
2. BLANCHARD, W.O. 'The World's greatest inland sea', *J.G.* 49. 1950. pp. 232–8.
3. PROUDMAN, J. *Dynamical Oceanography.* London, 1952, p. 75.
4. Nederland Met. Inst. *Middelandse Zee—oceanografishe en meteorologischie gegevews.* Amsterdam, 1957.
5. SCHOTT, H. U. *Oceanography for Meteorologists.* London, 1945. p. 179.
6. IDRAC, P. 'Recherches sur les mouvements et fluctuations de temperature', *Ann. Inst. Oceanog.*, 14. 1934. pp. 21–35, 231–2. See also VALLAUX, C. 'Les eaux Méditerranéen', *ibid*, 764. 1939. pp. 1–23.
7. ROMANOVSKY, V. *et alii. La Mer.* Paris, 1958.
8. DOUMEMGE, F. 'Problèmes de la Pêche en Méditerranée occidentale', *B.A.G.F.* 1958, pp. 7–23.
9. KING, C. A. M. *Oceanography for Geographers.* London, 1962, p. 106.
10. BERNARD, F. 'Comparaison de fertilité élémentaire entre les bassins S.E. et S.O. de la Méditerranée', *C.R. Acad. Sci.* 248. 1959, pp. 3633–65.
11. TORTONESE, G. 'General Remarks on the Mediterranean deep-sea fishes', *B. Inst. Ocean*, 1167. 1960. 14 pp. [He notes in this interesting article that one-fifth of the 543 species of Mediterranean fish are normally found below 200 m.]
12. EMILIANI, C. 'Pleistocene temperature variations in the Mediterranean', *Quat.* 2. 1955. pp. 87–98.
13. VAUFREY, R. 'Les éléphants nains des îles méditerranéennes et la question des isthmes pléistocènes', *Arch. Inst. Pal. Hum.* 1929, t. 6; also 'La question des isthmes méditerranéennes pléistocènes', *R.G.P.G.D.*, 1929, fasc. 4.
14. DE ANGELIS, R. *Exploitation et description des lagunes Saumâtres de la Médi-*

terranée. Cons. Gén. Pêches Médit. F.A.O. Et. et R. 1960, No. 12, 46 pp. [Useful summary of study with maps and bibliography.] Also, DOUMENGE, F. 'Aspect de la mise envalent du littoral Vénitien, *B.S.L.G.*, XXVIII. 1957, pp. 487–525.

15. MARRES, P. 'La pêche sue les côtes du Golfe du Lion', *Rapports du Congrès Internat. Géog*. Libson, 1949, tome iii, sect. IV. pp. 207–16.

16. DOUMENGE, F. *op. cit.* (No. 14).

17. JESSEN, O. *Die Strasse von Gibraltar*. Berlin, 1927. 283 pp.

18. SOLÉ SABARIS, L. 'Succession des fauns marines du Pliocène au Quaternaire sur les côtes médit d'Espagne et aux Baleares', *La Topographie et la Geologie des Profondeurs, op. cit.* pp. 283–98. [He believes that this sill was sufficiently important in Pliocene times to act as a faunal barrier between the north-east and the south-east coasts of Spain.]

19. GALTIER, G. 'La Côte sableuse du Golfe du Lion', *B.S.L.G.*, deuxième serie XXIX, 1958, pp. 149–416.

20. BOURCART, J. 'Les hypothèses sur la génèse des gorges sous-marines. Recherches sur les gorges sous-marines du Golfe du Lion', *Assoc. Oceans. Phys.*, No. 5, pp. 137; and *Marine Nationale Bull. Inf. C.O.E.C.*, 1949, pp. 317–30.

21. — 'Essai de carte sous-marine de l'Oust de la Corse', *R.G.P.G.D.* 1957, fasc. 1. pp. 31–6.

22. COLLET, L. W. 'Corse, Elbe et Apennin du point de viu tectonique', *B.S.G.F.*, VIII. 1938, pp. 737–53.

23. BOURCART, J. 'Morphologie du Precontinent des Pyrénées à la Sardaigne', *Coll. Internat.* 1959, *op. cit.* pp. 33–52.

24. SEGRE, A. 'La morfologia del Mare Tirreneo secondo i piu recenti studi', *R.G.I.* 1958, pp. 137–43.

25. — 'Observations générales sur l'orographic sous-marine de la Mer Tyrrhénienne', *Coll. Internat. 1959, op. cit.* pp. 53–9.

26. OTTMAN, F. and PICARD, J. 'Sur quelques movements tectoniques recents sur les cotes Nord et Est de la Sicilie', *C.R. des seances de l'Acad. Sc.*, t. 239. 1954. pp. 1230–31.

27. CASTANY, G. *Essai de synthèse géologique du territoire Tunisia-Sicilie*. Ann. Mins. Geol. Times 1956. 101 pp.

28. — 'La géologie profonde des Territoire Tunisia-Sicilie', *Coll. Internat. 1959, op. cit.* pp. 165–83.

29. DEBRAZZI E. and SEGRE, A. G. 'Le massime profundità del Mediterraneo', *R.G.I.*, LXVII. 1960. pp. 59–61.[Recent measurements indicate a depth of 16,150 feet near Cape Matapan.]

30. BLANC, A.C. 'Low levels of the Mediterranean Sea during the Pleistocene glaciation', *Q.J.G.S.*, 93. 1937. pp. 621–51.

31. MIGLIARDI TASCO, A., MAJONE, A. and D'ARRIGO, A. 'Caratteristiche fisiografiche dei litorali Italiani', *G. Genio Civile*, XCVIII. 1960. pp. 681–99. [This is a careful survey of the littoral changes on the Italian coasts since the surveys of Marsili in 1707, and of Cornaglia in 1888.]

32. GABERT, P. 'Une tentative d'évaluation du travail de l'érosion sur les massifs montagneux qui dominent la plaine du Pô, *R.G.A.* 1960, pp. 593–605.

33. See also classification by SION, J. 'Le Rôle des Articulations Littorales en Méditerranée', *A. de G.*, XLIII. 1934, pp. 372–9.

34. GUILCHER, A. 'Morphologie littorale du calcaire en Méditerranée occidentale (Catalonie et environs d'Alger)', *B.A.G.F.*, 241–2. 1954, pp. 50–8.

CHAPTER 4

THE ANATOMY OF THE LANDSCAPES

GENERAL WORKS ON STRUCTURAL GEOLOGY

BLUMENTHAL, M. *Géologie de la Méditerranée Occidentale*. Paris, 1931–4.
BIROT, P. and DRESCH, J. *La Méditerranée Occidentale*. Paris, 1953. pp. 3–37.
FURON, R. *La Paleogéographie*. Paris, 1959. pp. 351–82.
GLANGEAUD, L. 'Interpretation des caractères structuraux de la Méditerranée Occidentale', *B.S.G.F.* 1951. pp. 735–62.
KLEMME, H. D. 'Regional Geology of the Circum-Mediterranean Region', *B.A.A.P.G.*, 42. 1958. pp. 477–512.
MAULL, O. *Landerkunde von Südeuropa*. Leipzig and Vienna, 1929. 550 pp.
VON SEIDLITZ, W. *Discordanz und Orogenese der gebirge am Mittelmeer*. Berlin, 1931. 652 pp.
[Of these Furon's general summary is the clearest for the general reader. The regional work of Maull, though now dated, is still useful.]

QUATERNARY STUDIES

The standard work is J. K. CHARLESWORTH, *The Quaternary Era*. London, 1957. 2 vols., 1700 pp. F. E. ZEUNER, *Dating the Past* (3rd edn., 1952) is now outdated in its chronology. Much regional information is available in the journal *Quaternaria*, the guide books and the Acts of the Fourth International Congress of the Quaternary, Rome-Pisa, 1953, and of the Fifth International Congress of the Quaternary, Madrid-Barcelona, 1957.

REFERENCES

1. GLANGEAUD, L. 'Essai de classification geodynamique des chaines et des phenomenes orogeniques', *R.G.P.G.D.* 1957. pp. 200–20. Also 'Classification scalaire des sciences de la matière et leuts methodes', *Rev. Gen. des Sc.*, LXII. 1955. pp. 146–75.
2. CAILLEUX, A. et TRICART, J. 'Le problème de la classification des faits geomorphologiques', *A. de G.*, LXV. 1956. pp. 162–86.
3. UMBGROVE, J. H. F. *The Pulse of the Earth*. The Hague, 1947. See Fig. 183 and p. 298.
4. TERMIER, P. 'Les problèmes de la geologie tectonique dans la Méditerranée Occidentale'. *Rev. Gén. des sciences*, 22, 1911.
5. ARGAND, E. 'Sur la tectonique de l'Asie', *C.R. XIII Congr. Géol. Inter.* Liège, 1932. pp. 171–372.
6. STAUB, W. 'Gedanken zut Tektonik Spaniens: zur Kenntniss der Alpinen Leitlinien in Westlichen Mittelmeer Viert', *Jahrschr. d. Nat. forsch. ges.* Zurich, 1926. Also *Geol. Médit. Occid.* Barcelona, 1933.
7. VON SEIDLITZ, W. *op. cit.*
8. RUSSO, P. 'Contribution a l'étude tectonique de la Méditerranée Occidentale', *B.S.G.F.* 1947. pp. 81–95.
9. FALLOT, P. 'Essai de définition des traits permanents de la paléogeographique Secondaire dans la Méditerranée Occidentale', *B.S.G.F.* 1932. pp. 533–71.
10. KLEMME, *op. cit.*, suggests that neither convectional nor undulation theories are applicable to the Mediterranean. His view is that tectogenesis is the result of expulsion of material accumulated in the depressions.
11. HOLMES, A. 'Tectonic geology of the Mediterranean', rev. art. in *G.J.*, LXVIII 1931. pp. 161–3.

12. SUESS, E. *The Face of the Earth.*
13. STILLE, H. *Beitrage zur Geologie der Westlichen Mediterrangebiete.* Berlin. See also rev. art. by R. AIKEN, *G.J.*, LXXX. 1936. pp. 158–60.
14. KOBER, L. *Die Alpine Europa.* Berlin, 1931.
15. MARÍN, A. and FALLOT, P. 'Comparaison, stratigraphique entre l'extremité occidentale des zones bétique et penibétique d'Andalousie et Nord de l'arc Africain, C.R. séane. Acad. Scien. CXCI. Paris, 1930. pp. 144–6.
16. GLANGEAUD, L. 'Correlation chronolog. des phenomènes géodynamiques dans les Alpes, l'Apennin et l'Atlas', *B.S.G.F.* 1956, 6. pp. 867–91.
17. FURON, R. *op. cit.*
18. FALLOT, P. 'Essai de definition des traits permanents de la Palaeogéographie du Secondarie dans la Medit. Occid.', *B.S. Géol. Fr.*, (5), II. 1932, pp. 533–52.
19. KUENEN, P. 'L'Age d'un bassin méditerranéen' in *La Topographie et Géologie des Profondeurs Océaniques.* See pp. 157–64.
20. VON SEIDLITZ, W. *op cit.*
21. LLOPIS, LLADO, N. 'Types de chaînes alpidiques du littoral méditerranéen franco-espagnol et leurs rapports avec les Alpes françaises', *Comptes Rendus, Congrès Géol. Internat.*, XIII, II, 1954. pp. 261–79.
22. GLANGEAUD, L. 'Les deformations plio-quatern. de l'afrique du Nord', *Geol. Rundschau*, 43. 1955. pp. 181–96.
23. — 'Morphotectonique de la marge continentale nord-africaine', *B.S.G.F.*, (6) IV. 1956. pp. 751–72.
24. BEMMELEN, VAN R. W. 'Gravity field and orogenesis in the West-Mediterranean region'. *Geologie en Mijnbouwn* 8, 1952. pp. 306–15.
25. GLANGEAUD, L. 'Interprétation tectono-physique des caractères structuraux et paléogéographiques de la Méditerranée occidentale', *B.S.G.F.*, (6), I. 1951. pp. 735–62.
26. Comment by M. L. Picard in paper by Llopis Llado (see No. 21).
27. GILLET, S. 'Contribution a l'histoire du bassin Méditerranéen et euxinique au Neogene et Quaternaire', *Bull. Serv. Carte. Géol. Alsace-Lorraine*, X. 1957. pp. 49–57.
28. KUENEN, P. 'L'Age d'un bassin méditerranéen' (see No. 19).
29. Based on map by P. BIROT, *La Méditerranée Occidentale* (see General Works above). pp. 34–35.
30. MERLA, G. 'Geologia dell'Appennino Settentrionale', *B.S. Geol. It.*, LXX. 1951. pp. 95–382.
31. DEPÉRET, CH. 'La classification du Quaternaire et sa corrélation avec les niveaux prehistoriques', *C.R. Sc. Soc. Géol. Fr.* 1921. pp. 125–7.
32. LAMONTHE, GENERAL DE. 'Les anciennes lignes de rivages du Sahel d'alger', *Mem. Soc. Geol. Fr.*, IV ser., mem. I. 1911.
33. BLANC, A. C. 'Low levels of the Mediterranean during the Pleistocene glaciation', *Q.J.G.S.*, 93. 1937. pp. 621–51. Also 'La stratigraphie de la Plaine cotière de la Basse Versilia (Italie) et la transgression flandrienne en Méditerranée', *R.G.P.G.D.* 1936. pp. 129–60.
34. SACCHI, C. F. 'Les mollusques terrestres dans le cadre des relations biogeographiques entre l'Afrique du Nord et de l'Italie', *Vie et Milieu*, t. 9. 1958. pp. 11–52. Also see Solé Sabaris in *Colloques Internat. op. cit.* pp. 283–93.
35. TREVISAN, L. 'Problemi relativi all'epirogen si e all'eustatismo nel Pliocene e Pleistocene della Sicilia', *Atti Soc. Tosc. Sc. Nat.*, Pisa, Mem., LI. 1942.
36. DENIZOT, G. 'Observations sur le Quaternaire moyen de la Méditerranée Occidentale', *B.S.G.F.* 1935.
37. CASTANY, G. and OTTMAN, F. 'Le Quaternaire marine de la Méditerranée Occidentale', *R.G.P.G.D.* 1957. pp. 46–55.
38. CHOUBERT, G. 'Sur les rapports entre les formations marines et continentales quaternaires', *C.R. Ac. Sc.*, t. 237. Paris, 1953. p. 286.

39. OTTMAN, F., *Les Formations Pliocènes et Quaternaires sur le littoral corse.* Mém. Soc. Géol. Fr. 84, 1958, 176 pp.

40. BOURCART, J. *Les Frontières de l'Ocean.* Paris, 1952. pp. 86–7.

41. TREVISAN, L. 'Genèsise des terrasses fluviatiles en relation avec les cycles climatiques', *C.R. Congrès Internat. Géog.,* t. 11. Lisbon, 1949. pp. 511–28.

42. HERNÁNDEZ PACHECO, E. *Los Cinco Ríos.* Madrid, 1933.

43. GIGOUT, M. *Recherches sur le Quaternaire Marocaine.* Trav. de l'Institut Sc. Cherifien, no. 7. 1957.

44. BLANC, A. C. 'On the Pleistocene sequence of Rome', *Quat.* 4. 1956. pp. 95–110.

45. WOLDSTEDT, P. *Das Eiszeitalter Band.* Stuttgart, 1958. pp. 296–333, 376–92.

46. TRICART, J. and CAILLEUX, A. 'Action du froid quaternaire en Italie Peninsulaire', *Actes IV Congres I.N.Q.U.A.,* Tome I. Rome, 1956. pp. 136–42. See also NANGERONI, G. 'Fenomeni crionivali', *Rapports alla Commissione Morfologia Periglaciale XVIII Congress I.G.U.* Rio de Janeiro, 1957. 19 pp.

47. BUTZER, K. W. and FRANZLE, O. 'Observations on the pre-Würmian glaciation of the Iberian Peninsula', *Zeit. fur Geom.,* I. 1959. pp. 85–97.

48. RAYNAL, R. 'Les phenomènes periglaciaires en Maroc et leur place dans l'évolution morphologique', *Biul. peryglac.,* 4. Lodz, 1956.

49. BÜDEL, J. 'Die raumliche und zeitliche und Gliederung des Eiszeitlimas', *Naturwiss,* 36. 1949. pp. 105–12, 133–9. Also 'Neue wege der Eiszeitforschung', *Erdkunde,* 3. 1949. pp. 82–96.

50. BRINKMANN, R. *Las montañas—islas fosiles especialmente en España,* Pub. Doc. Geog. Nac. Bol. No. 8. 1932. pp. 24.

51. WILHEMY, H. *Klimamorphologie der Massengesteine.* Brunswick, 1958. p. 161.

52. KLAER, W. *Verwitterungsformen in Granit auf Korsika.* Pet. Mitt. Erg.—H.261. 1956

53. NANGERONI, G. 'Il carsismo e l'idrologia carsica in Italia', *Atti. del XVII Congress. Geog. Ital.* Bari, 1957. Relazioni pp. 82–112.

54. Consiglio Nazionale delle Ricerche, Centro di Studi per la Geografia Fisica *Ricerche sulla morfologia e idrografia carsica,* 7 vols. Bologna, 1948–56.

55. SCOTTI, P. 'Catasto e Cartografia delle Grotte Italiane', *Atti del XVII Congresso. Geog. Ital.* Bari, 1957. pp. 161–8.

56. CARANDELL, J. 'Un tipo cárstico en Andalusia. El Torcal de Antequera', *Bol. R. Soc. Esp. Hist. Nat.,* XXIII. 1923. pp. 233–7.

57. FOURNIER, F. *Climat et érosion* (doctorate thesis). Paris, 1960. pp. 73–4.

58. BIROT, P. *Les Pyrénées Orientales.* Paris, 1937. [For detailed discussion of these two rock types.]

59. ALMAGIÀ, R. *Studi geografici sulle frane in Italia,* Memorie della Soc. Geog. Ital., t. XIII, XIV. Rome, 1907–10.

60. DRESCH, J. 'Formes et limites climatiques et paleoclimates en Afrique du Nord', *A. de G.* 1934. pp. 56–9.

61. RAYNAL, R. 'Oscillations climatiques et évolution du relief au cours du quaternaire', *Notes Maroc,* 5. 1955. pp. 10–14.

62. DRESCH, J. 'Sur les pediments en Afrique Méditerranéenne et Tropicale', *C.R.I.G.U.,* Tome I. Lisbon, 1949. pp. 19–29.

63. BUDEL, J. 'Bericht uber klima-morphologische und Eiszeitforschunger in Nieder-Afrika', *Erdkunde.* 1950–1. pp. 104–14.

64. PUJOS, A. 'Terres rouges, noires, grises', *Soc. Sci. Nat. Phys. du Maroc. Trav. sect. Pedol.,* XII. 1957. pp. 69–96.

65. See useful summary of theories concerning red earths in JOFFE, J. S. *Pedology.* New Brunswick, 1949. Also BONIFAY, E. 'Age et signification des sols rouges méditerranéene en Provence', *C.R. Se. Ac. Sc.,* 244. 1957. pp. 3075–7.

66. MARCHELIN, P. *Observations sur des terres et des sols en région Méditerranéenne. t. I. Terres et sols en Costière.* Nice, 1947.

67. REIFENBERG, A. *The Soils of Palestine.* London, 1947.

68. MENSCHING, H. *Das Quartar in den Gebirgen Marokkos*, Pet Geog. Mitt., 256. Gotha, 1956. pp. 56–8.
69. BALOUT, L. *Préhistoire de l'Afrique du Nord*. Paris, 1955.
70. ALBAREDA, J. M. 'Mediterranean soils of the Spanish Levant and North Africa', *Trans. 4th Inter. Congr. Soil Sc.*, II. Amsterdam, 1950. pp. 185–6.
71. REIFENBERG, A. in *Comptes, rendus de la Conférence de Pedologie Méditerranéene*. Alger-Montpellier, 1947. pp. 161–3.
72. See views expressed by GEZE, B. 'Paleosols et sols dans l'evolution actuelle', *Ann. E.N.E. de Montpellier*, fasc. IV, XXVII. 1947. pp. 263–88. Also by DAUCHAUFUR, PH. *Pedologie*. Nancy, 1956.
73. KLINGE, H. 'Contribución al conocimiento de los suelos recientes, relictos y fosiles sobre roca caliza, del norte de España', *Anal. Edal. y Fis. Veg.*, 16, No. 2. 1957.
74. FRANZLE, D. 'Untersuchungen uber Ablagerungen und Boden im eiszeitlichen Gletschergebiet Norditalien', *Erd.*, 13. 1959. pp. 289–97.
75. KUBIENA, W. L. *The Soils of Europe*. London, 1953.
76. ALBAREDA, J. M. y GUTIERREZ, E. 'Mountainous Spanish soils', *Trans. 4th Inter. Congr. Soil Sci.*, I. Amsterdam, 1950. pp. 288–90.
77. DEL VILLAR, H. *Suelos de la Peninsula Luso-Ibérica*. Madrid, 1937.
78. — 'Contribución al estudio comparado de las "Tierras negras" de Andalucia y de Marruecos', *An. Edal. y Fis.*, IX. 1950. pp. 251–78.
79. DURAND, J. *Étude géologique, hydrogéologique et pedologique des croutes en Algerie* (These). Algers, 1952. pp. 43–168.
80. BALOUT, L. *Préhistoire de l'Afrique du Nord*. Paris, 1955. p. 62.
81. DESPOIS, J. 'Les croûtes calcaires et leurs origines', *A. de G.* 1954. pp. 59–60. And GIGNOUX, M. 'Sur les âges de la croûte en Maroc Occidentale', *C.R. Som. Soc. Geol. Fr.* 1948. p. 136.
82. TIXERONT, J. 'Conditions historiques de l'érosion en Tunisie', *Assoc. Internat. de l'Hydrol Sc.*, II. Brussels, 1951. pp. 73–81.
83. SACCARDY, L. 'Les methodes de defense et restauration des Sols en Algerie', FAO/SCM/65-C. 1958. MS.
84. U.N.E.S.C.O. *The Future of Arid Lands*. Washington, 1956. p. 45.
85. BLANC, A. C. 'Torre in Pietra, Saccopastore e Monte Circeo. La cronologia dei glacimenti e la paleogeografia quaternaria del Lazio', *B.S. Geol. It.* 1958. pp. 196–214—a fundamental study.
86. TRICART, J. 'Palaeoclimats, quaternaires et morphologie climatique dans le Midi méditerranéen', *Eiszeitalter und Gegenwarte*, II. pp. 172–88. Also 'Periglaciare et fluvioglaciare—essai de correlation du Quaternaire durancien', *Mem. du Centre et Doc. Carts. du C.N.R.S.* Paris, 1957.
87. BUDEL, J. *Naturwiss* (see No. 49).
88. BUTZER, K. W. 'Palaeoclimatic implications of Pleistocene stratigraphy in the Mediterranean area', *Ann. N.Y. Acad. Sc.* 1961. pp. 449–56.
89. CHARLESWORTH, J. K. *The Quaternary Era*, vol. 2. London, 1957. p. 1139.
90. WILLETT, H. C. 'The general circulation at the last (Würm) glacial maximum', *Geog. Ann.*, XXXII. 1950. pp. 179–187.
91. BUTZER, K. W. 'Mediterranean pluvials and the general circulation of the Pleistocene', *Geog. Ann.*, 39. 1957. pp. 48–53. See also 'The recent climatic fluctuations in lower latitudes and the general circulation of the Pleistocene' *Geog. Ann.*, 39. 1957. pp. 105–13.
92. FLOHN, H. 'Allgemeine atmospharische Zirkulation und Palaoklimatologie', *Geol. Rdsch.*, 40. 1952. pp. 153–78.
93. BUTZER, K. W. 'Climatic change in arid regions since the Pliocene' in *A History of Land Use in Arid Regions*, ed. by L. D. Stamp. U.N.E.S.C.O., 1961. pp. 31–56.

94. ADAMS, R. M. 'Survey of ancient water courses and settlements in central Iraq', *Sumer*, 14. 1958. pp. 101–3.
95. BRAIDWOOD, R. A. 'The Old World: post-paleolithic', *Nat. Acad. Sci.*, *Nat. Res. Council Publi. 565.* 1957. pp. 26–7.
96. TIXERONT, J. *op. cit.* (No. 82).
97. BALOUT, L. 'Pluviaux interglaciaires et préhistoire saharienne', *Trav. Inst. Recherche Sahar.*, 8. 1952. pp. 9–21.
98. DUBIEF, J. 'Note sur l'évolution du climat saharien au cours des derniers millenaires', *Actes du IV Congrès I.N.Q.U.A.*, 2. Rome, 1956. pp. 848–51.
99. BUDEL, J. *Erdk.* (No. 63).

CHAPTER 5

THE VEGETATION COVER

GENERAL WORKS

BIROT, P. and DRESCH, J. *La Méditerranée Occidentale.* Paris, 1953. pp. 56–78.
RIKLI, M. *Das Pflanzenkleid der Mittelmeerländer.*, 3 vols. Berne, 1943. [This is the major work, with exhaustive bibliography.]

REGIONAL STUDIES

Iberian Peninsula: *Geografía de España y Portugal*, ed. by M. de Terán: Tome II, *La Vegetación* by P. FONT QUER. Barcelona, 1954. pp. 145–271.
Die Pflanzenwelt Spaniens, 10-Internat. Pflanzengeographischen Exkursion. Berne, 1956.
Italy: TOURING CLUB ITALIANO, *Conosci l'Italia*: Vol. II, *La Flora.* Milan, 1958. 275 pp.
North Africa: BOUDY, P. *Économie forestière nord-africaine.* Paris, 1948–50.
MAIRE, R. *Flore de l'Afrique du Nord.*
Morocco: EMBERGER, L. *Aperçu général sur la végétation marocaine*, Mem. Soc. Sc. nat. Maroc. 1939.
Algeria-Tunisia: MAIRE, R. *Carte phytogéographique de l'Algérie et de la Tunisie.* Algiers, 1926.
MAIRE, R. and DE PEYERIMHOFF, P. *Carte forestières de l'Algérie et de la Tunisie*, Algiers, 1941.
[All these have extensive bibliographies.]

REFERENCES
1. GAUSSEN, H. 'Les Arbres méditerranéens', *Rev. des Eaux et Fôrets*, LXXIX. 1941. pp. 395–412, 471–89.
2. BRAUN-BLANQUET, J. 'Association végétale climatique et climax du sol dans le Midi Méditerranéen.' *Rev. des Eaux et Fôrets*, LXXII. 1934. pp. 1–7.
3. For example: BORDAS, J. *Les sols de la región du Bas-Rhône-essai de pedologie méditerranéene.* Paris, 1943.
   DAUCHAUFOUR, PH. *La Pédologie.* Nancy, 1956.
4. See 'Botanical studies in the Mediterranean region', in RAUNKIAER, C. *The Life Forms of Plants and Statistical Plant Geography.* Oxford, 1934. pp. 547–620.
5. ASHBY, E. 'Experimental work on xeromorphic structures', *School Sci. Rev.*, 15. 1934. p. 509.
6. KILLIAN, C. 'Recherches écologiques sur les fluctuations saisonières de la

transpiration chez les végétaux du climat mediterranéen', *Bull. Soc. Bot. Fr.*, 78. 1931. pp. 460–501.

7. — and FAUREL, A. 'Observations sur la pression osmotique des vegetaux désertiques et subdésertiques de l'Algerie', *Bull. Soc. Bot. Fr.*, LXXX. 1933. pp. 775–8.

8. OPPENHEIMER, H. R. 'Summer drought and water balance of plants growing in the Near East', *J. of Ecol.*, XXXIX. 1951. pp. 356–62.

9. SALVADOR, D. 'La fôret dans pays méditerranéene', *Rev. La Chêne*. 1931. pp. 10–37.

10. BRAUN-BLANQUET, J. 'Études sur la vegetation méditerranéene', *Bull. Soc. Bot. Fr.*, LXXI. 1924.

11. — *La Chênaie d'Yeuse méditerranéenne*, Mem. Soc. Etudes Sc. Nat. Nîmes. Montpellier, 1936.

12. PHILIPPIS, A. DE. 'La sughera ed il leccio nella vegetazione arborea mediterranea', *Bull. Silva Médit.*, X. 1935. pp. 9–109.

13. PAVIARI, A. 'L'Influenza dei boschi mediterranei sul clima', *Atti R. Acad. dei Georgofili*, XV. 1936. pp. 1–29. See also PAVIARI, A. 'Fundamentos ecológies, e tecnicos, da silvacultura nos paises mediterraneos', *Estudos e Informaçáo*, Direcc. Geral das Servicos Flor. e Aquae, 85. Feb. 1958. pp. 1–28.

14. MOLINIER, R., 'La végetation médit. dans ses relations avec les conditions de climat et l'action humaine', *Bull. Soc. for. Franche-Comté*, 28, 1955, 331–45.

15. TOURING CLUB ITALIANO. 'Macchia mediterranea in Italia', *L'Alpe*, No. 11–12. Milan, 1932.

16. SENNEN, F. 'La garrique du littoral, depuis Montpellier jusqu'à Sagunts', *Bull. Soc. Bot. Fr.* 1925.

17. BRAUN-BLANQUET, J. *Plant Sociology*, trans. by G. D. Fuller and H. S. Conard, 1st edn. London, 1932. 439 pp.

18. GAUCHER, G. 'Sur la national d'optimum climatique d'une formation pédologique', *C.R. Ac. Sc.*, 227. 1948. pp. 215–17.

19. GRACANIN, Z. in 'Recherches sur la regressión et la progression de la vegetation forestière et des sols sur le Karst', *Annals of the Forest Research Inst.*, Yugoslav Acad. Zagreb, 1955. pp. 11–145.

20. DAUCHAUFUR, PH. *op cit.* (No. 3).

21. BORDAS, J. *op. cit.*

22. GAUSSEN, H. 'Les sols et le climat méditerranéene de France', *Rev. la Chêne*. 1931. pp. 71–97.

23. DE OLIVEIRA, F. A. L. 'Quelques aspects se rapportant à leur evolution', 7eme session sur l'utilisation des terres dans la region médit. *FAO/SGM/60/5*, MS. 1960.

24. FISCHER, E. 'Der oedbaum', *Pet. Mit.*, 147. 1904. p. 147.

25. GAUSSEN, H. and PHILIPPIS, A. DE. 'Carte de delimitation et carte ecologique', *FAO/SCM/55*, MS. 1956. 22 pp.

26. LLOBET, S. 'El limite septentrional de la vid y el olivo en Cataluña', *10 Congresso Lit. del Instit. Est. Pirenaicos*, V. 1952. pp. 33–50.

27. FLAHAULT, C. and DURAND, A. 'Les limites de la region mériterranéenne en France', *Bull. Soc. Bot. Fr.*, XXXII. 1886. Also FLAHAULT, C. and DURAND, A. 'La distribution géographique des végétaux dans la region méditerranéenne française' in *Encycl. Biologique*. Paris, 1937. pp. 88–97.

28. TONIOLO, A. R. 'La distribuzione dell olivo e l'estensione della provincia climatica mediterranea nel Veneto occidentale', *Riv. Geog. Ital.*, XXI. 1914. pp. 2–45.

29. GAUSSEN, H. and BAGNOULS, F. 'Saison sèche et indice xerothermique', *Bull. Soc. d'histoire naturelle de Toulouse*, 88. 1953. pp. 193–239.

30. PRINCIPI, P. 'Le flora del Quaternario', *Atti Fac Agr. Univ. Firenze*, III. 1938.

W.M.W.—25

31. EMBERGER, L. 'Rapport sur les régions arides et semi-arides de l'Afrique du Nord' im U.N.E.S.C.O. *Les Bases Ecologiques de la Régéneration de la végétation des zones arides.* Paris, 1951.

32. MAIRE, R. and EMBERGER, L. *Tableau phytogéographie du Maroc.* Rabat, 1934.

33. GAUSSEN, H. *Vegetation de la moitié orientale des Pyrénées.* Paris, 1926.

34. LÜDI, W. *Die gliederung der vegetation auf der Apenninenhalbinsel, insbesondere der montanen und alpinen Höhenstufen.* Bern, 1944. 24 pp.

35. PHILIPPIS, A. DE. 'Classificazioni ed indici del clima in rapporto alla vegetazione forestale italiana', *N.G. Bot. It.*, 44. 1937. 169 pp.

36. EMBERGER, L. 'Remarques critiques sur les étages de végetation dans les montagnes marocaine', *Bull. Soc. Bot. Suisse.*, 46. 1936. pp. 614–31.

37. PRINCIPI, P. 'Le Flore del Paleogene', *Atti. Soc. Sc. Lett.*, 5. Genova, 1942. Also PRINCIPI, P. *'Le Flore del Neogene.* Florence, 1942.

38. TROTTER, A. 'Gli elementi balcano-orientali della flora italiana', *Atti Ist. Incoraggiamento'*, Ser. VI, 9. Naples, 1919.

39. GAUSSEN, H. 'L'influence du passé dans la repartition des Gymnospermes de la Pen. Iberique', *C.R. Congrès Internat. Géog.*, 111. 1949. pp. 805–21.

40. DEL VILLAR, H. 'L'aire du Callitris articulata en Espagna', *Bull. Soc. Bot. Fr.* 1938.

41. MARCHESONI, V. 'Richerche pollinologiche in sedimenti torbosi della pianura padana', *N.G. Bot. It.*, LXVI. 1959. pp. 336–9.
— 'Lineamenti paleobotanici dell' Interglaciale Riss-Würm nella pianura padana', *N.G. Bot. It.*, LXVII. 1960, pp. 306–11.
PAGANELLI, A. 'Il graduale impoverimento della flora forestale nel quaternario della pianura padana', *N.G. Bot. It.*, LXVIII. 1961. pp. 109–17.
— 'Richerche sul quaternario della Pianura Padana', *Rend. Ist. Univ. Camerino*, 2. 1961. pp. 83–96.

42. BONATTI, E. 'Pollen sequences from the sediments of the lake of Monterosi, Central Italy', MS. to be published in the *Proc. of the Connecticut Academy of Sciences.* See also MARCHESONI, V. 'Storia climatico-forestale dell' Appennino Umbro-Marchigiano', *Ann. Bot.*, XXV. 1957. pp. 1–39; and PAGANELLI, A. and SOLAZZI, A. 'Analisi pollinica sul deposito Pleistocenico di Pietrafitta (Umbria)', *Rend. Ist. Sc. Univ. Camerino*, 3. 1962. pp. 64–89.

43. LONA, F. and RICCARDI, E. 'Analisi pollinica dell' *Pollen and Spores*, 3. 1961. pp. 85–93.

44. CHIARRUGI, A. *Le epoche glaciali dal punto di vista botanico.* Rome, 1950.
PRINCIPI, P. 'Le Flore del Quaternario', *Atti. Fac. Agr. Univ.*, III. Florence, 1938.

45. ALLORGE, P. *Essai de Bryogéographique de la Peninsule Iberique.* Paris, 1947. 110 pp.

46. TEIXEIRA, C. 'A expansáo do Pinus Sylvestris L. no sudoeste da Europa', *Anais da Fac. de Ciencias do Porto*, XXIX. 1944. pp. 1–10.

47. LEMÉE, G. 'L'evolution de la fôret française au cours du Quaternaire d'après les analyses polliniques', *Revue forestière.* 1955.

48. GAUSSEN, H. 'L'histoire postglaciare de la végétation dans le sud-ouest de l'Europe', *Rev. gén. des Sc.*, XLIV. Paris, 1933. pp. 307–12.

49. MOLINIER, R. 'La vegetation méditerranéenne dans ses relations avec les conditions de climat et l'action humaine', *Bull. Soc. Forest. Franche-Comté.* 1955. pp. 331–45.

CHAPTER 6

THE WESTERN MEDITERRANEAN
AS A MAN-MADE WORLD

Two comprehensive bibliographies are:

EDELMAN, C. H. and EEUWENS, B. E. P. *Bibliography on Land and Water Utilization and Water Conservation in Europe.* Rome, 1955. 347 pp.

PLAISANCE, G. *Les formations végétales et paysages ruraux, lexique et guide bibliographique.* Paris, 1959. 418 pp.

GENERAL WORKS

ANDRÉ, JACQUES. *L'alimentation et la cuisine à Rome.* Paris, 1961. 259 pp. [A standard work on plants in Roman times.]

CARY, M. *The geographic background of Greek and Roman history.* Oxford, 1941. 331 pp. [Readable outline of the regional environment in relation to classical times.]

HEITLAND, W. *Agricola, a study of agricultural and rustic life in the Greco-Roman World from the point of view of labour.* Cambridge, 1921.

PARAIN, C. 'Roman and Medieval Agriculture in the Mediterranean area' in *The Cambridge Economic History of Europe*, ed. J. H. Clapham and E. Power, vol. I, Cambridge, 1941. pp. 118–27. [A useful outline of agrarian features.]

SEMPLE, E. C. *The Geography of the Mediterranean in relation to Ancient History.* London, 1932. 737 pp.

SINGER, C. *et alii. A History of Technology*, vol. I; *From early times to the fall of ancient empires.* Oxford, 1954.

WHYTE, R. O. 'Evolution of land use in south-western Asia in *A History of Land Use in Arid Regions*, ed. by L. D. Stamp. U.N.E.S.C.O., 1961. pp. 57–118. [Confused, but with useful bibliography.]

REFERENCES

1. POWELL, T. G. E. *The Celts.* London, 1959.
2. LAPEYRE, H. *Géographie de l'Espagne morisque.* Paris, 1959. 270 pp.
3. CLARK, G. *World Prehistory . . . an outline.* Cambridge, 1962. pp. 119–46.
4. BOSCH-GIMPERA, P. *El Poblamiento Antiguo y la Formacion de los Pueblos de España.* Mexico, 1944. 421 pp.
5. BLOCH, R. *The Etruscans.* London, 1958. p. 150.
6. HARDEN, D. *The Phoenicians.* London, 1962. pp. 25–43.
7. WOODHEAD, A. G. *The Greeks in the West.* London, 1962. pp. 31–71. See also DUNBABIN, T. J. *The Western Greeks.* London, 1948.
8. THEOPHRASTUS. *De Causis*, II, Ch. IV. pp. 2–3.
9. SCULLY, VINCENT. *The Earth, the Temple, and the Gods.* Yale, 1962.
10. STOTT-BEST, L. *M.T. Varro on Farming.* London, 1912. p. 9.
11. MUMFORD, LEWIS. *The City in History.* London, 1961. p. 205.
12. MARCAIS, G. 'Les jardins de l'Islam' in *Melanges d'histoire et d'archeologie de l'Occident musulman*, I. Alger. pp. 238–44.
13. RUPEREZ CUELLAR, A. *La Encina y sus Tratamientos.* Madrid, 1957. [See map.]
14. HARSHBERGER, J. 'Mediterranean garrigue and macchia', *Proc. Amer. Phil. Soc.*, 65. 1926.
15. CHOUARD, P. 'Observations sur la couverture végétale du modelé karstique', *B.S.B.F.*, 78. 1931.

16. LORENZI, A. 'L'Uomo e le Foreste', *R.G.I.*, XXV. 1918. pp. 141–65, 213–42. XXVI. 1919. pp. 47–57.

17. For general studies on deforestation see: GIORDANO, G. 'The Mediterranean Region', in *A World Geography of Forest Resources*, ed. by S. Haden-Guest, J. K. Wright, E. M. Teclaff. New York, 1956.
SEMPLE, E. C. 'Climatic and geographic influences on ancient Mediterranean forests and the lumber trade', *A.A.A.G.*, IX. 1919. pp. 13–37.
DARBY, H. C. 'The clearing of the woodlands in Europe', in *Man's Role in Changing the Face of the Earth*, ed. by W. L. Thomas, Jr. Chicago, 1956. pp. 183–216, especially pp. 184–88.

18. KUHNHOLTZ-LORDAT, G. *L'Écran Vert*. Paris, 1958. p. 112.

19. DEMOUGEOT, E. 'Le chameau et l'Afrique du Nord Romaine', *A.E.S.C.* 1960. pp. 209–47.

20. GEORGE, P. 'Anciennes et nouvelles fôrets en region Méditerranéen', *Ét. Rhod.* IX. 1933. pp. 85–120.

21. MIKESELL, M. W. 'Deforestation in northern Morocco', *Sci.*, 132. 1960. pp. 441–8.

22. EUBANKS, J. 'Navigation on the Tiber', *Class. Journ.*, XXV. 1930. pp. 683–95.

23. FREDERIKSEN, M. W. and WARD-PERKINS, J. B. 'The ancient road system of the central and northern Ager Faliscius', *Papers of Brit. Sch. Rome*, 25. 1957. pp. 67–208.

24. KUHNHOLTZ-LORDAT, G. *La Terre Incendie*. Paris, 1939.

25. ALBION, R. G. *Forests and Sea-Power*. Harvard, 1926.

26. LANE, F. C. *Venetian Ships and Shipbuilding of the Renaissance*. Baltimore, 1934. pp. 217–33.

27. BUFFAULT, P. 'Le déboseiment de l'Afrique du Nord', *Rev. des Eaux et Fôrets*, LXXIX. 1941, pp. 471–87.

28. LOMBARD, M. 'Le bois dans la Mediterranée Musulmane, VII–XIe siècles', *A.E.S.C.*, 14. 1951. pp. 234–54.

29. CAVAILLES, H. 'La question forestière en Espagne', *A. de G.*, XIV. 1905. pp. 318–31.

30. HOPFNER, H. 'La evolución de los bosques de Castilla la Vieja en tiempos históricos', *E.G.*, XV. 1954. pp. 415–30.

31. DUGELAY, A. 'Le fait vegétal de la fôret médit', *Rev. for. franc.* 7, 1955, 169–75.

32. SCLAFERT, TH. 'A propos du déboisement des Alpes du sud', *A. de G.*, XLII. 1933. pp. 266–77, 350–60.

33. BOUDY, P. *Économie forestière Nord-Africaine*, tôme 1. Paris, 1948. pp. 555–63, 629–75.

34. DRESCH, J. *L'agriculture en Afrique du Nord* (Cours de Sorbonne, Paris), tôme 1. p. 11.

35. KUHNHOLTZ-LORDAT, G. 'La silva, le saltus et l'ager de Garrigue', *Annals de l'école Nat. d'Agric.*, fasc. IV, XXVI. Montpellier, 1945. pp. 1–84.

36. — *L'écran vert* (see No. 18). p. 740.

37. LOUIS, M. *Préhistoire du Languedoc Méditerranéen et du Roussillon*. Nîmes, 1948. pp. 37, 53, 63.

38. ZEUNER, F. E. 'Domestication of animals' in Singer's *A History of Science, op. cit.* pp. 327–75.

39. REED, C. 'Animal domestication in the prehistoric Near East', *Sci.*, 130. 1959. pp. 1629–39.

40. Much has been written on the origins of cereals. For classic studies see CANDOLLE, DE. *Origines des plantes cultivees*. Paris, 1883. DARWIN, C. *The Variation of Animals and Plants*, 2 vols. London, 1885. HEHN, V. *The Wanderings of Plants and Animals from their first Home*. London, 1888. VAVILOV, N. I. 'The Origin, Variation, Immunity and Breeding of Cultivated Plants', trans. by K. S. Chester,

Chronica Botanica, 13. 1951. p. 164. SAUER, C. O. *The Agricultural Origins and Dispersals*, Amer. Geog. Soc. 1952, Series 2. New York, 1953, 110 pp.

41. HELBAEK, H. 'Archaeology and agricultural botany', *Annal. Rept. Inst. Archaeol.* London, 1953. pp. 44–59. See also the same author's article, 'Domestication of food plants in the Old World', *Sci.*, 130. 1959. p. 365.

42. ZOHARY, D. 'Studies on the origin of cultivated barley', *Bull. Res. Coun. Israel*, 9D. 1960. pp. 21–42.

43. JASNY, N. 'Competition among grains in classical antiquity', *Amer. Hist. Rev.*, XLVII. 1942. pp. 747–64.

44. — *Competition among Grains*. Stanford, 1940.

45. DESPOIS, J. 'Development of land use in northern Africa with references to Spain', in *A History of Land Use in Arid Regions*, ed. by L. D. Stamp. U.N.E.S.O., 1961. pp. 219–37.

46. GUYOT, A. L. *Origine des Plantes Cultivees*. Paris, 1949.

47. RIBEIRO, O. *Portugal*, vol. 5 of *Geografía de España y Portugal* ed. by M. de Téran. Barcelona, 1955. pp. 150–1.

48. LEFÉBVRE, TH. *Les modes de vie dans les Pyrénées Atlantiques Orientales*. Paris, 1933.

49. HAUDRICOURT, A. G. and HÉDIN, L. *L'homme et les plantes cultivées*. Paris, 1943. pp. 194–5.

50. LE DU and SACCARDY, L. 'Étude de quelques charbons préhistoriques de la région de Tebessa', *Rev. Africaine*. 1948. pp. 111–19.

51. CAMPS-FABRER, H. *L'olivier et l'huile dans l'Afrique Romaine*. Algiers, 1953. 95 pp.

52. BARADEZ, J. *Fossatum Africae*. Paris, 1949. p. 185.

53. SAUMAGNE, CH. 'Sur la législation relative aux terres incultes de l'Afrique Romaine', *Rev. Tunisienne*. 1922. pp. 57–116.

54. PERRIN, A. *La civilisation de la vigne*. Paris, 1938. pp. 31–45.

55. SIRAGO, V. A. *L'Italia agraria sotto Traino*. Louvain, 1958. 339 pp.

56. DION, R. *Histoire de la vigne et du vin en France des origins XIXe siècle*. Paris, 1959.

57. ISNARD, H. *La Culture de la vigne en Algérie*. Paris, 1952.

58. PLINY, *Hist. Nat.*, 15, 102.

59. VARRO, *Re Rustica*, 1, 41, 6.

60. PLINY, *Hist. Nat.*, 12, 13.

61. TOLKOWSKY, S. *Hesperides, a history of the culture and use of citrus fruits*. London, 1938. pp. 100–2, 108. See also ANDREWS, A. C. 'Acclimatization of Citrus fruits in the Mediterranean Region', *Agric. Hist.*, 35. 1961. pp. 35–46.

62. FONTAVELLA GONZALEZ, V. 'La evolución de los cultivos en las huertas levantinas de España', *C.R.C.I.G.*, vol. 3. Lisbon, 1949. pp. 291–2.

63. GAUSSEN, H. 'Les cultures en terrasses dans le bassin médit. occid', *A. de G.* 1927. pp. 276–8—review of work by J. Frödin, 'Om Terrasskulturen i vastra Medelharsom', *Lund Univ. Geog. Inst.*, No. 9. 1926.

64. DESPOIS, J. 'La culture en terrasses dans l'Afrique du Nord', *A.E.S.C.*, 11. 1956. pp. 42–50.

65. FRANK, T. *An Economic History of Rome*. London, 1927. pp. 7–12, 57.

66. BAILEY, C., ed. *The Legacy of Rome*. Oxford, 1923. pp. 470–2.

67. ALMAGIÀ, R. *L'Italia.*, vol. 2. Turin, 1959. pp. 677–726.

68. FRANK, T. *An Economic Survey of Ancient Rome*, vol. V. Baltimore, 1940. pp. 134–84.

69. See general reviews in: FAUCHER, D. *Geographie Agraire*. Paris, 1949. 382 pp. JUILLARD, E. and others. *Structures Agraires et Paysages Ruraux*, Annales de l'Est, Memoire no. 17. Nancy, 1957. pp. 98–118. MEYNIER, A. *Les paysages agraires*. Paris, 1958.

70. PAPASOGLI, G. *L'Agricoltura dei Etrusci e dei Romani.* Rome, 1942.
71. See following general works: BILLIARD, R. *L'agriculture dans l'antiquité d'après les Georgiques de Virgile.* Perugia, 1928; SINGER, C. *et alii. A History of Technology,* vol. 2. Oxford, 1956. pp. 81–139, 663–80; and STORR-BEST, L. *M. T. Varro on Farming.*' London, 1912. 375 pp.
72. VARRO, *Re Rustica,* 1, 10, 2. PLINY, *Nat. Hist.,* XVIII, 3, 9.
73. BARADEZ, J. *Fossatum Africae* (see No. 52).
74. CASTAGNOLI, F. *Le ricerche sui resti della centuriazione.* Rome, 1958. 53 pp. [A useful resumé with a comprehensive bibliography.]
75. FRACCARO, P. 'Agrimensura', article in *Enciclopedia Italiana*; and KISH, G. 'Centuriatio: Roman rectangular land survey'. *Surveying and Mapping,* XXII. 1962. pp. 233–44.
76. BRADFORD, J. 'Buried Landscapes in southern Italy', *Ant.,* XXIII. 1949. pp. 58–72.
77. — *Ancient Landscapes.* London, 1957. pp. 145–216.
78. INSTITUT GÉOGRAPHIQUE NATIONAL. *Atlas des Centuriations Romaines.* Paris, 1956.
79. CAILLEMER, A. and CHEVALIER, R. 'Les centuriations de l'Afrique vetus', *A.E.S.C.* 1954. pp. 432–60.
80. CASTAGNOLI, F. 'La centuriazione di Lucca', *Studi Etruschi,* XX. 1948. p. 285.
81. BLOCH, M. *Les caractères originaux de l'histoire rurale française,* new edn., ed. by R. Dauvergne. Paris, 1952–6.
82. AITKEN, R. 'Virgil's Plough', *J.R.S.,* XLVI. 1956. pp. 97–106.
83. NIGHTINGALE, M. 'Ploughing and Field Shape', *Ant.* 1953. pp. 20–6.
84. SION, J. 'Sur la structure agraire de la France méridionale', *B.S.L.G.* 1937. pp. 109–31. And also by the same author 'Sur la civilisation agraire méditerranéene', *B.S.L.G.* 1940. pp. 16–40.
85. FAUCHER, D. 'Polyculture ancienne et assolement biennial dans la France meridionale', *R.G.P.S.O.* 1934. pp. 241–55.
86. COPPOLANI, J. 'Cargèse-essai sur la géographic humaine d'un village corse', *R.G.A.* 1949. pp. 70–108.
87. WESTERMANN, W. L. 'The economic basis of the decline of ancient culture', *Amer. Hist. Rev.,* 20. 1919. p. 724.
88. BLANC, A. *La Croatia occidentale.* Paris, 1957. p. 138.
89. LE LANNOU, M. *Pâtres et Paysages de la Sardaigne.* Tours, 1941. pp. 187–99.
90. LE LANNOU, M. 'Sur les origines de l'Openfield', in *Livre jubilaire offert à Maurice Zimmerman.* Paris, 1949. pp. 111–18.
91. MINISTERIO DE AGRICULTURA, ESTUDIOS AGRO-SOCIALS. *El parcelamiento de la propiedad rústica en España.* 1954. 152 pp.
92. DESPOIS, J. *Le Hodna.* Paris, 1953.
93. — *La Tunisie orientale. Sahel et Basse Steppe,* 2nd edn. Paris, 1955.
94. HOUSTON, J. M. 'Land Use and Society in the Valencian Plain', in *Geographical Essays in Memory of Alan G. Ogilvie,* ed. by R. Miller and J. W. Watson. Edinburgh, 1959. p. 191.

CHAPTER 7

MODERN DEVELOPMENTS IN THE LANDSCAPES

REFERENCES

1. See subject developed in *Economic Survey of Europe, 1953.*
2. F.A.O. *Agricultural Yearbook.* Rome, 1956, 1958.

3. F.A.O. 'Mediterranean Development Project, Interim Report', 1957. MS.
4. CARRIER, E. H. *Water and Grass*. London, 1932. 434 pp. [A useful general study.]
5. CASCÓN, J. *Agricultura española*, Madrid, 1934, p. 198.
6. F.A.O. Silva Mediterranea: 'Las relaciones entre el bosque y la ordenacion de pastos desde el punto de vista tecnico y administrativo', FAO/SCM/60/6—. MS.
7. O.E.E.C. *Pasture and Fodder development in Mediterranean countries*. Paris, 1951.
8. For definition of the types of pastoral migration see the following general articles:

   ARBOS, PH. 'Geography of the Pastoral Life', *G.R.*, 13. 1923. pp. 559–75.

   BLACHE, J. 'Les Types de Migrations Pastorales Montagnardes', *R.G.A.*, 22. 1934. pp. 525–31.

   DAVIES, E. 'The Patterns of Transhumance in Europe', *G.*, XXVI. 1941. pp. 155–68.

   DEFFONTAINES, P. 'Essai de classification des genres de vie montagnardes', *R.G.H.E.*, No. 1. 1948. pp. 23–35.

   EVANS, E. E. 'Transhumance in Europe', *G.*, XXV. 1940. pp. 172–80.

   MÜLLER, E. 'Die Herdenwanderungen im Mittelmeergebiet', *Pet. Geog. Mitt.* 1938. pp. 364–70.

   For regional bibliography see references in Chapters 9 and 15.
9. LANTIER, R. 'Contributión archeologique a une étude de la vie pastorale primitive de la Méditerranée', *R.G.H.E.*, 4. 1949. pp. 78–9.
10. WHYTE, R. O. 'Mediterranean Survey, An example of fodder resources assessment', *World Crops*, 3. 1951.
11. F.A.O. *Agricultural Yearbook*. Rome, 1956.
12. RIDGEWAY, WM. 'The Homeric Land System', *J. Hell. Stud.*, VI. 1914. pp. 319–39.
13. GRILLOT, G. 'La jachère et l'humidité des sols au Maroc', *4th I.C.S.S. Amsterdam*, vol. 1. 1950. pp. 68–70.
14. BRYSSINE, G. and GRILLOT, G. 'Nouvelle contribution a l'étude de l'humidité des sols du Maroc', *Soc. Sciences Nat. du Maroc.*, vol. 2/3. 1951.
15. F.A.O. Silva Mediterranean. 'La production accessoire de la Forêt Mediterranéene', FAO/SCM/60. 1956. MS.
16. There is a considerable literature on citrus fruit. Apart from refs. 61 (Ch. 6) see WEBBER, H. J. and BATCHELOR, L. D., eds. *The Citrus Industry: History, Botany and Breeding*, vol. 1. Berkeley, California, 1943.
17. Based on various sources, especially F.A.O. and government statistics.
18. CHALLOT, J. P. *L'Arganier*. Paris, 1948.
19. Of the numerous references on irrigation the following are important: BRUNHES, J. *L'irrigation dans la Peninsula Iberique et dans l'Afrique du Nord*. Paris, 1902; and SCOTT-MONCRIEFF, C. *Irrigation in Southern Europe*. London, 1868.
20. WITTFOGEL, K. A. 'The Hydraulic Civilizations', in Thomas, W. L., Jr., ed. *Man's Role in Changing the Face of the Earth*. Chicago, 1956. pp. 152–64.
21. F.A.O. '*Mediterranean Development Project*. Rome, 1960.
22. CASIMIRO, A. *Conquista da Terra*. Lisboa, 1940. [A useful summary of the relevant legislation.]
23. Copied from MS map in Institute of Geography, University of Lisbon.
24. FEIO, M. *Le Bas Alentejo et l'Algarve*. U.G.I. Congrès Internat. Géog. Lisbon, 1949. p. 83.
25. SILBERT, A. 'Le progrès agricole dans les plaines mediterranéennes: une exploitation modernisée de l'Alentejo', *R.G.P.S.O.*, XXIX. 1958. pp. 5–20.
26. JUNTA AUTÓNOMA DAS OBRAS DE HIDRÁULICA AGRÍCOLA. *Estudos e Obras*. Lisboa, 1939–40.

27. JUNTA AUTÓNOMA DAS OBRAS DE HIDRÁULICA AGRÍCOLA. See reports on each scheme, 1949 et seq.
28. JUNTA DE COLONIZACAO INTERNA. Reconhecimento dos baldios do continente. Lisboa, 1939.
29. Excellent detailed statistics are published in
30. PINA MANIQUE, L. DE. A Fragmentacao da Propriedade rustica. Lisboa, 1935. p. 13.
31. For general summaries see: HOUSTON, J. M. 'Irrigation as a solution to Agrarian Problems in Modern Spain', G.J., CXVI. 1950. pp. 55–63; and LAUTENSACH, H. 'Sobre la geografía del regadío', E.G. 1950. pp. 515–47.
32. MARTÍNEZ DE BUGANDA, E. 'The Spanish national irrigation plan', Inter. Inst. Agric., Monthly Bull. Ec. Soc., 25. 1934. p. 241.
33. SERMET, J. 'La renouveau economique de l'Espagne', R.G.P.S.O., XXX. 1959. pp. 193–239.
34. M. DE OBRAS PUBLICAS. Las Riegos de Espana. Madrid, 1956.
35. INSTITUTO NACIONAL DE COLONISACIÓN. Resumen de la actuación del I.N.C. Madrid, 1956.
36. NAYLON, J. 'Land consolidation in Spain', A.A.A.G., 49. 1959. pp. 361–73.
37. CONSEJO DEL ESTADO. El Plan Badajiz. Madrid.
38. — El Plan de Jaen.
39. CEBELLOS, I. 'Repoblacion forestal española en los ultimos anos 1940–1960', E.G. 1960. pp. 497–508.
40. Internat. Bank for Reconstruction and Devel., The Econ. Development of Spain, Baltimore, 1962, pp. 266–9, 317–20.
41. BOTTALICO, M. Land Reclamation. Bari, 1958. pp. 6, 10, 13–15, 17.
42. O.E.E.C. Economic Survey of Europe. 1953.
43. On the South, a fundamental work is VÖCHTING, F. La Questione Meridionale Napoli, 1955. 656 pp. It contains a full bibliography.
44. There are numerous studies of this kind, but a convenient summary is in: BENEVENTANI, E. La Bonifica integrale. Milano, 1929.
45. There are numerous articles on the Pontine reclamation schemes, but the following are the most useful: FROST, R. S. 'The reclamation of the Pontine Marshes', G.R. 1934. pp. 584–95; JACQUARD, R. 'L'Assainissement des marais pontins', A. de G., 45. 1936. pp. 486–501; KISH, G. 'The Pontine Marshes', Can. Geog. Journ., 52. 1956. pp. 118–25; and SIR J. RUSSELL. 'Agricultural Colonization in the Pontine Marshes and Libya', G.J., 94. 1939. pp. 273–92.
46. DOZIER, L. C. 'Establishing a framework for development in Sardinia: the Campidano', G.R. 1957. pp. 490–506.
47. BARBERO, G. 'La Transformazione fondiaria irrigua nella piana del destra Sele', in Economia delle transformazioni fondiarie, vol. I. Naples. pp. 233–434.
48. BIGNARDI, D. Land Reclamation in Italy. Rome, 1953. p. 10.
49. Of the numerous references to land reform the following may be selected: VÖCHTING, F. op. cit. (see no. 43); ROSSI-DORIA, M. Riforma agraria e azione meridionalista. Roma, 1948.
50. ENTE MAREMMA. La riforma fondiaria in Maremma. Rome, 1955. 158 pp.
51. I.N.I.E. La riforma agraria in Puglia, Lucania, Molise. Bari, 1956.
52. OPERA PER LA VALORIZZAZIONE DELLA SILA. Le realizzazioni della riforma in Calabria. Novara, 1959.
53. ROCHEFORT, R. Le travail en Sicilie, étude de géographie sociale. Paris, 1961. 363 pp. [A comprehensive survey of Sicily's social problems.]
54. DICKINSON, R. E. 'Agrarian Reform in S. Italy', E.G. 1954. pp. 157–76.
55. CASSA PER IL MEZZOGIORNO. The 'Cassa per il Mezzogiorno' and the economic development of Southern Italy. Rome, 1963. 107 pp.
56. ALEMANNI, M. M. 'Insediamento umano bonifica e riforma nei territori lati-

fondistici'. *Atti XII Reunione Sci della Soc. Ital. di Econ. Demoz. e Stat.*, IV. Rome, 1950. pp. 1–31.

57. These problems are raised in NELSON, L. *Land Reform in Italy.* Washington, D.C., 1956.

58. Two useful summaries are contained in: BIROT, J. and DRESCH, J. *La Méditerranée Occidentale.* Paris, 1953. pp. 477–80, 505–19; and DESPOIS, J. *L'Afrique du Nord.* Paris, 1949. pp. 355–422, 544–51. The latter volume has a comprehensive bibliography. See also DRESCH, J. 'L'agriculture de l'Afrique du Nord' (Cours de Sorbonne—mimeographed). Paris, 1956. 221 pp.

59. Standard works on French colonisation are: BEAUDICOURT, L. DE. *Histoire de la Colonisation de l'Algérie.* Challamel, 1860. 584 pp. CONGRÈS DE LA COLONISATION RURALE. *La Colonisation rurale dan les principaux pays de peuplement.* Alger, 1930. 755 pp. PEYERIMHOFF, M. *Enquête sur les resultats de la colonisation officielle de 1871à, 1875,* 2 vols. Alger, 1906. 363 and 601 pp. PIQUET, V. *La colonisation française dans l'Afrique du Nord.* Paris, 1912. 538 pp.

60. FRANC, J. *La colonisation de la Mitidja.* Paris, 1928. 577 pp.

61. TINTHOIN, R. *Colonisation et evolution des genres de vie dans la region Ouest d'Oran de 1880 a 1885.* Oran, 1947. 389 pp.

62. ISNARD, H. *Histoire de la vigne en Algérie.* Also 'Vigne et Colonisation in Algérie', *A.H.E.S.* 1947. pp. 288–300.

63. BERNARD, A. 'Le "dry-farming" et ses applications dans l'Afrique du Nord', *A. de G.*, XX. 1911. pp. 411–30.

64. CHEVALIER, L. *Le probleme demographique nord-Africain.* Paris, 1947. 221 pp.

65. TOUMIEROUX, J. A. *L'oleiculture en Tunisie.* Tunis, 1929. 373 pp.

66. MILLIOT, L. *Les terres collectives* (*Blad djemaa*). 1922. 310 pp.

67. AMPHOUX, M. 'L'evolution de l'agriculture européenne au Maroc', *A. de G.*, XLII. 1933. pp. 175–85.

68. SONNIER, A. 'Les merjas de la plaine du Rharb', *B.E.Ma.* 1935. pp. 118–23.

69. The following articles summarise the significance of Algerian schemes of irrigation: MAZUREL, Y. 'Le problème de l'irrigation en Algérie et le systeme de grands barrages', *B.S.G. Marseille.* 1944–7. pp. 21–42; ROESSINGER, E. 'Barrages, irrigation et houille blanche en Algerie', *B.S. neufchâteloise de G.* 1946.

70. BERKALOFF, F. and TIXERONT, M. *Carte du ruissellement annuel moyen en Tunisie et notice.* Tunis, 1957. 10 pp.

71. HOUSTON, J. M. 'The significance of irrigation in Morocco's economic development', *G.J.*, CXX. 1954. pp. 514–28. Also LE MOIGNE, J. 'Hydraulique et irrigation au Maroc', *R.G.M.* 1931. pp. 289–306.

72. CELERIER, J. 'Travaux de petite hydraulique dans le Sud Marocain', *A. de G.* 1938. pp. 534–9.

PART II: THE IBERIAN PENINSULA

CHAPTER 8

STRUCTURES AND LANDFORMS

ATLASES AND MAPS

Generalstab des Heeres. *Militargeographischen studie uber Spanien und Portugal.* 1940–1. This contains 220 pp. text, 243 pp. photos, 7 maps and 148 town plans.

SIEX BARRAL, S. A., ed. *Atlas Geográfico Mundial y especial España Barcelona.* 1957. [139 maps.]

Aguilar. *Neuvo Atlas de España*. Madrid, 1961. The best up-to-date atlas with 352 maps, 139 photos.
— *Atlas de Portugal*, 2nd edn. Lisbon, 1958. [With 40 maps, and text.]
The topographic maps of the Iberian Peninsula do not show a high standard of accuracy, especially in the depiction of contours, but especially on the Spanish 1/50,000 sheets care is taken to show several features of land use.

Spain

Instituto Geográfico y Catastral of Madrid. 1/50,000 sheets have appeared since 1875. Copied by G.S.G.S. and A.M.S. 781–7 in 1943–4.
— 1/500,000. Copied by G.S.G.S. and A.M.S.
Servicio Geográfico del Ejercito. 1/100,000 sheets have appeared since 1920. Copied by G.S.G.S. 4109, and by A.M.S.
— 1/200,000.
Instituto Geográfico y Catastral of Madrid. 1/1 million, *Mapa Fisico*, 1930. 1/500,000.
Instituto Geológico y Minero de España. 1/1 million. *Mapa Geológico de España y Portugal*, 1952.
Instituto Nacional de Investigaciones Agronomicas. 1/1 million. *Mapa vinicola nacional*, 1959.

Portugal

Istituto Geográfico e Catastral. 1/20,000. *Carta Corografica de Portugal* (towns).
— 1/50,000. *Carta Corográfica de Portugal* since 1900. Copied by G.S.G.S. 4145, 1940–2 and A.M.S.
— 1/100,000. 1856–1904. New edition of 1950.
— 1/250,000. *Carta Itineraria de Portugal*, 1904–24. Copied by G.S.G.S. 4148, 4455, 1941–7, and by A.M.S. M501, 1959.
— 1/600,000. *Carta Hipsometrica de Portugal*, 1955.
— 1/1 million. *Carta Hipsometrica*.
— 1/500,000. *Carta, Distribuicao da populacao de Portugal*. By O. Ribeiro (1940 census), 1951.
Estacao Agronomica Nacional. 1/500,000. *Carta Ecologia de P. de Pina Manique e Alburquerque*, 1952, with booklet.
Plan do Fomento Agricola. 1/250,000. *Carta de l'Eucalyptus*.

GENERAL WORKS

Of the numerous textbooks on the Iberian Peninsula the following are standard works:
BIROT, P. et DRESCH, J. *La Méditerranée et le Moyen-Orient*, tome I, *La Méditerranée Occidentale*. Paris, 1953. 552 pp.
ECHEVERRÍA, L. M. *España, e pais y los habitantes*. Mexico, 1940. 488 pp.
Geographical Handbooks, Naval Intelligence Division. *Spain and Portugal*, 4 vols. 1944.
HERNÁNDEZ-PACHECO, E. *Síntesis Fisiográfica y Geológica de España*. Madrid, 1934. 584 pp.
SORRE, M. *Méditerranée: Peninsules Méditerranéennes* (*Espagne-Portugal*), Geog. Universelle, tome VII, part one. Paris, 1934. 228 pp.
TERÁN, M. DE, ed. *Geografía de España y Portugal*. Barcelona (vols. I, II, IV, V published by 1958).
Other works are referred to under chapters 11–13.

REFERENCES

1. LAUTENSACH, H., and MAYER, E. 'Iberische Meseta und Iberische Masse'. *Z. Geomorphol.* 5, 1961. pp. 161–80.
2. CARBONELL, J. 'Ideas sobre la tectonica de Espana', *R. Acad. Cien. Bellas Letras y Nobl. Artes de Córdoba.* 1926. 83 pp.
3. CARLE, W. 'Ergebnisse geologischer Untersuchungen im Grundgebirge von Galicien', *Geotekt. Forsch.*, 6. 1945. pp. 13–36.
4. SAENZ CLEMENTE, A. 'Estructura general de la cuenca del Ebro', *Est. Geol.*, 111. 1942. pp. 249–69.
5. COTELO NEIVA, J. M. 'Manifestações da actividade magmatica em Portugal', *Bull. Soc. Geol. Port.* IV. 1944. pp. 41–60.
6. BOTELLA, F. 'Apuntes paleográficos. España y sus antiguos mares', *Bol. R. Soc. Geog. Nac.* II, 1886, pp. 143–66; 211–29, 276–314, 461–98; XVI, 216–31; XVII, 129–60; XXI, 37–113.
7. STILLE, H. 'Sobre los enlaces de las cadenas de montañas del Mediterráneo occidental, *Inst. José de Acosta.* Madrid, 1942. pp. 25–70.
8. CARBONELL, A. 'Contribución al estudio de la geología y de la tectónica andaluza', *Bol. Inst. Geol. y Min. Esp.* XLIX, 1927. pp. 81–215.
9. MARIN, A. 'La depresión del Ebro. La tectónica y los yacimientos minerales', *Bol. Inst. Geol. y Min. Esp.* LVII, 1945. pp. 1–52.
10. FERNANDEZ NAVARRO, L. *Paleogeografía. Historia geológica de la Península Ibérica.* Madrid, 1916. 238 pp.
11. STAUB, R. 'Gedanken zur Tektonik Spaniens Vierteljahrschr. d. Naturforsch', *Gess. Zurich*, LXXI, 1926. pp. 196–261.
12. HERNANDEZ PACHECO, F. 'Sintesis orográfica y orogenica de la peninsula Ibérica', *Bol. R. Soc. Esp. Hist. Nat.* LIII, 1955. pp. 23–42.
13. FISCHER, T. *Mittelmeer-Bilder.* Berlin, 1906. pp. 236–77.
14. SCHWENZNER, J. *Zur morphologie das Zentralspanischen Hochlandes*, Geog. Abhand. 3 ser. X, Stuttgart, 1937. 128 pp.
15. FEIO, M. *A evolucao do relevo do Baixo Alentejo e Algarve.* Lisbon, 1951. 186 pp.
16. HERNANDEZ-PACHECO, F. *Fisiografía e historia geológica de la altiplanicie de Castilla la Vieja.* Publ. Univ. Valladolid. 1930. 6 pp.
17. SOLÉ SABARÍS, L. In *Geografía de España.* (See General Works).
18. ALIA MEDINA, M. 'Sobre la tectónica profunda de la fosa del Tajo', *Notas y Commun. Inst. Geol. y Min. Esp.* 1960, 58. pp. 125–62.
19. ASENSIO AMOR, I. 'Genesis y cronologia de las arenas de Torrelodones', *An. Soc. Esp. Prog. Cis.*, 1960, pp. 75–84; also, SOS, BAYNAT, V., 'Observaciones sobre la formacion y la edad de los ranas', Cur. y Conf. Inst. Lucas Mallada 1957, 4, pp. 33–6; and the series of papers devoted to this subject in *C.R. Internat. Congrès Geog.*, Lisbon, 1949, tome 11, pp. 87–131, 149–59.
20. ROYO GOMEZ, E. 'El Terciario continental de la cuenca alta del Tajo', sheet 560, Alcalá de Henares, *Inst. Geol. y Mineral. Esp.* Madrid, 1928. pp. 17–89.
21. SOLÉ SABARÍS. *Geografía de España, op. cit.*, p. 212–14.
22. FEIO, M. *Os terracos da Guadiana a jussante do Ardilla.* Lisbon, 1947. 82 pp.
23. MABESONNE, J. M. 'Tertiary and Quaternary sedimentation in a part of the Duero basin', *Leidse Geol. Med.*, 24, 1959, pp. 31–180; also, NOSSIN, J. J. 'Geomorphological aspects of the Pisuerga drainage area', *ibid.*, pp. 283–406.
24. BIROT, P. et SOLÉ SABARÍS, L. 'Recherches morphologiques dans l'W. de la Péninsule Ibérique', *Mém. et Doc. C.N.R.S.* Paris, IV, 1954. pp. 10–60. [Important work.]
25. HERNÁNDEZ PACHECO, F., *et alia, INQUA.* V Congrès internat. *Excursión a las Cantabrians.* 1957. 70 pp.
26. VIDAL BEX, C. 'Ensayo sobre la interpretación morfológica y tectónica de la

Cordillera Central en el segmento comprendido en la provincia de Avila', *Bol. R. Soc. Esp. Hist. Nat.* XXXVII, 1937. pp. 79–106.

27. HERNÁNDEZ-PACHECO, F. *INQUA.* V Congrès internat. *Excursión CI. Gredos.* 1957. 58 pp.

28. BIROT, P. Y SOLÉ SABARÍS, L. *Investigaciones sobre la morfología de la Cordillera Central.* Inst. Juan Sebastian Elcano, Madrid, 1954.

29. VIDAL BOX, C. 'Nuevas aportaciones al conocimiento geomorfológico de la Cordillera Central', *E.G.* IX, 1948.

30. HERNANDEZ-PACHECO, E. 'El meandro encajodo del Tajo en torno de Toledo', *Bol. R. Soc. Esp. Hist. Nat.* XXX. 1930. pp. 116–29.

31. RIBA, O. *INQUA.* V Congres internat. *Excursión C2.* Terrasses du Manzanares et du Jarama aux environs de Madrid, 1957. 55 pp.

32. ROYO GÓMEZ, J. 'Los límites del Terciario y del Cuaternario en la cuenca alta del Tajo', *Mem. hoja 559, Inst. Geol. y Min. Esp.* 1929.

33. HERNÁNDEZ-PACHECO, F. Y RODRIGUEZ MELLADO, M. T. 'La evolucion geomorfologica de las zonas orientales de la Mancha', *Bol. R. Soc. Esp. Hist. Nat.* XLV, 1947.

34. PLANCHUELO PORTALES, G. *Estudio del Alto Guadiana y de la Altiplanicie del Campo de Montiel.* Madrid, 1954. pp. 43–62.

35. VIDAL BOX, C. 'La edad de la superficie de erosión de Toledo y el problema de sus montes-islas', *Rev. Las Cien.* IX, 1944.

36. HERNÁNDEZ-PACHECO, F. *Estudio de la region volcánica central de España.* Mem. R. Acad. Cien. Exact. Fis. Nat. Madrid, 1932.

37. BIROT, P. In *La Méditerranée Occidentale, op. cit.* p. 143.

38. HERNÁNDEZ-PACHECO, F. *Ensayo morfologico de Extremadura.* Madrid, 1947.

39. — 'El segmento medio de las Sierras Centrales de Extremadura', *Las Ciencias,* IV, 1939. pp. 361–97.

40. BIROT, P. In *La Méditerranée Occidentale* (see Ch. 1). p. 145.

41. CARBONELL, A. *La linea tectónica del Guadalquivir,* XIV Cong. Géol. Internat. Excurs. A–4, Inst. Geol. y Min. Esp. 201 pp.

42. BIROT, P. and FEIO, M. 'Notes sur la morphologie du Portugal meridionale', in *Melanges Géographiques Faucher.* Toulouse, 1948.

43. BIROT, P. 'Les surfaces d'erosion du Portugal central et septentrional', *C.R. Congrès Internat. Géog.,* Lisbon, 1949.

44. FEIO, M. 'Notas geomorfologicas a depressao de Regua-Verin', *Com. Ser. Geol. Port.* XXXII, 1951. pp. 5–46.

45. ZBYSZEWSKI, G. 'La Quaternaire du Portugal', *B. Soc. Geol. Port.* XIII, 1958. 227 pp.

46. FEIO, M. *op. cit.* (No. 15).

47. — *Le bas Alentejo et l'Algarve, Livret-guide de l'exursión E,* Congrès Internat. Géog. Lisbon, 1949. 202 pp.

48. ZBYSZEWSKI, G. *Observations sur la structure et la morphologie du Bas Alentejo et de l'Algarve',* Inst. Fran. au Port. 1939.

49. PEREIRA DE SOUSA, F. L. 'La serra de Monchique', *Bull. Soc. Geol. Fr.* XXVI. 1926.

50. MEDEIROS-GOUVEA, A. de. *Algarve-aspectos fisiográficos.* Lisbon, 1938.

51. RAU, V. et ZBYSZEWSKI, G. *Estremadura et Ribatejo, Livret-guide de l'excursión D.* Congrès Internat. Géog. Lisbon, 1949. 146 pp.

52. Ibid.

53. FERNANDES MARTIN, A. *Le Centre Littoral et le massif calcaire d'Estremadura. Livret-guide de l'excursión B.* Congrès Internat. Géog. Lisbon, 1949. 96 pp.

54. RIBEIRO, O. *Le Portugal Central. Livret-guide de l'excursión C.* Congrès Internat. Géog. Lisbon, 1948. 180 pp.

55. — 'Estructura e relevo da Serra da Estrela', *Bol. R. Soc. Esp. Hist. Nat.* 1954. pp. 549–66.
56. — 'Tres notas de geomorfologia da Beira Baixa', *Com. Ser. Geol. Port.* XXXII, 1951. pp. 5–28. Also, DIAS J. MINHO. *Trás-os-Montes, Haut-Douro. Livret-guide,* Congres Internat. Geog. Lisbon, 1949. 125 pp.
57. BOURCART, J. 'Le marge continentale. Essai sur les trangressions et regressions marines', *B. Soc. Geol. Fr.* 5a. ser. VIII, 1938. pp. 393–448.
58. CARLÉ, W. 'Gänge als Zeitmarken und tektonischen Bezugaflächen. Mit einem Beitrag zu Region Geol. Galiciens', *Geol. Rundschau,* XXXI, 1940. pp. 230–40.
59. DANTÍN CERECEDA, J. *Regiones naturales de España* I., Madrid, 1942, pp. 89–388.
60. PARGA PONDAL, I. *Observación, interpretación y problemas geológicas de Galicia.* La Coruña, Real Acad. Gallega. 1960. 54 pp.
61. BIROT, P. 'Espagne: Progrès récents dans la connaissance de la géomorphogie et de la structure de l'Espagne septentrionale', *A. de G.* 375, 1960. pp. 548–50.
62. HERNÁNDEZ-PACHECO, F. 'Geomorfologia de la cuenca media del Sil', *Mem. R. Acad. Cien. Exact. Fis. y Nat.* XIII, 1949. 114 pp.
63. LLOPIS LLADO, N. 'El relieve de la region central de Asturias', *E.G.* XV, 1954. pp. 501–19.
64. SCHEU, E. 'Das Kantabrische Gebirge und die spanische Riviera', *Mitt. Ges Erdkunde,* XLIX, 1925–9, pp. 7–136. See also the following on the controversy over the origin of the *rasas*: HERNÁNDEZ-PACHECO, F. y ASENSIO AMOR, I. 'Materiales sedimentarios sobre la rasa cantabrica', *B.R. Soc. Esp. Hist. Nat.* LVII, 1959, pp. 75–100; and HÉRNANDEZ-PACHECO, F., *et alii. INQUA. Livret-guide, Excursión, Cantabrians,* 1957.
65. HERNÁNDEZ-PACHECO, F. 'Nueva hipotesis de la formacion tectónica de los Picos de Europa', *Invest. y Progr.,* XV, 1944. pp. 215–27.
66. RAT, P. *Les pays crétacés basco-cantabriques.* Pub. Univ. Dijon. XVIII, 1959. 528 pp.
67. BIROT, P. et SOLÉ SABARÍS, L. 'Sur un trait morphologique paradoxal des massifs cristallins de la Cordillere Centrale Iberique', *B.A.G.F.,* 1951. pp. 94–9.
68. AITKEN, R. 'Datos geológicos sobre el Norte de la Demanda', *Bol. R. Soc. Esp. Hist. Nat.* XXXII, 1932. pp. 309–10.
69. SOLÉ SABARÍS, L. y RIBA ARDEIUS, O. 'El relieve de la Sierra de Albarracin y zonas limitrofes de la Cordillera Ibérica', *Teruel Inst. Est. turolensis,* 7, 1951. pp. 1–27.
70. BOMER, B. 'Aspectos morfológicas de la cuenca de Calatayud-Daroca y de sus zonas marginales', *E.G.,* 1960. pp. 393–402.
71. HERNÁNDEZ-PACHECO, F. 'Sintesis geomorfologica del pais vasco en las limites de Guipuzcoa y Navarra', *Bol. R. Soc. Esp. Hist. Nat.* 1950. pp. 5–23.
72. ARANEGUI, P. *Geología y Geografía del pais vasco.* Com. Invest. Geog. Geol. y Prehist. Mem. 2. 1936. 141 pp.
73. LAMARE, P. 'La structure geologique des Pyrenees Basques', Primer Congrès Internat. Piren. Zaragoza, 1950. pp. 1–44; also SERMET, J. 'Le problème de la limite géographique occidentale des Pyrenees', *Mem. de l'acad. Sci. Toulouse.* 1958. pp. 99–144.
74. SOLÉ SABARÍS, L. *Los Pirineos.* Barcelona, 1951. pp. 21–129.
75. BIROT, P. 'Sur quelques contrastes fundamentaux dans la structure et la morphologie des Pyrenées', *Inst. Est. Pir.* 1950. 9 pp.
76. — *Recherches sur le morphologie des Pyrénées Orientales franco-espanoles.* Thesis. Paris, 1937. 318 pp.
77. LLOPIS LLADO, N. 'El relieve del alto valle del Aragón', *Pir.,* III, 1947. pp. 81–166.
78. SOLÉ SABARÍS, L. *Los Pirineos, op. cit.* pp. 110–29.

79. ALIMEN, H., *et alii. INQUA.* V Congres Internat. *Livret Guide de Excursión Ni.* 1957. 107 pp.
80. BIROT, P. *Recherches sur le morphologie des Pyénées Orientales, op. cit.*
81. SAENZ CLEMENTE, A. 'Estructura general de la cuenca del Ebro', *E.G.* III, 1942. pp. 249–69.
82. SOLÉ SABARÍS, L. 'Terrazas cuaternarias deformadas de la cuenca del Ebro', *Mem. R. Acad. Ciencias y Artes,* XXXI, 7. Barcelona, 1953. pp. 239–59.
83. GARCÍA SAINZ, L. 'Los principales rasgos morfológicos del Ebro medio', *Las Ciencias,* IV, 1939. pp. 528–38.
84. LLOPIS LLADO, N. *Contribución al conocimiento de la morfostructura de los Catalánides.* Con. Sup. Invest. Cient. Inst. Lucas Mallada. Barcelona, 1947. 372 pp.
85. LLOBET, S. 'Las terrazas del alto rio Ter', *Actas 3er. Congresso Est. Piraicos.* Gerona, 1958.
86. LLOPIS LLADO, N. 'Tectomorfología del macizo del Tibidabo y valle inferior del Llobregat', *E.G.,* III, 1942. pp. 321–83.
87. LLOBET, S. *El medio y la vida en el Montseny.* Barcelona, 1947. pp. 11–33.
88. SAN MIGUEL DE LA CAMARA, M. Y MARCET, J. *La region volcanica de Oloy.* XIV Congr. Geol. Internat. Excursion C-4, Inst. Geol. y Min. Esp. 1926. pp. 39–216.
89. LLOPIS LLADO, N. 'Morfologia dec los relieves de pudingas de Sant Llorens del Munt, Sierra de l'Obach', *E.G.* V, 1945. pp. 687–814.
90. FALLOT, P. 'Etat de nos connaissances sur la structure des chaînes bétique et subbétique', *Livre jub. centenaire Soc. géol. Fr.* I, 1930. pp. 279–305.
91. JESSEN, O. *Die Strasse von Gibraltar.* Berlin, 1927. 283 pp.
92. BIROT, P. 'Notes sur l'évolution morphologique des Chaînes Bétiques Centrales', *B.A.G.F.,* 212–3, 1950. pp. 122–8.
93. GAVALA, J. 'La geología del Estrecho de Gibraltar', *B. Inst. Geol. y Min. Esp.,* LI, 1929. pp. 3–35.
94. A comprehensive bibliography on the region is listed by: SOLÉ SABARÍS, L. y MORENO, I. 'Bibliografía geológica y fisiográfica de las Cordilleras Beticas', *Bol. Univ. Granada,* XIV, 1942. pp. 467–570.
95. CARANDELL, J. 'La morfologia de Sierra Nevada. Ensayo de su interpret acion tectónica', *Rev. R. Acad. Cien. Fis. Quim. y Nat.,* IX, Madrid, 1921. pp. 43–76.
96. ORUETA, D. Y RUBIO, E. *La Serranía de Ronda, Excursión A-2.* XIV Congr. Geol. Internat. Inst. Min. y Min. Esp. Madrid, 1926. 160 pp.
97. SOLÉ SABARÍS, L. et BIROT, P. 'L'évolution morphologique de la zone sub-bétique orientale', *B.A.G.F.,* 251, 1955. pp. 118–24.
98. AGUIRRE, E. 'Notes sobre estratigrafia de las depresiones andaluzas', *Est. Geol.,* 38, 1958. pp. 121–6.
99. REY PASTOR, A. 'Estudio morfo-tectonico de la falla del Guadalquivir', *Rev. de Geofisica,* XIV, 1955. pp. 101–37.

CHAPTER 9

THE RURAL LANDSCAPES

REFERENCES

1. BRUNHES, J. *L'irrigation dans la Péninsule Ibérique.* Paris, 1902.
2. SORRE, M. In *Geographie Universelle,* tome VII, Paris, 1934. Part 1, p. 81.
3. DANTÍN CERECEDA, J. and RAVENGA CARBONELL, A. 'Las lineas y zonas Isoxeras de España segun los indices thermopluviometricos, *E.G.,* 1941. pp. 35–92.

4. LAUTENSACH, H. 'Die niederschlagshöhen auf der Iberischen', *Pet. Mitt.* 1951. pp. 145–60.
5. BIROT, P. 'Sur une nouvelle fonction d'aridité appliquée au Portugal', *Anais de Faculdade de Ciencias do Porto*, 1945.
6. TAMÉS, C. 'Bosquejo del clima de España segun la clasificación de C. W. Thornthwaite', *Bol. Inst. Nac. Invest. Agron.*, 1949. pp. 49–123.
7. LLORENTE, J. 'La clasificación de climas, según Thornthwaite, aplicada a España', *Las Ciencias*, XII, 1947. pp. 772–81.
8. See summary of views in article by FERNANDEZ ALONSO, F. 'Ensayo de revisión de los conceptos "Iberia Humeda" e "Iberia Seca" ', *E.G.*. 1957. pp. 5–35.
9. LOPEZ GOMEZ, J. and A. El Clima de España segun la clasificación de Köffren', *E.G.*, 1959. pp. 167–88.
10. WALTER, H. und LIETH, H. *Klimadiagramm Weltatlas.* Jena, 1960.
11. LAUTENSACH, H. 'El ritmo de las estaciones en la Peninsular Ibérica', *E.G.*, 1956. pp. 443–60.
12. DEL VILLAR, E. H. *Suelos de la Peninsula Luso-Ibérica*, Madrid, 1937, pp. 416; see also TAMÉS, C. *Los grupos principales de suelos de la España Peninsular.* M. de Agricultura, Madrid, 1957.
13. WILLKOMM, M. *Die Strand- und Steppengebiete der Iberischen Halbinsel und deren Vegetation.* Leipzig, 1852.
14. REYES, PROSPERE, *Las Estepas de España.* Madrid, 1915, 304 pp.
15. DEL VILLAR, E. H. 'Avance geobotánico sobre la pretendida "Estepa Central" de España', *Ibérica.* 1925.
16. DANTÍN CERECEDA, J. 'La aridez y el endorreismo en España', *E.G.*, 1940, pp. 75–117; 1942, pp. 505–96.
17. NAVARRO GARNICA, M. 'Destino de las tierras españolas', FAO/SCM/60/SB. 1960.
18. Based on *World Forest Atlas.* Hamburg, 1956.
19. RUPEREZ CUELLAR, A. *La encina y sus tratamientos.* Madrid, 1957.
20. M. DE AGRICULTURA. *Pinares de la Meseta sur del Duero* (Mapa Agronómico Nacional hoźa 429). Madrid, 1951. 245 pp.
21. F.A.O./S.C.M. Report on Poplars, Rome, 1956, MS.
22. F.A.O./S.C.M. Report on Eucalyptus in Portugal, Rome, 1959, MS.
23. 'Los relaciones entre el bosque y la ordenación de pastos', FAO/SCM/60/6-B. 1960.
24. CARO BAROJA, J. 'Régimenes sociales y económicas de la España Preromana', *R.I.S.*, 1, 1943. pp. 149–90.
25. On transhumance an extensive bibliography now supersedes the pioneer study by FRIBOURG, 'La transhumance en Espagne', *A. de G.*, 1910. pp. 231–44.
26. CASA TORRES, J. M. 'Transhumance in Spanish Navarra', *Congrès Internat. Geog.* Tome 2. Lisbon, 1949. pp. 12–13.
27. FLORISTAN, A. 'Juntas y Mestas ganaderas en las Bardenas de Navarra', *Actes Primer Congreso Int. E.P.* Tome V. San Sebastian, 1950. pp. 111–30.
28. LLOBET, S. *El Medio y la Vida en Andorra.* Barcelona, 1947. 343 pp.
29. LLOBET, S. and VITA VALENTÍN, S. 'La Trashumancia en Cataluna', *C.R. Congrès Internat. Géog.* Tome 2. Lisbon, 1949. pp. 36–47.
30. M. DE AGRICULTURA. *El Pastoreo en los montes: contribución al estudio pastoral del Levante Español.* Madrid, 1956. 119 pp.
31. KLEIN, J. *The Mesta.* Cambridge (Harvard), 1920.
32. DANTÍN CERECEDA, J. 'Cañadas ganaderas españolas', *Cong. do Mundo Portug, Pub.*, XVIII, 1940, pp. 682–96; see also AITKEN, R. 'Routes of Transhumance on the Spanish Meseta', *G.J.*, CVI, 1945. pp. 59–69.
33. FLORISTAN, A. *La Ribera Tudelana de Navarra.* Zaragoza, 1951. pp. 112–19.
34. AITKEN, R. 'Wheat growing in Old Castile', *J. of Tyneside Geog. Soc.*, 1937.

35. CEBALLOS, L. and MARTÍN BOLANOS, M., *Estudio sobre la vegetación forestal de la provincia de Cadiz*, Madrid, 1930, p. 27.
36. PEREIRA, G. 'Les Vignobles du Nord du Portugal', *R.G.P.S-O.*, 111, 1932. pp. 202–33.
37. GALTIER, M. G. 'Le vignoble espanol d'aujourd'hui', *B.A.G.F.*, 1950. pp. 96–103.
38. There are numerous references on irrigation, notably: MARKHAM, R. C., *Report on irrigation in eastern Spain*, London, 1866–7; SCOTT, C. C., Irrigation in southern Europe, London, 1868; 1ero *Cong. Nac. de Riegos*, 3 vols., 1914; and *Junta Consultiva Agrónimca*, 2 vols., 1918.
39. JAUBERT DE PASSÁ. *Canales de riego de Cataluña y el reino de Valencia*. Madrid, 1844.
40. LAUTENSACH, H. 'Sobre la geografía del regadío', *E.G.*, 1950, pp. 515–47; also HOUSTON, J. M., 'Irrigation as a solution to agrarian problems in Spain', *G.J.*, CXVI, 1950, pp. 55–63.
41. COMITE ESPAÑOL DE REIGOS Y DRENAJES. *Los Riegos de España*. Madrid 1956.
42. GUILLE N Y RODRIQUEZ DE CEPADA. *El Tribunal de Agua*. Valencia, 1920.
43. HOUSTON, J. M. 'Social geography of rice cultivation in Spain', *Indian Geog. Soc., Jubilee vol*. 1951. pp. 36–40.
44. GARCÍA DE OTEYZA, L. 'Los regimenes de explotación del suelo nacional', *R. Est. Agro-Sociales*. 1952. pp. 49–61.
45. GARCÍA-BADELL, G. 'El regimen de la propiedad de nustro suelo agrícola y el problema de los mini fundios', *Bol. R. Soc. Geog.*, LXXVII, 1942, pp. 647–85; and *E.G.*, 1946, pp. 171–223; see also DUMONT, R., *Types of Rural Economy*, London, 1957, pp. 209–28.
46. LIMA BASTO, E. A. *Inquerito Economico-Agricola*. Lisbon, 1936.
47. CARRIÓN, P. *Los Latifundios en España*. Madrid, 1932.
48. SILBERT, A. 'Le progrès agricola dans les plaines mediterranèenes: une exploitation modernisée de l'Alentejo', *R.G.P.S-O.*, XXIX, 1958. pp. 5–20.
49. QUARTIM, L., *Problemas da vide rural*, Lisbon, 1945.
50. NAYLON, J. 'Progress in land consolidation in Spain', *A.A.A.G.*, 1961, pp. 335–8.
51. BIROT, P. and BRUNET, L. 'Notes sobre los estructuras agrarias de N.O. de la Péninsula Ibérica', *E.G.*, 1954; see also HAYES, R. D., 'A peasant economy in N.W. Portugal', *G.J.*, LXXII, 1956, pp. 54–70.
52. CARO BAROJA, J. *Los Pueblos del norte de España*, Madrid, 1943. 241 pp.; also DAVID, P., *Etudes historiques sur la Galice et le Portugal du VI au XII siécles*, Coimbra, 1947.
53. TERÁN, M. 'Vaqueros y cabanas en los montes de Pas', *E.G.*, 1947. pp. 493–536.
54. VILÁ VALENTÍN, J. 'Un nombre mal empleado: Los Montes Universales', *E.G.*, 1956. pp. 41–59.
55. LOPEZ GOMEZ, A. 'Valdelaguna: colectivismo agrario en los montañas burgalesas', *E.G.*, 1954. pp. 551–67.
56. BARRÈRE, P. 'Types d'organisation des terroirs en Haut-Aragon', *Actes Primer Congreso Int. E.P. San Sebastian*, tomo V, 1950. pp. 249–68.
57. ASSO, J. I. *Historia de la Economia politica de Aragon*. 1798 (new edn. 1947).
58. MADOZ, P. *Diccionario Geográfico Estadistico e Historico de España*. Madrid, 1848–50.
59. COSTA, J. *Colectivismo agrario de España*. Madrid, 1915. 646 pp.
60. CABO ALONSO, A. 'El colectivismo agrario en tierra de Sayago', *E.G.*, 1956. pp. 593–658.
61. GARCÍA FERNANDEZ, J. 'Horche (Guadalajara): Estudio de estructiva agraria', *E.G.*, 1953. pp. 193–239.
62. FLORISTAN, A. *La Ribera Tudelana de Navarra*. Zaragoza, 1951. 316 pp.
63. BARCELANO, P. B. 'Evolución de la estructura agraria del termino de Ocaña', *E.G.*, 1956. pp. 185–206.

CHAPTER 10

POPULATION AND SETTLEMENT

References on these subjects are legion, so only the major items are here listed.

GENERAL WORKS

CARO BAROJA, J. *Los Pueblos de España*. Madrid, 1946. 495 pp. [Contains detailed bibliography. Somewhat speculative, but stimulating work.]

BRAUDEL, F. La *Méditerranée et le monde méditerranéen a l'époque de Philippe II*. Paris, 1949. 1160 pp. [The standard work on the historical geography of the sixteenth century.]

JÜRGENS, O. *Spanische Städte*. Hamburg, 1926, with atlas containing 27 town plans.

HOYOS SAINZ, L. DE. *La densidad de población y el acrecentamiento en España*. Madrid, 1952. 302 pp.

HOYOS SANCHO, N. *La Casa Tradicional en España*, 2nd edn. 1959. 28 pp.

LAUNTENSACH, H. *Maurische Zuge im geographischen Bild der Iberischen Halbinsel*. Bonner geogr. Abh. 1960, No. 28. 98 pp.

SCHULTEN, A. *Iberische Landeskunde: Geographie des antiken Spanien*. Strasbourg/Kehl, 1955. 462 pp. [The standard work on the historical geography of ancient times.]

TORRES BALBAS, L., *et alii. Resumen histórico del urbanismo en España*. Madrid, 1954. 227 pp. [A useful summary of urban studies in Spain.]

REFERENCES

1. MENÉNDEZ PIDAL, R. *Spaniards in their History*, trans. by W. Starkie. London, 1950. p. 179.
2. HOUSTON, J. M. 'Population changes in Spain', 18th *Internat. Geog. Congress* Rio de Janeiro, 1956. MS.
3. VINAS, C. *Relaciones de los pueblos de España, ordenados por Filipe II*, Reinos de Toledo, I. Madrid, 1951. 575 pp.
4. LEPEYRE, H. *Géographie de l'Espagne Morisque*. Paris, 1959. 304 pp.
5. M. DE TRABAJO Y PREVISIÓN. *Depoblación y Repoblación de España, 1482–1920*. Madrid, 1929.
6. SCHWALBACH, L. 'A populaçao portuguese', *Rev. Fac. Letras de Coimbra*. 1948. 48 pp.
7. ALZINA CAULES, J. 'Investigaciones analitica sobre el moviemento de población en Catalunia', *Cuadernas de Inf. Ec. y Soc.* Barcelona, 1955. pp. 15–46.
8. RUIZ ALMANSA, R. *La Población de Galicia, 1500–1945*. Madrid, 1948.
9. LOPEZ, T. Censo de poblacion de las provincias y partidos de la corona de Castilla en el siglo XVI. Madrid, 1829.
10. COLAÇÃO, J. *Cadastro de populaçao do Reino (1527)*. Lisboa, 1929.
11. RIBEIRO, O. *Geografia da populaçao em Portugal* (en colaboracion con N. Cardigos). Lisboa, 1946.
12. REGLA, J. 'La expulsion de los Moriscos y su consecuencias', *Hisp.* 1953. pp. 215–67, 402–79.
13. HAMILTON, E. J. *Money, Prices and Wages in Valencia, 1609*. Harvard, 1936.
14. CARO BAROJA, J. *Los Moriscos del reino de Granada*. Madrid, 1957. 305 pp.
15. PARDO PEREZ, M. P. *La población de Zaragoza*. Zaragoza, 1959. 206 pp.
16. JIMENEZ DE GREGORIO, F. 'La poblacion de la Jara Cacerena', *E.G.* 74, 1959. pp. 21–80.
17. — *Notas para una geografía de la población murciana*. Murcia, 1956. 152 pp.

18. JIMENEZ CASTELLO, M. *Población de Navarra*. Zaragoza, 1958. 192 pp.
19. BALLESTER ROS, I. 'La densimetría muncipal de la region valenciana', *B.R. Soc. Geog.*, XCII, 1956. pp. 7–44.
20. DANTÍN CERECEDA, J. 'Distribucion de la poblacion de Galicia', *Junta Ampli. Est. e Inv. Cient.* 1925.
21. SCHULTEN, A. *Iberische Landeskunde* (as above).
22. SAMPAIO, A. *As vilas do norte de Portugal. Estudos Históricos e Economicos.* Oporto, 1923.
23. SCHULTEN, A. 'Land und Leute in Numancia', *Deutsche Zeitung fur Spanien.* Barcelona, 1930.
24. WISEMAN, F. J. *Roman Spain.* London, 1956. 232 pp.
25. LACARRA, J. M. 'El desarrollo urbano de las ciudades de Navarra y Aragon en la edad media', *Pirin.*, 6. 1950. pp. 5–34.
26. LOPEZ CUEVILLAS, F. y LORENZO FERNANDEZ, J. 'Las habitaciones de los Castros', *Cuad. Est. Gall.*, 5, II, 1946–7. pp. 5–74.
27. GONZALEZ, N. *Burgos, la ciudad marginal de Castilla.* Burgos, 1958. 308 pp.
28. AVRIAL y FLORES, J. M. 'Segovia, ciudad de arte', *Est. Seg.*, 6, 1954, p. 391; also, REPOSA RODRIGUEZ, A., 'Notas para el estudio de la ciudad de Segovia en los siglos XII–XIV', *Est. Seg.* 1949, pp. 273–319.
29. TEIXERA DE CASTRO, A. *Monografia da cidade de Porto.* Lisboa, 1926.
30. TORRES BALBAS, L. 'Soria', *Celt.*, III, 1952. pp. 7–21.
31. LACARRA, J. M. 'El desarrollo urbano de las ciudades de Navarra', *loc. cit.* (No. 25).
32. GARCIA PRADO, J. *La ciudad de Logroño, Estudio geográfico.* Logroño, 1949. 243 pp.
33. TORRES BALBAS, L. 'Estructura de las ciudades hispanomusulmanes: la medina, los arrabales y los barrios', *Al-And.* 1953. pp. 149–77.
34. — 'Extension y demografía de las ciudades hispanomusulmanes', *Stud. Islam*, 1955. pp. 42–54.
35. SÁNCHEZ-ALBORNOZ, C. *Una ciudad hispano-cristiana hace un millnio.* Buenos Aires. 206 pp.
36. RICARD, R. 'La plaza mayor en Espagne et en America Espagnoles', *A.H.E.S.*, 1947. p. 433.
37. — 'Les chemins de St Jacque et les sauvetés de Gascogne', *A.M.*, 63, 1951. pp. 293–304.
38. SAMPAIO, A. As vilas do norte de Portugal (see No. 22).
39. TORRES BALBAS, L. *Resumen Histórico del Urbanismo en España* (see General Works above). pp. 60–67.
40. ORTIZ DE VILLAJOS, C. G. *Santa Fé.* Granada, 1929. pp. 9, 34, 38.
41. JURGENS, O. *Spanische Städte* (see General Works above).
42. CARO BAROJA, J. *Razas, Pueblos y Linajes.* Madrid, 1957. pp. 201–32.
43. MELON, A. y GARDEJUELA, R. DE. 'El crecimiento de las ciudades espanola', *Geogr.*, 1954. pp. 96–106.
44. MALUQUER DE MOTES, M. 'Los pueblos de la Espana celtica', *Historia de España*, tomo I, vol. III, pt. I. p. 94.
45. CARO BAROJA, J. *Los Pueblos del Norte de la Peninsula Ibérica.* Madrid, 1943.
46. RUIZ ALMANSA, J. *La población de Galicia* (see No. 8). p. 312.
47. CASAS TORRES, J. M. *La Vivienda y los Núcleos de Población.* Madrid, 1944.
48. SANCHEZ-ALBORNOZ, C. *Ruinas y extinción del municipio romano en España e las instituciones que le reemplazan.* Buenos Aires, 1943.
49. HINOJOSA, E. DE. 'Las Behetrías: la encomendación en Asturias, León y Castilla', *A.H.D. Esp.*, I, 1924. p. 158.
50. QUELLE, O. 'Densidad de poblacion y tipos de poblmiento de distintas regionas espanolas', *E.G.*, XIII, 1952. pp. 699–720.

51. Ibid., p. 717.
52. LOPEZ-BONILLA, V. C. *Las Repoblación de la Mancha por las ordenes militares.*
53. GUTTON, F. *L'Ordre de Calatrava.* Paris, 1955. 240 pp.
54. CAYIGAS, I. DE LAS. *Andalucia Musulmana. Aportaciones a la delimitación de la frontera del Andalus.* Madrid, 1950. 92 pp.
55. LACARRA, J. M. *et alii. La Reconquista en España.*
56. JESSEN, O. 'Las viviendas trogloditicas en los paises mediterraneos', *E.G.,* 1955. pp. 137–58.
57. CORREA, A. A. MENDES. *Os povos primitivos da Lusitania.* Porto, 1924.
58. CASAS TORRES, J. M. *La Vivienda y los Nucleos de la Población.* (see no. 47).
59. DAUMAS, M. 'La maison rurale dans les hautes vallées de l'Esera et de l'Isabena', *Actas Tercer Congreso Internac. Est. Pirin.* Gerona, 1958. pp. 58–62.
60. CAMPS U ARBOIX, J. DE. *La Masía Catalana.* Barcelona, 1959. 281 pp.
61. LARREA Y RECALDE, J. 'Establecimientos humanos y casa rural', *An. Eusko-Folklore,* 1926. pp. 1–124.
62. CARO BAROJA, J. 'En las Campiña de Córdoba', *Rev. Dial. Trad. Populares,* XII, 1956. pp. 270–99.
63. CARLE, W. 'Los horreos en el noroeste de la peninsula Ibérica', *E.G.,* IX, 1948. pp. 275–95.

CHAPTER 11

THE REGIONS OF SPAIN: PERIPHERAL PROVINCES

NORTHERN REGIONS

Most important is *Geografía de España y Portugal* (ed. by M. de Terán) tomo IV–I, 1958. pp. 9–225.

1. Galicia

A useful bibliography is contained in Rio Barja, E. J. *Bibliografía de geografía económica de Galicia.* Vigo, 1960. 254 pp.

BELLOT, F. *Sinopsis de la vegetación de Galicia.* Madrid, 1951.

CARRERAS CANDI, T. *Geografía general del reino de Galicia.* Barcelona. 5 vols. [Factual and verbose.]

CASTROVIEJO BLANCO-CICERON, J. M. *Galicia guia espiritual de una tierra.* Madrid, 1960. 635 pp.

DANTÍN CERECEDA, J. *Regiones naturales de España.* Madrid, 1952. pp. 87–347.

— 'Distribución de la poblacion de Galicia', *Junta Ampli. Est. e Inv. Cient.* 1925.

CARLE, W. 'Las rias gallegas', *E.G.,* X. 1949. pp. 323–30.

DOBBY, E. H. G. 'Galicia', *G.R.* 1936. pp. 555–80.

NIEMEIR, G. 'Tipos de población rural en Galicia', *E.G.,* XIV, 1944. pp. 301–29.

OTERO PEDRAYO, R. *Paisajes y tipos de Galicia.* Vigo, 1929.

RUIZ ALMANSA, J. *La población de Galicia, 1500–1945,* Vol. I. Madrid, 1948. 327 pp. [An important work.]

2. The Asturias

CALINDO, J. L. M. 'El hombre y los Picos de Europa en Valdeon', *B.S. Soc. Esp. Nat. Hist. L,* 1952. pp. 59–80.

DANTIN CERECEDA, J. 'Distribución geografica de la escanda asturiana', *E.G.* 1941. pp. 739–97.

DIAZ CANEJA, J. *Paisajes de reconquista.* Madrid, 1926.

FIGAR, G. *Panorama actual de la actual agricultura asturiana.* Conf. sobre Economia asturiana. Oviedo, 1955–6.

GARCÍA PRADO, J. *La villa de Gijon. Estudio de geografia urbana.* Gijon, 1954.

KRUGER, F. 'Las Branas. Contribucion a lá historia de las construcciones circulares en la zona astur-galaica-portuguesa', *Bol. I.E. Ast.,* Vol. VIII, 1949.

LASCOMBES, G. 'La vegetation des Picos de Europa. Les paysages forestiers', *Bull. Soc. Nat. Hist.,* 79. Toulouse, 1944.

ROBERT, D. 'La region de Santander. Étude de géographie économique et humaine', *A. de G.,* XLV, 1936. pp. 1–18.

SERMET, J. 'El puerto de Santander', *E.G.,* IX, 1948. pp. 637–47.

TERAN, M. 'Vaqueiros y cabañas en los Montes de Pas', *E.G.,* VIII, 1947. pp. 7–50.

4. The Basque Lands

BOESCH, H. 'Die natur im Baskenland', *Helv.,* X, 1955. pp. 136–44.

CARO BAROJA, J. *Los Vascos.* San Sebastian, 1949. 559 pp. [An ethnographic study of much interest.]

CARRERAS CANDI, E. *Geografía general del pais vasco-navarro,* 4 Vols. Barcelona, 1910–21. [Factual and verbose.]

ESCAGUES DE JAVIERRE, I. 'La trasformacion económica de Vizcaya', *Las Ciencias,* XXIV, 1959. pp. 741–62.

GAUSSEN, H. 'Le climat et le sol du Pays Basque', *Bull. Soc. Bot. Fr.* 1941

GUINEA, E. *Vizcaya y sus paisaje vegetal.* Bilbao, 1950. 440 pp.

LEFÈBVRE, TH. *Les môdes de vie dans les Pyrénées Atlantiques orientales.* Paris, 1933. [Doctorate thesis.]

SERMET, J. 'Sur certains traits geographiques permanents du pays Basque Espangol', in *Homenaje a D. Joaquin Mendizabal Gortazar, Miscelanea de Estudios.* San Sebastian, 1956. pp. 399–442.

EASTERN SPAIN

DEFFONTAINES, P. y DURLAIT, M. *La España del Este. Cataluna, Baleares, Valencia,* translated by M. Teresa Mongui. Barcelona, 1958. 256 pp.

1. Eastern Catalonia

BLASI, P. *Les Terres Catalanes.* Barcelona, 1957. 741 pp.

DEFFONTAINES, P. *La catalogue, vue por un géographe.* Barcelona, 1960. 73 pp.

— 'Introduction a une géographie de la Catalogue', *Medit.,* I, 1959. pp. 47–65.

— 'Essai de description régionale de la Catalogue' *Medit.,* 4, 1962. pp. 1–50.

DOBBY, E. H. G. 'The Ebro delta', *G.J.,* LXXXVII, 1936. pp. 455–69.

— 'Catalonia; the geographic basis of its regionalism', *G.R.,* XXVIII, 1938. pp. 224–49.

LLOBET, S. *El medio y la vida en el Montseny.* Barcelona, 1947. 518 pp. [A doctorate thesis of value.]

SOLÉ SABARÍS, L., ed. *Geografia de Catalunya.* Barcelona, 1958. [The best regional survey of any area of Spain, published in a series of parts, and written in the Catalan dialect. It is magnificently illustrated.]

SORRE, M. *Les Pyrénées Orientales.* Paris, 1913. [A classic work on landscapes.]

VILAR, P. *Resum de geografia de Catalunya:* I, *Aspecte fisic;* II, *Aspecte huma, El Litoral;* III, *El Prelitoral.* Barcelona, 1928–29–30.

— 'Le port de Barcelone', *A. de G.,* XLIII. 1934. pp. 489–509.

VILAR VALENTI. 'El origen de la industria catalana moderna', *E.G.,* XXI, 1960. pp. 5–40.

2. Valencian Levante

CARRERAS Y CANDI, F. *Geografía general del reino de Valencia.* Barcelona, 1920–27. 5 Vols. [Voluminous but factual and much of it non-geographical.]

CASAS TORRES, J. M. *La vivienda y los núcleos de población rurales de la Huerta de Valencia.* Madrid, 1944. 328 pp. [A doctorate thesis of importance.]

FONTAVELLA GONZALEZ, V. *La Huerta de Gandia.* Zaragoza, 1952. 404 pp. [Another doctorate thesis, well produced.]

GAISE, ed. *El Futuro de Valencia.* Valencia, 1959. 273 pp. [Future planning proposals for this city.]

GIL, A. 'La evolucion económica de Requeña y sus comarca', *E.G.*, XIV, 1953. pp. 49–68.

GINER, BOIRA, V. *El Tribunal de las Aguas de la Vega de Valencia, 960–1960.* Valencia, 1960. 41 pp.

HOUSTON, J. M. 'Urban geography of Valencia. The regional development of a huerta city', *Trans. I.B.G.*, 1949. pp. 19–35.

— 'Land use and society in the plain of Valencia', in *Geographical Essays in memory of Alan G. Ogilvie.* Edinburgh, 1959. pp. 166–94.

LÓPEZ GÓMEZ, A. 'Evolucion agraria de la Plana de Castellon', *E.G.*, XVIII, 1957. pp. 309–60.

3. Alicante Levante

JESSEN, O. 'El palmeral y la ciudad de Elche', *E.G.*, XII, 1951. pp. 111–30.

LOPEZ GOMEZ, J. 'El puerto de Alicante', *E.G.*, XVI, 1955. pp. 511–83.

4. Murcian Levante

JIMENEZ DE GREGORIO, F. 'Geografía del Mar Menor y de su ribera', *E.G.*, XIX, 1958. pp. 23–54.

MONBEIG, P. 'Les transformations économiques dans les huertas et la region entre Alicante et Murcie', *A. de G.*, XXXIX, 1930. pp. 597–606.

LLOBET, S. 'Utilización del suelo y economía del agua en la region semiarida de Huercal-Overa, Almeria', *E.G.*, XIX, 1958. pp. 5–21. [This study is just outside this region but it is very apposite.]

REPARAZ, E. DE. 'La zona piu arida d'Europa', *B.S.G. It.*, Ser. VI, X, 1933. pp. 157–62.

RIVISTA FINANCIERA DEL BANCO DE VIZCAYA. *Alicante y Murcia.* Bilbao, 1953. [A useful factual survey of economic conditions.]

CHAPTER 12

THE REGIONS OF SPAIN: THE CENTRAL AND SOUTHERN PROVINCES

ARAGÓN AND NEIGHBOURING PROVINCES

1. The Pyrenees

There are many publications on this region, with exhaustive bits of references in the books of Sole and Sorre. References to the many excellent monographs on the French Pyrenees are not included. The following journals also contain many relevant articles: *Butlletí del Centre Excursionista de Catalunya* (Barcelona), *Pirineos* (Saragossa), *Revue de Géographie des Pyrénées et du Sud-Ouest* (Toulouse) and *Actas del Primer Congreso Internacional de Estudios Pirenaicos*, San Sebastián, toms I–V, 1950. The best guide book is JOANNE, A. *Pyrénées* (*Les Guides Bleu*). Paris, 1933. 512 pp.

Fundamental monographs are:

BIROT, P. *Recherches sur la morphologie des Pyrénées Orientales franco-espagnoles·* Paris, 1937. 318 pp.

— *Etude comparée de la vie rurale pyrénéenne dans les pays de Pallars (Espagne) et de Couserans (France)*. Paris, 1937. 120 pp.

GAUSSEN, H. *Végétation de la moitié orientale des Pyrénées. Sol, climat, vegetation.* Paris, 1926. 559 pp.

— *Géographie botanique et agricole des Pyrénées Orientales.* Paris, 1934. 353 pp.

LLOBET, S. *El Medio et la Vida en Andorra.* Barcelona, 1947. 347 pp.

SOLÉ SABARÍS, L. *Los Pirineos: El medio y el hombre.* Barcelona, 1951. 624 pp.

SORRE, M. *Les Pyrénées.* Paris, 1933. 216 pp.

2. The Ebro Valley

There is a comprehensive bibliography in CASAS TORRES, J. ML. and FLORISTAN Y SEMANES, A. *Bibliografía geográfica de Aragón.* Zaragoza, 1945.

Important studies are:

CASAS TORRES, J. M. 'Unidad y variedad geográfica del Valle del Ebro', Conference at Santander, Vol. I, 1952. pp. 41–84.

CONFEDERACIÓN HIDROGRÁFICA DEL EBRO. *Memoria (1936–45).* Zaragoza, 1946. 184 pp.

DANTÍN CERECEDA, J. 'Distribución y extensión del endorreismo aragonés', *E.G.,* Madrid, 1942. pp. 505–595.

— 'El medio físico aragonés y el reparto de su población', *E.G.,* 1942. pp. 51–162.

FERRER REGALES, M. 'La personalidad geográfica de Monegros', *Geograf.,* 1960. pp. 59–88.

FLORISTAN SEMANES, A. *La Ribera Tudelana de Navarra.* Zaragoza, 1951. 303 pp.

GARCÍA SÁENZ, L. 'Las regiones del Ebro medio y sus zonas de regadío', *E.G.,* 1942. pp. 469–97.

LORENZO PARDO, M. *La conquista del Ebro.* Zaragoza, 1931. 313 pp.

NAGORE, D. *La agricultura y ganadería de Navarra.* Pamplona, *c.* 1923. 313 pp.

SCHMIDT, T. *Das klima von Aragonien und Altkastilien auf Grand der spanischen Witterbeobachtungen der Jahre 1906 bis 1925.* Giessen, 1935. 136 pp.

3. The Iberian Cordillera

AITKEN, R. 'The Sierra Demanda', *Geol. Mag.* 1933.

CHUDEAU, R. 'La Plateau de Soria', *A. de G.,* 1, 1892. pp. 279–86.

GOMEZ CHICO, R. 'Las comarcas geográficas sorianas', *Celt.,* 2, 1951. pp. 357–74.

— *Soria es así.* Soria, 1953.

MIRALBÉS, M. 'La actividad ganadera en la provincia de Soria', *Celt.,* 1955. pp. 177–217.

— *Contribución al estudio económico de Soria.* Zaragoza, 1957.

SÁENZ GARCÍA, C. 'Marco geográfico de la altimeseta soriana', *Celt.,* 1951. pp. 69–80.

TORRES BALBAS, L. 'Soria: interpretación de sus origines y evolución urbana' *Celt.,* 1952. pp. 7–31.

VILA VALENTÍ, J. 'Un nombre mal empleado: Los Montes Uinversales', *E.G.,* 1956. pp. 41–59.

THE MESETA

1. The Northern Tableland

BIELZA LAGUNA, V. *Las comarcas naturales de la provincia de Valladolid.* Valladolid, 1953.

CABO ALONSO, A. 'El colectivismo agrario en tierra de Sayago', *E.G.*, 1956. pp. 591–656.

DANTÍN CERECEDA, J. 'La cuenca endorreica de la Nava' (Palencia), *Las Ciencias.* Madrid, 1931.

DOMÍNGUEZ, M. *Regiones naturales y comarcas de la provincia de León.* León, 1952.

GARCÍA FERNANDEZ, J. 'El modo de vida pastoral en la Tierra de Segovia', *B.S.G.M.*, 1949.

GONZÁLEZ GARRIDO, J. *Horizontes de Castilla. La Tierra de Campos region natural.* Valladolid, 1941.

GONZÁLEZ IGLESIAS, L. *La casa albercana.* Salamanca, 1945.

HOPFNER, H. *Die Ländlichen Siedelungen der altkastilischen Meseta.* Hamburg, 1939.

LÓPEZ GÓMEZ, A. 'Valdelaguna', *E.G.*, 1954. pp. 551–68.

MARTÍN GALINDO, J. L. 'La cuidad de León', *E.G.*, 1957. pp. 95–150.

RODRIGUEZ, B. *Estudio de la ganadería leonesa.* León, 1955. 150 pp.

SÁNCHEZ-ALBORNOZ, C. *Una ciudad hispano—christiana hace un milenio.* Buenos Aires, 1947. 206 pp.

SÁNCHEZ GÓMEZ, J. C. *Estudio geográfico regional de Valdecorneja,* Pub. S. Geog. Nac., Series B, No. 11. Madrid, 1932.

TEIJON LASO, E. 'Los modos de vida en la dehesa salmantina', *E.G.*, 1948. pp. 377–420.

2. The Central Cordillera

CASAS TORRES, J. M. 'Sobre la geografía humana del Valle del Lozoya', *E.G.*, 1943. pp. 781–828.

DANTÍN CERECEDA, J. 'La población de la Sa de Guadarrama, *Actas Cong. Sevilla Assoc. Esp. Prog. Ciencias*, VI, Madrid, 1918. pp. 181–200.

LEGENDRE, M. *Las Hurdes.* Bordeaux, 1927.

SCHMIEDER, O. 'La Sierra de Gredos', *E.G.*, 1953. pp. 421–40, 629–53.

3. The Tagus Valley and Madrid

COURTNEY, P. P. 'Madrid, the circumstances of its growth', *G.*, 1959. pp. 22–34.

GUINARD, P. and MONBEIG, P. 'Madrid', *A.G.*, XLI, 1932. pp. 481–499.

JIMÉNEZ DE GREGORIO, F. 'La población en la Jara toledana', *E.G.*, 1950, pp. 201–50; 1951, pp. 527–82.

Madrid. Información sobre la Cuidad. Madrid, 1929.

ORS PEREZ-PEIX, V. DE. *Cartas sobre Madrid.* Madrid, 1960. 67 pp.

RAMOS, D. 'Notas sobre la geografía del Bajo Tajuna', *E.G.*, 1947. pp. 41–154.

RUIZ ALMANSA, J. 'Estructura y evolución de la población de Madrid', *R.I.S.*, 1945, pp. 245–67; 1946, pp. 389–411.

4. The Tablelands of New Castile

BARCELÓ PONS, B. 'Evolución de la estructura agraria del termino de Ocaña', *E.G.*, 1956. pp. 184–206.

DANTÍN CERECEDA, J. *La población de la Mancha Española en el centro de su maximo endorreismo.* Soc. Geog. Nac. Madrid, 1932.

GARCÍA FERNÁNDEZ, J. 'Horche (Guadalajara). Estudio de estructura agraria', *E.G.*, 1953. pp. 193–240.

HERNÁNDEZ PACHECO, F. *Avance al estudio de las comarcas naturales del sudoeste de Castilla la Nueva y de la Sa Morena*. Madrid, 1934.

HOYOS SANCHO, N. 'La vida pastoril en la Mancha', *E.G.*, 1948. pp. 623–36.

JESSEN, O. 'La Mancha', *E.G.*, 1946. pp. 246–312, 479–524.

PLANCHUELO, G. *Estudio del Alto Guadiana y la altaplanicie del Campo de Montiel*. Madrid, 1954. 189 pp.

QUELLE, O. 'Población de la provincia de Toledo', *E.G.*, 1952. pp. 161–77.

ROMERO DE CASTILLA, M. 'Ocaña, Urbs de la gens de los Olcades', *E.G.*, 1944. pp. 881–92.

5. Extremadura

CORCHON, J. 'Relaciones topográficas referentes a Extremadura', *E.G.*, 1949. pp. 299–322.

HERNÁNDEZ PACHECO, F. 'Rasgos geografico—geologicos del valle de Alcudia en relacion con sus caracteristicas agropecuarias', *Bol. Inst. Reforma Agraria*, 18, 1933. pp. 217–41.

HOYOS SANCHO, N. 'Sobre la antigua Vettonia y la actual Extremadura', *E.G.*, 1953. pp. 409–20.

PRESIDENCIA DEL GOBIERNO. *Plan de obras colonización, industrialización y electrificación Provincia de Badajaz*. Madrid, 1951. 156 pp.

SERMET, J. *L'Espange du Sud*. Paris, 1953. pp. 351–88.

ANDALUSIA

The two fundamental works are those of Niemeier and especially of Sermet.

BOISSIER, E. *Voyage botanique dans le midi de l'Espagne pendant l'année 1837*. Paris, 3 vols., 1839–45.

BONSOR, G. 'Les colonies agricoles de la vallée du Betis', *Rev. Archael*, XXXV, 1899.

— 'Les villes antiques du detroit de Gibraltar', *Bull. hispanique*, XX, 1918. pp. 141–8.

BOSQUE MAUREL, J. 'Geografía urbana de Granada', *E.G.*, 1956. pp. 461–73.

CABANÁS, R. 'Notas para el estudio del "habitat" en la provincia de Jaén', *E.G.*, 1956. pp. 373–414.

CARANDELL, J. *Distribución y estructura de la propiedad rural en la provincia de Córdoba'*. Madrid, 1934.

CARO BAROJA, J. *Razas, Pueblos y Linajes*. Madrid, 1957. 353 pp. (especially pp. 181–259).

CEBALLOS L. and MARTÍN BOLANOS, M. *Estudio sobre la vegetación forestal de la provincia de Cadíz*. Madrid, 1930.

CEBALLOS L. and VICIOSO, C. *Estudio sobre la vegetación y la flora florestal de la provincia de Malaga*. Madrid, 1933.

FOSTER, A. 'The Malaga raisin district', *J.G.*, XXXVII, 1938.

LE BOURDIEC, P. 'Bassin de l'Ebre et Plaine Andalouse', in *Géographie*, Centre de Doc. Univ. Paris C. 1959. pp. 45–53.

LÉVI-PROVENCAL, E. *L'Espagne musulmane an Xème siècle*. Paris, 1932. (See pp. 159–70 on latifundia.)

NIEMEIER, G. *Siedlungsgeographische Untersuchungen in Niederandalusien*. 1935.

PRESIDENCIA DEL GOBIERNO. *Plan de obras colonización, industrialización y electrificación de la provincia de Jaén*. Madrid, 1952. 216 pp.

SCHULTEN, A. *Iberische Landeskunde: Geographie des antiken Spanien*. Strasbourg, 1957. 600 pp. (See especially pp. 355–87, 399–414, 445–517.)

SERMET, J. *L'Espagne du Sud*. Paris, 1953. 422 pp.

TERRERO, J. 'La "tierra llana" de Huelva', *E.G.*, 1952, pp. 671–698; 1954, pp. 5–58.

TORRES BALBAS, L. 'La estructura de las ciudades hispano-musulmanas', *Al-Andalus*, XVIII, 1953. pp. 149–77.

CHAPTER 13

THE REGIONS OF PORTUGAL

GENERAL WORKS

A useful bibliography is: LAUTENSACH, H. with the collaboration of FEIO, M. *Bibliografía geográfica de Portugal*. Lisbon, 1948. It contains 2,347 items.

BIROT, P. *Le Portugal*. Paris, 1950. 215 pp. An excellent, concise outline.

GIRÃO, A. DE AMORÍM. *Geografía de Portugal*. Oporto, 1940. 510 pp.

LAUTENSACH, H. *Portugal auf Grund eigener Reisen und der Literatur:* I. *Das Land als Ganzes*, Pettermans Geog. Mitt., XLVI, 1932; II. *Die portugiesischen Landschaften*, Id, 1937. [This is still a fundamental survey of Portugal.]

RIBEIRO, O. *Portugal, o Mediterraneo e o Atlantico*. Coimbra, 1945. [A stimulating synthesis of the character of Portugal.]

— *Portugal*, tomo V of *Geografía de España y Portugal*, ed. by M. Terán. Barcelona, 1955, 288 pp. [The best general survey of the country.]

STANISLAWSKI, D. *The individuality of Portugal*. Univ. of Texas, Austin, 1959. 248 pp. [A politico-historical survey.]

SORRE, M. *Le Portugal*, Vol. VII of the *Géog. Universelle*. Paris, 1934. pp. 202–28.

REGIONAL REFERENCES

THE NORTH

DIAS, J. *Minho, Trás-os-Montes, Haut-Douro*. Livre-guide, Congrès Intérnat. Géog., 1949. 125 pp.

DOBBY, E. H. G. 'Economic geography of the Port Wine Region', *Econ. Geog.*, XII, 1936. pp. 311–23.

ENJALBERT, H. 'Un vignoble de renommée mondiale. L'alto Douro', *Cahiers d'Outre-Mer*, 1949. pp. 1–24.

HAYES, R. D. 'A peasant economy in N.W. Portugal', *G.J.*, CXXII, 1956. pp. 54–70.

TABORDA, V. *Alto Trás-os-Montes, Estudo Geográfico*. Coimbra, 1932.

THE TRANSITIONAL REGIONS

AMORIM GIRÃO, A. DE et alii. *Coimbra e Arredores*. Coimbra, 1939.

— *Excursoes no Centro de Portugal*. Coimbra, 1939.

BACILLARS BEBIANO, J. *O porto de Lisboa: estudo de historia economica*. Lisboa, 1960, 154 pp.

FERNANDES MARTIN, A. *O Esforco do Homem na Bacia do Mondego*. Coimbra, 1940.

— *Le Centre Littoral et le Massif Calcaire d'Estremadura*, Livret-guide de l'excursión B. Congrès Internat. Géog. Lisbon, 1949. 96 pp.

FRAZÃO, E. M. 'A autonomia regional do Ribatejo sob o aspecto agro-climatico', *Bol. da Junta de Prov. do Ribatejo*, I, Lisbon, 1940.

FIORILLO, A. 'La Costa do Sol e la colline di Sintra', *L'Univ.*, XL, 1960. pp. 919–32.

RAU, V. et ZBYSZEWSKI, G. *Estremadura et Ribatejo*, Livret-guide de l'excursión D. Congrès Internat. Géog. Lisbon, 1949. 146 pp.

RIBEIRO, O. *Le Portugal Central*, Livret-guide de l'excursion C. Congrès Internat. Géog. Lisbon, 1949. 180 pp.

— 'Le site et la croissance de Lisbonne', *B.A.G.F.*, 1938.

SCHNEIDER-CARIUS, K. 'Die Niederschlagsverhaltnisse von Lissabon', *Stuttgarter G. Studien*, 69, 1957. pp. 235–46.

THE SOUTH

BIERHENKE, W. 'Observaciones sobre le cultura popular del Bajo Algarve, *B.R. Soc. G. Madrid*, 89, 1953. pp. 427–48.

FEIO, M. *Le Bas Alentejo et l'Algarve*, Livret-guide de l'excursión E. Congrès Internat. Géog. Lisbon, 1949. 207 pp.

— *A evolucao do relevo do Baixo Alentejo e Algarve*. Lisboa, 1951. 186 pp.

FERRO, G. 'Alentejo, il granaio del Portogallo', *Univer.*, 36, 1956. pp. 399–402.

— 'L'Algarve (monografia regionale)', *Ann. Ric. Studi G. Genova*, 12, 1956. pp. 1–40, 57–124, 131–87. [See also other articles in same publication for 1954, 1955.]

PART III: ITALY

CHAPTER 14

STRUCTURE AND LANDFORMS

ATLASES AND MAPS

CONSOCIAZIONE TURISTICA ITALIANA. *Atlante Fisico, Economico d'Italia*. G. Dainelli. Milan, 1939. (82 sheets and 508 maps). [This is of fundamental importance.]

ISTITUTO GEOGRAFICO DE AGOSTINI. *Atlante Produzione, Commercio e Agricole*. Novara, 1927. (69 sheets).

ISTITUTO NAZIONALE DI ECONOMIA AGRARIA. *Carta dei tipi d'Impresa nell Agricoltura Italiana*. Rome, 1958. (16 maps at 1/750,000 and 46 pp. text).

ISTITUTO GEOGRAFICO MILITARE. 1/25,000. Begun in 1870. Also some sheets shown stereoscopically. 1936–7. 1/50,000 (G.S.G.S. 4229). Begun in 1863, revised since 1939.

1/100,000. Begun in 1883. G.S.G.S. 4164, 1943–46, is based on revision of 1928–45. An Italian archaeological edition with catalogued lists and pamphlet for each sheet was begun in 1949. 1/200,000. Begun since 1950.

TOURING CLUB ITALIANO. *Carte Generale*. 1/500,000. Begun in 1937 and revised since then.

Carta della Utilizzazione del suolo d'Italia. 1/200,000—commenced in 1956. [Of much importance.]

Carta delle zone Turistiche—coloured reproductions and improvements of official 1/50,000 and 1/25,000 maps of a few special areas, such as the Naples district, the Riviera and some mountain areas.

ISTITUTO GEOLOGICO. *Carta Geologica d'Italia*. 1/1,000,000. 1931. 1/100,000. Many sheets published, but not all on sale.

MINISTERO DELL' INDUSTRIA E DEL COMMERCIO. *Carta Geologica d'Italia*. 1/1,000,000, 1961.

CONSIGLIO NAZIONALE DELLE RICHERCHE. *Carta della Densita della Popolazione in Italia*, 1/1,500,000, 1951.

MANCINI, F. *Carta dei souli Italia*, 1/1,500,000, 1960.

GENERAL WORKS

Italy has a wealth of geographical material comparable to that of France and Germany. It is only possible therefore to enumerate the main items. Perhaps no other European country has better bibliographical sources in geography. A *Bibliografia geografica dell'Italia* was commenced in 1900 as an annual supplement to the

Revista Geografica Italiana; it has not been produced without interruption since then. In 1959 a series of regional bibliographies was initiated under the auspices of the Consiglio Nazionale delle Ricerche, of which the following have now appeared: *Lazio*, edited by E. Migliorini (1,298 items); *Campania*, E. Migliorini (1,543 items); *Liguria*, G. Ferro (1,318 items); *Sicilia*, M. Teresa di Maggio (2,402 items); and *Sardegna*, A. Terrosu Asole (1,598 items). Less geographical is W. O. Hassall, *A select Bibliography of Italy*, London, 1946.

Apart from those textbooks dealing with the Mediterranean (listed on p. 725) there are the following in order of publication:

FISCHER, T. *La Penisola Italiana*. Turin, 1902. 498 pp. [Still useful.]

DEECKE, W. *Italien*. Berlin, 1898. English translation, 1904. 485 pp.

MORI, A. *L'Italia. Caratteri generali*. Milan, 1936. 565 pp. [A work of variable quality in collaboration with various writers.]

MILONE, F. *L'Italia nell'economia delle sue regioni*. Turin, 1955. 1,296 pp. [An exhaustive treatment of Italian economic geography, treated by regions. But the maps are not systematic for each territory.]

ALMAGIA, R. *L'Italia*. Turin, 1959. Vol. I. 670 pp; Vol. II. 1,320 pp. [A lavishly illustrated production, this work is somewhat old-fashioned on geomorphology and disappointing on regional descriptions. It is thorough on economic and urban aspects.]

There are also the splendid monographs published by the Touring Club Italiano, of which the following are especially relevant:

CONOSCI ITALIA. Vol. I, *L'Italia Fisica*. Milan, 1957. 320 pp.

— Vol. II, *La Flora*. Milan, 1958. 275 pp.

— Vol. VII, *Il Paesaggio*. Milan, 1963. 232 pp. Text by A. Sestini.

All are magnificently illustrated with coloured photographs and have authoritative texts. The seventh volume is a masterpiece of regional geography. Under the initial direction of the late Prof. R. Almagìa the Unione Tipografico-Editrice Torinese have published a number of regional geographies for the Italian *regioni* since 1960; these are listed under the references for chapters 17 and 18.

REFERENCES

1. CAPELLO, C. F. *et alii. Les phenomènes karstiques et l'hydrologie souterraine dans certaines regions de l'Italie*. Assoc. Internat. d'hydrologie, No. 37, 1956.
2. DE LORENZO, G. *Geologia dell'Italia meridionale*, 2nd edn. Napoli, 1937, 326 pp.
3. MERLA, G. 'Geologia dell'Appennino settentrionale', *B. Soc. Geol. It.*, LXX, 1951. pp. 95–382.
4. SACCO, F. *La Puglia*. Bari, 1911.
5. ALMAGIA, R. *Studi geografici sulle frane in Italia*, 2 vols. Roma, 1907, 1910.
6. PENTA, F. *Frane e movimenti franosi*, 2nd edn. Roma, 1956.
7. Much has been written on Italian vulcanology—see JOHNSTON-LAVIS, H. J. and A. *Bibliography of the Geology and Eruptive Phenomena of the more important Volcanoes of Southern Italy*. London, 1918. 374 pp.
8. DE LORENZO, G. 'I vulcani di Napoli', *Nuova Antologia*, 98, 1902. pp. 684–95.
9. ALFANO, G. B. *Il Vesuvio e le sue eruzioni*, 2nd edn. Pompei, 1929. 50 pp.
10. See GUNTHER, R. T. *A Bibliography of Topographical and Geological Works on the Phlegraen Fields*, Royal Geog. Soc. London, 1908. 90 pp.
11. BLANC, A. C. *Le Pliocene et le Quaternaire aux alentours de Rome*, INQUA IVe Congres Internat. Rome, 1953. 35 pp.
12. BENEO, E. 'Tentativo di sintesi tettonica dell'Italia peninsulare e insulare', *B. Soc. Geol. It.*, LXVIII, 1949. pp. 66–80.
13. SACCO, F. *L'Appennino Settentrionale e Centrale*. Torino, 1904.
14. STAUB, R. 'La Structure des Alpes entre Savone et Genes', *C.R. Soc. Geol. Fr.*, 1937. pp. 129–31.

15. GIGNOUX, M. 'Sur les formations marines pliocenes et quaternaires de l'Italie du Sud et de la Sicilie', *Ann. de l'Univ. de Lyon*, fasc. 13, 1913. 693 pp.

16. MAXIA, C. 'Contributi alla geologia del Lazio', *B. Ufficio geol.*, 70, 1945–6. pp. 1–32.

17. GABERT, P. *Les Plaines occidentales du Pô et leurs Piedmonts*. GAP. 1962. pp. 492–6.

18. NANGERONI, G. *et alii*. *Studi sul glaciale quaternario della Lombardia*. Atti Soc. It. Sc. Nat., XCIII, Milano, 1954.

19. LOSACCO, U. 'La glaciazione quaternaria nell'Appennino settentrionale', *R.G.I.*, 1949. pp. 90–152, 196–272. [Contains important bibliography].

20. SUTER, K. 'Die eiszeitliche Vergletscherung des Zentralapennins', *Vierteljahrschrift der Naturforsch*, Zurich, 1934. pp. 242–53.

21. NANGERONI, G. *et alii*. *Studi sul glaciale* (see No. 18).

22. BOURCART, J. *Géographie du Fond des Mers*. Paris, 1949. pp. 88–9.

23. ALBANI, D. 'Le foci del Po secondo le ultime ricognizioni aeree, *R.G.I.*, 1948. pp. 225–54.

24. GABERT, P. *op. cit.* (see no. 17, pp. 75–105).

25. NANGERONI, G. 'Appunti sull'origine di alcuni laghi prealpini lombardi', *Atti Soc. It. Sc. Nat.*, 1956.

26. — *et alii*. *Studi sul glaciale* (see No. 18).

27. DESIO, A. *Caratteri fisici e geologici della provincia di Milano*. Roma, 1938.

28. LIPPARINI, T. 'I terrazzi fluviali dell "Emilia" ', *Com. Naz. Geog. del C.N.R. Bologna*, fasc. I, 1935.

29. MARINELLI, O. 'Sull'età dei delta dei fiumi italiani', *La Geog.*, XIV, 1926. pp. 21–9.

30. ORTOLANI, M. 'Contributo alle ricerche sull'antico delta padano', *Atti del XV Congresso geog. It.*, vol. II. Torino, 1950. pp. 855–60.

31. BONI, A. 'L'alto bacino orientale del Piave', *Topografia, geologia, morfologia, idrografia*, Mem. 1st. lombard. sci. lett., Milan, 1937.

32. MARINELLI, O. 'La maggiore discordanza tra orografia e idrografia nell' Appennino', *R.G.I.*, 1926. pp. 65–74.

33. SESTINI, A. 'Delimitazione delle grandi regioni orografico-morfologiche dell' Italia', *R.G.I.*, 1944. pp. 16–29.

34. ROVERETO, G. *Liguria Geologica*, Mem. Soc. Geol. It., II. Roma, 1939. 743 pp.

35. SESTINI, A. 'Osservazioni geomorfologiche suu'Appennino Tosco-Emiliano fra il Reno e il Bisenzio', *Atti Soc. Toscana Sc. Nat.*, Firenze, 1939.

36. MERLA, G. 'Geologia dell'Appennino settentrionale' (see No. 3).

37. PELLETIER, J. 'Le relief de l'Apennin settentrional. Faits et problèmes de la partie occidentale', *R. Geog. Lyon*, XXXIV, 1959. pp. 89–111.

38. BIROT, J. 'Grands traits de la structure et du relief de l'Apennin', *A. de G.*, 1939. pp. 22–40.

39. DU RICHE PRELLER, C. S. *Italian Mountain Geology*. London, 1924. pp. 105–93.

40. MIGLIORINI, C. 'I cunei composti nell'orogenesi', *B. Soc. Geol. It.*, LXVII, 1948. pp. 31–142.

41. DEMANGEOT, J. 'Les aplanissements villafranchiens de l'Apennin central', *Contribi de Sc. Geol.*, Roma, 1952. pp. 96–105.

42. BALLY, A. et DEMANGEOT, J. 'Remarques sur la morphologie de la Majella', *Contributi Sc. Geol.*, II. pp. 39–45.

43. CASTIGLIONI, B. *Ricerche morfologiche sui terreni pliocenici dell'Italia centrale*, 1st Geog. Univ. Roma, 1935. 160 pp.

44. PFALZ, R. *Morphologie des toskanisch-umbrischen Apennin*. Leipzig, 1932.

45. ORTOLANI, M. e MORETTI, A. *Il Gran Sasso d'Italia. Vertiente meridionale*, Consiglio Nazionale delle Ricerche. Bologna, 1950.

46. DEMANGEOT, J. 'L'Arc Abruzzais externe, étude tectonique', *La Ricerca Sc.*, 21, 1951. pp. 904–39.

47. MARINELLI, O. 'La maggiore discordanza tra orografia e idrografia nell'-Appennino (see No. 32).

48. CASTALDI, F. 'Manifesta zioni di carsismo attivo e di carsismo morto nella costiera amalfitana della penisola sorrentina', *Ann. Ist. sup. di sc. e lett. s. Chiara*, Napoli, 4, 1953. pp. 341–52.

49. MINUCCI, E. 'Il mare pliocenico nella Campania', *Mem. Geol. e Geog.*, Vol. III, 1932–3. pp. 229–356.

50. KAYSER, B. *Recherches sur les sols et l'érosion en Italie meridionale.* Lucania. Paris, 1961. 127 pp.

51. Quoted by BIROT, P. and DRESCH, J. *La Mediterranée Occid.* op. cit. p. 291.

52. GIGNOUX, M. 'La Calabre', *A. de G.*, XVIII, 1909. pp. 142–61.

53. KANTEN, H. *Kalabrien.* Hamburg, 1930.

54. JABOLI, D. e ROGER, A. 'Esquisse structurale de la Fosse Bradanique', *C.R. XIX Congrès Geol. Inter*, Sec. IX, Alger, 1954.

55. REINA, C. 'Sulla geomorfologia della regione pugliese', *Atti XVII Congr. Géog. It., Comunicazioni*, III, Bari. pp. 247–55.

56. CASTIGLIONI, B. *Ricerche morfologiche sui terreni pliocenici* (see No. 43).

57. PFALZ, R. *Morphologie des toskanisch-umbrischen Apennin, op. cit.*

58. PANTANELLI, D. 'Storia geologica dell'Arno', *B.R. Soc. Geol. It.*, XIX, 1900. pp. 419–36.

59. DEECKE, W. *Italien* (as above). p. 102.

60. MORI, A. 'La sesta escursione geografica interuniversitaria nella Maremma Grossetana e nel-l'Amiata', *B.R.S.G.I.*, VIII, 1931. pp. 532–55.

61. RICHE PRELLER, C. S. DU. *Italian Mountain Geology*, Part III. London, 1923. pp. 14–41.

62. BLANC, A. C. *et alii*. *Le Pliocene et le Quaternaire aux alentours de Rome*, INQUA IVe. Congrès Internat. 1953. 35 pp.

63. MERLA, G. ed. *Il Tevere. Monografia Idrologia.* Roma, 1938. Vol. I, Part II. 130 pp.

64. D'ARRIGO, I. 'Sulle fasi di regime del litorale deltizo del Tevere', *Ann. Lav. Pub.*, fasc. 3, Roma, 1932. pp. 1–38.

65. BLANC, A. C. e SEGRE, A. G. *Excursion au Mont Circe.* INQUA, IVe. Congrès Internat. Rome, 1953. 108 pp.

66. RITTMAN, A. 'Sintesi geologica dei Campi Flegrei', *B.S. Geol. It.*, 69, 1950. pp. 117–28.

67. DEMANGEOT, J. 'Le volcanisme des Champs Flegreens', *Rev. Géog. Lyons*, XXVII, 1952. pp. 35–43.

68. VECCHIA, O. 'La Sicilia e le aree circostanti', *Ann. de Geofisica*, VIII, 1955. pp. 23–58.

69. CIPOLLA, F. 'Osservazioni geomorfologiche sul litorale tirreno della Sicilia. Nota preliminare', *B.S. Sc. Nat. Ec. di Palermo*, XIII, 1931. pp. 19–33.

70. TONGIORGI, E. e TREVISAN, L *Sicilie*, INQUA, IVe. Congrès Internat. Roma, 1953, 36 pp.

71. RIGO, E. e CORTESINI, A. 'Contributo alla conoscenza strutturale della Sicilia sud-orientale', *B. Serv. Geol.*, 81, fasc. 2–3, 1959. pp. 349–69.

72. POLI, E. 'Genesi e morfologia di alcune grotte dell'Etna', *B.S.G.I.*, XII, 1959. pp. 452–63.

CHAPTER 15

THE RURAL LANDSCAPES

1. General summaries of climate in Italy are contained in the following: Almagià, R. *L'Italia*. Turin, 1959, vol. 1, pp. 411–29; and Touring Club Italiano. *Conosci l'Italia*, vol. 1, *L'Italia Fisica*. Milan, 1957. pp. 21–63.
2. Servizio Idrografico del Ministero dei L.L.P.P. *Carte delle precipitazioni atmosferiche in Italia*. Rome, 1957.
3. BONASERA, F. 'Il Problema dello studio scientifico del clima della regione marchigiana', *Atti XVII Congresso Geog. Ital.* Bari, 1957. Vol. 2, pp. 228–31.
4. FERRINI, F, *Le piogge nell' Italia meridionale*. Florence, 1931.
5. TULLI, A., 'La distribuzione dei venti in Liguria e il consequente valore antropogeografico'. *Atti Soc. Lig. Sc. Nat. Geogr.*, XXIII, 1912. pp. 97–146.
6. EREDIA, F. *Distribuzione della temperatura dell' aria in Italia*. Rome, 1942. (Together with detailed map).
7. FERRINI, F. *op. cit.*
8. GIACOBBE, A. *Schema di una teoria ecologica per la classificazione della vegetazione Italiana*. Comitato Nazionale per la Geografia. Bologna, 1938. 87 pp.
9. GIACOBBE, A. 'Le basi concrete per una classificazione evologica della vegetazione italiana'. *Archivio Botanico*, 1947–49.
   See also, EMBERGER, L. 'La végétation de l'Italie d'après A. Giacobbe', *Recueil des Trav. et Lab. de Bot.*, *Géol. Zoolog.* Montpellier, 1953. pp. 19–29.
10. GAMS, H. *Zur Geschichte, Klimatischen Begrenzung und Gliederung der immergrünen Mittelmeerstrufe*. Ergebn. d. Internat. Pflanzengeogr. Exkursion d. Mittelitalien, 1934. Zurich, 1935.
11. NEGRI, G. 'Richerche sulla distribuzione altimetrica della vegetazione in Italia. Introduzione'. *Nuovo Giorn. Bot. It.* n.s. XLI, 1934. pp. 327–641.
12. DE PHILIPPIS, A. *Classificazioni ed indici del clima in rapporto alla vegetazione forcstale Italiana*. Comitato Nazionale per la Geog. Bologna, 1937. 169 pp.
13. GIACOBBE, A. *op. cit.* (see note 8).
14. DE PHILIPPIS, A. 'Le sughera ed il leccio nella vegetazione arborea mediterranea', *Bull. de la Silva* Mediterranea, X, 1935. pp. 9–109.
15. CHIARUGI, A. *La vegetazione dell' Appennino nei suoi aspetti di ambiente e di storia del popolamento* montano. Rome, 1935.
16. NEGRI, G. 'Considerazioni sulla classificazione dei piani altimetrici della vegetazione in Italia'. *R.G.I.* LIV, 1947. pp. 17–30, 79–91.
17. DE PHILIPPIS, A. *Classificasioni ed indica del clima, op cit.*
18. PRINCIPI, P. *I Terreni d'Italia*. Rome, 1943. 242 pp. [Contains important bibliography.]
19. MANCINI, F. 'Carta dei suoli d'Italia', *Agricolture*, 1960. pp. 14–45. [Contains soil map on scale of 1:500,000.]
20. PRINCIPI, P. 'Attraverso l'Italia pedologica. I terreni agrati del Lazio', *L'Italia Agricola*, 88, 1951. pp. 86–101. [Map.]
21. — P. *I Terreni d'Italia, op. cit.* pp. 19–20.
22. For general summaries of vegetation see: BEGUINOT, A. *Gli aspettie le origini della vegetazione d'Italia*. Modena, 1928; RIKLI, M. *Des Pflanzenkleid der Mittelmeerländer*. Berne, 1943–48, 3 vols.; Milan, Touring Club Italiano, *Conosci Italia*, vol. 2, *La Flora*. 1958. 394 pp.
23. CARY, M. *The Geographic Background of Greek and Roman History*. Oxford, 1949, p. 143.
24. SIRAGO, V. A. *L'Italia agraria sotto Traiano*. Louvain, 1958.
25. CHILVER, G. E. F. *Cisalpine Gaul*. Oxford, 1941. pp. 129–61.

26. LORENZI, A. 'L'Uomo e la foreste'. *R.G.I.* 1918 XXV, pp. 141–65, 213–42; 1919, XXVI, pp. 47–57.

27. Istituto Nazionale di Economia Agraria. *Annuario dell' Agricoltura Italiana*, XV. Milan, 1962. pp. 237–42.

28. SPERANZA, F. *Dei limiti altimetrici della vegetacione sull' Etna*, Catania, 1960.

29. Summarised from data in *Conosci Italia. La Flora, op. cit.*

30. *Atti del Convegno nazionale del bosco ceduo, con particolare riguordo alla macchia mediterranea.* Siena, 1958. p. 29.

31. ZODDA, G. 'Studi sulla flora. IV. Azione antropica sul bosco, del ceppo (Bosco Matese)'. *N.G. Bot. It.*, LXVI, 1959. pp. 253–64.

32. PAVARI, A. 'Basi ecologiche e techniche della silva coltura ner paesi meditertanei'. *Monte e Boschi*, 5 (10), 1954. pp. 435–52.

33. Instituto Centrale di Statistica. *Annuario Statistico Italiano*. Rome, 1959.

34. FRANCIOSA, L. *La transhumancia nell' Appennino centromeridionale.* Mem. geog. econ. C.N.R. IV. Naples, 1951. 99 pp.

35. ROSTOVTZEFF, M. *Social and Economic History of the Roman Empire.* Oxford, 1926, pp. 183–7.

36. BIROT, P. and DRESCH, J. *La Méditerranée et le Moyen-Orient*, tome 1, Paris, 1953, pp. 355–6.

37. MEDICI, G. *Land Property and Land Tenure in Italy.* Bologna, 1952. p. 40.

38. FRANK, T. *An Economic Survey of Ancient Rome*, vol. 1. Baltimore, 1933, pp. 368–9.

39. PRESTIANNI, N. *L'Economia agraria della Sicilia.* Palermo, 1947. 268 pp.

40. DESPLANQUES, H. 'Contribution à l'étude des pay sages ruraux au Italie centrale', *Geographie et Histoire Agraires. Colloques Internat.* Nancy, 1957. pp. 97–104.

41. BILLIARD, R. *L'Agriculture dans l'antiquité d'après les Georgiques de Virgile.* Perugia, 1928. 538 pp.

42. COLUMELLA, *De Agricola*, II, 4.

43. PLINY, *Historia Naturalis*, XIV, 3; XVII.

44. COLUMELLA, *De Agricola, op. cit.*

45. DESPLANQUES, H. 'Il paessaggio rurale della coltura promiscua in Italia'. *R.G.I.* LXVI. 1959. pp. 29–64.

46. Istituto Centrale di Statistica, *Catasto Agrario.* Rome, 1929.

47. DESPLANQUES, *op. cit.* pp. 51–57.

48. — *op. cit.* pp. 47–8.

49. LANDESCHI, G. B. *Saggi di agricoltura.* Florence, 1770. p. 202.

50. SERENI, E. 'Note per una storia del paessaggio agrario emiliano' in *Le campagne emiliane nell' epoca moderna.* Milan, 1957. pp. 5–35.

51. POLYBIUS, ii. 15.

52. STRABO, IV, p. 202.

53. BEY, ISMAIL SIRRY. *Irrigation in the valley of the River Po.* Cairo, 1902. pp. 64–75.

54. ORTOLANI, M. *La Pianura Ferrarese.* Mem. di Geog. Econ. Naples, XV, 1956. 197 pp.

55. MIGLIORINI, E. *Veneto.* Turin, 1962, pp. 255–62.

56. Istituto Nazionale di Economia Agraria. *Ricerche sull' economia della irrigazione.* Rome, 1931–37. 3 vols.

57. PARETI, R. *Sulle bonificazioni, risaie ed irrigazioni del Regno d'Italia.* Milan, 1865. [A fundamental source-book on the subject.]

58. ALMAGIA, R. *L'Italia*, tome II. Turin, 1959. pp. 677–79.

59. O.E.E.C. *An Economic Survey of S. Europe.* 1953.

60. LONGOBARDI, C. *Land-Reclamation in Italy.* transl. by O. R. AGRESTI. London 1936, 243 pp.

61. DICKINSON, R. E. 'Land Reform in southern Italy', *E.G.*, 1954. pp. 157–176.
62. MERLINI, G. *Le Regioni Agrarie in Italia*. Bologna, 1948. 178 pp. [A useful, regional summary.]
63. MEDICI, G. *op. cit.* pp. 27–36.
64. Istituto nazionale di economia agraria. *L'Economia agraria della Campania*. Rome, 1948. pp. 101–2.
65. BIROT, P. and DRESCH, J., *op. cit.*, p. 327.
66. MEDICI, G., *op. cit.* pp. 144–7.
67. PAPASOGLI, G. *L'Agricoltura dei Etrusci e dei Romani*. Rome, 1942.

CHAPTER 16

THE POPULATION AND SETTLEMENTS OF ITALY

A useful bibliographical guide is: LUCHETTI, A. 'Guida bibliografica allo studio degli insediamenti in Italia', *Mem. Geog. antr.*, VIII, 1953, fasc. III (681 items listed), Rome, 1954. See also, SALINARI, M. E. 'Bibliografia degli scritti di geografia urbana, 1901–1944', *Mem. Geog. antr.*, II, 1947, fasc. II. pp. 1–89 (with 264 items on Italy, includes references to other countries also).

1. SESTINI, A. 'Il paesaggio antropogeografico come forma di equilibrio', *B.S.G.I.*, 1947, pp. 1–8; also, 'Le fasi regressive nello sviluppo del paesaggio antropogeografico', *R.G.I.*, LIV, 1947, pp. 153–71.
2. See Touring Club Italiano, *L'Italia storica*, Milan, 1961, 288.
3. WISE, M. J. 'Population pressure and natural resources, some observations upon the Italian population', *Econ. Geog.*, 1954. pp. 144–56.
4. BELOCH, J. *Bevolkerungsgechichte Italiens*. Berlin. Vol. 1, 1937, 284 pp.; vol. 2, 1940, 312 pp. [This is the standard work on Italy's early population.]
5. GUISTI, U. *Caratteristiche ambientali Italiane: agrarie-sociali-demografiche, 1815–1942*. Roma, 1943. 346 pp. [Contains much useful demographic data.]
6. FRANCIOSI, L. 'Sviluppo e centri del littorale italiano', *B.S.G.I.*, 1938. pp. 834–51.
7. SCANO, G. 'Distribuzione, aumento e densità della popolazione italiana'. *R.G.I.*, XXIV, 1917, pp. 289–306, 366–77; XXV, 1918, pp. 36–41, 111–16; 243–8; XXVII, 1920, pp. 37–42; XXVIII, 1921, pp. 103–8, 157–62; XXIX, 1922, pp. 197–203; XXX, 1923, pp. 50–6, 158–68; XXXI, 1924, pp. 159–75.
8. TONIOLO, A. R. 'Studies of depopulation in the mountains of Italy', *G.R.*, 1937, pp. 473–77; also BARBIERI, G., 'I mestieri degli emigranti e alcune caratteristiche correnti di emigrazione della montagna italiana', *Studi Geogr. pubbl. in onore del Prof. R. Biasutti. Suppl. a Riv. Geogr. It.*, LXV, 1958. pp. 45–65.
9. *Lo spopolamento montano in Italia.* C.G.C.N.R. e Ist. Naz. Econ. Agr., 11 vols. 1932–9. [This is the major study of mountain depopulation.]
10. GUISTI, U. *Op. cit.* pp. 301–34.
11. *Lo spopolamento montano, op. cit.*, Part VI, *L'Appennino Emiliano-Tosco-Romagnolo*. Roma, 1934. 219 pp.
12. TONIOLO, A. R. 'Modificazioni del paesaggio geografico nelle zone di bonifica e suoi riflessi sul modo di vita degli abitanti', *Atti XXIV Riunione So. It. per il Progresso del lev Sc.* (Palermo, 1935), III. Roma, 1936. pp. 308–10. See also, BALDACCI, O. 'Recenti trasformazioni del paesaggio umano nella Italia meridionale', *Atti XVII Congresso Geog. It. Relazioni*, vol. II. Bari, 1957. pp. 347–84.
13. MCNEE, R. B. 'Rural development in the Italian South', *A.A.A.G.*, 1955. pp. 127–51.
14. MORI, A. 'Agglomerati rurali tipici nella Maremma grossetana', *C.R.I. Geog. Amsterdam*, Sect. A, 1938. pp. 115–28.

BIBLIOGRAPHY 769

15. BEVILACQUA, E. Marche, *op. cit.* pp. 115–9.
16. MORI, A. 'Sul popolamento recente di alcuni comuni costieri del Lazio, *Atti Congr. Internaz. Studi Pop.*, IX, 1933. pp. 485–96.
17. FERRANTINI, A. 'Variazioni della popolazione nel Piemonte, Valle d'Aosta e Liguria del 1848', *Atti XV Cong. Geog. It. Torino*, I, 1950. pp. 431–9.
18. CANDIDA, L. 'Aspetti geografici delle variazione di popolamento nelle Venezia nel trentennio, 1901–31', *C.R.C.I.Geog.*, Sect. A, Amsterdam, 1938. pp. 48–61.
19. ACHER, G. 'Les migrations a travers les Alpes', *A. de G.*, LXIV, 1955. pp. 340–58.
20. SOMOGYI, S. 'La mobilita interna della popolazione italiana', *Riv. It. Ec. Demogr. e Stat.*, XIV, 1960. pp. 17–44.
21. COLETTI, F. *La popolazione rurale in Italia.* Piacenza, 1925.
22. PARLATO, G. 'L'emigrazione italiane nel mondo', *L'Univ.*, 30, 1950. pp. 726–43.
23. BARBERIS, C. *Le migrazioni rurali in Italia.* Milano, 1960. 238 pp.
24. PINNA, M. *La carta della densità della popolazione in Italia.* (Censimento 1951). Roma, C.N.R. 1960. 76 pp. [A useful summary.]
25. ROSTER, G. 'Influence del clima su la distribuzione e la densita dell popolazione italiana', *Atti R. Acc. dei Georgofili*, IX, 1912. pp. 13–27.
26. PINNA, *op. cit.*
27. SESTINI, A. 'Densità tipiche di popolazione in Italia secondo le forme di utilizzazione del suolo', *R.G.I.*, LXVI, 1959. pp. 231–41.
28. VANNI, M. 'Limiti e popolazione delle più grande città italiane', *L'Univ.*, 38, 1958. pp. 81–94.
29. BRADFORD, J. 'Buried landscapes in Apulia', *Ant.*, XXIII, 1949. pp. 58–72.
30. WARD-PERKINS, J. B. 'Early Roman towns in Italy', *Town Planning Rev.*, 26, 1955. pp. 127–54.
31. — 'The problem of Etruscan origins', *Harvard Studies in Class. Philol.*, 64, 1959. pp. 1–26.
32. LAVEDAN, P. *Histoire de l'urbanisme. Antiquité-Moyen Age.* Paris, 1926. pp. 98–111.
33. MACIVER, D. R. *Greek Cities in Italy and Sicily.* Oxford, 1931. 226 pp. Also KIRSTEN, E. *Die Griechische Polis als historisch-geographisches*, Colloqium. G. Bonn, 1955. 154 pp.
34. Touring Club Italiano. *Conosci L'Italia*, vol. IV, *Arte e Civilta nell'Italia antica.* Milano, 1960. 256 pp.
35. RENOUARD, Y. *Les villes d'Italie de la fin du Xe. siècle au début XIVe. siècle*, Les Cours de Sorbonne, parts I, II, III. Paris, 1960.
36. FOTHERINGHAM, J. *The Towns of Italy.* London, 1910.
37. ALMAGIA, R. 'The repopulation of the Roman Campagna', *G.R.*, 1929. pp. 529–55.
38. LOPEZ, R. S. 'The trade of medieval Europe: the South', in *The Cambridge Economic History*, vol. 2, 1952. pp. 257–354.
39. FLEURE, H. J. 'Cities of the Po Basin', *G.R.*, 1924. pp. 345–61.
40. PICCINATO, L. 'Urbanistica medioevale', in Giovannoni *et alii*, *L'Urbanistica dall' antichita ad oggi*, Firenze, 1943. pp. 63–89.
41. WARD-PERKINS, J. B. 'Etruscan Towns . . . The historical geography of southern Etruria', *G.J.*, CXXVIII, 1962. pp. 380–405.
42. MARCELLINO, V. 'Sulle piante topografiche della citta di Palermo', *Arch. Stor. Sic.* 1948. pp. 199–223.
43. WILLEMSEN, C. S. and ODENTHAL, D. *Apulia.* London, 1959. pp. 9–18.
44. MORI. 'Sulla formazione di nuovi centri abitati in Sicilia negli ultimi quattro secoli', *R.G.I.*, XXVII, 1920. pp. 149–77.
45. GRIBAUDI, D. 'Geografia agraria e forma del popolamento rurale', *Atti XIV Congr. Geog. It.*, Bologna, 1947. pp. 187–97.

46. SCHOLZ, H. 'Tipi d'insediamento rurale nella Sicilia centrale', *Atti XVII Congr. Geog. It.*, vol. III, Barri, 1957. pp. 364–67.
47. BIASUTTI, R. 'Ricerche sui tipi degli sediamenti rurali in Italia', *Mem. Soc. Geog. It.*, XVII, Roma, 1932. pp. 5–25.
48. D'ADDARO, R. 'L'agglomeramento della popolazione nei compartimenti italiane', *Ann. di Statistica*, XVI, 1931. pp. 59–118.
49. DICKINSON, R. E. 'Dispersed settlement in Southern Italy', *Erdk.*, 1956. pp. 282–97.
50. LORENZI, A. 'Studi sui tipi antropogeografici della pianura padana', *R.G.I.*, XXI, 1914. pp. 269–354; 401–50; 497–530; 576–604.
51. CARACI, G. 'Le corti lombarde e l'origine della corte', *Mem. Soc. Geog. It.*, Roma, 1932. pp. 26–72.
52. Consiglio Nazionale delle Ricerche. Centro di Studi per la Geografia Etnologica, *Ricerche sulle dimore rurali in Italia*, ed. by R. Biasutti, with 19 volumes published between 1938 and 1958. The best general guide to this subject is by NANGERONI, G., *Geografia delle dimore e degli insediamenti rurali*, Milano, 1946, 96 pp.

CHAPTER 17

NORTHERN ITALY

The major studies of regional geography in Italy are being published by UTET, *Le Regioni d'Italia*. The first volumes were edited by the late R. Almagià, and are referred to below under the various regions. More useful to the general reader are the short articles by F. Milone, that summarise his great work, *L'Italia nell'economie delle sue regioni*, Torino, 1955, 1,296 pp. These articles are published by the Banco di Roma as 'Regional structure of Italian economy', in the *Review of the Economic Conditions of Italian Economy* as follows: XIV, No. 1, 1960, pp. 28–56; No. 2, pp. 149–77; No. 3, pp. 483–506; No. 6, pp. 602–30; XV, 1961, No. 2, pp. 124–57; No. 4, pp. 317–42; No. 6, pp. 528–61; XVI, 1962, No. 3, pp. 207–39.

NORTHERN ITALY

FLEURE, H. J. 'Cities of the Po Basin', *G.R.*, 1924. pp. 345–61.
GACHON, L. 'Comparazione tra el paesaggio dell'Italia settentrionale e quello della Francia meridionale', *R.G.I.*, LXI, 1954. pp. 1–24.
LEHMANN, H. 'Das Landschaftgefuge der Padania', *Frankfurter Geogr. Hefte*, 37, 1961. pp. 87–158. See review by A. SESTINI, *R.G.I.*, LXIX, 1962. pp, 271–6.
ROBERTSON, C. J. 'Agricultural regions of the North Italian Plain., *G.R.*, 1938. pp. 573–96.

THE WESTERN PLAIN

1. Liguria

LAMBOGLIA, C. 'L Riviera dei fiori ed il suo entroterra sotto il riguardo turistico ed economico', *Atti XVI Congr. Geog. It. Padava-Venezia*, 1954. pp. 691–702.
MERLO, C. *Liguria* (dir. R. Almagià), Torino, 1962. 539 pp. [The best regional work.]
RODGERS, A. L. 'The port of Genoa', *Aî.A.A.G.*, XLVIII, 1958. pp. 319–51.
REVELLI, P. *Figurazioni cartografiche della citta di Genova (1435–1935)*. Genova, 1936. 78 pp.
ROVERETO, G. 'La storia delle fasce dei liguri', *Le Vie d'Italia*, XX. 1942. pp. 529–35.

SCARIN, E. 'La XXIV Escursione geografica interuniversitaria italiana nella Liguria orientale', *Ann. Ric. St. Geog.*, XV, Genova, 1959. pp. 69–102.
— 'La Casa rurale nella Liguria', *Ann. Ric. Sc Geog.*, XIII, 1957. pp. 1–96, 104–231.
ROSSO, G. *XIII Escursione geografica interuniversitaria.* Genova, 1939. 72 pp.

2. Piedmont

DONNA, C. *Lo sviluppo storico delle bonifiche e delle irrigazioni in Piedmonte.* Torino, 1939.
GRIBAUDI, D. *Piedmonte e Val d'Aosta* (dir. R. Almagia). Torino, 1960. 601 pp. [The best work.]
— 'La posizione geografica e lo sviluppo di Torino'. Torino, 1908.
LORENZI, A. 'Studi sui tipi antropogeografici della pianura padana', *R.G.I.*, XXI 1914. pp. 269–354, 402–450, 495–530, 576–604.
OGILVIE, A. G. 'Natural and cultivated vegetation in the eastern Dora Baltea basin' *S.G.M.*, LIII, 1937. pp. 249–65.
ROMITI, G. *La sistemazione del bacino idrografico del Po nella regione piedmontese.* Torino, 1959.

3. Lombardy

BONATO, C. *L'economia agraria della Lombardia.* Milano, 1952.
BERTOSSI, T. e CHIESA. 'La densità della popolazione in Lombardia', *L'Univ.* 1951.
CARACI, G. *Le corti lombarde e l'origine della corte*, Mem. Soc. Geog., 17, Rome, 1932. pp. 26–72.
PECORA, A. *La provincia di Pavia.*, Mem. di Geog. antr. Roma, 1954.
— 'Pavia: saggio di geografia urbana', *R.G.I.*, 1954. pp. 277–322.
— 'Contributi allo studio geografico della città di Milano', *B.S.G.I.*, 1953. pp. 419–24.
PRACCHI, R. 'La distribuzione della popolazione nel triangolo lariano', *R.G.I.* 1941. pp. 184–207.
— *Lombardia* (dir. R. Almagià). Torino, 1960. 562 pp. [The best survey of Lombardy.]

THE EASTERN PLAIN

1. Veneto

BONI, A. *L'alto bacino orientale del Piave. Topografia, geologia, morfologia, idrografia.* (Mem. Ist. lomdardo sc. e. lett.) Milano, 1937.
CANDIDA, L. 'Aspetti geografici della variazione di popolamento nella Venezia 1901–31', *C.R. Congr. Geog. Internat.* Amsterdam, 1938. Sect. A-F.
— *La casa rurale nella pianura e nella collina venea.* Firenze, 1959.
— *I Colli Euganei.* Venezia, 1959. 93 pp.
GASPARETTO, M. L. *Il Polesine; studio di geografia economica.* Padova, 1960, 337 pp.
MIGLIORINI, E. *Veneto.* (Dir. R. Almagià). Torino, 1962. 515 pp. [A serious and valuable work on a region little studied.]

2. Emilia-Romagna

ARMANDI, E. R. 'Regioni e centri turistici nell'Emilia-Romagna', *Atti del XVII Congr. Geog. Ital.*, vol. I. Bari, 1957.
GAMBI, I. *L'insediamento umano nella regione della bonifica romagnola*, Mem. di Geog. Antr., III. Roma, 1948. 219 pp.

EDLOWSKI, E. 'Profilo delle foreste demaniali, di Bologna e di Ferrara', *Monte e Boschi*, XI., 1960. pp. 531–53.

ORLANDINI, J. *Rimini: Ricerche di geografia urbana*, Centro Stude Geog. antr., VII. Roma, 1953.

ORTOLANI, M. *La pianura ferrarese*, Mem. di Geog. econ., XV, Napoli, 1956. 200 pp.

PERDISA, L. *Monografia economico-agraria dell'Emilia*. Bologna, 1938.

ROLETTO, G. 'Le cadre geographique de Bologne', *R.G.A.*, XIV, 1926. pp. 447–71.

TOSCHI, U. *Emilia-Romagna*. (Dir. R. Almagià). Torino, 1961. 485 pp. [An excellent survey.]

CHAPTER 18

THE REGIONS OF PENINSULAR ITALY

1. The Adriatic Coastlands of the Marches, Abruzzi, and Molise

BEVILACQUA, E. 'L'insediamento umano nei bacini del Cesano e del Misa', *B.S.G.I.*, 1949. pp. 9–26.

— *Marche*. (Dir. R. Almagià). Torino, 1961. 418 pp. [The most useful regional summary of the Marches.]

BONASERA, F. *Fano, studio di geografia urbana*, Ist. Geog. Univ. Roma, 1951.

— *Studi geografici recentemente compiuti e de compiere sulle Marche*. Ancona, 1955. 118 pp. [25 years of bibilographical items.]

EMILIANI, A. 'La distribuzione della popolazione nel bacino dell'Esino', *B.R.S.G.I.*, 1932. pp. 142–63.

— *Ancona*. Mem. di Geog. antr., X. Roma, 1955.

ORTOLANI, M. 'Il litorale piceno', *B.S.G.I.*, 1937.

— 'Il litorale abgruzzese', *B.S.G.I.*, 1956. pp. 138–51.

— 'Il subappennino abruzzese', *R.G.I.*, LXVIII, 1960. pp. 13–20.

PRINCIPI, P. 'I terreni agraria delle Marche', *L'Italia agricole*, 85, Roma, 1948. pp. 45–54.

PULLÌ, G. 'I Monti Sibillini', *L'Univ.*, 1939.

RICCARDI, M. 'Carta della distribuzione della popolazione sparsa e dei centri in Abruzzio', *B.S.G.I.*, 1950. pp. 149–62.

2. Umbria

BEVILACQUA, E. 'Perugia', *Mem. Geog. antr.* Roma, 1950.

BONASERA, F. 'Nota geografichi sul bacino del Lago Trasimeno', *Atti di Rie e Studi di Geog.*, XVI, 1960. pp. 109–40.

DELLA VALLE, C. 'Una escursione della Società Geografica It. nel bacino del Nera-Velino', *B.S.G.I.*, 1952. pp. 145–57.

DESPLANQUES, H. 'Assise', *Pub. Ste. Géog.* Lille, 1950–3. pp. 20–53.

FROSINI, P. 'Il lago Trasimeno e il suo antico emissario', *B.S.G.I.*, XI, 1958. pp. 6–15.

IACONI, I. 'Saggio di carta antropogeografica della Valle Umbra', *Mem. di Geog. Antr.*, Roma, 1953. pp. 7–80.

RICCARDI, R. *Ricerche sull'insediamento umano nell'Umbria*, Mem. Roma, 1931.

3. Tuscany

Accademia economico-agraria dei Georgofili. *Il bacino dell'Arno*. Florence, 1955. 290 pp.

BARBIERI, G. 'Il Mugello. Studio di geografia umana, *R.G.I.*, LX, 1953. pp. 89–133.

DELLA VALLE, C. *Lecco e il suo territorio. Studio antropogeografico*, Mem. Soc. Geog. It., XXI. 1954. 192 pp.
— 'XXII L'Escursione dell'Univ. di Roma e della Soc. Geog. all'Isola d'Elba e nella Toscana occidentale', *B.S.G.I.*, 1958. pp. 287–338.
FULLER, G. T. *Elba*, Geog. Field Group. Nottingham, 1958.
GAMBI, L. 'Le escursione geografica interuniversitaria in Toscana', *R.G.I.*, LXIII, 1956. pp. 287–99.
GIGLI, F. 'La densita de popolazione in Toscana nei sec. XIV e XVIII', *R.G.I.*, LXI, 1954. pp. 265–76.
HERLICHY, D. *Pisa in the early Renaissance—a study in urban growth*. Baltimore, 1954.
MANSINI, E. 'Le origini di Firenze', *L'Univ.*, VI, 1925. pp. 507–31.
MORI, A. *et alii. Notizie geografiche sull'Isola d'Elba*. Pisa, 1960. 71 pp.
NICE, B. *Le Alpi Apuane. Studio antropogeografico*, Mem. di Geog. antr., VII. Roma, 1952. 212 pp.
PEDRISCHI, L. 'Aspetti geografica della trasformazione fondiario-agraria in Maremma e nel Fucino', *B.S.G.I.*, 1953. pp. 283–97.
— 'Due particolare idrografici della pianura costiera pisanolucchese', *R.G.I.*, LXI, 1954. pp. 229–36.
LUCIO, G. 'La XXII Escursione geografica Interuniv. in Toscana', *R.G.I.*, LXII, 1956. pp. 287–99.
PINNA, M. *et alii. Contributi alla geografia della Toscana Pubbl. Ist. Geog.* Pisa, 1959. 165 pp.
PRINCIPI, P. 'Il terreni agraria della Toscana', *L'Italia agric.*, 85, 1948. pp. 253–65.
STORAI, T. 'L'Opera di modificaziobe dell'uomo sul suolo della Toscana', *B.S.G.I.*, 1947. pp. 241–55.

4. Latium

ALMAGIÀ, R. 'The repopulation of the Roman Campagna', *G.R.*, 1929. pp. 529–55.
— *Geografia del Lazio*. Roma, 1955. 136 pp. [A concise, useful outline.]
— 'Intorne ad alcune caratteristiche geografische della regione pontine', *L'Univ.*, XXXIX, 1959. pp. 371–82.
ASHBY, T. *The Roman Campagna in classical times*. London, 1927. 256 pp. [A standard work on classical topography.]
AUDIN, A. 'La naissance de Rome', *R.G.A.*, XXXI, 1956. pp. 21–31.
CASTAGNOLI, F. *et alii. Storia di Roma*, vol. 22: *Topografia e Urbanistica di Roma*, Ist. Studi Romani. Roma, 1960. [This is an exhaustive work of reference.]
DAVIS, W. M. 'The seven hills of Rome', *J.G.*, IX, 1911. pp. 197–202, 230–3.
FERRANTINI. 'I limiti altimetrici della vegetazione nel Vulcano Laziale', *R.G.I.*, 49, 1942. pp. 18–34.
FRACCARO, P. 'Di alcuni antichissimi lavori idraulici di Roma e della Campagna', *B.S.G.I.*, 1919. pp. 186–215.
— 'I fattori geografici della grandezza di Roma', *La Geog.*, 14, 1926. pp. 84–101.
JUDSON, S. and KAHANE, A. 'Underground drainageways in southern Etruria and northern Latium', *Paper of the Brit. School at Rome*, XXXI, 1963. pp. 74–99.
LE GALL, J. *Le Tibre fleuve de Rome dans l'antiquite*. Paris, 1953. 367 pp. [A doctorate thesis with much valuable data.]
MORANDINI, G. *I Monti Lepini. Studio antropogeografico*, Mem. Geog. antr., I. 1946. 180 pp.
RICCARDI, M. 'Il bacino di Fondi', *B.S.G.I.*, 1959. pp. 27–99.
SAFLUND, G. 'Ancient Latin cities of the hills and the plains. A study in the evolutions of the settlement in ancient Italy', *Opuscola archaeologica*, I, 1934. pp. 64–86.
SERONDE, A. M. 'Rome. Étude d'evolution urbaine', *B.A.G.F.*, 1954. pp. 121–7.
TOSCHI, U. 'The Vatican city. From the standpoint of political geography', *G.R.*, 1931. pp. 529–38.

WARD-PERKINS, J. 'Etruscan Towns, Roman roads and medieval villages: the historical geography of southern Etruria', *G.J.*, CXXVIII, 1962. pp. 389–405.
ZEPPEGGO, L. 'Nell'alto Lazio, lungo l'Aniene', *La Vie d'Italia*, 1956. pp. 968–76.

SOUTHERN ITALY

A useful general reference is still that of AHLMANN, H. W. 'Études de géographie humaine sur l'Italie subtropicale', *Geog. Ann.*, VII, 1925, pp. 257–322; 1926, pp. 74–124.

1. Campania

CASTALDI, F. *Itineratia salernitani*. Salerno, 1949. 142 pp.
DAINELLI, G. 'Guida della escursione alla Penisola Sorrentina', *Atti dell'XI Congr. Geog.*, vol. IV, Napoli, 1930. pp. 59–97.
FRANCIOSA, L. *Il Cilento*. Salerno, 1950. 196 pp.
Ist. Naz. di Econ. agraria. *L'Economia agraria della Campania*. Roma, 1948. 276 pp.
KANT:R, H. 'Ischia und Capri', *Z. deutsch. Gesell. Erdkunde*, 1926. pp. 409–24.
LANGELLA, V. 'Lineamenti geografici della pianura del Sarno', *R.G.I.*, LXVI, 1959. pp. 338–74.
MAIURI, A. *Passeggiate campane*. Firenze, 1950. 421 pp. [A study in classical topography.]
RICCARDI, M. 'Il bacino di Fondi', *B.S.G.I.*, 1959. pp. 27–99.
RUOCCO, D. *I Campi Flegrei. Studio di geografia agraria*, Mem. Geog. econ. XI. Napoli, 1954. 99 pp.
SPANO, G. *Le Campania felice nelle èta piu remote*. Napoli, 1941. 444 pp.
UNGER, L. 'Rural settlement in the Campania', *G.R.*, 1953. pp. 506–24.

2. Basilicata

ARMIGNACCIO, V. 'Potenza: ricerche de geografia urbana', *R.G.I.*, LX, 1953. pp. 19–49.
FRANCESCA, L. 'Distribuzione della popolazione nella Lucania in rapporto alle condizioni litologiche', *B.S.G.I.*, 1946. pp. 65–78.
KAYSER, B. *Recherches sur les sols et l'érosion en Italie meridionale: Lucanie*. Paris, 1961. 127 pp. [Summary of doctorate thesis.]
RANIERI, L. *La regione del Vulture. Studio di geografia agraria*, Mem. Geog. econ., VIII. Napoli, 1953.
— *Basilicata*. (Dir. R. Almagià.) Torino, 1961. 429 pp. [The best regional study in this little known region.]
TICHY, F. 'Die entwaldungsvorgaenge des 19. Jahrhunderts in der Basilica', *Erdkunde*, XI, 1957. pp. 288–96.

3. Apulia

AMATI, A. *Bari. Studio de geografia urbana*, Mem. Geog. antr. Roma, 1948.
Atti del XVII Congresso Geog. It., vol. IV, *Guida alle escursioni*. Bari, 1957. 196 pp.
BALDACCI, O. *Puglia*. (Dir. R. Almagià.) Torino, 1962. 550 pp. [The best regional outline.]
COLAMONICO, C. *Memoria illustrativa della carta utilizzazione del suolo della Puglia*. Roma, 1960. 224 pp.
FRANCIOSA, L. 'Aspetti antropogeografici del Gargano', *L'Univ.*, XXXVIII, 1957. pp. 313–26.
PECORA, A. 'Manfredonia e il suo territorio', *R.G.I.*, LXVII, 1960. pp. 237–67.
RICCARDI, M. 'Escursione della Soc. Geog. It. in Puglia e Basilicata', *B.S.G.I.* 1953. pp. 212–23.

TOSCHI, U. 'Tipi di paesaggi e paesaggi tipici in Pugli e in Emilia', *Studi geo. in onore A. R. Toniolo.* Milano, 1952. pp. 197–237.

WIRTH, E. 'Die Murgia dei Trulli (Apulien)', *Die Erde,* 1962. pp. 249–78.

4. Calabria

BALDACCI, O. *La Serra. Monografia antropogeografia di una regione Calabrese,* Mem. Geog. antr. Roma, IX. Roma, 1954. 253 pp.

BELLA, P. de. 'La Calabria e l'emigrazione', *B.S.G.I.,* 1924. pp. 549–60.

CREA, G. L. 'Aspromonte ed i suoi boschi', *Monti e Boschi,* VII, 1956. pp. 67–79.

GIGNOUX, M. 'La Calabre', *A. de G.,* XVIII, 1909. pp. 141–61.

GRIBAUDI, D. 'L'Escursione della Soc. Geog. It. in Calabria', *B.S.G.I.,* 1960. pp. 217–43.

KANTER, H. *Kalabrien.* Hamburg, 1930.

LACQUANTI, L. *XVIII Escursione interuniversitaria, Calabria meridionale.* Palmi, 1951. 20 pp.

MEYRIAT, J. (ed.). *La Calabre.* Paris, 1960. [See especially pp. 1–53.]

MILONE, F. *Memoria illustrativa della carta della utilizzazione del suolo della Calabria.* Napoli, 1956. 101 pp.

SICILY

BRUNO, F. *et alii.* 'Le piante officinali spontanee della Sicilia', *Lav. dell'Ist. Botan. e Giardino col. Palermo,* XVII. 1960. pp. 131–521.

Congreso Geog. Ital. VII, *Palermo e la Conca d'oro.* Palermo, 1911. 412 pp.

DELLA VALLE, C. 'L'Escursione della Soc. Geog. It. in Sicilia', *B.S.G.I.,* 1958. pp. 287–338.

FLORIDA, S. *La Sicilia nei tempi antichi.,* I. Catania, 1944. 108 pp. [This is the standard work on classical topography.]

KOEGEL, L. 'Der Aetna über dem sizilischen Landschauftsblock', *Erd.,* VIII, 1940. pp. 145–60.

LAURE, G. 'I boschi siciliani nella preistoria, nella storia, nell'attualita', *Monti e Boschi,* IV, 1953. pp. 253–61.

MILONE, F. *Memoria illustrativa della carta della utilizzazione del suolo della Sicilia.* Roma, 1959. 210 pp.

— *Sicilia: la natura e l'uomo.* Torino, 1960. 466 pp. [The best regional study on the island, with useful historic perspective.]

PHILIPPSON, A. 'Die Landschaften Siziliens', *Erd,* 1934. pp. 321–42.

SPERANZA, F. *Dei limiti altimetrici della vegetacione sull'Etna.* Catania, 1960, 110 pp.

PART IV: PERIPHERAL LANDS OF THE NORTHERN MEDITERRANEAN AND THE MEDITERRANEAN ISLANDS

CHAPTER 19

THE YUGOSLAV LITTORAL

ATLASES AND MAPS

Znanje, Zagreb: Geografiski Atlas Jugoslavije. 1/500,000. 1961.

Collection de Cartes de la Soc. Geog. Beograd. Belgrade. 1931. [Includes a morphological map prepared by P. S. Jovanovic, 1/1,200,000.]

Vojni Geografski Institut: Maps of 1/50,000.
Serbian General Staff: 95 sheets of 1/75,000.
'Ucila-Mladost', Zagreb: Tourist map of the Adriatic Coast. *c.* 1/390,000. 1960.
Ekomoska Karta F.N.R: 1/500,000. 1960.
Jugoslavija. Autokarta. 1/850,000. 1962.
Jugoslovensko Stampasko Preduzece. Geoloska Karte. 1/500,000. 1953.

For reference to other earlier maps, see Naval Intelligence Division, *Geographical Handbooks*, vol. 1. Jugoslavia. pp. 279–95.

BIBLIOGRAPHY

As the great majority of references are in Serbo-Croat it seemed unnecessary to list them. Only a very few items in other languages are therefore listed. For further references see B. Z. Milojevic, *Geography of Yugoslavia, a selective bibliography.* Washington, 1955. 72 pp. [With 830 items listed.]

ADAMOVIĆ, L. *Die Pflanzenwelt der Adrialander.* Jena, 1929.
BLANC, A. *La Croatie Occidentale*, Inst. d'Études Slaves. Paris, 1957. 496 pp. [A first-class work dealing with the imprint of traditional economies on the landscapes.]
CADIŽ. 'Sur une classification des types de temps', *Météorol.*, 1957, pp. 317–23.
DAINELLI, G. *La Dalmazia.* Novara, 1918.
GEORGE, P. 'Vie rurale et maritime dans la Kvarner yougaslave, *B.A.G.F.*, 1948, pp. 81–9.
— 'Quelques formes karstiques de la Croatie occidentale et de la Slovenie meridionale', *A. de G.*, 1948, pp. 298–307.
GREIM, G. 'Die Insel Arbe (Rab)', *Geog. Ges. in Munchen*, XIX, 1926. pp. 143–84.
JOHNSTON, W. B. and CRKVENČIĆ, I. 'Changing peasant agriculture in north-western Hrvatsko-Primorge', *G.R.*, 1954. pp. 352–72.
MILOJEVIĆ, B. Ž. 'Littoral et iles dinariques dans le Royaume de Yougoslavie', *Memoires de la Societé de Géographie de Beograd*, vol. II, 1933. pp. 1–226. [This contains the substance of seven articles published in 1927 and later material.]
— 'Les bouches de Kotor', *B. de G. Fac. Lettres d'Aix-en-Provence*, LXVII, 1956. pp. 5–20.
— *Les vallées principales de la Yougaslavie, recherches géog.* Belgrade, 1958. 160 pp. [A useful summary.]
NIEMEIER, G. 'Hvar, als Type der Mittel und Sud Dalmatischen Inseln', *Geog. Ges. in Munchen*, XXI, 1928. pp. 127–58.
O.N.U., F.A.O. *Project F.A.O. de developpment méditerranéen. Yougoslavie, rapport national.* Belgrade, 1959. 130 pp.
ORTOLANI, M. 'Le isole dalmate', *R.G.I.*, LV, 1948. pp. 186–203; 255–76.

CHAPTER 20

MEDITERRANEAN FRANCE

ATLASES AND MAPS

Comité National de Géographie. Atlas de France, commenced in 1933; latest edition, 1961. Invaluable source of data.

French topographic maps are of the highest standards. Most of the Midi is now covered by the 1/50,000 sheets.

INSTITUT GEOGRAPHIQUE NATIONAL (formerly ¡Service Geographique de l'Armee):
— Carte d'État-Major, 1/80,000. Issued in 1818–78, and revised periodically since.
— Nouvelle Carte de France, 1/50,000. First produced in 1922 and still being completed for the whole country. G.S.G.S. 1/50,000 sheets, however, are enlarged from the old 1/80,000 edn.
— 1/100,000. Issued since 1922.
— 1/200,000. Types 1880, 1912.
— 1/250,000. Produced for the M. des Travaux, 1936 and copied by G.S.G.S. 4042. The G.S.G.S. 2738 series on same scale were recast from the 1914/18 series.
— 1/500,000. Produced in 1871 and 1925.
— 1/1 million. G.S.G.S. 2758.
SERVICE DE LA CARTE GÉOLOGIQUE. 1/80,000. Geological detail superimposed on the topographic sheets.
— 1/50,000. Issued since 1945.
— 1/500,000. Detail superimposed in colours upon black edition of 1871.
— 1/1 million. First edition, 1905, latest, 1961.
INSTITUT GEOGRAPHIQUE NATIONAL. Carte de la Vegetation de la France,
— 1/1 million. First edition, 1905, latest, 1961.
1/200,000. A few sheets have appeared, prepared by H. Gaussen.

Numerous specialised maps usually at scales of 1/1,4000,000 or larger have been prepared by various government departments. For more detailed reference to topographic maps see Naval Intelligence Division, Geographical Handbooks, vol. 1. France. pp. 233–51.
Probably no other region of the Mediterranean has such a voluminous literature. References can only be very selective.

Bibliographies are contained in several general works but note especially MARRES, P. 'Bibliographie géographique de Languedoc Mediterranéene et du Roussillon', *B.S.G.L.*, XIX. 1948. pp. 12–45.

GENERAL WORKS

BAULIG, H. *Le Sud-Est du Massif Central*, Excursion A2, Congrès Int. Géog. Paris, 1931. 26 pp.
BÉNÉVENT, E. *Provence Rhodanienne et Littorale*, Excursion B3, Congrès Int. Géog. Paris, 1931. 35 pp.
BLANCHARD, R. *Le comté de Nice, étude géographique.* 1960.
CARRÈRE, P. et DUGRAND, R. *La Région Méditerranée.* Paris, 1960. 160 pp. [A useful outline of demographic and economic features.]
DEMANGEON, A. *France économique et humaine.* Paris, 1946–48. Géog. Universelle, tome VI. Part I, 1946, pp. 348–68; part II, 1948, pp. 507–38, 629–50, 771–7. [A fundamental work.]
DEFFONTAINES, P. and JEAN-BRUNHES DELAMARRE, M. *Atlas Aérien*, tome 1. Paris, 1955. 184 pp. [Excellent illustrations.]
DE MARTONNE, EMM. *France physique.* Paris, 1947. Géog. Universelle, tome VI. Part I, pp. 212–24, 237–41, 276–9, 308–10, 317–20, 365–6, 386, 405–6. [A standard work of first importance.]
DUGRAND, R. *Villes et Campagnes en Bas-Languedoc.* Paris, 1963. 638 pp. [An excellent doctorate work that appeared after this chapter was written.]
FAUCHER, D., ed. *La France tourisme*, tome 1. Paris, 1951. pp. 228–327. [Lucid and comprehensive.]
GEORGE, P. *La région du Bas-Rhône.* Paris, 1935. 691 pp. [Doctorate thesis: his views on erosion surfaces are debatable.]

— *Etudes géographique sur le Bas-Languedoc: La région montpelliéraine.* Paris, 1938. 148 pp.

LAUTIER, G. *Le Sud-Ouest méditerranéen (Bas Languedoc et Roussillon).* Paris, 1928. 186 pp.

LENTHÉRIC, C. *The Riviera, ancient and modern,* trans. by C. West. London, 1895. 540 pp.

LIVET, R. *Habitat rural et structures agraires en Basse-Provence.* Aix-en-Provence, 1962. 465 pp. [A doctorate thesis that appeared after this chapter was written.]

MONKHOUSE, F. J. A. *Regional Geography of Western Europe.* London, 1959. pp. 401–46. [A useful factual outline.]

SION, J. *La France Méditerranéenne.* Paris, 1934. 222 pp. [Contains a useful bibliography.]

SELECTED REFERENCES

1. BLANCHARD, R. 'La limite septentrionale de l'olivier dans les Alpes française', *La Géog.,* 1900. pp. 225–301.

2. GAUSSEN, H. 'Limite et écologie des pays méditerranéens', *F.A.O.-S.C.M.,* 55.

3. EMBERGER, L. 'Les limites de l'aire de végétation méditerranéene en France', *B.S.H.N.,* 78, 1943. pp. 159–80.
   See also RAMPAL, A. 'Les limites naturelles de la région provençale', *B.S.G. Marseille,* 41.

4. NICOD, J. 'Grandeur et decadence de l'oleiculture provencale', *R.G.A.,* 1956.

5. GIGNOUX, M. *Stratigraphic Geology,* trans. by G. G. Woodford. San Francisco, 1955. p. 428 et seq. [A standard work.]

6. GALTIER, G. 'La côte sableuse du Golfe du Lion', *B.S.L.G.,* XXIX, 1958. pp. 149–416. [This contains much useful material and comprehensive bibliography.]

7. BOURCART, J. 'Contribution à la connaissance du socle sous-marin de la France de long de la côte medit.', *Congrès Geol. Internat. C.R.* Algers, 1952, sect. IV, fasc. IV, 1953. pp. 25–64;
   also *Etude des sediments pliocènes et quaternaires du Roussillon.* Bull. des services de la carte géol. de la France et des topographies souterrains. No. 218, tome XLV, 1945. 82 pp.;
   and PERPILLOU, A. 'Un problème de morphologie sous-marine', *A. de G.,* 1947. pp. 241–63.

8. DENIZOT, G. 'Le Pliocène dans la vallée du Rhône', *E.R.,* XVII, 1952. pp. 327–57;
   also GEORGE, P. 'Essai de synthese de l'histoire morphologique des pays du Bas-Rhône et du Bas-Languedoc au Pliocène et au Quaternaire', *E.R.,* XVIII, 1943. pp. 181–9.

9. GEORGE, P. 'Les surfaces d'aplanissement dans la région du Bas-Rhône', *A. de G.,* XLII. 1933. pp. 477–88.
   also DENIZOT, G. 'Cycle pliocène et surface topographique antéquaternaire sur le sol français', *B.A.G.F.,* 106. 1937. pp. 82–91.

10. DENIZOT, G. 'Les anciens rivages de la Méditerranée française', *Bull. Int. Ocean,* 992. 1951. 56 pp.

11. MATTES, P. et alia, 'La XXXVIIᵉ Excursion Interuniversitaire', *A. de G.,* LXIII, 1954, pp. 321–38, 401–15.

12. TRICART, J. 'Paléoclimats quaternaires et morphologie climatique dans le Midi Méditerranéen', *E. und G.,* II, 1952. pp. 193–213.
    — 'Periglaciare et fluvioglaciare: essai de corrélation du Quaternaire de la Durance', *Mem. Doc. Centre Doc.* Paris 4, 1954. pp. 171–202.

13. RUSSELL, R. J. 'Geomorphology of the Rhône delta', *A.A.A.G.,* 1944. pp. 149–254;

also OLDHAM, R. D. 'The age and the origin of the lower Rhône', *Q.J.G.S.*, XC, 1934. pp. 445–61;
— 'Historic changes of the delta of the Rhône', *Q.J.G.S.*, LXXXVI, 1930. pp. 64–92;
and RAZARET, C. D. R. 'L'évolution actuelle du delta du Rhône', *C.R.A.S.*, 228, 1949. pp. 1238–9.

14. LENTHÉRIC, C. 'Le Littoral d'Aigues-Mortes au XIIIme et au XIVme siècle', *Mem. Acad. du Gard.* 1869. pp. 173–233.

15. ARBOS, PH. 'La Plaine du Roussillon', *A. de G.*, XIX. 1910. pp. 150–62.

16. MALAURIE, J. 'Le relief des Corbières Orientales', *A. de G.*, LIX, 1950. pp. 259–68.

17. BAULIG, H. *Le Sud-Est du Massif Central* (as above). p. 17.

18. BÉNÉVENT, E. 'La XXXVIIIe Excursion Géographique Interuniversitaire Basse Provence, Bas-Languedoc oriental', *A. de G.* 1954.

19. BOURCART, J. *De la frontière italienne à Antibes*, INQUA, Excursion c. Rome, 1953. pp. 14–15.

20. The classic study is the doctorate thesis of PARDÉ, M. *Le Régime du Rhône*, 2 vols. Lyon, 1925. 888 and 440 pp.

21. ROUGÉ, J. 'Hydrologie de l'Hérault', *B.S.L.G.*, XXX, 1959. pp. 3–193;
also QUESNEL, B. 'La défense contre les inondations en Roussillon, Confluent et Vallespir', *A.F.P.E.M.*, XII. 1946. pp. 81–103.

22. DE MARTONNE, E. *La France*, Paris, 1947, Géog. Universelle, tome VI. Part 1, 1947, pp. 317–21;
also GALTIER, G. *Le vignoble du Languedoc Med. et du Roussillon*, tome 1. Montpellier, 1960. pp. 38–81.

23. There are numerous important studies on plant geography, especially the following:
FLAHAULT, CH. 'La Distribution géographique de la végétation dans la région méditerranéene française', *Encycl. Biologique*, XVIII, Paris, 1937. 186 pp.
BRAUN-BLAQUET *et alii*. *Les Groupements Végétaux de la France méditerranéene*. 1952. 198 pp.

24. GAUSSEN, H. *La Végétation de la moitié orientale des Pyrénées. Sol, Climat. Végétation.* Paris, 1926. 560 pp.

25. HARDY, M. 'La Géographie et la Végétation du Languedoc entre l'Hérault et la Vidourle', *B.S.G.M.*, XXVI, 1903. pp. 121–267.

26. ARÈNES, J. *Les Associations Végétales de la Basse-Provence.* Paris, 1928. 248 pp.

27. MAGNE, M. 'Le Chataignier dans le Gard historique état actuel avenir', *Comm. du Chataignier, Bull. Tech. No. 5*, Nancy. 1958;
also MARCELIN, P. 'La prehistoire et la fôret dans les Cévennes', *R.E.F.*, 1939.
— 'Essai sur le deperissement de la châtaigneraie', *Semaine International de Chataignier.* Sept., 1950.

28. DUTILLOY, F. et SERRE, G. DE LA. *Région Méditerranée—partie orientale de la chaîne des Pyrénées et Corse*, Assoc. Nat. du Bois. Paris, 1947. 59 pp.

29. BÉNÉVENT, E. 'La vielle économie provençale', *R.G.A.*, 1938. pp. 531–71.

30. On soils see especially:
BORDAS, J. *Essai d'agronomie méditerranéenne.* Avignon, 1946. 290 pp.
— *Les Sols de la région du Bas-Rhône.* Paris, 1943.
MARCELIN, P. *Terres et Sols en Costiere.* Nîmes, 1947.

31. STRABO,

32. DICKINSON, O. *Les espèces survivantes tertiares du Bas-Languedoc.* Montpellier, 1934. 159 pp.

33. AYMARD, A. 'L'interdiction des plantations de vignes en Gaule Narbonnaise', *Mélanges Faucher*, 1. pp. 27–47;

see also GALTIER, G. 'La création du vignoble Languedocien', *Cahiers de Préhistoire et d'Archéologie*, 1959. pp. 121–42.

34. GEORGE, P. 'Anciennes et nouvelles fôrets en région médit', *E.R.*, IX, 1933. pp. 85–120.

35. SION, J. 'Sur la structure agraire de la France Médit', *B.S.L.G.*, VIII, 1937. pp. 111–31; IX, 1938. pp. 8–11;

also BERNARD, J. 'Contribution à l'étude de la structure agraire de la plaine littorale Montpelliéraine, *B.S.G.L.*, XXVIII, 1957. pp. 175–241, 249–338.

36. JOURDAIN, F. 'La Plaine entre Montpellier et le bassin de Thau, *B.S.L.G.*, 1959. pp. 197–363.

37. NICOD, J. 'Les Chemins ruraux en Basse-Provence', in *Mélanges Géog. offerts au Doyen E. Bénévent*, 1954. pp. 271–87.

38. LENTHERIC, C. *Les Villes mortes du golfe de Lyon*, 6th edn. Paris, 1898. 524 pp.

39. PEYRE, M. 'Irrigation de la Basse Durance', *A. de G.*, XXXVII. 1927. pp. 40–57.

40. LIVET, R. 'Les chemins ruraux en Basse-Provence', *Mélanges . . . á E. Bénévent* (as above). pp. 241–53.

41. SORRE, M. 'La transhumance dans la région montpelliéraine,' *B.S.L.G.*, 1912. pp. 1–40;

also FOURNIER, J. 'Les chemins de transhumance . . . au XVIIIᵉ siècle', *Bull. de Géog. Hist.*, 1900. p. 25.

42. DAINVILLE, F. DE. 'Cartes anciennes du Languedoc (XVI–XVIII siècles)', *B.S.L.G.*, XXXI, 1960. pp. 87–303;

also DAINVILLE, F. DE. 'La carte de Cassini et son intérêt géographique', *B.A.G.F.*, 251, 1955. p. 138.

43. AGNEW, S. 'The vine in Bas Languedoc', *G.R.*, 1946. pp. 67–79.

44. YOUNG, A. *Voyages en France*, edit. see p. 687.

45. GALTIER, G. *Le vignoble du Languedoc* (see No. 22). [Tome I, pp. 123–6—has very comprehensive bibliography on the subject of the development of viticulture.]

46. NICOD, J. 'Grandeur et decadence de l'olei-culture' (see No. 4).

47. FONCIN, M. 'La culture des fleurs et primeurs sur la Côte d'Azur, *A. de G.*, XXV, 1916. pp. 241–62.

48. MEGY, R. 'Note sur Lavande, Lanvandin et Foire-Exposition dans les Basses Alpes', *Med.*, 1, 1960. pp. 120–4.

49. GEORGES, P. 'Problèmes, agricoles de l'aménagement hydrauliques du Bas-Rhône', *Melanges à E. Bénévent, op. cit.* pp. 223–33;

also PRÉVOT, V. 'La culture du riz de Camargue', *L'Inform. Géog.*, 1953. pp. 13–20.

50. GRAVIER, J. F. et PERRIN, N. 'L'aménagement du Bas-Rhône et du Languedoc', in Institut nat. d'études démog., *Région Languedoc Roussillon*, No. 30. Paris, 1957. pp. 47–60.

51. Three important studies of population are:

PRESSAT, R. 'La population, situation actuelle et prospectives', *Région Languedoc Roussillon, op. cit.* pp. 25–46.

CARRÈRE, P. at DUGRAND, R. *La Region Mediterranée* (see General Works). pp. 24–49.

ACHER, G. 'L'évolution du peuplement dans le department des Alpes Maritimes', *R.G.A.*, 44. 1956. pp. 497–522.

CALLON, M. G. 'Le mouvement de la population de la des Bouches-du-Rhône', *B.S.G.E.C.*, Marseille 51, 1930. pp. 5–35.

52. AGNEW, S. 'Rural Settlement in Bas Languedoc', *G.*, 1946. pp. 65–74.

53. See careful historic study of BRUTAILS, J. A. '*Étude sur la condition des populations rurales en Roussillon au Moyen Age*. 1891.

54. MERCIER, J. 'L'Habitation rurale provençale—le vent et le soleil', *R.G.A.*, XXXI, 1943. pp. 525–33.

55. LIVET, R. *Habitat rural, op. cit.*

56. Two useful summaries of the towns are given in SION J. *La France Médit.* (see General Works). pp. 174–201; and DEMANGEON, A. *France Humaine* (see General Works), part I, pp. 361–3, 364–8; part II, pp. 510–18, 531–3, 629–48.

57. BERNE, P. 'Aigues Mortes et ses environs', *B.S.L.G.*, 2, VI. 1935. pp. 61–96; see also 'Les villes militaires de Bas-Languedoc', *B.S.L.G.*, XL, 1917. pp. 42–66, 109–45, 263–495.

58. CARRÈRE et DUGRAND, *op. cit.* p. 41.

59. INSTITUT GÉOGRAPHIQUE NATIONAL, *Régions géographiques de la France*, Paris, 1950.

60. BIROT, P. *Recherches sur la morphologie des Pyrénées Orientales franco-espagnoles.* Paris, 1937. 318 pp.; and SORRE, M. *Les Pyrénées Méditerranéenes, étude de géographie biologique.* Paris, 1913. 508 pp.

61. BÉNÉVENT, E., *Languedoc.* Visages des Provences, 1950, pp. 5–52.

62. JOURDAIN, F. 'La Plaine entre Montpellier et le bassin de Thau', *op .cit.*

63. GEORGE, P. 'La Gardiole. Étude morphologique', *B.A.G.F.*, 98. 1936. pp. 92–99.

64. MARRES, P. *La Costière du Gard.* Nîmes, 1950. 19 pp.

65. BILLANGES, A. 'Au sujet des garrigues Languedociennes', *E.R.*, 20, 1945. pp. 125–6.

66. MARRES, P. 'La modernisation de l'économie du Bas-Languedoc et des Cévennes méridionales, *B.S.L.G.*, XXV, 1954. pp. 5–47.

67. — 'Modernisation de la vie rurale cévenole' *Mélanges . . . à E. Bénévent.* 1954. pp. 255–69.

68. BAULIG, H. 'La Crau et la glaciation Würmienne', *A. de G.*, XXXVI, 1927. pp. 499–508.

69. Other studies on the Rhône delta not already referred to are:
FRANÇOIS, L. 'Évolution actuelle des emboucheurs du Rhône et des côtes de Camargue', *B.A.G.F.*, 74, 1931. pp. 134–7.
— 'L'Etude sur l'évolution actuelle des côtes de Camargue', *E.R.*, XIII, 1937. pp. 71–126.
KRUIT, C. *Sediments of the Rhône delta.* The Hague, 1955. 140 pp.

70. GEORGES, P. 'Les paysages et l'évolution géographique de la Camargue', *Le Chêne*, 16, 1930. pp. 3–15; also GIBB, R. W. 'La Camargue', *G.*, 27, 1942. pp. 63–6; and PRÉVOT, V. 'La culture du riz. de Camargue', *L'Inf. Géog.*, 17, 1953. pp. 13–20.

71. RONCAYOLO, M. 'Evolution de la banlieue marseillaise dans la basse vallée de l'Huveaune', *A. de G.*, LXI, 1952. pp. 342–56.

72. VASSEUR, L. V. 'Le port de Marseille', *L'Inf. Géog.* 1958.

73. BÉNÉVENT, E. 'Sur l'agencement et l'évolution du relief de la Basse-Provence calcaire', *A. de G.*, XLVI, 1937. pp. 494–508.
See also:
BAILEY, E. 'Some aspects of Provencal tectonics', *Q.J.G.S.*, 108, 1952. pp. 135–55.
DUFAURE, J. J 'Contacts entre Provence cristalline, Provence calcaire et Prealpes du sud', *B.A.G.F.*, 278, 9, 1958. pp. 63–79.
LUTAUD, L. 'La tectogenèse et l'évolution structurale de la Provence', *R.G.P.G.D.*, 2me Ser. 1, 1957. pp. 103–12.

74. VAUMAS, E. DE. 'Le relief de la Sainte-Baume', *A. de G.*, XLVI, 1937. pp. 580–90.

75. BILLEREY, A. 'Un rejeu quaternaire de la montagne Ste. Victoire', *Médit.*, 1, 1960. pp. 3–13.

76. JOURNAUX, A. 'Etude morphologique de la basse vallée de l'Aix', *B.A.G.F.*, 218–9, 1951. pp. 108–16.
77. QUENIN, A. 'Les fôrets provençales—leur défense contre l'incendie', *B.S.G.M.*, 49, 1928. pp. 1–23;
   also NICOD, J. 'Sur le rôle de l'homme dans la dégradation des sols et du tapis végétal en Basse-Provence calcaire', *R.G.A.*, 39, 1956. pp. 739–48.
78. SELAFERT, T. 'Usages agraires dans les régions provençales avant le XVIIIᵉ siècle—les assolements', *R.G.A.*, 29, 1941. pp. 471–92;
   also PERPILLON, A. 'Types d'évolution de quelques paysages agricoles médit', *Mélanges . . . à E. Bénévent, op. cit.*
   and LAGET, G. DE. 'Paysages et gens de Provence', *G. Soc. G. et E. Col. Marseille*, 62, 1942–3. pp. 17–26.
80. CHARDONNET, J. 'La côte française de Marseille à Menten. Etude de morphologie littorale', *B.S.R.C.*, Egypte 23. 1950. pp. 185–264.
   — 'Les calanques provençales, origine et divers types', *A. de G.*, LVII, 1948. pp. 289–97.
   CORBEL, J. 'Un karst méditerranée de basse altitude—le massif des Calanques', *R.G.L.*, XXXI, 1956. pp. 129–36.
81. MASUREL, Y. 'Observations sur la structure et la morphologie des îles d'Hyènes', *A. de G.*, LXII, 1953. pp. 241–58.
82. BÉRARD, A. 'Les conditions des establissements maritimes sur la côte de Provence dans l'antiquité', *A. de G.*, XXXVI, 1927. pp. 413–35.
83. CHARDONNET, J. *Les Massifs anciens Provencaux, étude morphologique*, Inf. Géog. Nat. Paris, 1952. 30 pp.
84. DUTILLOY and SERRE, *op. cit.* (see No. 28).
85. JUILLARD, E. 'La côte des Maures, son évolution économique et sociale depuis cent ans', *R.G.A.*, XLV, 1957. pp. 289–350.
86. TESSIER, L. F. 'La végétation des Alpes Maritimes', *La G.B.S.G.*, XXVIII, 1913. pp. 119–25.
87. DEWITTE, J. *The Story of the Four towns, Nice, Monaco, Cannes and Menten*; also BENIAMINO, O. 'Nice et Antiles—capitales azuréennes', *R.G.A.*, XXXVIII, 1958. pp. 495–508.

CHAPTER 21

THE ISLANDS OF THE WESTERN MEDITERRANEAN

MAPS

For atlases and maps see under appropriate countries.

GENERAL REFERENCES

AUBERT DE LA RUE, E. *L'homme et les Îles*. Paris, 1935. 191 pp.
MENSCHING, H. 'Mallorca—Korsika—Sardinien', *Die Erde*, VIII, 1956. pp. 39–52.

Corsica

ALBITRECCHIA, A. *La Corse*. Paris, 1933. [An authoritative work.]
— 'Bonifacio', *B.A.G.F.*, 28, 1940. pp. 38–44.
ALLORGE, P., ed. *Histoire de peuplement de la Corse. Étude biogéographie*. Paris, 1926.
ANFOSSI, M. G. 'Recherches sur la distribution de la population en Corse', *R.G.A.*, VI, 1918. pp. 71–135.

ARRIGHI, M. 'Le pays de Porto et de Sagone', *A. de G.*, XLII, 1933. pp. 500–5.

BIROT, P. and JÉREMINE, E., Recherches sut le comportement de l'érosion différentielle dans les roches granitiques de Corse, *C.I.G.* Lisbon, 11, 1949, p. 243.

BLACHE, J. 'Les grands traits de la morphologie de la Corse', *R.G.A.*, XX, 1932. pp. 627–53.

BOTTIGLIONI, G. *Atlante linguistico etnografico Italiana della Corsica.* Pisa, 1933. [A monumental ethnic study in 7 vols. and with 1,400 maps (1/400,000).]

BOURCART, J. 'Essai de carte sous-marine de l'oust de la Corse', *R.G.P.G.D.*, 1957. pp. 31–6.

CARLOTTI, J. *Monographie agricole de la Corse.* Ajaccio, 1936. [The only survey of its kind for Corsica.]

COPPOLANI, J. 'Cargese', *R.G.A.*, XXXVII, 1949. pp. 70–106.

DRESCH, J. 'Les anciens glaciers corses', *B.A.G.F.*, 140–1. 1941. pp. 115–20.

FAUCHER, D., ed. *La France Geographie Tourisme,* vol. 1. Paris, 1951. pp. 261–7.

GUISLAIN, A. 'La forèt Corse', *Rev. et. forêts.*, 3. 1955–6.

KLAERE, W. *Verwitterungsformen im Granit auf Korsika,* Petermanns G. Mitt., 261, 1956. 146 pp. [A detailed study of granite weathering.]

LEFEBVRE, P. 'La population de la Corse', *R.G.A.*, XLV, 1957. pp. 557–75.

MEJEAN, P. 'Notes sur la Maison Corse', *R.G.A.*, XX, 1932, pp. 655–76.

METRO, A. 'Les Suberais de la Corse', *FAO/SCM/LG./2–B.* 1958.

OTTMAN, F., see p. 734 no. 39. [Fundamental on chronology.]

PIERETTI, A. 'Les forms d'exploitation et de peuplement d'une plaine Mediterranean', *Bol. Soc. Géog. et Écon. Col.* Marseille, 63, 1947. pp. 7–20.

— 'En Corse—le desert des Agriates', *R.G. Lyon,* 26, 1951. pp. 155–63.

ROL, R. 'La vegetation forestière de la Corse', *R.F.F.*, 12, 1955.

RONDEAU, A. 'Problèmes de morphologie régionale en Corse', *B.A.G.F.*, 257/8, 1956. pp. 49–61. [A useful up-to-date summary.]

SIMI, P. 'Nebbio', *R.G.A.*, XLV, 1957. pp. 711–62.

VILLAT, L. *et alii,* eds. *Visages de la Corse.* Paris, 1951. [A popular summary of its geography and history.]

VILLIEN-ROSSIE, M. L. *Petite Géographie du départment de la Corse.* Paris, 1949. [A school textbook.]

WAGNER, G. 'The island that does not want to die', *Yale Review,* 50, 1961. pp. 405–15.

Sardinia

ASOLI, A. and PINNA, M. *Contributi alla geografia della Sardegna.* Univ. di Cagliari, 1951. 37 pp.

Atti del XII Congresso geofrafico italiano, 1934. Cagliari, 1935. [Contains many articles on Sardinia—see note in *G.J.*, LXXXVIII.]

BALDACCI, O. *Le casa rurale in Sardegna.* Rome, 1952. 22 pp. [Indispensable to the study of house types.]

BEGUINOT, A. 'Le macchia-foresta nella Sardegna settentrionale edi suoi principali tipi', *Bull. Ist. R. Univ. di Sassari,* vol. 1, mem. VIII. 1923.

DEL RIO, C. 'La Barbagia', *R.G.I.*, 48, 1941. pp. 262–71.

DOZIER, C. L. 'Establishing a framework for development in Sardinia: the Campidano', *G.R.*, 1957. pp. 490–506.

LE LANNOU, M. *Pâtres et Paysans de la Sardaigne.* Tours, 1941. 364 pp. [An excellent study in human geography.]

— 'Récherches morphologiques en Sardaigne', *A. de G.*, LII, 1943. pp. 33–48.

— 'Sardaigne', *R.G. Lyon,* 26, 1951. pp. 113–29.

— and PELLETIER, J. 'La XLII Excursión Géographique Interuniversitaire vieille et nouvelle Sardaigne', *A. de G.*, LXIX, 1960. pp. 561–83.

'L'Escursione in Sardegna della Soc. Geog. Ital.', *B.S.G.I.*, 1956. pp. 300–43.

LEVI, D. 'Sardinia: Isle of Antithesis', *G.R.*, 1943, pp. 630–54.

LILLIU, G. 'The Nuraghi of Sardinia', *Ant.*, 33. 1959. pp. 32–8.

MARROU, H. I. 'Un historian en Sardaigne', *R.G. Lyon*, 26, 1951. pp. 141–6.

MILONE, F. *L'Italia nell Economia delle sue Regions*. Turin, 1955. pp. 1032–91. [A useful summary of economic changes.]

MORI, A. *Le saline della Sardegna*, Mem. Geog. Econ. Naples, 3, 1950. 124 pp.

— and SPANO, B. *I Porti della Sardegna*, Mém. Geog. Econ. Naples, 1952. 237 pp.

PAMPALONI, E. *L'Economia agraria delle Sardegna*. Rome, 1947. 273 pp. [A fundamental study on agrarian matters.]

PELLETIER, J. 'Notes sur la morphologie de la Gallura', *R.G. Lyon*, 26, 1951. pp.147–53.

— *Le relief de la Sardaigne*, Mem. et Doc. de l'Inst. d'Etudes rhod., 13. Lyons, 1960. [The first comprehensive study of modern morphological problems in Sardinia.]

PINNA, M. *Il Clima della Sardegna*, Pub. Ist. Geog. Univ. Pisa, 1954. 104 pp.

— and CORDA, L. *La distribuzione della popolazione e i centri abitati della Sardegna*. Pub. Ist. Geog. Univ. Pisa, 1956–7. 190 pp. [Both these memoirs are fundamental on their respective subjects.]

SCHEU, E. 'Sardinien. Landeskundliche Beitrage', *Mitt. der Gesellschaft fur Erdkunde zu Leipzig fur 1919 bis 1922.*

SPANO, B. *Le Gallura*, Mem. Geog. Antrop. Rome, 13, 1947. 220 pp. [The best study on this region.]

VARDABOSSO, S. 'Le peneplaine hercynienne de la Sardaigne du Centre Est', *R.G., Lyon*, 26, 1951. pp. 113–29.

VINELLI, M. 'Water Conservation in Sardinia', *G.R.* 1926. pp. 395–402.

WALKER, W. G., ed. *Sardinian Studies*. Le Play Society. London, 1938. 60 pp.

The Balearic Islands

BUTLAND, G. J., ed. 'Ibiza, a report of geographical field works', The Geog. Field Group, 1955. MS [A useful geographical summary of Ibiza.]

COLOM, G. *Biogeografía de las Balearics*. Palma, 1957. 568 pp. [A comprehensive work.]

DALLIMORE, W. 'Agriculture and Horticulture in Majorca', *Kew Bull. of Miscell. Inf.*, 9, 1927. pp. 369–74.

DARDER, B. and FALLOT, P. *L'Ile de Majorque*, Excursion C 5 XIVe Congrès Géol. Internat. Madrid, 1926.

FALLOT, P. *Étude géologique de las Sierra de Majorque*. Paris–Liège, 1922. 480 pp. [A fundamental work.]

— 'Le probleme de l'ile de Minorque', *B.S. Geol. Fr.*, IV, series 2, XXIII, 1923. pp. 3–44.

— 'Esquisse morphologique des iles Baleares', *R.G.A.*, XI, 1923. pp. 421–48. [A useful morphological summary.]

FOSTER, G. M. 'The Feixes of Ibiza', *G.R.*, 1952. pp. 227–37.

GILBERT, E. W. 'The Human Geography of Mallorca', *S.G.M.*, 50. 1934. pp. 129–42.

— 'Influences of the British Occupation on the Human Geography of Menorca', *S.G.M.*, 52, 1936. pp. 375–90.

INQUA. V Congrès Internat. Livret Guide de l'Excursion L, *Levant et Majorque*. Madrid–Barcelona, 1957. 52 pp. [Contains exhaustive bibliography on the Quaternary.]

KNOCHE, H. *Flora Balearica: Étude Phytogéographique sur les Îles Baleares*, 4 vols. 1921–3. [The fundamental botanical study of the Balearics.]

MENSCHING, H. 'Karst y Terra Rossa en Mallorca', *E.G.*, XVII, 1956. pp. 659–72.

MONBEIG, P. 'Vie de relations et specialisation agricole. Les Baleares an XVIIIe siècle', *A.H.E.S.*, IV, 1932. pp. 538–48.

RIBAS DE PINA, M. 'El habitat rural en le Isla de Mallorca a fins del siglo XVIII y en la actualidad', *B.S.G.N.*, 72, 1932. pp. 259–88.

RICCARDI, R. 'Viaggro a Maiorca', *B.R.S.G.*, VI, 1931. pp. 747–61.

VILAR, P. 'Le clima de Minorque', *R.G.A.*, XXI, 1933. pp. 831–39.

VILA VALENTÍN, J. 'Formentera. Estudio de Geografía Humana', *E.G.*, XI, 1950. pp. 389–442.

— 'Ibiza y Formentera, Islas de la Sal', *E.G.*, XIV, 1953. pp. 3–48.

The Maltese Islands

BOWEN-JONES, H. *et alii. Malta.* Durham, 1961. 356 pp. [Comprehensive survey of land use, which has appeared since this section was written.]

BULMER, B. F. and STORMONTH, K. *The Rainfall of Malta.* Air Ministry Meteorol. Office, scientific paper No. 3. London, 1960. 20 pp.

BUXTON, L. H. D. 'Malta: an anthropogeographical study', *G.R.*, 1924. pp. 75–87.

Central Office of Statistics. *Census of Production for 1955.* Valletta, 1958. 139 pp.

— *Census of Agriculture, 1957.* Valletta, 1959. 52 pp.

— *Census 1957, The Maltese Islands. Report on Population and Housing.* Valletta, 1960. 276 pp.

EVANS, J. V. *Malta.* London, 1959. 256 pp. [An archaeological summary.]

FLEMING, J. B. 'Notes on Rural Malta', *S.G.M.*, LXII, 1946. pp. 56–60.

HOBBS, W. H. 'The Maltese Islands: a tectonic-topographic study', *S.G.M.*, XXX, 1914. pp. 1–13.

HYDE, H. P. T. 'Malta', *Die Erde*, V, 1953, pp. 224–40.

LANG, D. M. *Soils of Malta and Gozo.* H.M.S.O. London, 1960. [Includes soils map.]

MORRIS, T. L. *The Water Supply Resources of Malta.* Valletta, 1951. 125 pp.

MURRAY, J. 'The Maltese Islands with special reference to their geological structure', *S.G.M.*, VI, 1890. pp. 440–88.

REED, F. R. C. *The Geology of the British Empire.* London, 1921. pp. 7–14.

ROBINSON, G. W. S. 'The Distribution of Population in the Maltese Islands', *G.*, XXXIII, 1948. pp. 69–78. [A useful summary of Malta's population problems.]

PART V: NORTH-WEST AFRICA (THE MAGHREB)

CHAPTER 22

THE MAGHREB—ITS LANDFORMS AND ECOLOGICAL FEATURES

ATLASES AND MAPS

Atlas des Colonies Françaises, Protectorats, et territoires sous mandat de la France. Paris, 1932. [Text and maps.]

Algérie: Atlas historique, géographique, et économique. Paris, 1934. [Text and maps.]

Tunisie: Atlas historique, géographique, et économique. Paris, 1936.

Atlas du Maroc. [This is in preparation with total of 54 sheets, together with a useful series of commentaries, for each sheet. Comité de Géographie du Maroc, Rabat.

Carte Géologique Internationale de l'Afrique (1/5,000,000). Paris, 1936.

Carte Géologique du Nord-Ouest de l'Afrique XIX Internat. Geol. Congress, Algiers. 1952 (2 sheets, 1/2,000,000).

Institut Géographique National. Carte du Sahara (2 sheets, 1/100,000). 1961.
Institut Géographique National Maroc, Tunisie 1/50,000.
Michelin Maroc, Algérie-Tunisie (2 sheets, 1/1,000,000). 1955-6, 1958.
Service de la Carte Géologique (1/50,000 sheets and 'memoirs'—a few sheets).
Service des Mines Carte Géologique (1/1,500,000). 1936.
Service des Mines de l'Industrie et de l'Énergie. Carte géologique de la Tunisie (1/500,000). 1951 (3) and booklet.
Service Géographique de l'Armee and subsequently Institut Géographique National have published various topographical maps:
  1:500,000 all the Maghreb; also new editions.
  1:200,000 regular edition covers all Algeria and Tunisia but there is only a pro-visional edition for Morocco.
  1:100,000 all Tunisia except extreme north and south. Provisional edition for rest of Morocco, except south.
  1:50,000 all Algerian and Tunisian Tell, and coastal area of Morocco; only some areas of interior.
Servicio Geográfico del Ejercito has provisional edition of the former Spanish Morocco (1/50,000). 1928-59.
Many of the topographical maps of varying scale, have also been reproduced by the Geographical Section, General Staff.

Délégation Générale du Gouvernement en Algérie. *Algérie Limites Administratives* (1/600,000). 1960, 2 sheets.
— *Voies de Communication* (1/1,500,000). 1960, 1 sheet.
GAUSSEN, H. and VERNARD, A. *Carte des pluies en Algerie au 1/500,000.* 1958.
— *Carte des pluies en Tunisie en 1/500,000.* 1958.
— *Carte internationale du tapis vegetal a 1/1,000,000* with some sheet pamphlets.
Inspection Générale de l'Agriculture. *Carte de Reconnaissance des Sols d'Algérie* (1/200,000). 1955, 3 sheets and booklets.
— *Carte des Sols d'Algérie* (1/500,000). 1954, 7 sheets and booklets.
Institut Geographique National. *Carte des Tribus* (Maroc) (1/500,000). 1958.
MAIRE, R. *Carte phytogéographique de l'Algérie et de la Tunisie.* Alger, 1926, with booklet.
PEYERIMHOFF, P. DE. *Carte forestière de l'Algérie et de la Tunisie.* Alger, 1941, with booklet.

GENERAL WORKS

DESPOIS, J. *L'Afrique du Nord*, 2nd edn. Paris, 1958. 624 pp.
DRESCH, J. 'L'Afrique du Nord: Les Problèmes Physiques', in BIROT, P. and DRESCH, J. *La Mediterranée Occidentale.* Paris, 1953. pp. 391–452.
[These are the two best works and have comprehensive bibliographies.]
There are numerous other general works but the best are:
BERNARD, A. *L'Afrique du Nord.* Géographie Universelle, tome XI, part 1. Paris, 1937. 284 pp.
CÉLÉRIER, J. *Le Maroc.* Paris, 1948. 180 pp.
DESPOIS, J. *La Tunisie.* Paris, 1961. 224 pp.
DRESCH, J. GIGOUT, M., JOLY, F., LE COZ, J. and RAYNAL, R. *Aspects de la géo-morphologie du Maroc*, Notes et Memoires, No. 96, Division des Mines et de la Géologie, Service Géologique. Casablanca, 1952. 182 pp.
L'Encyclopédie coloniale et maritime, 4 vols. Paris, 1946-7.
LARNAUDE, M. *Algérie.* Paris, 1950. 230 pp.
MENSCHING, H. *Marokko, die Landschaften in Maghreb.* Heidelberg, 1958. 254 pp.
Naval Intelligence. *Geographical Handbook* (on the three territories, 5 volumes 1942).

Useful also are the excursion guides of the International Geological Congress, Algiers, 1952, and *Excursion B4 Algeria, Sahara Algérien*, of the International Geography Union Congress, Paris, 1931.

REGIONAL MONOGRAPHS

COQUE, R. *La Tunisie Presaharienne, étude géomorphologique.* Paris, 1962. 476 pp. [Fundamental on Quaternary morphology.]

DESPOIS, J. *La Tunisie orientale, Sahel et Basse Steppe.* Paris, 1940. 616 pp.

— *Le Hodna.* Paris, 1953. 409 pp.

DRESCH, J. *Essai sur l'évolution du relief dans la región prérifaine.* Paris, 1933. 156 pp.

— *Recherches sur l'évolution du relief dans le massif central du Grand Atlas, le Haouz et le Sous.* Paris, 1941. 708 pp. [Both fundamental works.]

JOLY, F. *Études sur le relief du sud-est marocain.* Trans. Inst. Sc. Chérif., No. 10. Rabat, 1962. [Detailed geological and morphological study of an area unknown before 1942.]

POUQUET, J. *Les Monts du Tessala. Essai Morphogénétique.* Paris, 1952. 351 pp.

RAYNAL, R. *Plaines et Piedmonts du Bassin de la Moulouya—Étude Géomorphologique.* Rabat, 1961. 617 pp. [Fundamental on study of pediments.]

SELTZER, P. *Le climat de l'Algerie.* Algiers, 1946. 219 pp. [The only significant, regional study of climate in North Africa.]

REFERENCES

1. BOURCART, J. 'Les peneplaines du Maroc et du Sahara', *Mél. Gautier*, 1937. pp. 55–75.

2. BIROT, P. and JOLY, F. 'Observations sur le glacis d'erosion et les reliefs granitiques au Maroc', *Mém. et Doc. C.N.R.S., 1952.*

3. MARTONNE, E. DE, CÉLÉRIER, J. and CHARTON, A. 'Le massif de Rehamma', *A. de G.*, 1924.

4. FALLOT, P. and MARIN, A. *La Cordillera del Rif.* Madrid, 1939.

5. FURON, R. *Geologie de l'Afrique.* Paris, 1950. 349 pp. [See especially pp. 1–90.]

6. DRESCH, J. 'Stratigraphie et paleogeographie de l'Afrique du Nord', *A. de G.*, L1., 1942. pp. 304–12.

7. JOLY, R. *Études sur le relief du sud-est Marocain* (as above); also CHOUBERT, G. 'Note au sujet du terme Anti-Atlas', *R.G.M.*, 1943. pp. 20–37.

8. DRESCH, J. 'La structure de l'Afrique du Nord', *L'Inf. Géog.* 1942–5. pp. 46–53.

9. CASTANY, J. *Étude geologique de l'Atlas tunisien oriental.* Tunis, 1951. 632 pp. [A fundamental work on this subject.]

10. DALLONI, M. 'Notes sur la classification du Pliocène supérieur et du Quaternaire de l'Algérie', *B.S.G. Oran*, LXI, 1940. pp. 8–43.

11. DRESCH, J. *Recherches . . . sur . . . Grand Atlas . . . Sous* (See Regional Monographs).

12. CHOUBERT, G. 'Note preliminaire sur le Pontian au Maroc', *B.S.G.F.* 5e. ser. VX, 1945. pp. 677–774; also GLANGEAUD, L. 'Les surfaces d'aplanissement d'âge tertiaire dans le nord de la province d'Alger et leurs deformations', *C.R.C.I. de géog.*, 11. Paris, 1931. pp. 571–87.

13. A useful summary of views is contained in ASWAD, H. 'Some aspects of the geomorphology of Morocco related to the Quaternary climate', *G.J.*, CXXIX, 1963. pp. 129–39.

14. DRESCH, J. 'Forms et limites climatiques et paléoclimatiques en Afrique du Nord', *A. de G.*, LXII, 1954. pp. 56–9.

15. — 'Les changements de climat et les mouvements du sol en Afrique du Nord au cours du Plio-Quaternaire', *I.G.*, 24, 1960. pp. 107–13.

16. COQUE, R. *La Tunisie Pré-Saharienne, op. cit.* p. 419.

17. DRESCH, J. 'Sur les pediments en Afrique Méditerranéenne et tropicale', *C.R.C.I. de géog.*, I, Lisbon, 1949. pp. 19–28.

18. MENSCHING, H. 'Glacis, Fussflache in Marokko', *Petermanns Geog. Mitt.*, 98, 1954. pp. 171–6.

19. JOLY, F. 'Pédiments et glacis d'erosion dans le sud du Maroc', *C.R.C.I. géog.*, I, Lisbon, 1949. pp. 110–25; also COQUE, R. 'Glacis d'erosion dans le sud tunisien', *C.R.C.I. géog.* Rio de Janiero, 1956. *Resumé comm.* pp. 28–9.

20. There is now a growing volume of research on the N. African crusts, chief of which are as follows:

    DURAND, J. *Étude géologique, hydrogéologique et pédologique des croutes en Algérie*, Gvt. Gén. Algérie. Algiers, 1953. 209 pp.

    — *Les croutes calcaires s.l. d'Afrique du Nord etudiés a la lumière de la Bio-Rhexistasie*, Gvt. Gen. Algérie. Algiers, 1957. 23 pp.

    also COQUE, R. 'les croûtes gypseuses du Sud tunisien', *Bull. Soc. Sc. nat. Tunisie*, VIII, 1955. pp. 217–36.

21. CHOUBERT, G. at alii. 'Essai de classification du Quaternaire continental du Maroc', *C.R. Acad. Sci*, 243. Paris, 1956. pp. 504–6.

22. COQUE, *La Tunisie Pre-saharienne* (see No. 16). p. 363.

23. LEROIR-GOURHAN, A. 'Resultats de l'analyse pollinique du gisement d'El Guettar', *Bull. Soc. pré hist. fr. LV*, 1958. pp. 546–51.

24. JOLY, F. 'Place des pays de Piedmont dans le vie economique et humaine du Maroc', *N.M.*, 13. 1960. pp. 97–102.

25. BÜDEL, J. 'Bericht Uber Klima-Morphologische und Eizeitforschungen in Nieder-Afrika', *Erd.* 1950–1. pp. 104–14.

26. MENSCHING, H. *Das Quartär in den Gebergen Marokkos.* Petermanns Mitt. Ergzh., 256. Gotha, 1956.

27. PUJOSA, A. 'Terres rouges, noires, grises, problèmes de coloration et de datation des sols méditerranéens étudiés en Afrique du Nord', *Soc. Sc. nat. et phys. du Maroc: Trav. section de Pedologie*, 12, 1955. pp. 71–96.

28. CÉLÉRIER, J. and CHARTON, 'Profils en long des course d'eau morocains', *A. de G.* 1924. pp. 286–96; also GAUTIÊR, E. F. 'Profils en long des cours d'eau en Algérie-Tunisie, *A. de G.*, XX. 1911. pp. 351–431.

29. DUBIEF, J. *Essai sur l'hydrologie superficielle au Sahara*, Gvt. gen. de l'Algérie. Algiers. 457 pp.

30. DRESCH, J. 'Notes sur les formes glaciaires et periglaciaires dans le Moyen Atlas, le bassin de la Moulouya et le Haut Atlas oriental', *Notes Serv. geol. Maroc.*, 7, 1953. pp. 111–23.

31. MENSCHING, H. *Marokko* Heidelberg, 1958. pp. 29–30.

32. RAYNAL, R. 'Quelques aperçus sur l'existence et l'importance des phénomènes periglaciaires pre-wurmiens au Maroc', *Congrès et Colloques de l'Université de Liège*, 17, 1960. pp. 109–22.

33. For general outline, see MARTONNE, E. DE. 'La structure géographique de l'Afrique du Nord francaise', *A. de G.* 1933; also RUSSO, P. 'Le relief de l'Afrique du Nord', *E.R*, 1942.

34. FALLOT and MARIN. *La Cordillera del Rif.*

35. RAYNAL, R. *Plaines et Piedmonts du bassin de la Moulouya* (see Regional Monographs).

36. GAUTIER, M. *Structure de l'Algérie*. Paris, 1920. 240 pp.

37. POUQUET, J. *Les Monts du Tessala*. Paris, 1952. 351 pp.

38. GLANGEAUD, L. 'Les deformations plio-quaternaires de l'Afrique du Nord', *Geologische Rundschau*, 43–1. Stuttgart, 1955. pp. 181–96.

40. FICHEUR, E. *Description géologique de la Kabylie du Djurdjura, etude spéciale des terraines tertiaines*. Algiers, 1890. 476 pp.

41. SOLIGNAC, M. *Étude géologique de la Tunisie septentrionale*. 1927. 757 pp.

42. DRESCH, J. 'La region pre-rifaine. Essai morphologique', *A. de G.*, LXXIX, 1930. pp. 395–415.

43. TERMIER, H. *Études géologiques sur le Maroc central et le Moyen Atlas septentrional.* Rabat, 1936. 1,566 pp.

44. BEAUDET, G. 'Paysages et Problèmes morphologiques du Plateau Central Marocain', *N.M.*, 13, 1960. pp. 26–32.

45. MARIN, PH. 'Le Maroc Central; aperçu structural et orogénique', *N.M.*, 11, 1959. pp. 16–25.

46. MARTONNE, E. DE, CÉLÉRIER, J. and CHARTON, A. 'Le massif des Rehamna. Étude morphologique', *A. de G.*, XXXIII, 1924. pp. 244–56.

47. GIGNOUT, M. *Etudes géologiques sur la Méséta Marocaine Occidentale*, Trav. Inst. Sc. Chérif., 1. 1951. 507 pp.

48. GAUTIER, M. 'Le Moyen Atlas', *Hesp.* 1925–6.

49. DRESCH, J. *Recherches sur l'evolution du relief dans le Massif central du Grand Atlas* (see Regional Monographs).

50. DRESCH, J. 'De la Sierra Nevada au Grand Atlas. Formes glaciaires et forms de nivation', *Mél. Gautier.* pp. 194–212.

51. JOLY, A. 'Le plateau steppien d'Algérie. Relief et structure', *A. de G.*, XVIII, 1909. pp. 162–73, 238–52.

52. GAUTIER, M. *Le problème hydraulique du Chottech Chergui.* Algiers, 1947. 34 pp.

53. RAYNAL, R. *Plaines et piedmonts du bassin de la Moulouya* (see Regional Monographs).

54. RUSSO, P. 'La morphologie des Hauts plateaux de l'Est Marocain', *A. de G.*, LVI, 1947. pp. 36–48.

55. DESPOIS, J. *L'Afrique du Nord, op. cit.* p. 66.

56. — *Le Hodna* (see Regional Monographs).

57. MITARD, A. E. 'Grands traits géographiques de l'Aurès', *R.G.A.*, 1941. pp. 577–78; also MITARD, A. E. 'Considerations sur la subdivision morphologique de l'Algérie orientale', *R. Afr.*, LXXXI, 1937. pp. 561–70.

58. CASTANY, G. *Étude geologique de l'Atlas tunisien oriental* (see No. 9); also 'Les fosses quaternaires d'effondrement de Tunisie', *Int. Geol. Cong. Rept.*, XVIII Session, part XIII. London, 1948. pp. 38–44.

59. COQUE, R. *La Tunisie Présaharienne* (see Regional Monographs).

60. JOLY, R. *Études sur le Relief du Sud-Est Marocain* (as above).

61. — *et alii. Les Hamadas sud-Marocaines*, Trav. Inst. Sc. Chérif., 2, 1954. 289 pp.

Climate

62. PÉDELABORDE, P. and DELANNEY, H. 'Recherches sur les types de temps et le mecanisme des pluies en Algérie', *A. de G.*, LXVII, 1958. pp. 216–44.

63. REX, D. F. 'Blocking action in the middle troposphere and its effect upon regional climate', *Tellus.* 1950. p. 206.

64. QUENEY, P. 'Types de temps en Afrique du Nord et au Sahara septentrional', Trav. Inst. Mét. et Phys. Globe d'Algérie, No. 3, 1949. pp. 7–41.

65. CAPOT-REY, R. 'Études récentes sur le climat de l'Afrique du Nord et du Sahara', *A. de G.*, LV, 1946. pp. 39–48.

66. SELTZER, P. *Le climat de l'Algérie* (see Regional Monographs).

67. NOIN, D. 'Types de temps d'été au Maroc', *A. de G.*, LXXII, 1963. pp. 1–12.

68. ISNARD, H. 'La répartition saidonnière des pluies en Algéiie', *A. de G.*, LIX, 1960. pp. 354–61.

69. — 'La répartition saisonnière des pluies au Maroc', *A. de G.*, LXVII, 1958. pp. 39–42.

70. — 'La répartition saisonnière des pluies en Tunisie', *A. de G.*, LXI, 1952. pp. 357–62.

71. DEBRACH, J. and BIDAULT, G. 'Le climat de la montague marocaine', *Maroc médical*. 1939.

72. HOUSTON, J. M. 'The significance of irrigation in Morocco's economic development', *G.J.*, CXX, 1954. pp. 314–28.

73. DROUHIN, G. 'The problem of water resources in North-west Africa', *Arid Zone Programme*, 1. U.N.E.S.C.O., 1953. pp. 9–41.

74. TIXEROUT, J. *L'équipment de la Tunisie: 'Les Eaux souterraines'*, Direction des Travaux Publics. Tunis, 1950.

75. For an important bibliography on the subject see: WILBERT, J. 'Liste d'ouvrages et articles concernant l'étude des sols et ses divers aspects au Maroc et en Afrique du Nord', *Soc. Sc. Nat. et Phys. Travaux de la section de Pédologie*, tomes 13–14. Rabat, 1958–9. pp. 205–31.

76. DALLONI, M. *Géologie appliquée de l'Algérie*. Paris, 1939. 888 pp.; also PONCET, J. *Les rapports entre le modes d'reploitation agricole et l'erosion des sols en Tunisie*. Pub. Sec. d'État à l'Agric., No. 2. Tunis, 1962. 169 pp.

77. The fundamental work on N. African forests is: BOUDY, P. *Économie Forestière Nord Africaine*, 4 vols. Paris, 1948.

78. EMBERGER, L. 'Remarques critiques sur les étages de végétation dans les montagnes marocaines', *Ber. Schweiz. bot. Ges.*, XIVI, 1936. pp. 614–31.

79. BUDEL, J. 'Berich Uber Klima—Morphologische' (see No. 25). p. 106.

80. MAIRE, R. *Études sur la vegetation et la flore du Grand Atlas et du Moyen Atlas marocains*. Marseilles, 1924. 220 pp.

81. MIKESELL, M. W. *Northern Morocco, a cultural geography*. Berkeley, 1961. p. 28.

82. EMBERGER, L. 'Contribution à la connaissance des Cèdres', *Rev. de Bot. Appliq. et d'Agric.* Trop., 18, 1938. pp. 77–92.

83. PUJOS, A. 'Quelques applications des données de la géographie physique aux etudes d'ecologie vegetale', *R.G.M.*, 1962. pp. 87–91.

84. DE PEYERIMHOFF. *Carte forestière de l'Algérie et de la Tunisie* (with *Notice*). Algiers, 1941.

85. BRAUN-BLANQUET, J. and MAIRE, R. 'Études sur la végétation et la flore marocaines', *Bull. Soc. Bot. Fr.*, IXVIII, 1921. pp. 1–224.

86. EMBERGER, L. *Les Arbres du Maroc, et comment les reconnaître*. Paris, 1938. p. 117.

87. SUMMERS, T. W. 'Some impressions of Algerian Forestry', *Emp. For. Jour.*, XVIII, 1939. p. 235.

88. MÉTRO, A. and SAUVAGE, CH. *Flore des vegetaux ligneux de la Mamora*. Soc. Sci. Nat. et Phys. du Maroc. Rabat, 1955.

89. EMBERGER, L. *Aperçu general sur la vegetation du Maroc*. Bern, 1939. p. 101.

90. CHEVALIER, A. 'Les jujubiers ou zizyphus de l'ancien monde et l'utilisation de leurs fruits', *Rev. Bot. Appl. Agric. Trop.*, 27, 1947. pp. 470–82.

91. KILLIAN, C. 'La vegetation autour du chott Hodna, indicatrice des conditions culturales et son milieu edaphique', in *Desert Research*, Proc. Internat. Symposium, May 7–14, 1952. U.N.E.S.C.O., Jerusalem. pp. 241–58.

CHAPTER 23

THE MAGHREB—ITS RURAL LANDSCAPES, POPULATION AND SETTLEMENT

REFERENCES

1. DESPOIS, J. *L'Afrique du Nord*. Paris, 1949. p. 97; and 'Development of land use in Northern Africa', in *A History of Land Use in Arid Regions*, ed. by L. Dudley Stamp. U.N.E.S.C.O., 1961. pp. 219–38.

2. DRESCH, J. 'L'Afrique du Nord', in *La Méditerranée et le Moyen Orient*. Tome I, *La Méditerranée Occidentale*, by P. Birot and J. Dresch. Paris, 1953. pp. 453–7.

3. CAMPS-FABRER, H. *L'Olivier et L'Huile dans L'Afrique Romaine*, Gouvernement Général de L'Algérie, Service des Antiquités, Missions Archéologiques. Algiers, 1953.

4. *L'Atlas des centuriations romaines en Tunisie*. Institut Géographique Nationale. Paris, 1954. See also A. CAILLEMER et A. CHEVALIER. 'Les centuriations romaines de l'Africa vetus', *A.E.S.C.*, 1954, pp. 433–60, and 'Les centuriations romaines de Tunisie', *ibid.*, 1957, pp. 275–86.

5. BARADEZ, J. *Vue aérienne de l'organisation Romaine dans le Sud-Algérien*. Paris, 1949.

6. DESPOIS, J. 'La culture en terrasses en Afrique du Nord', *A.E.S.C.*, 1956. pp. 42–50.

7. DEMOUGEOT, E. 'Le chameau et L'Afrique du Nord romaine', *A.E.S.C.*, 1960. pp. 210–47.

8. ISNARD, H. *La Vigne en Algérie*, 2 vols. Gap, 1951–4.

9. REINHARD, M. and ARMENGAUD, A. *Histoire Générale de la Population*. Paris, 1961. p. 545.

10. MIKESELL, M. W. *Northern Morocco: a Cultural Geography*, vol. 14, University of California Publications in Geography. 1961. p. 59.

11. DESPOIS, J. *L'Afrique du Nord* (see No. 1). pp. 355–6 and 364.

12. ISNARD, H. 'Agriculture européenne et agriculture indigène en Algérie, *Cahiers d'Outre-Mer*, 1959, pp. 147–59; J. GADILLE. 'L'agriculture européenne au Maroc', *A. de G.*, 66, 1957, pp. 144–58.

13. DUMONT, R. 'Les Données Agricoles', in *Industrialisation de L'Afrique du Nord*, by C. Celier *et alii*. Paris, 1952. p. 50.

14. BESSIS, A., MARTHELOT, P., MONTETY, H. DE, PAUPHILET, D. *Le Territoire des Ouled Sidi Ali Ben Aoun*. Paris, 1956.

15. LEHURAUX, L. *Le nomadisme et la colonisation dans les Hauts Plateaux de l'Algérie*, Paris, 1931; and *Où va le nomadisme en Algérie?* Algiers, 1948.

    CLARKE, J. I. 'Des problèmes du nomadisme estival vers le nord de la Tunisie', *B.A.G.F.*, No. 288, 1952, pp. 134–41; and 'Summer Nomadism in Tunisia', *Econ. Geog.*, 31, 1955. pp. 157–67.

16. HOUSTON, J. M. 'The significance of irrigation in Morocco's economic development', *G.J.*, 120, 1954. pp. 314–28.

17. PONCET, J. 'La mise en valeur de la basse vallée de la Medjerda', *A. de G.*, 65, 1956. pp. 199–222.

18. DESPOIS, J. *L'Afrique du Nord* (see No. 1). pp. 215–392.

19. DRESCH, J. *L'Afrique du Nord* (see No. 2). pp. 451–73, 493–8, and 505–7.

20. GERLINGS, J. H. J. and JONGMANS, D. G. 'The Aït Atta: from Nomadic to Settled Life', *Royal Tropical Institute Amsterdam, Department of Cultural and Physical Anthropology*, vol. 50. 1955.

21. DESPOIS, J. 'L'Atlas Saharien occidental d'Algérie: Ksouriens et pasteurs', in *Mélanges géographiques canadiens offerts à Raoul Blanchard*. Quebec, 1959. pp. 403–15.

22. CLARKE, J. I. 'Studies of semi-nomadism in North Africa', *Econ. Geog.*, 35, 1959. pp. 95–108.

23. BARDIN, P. 'Les jebalia de la région de Gafsa. Étude des populations berbères des massifs montagneux à L'Est de Gafsa', *R.T.*, 1939. pp. 87–126.

24. DESPOIS, J. *Le Hodna*. Paris, 1953. 409 pp.

25. DRESCH, J. *Documents sur les genres de vie de montagne dans le Massif central du Grand Atlas*, 2 vols. Tours, 1941.

26. DESPOIS, J. *La Tunisie Orientale. Sahel et Basse Steppe*, 2nd edn. Paris, 1955. 616 pp.

27. SEKLANI, M. 'La population de la Tunisie. Situation actuelle et évolution probable jusqu'en 1986', P. 16. 1961. pp. 473–504.

28. CHEVALIER, L. *Le Problème Démographique Nord-Africain*, Institut National d'Études Démographiques, Travaux et Documents, Cahier No. 6, 1947; BEAUJEU-GARNIER, J. *Géographie de la Population*, Vol. 2, Paris, 1958; GOOD, D. 'Notes on the Demography of Algeria', *Population Index*, 27, 1961. pp. 3–32.

29. *Groupe d'études des relations financières entre la métropole et L'Algérie: rapport général.* Algiers, 1955.

30. DESPOIS, J. *La Tunisie*. Paris, 1961. pp. 204–5. See also Publications de l'Institut des Hautes Études de Tunis. *Mémoires du Centre d'Études de Sciences Humaines*, vol. 3; SEBAG, P. *Enquête sur les Salariés de la Région de Tunis*, 1956, and *Niveaux de vie liés à l'Agriculture*, 1957.

31. BURNET, E. 'Enquête sur L'alimentation en Tunisie', *Archives de l'Institut Pasteur, Tunis*, 28, 1939, pp. 407–578; ROCHE, J., UZAN, M. and DAVID, M. 'Enquêtes alimentaires en Tunisie', *B.E.S.T.*, 1952; *C.T.*, No. 12, 1955.

32. BOUSQUET, G. H. 'L'Islam et la limitation voluntaire des naissances', *P.*, vol. 5. 1950. pp. 121–8.

33. MONTAGNE, R. *Naissance du Prolétariat Marocain*, Paris, 1951; GLAUERT, G. 'Veränderungen in den Bevölkerungsstruktur Nord-Afrikas in den letzen Jahrzehnten', *Die Erde*, 88, 1957, pp. 298–319; CLARKE, J. I. 'Emigration from Southern Tunisia', 42, 1957, pp. 96–104; *Les Algériens en France*, Études sociales nord-africaines, Paris, 1955.

34. BEHR, E. *The Algerian Problem*. 1961. p. 241.

35. LEPIDI, J. 'L'évolution de la population et le problème démographique en Tunisie', *La Documentation Française*. Paris, 26 June 1957.

36. PONCET, J. 'L'évolution du peuplement tunisien à L'époque récente', *A. de G.*, 68, 1959. pp. 247–53.

37. BOUSQUET, G. H. *Les Berbères*. Paris, 1957. p. 16.

38. MIKESELL, M. W. *op. cit.* 1961. pp. 33–7.

39. MONTAGNE, R. *La Civilisation du désert: nomades d'Orient et d'Afrique*. Paris, 1947. p. 256.

40. CHOURAQUI, A. *Les Juifs d'Afrique du Nord*. Paris, 1952.

41. REINHARD, M. and ARMANGAUD, A. *op. cit.* (see No. 9). p. 565.

42. MARCHAND, H. F. *Les mariages franco-musulmans*. Algiers, 1955.

43. LE TOURNEAU, R. *Fès avant le Protectorat: étude économique et sociale d'une ville de l'occident musulman.* Casablanca, 1949.

44. CÉLÉRIER, J. *Maroc.* Paris, 1948. p. 98.

45. BERQUE, J. 'Medinas, villeneuves et bidonvilles', *C.T.*, 21–2, 1958. pp. 5–42.

46. MIKESELL, M. W. 'The role of tribal markets in Morocco', *G.R.*, 48, 1958. pp. 444–511.

47. MARÇAIS, G. 'La conception des villes dans L'Islam', *R.M.*, 10, 1945. p. 525. See also, LE TOURNEAU, R. *Les Villes musulmanes de l'Afrique du Nord*, Bibliothèque de l'Institut d'Études supérieures islamiques, II. 1957.

48. LE TOURNEAU, R., PAYE, L. and GUYOT, R. 'Le corporation des tanneurs et l'industrie de la tannerie à Fès', *Hesp.*, 21, 1955. pp. 167–240.

49. LARNAUDE, M. *Algérie*. Paris, 1950. p. 187.

50. SEBAG, P. *L'évolution d'un ghetto nord-africain. Le hara de Tunis.* Paris, 1959.

51. — 'Le bidonville de Borgel, Tunisie', *C.T.*, 23–4, 1958, pp. 267–309; SEBAG, P. *et alii. Un Faubourg de Tunis, Saïda Manoubia.* Paris, 1960.

52. WICHE, K. 'Marokkanische Stadttypen', in *Festschrift zur Hundertjahrfeier der geographischen Gesellschaft in Wien, 1856–1956.* Vienna, 1957. pp. 485–527; 'Maroc: les villes', in *Encyclopédie Mensuelle d'Outre-Mer*. Paris, 1954.

53. BERNARD, A. *Afrique septentrionale et occidentale.* (*Geographie Universelle*, Part 1. Paris, 1937. Tome XI). p. 89.

54. FEILBERG, C. G. *La Tente Noire.* Copenhagen, 1944. pp. 36–58.

55. DESPOIS, J. 'Les greniers fortifiés de L'Afrique du Nord', *C.T.*, 1, 1953, pp. 38–60; JACQUES-MEUNIÉ, J. *Greniers-citadelles au Maroc*, 2 vols, Paris, 1951.

56. PLANHOL, X. DE. *Nouveaux villages Algérois*, Publications de la Faculté des Lettres et Sciences Humaines d'Alger, vol. 39. Paris, 1961.

57. CELERIER, J. 'L'idée de région naturelle en Afrique du Nord' (2ᵉˑ Congrès de la Féd. des Soc. Sav. de l'Afrique du Nord), *Rev. Afr.* (Algiers), I, 1936. pp. 95–124.

58. RAYNAL, R. 'Quelques aperçus géographiques sur l'évolution des régions humaines du Maroc', *Hesp.*, 1952. pp. 1–16.

59. DESPOIS, J. 'Régions naturelles et Régions humaines en Tunisie', *A. de G.*, 1942. pp. 112–28.

INDEX